SRA®

MATH

Explorations and Applications

Make thinking a basic skill on the road of life.

Solve the persistent problems of teaching elementary mathematics by teaching children how to *think* mathematically.

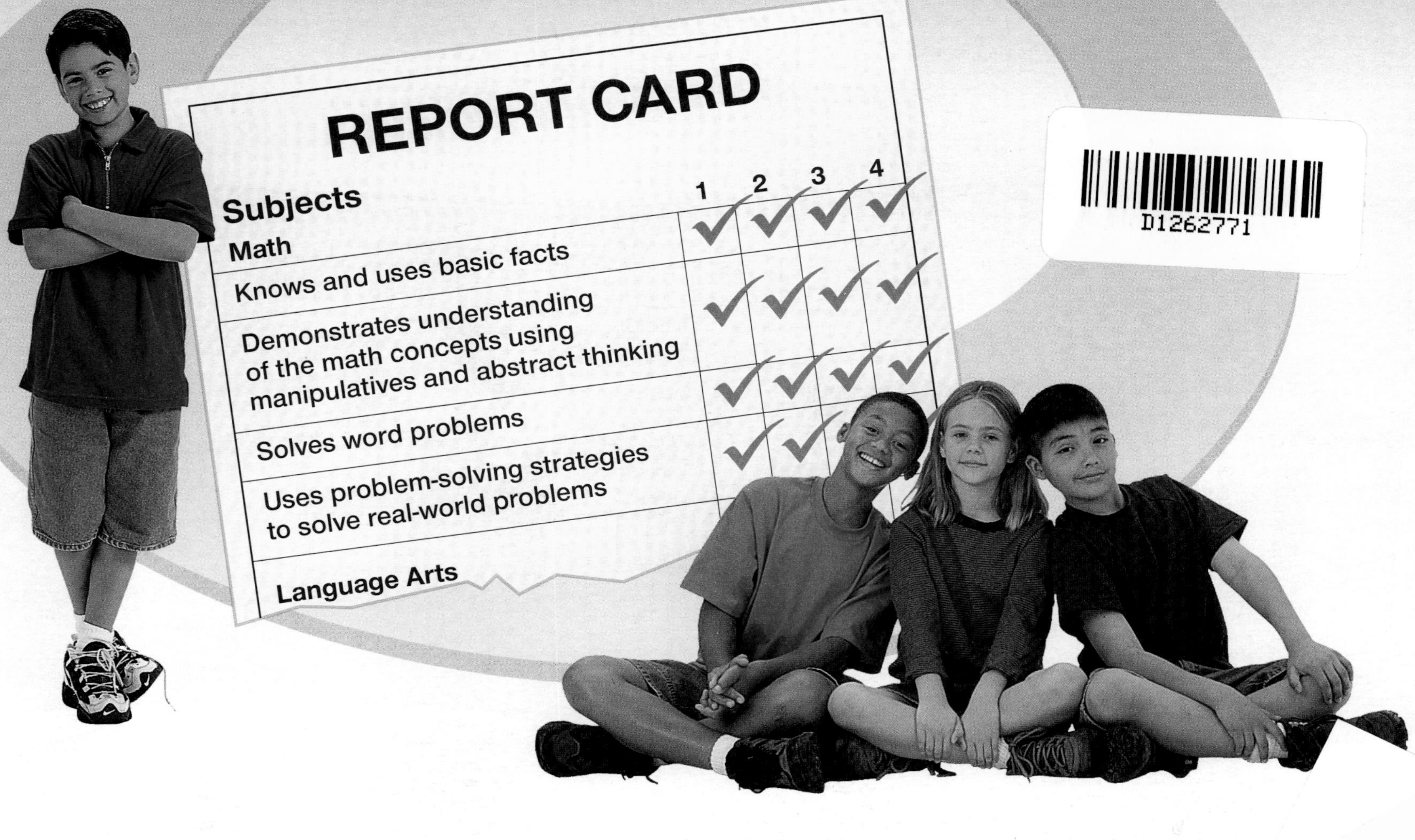
REPORT CARD
Subjects
1 2 3 4
Math
Knows and uses basic facts
Demonstrates understanding of the math concepts using manipulatives and abstract thinking
Solves word problems
Uses problem-solving strategies to solve real-world problems
Language Arts

Introducing

SRA MATH
Explorations and Applications

Take the right path to teaching mathematics.

This comprehensive, research-based program challenges students to think every day, on every page, at every juncture. It's the answer that teachers need to make math instruction effective and math learning enjoyable.

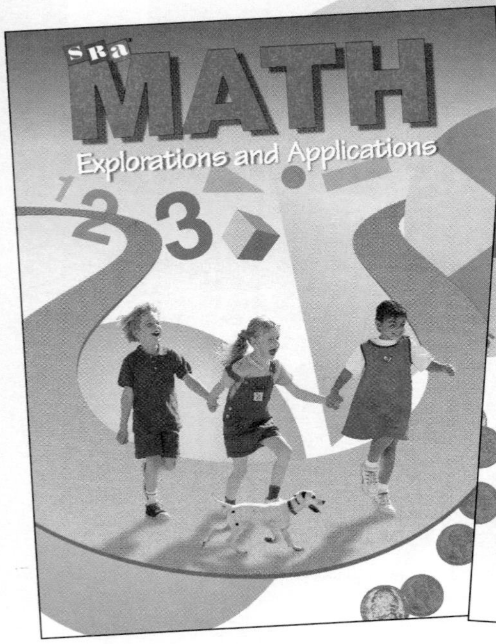

Level K

Level 1

Level 2

Level 3

Level 4

Level 5

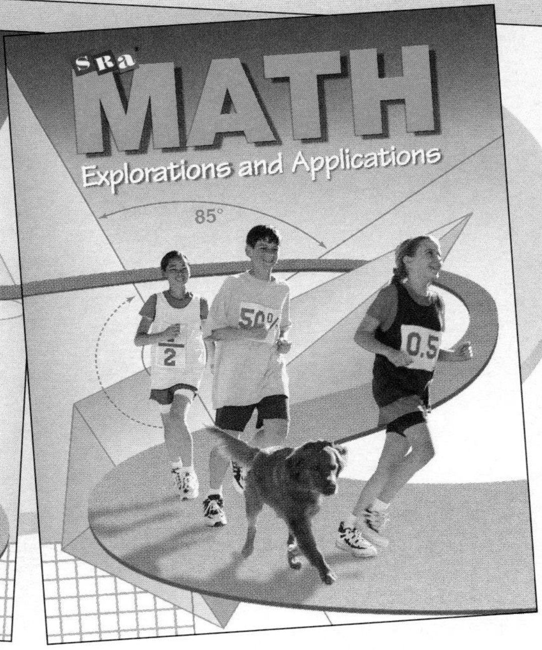

Level 6

Also Available

- **Professional Development Handbook**
- **Program Video**
- ***Minds on Math***
- ***Math CrossSections***
- ***Science, Math & YOU***
- ***Cooperate 1, 2, and 3***
- ***Junior Thinklab™***
- ***Thinklab™***
- ***Thinklab™ 2***
- ***Scoring High in Math***

It's mathematics, taken off the beaten path.

***Math Explorations and Applications* helps students learn the real basics: traditional arithmetic skills, computation, and problem solving.**

- **Concept Integration.** The program's organization, scope, and sequence allow integration and thorough study of math concepts.
- **In-Depth Study.** Lessons devote the number of pages needed to teach a concept, not artificially dividing every topic into the same lesson length. Sometimes it takes more than two pages to effectively cover the important points in a lesson.
- **Concepts in Context.** Skills and concepts are taught and retaught in different contexts—never in isolation.

- **Variety of Presentations.** Explore, Practice, Problem Solving, and Projects address a variety of learning styles so that students stay interested and motivated as they learn to think.
- **Cumulative Review of Content.** Once a skill has been introduced, it is integrated, practiced, and reviewed in mixed practice and in context throughout the grade level. Lesson by lesson, students accumulate the skills they need to master more complicated math concepts, as they continually review previously introduced skills.
- **Life-Long Learning.** As they see mathematics used to solve realistic problems, students begin to view strong math skills as useful, lifelong tools they can use both inside and outside the classroom.
- **Focus on Computation *and* Problem Solving.** *Math Explorations and Applications* develops and provides practice of traditional skills in problem-solving settings such as games. This makes efficient use of teacher and student time and effort.

Take along the essentials for the journey.

Core Materials

- Student Editions (K–2) in consumable format that introduce, integrate, and practice concepts and skills
- Student Editions (3–6) in hardbound format filled with lessons that integrate concept development, practice, and problem solving
- Thinking Story Books (Levels 1–3) for teachers to read to the class
- Teacher's Guides that provide the road map along with practice, reteaching, and enrichment support
- Basic Manipulative Kits needed for Cube Games and Mental Math Activities

Lesson Support Materials

- Practice Activities in Workbook and Blackline Master formats
- Enrichment Activities in Workbook and Blackline Master formats
- Reteaching Activities in Workbook and Blackline Master formats
- Assessment Masters
- Home Connections Masters
- Literature Library (K–3)

Manipulative Support Materials

- Game Mat Packages (K–6) for skill practice and problem solving
- Primary Manipulative Kit (K–2) to introduce basic concepts
- Primary Overhead Manipulative Kit (K–2)
- Intermediate Manipulative Kit (3–6) for variety in concept presentation
- Intermediate Overhead Manipulative Kit (3–6)
- Teacher Manipulative Kit for classroom demonstrations

Technology Support Materials

- *Math Explorations and Applications* Software (1–6) provides extra skill practice for every lesson.
- *The Cruncher* (4–6) offers a student-friendly spreadsheet application for appropriate lessons.
- *My Silly CD of Counting* CD-ROM (K) helps build the concept of counting.
- TI-108™ Calculator Package (K–3)
- Math Explorer™ Calculator Package (4–6)
- Primary Overhead Calculator (K–3)
- Intermediate Overhead Calculator (4–6)

Professional Development

- Professional Development Handbook
- Program Video

Developing concepts in context paves the road to understanding.

Math Explorations and Applications **introduces and integrates concepts so that students make connections and build on what they already know.**

- **Early Introduction of Concepts.** An early age-appropriate introduction to concepts such as algebra, geometry, multiplication, and division builds understanding and connections from the very beginning. Because most students actually begin to use the principles of more advanced math concepts like algebra long before the eighth grade, *Math Explorations and Applications* helps students feel comfortable with these concepts from the very start.

- **Core Concept Development at Every Level.** Operations, thinking skills, problem solving, mental math, estimation, data organization, geometry, probability, and statistics are emphasized at all grade levels.

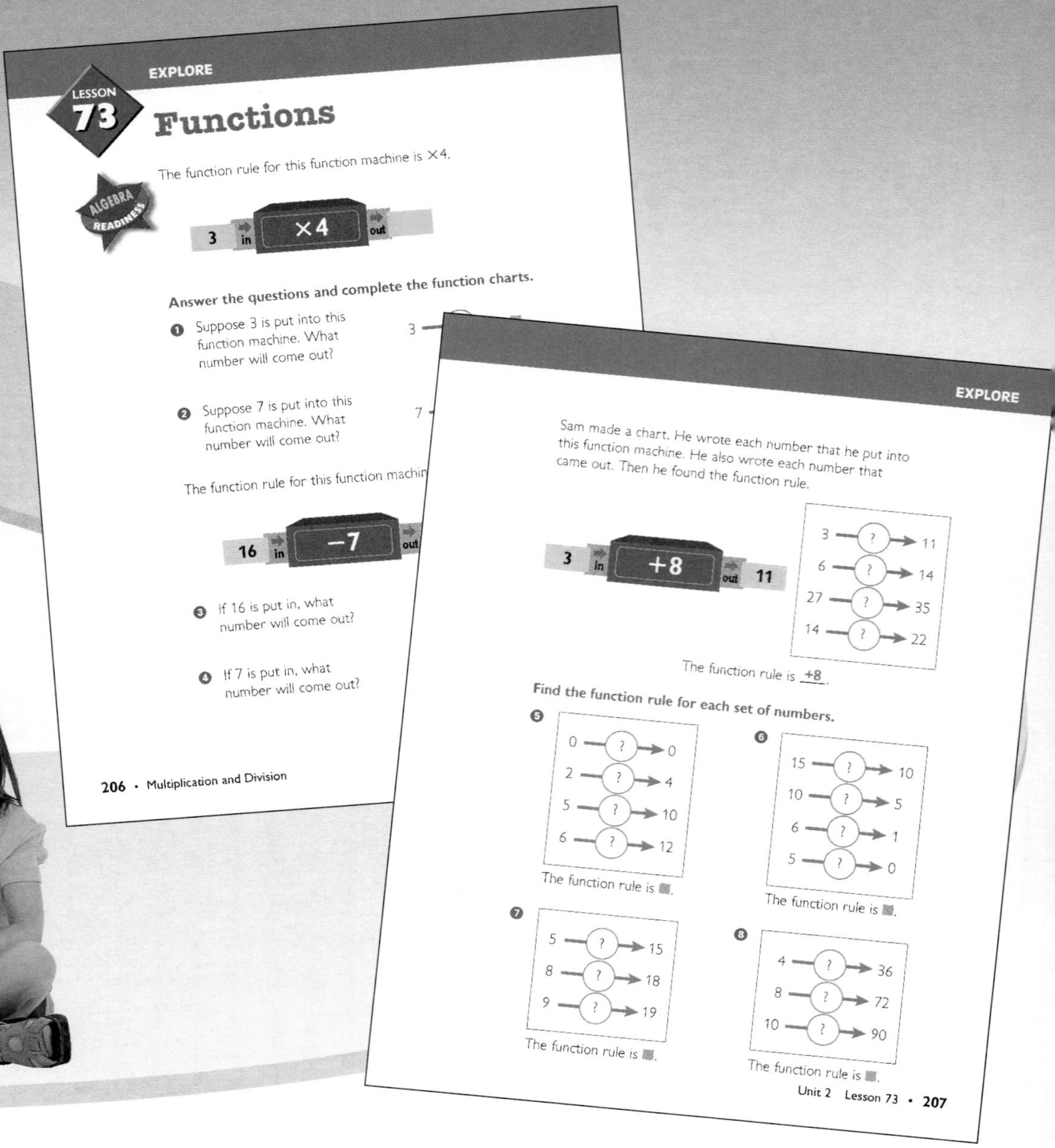

EXPLORE

LESSON 73

Functions

ALGEBRA READINESS

The function rule for this function machine is ×4.

3 in ×4 out

Answer the questions and complete the function charts.

1. Suppose 3 is put into this function machine. What number will come out?
2. Suppose 7 is put into this function machine. What number will come out?

The function rule for this function machin

16 in −7 out

3. If 16 is put in, what number will come out?
4. If 7 is put in, what number will come out?

206 • Multiplication and Division

EXPLORE

Sam made a chart. He wrote each number that he put into this function machine. He also wrote each number that came out. Then he found the function rule.

3 in +8 out 11

3 → ? → 11
6 → ? → 14
27 → ? → 35
14 → ? → 22

The function rule is +8.

Find the function rule for each set of numbers.

5. 0 → ? → 0; 2 → ? → 4; 5 → ? → 10; 6 → ? → 12
The function rule is ■.

6. 15 → ? → 10; 10 → ? → 5; 6 → ? → 1; 5 → ? → 0
The function rule is ■.

7. 5 → ? → 15; 8 → ? → 18; 9 → ? → 19
The function rule is ■.

8. 4 → ? → 36; 8 → ? → 72; 10 → ? → 90
The function rule is ■.

Unit 2 Lesson 73 • 207

Level 3

◆ **Concepts in Context.** Concepts are developed in different contexts to help students recognize their natural connections. For example, the concept of fractions is developed in relation to time, money, and measurement.

◆ **Intelligent Use of Manipulatives.** Intelligent use of hands-on activities and manipulatives establishes concepts in the concrete, showing students a variety of ways to solve a problem. Students are encouraged to use these tools where appropriate, then to move beyond these tools as quickly as possible toward the goal of abstract thinking.

◆ **Realistic Problem-Solving Models.** Exciting **Act It Out** lessons model problem-solving strategies by having students physically work through new concepts.

◆ **Emphasizing Natural Concept Relationships**
By drawing on the natural relationships that exist among concepts, students learn to make connections between concepts so that they can understand them more effectively.

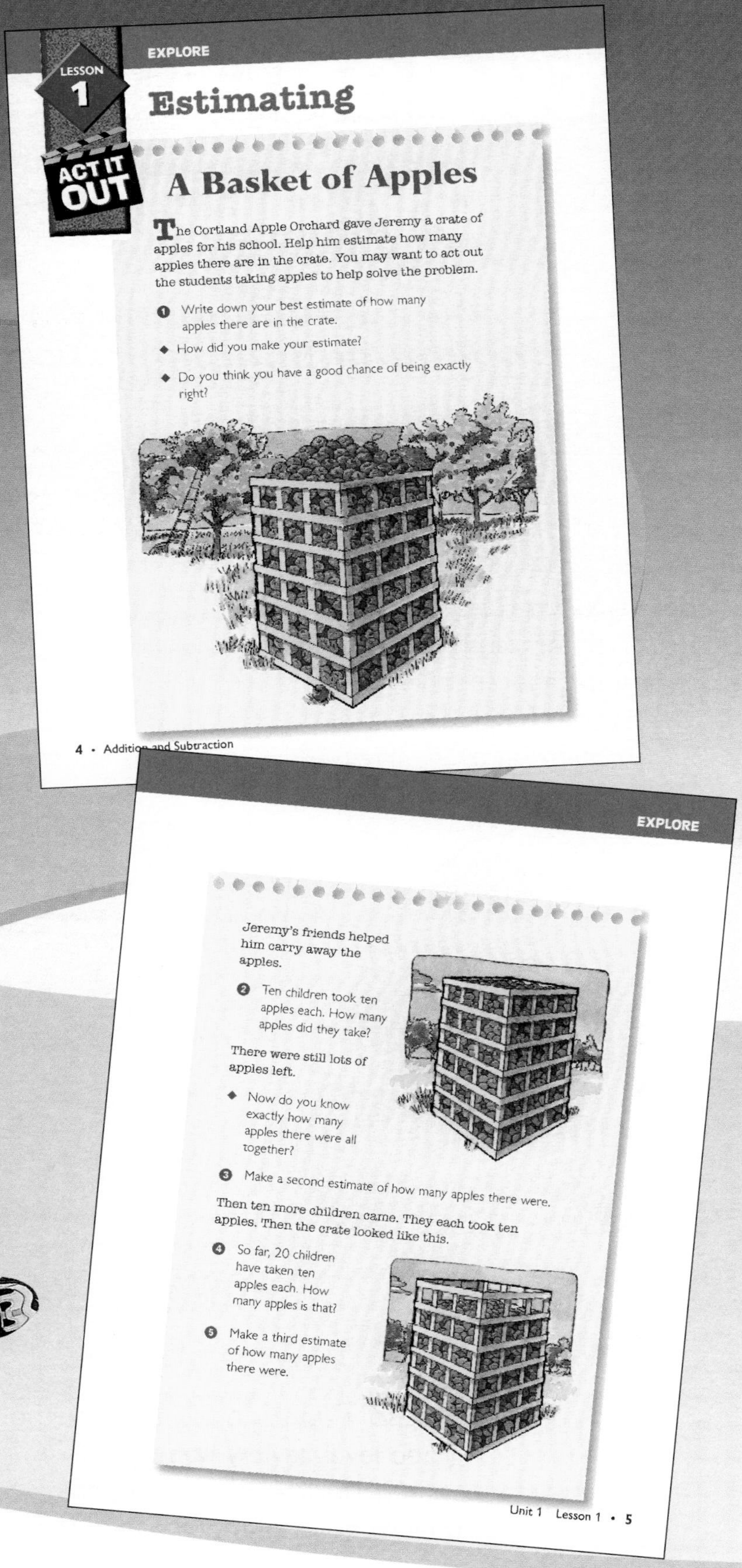
LESSON 1

ACT IT OUT

EXPLORE

Estimating

A Basket of Apples

The Cortland Apple Orchard gave Jeremy a crate of apples for his school. Help him estimate how many apples there are in the crate. You may want to act out the students taking apples to help solve the problem.

1. Write down your best estimate of how many apples there are in the crate.

◆ How did you make your estimate?

◆ Do you think you have a good chance of being exactly right?

4 • Addition and Subtraction

EXPLORE

Jeremy's friends helped him carry away the apples.

2. Ten children took ten apples each. How many apples did they take?

There were still lots of apples left.

◆ Now do you know exactly how many apples there were all together?

3. Make a second estimate of how many apples there were.

Then ten more children came. They each took ten apples. Then the crate looked like this.

4. So far, 20 children have taken ten apples each. How many apples is that?

5. Make a third estimate of how many apples there were.

Unit 1 Lesson 1 • 5

Level 4

Step by step, students learn the basics by heart and mind.

Computational skills are essential for efficient mathematical thinking. But skill practice can be enjoyable and is one more opportunity to challenge students to think mathematically.

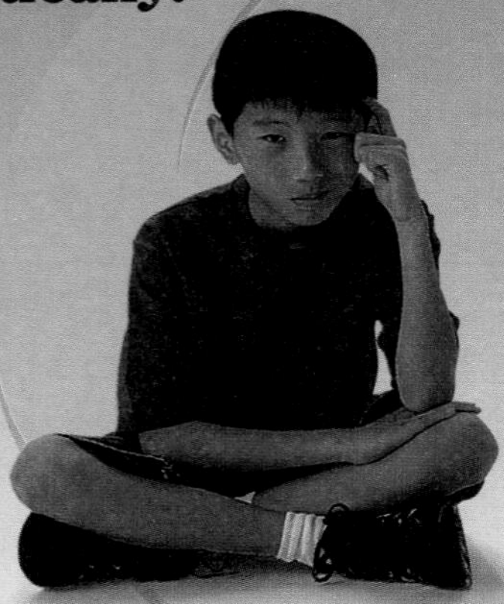

- **Practice** pages often have hidden patterns that help students understand number relationships and encourage mathematical thinking on every problem on every page.

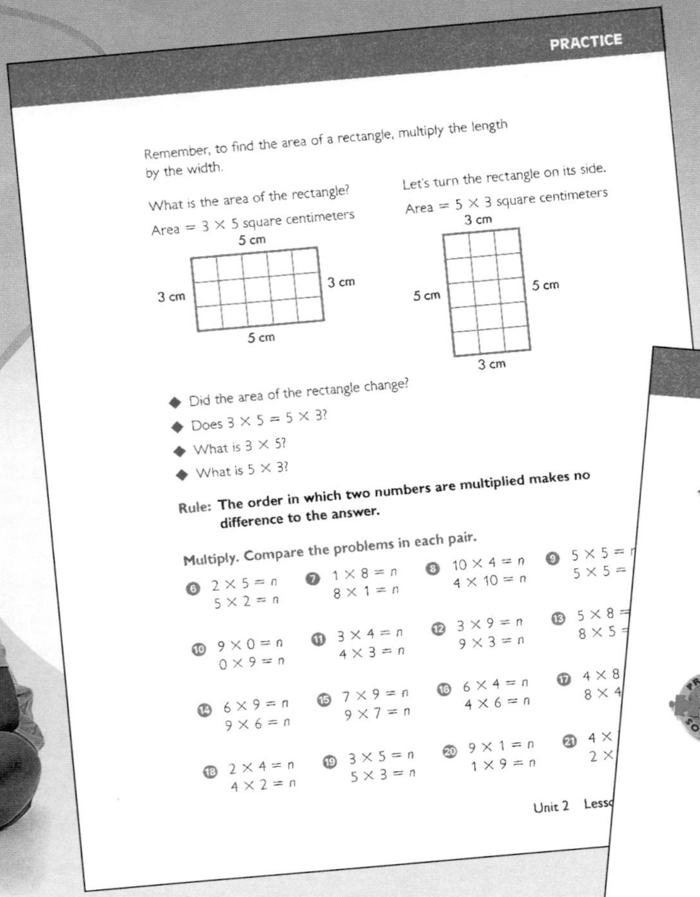
PRACTICE

Remember, to find the area of a rectangle, multiply the length by the width.

What is the area of the rectangle?
Area = 3 × 5 square centimeters

Let's turn the rectangle on its side.
Area = 5 × 3 square centimeters

- Did the area of the rectangle change?
- Does 3 × 5 = 5 × 3?
- What is 3 × 5?
- What is 5 × 3?

Rule: The order in which two numbers are multiplied makes no difference to the answer.

Multiply. Compare the problems in each pair.

6. 2 × 5 = n; 5 × 2 = n
7. 1 × 8 = n; 8 × 1 = n
8. 10 × 4 = n; 4 × 10 = n
9. 5 × 5 = n; 5 × 5 =
10. 9 × 0 = n; 0 × 9 = n
11. 3 × 4 = n; 4 × 3 = n
12. 3 × 9 = n; 9 × 3 = n
13. 5 × 8 =; 8 × 5 =
14. 6 × 9 = n; 9 × 6 = n
15. 7 × 9 = n; 9 × 7 = n
16. 6 × 4 = n; 4 × 6 = n
17. 4 × 8; 8 × 4
18. 2 × 4 = n; 4 × 2 = n
19. 3 × 5 = n; 5 × 3 = n
20. 9 × 1 = n; 1 × 9 = n
21. 4 ×; 2 ×

Unit 2 Lesso

Level 4

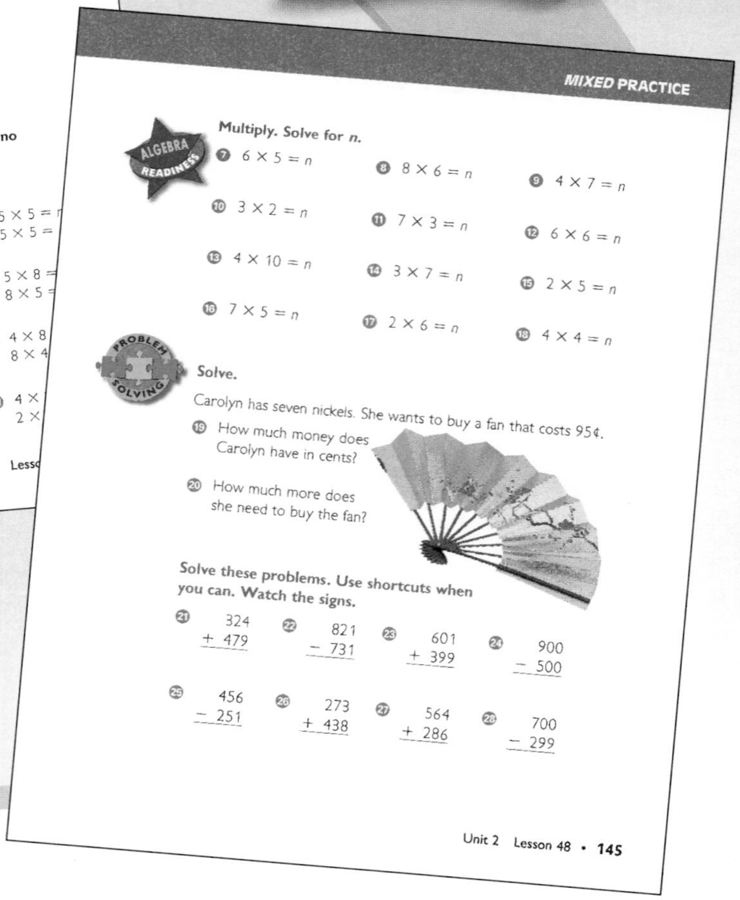
MIXED PRACTICE

Multiply. Solve for n.

7. 6 × 5 = n
8. 8 × 6 = n
9. 4 × 7 = n
10. 3 × 2 = n
11. 7 × 3 = n
12. 6 × 6 = n
13. 4 × 10 = n
14. 3 × 7 = n
15. 2 × 5 = n
16. 7 × 5 = n
17. 2 × 6 = n
18. 4 × 4 = n

Solve.

Carolyn has seven nickels. She wants to buy a fan that costs 95¢.

19. How much money does Carolyn have in cents?
20. How much more does she need to buy the fan?

Solve these problems. Use shortcuts when you can. Watch the signs.

21. 324 + 479
22. 821 − 731
23. 601 + 399
24. 900 − 500
25. 456 − 251
26. 273 + 438
27. 564 + 286
28. 700 − 299

Unit 2 Lesson 48 • 145

Level 3

- **Mixed Practice** pages throughout each grade level review concepts from all lessons and encourage students to think about what they're doing and how they do it.

Multiplication Table Game

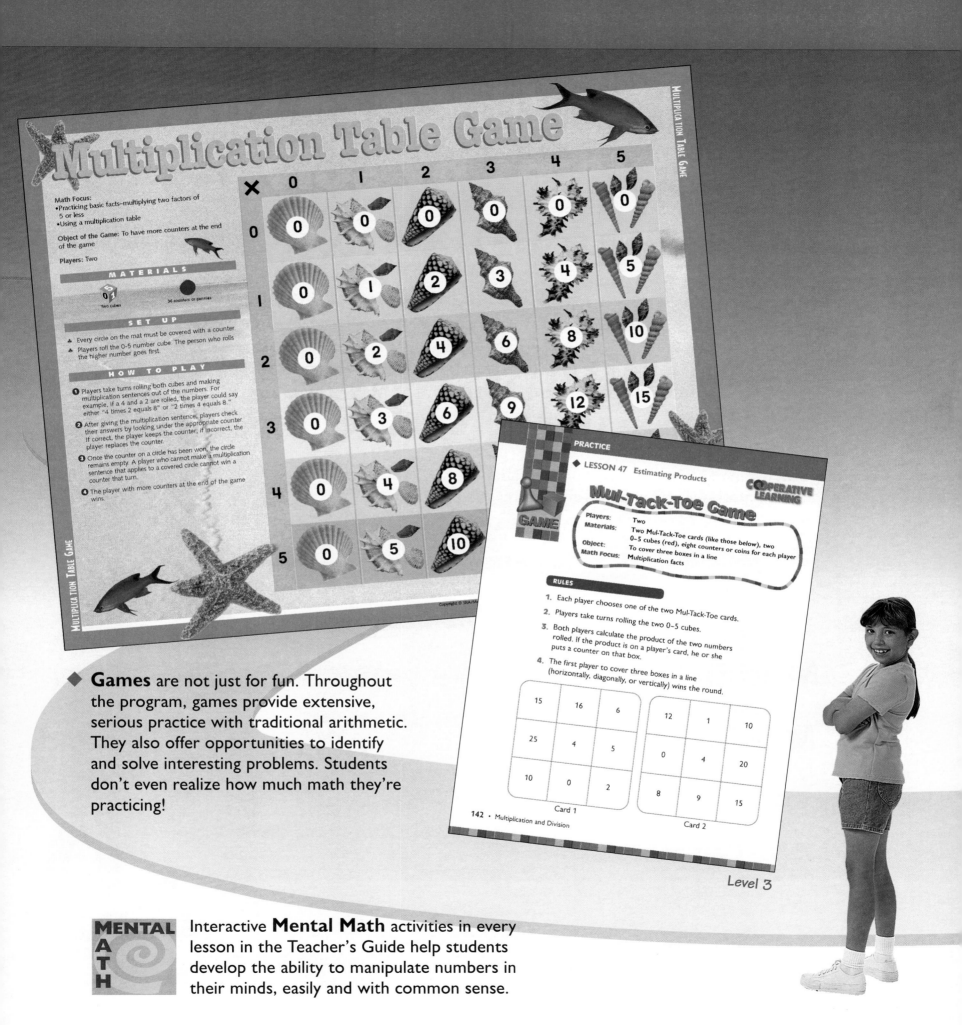

Math Focus:
•Practicing basic facts–multiplying two factors of 5 or less
•Using a multiplication table

Object of the Game: To have more counters at the end of the game

Players: Two

MATERIALS

Two cubes
36 counters or pennies

SET UP

- Every circle on the mat must be covered with a counter.
- Players roll the 0-5 number cube. The person who rolls the higher number goes first.

HOW TO PLAY

1. Players take turns rolling both cubes and making multiplication sentences out of the numbers. For example, if a 4 and a 2 are rolled, the player could say either "4 times 2 equals 8" or "2 times 4 equals 8."
2. After giving the multiplication sentence, players check their answers by looking under the appropriate counter. If correct, the player keeps the counter; if incorrect, the player replaces the counter.
3. Once the counter on a circle has been won, the circle remains empty. A player who cannot make a multiplication sentence that applies to a covered circle cannot win a counter that turn.
4. The player with more counters at the end of the game wins.

×	0	1	2	3	4	5
0	0	0	0	0	0	0
1	0	1	2	3	4	5
2	0	2	4	6	8	10
3	0	3	6	9	12	15
4	0	4	8			
5	0	5	10			

MULTIPLICATION TABLE GAME

MULTIPLICA TION TABLE GAME

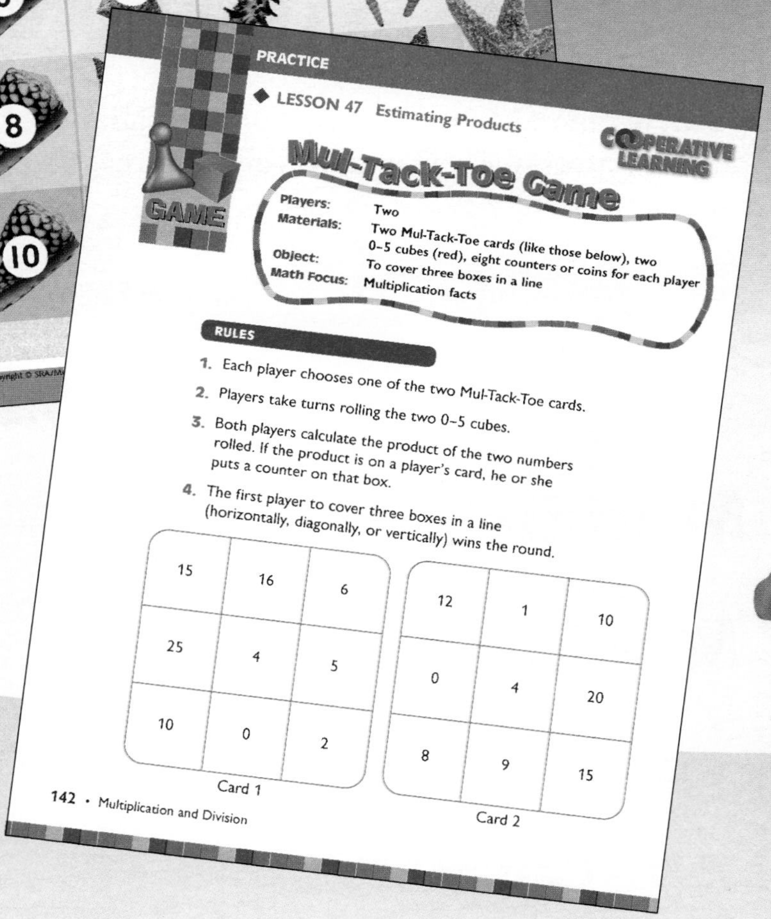

PRACTICE

◆ LESSON 47 Estimating Products

GAME

COOPERATIVE LEARNING

Mul-Tack-Toe Game

Players: Two
Materials: Two Mul-Tack-Toe cards (like those below), two 0–5 cubes (red), eight counters or coins for each player
Object: To cover three boxes in a line
Math Focus: Multiplication facts

RULES

1. Each player chooses one of the two Mul-Tack-Toe cards.
2. Players take turns rolling the two 0–5 cubes.
3. Both players calculate the product of the two numbers rolled. If the product is on a player's card, he or she puts a counter on that box.
4. The first player to cover three boxes in a line (horizontally, diagonally, or vertically) wins the round.

15	16	6
25	4	5
10	0	2

Card 1

12	1	10
0	4	20
8	9	15

Card 2

142 • Multiplication and Division

Level 3

◆ **Games** are not just for fun. Throughout the program, games provide extensive, serious practice with traditional arithmetic. They also offer opportunities to identify and solve interesting problems. Students don't even realize how much math they're practicing!

MENTAL MATH

Interactive **Mental Math** activities in every lesson in the Teacher's Guide help students develop the ability to manipulate numbers in their minds, easily and with common sense.

Children learn to solve problems by solving problems.

Problem-solving strategies are integrated throughout *Math Explorations and Applications*, never taught in isolation. Instead of memorizing rote strategies, students learn to recognize a problem, select an appropriate strategy, solve the problem, and reflect on their reasoning.

- **Thinking Stories** model mathematical thinking and problem-solving strategies. They demonstrate that real-life "problems" can appear in unexpected places.

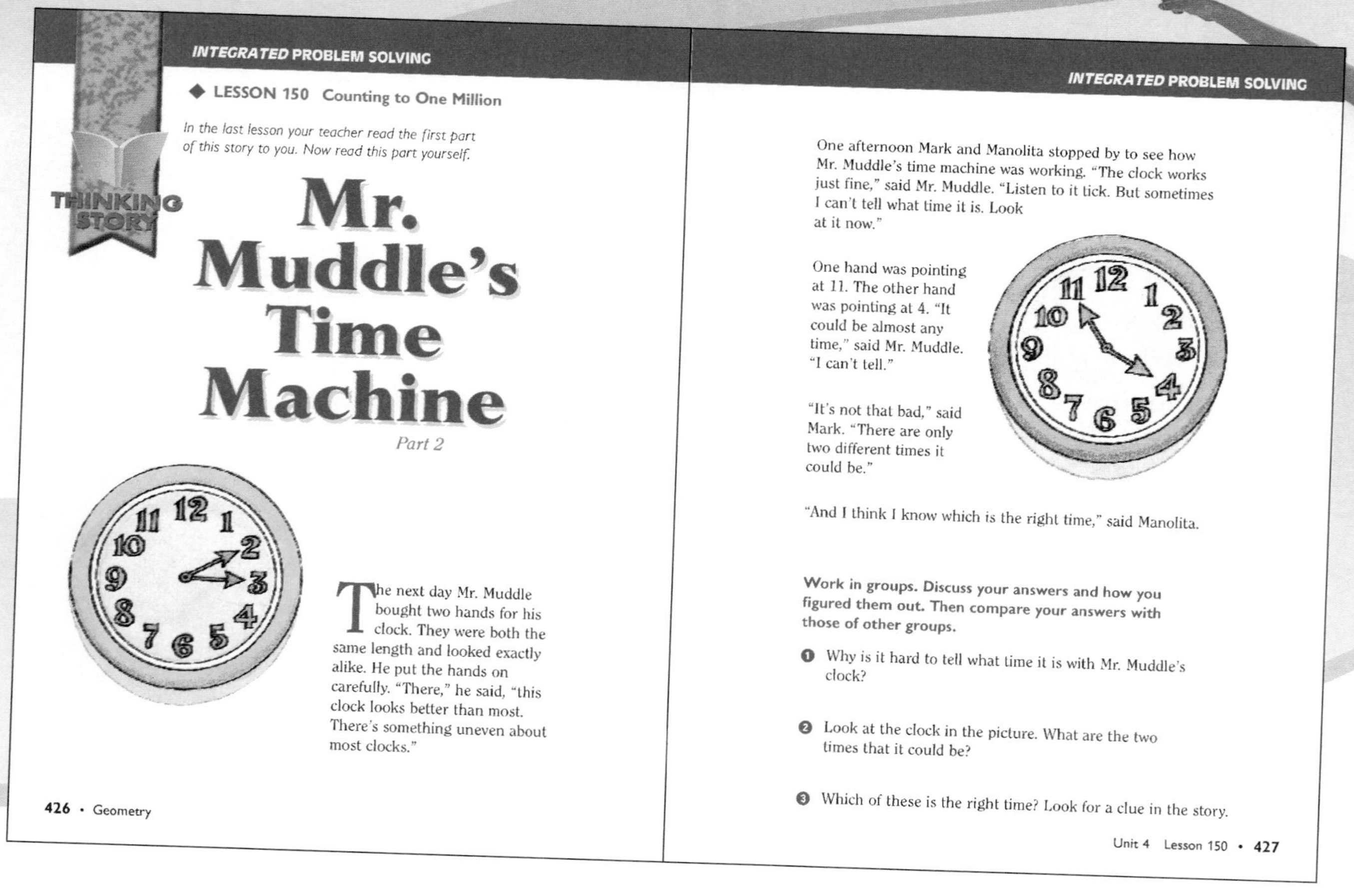

INTEGRATED PROBLEM SOLVING

◆ LESSON 150 Counting to One Million

In the last lesson your teacher read the first part of this story to you. Now read this part yourself.

THINKING STORY

Mr. Muddle's Time Machine

Part 2

The next day Mr. Muddle bought two hands for his clock. They were both the same length and looked exactly alike. He put the hands on carefully. "There," he said, "this clock looks better than most. There's something uneven about most clocks."

426 • Geometry

INTEGRATED PROBLEM SOLVING

One afternoon Mark and Manolita stopped by to see how Mr. Muddle's time machine was working. "The clock works just fine," said Mr. Muddle. "Listen to it tick. But sometimes I can't tell what time it is. Look at it now."

One hand was pointing at 11. The other hand was pointing at 4. "It could be almost any time," said Mr. Muddle. "I can't tell."

"It's not that bad," said Mark. "There are only two different times it could be."

"And I think I know which is the right time," said Manolita.

Work in groups. Discuss your answers and how you figured them out. Then compare your answers with those of other groups.

1. Why is it hard to tell what time it is with Mr. Muddle's clock?
2. Look at the clock in the picture. What are the two times that it could be?
3. Which of these is the right time? Look for a clue in the story.

Unit 4 Lesson 150 • 427

Level 3

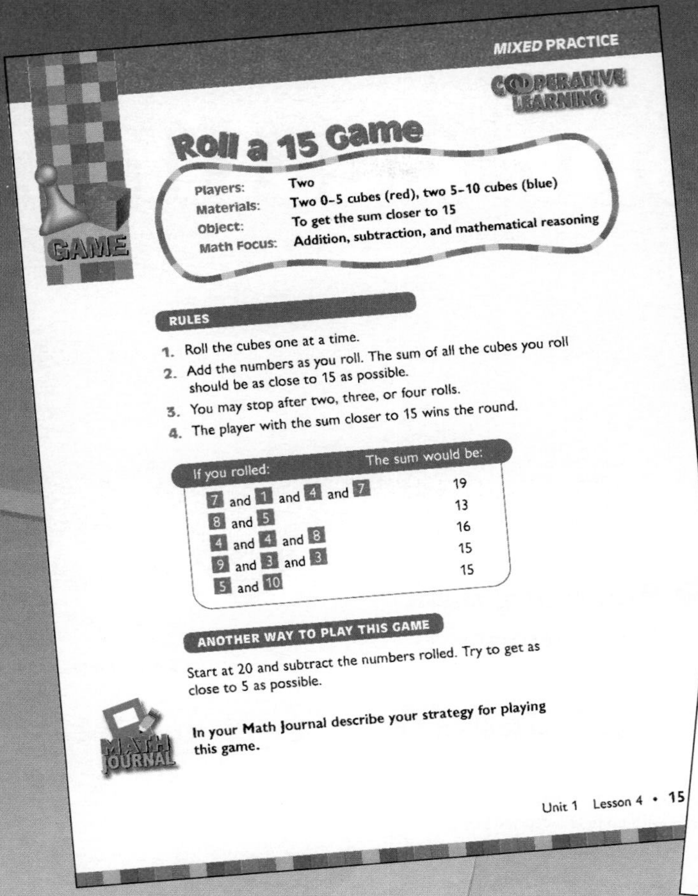

MIXED PRACTICE

COOPERATIVE LEARNING

GAME

Roll a 15 Game

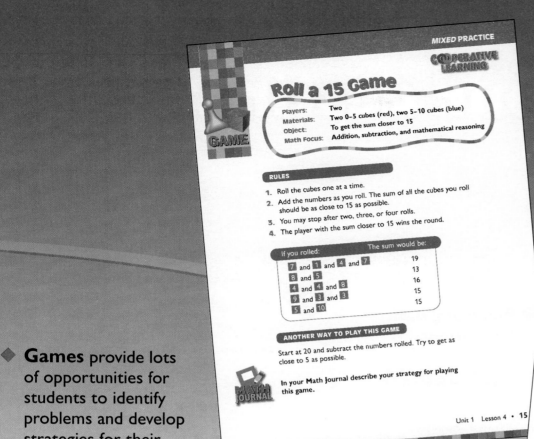

Players: Two
Materials: Two 0–5 cubes (red), two 5–10 cubes (blue)
Object: To get the sum closer to 15
Math Focus: Addition, subtraction, and mathematical reasoning

RULES

1. Roll the cubes one at a time.
2. Add the numbers as you roll. The sum of all the cubes you roll should be as close to 15 as possible.
3. You may stop after two, three, or four rolls.
4. The player with the sum closer to 15 wins the round.

If you rolled:	The sum would be:
7 and 1 and 4 and 7	19
8 and 5	13
4 and 4 and 8	16
9 and 3 and 3	15
5 and 10	15

ANOTHER WAY TO PLAY THIS GAME

Start at 20 and subtract the numbers rolled. Try to get as close to 5 as possible.

MATH JOURNAL In your Math Journal describe your strategy for playing this game.

Unit 1 Lesson 4 • 15

Level 4

◆ **Games** provide lots of opportunities for students to identify problems and develop strategies for their solution.

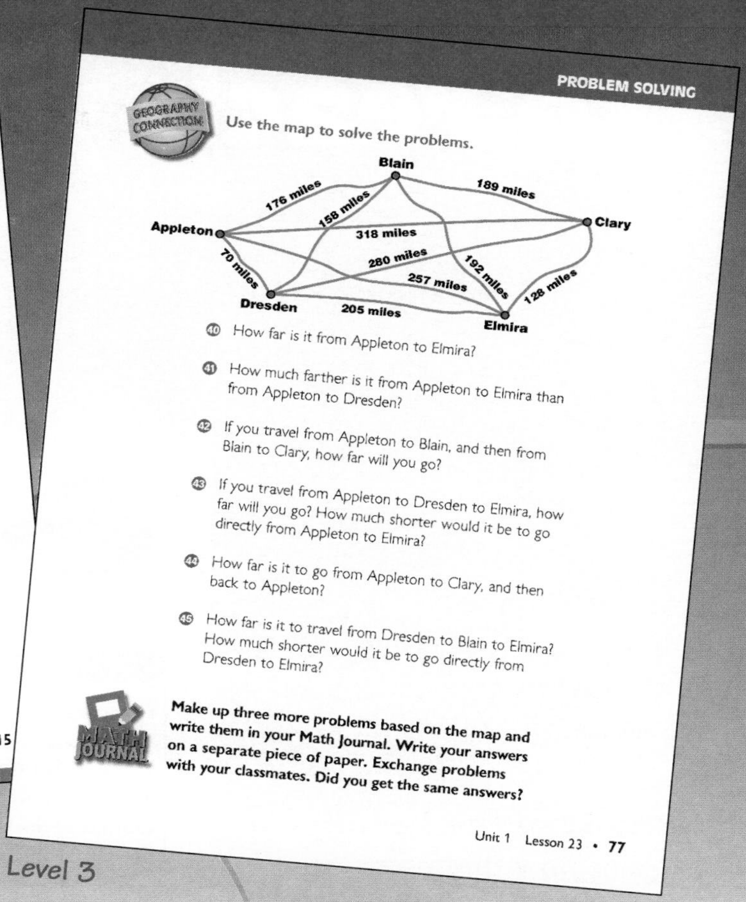

PROBLEM SOLVING

GEOGRAPHY CONNECTION Use the map to solve the problems.

40 How far is it from Appleton to Elmira?

41 How much farther is it from Appleton to Elmira than from Appleton to Dresden?

42 If you travel from Appleton to Blain, and then from Blain to Clary, how far will you go?

43 If you travel from Appleton to Dresden to Elmira, how far will you go? How much shorter would it be to go directly from Appleton to Elmira?

44 How far is it to go from Appleton to Clary, and then back to Appleton?

45 How far is it to travel from Dresden to Blain to Elmira? How much shorter would it be to go directly from Dresden to Elmira?

MATH JOURNAL **Make up three more problems based on the map and write them in your Math Journal. Write your answers on a separate piece of paper. Exchange problems with your classmates. Did you get the same answers?**

Unit 1 Lesson 23 • 77

Level 3

◆ **Projects** at the end of each unit allow students to solve complex problems, many of which require outside research and data analysis.

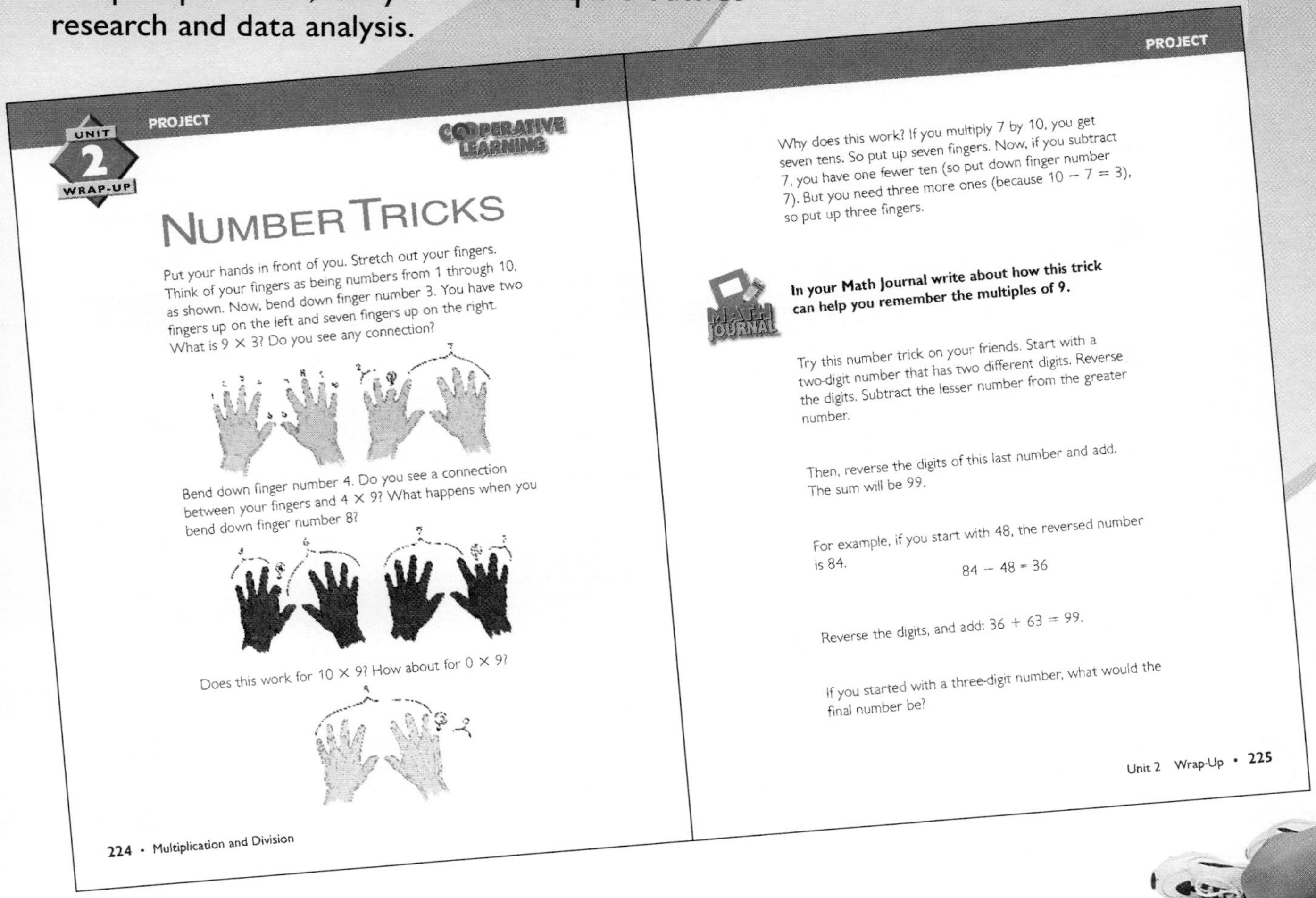

UNIT 2 WRAP-UP

PROJECT

COOPERATIVE LEARNING

NUMBER TRICKS

Put your hands in front of you. Stretch out your fingers. Think of your fingers as being numbers from 1 through 10, as shown. Now, bend down finger number 3. You have two fingers up on the left and seven fingers up on the right. What is 9 × 3? Do you see any connection?

Bend down finger number 4. Do you see a connection between your fingers and 4 × 9? What happens when you bend down finger number 8?

Does this work for 10 × 9? How about for 0 × 9?

224 • Multiplication and Division

PROJECT

Why does this work? If you multiply 7 by 10, you get seven tens. So put up seven fingers. Now, if you subtract 7, you have one fewer ten (so put down finger number 7). But you need three more ones (because 10 − 7 = 3), so put up three fingers.

MATH JOURNAL **In your Math Journal write about how this trick can help you remember the multiples of 9.**

Try this number trick on your friends. Start with a two-digit number that has two different digits. Reverse the digits. Subtract the lesser number from the greater number.

Then, reverse the digits of this last number and add. The sum will be 99.

For example, if you start with 48, the reversed number is 84. 84 − 48 = 36

Reverse the digits, and add: 36 + 63 = 99.

If you started with a three-digit number, what would the final number be?

Unit 2 Wrap-Up • 225

Level 3

◆ **Word Problems** throughout the student books are carefully crafted to involve multiple operations, cumulative content, and sometimes, insufficient information so that students always have to think.

To reach your destination,

***Math Explorations and Applications* gives teachers the support they need to challenge students to think mathematically, not to just complete exercises.**

- **Lesson Planner** offers a quick overview of the lesson objectives, materials, and resources.
- **Context of the Lesson** explains how this lesson fits into sequence with others.
- A clear, three-step lesson plan lays out how to **Warm-Up, Teach,** and **Wrap-Up** each lesson.
- **Problem of the Day** presents an interesting problem for students to ponder in every lesson.
- **Mental Math** provides basic fact and abstract-thinking practice in every lesson.
- **Why teach it at this time?** or **Why teach it in this way?** provides an explanation of the authors' philosophy as it relates to this specific lesson.

LESSON 106

Student Edition pages 298–299

Practicing Basic Operations

LESSON PLANNER

Objectives

✓ to assess mastery of students' ability to add and subtract decimals (with up to two decimal places)

▶ to provide practice in adding and subtracting decimals

Context of the Lesson This is the 15th of 15 lessons on decimals. This lesson also contains the 22nd of 24 Mastery Checkpoints.

Materials	Program Resources
graph paper (optional)	Thinking Story Book, pages 88–89
play money (optional)	Practice Master 106
	Enrichment Master 106
	Assessment Master
	For extra practice: CD-ROM* Lesson 106

1 Warm-Up (5 minutes)

Problem of the Day Present this problem: Fay called her friend Samir and asked him to meet her at the library. Fay lives 3.4 kilometers away from the library, while Samir lives 1.62 kilometers away. Who must travel farthest to the library? (Fay: 3.4 > 1.62) How much farther? (1.78 km: 3.40 − 1.62 = 1.78)

MENTAL MATH Review addition and subtraction of decimals. On the chalkboard write: 4.2 − 1.14 = ____. Show that the problem can be done by changing 4.2 to the equivalent 4.20 and then subtracting. Then have students respond quickly by writing their answers on paper as you read the following problems aloud.

a. 3.57 − 2.4 = (1.17) b. 15.63 − 4.7 = (10.93)
c. 5.3 − 2.02 = (3.28) d. 9.1 + 6.04 = (15.14)
e. 8.35 + 3.2 = (11.55) f. 7.06 − 1.3 = (5.76)

MIXED PRACTICE

LESSON 106

Practicing Basic Operations

Solve these problems. Watch the signs.

1. 5.3 − 2.1 = **3.2**
2. 5.47 − 3.6 = **1.87**
3. 2.4 − 1.87 = **0.53**
4. 4.71 + 5.62 = **10.33**
5. 5.62 + 4.71 = **10.33**
6. 5.62 − 4.71 = **0.91**
7. 3.8 + 1.2 = **5.0**
8. 4.07 − 3.7 = **0.37**
9. 12.13 − 8.6 = **3.53**
10. 5.81 − 3.28 = ■ **2.53**
11. 9.03 + 9.3 = ■ **18.33**
12. 2.66 − 1.7 = ■ **0.96**
13. 7.56 + 9.33 = ■ **16.89**
14. 4.2 − 1.75 = ■ **2.45**
15. 3.44 − 2.07 = ■ **1.37**
16. 5.4 + 8.17 = ■ **13.57**
17. 12.1 + 4.79 = ■ **16.89**

Number correct ■

RETEACHING

Students who fall short of the mastery objective should be checked to determine the nature of the difficulty. If the trouble lies with multidigit addition and subtraction of whole numbers, reteach the appropriate algorithms using concrete materials. If the difficulty is adding and subtracting decimals, have students solve problems both with and without concrete objects such as play money*. Use graph paper if students have difficulty lining up the decimal points and columns.

PRACTICE p. 106

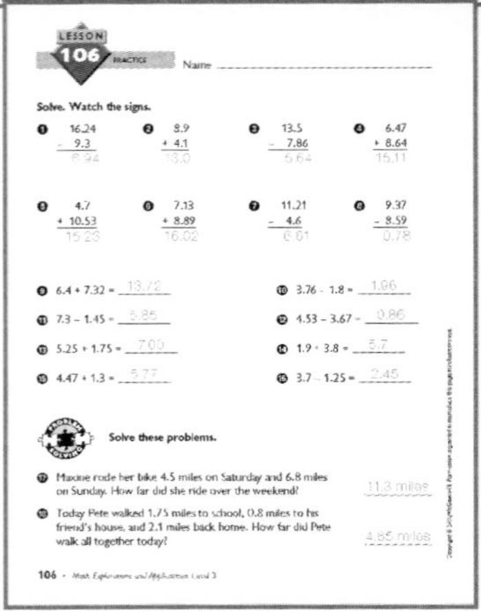

*available separately

you need a clear road map.

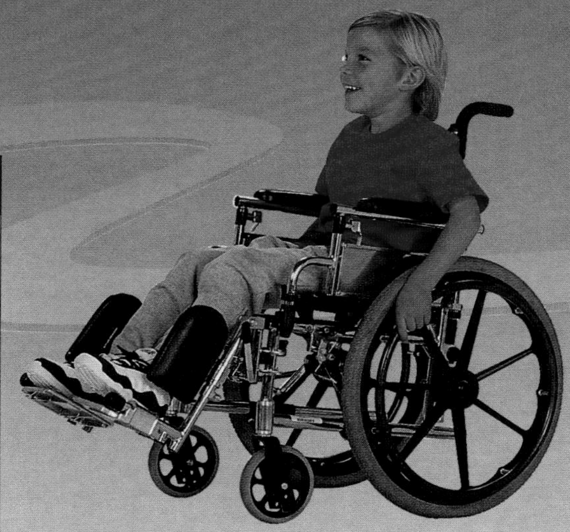

Solve.

18. Each time Amy adds a book to her bookshelf, she records how much room is left on the shelf. All her books are the same thickness. Copy and complete Amy's table.

Space on Amy's Bookshelf

Number of Books	5	6	7	8	9	10	11	12	13
Space Used	1.03	0.99	0.95	0.91	0.87	0.83	0.79	0.75	0.71

MATH JOURNAL

Make up five problems using the map below and solve them. Write your problems in your Math Journal and explain how to solve them.

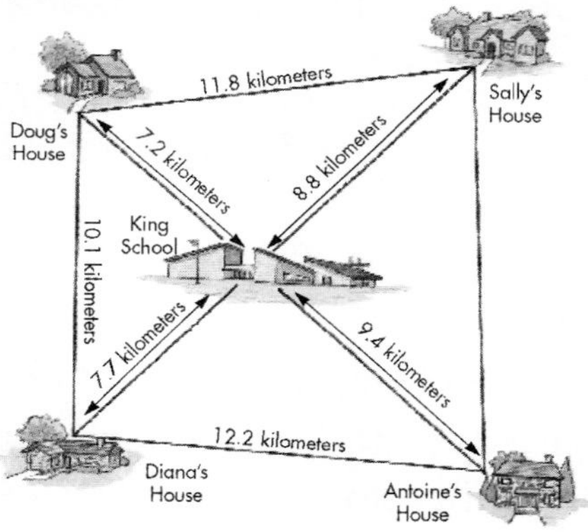

❷ Teach

Using the Student Pages Tell students that the problems on page 298 are a test. Allow students enough time to finish. When all students have finished, have them proofread their papers as a group. Remember to focus attention on the number of correct rather than the number of incorrect answers. Then have students complete page 299.

Using the Thinking Story Have students complete three problems from among those following "Mosquito Lake" on pages 88–89 of the Thinking Story Book.

❸ Wrap-Up

5 MINUTES

In Closing Ask students what they must remember to do when adding or subtracting numbers with decimals. Students should say they must write more zeros as necessary so that each number in the problem has the same number of decimal places.

Mastery Checkpoint 22

Students should demonstrate mastery of the addition and subtraction of decimals (with up to two decimal places) by correctly answering 12 of the 17 problems on page 298. The results of this assessment may be recorded on the Mastery Checkpoint Chart. You may also wish to assign the Assessment Master on page 41 to determine mastery.

ENRICHMENT p. 106

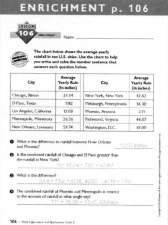

LESSON 106 ENRICHMENT Name

GEOGRAPHY CONNECTION

The chart below shows the average yearly rainfall in ten U.S. cities. Use the chart to help you write and solve the number sentence that answers each question below.

City	Average Yearly Rain (in inches)	City	Average Yearly Rain (in inches)
Chicago, Illinois	33.34	New York, New York	42.82
El Paso, Texas	7.82	Pittsburgh, Pennsylvania	36.30
Los Angeles, California	12.08	Phoenix, Arizona	7.11
Minneapolis, Minnesota	26.36	Richmond, Virginia	44.07
New Orleans, Louisiana	59.74	Washington, D.C.	39.00

1. What is the difference in rainfall between New Orleans and Phoenix? 52.63 inches
2. Is the combined rainfall of Chicago and El Paso greater than the rainfall in New York? no; 33.34 + 7.82 < 42.82
3. What is the difference? 33.4 + 7.82 = 41.16; 42.82 − 41.16 = 1.66
4. The combined rainfall of Phoenix and Minneapolis is nearest to the amount of rainfall in what single city? 7.11 + 26.36 = 33.47; Chicago

106 • Math Explorations and Applications Level 3

ASSESSMENT p. 41

UNIT 3 **Mastery Checkpoint 22** Addition and subtraction of decimal numbers (Lesson 106)

Name

The student demonstrates mastery by correctly answering at least 12 of the 15 problems.

Solve. Watch the signs.

1. 4.37 + 5.63 = 10.00
2. 9.3 − 5.5 = 3.8
3. 27.32 + 4.1 = 31.42
4. 8.8 − 6.22 = 2.58
5. 4.73 + 2.62 = 7.35
6. 5.54 + 4.73 = 10.27
7. 3.43 − 2.62 = 0.81
8. 5.05 − 4.5 = 0.55
9. 4.6 + 2.4 = 7.0
10. 6.21 − 5.03 = 1.18
11. 3.7 − 1.85 = 1.85
12. 4.2 + 9.15 = 13.35
13. 9.52 − 8.62 = 0.90
14. 5.72 + 6.28 = 12.00
15. 1.36 + 7.89 = 9.25

Math Explorations and Applications Level 3 • 41

Assessment Criteria

Did the student . . .

✓ make up at least five word problems with solutions based on page 299?

✓ demonstrate mastery of the addition and subtraction of decimals?

Homework To reinforce the lesson concept, have students play the "Harder Rummage Sale" game with a household member.

Level 3

◆ **Program Resources** are referenced at point of use.

◆ **Mastery Checkpoint** provides opportunities for teachers to check for student understanding of core skills and concepts.

◆ **Practice, Enrichment,** and **Reteaching** blackline masters and strategies are included for every lesson.

◆ **Assessment Criteria** tie informal assessment to the Lesson Objectives.

◆ **Homework** ideas are always included in Levels 3–6 for added practice and reinforcement.

Assessment tools help students stay on track.

Math Explorations and Applications **aligns teaching and assessment to support learning. With a variety of options, teachers can select appropriate methods to monitor student progress.**

Self-Assessment. *Are You Shiny or Rusty?* activities offer nonthreatening timed tests so that students can see how quickly and accurately they can recall the basic arithmetic facts.

Performance Assessment. Strategies in the Teacher's Guide and the Assessment Book provide opportunities for students to show what they know.

Portfolio Assessment. Suggestions throughout the Teacher's Guide give students an opportunity to demonstrate their mathematical growth.

Informal Assessment

- **Assessment Criteria.** In every lesson teachers are reminded what to look for as they informally assess student responses.
- **Varied Opportunities.** Every Game, Thinking Story, and Act It Out provides an opportunity for teachers to informally assess students' mathematical thinking.
- **Mental Math Exercises.** Daily interactive Mental Math activities offer opportunities for informal assessment and self-assessment.

Formal Assessment

- **Unit Assessment.** Mid-Unit Reviews, Unit Reviews, and Unit Tests provide ready-made formal assessment of students' comprehension.
- **Mastery Checkpoints.** These checkpoints and corresponding evaluations in the Assessment Books indicate times that teachers can check for mastery of specific skills and concepts.
- **Mastery Checkpoint Charts.** Mastery Checkpoints give teachers an easy way to keep track of students' mastery of specific skills.
- **Standardized-Format Tests.** Multiple-choice computation tests provide practice taking standardized tests at the same time they provide one more opportunity to assess students' math skills.

SRA®

MATH

Explorations and Applications

It will change the way students think about math . . . for a lifetime.

***Math Explorations and Applications* is a program with proven results for more than 25 years.**

- The program was developed one grade level at a time, building on valuable field test results to ensure consistency and continuity throughout all grade levels.
- Successfully field-tested in urban, suburban, and rural schools, *Math Explorations and Applications* ensures effectiveness in any teaching situation.
- Teaching strategies throughout the program are based on substantial bodies of research indicating how children learn best.
- Written and updated by a team of distinguished and committed authors, *Math Explorations and Applications* reflects time-tested strategies with proven results.
- We have listened carefully to teachers who use the program. This edition of *Math Explorations and Applications* reflects the many valuable suggestions and comments we have received from talented teachers over the years. We look forward to receiving your comments.

Exceeds ~~Meets~~ NCTM Standards!

Authorship

Dr. Stephen S. Willoughby

Mathematics Educator

Stephen S. Willoughby has taught mathematics at all levels, from first grade through graduate courses in schools in Massachusetts, Connecticut, Wisconsin, New York, and Arizona, including the University of Wisconsin and New York University. He is now Professor of Mathematics at the University of Arizona. He received bachelor's and master's degrees from Harvard University and a doctorate from Columbia University.

Dr. Willoughby was President of the National Council of Teachers of Mathematics from 1982 to 1984 and Chairman of the Council of Scientific Society Presidents in 1988. He was a member of the national Board of Advisors for SQUARE ONE TV, chairman of the United States Commission on Mathematics Instruction, and a member of the Education Testing Services Mathematics Advisory Committee for the successor to the National Teacher's Examination, and is now a member of the Education Advisory Panel of New American Schools Development Corporation (NASDC).

Dr. Willoughby has published more than 200 articles and books on mathematics and mathematics education and was senior author of the innovative K–8 mathematics series *Real Math™* published by Open Court.

Dr. Carl Bereiter

Cognitive Psychologist

Carl Bereiter is a professor in the Centre for Applied Cognitive Science, Ontario Institute for Studies in Education, University of Toronto. He holds a Ph.D. in educational psychology from the University of Wisconsin. He has done research and developed educational materials in such diverse areas as preschool education, thinking skills, writing, elementary school mathematics, and science understanding. He is also active in the development of advanced computer-based technology for schools. His scholarly contributions have been recognized by award of a Guggenheim Fellowship, appointments to the Center for Advanced Study in the Behavioral Sciences, election to the National Academy of Education, and an honorary Doctor of Laws from Queens University. His books include *Arithmetic and Mathematics* (1968), *Thinking Games* (1975 with Valerie Anderson), *The Psychology of Written Composition* (1987, with Marlene Scardamalia), and *Surpassing Ourselves: An Inquiry into the Nature and Implications of Expertise* (1993, also with Marlene Scardamalia) and the forthcoming *Education and Mind in the Knowledge Age.*

Dr. Peter Hilton

Mathematician

Peter Hilton is Distinguished Professor of Mathematics Emeritus at the State University of New York (Binghamton) and Distinguished Professor at the University of Central Florida. He holds M.A. and Doctorate of Philosophy degrees from Oxford University and a Ph.D. from Cambridge University. He has an honorary doctorate of humanities from Northern Michigan University, an honorary doctorate of science from the Memorial University of Newfoundland, and an honorary doctorate of science from the Autonomous University of Barcelona. In addition to his activity in research and teaching as a mathematician, he has a continuing interest in mathematics education and has served on many national and international committees and as chairman of the United States Commission on Mathematics Instruction. Dr. Hilton is the author of several important books, his most recent being *Mathematical Reflections,* jointly with Derek Holton and Jean Pedersen, and many research articles on algebraic topology, homological algebra, group theory, and category theory.

Dr. Joseph H. Rubinstein

Biologist and Educator

Joseph H. Rubinstein is Professor of Education and Chairperson of the Department of Education at Coker College, Hartsville, South Carolina. He received B.A., M.S., and Ph.D. degrees in biology from New York University, completing his studies in 1969. His interest in elementary education was kindled by his participation in the late 1960s in an experimental science curriculum development project, the Conceptually Oriented Program in Elementary Science (COPES). During that time he worked in the New York City public schools helping elementary school teachers implement science programs in their classrooms. Dr. Rubinstein served as the Director of Open Court Publishing Company's Mathematics and Science Curriculum Development Center during the development of *Real Math™,* the precursor to *SRA Math Explorations and Applications.* In 1984 he joined the faculty of Coker College, where his principal duties include training prospective teachers to teach mathematics and science.

Reviewers

Dr. Prentice Baptiste
Manhattan, KS

Debney Biggs
Shreveport, LA

Pat Dahl
Vancouver, WA

Karen Hardin
Houston, TX

Susan Humphries
BelAir, MD

Tucky Marchica
Inverness, IL

Dr. Marilyn Neil
Birmingham, AL

Bill Smith
Haddonfield, NJ

Bob Winkler
Overland Park, KS

Game Mat Testers

Grace Brethren Elementary School
Columbus, OH

Huber Ridge Elementary School
Westerville School District
Westerville, OH

St. Paul's Elementary School
Columbus Diocese
Westerville, OH

Tremont Elementary School
Upper Arlington School District
Upper Arlington, OH

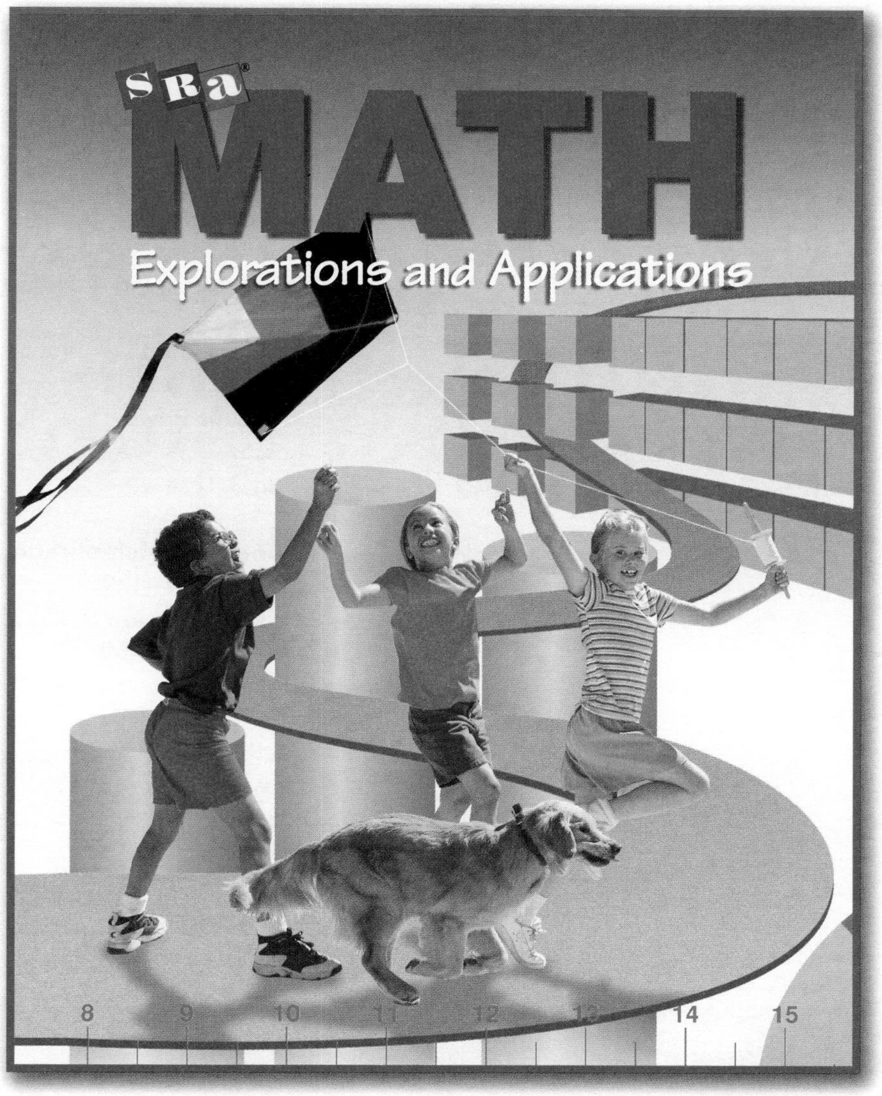

Stephen S. Willoughby
Carl Bereiter
Peter Hilton
Joseph H. Rubinstein

SRA/McGraw-Hill
A Division of The ***McGraw-Hill*** *Companies*

Printed in the United States of America.

Send all inquiries to:
SRA/McGraw-Hill
250 Old Wilson Bridge Road, Suite 310
Worthington, OH 43085

ISBN 0-02-687853-4

1 2 3 4 5 6 7 8 9 VHP 02 01 00 99 98 97

TABLE OF CONTENTS

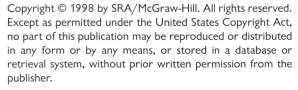

SRA/McGraw-Hill
A Division of The ***McGraw·Hill*** *Companies*

Printed in the United States of America.

Send all inquiries to:
SRA/McGraw-Hill
250 Old Wilson Bridge Road, Suite 310
Worthington, OH 43085

ISBN 0-02-687862-3

1 2 3 4 5 6 7 8 9 WEB 02 01 00 99 98 97

Acknowledgments

Photo Credits

p. T1, (l) ©Jeff Smith/Fotosmith; (r) ©Timothy Fuller; **T3,** ©Aaron Haupt; **T4,** ©Jeff Smith/Fotosmith; **T5,** ©Aaron Haupt; **T6,** ©Jeff Smith/Fotosmith; **T7,** ©Jeff Smith/Fotosmith; **T8,** (l) ©Jeff Smith/Fotosmith; (r) ©Timothy Fuller; **T9,** ©Jeff Smith/Fotosmith; **T10,** ©Jeff Smith/Fotosmith; **T11,** ©Jeff Smith/Fotosmith; **T13,** ©Jeff Smith/Fotosmith; **T14,** ©Timothy Fuller; **T15,** ©Jeff Smith/Fotosmith; **T32, T33, T200D,** ©1997/PhotoDisc.

Cover Credits

Front cover photo, ©Timothy Fuller; **Design and Illustration,** Morgan-Cain & Associates; **Back cover photo,** ©Timothy Fuller and Jeff Smith/Fotosmith.

TEACHING THE PROGRAM

Math Explorations and Applications is based upon the idea of making mathematics real for students. It builds upon what children already know when they enter school and upon what they learn from their experiences outside school. It helps children see that mathematics is useful and important in their own lives, and it makes learning mathematics enjoyable.

Math Explorations and Applications is based upon everyday teaching and learning. In the Teacher's Guide are all the activities that go together to make up the total learning experience. These activities have been tried, criticized, revised, and tried again by hundreds of teachers.

Math Explorations and Applications is based upon sound theory, research, and extensive field testing. It is a program that works.

In every grade the program emphasizes thinking skills, problem-solving strategies, real applications, mental arithmetic, estimation, approximation, measurement, organizing data, geometry, probability, statistics, and algebra. In addition, computational skills are introduced at appropriate levels and are reviewed and maintained in that level and in subsequent levels.

PROGRAM ORGANIZATION

There are three ways that *Math Explorations and Applications* has been carefully organized to introduce and reinforce concepts.

Early Introduction of Concepts

Math Explorations and Applications makes a point of exposing students to core problems and concepts from the beginning. For example, in traditional teaching, students first learn the plus sign and later are introduced to the minus sign. When signs are introduced one at a time, students learn to pay no attention to the sign because it is always the same. Students are trained in this way not to figure out the problem but to follow the pattern.

Similar confusion arises in the traditional teaching of subtraction of multidigit numbers. First, children learn to subtract with numbers that require no regrouping (65 – 32, for example). When they are later introduced to regrouping (62 – 35, for example), they are often confused because they have learned an easy and automatic way to subtract, which turns out to work only sometimes.

In *Math Explorations and Applications*, plus and minus signs are introduced at the same time in Level 1. In Level 2, multidigit subtraction problems that require regrouping, as well as those that do not, are introduced early on. Core mathematical concepts are emphasized in an age-appropriate manner at every level. The early introduction of concepts causes much less trouble and confusion later on because students don't have to unlearn patterns that they have begun to rely on. Furthermore, when students reach middle school and high school, they will already have a firm foundation in core mathematical concepts such as probability, statistics, geometry, and algebra.

Revisiting Concepts

While it is convenient to package teaching into neat, isolated units that deal with a single topic, the learning that goes on in children's minds cannot be so neatly packaged. Children learn, forget, and relearn. They catch a glimmer of an idea, lose it, catch it again, and finally get hold of it firmly enough that it becomes a solid part of understanding. In *Math Explorations and Applications*, concepts like inequalities, missing addends, and base 10 are developed and reviewed continuously over the whole year so that they become part of the child's working knowledge.

Throughout the year concepts and skills are introduced and reappear again and again in subsequent lessons and in Mixed Practice so that students never lose them. For example, basic addition, subtraction, multiplication, and division are a major focus of at least one third of the lessons in Level 3 and are practiced in virtually every Practice and Mixed Practice exercise.

Presenting Concepts in Different Contexts

In Level 4 of *Math Explorations and Applications*, multiplication is introduced and reinforced in more than 50 lessons throughout the entire year in all the following contexts:

- one-digit number multiplication
- two-digit number multiplication
- three-digit number multiplication
- algebra readiness
- area
- commutative property (order of factors)
- decimals
- division
- conversion graphs
- multidigit numbers
- money
- multiplication facts
- multiples of 10
- powers of 10
- problem solving
- repeated addition
- skip counting
- square numbers
- whole numbers

The thoughtful organization at every level of *Math Explorations and Applications* ensures that students are introduced to mathematics concepts and skills in context at appropriate age levels. They encounter these concepts and use these skills again and again throughout the year and in subsequent years in different, age-appropriate contexts.

> ***"There are reasons for almost everything we do in mathematics. Children should be encouraged to discover, or at least see, those reasons. Understanding the reasons will help them remember how to do the mathematics; but more important, it will help them understand that the mathematics is related to their reality and that mathematics can be used to help them understand the real world."***
>
> —Stephen S. Willoughby
> *Mathematics Education for a Changing World*

COMPONENTS CHART

A variety of resources that present math concepts in a way all students can learn!

Components	Levels						
	K	1	2	3	4	5	6
Student Edition	✓	✓	✓	✓	✓	✓	✓
Teacher's Guide	✓	✓	✓	✓	✓	✓	✓
Thinking Story Book		✓	✓	✓			
Game Mat Package	✓	✓	✓	✓	✓	✓	✓
Reteaching Masters		✓	✓	✓	✓	✓	✓
Reteaching Workbook		✓	✓	✓	✓	✓	✓
Reteaching Workbook TE		✓	✓	✓	✓	✓	✓
Practice Masters	✓	✓	✓	✓	✓	✓	✓
Practice Workbook	✓	✓	✓	✓	✓	✓	✓
Practice Workbook TE	✓	✓	✓	✓	✓	✓	✓
Enrichment Masters	✓	✓	✓	✓	✓	✓	✓
Enrichment Workbook	✓	✓	✓	✓	✓	✓	✓
Enrichment Workbook TE	✓	✓	✓	✓	✓	✓	✓
Assessment Masters	✓	✓	✓	✓	✓	✓	✓
Home Connections Masters	✓	✓	✓	✓	✓	✓	✓
Literature Library	✓	✓	✓	✓			
Primary Manipulative Kit	✓	✓	✓				
Primary Overhead Manipulative Kit	✓	✓	✓				
Intermediate Manipulative Kit				✓	✓	✓	✓
Intermediate Overhead Manipulative Kit				✓	✓	✓	✓
Teacher Manipulative Kit	✓	✓	✓	✓	✓	✓	✓
Basic Manipulative Kit	✓	✓	✓	✓	✓	✓	✓
Primary Overhead Calculator	✓	✓	✓	✓			
Intermediate Overhead Calculator					✓	✓	✓
TI-108™ Calculator Package	✓	✓	✓	✓			
Math Explorer™ Calculator Package					✓	✓	✓
Math Explorations and Applications CD-ROM Program		✓	✓	✓	✓	✓	✓
The Cruncher CD-ROM Program and Guide					✓	✓	✓
My Silly CD of Counting CD-ROM	✓						
Professional Development Handbook	✓	✓	✓	✓	✓	✓	✓
Program Video	✓	✓	✓	✓	✓	✓	✓
Teacher Management System	✓	✓	✓	✓	✓	✓	✓

PROGRAM MANAGEMENT

In *Math Explorations and Applications* there are a variety of resources for students and teachers to use to introduce and demonstrate concepts and to practice math skills. These carefully integrated materials each play an important and well-thought-out role in the program as a whole.

TEACHER'S GUIDE

This comprehensive manual gives specific advice for every lesson and lesson component, as well as teaching tips, explanations, and background information.

STUDENT EDITION

The Student Edition provides practice with written problems. It is also used to present games and activities. It is not, however, the main source of concept presentation or skill practice. Student Edition pages supplement the teacher's concept presentation and the practice provided by Mental Math exercises, activities, games, and Thinking Stories.

BASIC MANIPULATIVES

Basic Manipulatives—**Number Cubes, Number Wheels, and Number Strips**—are used throughout *Math Explorations and Applications* in Games and in Mental Math activities that appear in the Teacher's Guide. The Basic Manipulatives allow all students to participate in every Mental Math activity in a nonthreatening way. Mental Math activities provide essential, regular practice in basic math facts. Furthermore, they allow the teacher to informally assess each student's mathematical skill.

The Number Cubes used at Levels 1 and 2 allow students to make any integer from 0 through 100. The students use the cubes to form numbers in games and to show answers during Mental Math exercises. In Levels 3–6, students use Number Wheels for display. Each wheel can be dialed to show any digit from 0 to 9. The wheels allow students to make any integer from 0 through 99,999.

Most Mental Math activities are done in the following three steps. The pace should be lively enough to keep things moving yet not so fast that students have insufficient time to think.

1. **"Find."** The teacher presents the problem either orally or on the chalkboard. The students find the answer and arrange their Number Cubes or Number Wheel in a position to display it.
2. **"Hide."** The students hide the answer against their chests. The teacher waits for most of the students to have an answer. Teachers do not need to wait for every student to find and hide an answer, but long enough so that students who are making progress toward a solution have time to finish. Add a "peek-to-be-sure" step to keep all students involved while waiting for the next command.
3. **"Show."** The students hold up their Number Cubes or Number Wheel so that the teacher can see the response. The teacher quickly checks the responses, shows or tells the correct answer, and quickly moves to the next problem. Only the teacher and the students who got a wrong answer need know about it. Teachers can give these students extra teaching later on.

PRIMARY AND INTERMEDIATE MANIPULATIVE KITS

In the real world, students experience number in many different representations. If in mathematics instruction they are given only one way of representing number—whether with rods, blocks, coins, sticks, or tally marks—they are liable to become dependent upon that one method. In *Math Explorations and Applications* all these ways—and more—of representing number are used.

Whenever appropriate, manipulatives are used to show the connection between the real world and the mathematics. The use of manipulatives is discontinued after a sufficient connection has been made so that the abstract nature of mathematics is not obscured.

LESSON SUPPORT MATERIALS

A variety of extra activities is available to support lesson concepts and skills. Activities in the Practice Workbook provide extra practice in computational skills. Enrichment activities offer extensions, and Reteaching activities help those who have not yet grasped the lesson concept or skill. These activities are keyed to each lesson. Assessment masters provide the Mastery Checkpoints, Mid-Unit Reviews, and Unit Tests.

TECHNOLOGY SUPPORT MATERIALS

- ◆ Calculators are suggested for use in appropriate lessons.
- ◆ SRA **Cruncher** suggestions are also provided at point of use when a spreadsheet application would be appropriate or would facilitate solving a problem.
- ◆ The *Math Explorations and Applications* Software provides extra practice for specific skills in a motivating format.

PACING

Math Explorations and Applications is intended to be taught at a lively pace but not to be rushed through at the expense of achievement. Lessons are generally written to fill a 45-minute time period. Teachers should move quickly from activity to activity. Introductions and lesson closures should be short because these tend to be ineffective and often lose students' attention.

The efficient lesson plans in *Math Explorations and Applications* help teachers gives their students the chance to practice skills, to solve thinking problems, and to do enrichment activities. Here are some tips for using the resources efficiently.

Be prepared. Having necessary materials ready is, of course, important. To help, sections in the Lesson Plans entitled "Looking Ahead" and "Materials" will be useful. This is a good reason to read the lesson in advance.

Watch the clock. The clock can tell a teacher when he or she has concentrated on an activity too long, even before students show signs of restlessness. Teachers should keep an eye on the clock to make sure they don't spend too much time talking or shifting from one activity to another.

Extend lessons to more than one day. Teachers may occasionally find it necessary to spend an extra day on some lessons. This is expected. It is recommended that more than one day be spent on many lessons. The time gained by extending a lesson should go to more teaching and drill on related skills, to related games, or to a review of prerequisite skills.

> *"Whole-class response activities encourage practice, allow students to correct their own errors, and allow the teacher to identify difficulties that individual students are having or that are common to the entire class."*
>
> —Stephen S. Willoughby
> *Mathematics Education for a Changing World*

If you have more than forty-five minutes a day for math. Below are some ideas for extending parts of the lessons.

- Lengthen game periods by five minutes each (more when new games are introduced).
- Repeat whole-group activities when you feel that the students will remain interested.
- Lengthen Mental Math exercises by up to five minutes.
- Lengthen demonstrations and seminars by two or three minutes at most.
- Use the Enrichment masters.

If you have less than forty-five minutes a day for math. Many teachers will be tempted to forgo Games or Thinking Stories in a time crunch, but these elements of *Math Explorations and Applications* are vital for developing mathematical intelligence, without which computational skills have little value. Try these suggestions if there is little time.

- Present the Thinking Stories during reading or some other time outside the regular math period.
- Conduct games outside the regular math period. Set up game-playing sessions every Friday, for example. Be aware, however, that not all games can be transferred to special sessions, because sometimes a game provides practice that will help students complete a particular lesson.
- Complete Mental Math exercises during five-minute periods at the beginning or end of the day or right before or after lunch. These sessions are not always essential to a particular lesson, but they do provide regular drill with Mental Math and basic math facts.

ASSESSMENT

Math Explorations and Applications is unusually rich in opportunities to keep track of–and do something about–individual student progress.

In the Teacher's Guide

Each lesson in the Teacher's Guide provides at least two different assessment suggestions. One is Assessment Criteria, which provides questions teachers can ask themselves as they observe students completing the lesson activities. Additional suggestions include the following:

- Informal assessment (interviews, observation, and oral assessment)
- Formal assessment (Tests, Reviews, Mastery Checkpoints, and Mastery Checkpoint Masters)
- Self-Assessment
- Portfolio and Performance Assessment

In the Student Edition

A formal Mid-Unit Review as well as a Unit Review and a Unit Test are provided in the Student Edition in Levels 1–6. Self-Assessments and timed tests are included throughout the Student Editions for students to evaluate their own performances.

In the Assessment Book

In the Assessment Book, there is a master for each Mastery Checkpoint, and an additional Mid-Unit Review and two Unit Tests, one in standardized (multiple-choice) format. Each unit also provides Performance Assessment activities and Portfolio Assessment suggestions. The Assessment Book includes additional information on the various alternative assessment options that are provided in the program, as well as suggestions for using rubrics to grade these assessments.

Informal Daily Assessment

Use Mental Math, Games, Thinking Stories, and Student Edition pages for day-to-day observation and assessment of how well each student is learning the skills and grasping concepts. Because of their special nature, these activities are an effective and convenient means of monitoring. Games, for example, allow the teacher to watch students practice particular skills under conditions more natural to students than most classroom activities. Mental Math activities allow the teacher to get feedback from each student, to give immediate feedback to each student, and to keep all the students actively involved.

To follow through on daily monitoring, consider the Reteaching strategy or master in each lesson to provide immediate help to students who are having difficulty.

Mastery Checkpoints and Charts

To help teachers formally yet conveniently monitor the progress of each student, there are more than 20 skills identified at each grade level that are important for future progress. These skills are listed on the Mastery Checkpoint Chart in the Assessment Book for each grade level. Each skill is described in detail in the Mastery Checkpoint section of the Teacher's Guide lesson in which teachers can formally assess that skill. These Mastery Checkpoints are an opportunity for teachers to monitor how well students have mastered basic skills and to provide extra help to those who are having trouble. Mastery Checkpoints are placed in the lesson in which most, but not all, of the students are expected to have achieved adequate proficiency in the skill. Teachers should not hold up the class waiting for every student to demonstrate success.

Using the Mastery Checkpoint Chart

- Fill in the names of all the students in the class.
- When a Mastery Checkpoint is encountered in the Teacher's Guide, follow the suggestions for observing and assessing each student's success.
- ✓ Place a check mark in the appropriate column of the Mastery Checkpoint Chart beside the name of each student who demonstrates success on the objective in question.
- **P** Pencil in a *P* in the appropriate column for each student who grasps the concept but still needs further practice to sharpen his or her skill. Assign extra practice to students whose names you marked with a *P*.
- **T** Pencil in a *T* for each student who has not yet grasped the idea and needs further teaching. Give extra teaching or Reteaching to students whose names you marked with a *T*.
- Change Ts to Ps and Ps to check marks when students demonstrate success on the objective. Do not hold up the entire class, however, waiting for all students to demonstrate success. More teaching and practice on a particular skill is always given in a later lesson, usually the following one. At that time teachers can focus on those students who need extra help.

> *"Observation of game-playing activity resembles observation of real-life-out-of-school activities as closely as anything we are likely to see in school. Such observation will often give greater insight into a child's thought patterns than anything else the teacher can do."*
>
> –Stephen S. Willoughby
> *Mathematics Education for a Changing World*

MANIPULATIVE KITS

Component	Game Mat Package (K-6)	Basic (K)	Basic (1-2)	Basic (3-6)	Primary (K-2)	Primary Overhead (K-2)	Intermediate (3-6)	Intermediate Overhead (3-6)	Teacher (K-6)
Angle Ruler							✓		
Attribute Blocks					✓	✓			
Base-10 Blocks				✓	✓	✓	✓		
Beakers									✓
Bills	✓*					✓		✓	
Classifying Counters					✓				
Clock Faces (demonstration or individual)					✓	✓	✓	✓	✓
Coins	✓*					✓		✓	
Counters (opaque or two-sided)	✓				✓	✓	✓	✓	
Cubes (interlocking)					✓		✓		
Decimal Set							✓		
Dual-Dial Scale									✓
Fraction Cubes							✓		
Fraction Tiles					✓	✓		✓	
Funnels							✓		
Geoboard					✓	✓			
Geometric Solids					✓				
Geometric Volume Set							✓		
Math Balance									✓
Metric Grids								✓	
Mirrors					✓		✓		
Number Cubes–0-5 and 5-10 Units	✓	✓	✓	✓					
Number Cubes–0-5 and 5-10 Tens			✓						
Number Line (walk-on)					✓				
Number Strips		✓	✓						
Number Tiles						✓		✓	
Number Wheels				✓					
Pattern Blocks					✓	✓			
Place Markers	✓								
Place Value Pad							✓		
Precision Balance									✓
Protractors							✓		
Shape Set						✓		✓	
Spinners and Dice (blank)						✓	✓	✓	
Stopwatch									✓
Tape Measure					✓		✓		
Thermometer (classroom, demonstration, or individual)					✓	✓	✓	✓	✓
Venn Diagram/Graphing Mat									✓

*not in the Kindergarten package

PRACTICE AND PROBLEM SOLVING

GAMES AND THINKING STORIES

GAMES

Games do not provide just fun or enrichment in *Math Explorations and Applications;* they are a vital, almost daily part of the program. Games give students a chance to develop their mathematical skills and understandings in situations in which those skills and understandings count. Games provide practice. They give students a means of becoming proficient in the mathematical skills to which they've been introduced. Some games give students a chance to work out important mathematical ideas and problem-solving strategies. Games also give the teacher an opportunity for informal assessment. By observing game-playing sessions, teachers can quickly assess how well individual students have learned the skill being practiced.

Each game involves the use of specific skills, but there is usually also a certain amount of luck involved, so the more able student does not always win. When a lesson plan prescribes a game, it does so because the principal skills involved in that game need attention at that time. Some lesson plans suggest that students play games of their choice. The Game Directory lists principal skills involved in each game to help the teacher select those games that will give each student an appropriate form of practice. Game Mats and Cube Games are the two types of games used in *Math Explorations and Applications*.

GAME MATS

Many of the games in *Math Explorations and Applications* are board games found in the Game Mat package for each grade level. There are five Game Mats in Kindergarten, 13 in Levels 1–3, and 14 in Levels 4–6. In each Game Mat package there are 15 copies of each Game Mat, as well as enough counters, place markers, Number Cubes, and money so that the entire class can play a game at the same time. Also included is A Guide for Using the Game Mats and an overhead transparency of each game for introducing the games to the class. Many of the Game Mats are offered in both a standard and a harder version. A copy of each game can also be found in the back of this Teacher's Guide.

CUBE GAMES

Many games don't require Game Mats. They use Number Cubes or sometimes require no materials at all. These games, presented in the Student Edition in Levels 3–6 and in the Teacher's Guide in Levels K–2, reinforce basic math skills and involve mathematical reasoning.

INTRODUCING GAMES

Here are some tips for making sure that games are played correctly.

- Familiarize yourself with each game by playing it before showing the students how to play it.
- Show, don't just tell, how a game is played. Games should be demonstrated in front of the class when they are first introduced. Overhead Game Mats are provided for this purpose. Verbalize the rules as you demonstrate.
- Make sure each student can see when a game is demonstrated.
- Supervise to see that students get off to the right start after you've introduced a game.
- Let students who know the game rules help those who haven't played it.

ORGANIZING SUCCESSFUL GAME SESSIONS

- Mixing ability levels from time to time, however, keeps some students from having an oppressive sense of their slowness.
- Change groupings from day to day. Students can learn different things by playing with different partners.
- Assign a referee to each group. The referee sees that the rules are followed, reminds players when it is their turn, settles disputes, keeps track of scores, and in some games acts as banker. Associate a sense of honor and responsibility around the role of the referee so that students will be willing to serve as referee.
- Encourage students to play games during free time—in school and at home—as well as during the scheduled game periods.
- Allow students to make up and name their own variations of the games. Whenever students regularly misinterpret a rule, there's a good chance they have discovered a new and, to them, more interesting version of the game. Be alert, however, to avoid versions that reduce the skill-practice value of the game.
- Encourage parents, teacher aides, or older students to participate in game-playing sessions with students.
- Stress enjoyment rather than competition. Emphasize sportsmanship, fair play, and giving each player a turn.
- Teach students to control their excitement and to speak in a low voice.
- Make Game Mats accessible. Store Game Mats so that students can find and return them by themselves.

THINKING STORIES

Thinking Stories are an essential part of *Math Explorations and Applications*. The stories and related thinking problems tap into the child's world of fantasy and humor. They are aimed at developing quantitative intelligence—creativity and common sense in the use of mathematics. The stories allow students to discover the power of their own mathematical common sense and of their innate capacity for reasoning. The stories and problems are filled with surprises, so students cannot apply arithmetic routinely. Instead they must apply mathematical common sense to choose which operation to use, to recognize which data are relevant to the questions asked, to determine whether an answer is absurd, and to decide when calculation isn't necessary.

THINKING STORY CHARACTERS

The various characters in the stories appear in all grade levels. The children in the stories age with each grade level so that they are about the same age as the students reading the stories. All the characters have peculiar thinking patterns that students come to know. Mr. Muddle, for example, is always forgetting things. Ferdie jumps to conclusions, and Mr. Breezy provides too much information. Students are challenged to listen carefully and to try to outthink the characters.

READING THE THINKING STORIES

The Thinking Stories are designed to be read to students. They appear in the Teacher's Guide and in separate Thinking Story books in Levels 1–3. At Levels 4–6 the Thinking Stories appear in three to five or more parts in the student book so that students have an option to read them individually or in groups, depending upon their reading abilities. As the stories unfold, students are asked questions that prompt them to think ahead of the characters—to spot what is wrong with what a character has done or said, to anticipate what is going to happen as a result, or to think of other possibilities that the character hasn't considered.

Following each story is a selection of short problems. Like the story questions, these problems generally require more thinking than computation and have a mixture of difficulty levels.

PACING

Most teachers spend about 15 minutes reading a Thinking Story and discussing the corresponding questions. In many lessons teachers may spend about five minutes on three or four of the questions that follow the story.

The Introduction to the Storybook for Levels 1–3 contains a briefing on the characters and useful hints on presenting stories and problems.

TEACHING THE BASICS IN K–3

Math Explorations and Applications does not take the traditional route of teaching basic computation in the early grades. Because developing a solid mathematics skills foundation in the early grades is so important to future success in mathematics, concentrating on helping students understand from the very beginning is essential.

TEACHING ADDITION AND SUBTRACTION

In *Math Explorations and Applications*, addition and subtraction are taught together so that students can see the relationship between the operations. Many traditional programs teach one operation and then the other. This seems simple and straightforward and would be appropriate if the two operations were not related. By teaching the operations at the same time, students learn to think about what they are doing rather than simply memorizing patterns, and they also learn the relationship between addition and subtraction.

PLACE VALUE

Research shows that many of the difficulties students have with mathematics can be traced to a faulty understanding of place value, a problem that often develops in the early grades. *Math Explorations and Applications* takes great care to develop this concept carefully and systematically. The use of expanded counting in early grades is one practical solution for meeting this need.

Once students begin working with numbers above 10, they often have difficulty understanding the significance of the ones position and the tens position. As students encounter addition and subtraction with regrouping, a knowledge of place value becomes even more important. Students commonly make mistakes such as 27 – 18 = 11 because they do not understand place value and simply subtract the greater number from the lesser number, regardless of whether it is in the subtrahend or minuend position.

Teaching expanded counting from the beginning helps students understand the true value of a number. They recognize that the number 57, for example, is really five tens and seven.

For example, for the numbers 19, 20, 21, 22 instead of counting "nineteen, twenty, twenty-one, twenty-two" expand the counting to "ten and nine, two tens, two tens and one, two tens and two."

To encourage students to visualize place value, in addition to the careful use of base-10 manipulatives, in the beginning and when appropriate, digits in the tens place are written larger than the digits in the ones place: 19, 20, 21, 22.

Expanded counting helps young students understand the base-10 structure of our number system. The expanded oral form helps show the relationship between 1 and 11, between 2 and 12, and so on. The expanded written form helps show that even though the numeral 9 represents a greater quantity than the numeral 1, the 1 in 19 represents a greater quantity than the 9.

By the end of Level 1 and by Level 2 most students will change over to a more conventional way of writing and saying numbers. This transition is usually quite smooth. Those students who still have problems understanding place value or difficulty with regrouping even in Level 3, however, may benefit from the oral and written demonstration of expanded counting.

> ***"Whenever possible, addition and subtraction should be taught at about the same time so that learners can contrast the two and so that problems can be presented that are not all solved by using the same operation."***
>
> —Stephen S. Willoughby
> *Mathematics Education for a Changing World*

> ***"Often, when addition and subtraction are taught at about the same time, teachers complain that children are confused. It is true that children find it much easier to learn only one algorithm at a time, then practice that algorithm for a long time, then solve "problems" using only that algorithm, and then go on to something else. The difficulty with such a procedure is that it pretty much eliminates the need for the learner to think. When the time comes to decide which operation is appropriate, the pupil is unlikely to have given enough thought to what the operations mean to be able to make intelligent decisions."***
>
> —Stephen S. Willoughby
> *Mathematics Education for a Changing World*

TEACHING THE BASICS IN K–3 (Continued)

FINGER SETS

Allowing students to use their fingers as manipulatives to count or to add and subtract is often frowned upon. Some experts fear that students will become too dependent on this method. However, the fact remains that most young students use their fingers in mathematics whether or not they are allowed to do so.

In ***Math Explorations and Applications***, teachers teach students to use their fingers in a systematic way. Students learn to form "standard" finger sets, with each set representing a specific number. In this way, students will be able to recognize, for example, seven or eight fingers visually and kinesthetically without having to count individual fingers. Eventually, students will be able to abandon the use of their fingers and depend more and more upon mental operations.

The illustration below demonstrates the standard way of forming finger sets. Either hand may be used for the numbers 0 through 5. The number 1 is represented by the thumb.

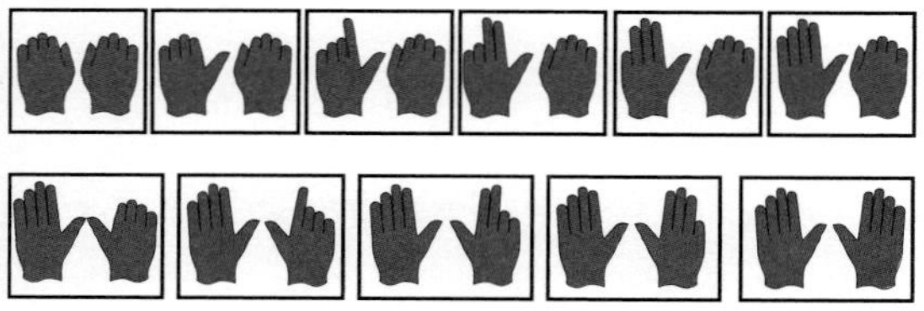

Students may enjoy learning a counting song, such as "This Old Man," "Five Little Ducks," "Over in the Meadow," or "Roll Over," as they learn to count with finger sets. Music addresses yet another intelligence and often helps young students remember what they might otherwise easily forget.

Eventually students will be able to form the finger set for each number the teacher requests and recognize each finger set by sight. This will reduce or eliminate the need to count fingers.

Children use finger sets as one of several ways to represent numbers. In addition to finger sets, students learn to use counters, number lines, number strips, tally marks, play money, and the numerals themselves. Thus they do not become overly dependent on any one method of representing numbers.

Moving from Concrete to Mental Math

As students move from concrete to Mental Math, the teacher should phase out the use of finger sets. Students should have abandoned the use of finger sets by the end of Level 1. Following are the stages in this process:

1. Students learn to form the standard finger sets for 0 through 10.
2. Students learn to recognize the standard finger sets by sight and feel without counting fingers.
3. Students learn to add or subtract with finger sets. For example, if they are adding 4 + 3, they show the finger set for 4 and count fingers to add 3. However, they recognize the answer, 7, without counting fingers.
4. Students learn to add or subtract with finger sets out of sight. They can feel the finger sets, but they cannot see them.
5. Students learn "statue" arithmetic. At this stage students only imagine themselves raising or lowering their fingers to add or subtract. For example, for 6 – 2, they show the finger set for 6, then imagine two fingers being lowered. They imagine the remaining finger set and thus get the answer, 4.
6. Students no longer need to use finger sets. They have moved from concrete to Mental Math.

Establishing a firm foundation of math skills and mathematical thinking at K–3 will enable students to enjoy and succeed in mathematics throughout their lives.

> ***"If we teach children to use their fingers intelligently in the early grades, they should be more able to get along without using them later."***
>
> —Stephen S. Willoughby
> *Mathematics Education for a Changing World*

Contents

UNIT 1

Addition and Subtraction 1

■ Application ● Preteaching ▲ Revisiting

UNIT 2 Two-Digit Addition and Subtraction 99

■ Application ● Preteaching ▲ Revisiting

■ Application ● Preteaching ▲ Revisiting

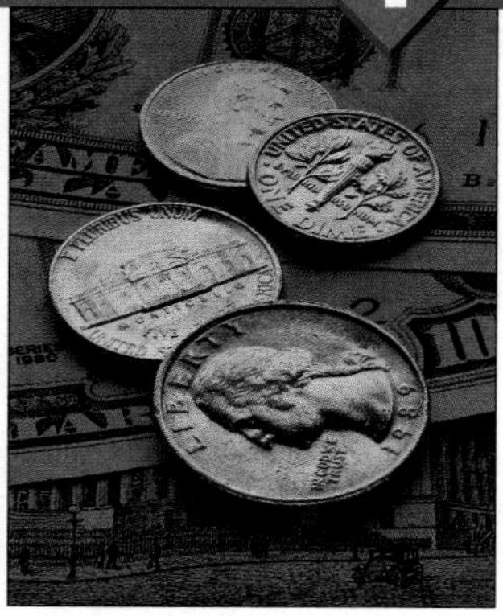

■ Application ● Preteaching ▲ Revisiting

■ Application ● Preteaching ▲ Revisiting

PACING

HOW TO PACE THE PROGRAM

The lessons in this book are designed to be taught at a lively pace. Students should move quickly from activity to activity. In this way, they will remain alert and interested in what they are learning.

The lively pace is also important because there is much for students to learn at this grade level. Yet, 45 minutes a day is about all that most teachers can devote to mathematics. Therefore, it's important to get as much from those minutes as possible. Here are some tips to help you make the most of your time:

Tips for Making the Most of Your Time

- **Prepare items you'll need for a lesson ahead of time.** See the Lesson Planner sections titled Materials and Program Resources for a complete listing of the items you'll need. The Looking Ahead feature under the Wrap-Up alerts you to any advance preparation needed for an upcoming lesson.
- **Read the lesson plan in advance.** This will save you time and make the lesson run more smoothly.
- **Keep introductions and explanations brief.** You will lose your students' attention if you try to say too much.

HOW TO EXTEND YOUR LESSONS

You might need to spend an extra day teaching some lessons. Lessons that might take an extra day are noted in the individual Lesson Planner and in the Unit Overview Planning Chart—but only you can be the judge. When you decide to let a lesson run two days, try dividing it as follows:

Day 1

- Do all suggested activities, but not the Student Edition pages.
- Use extra time to review the skills students will need for the lesson.
- Modify the Reteaching Strategy/Master and Practice Master for use with the entire class.
- Don't greatly lengthen the demonstration period (K–3).

Day 2

- Review the Mental Math or Number Wheel, or Number Cube Exercises from the preceding day.
- Provide additional teaching and practice on related skills.
- Devote time to a related Cube Game or Game Mat.
- Allow plenty of time for students to do the Student Edition activities.

WHEN YOU HAVE MORE THAN 45 MINUTES FOR MATH

Tips for Making the Best Use of Extra Time

- Lengthen game periods by five minutes each (more when new games are introduced).
- Repeat whole-group activities when you feel that students will remain interested.
- Lengthen Mental Math, Number Wheel, or Number Cube exercises by up to five minutes each.
- Lengthen demonstrations and activities by two or three minutes at most.
- Use the Reteaching, Practice, and Enrichment Masters. You might also want to use the various Cross-Curricular Connections strategies provided throughout the Teacher's Guide.

WHEN YOU HAVE FEWER THAN 45 MINUTES FOR MATH

Tips for Making the Best Use of Less Time

- Don't eliminate the games or the Thinking Stories. These help develop mathematical intelligence.
- Do the Thinking Story activities outside the regular mathematics period. There might be time the first thing in the morning, right after lunch, or when you have a read-aloud period.
- Conduct games outside the regular mathematics period—every Friday, perhaps— especially if you have another adult or older student to assist you. If a game provides practice that will help students do the Student Edition exercise, play the game during the lesson.
- Conduct Mental Math on basic facts outside the regular mathematics period.
- Reduce a few lesson components by a minute or two.
- Introduce the Problem of the Day at the start of school each morning instead of at the start of the regular mathematics period.

UNIT 1

Addition and Subtraction

REVIEWING AND EXPANDING BASIC FACTS

OVERVIEW

In this unit students count and write numbers through 100, count and regroup money amounts, and read a calendar. Students investigate basic facts in addition and subtraction by counting and work up to using an algorithm for adding tens and ones. The emphasis is on student experience and on using basic facts to solve problems. In addition, students read pictographs and bar graphs and measure length in both customary and metric units.

Integrated Topics in This Unit Include:

- counting and writing numbers through 100
- counting and regrouping money
- finding missing numbers on a calendar and naming days of the week
- adding and subtracting facts
- using addition tables
- finding missing addends
- understanding the commutative property
- applying addition and subtraction in word problems
- reading pictographs, vertical bar graphs, and horizontal bar graphs
- reviewing tens and ones
- reviewing money
- counting by tens
- measuring in centimeters and meters
- measuring in inches, feet, and yards
- estimating length
- finding perimeter by measuring

MISSING ADDENDS
INTRODUCING GRAPHS

> “Children must understand numbers if they are to make sense of the ways numbers are used in their everyday world. They need to use numbers to quantify, to identify location, to identify a specific object in a collection, to name, and to measure. Furthermore, an understanding of place value is crucial for later work with numbers and computation.”
>
> —*NCTM Curriculum and Evaluation Standards for School Mathematics*

GAMES

Motivating Mixed Practice

Games provide **basic math skills** practice in cooperative groups and develop **mathematical reasoning.**

Tracing and Writing Numbers Game	Lesson 1	page 3
Counting and Writing Numbers Game	Lesson 2	page 5
Yard Sale Game	Lesson 3	page 8
Calendar Game	Lesson 4	page 9
Frog Pond Game	Lesson 8	page 18
Addition Table Game	Lesson 13	page 28
Harder Addition Table Game	Lesson 14	page 30
Roll 15 Game	Lesson 18	page 38
Missing Number Game	Lesson 19	page 40
Roll 20 to 5 Game	Lesson 22	page 48
Space Game and Harder Space Game	Lesson 24	page 52
What's the Problem?	Lesson 26	page 56
Roll a Number Game	Lesson 32	page 68
Get to 100 by Tens or Ones Game	Lesson 36	page 76
Roll a Number Game	Lesson 38	page 80

THINKING STORY

Integrated Problem Solving

Thinking Stories provide opportunities for students to work in **cooperative groups** and develop **logical reasoning skills** while they integrate **reading skills** with mathematics.

Measuring Bowser	Lesson 3	Thinking Story Book pages 6–11
The Amazing Number Machine Makes Mistakes	Lesson 11	Thinking Story Book pages 12–17
Mr. Muddle Takes a Test	Lesson 21	Thinking Story Book pages 18–23
Ferdie Knows the Rules	Lesson 27	Thinking Story Book pages 24–29
Portia's Rules	Lesson 36	Thinking Story Book pages 30–35
Paint Up, Fix Up, Measure Up	Lesson 42	Thinking Story Book pages 36–41

Story Summaries In “Measuring Bowser,” Mr. Breezy asks some of the children to help him measure and weigh the dog, Bowser.

“The Amazing Number Machine Makes Mistakes” focuses on common errors in arithmetic, subtracting when it should add, and so on.

“Mr. Muddle Takes a Test” focuses on everyday uses of addition, subtraction, and common sense.

“Ferdie Knows the Rules” explores rules and their exceptions. Story problems emphasize using arithmetic in everyday situations.

“Portia's Rules” focuses on testing rules. Portia hypothesizes and tests her hypotheses.

“Paint Up, Fix Up, Measure Up” focuses on Mr. Muddle's effort to fix and paint his house.

PROJECT

Making Connections

The Unit Project establishes more real-world connections. Students work in **cooperative groups** to solve problems and communicate their findings.

In the Unit Project students create an address and phone book of local or imaginary businesses. Students may begin this project any time after Lesson 21.

Addition and Subtraction Lesson Plans

	LESSON	PACING	PRIMARY OBJECTIVES	FEATURE	RESOURCES	NCTM STANDARDS
1	Counting and Writing Numbers 3–4	1 day	to review writing the numbers 0 through 100 and introducing estimating	Game	Practice Master 1 Enrichment Master 1	5, 6
2	More Counting and Writing 5–6	1 day	to continue to review counting numbers through 100	Game	Reteaching Master Practice Master 2 Enrichment Master 2	3, 6
3	Counting and Regrouping Money 7–8	1 day	to review counting and regrouping money	Thinking Story, Game	Practice Master 3 Enrichment Master 3	1, 2, 3, 4, 6
4	Numbers on the Calendar 9–10	1 day	to review reading a monthly calendar and give students an understanding of its structure	Thinking Story, Game	Practice Master 4 Enrichment Master 4	3, 4, 10
5	Writing Numbers 11–12	1 day	✓ to evaluate students' ability to count and write numbers from 1–100	Thinking Story	Practice Master 5 Enrichment Master 5 Assessment Master pp. 7–8	6
6	Adding and Subtracting by Counting 13–14	1 day	to review mental addition and subtraction of 0, 1, 2, and 3	Thinking Story	Practice Master 6 Enrichment Master 6	1, 2, 3, 4, 7, 8
7	Counting Up or Down 15–16	1 day	to continue and review mental addition and subtraction of 0, 1, 2, and 3	Thinking Story	Practice Master 7 Enrichment Master 7	1, 2, 3, 4, 7, 8
8	Addition Facts 17–18	1 day	to review addition facts	Thinking Story, Game	Practice Master 8 Enrichment Master 8	1, 2, 3, 4, 8
9	Double Addends to Ten 19–20	1 day	to provide review of double addends through 10 + 10		Reteaching Master Practice Master 9 Enrichment Master 9	3, 4, 8
10	Addition Facts Review 21–22	1 day	to provide review of the nines addition facts by relating them to the tens addition facts		Practice Master 10 Enrichment Master 10	8
11	Commutative Property 23–24	1 day	to provide review of the commutative property for addition	Thinking Story	Practice Master 11 Enrichment Master 11	2, 4, 7, 8
12	Reviewing Addition Facts 25–26	2 days	to reinforce students' knowledge of basic addition facts	Thinking Story	Practice Master 12 Enrichment Master 12	8
13	Addition Table 27–28	1 day	to review the use of an addition table	Thinking Story, Game	Practice Master 13 Enrichment Master 13	4, 8
14	Practicing Addition Facts 29–30	1 day	to identify addition facts and strategies students have mastered	Thinking Story, Game	Reteaching Master Practice Master 14 Enrichment Master 14	1, 2, 3, 4, 8
15	Addition Fact Review 31–32	1 day	to provide review of addition facts with sums from 1–10	Thinking Story	Practice Master 15 Enrichment Master 15	1, 2, 3, 4, 8, 13
16	Addition Checkpoint 33–34	1 day	to provide practice with addition in a realistic situation	Thinking Story	Practice Master 16 Enrichment Master 16	1, 2, 3, 4, 8
17	Additional Practice 35–36	1 day	✓ to identify facts students have and have not mastered		Reteaching Master Practice Master 17 Enrichment Master 17 Assessment Master pp. 9–10	1, 2, 3, 4, 8
18	Subtraction Involving 0, 1, and 2 37–38	1 day	to review subtraction facts	Thinking Story, Game	Practice Master 18 Enrichment Master 18	7, 8
19	Missing Addends 39–40	1 day	to provide review in supplying missing addends	Game	Practice Master 19 Enrichment Master 19	3, 7, 8
20	Functions 41–42	1 day	to demonstrate patterns using function machines		Practice Master 20 Enrichment Master 20	7, 8, 13
	Mid-Unit Review 43–44				Assessment Master pp. 11–12	
21	Missing Addends and Subtraction 45–46	1 day	to provide review with missing addend problems and show how they are related to subtraction	Thinking Story	Reteaching Master Practice Master 21 Enrichment Master 21	1, 2, 3, 4, 7, 8

	LESSON	PACING	PRIMARY OBJECTIVES	FEATURE	RESOURCES	NCTM STANDARDS
22	Using an Addition Table to Subtract 47–48	1 day	to introduce the use of addition table for subtraction	Thinking Story, Game	Practice Master 22 Enrichment Master 22	1, 2, 3, 4, 7, 8
23	Adding and Subtracting 49–50	1 day	to review subtraction facts with 10 or 9	Thinking Story	Practice Master 23 Enrichment Master 23	1, 2, 3, 4, 8
24	Subtraction Facts 51–52	1 day	to identify subtraction facts that have and have not been mastered	Game	Reteaching Master Practice Master 24 Enrichment Master 24	1, 2, 3, 4, 8
25	Reviewing Subtraction Facts 53–54	1 day	to continue to review known subtraction facts	Thinking Story	Practice Master 25 Enrichment Master 25	8
26	Practicing Subtraction Facts 55–56	1 day	to encourage students to begin memorizing subtraction facts with a minuend of 13, 14, 15, and 16	Game	Practice Master 26 Enrichment Master 26	1, 2, 3, 4, 8
27	More Subtraction Practice 57–58	1 day	to provide practice with subtraction word problems	Act It Out, Thinking Story	Reteaching Master Practice Master 27 Enrichment Master 27	1, 2, 3, 4, 8
28	Subtraction Checkpoint 59–60	1 day	✓ to assess students' mastery of basic subtraction facts	Thinking Story	Practice Master 28 Enrichment Master 28 Assessment Master pp. 13–14	1, 2, 3, 4, 8
29	Using a Calculator 61–62	1 day	to introduce students to calculators		Practice Master 29 Enrichment Master 29	8
30	Addition and Subtraction 63–64	1 day	to provide practice with addition and subtraction facts	Thinking Story	Practice Master 30 Enrichment Master 30	1, 2, 3, 4, 8
31	Applying Addition and Subtraction 65–66	1 day	to provide practice solving word problems	Thinking Story	Practice Master 31 Enrichment Master 31	1, 2, 3, 4, 8
32	Adding and Subtracting Three Numbers 67–68	1 day	to introduce addition and subtraction of three numbers	Game	Reteachng Master Practice Master 32 Enrichment Master 32	7, 8
33	Pictographs 69–70	1 day	to demonstrate how to read a pictograph		Practice Master 33 Enrichment Master 33	2, 4, 11
34	Vertical Bar Graphs 71–72	1 day	to show students how to read a bar graph		Practice Master 34 Enrichment Master 34	2, 4, 11
35	Horizontal Bar Graphs 73–74	1 day	to provide practice in reading horizontal bar graphs		Reteaching Master Practice Master 35 Enrichment Master 35	2, 4, 11
36	Place Value—Base Ten 75–76	1 day	to review counting the tens and ones in numbers less than 100	Thinking Story, Game	Practice Master 36 Enrichment Master 36 Assessment Master p. 15	4, 6
37	Place Value—Using Money 77–78	1 day	to review using coins to make given amounts of money	Thinking Story, Game	Practice Master 37 Enrichment Master 37	4, 6, 11
38	Counting by Tens 79–80	1 day	to provide review in and extend students' knowledge of base-10 numeration system	Thinking Story, Game	Reteaching Master Practice Master 38 Enrichment Master 38	7, 8, 13
39	Measuring Length—Centimeters 77–78	1 day	to introduce the centimeter as a standard metric unit of length		Practice Master 39 Enrichment Master 39	1, 2, 3, 4, 9, 10
40	Measurement—Meters and Centimeters 83–84	1 day	to demonstrate the relationship between centimeters and meters		Practice Master 40 Enrichment Master 40	4, 10
41	Measuring Length—Inches 85–86	1 day	to introduce the inch as a standard unit of length		Practice Master 41 Enrichment Master 41	4, 10
42	Measurements—Yards, Feet, and Inches 87–88	1 day	to have students practice measuring length in inches, feet, and yards	Thinking Story	Reteaching Master Practice Master 42 Enrichment Master 42	4, 10
43	Estimating Length 89–90	2 days	to provide practice in measuring length in metric units	Thinking Story	Practice Master 43 Enrichment Master 43 Assessment Master pp. 16–17	10
44	Measurements—Perimeters 91–92	1 day	to provide practice in finding the perimeter of objects	Thinking Story	Practice Master 44 Enrichment Master 44	4, 9, 10
45	Unit Test 93–96		to review addition and subtraction		Assessment Master pp. 18–22	
46	Extending the Unit 97–98		to review addition and subtraction	Project		

UNIT CONNECTIONS

INTERVENTION STRATEGIES

In this Teacher's Guide there will be specific strategies suggested for students with individual needs—ESL, Gifted and Talented, Special Needs, Learning Styles, and At Risk. These strategies will be provided at the point of use. Here are the icons to look for and the types of strategies that will accompany them:

ESL

English as a Second Language

These strategies, designed for students who do not fluently speak the English language, will suggest meaningful ways to present the lesson concepts and vocabulary.

GIFTED & TALENTED

Gifted and Talented

Strategies to enrich and extend the lesson will offer further challenges to students who have easily mastered the concepts already presented.

SPECIAL NEEDS

Special Needs

Students who are physically challenged or who have learning disabilities might require alternative ways to complete activities, record answers, use manipulatives, and so on. The strategies labeled with this icon will offer helpful methods of presenting lesson concepts to these students.

LEARNING STYLES

Learning Styles

Each student has a unique learning style. The strategies labeled with this icon address a variety of learning modalities, such as tactile/kinesthetic, visual, and auditory.

AT RISK

At Risk

These strategies highlight the relevancy of math skills and concepts to the world outside the classroom. They are directed toward students who appear to be at risk of dropping out of school before graduation.

TECHNOLOGY CONNECTIONS

The following software, designed to reinforce and extend lesson concepts, will be referred to throughout this Teacher's Guide. It might be helpful to order this software or check it out of the school media center or local community library.

TECHNOLOGY CONNECTION

Look for this **Technology Connection** *icon.*

- *Mighty Math Zoo Zillions* from Edmark, Mac, IBM, for grades K–2 (software)
- *Schoolhouse Rock—Math Rock* from Creative Wonders, Mac, IBM, for grades 1–6 (software)
- *Number Connections* from Sunburst Communications, Mac, for grades K–3 (software)
- *Math for Beginners: Addition/Subtraction* from Coronet/MTI for grades K–3 (laser disc)
- *Talking Addition and Subtraction* from Orange Cherry, Mac, for grades K–3 (software)
- *Math Rabbit* from The Learning Company, Mac, IBM, for grades K–2 (software)
- *Dancing Dinos* from Micrograms, Mac, IBM, for grades 1–3 (software)

CROSS-CURRICULAR CONNECTIONS

This Teacher's Guide offers specific suggestions for connecting the math skills and concepts presented in the unit with other subject areas and with real-world situations. These strategies will be provided at the point of use.

Look for these icons:

- Geography
- Health
- Social Studies
- Music
- Science
- Math
- Art
- Physical Education
- Language Arts

LITERATURE CONNECTIONS

Relevant fiction and nonfiction books are suggested throughout the Teacher's Guide at the point where they could be used to introduce, reinforce, or extend specific lesson concepts. You might want to locate these books in your school or your local community library.

Look for this **Literature Connection** *icon.*

- *Yoshi 1, 2, 3* by Yoshi, Picture Book Studio, 1991
- *Old Dame Counterpane* by Jane Yolen, Philomel Books, 1994
- *26 Letters and 99 Cents* by Tana Hoban, Greenwillow Books, 1987
- *Only Six More Days* by Marisabina Russo, Greenwillow Books, 1988
- *One Tortoise, Ten Wallabies* by Jakki Wood, Bradbury Press, 1994
- *Counting Our Way to Maine* by Maggie Smith, Orchard Books, 1995
- *From One to One Hundred* by Terri Sloat, Dutton Children's Books, 1991
- *I Spy Two Eyes: Numbers in Art* by Lucy Micklethwait, Greenwillow Books, 1993
- *Counting Wildflowers* by Bruce McMillan, Lothrop, Lee & Shepard Books, 1986
- *Counting* by Henry Pluckrose, Childrens Press, 1995
- *One Green Island* by Charlotte Hard, Candlewick Press, 1995
- *12 Ways to Get to 11* by Eve Merriam, Simon & Schuster Books for Young Readers, 1993
- *Ten Sly Piranhas* by William Wise, Dial Books for Young Readers, 1993
- *Amelia's Nine Lives* by Lorna Balian, Abingdon Press, 1986
- *Mouse Count* by Ellen Stoll Walsh, Harcourt Brace Jovanovich, 1991
- *Play Ball: Sports Math* pp. 62–63 "Caledonia and the Calculator," Time-Life for Children, 1993
- *Ten Little Animals* by Laura Jane Coats, Macmillan, 1990
- *How Do Octopi Eat Pizza Pie?—Pizza Math*, pp. 6–7 Time-Life for Children, 1992
- *1 + 1 Take Away Two!* by Michael Berenstain, Western Pub. Co., 1991
- *My First Number Book* by Marie Heinst pp. 30–31, "How Many Are Left?" Dorling Kindersley, 1992
- *Dinosaurs Depart* by Bob Barner, Bantam Doubleday Dell, 1996

ASSESSMENT OPPORTUNITIES AT-A-GLANCE

LESSON	PORTFOLIO	PERFORMANCE	FORMAL	SELF	INFORMAL	MULTIPLE CHOICE	MASTERY CHECKPOINTS	ANALYZING ANSWERS
1		✓						
2					✓			✓
3					✓			
4		✓						
5			✓				✓	
6				✓				✓
7					✓			✓
8		✓						
9					✓			
10					✓			
11					✓			
12	✓							
13					✓			
14					✓			
15				✓				
16				✓				
17			✓				✓	
18					✓			
19				✓				
20					✓			
Mid-Unit Review			✓					
21		✓						
22					✓			
23				✓				
24				✓				
25				✓				
26					✓			
27				✓				
28			✓				✓	✓
29		✓						
30					✓			
31					✓			
32					✓			
33		✓						
34					✓			
35			✓		✓		✓	
36				✓				
37		✓						
38		✓						
39		✓						
40		✓						
41		✓						
42					✓			
43			✓				✓	✓
Unit Review			✓	✓		✓		
Unit Test			✓	✓		✓		

ASSESSMENT OPTIONS

PORTFOLIO ASSESSMENT

Throughout this Teacher's Guide are suggested activities in which students draw pictures, make graphs, write about mathematics, and so on. Keep students' work to assess growth of understanding as the year progresses.

Lesson 12

PERFORMANCE ASSESSMENT

Performance assessment items focus on evaluating how students think and work as they solve problems. Performance assessment can be found throughout the unit. Rubrics and guides for assessment are in the front of the Assessment Masters book.

Lessons 1, 4, 8, 21, 29, 33, 37, 40, and 41

FORMAL ASSESSMENT

A Mid-Unit Review and a Unit Test help assess students' understanding of concepts, skills, and problem solving. The *Math Explorations and Applications* CD-ROM Test Generator can create additional unit tests at three ability levels. Also, Mastery Checkpoints are provided periodically throughout the unit.

Lessons 5, 17, 28, 35, 43, Mid-Unit Review, Unit Review, and Unit Test

SELF ASSESSMENT

Throughout the program, students evaluate their math skills through self-assessment activities.

Lessons 6, 15, 16, 19, 23, 24, 25, 27, 36, and 44

INFORMAL ASSESSMENT

A variety of assessment suggestions are provided, including interviews, oral questions or presentations, and debates. Also, each lesson includes Assessment Criteria—a list of questions about each student's progress, understanding, and participation.

Lessons 2, 3, 7, 9, 10, 11, 13, 14, 18, 20, 22, 26, 30, 31, 32, 34, 35, and 42

MULTIPLE-CHOICE TESTS (STANDARDIZED FORMAT)

Each unit includes a Unit Test in standardized format, presenting students with an opportunity to practice taking a test in this format.

MASTERY CHECKPOINTS

Mastery Checkpoints are provided throughout the unit to assess student proficiency in specific skills. Checkpoints reference appropriate Assessment Masters and other assessment options. Results of these evaluations can be recorded on the Mastery Checkpoint Chart.

Lesson 5, 17, 28, 35, and 43

ANALYZING ANSWERS

Analyzing Answers suggests possible sources of student error and offers teaching strategies for addressing difficulties.

Lessons 2, 6, 7, 28, and 43

Look for these icons:

> ***"In order to develop mathematical power in all students, assessment needs to support the continued mathematics learning of each student."***
>
> *—NCTM Assessment Standards*

ASSESSING INDIVIDUAL PROGRESS

WHAT TO EXPECT FROM STUDENTS AS THEY COMPLETE THIS UNIT

WRITING AND COUNTING NUMBERS

Use students' answers to page 11 or Assessment Master pages 7 and 8 to assess their mastery of writing and counting numbers from 0–100 and of numerical sequences through 100.

ADDITION FACTS

At this time most students should demonstrate mastery ofbasic addition facts. Use the results of the speed test students completed on page 35 or Assessment Master pages 9 and 10 to assess students' knowledge of basic addition facts.

SUBTRACTION FACTS

At this time most students should be proficient in the basic subtraction facts. You may use page 59 or Assessment Master pages 13 and 14 to assess students' mastery of subtraction facts.

STORYBOOK PARTICIPATION

At this time you might want to formally assess the students' participation in the storybook portion of the lessons. Try to call more often on those students who do not participate as much, especially for the easier problems. It is desirable to use Number Cubes for responding as often as possible, particularly if you find it difficult to get whole-group participation. You may use Assessment Master page 15 to assess students participation.

By this time most students should be able to measure the length and weight of objects. You may use page 90 or Assessment Master pages 16 and 17 to assess students' accuracy.

UNIT 1

PROGRAM RESOURCES

THESE ADDITIONAL COMPONENTS OF *MATH EXPLORATIONS AND APPLICATIONS* CAN BE PURCHASED SEPARATELY FROM SRA/MCGRAW-HILL.

LESSON	BASIC MANIPULATIVE KIT	GAME MAT PACKAGE	TEACHER KIT	OPTIONAL MANIPULATIVE KIT	OVERHEAD MANIPULATIVE KIT	*MATH EXPLORATIONS AND APPLICATIONS* CD-ROM	LITERATURE LIBRARY
1	Number Cubes			counters		Lesson 1	The Apple Thief
2	Number Cubes					Lesson 2	The Three Billy Goats Gruff
3	Number Cubes	Yard Sale and Harder Yard Sale Games			bills, coins	Lesson 3	
4	Number Cubes	Calendar Game				Lesson 4	
5	Number Cubes					Lesson 5	
6	Number Cubes					Lesson 6	
7	Number Cubes					Lesson 7	Animal Orchestra
8	Number Cubes	Frog Pond and Harder Frog Pond Games				Lesson 8	
9	Number Cubes					Lesson 9	
10	Number Cubes					Lesson 10	
11	Number Cubes					Lesson 11	
12	Number Cubes					Lesson 12	
13	Number Cubes	Addition Table and Harder Addition Table Games			bills, coins	Lesson 13	
14	Number Cubes	Harder Addition Table Game				Lesson 14	Squeeze In
15	Number Cubes			base-10 blocks		Lesson 15	
16					bills, coins	Lesson 16	
17	Number Cubes			clock		Lesson 17	
18	Number Cubes					Lesson 18	
19	Number Cubes		balance			Lesson 19	
20	Number Cubes					Lesson 20	
21	Number Cubes					Lesson 21	
22	Number Cubes					Lesson 22	
23	Number Cubes			base-10 blocks		Lesson 23	
24	Number Cubes	Space Game				Lesson 24	
25	Number Cubes					Lesson 25	
26	Number Cubes					Lesson 26	
27	Number Cubes				bills, coins	Lesson 27	
28	Number Cubes			clock		Lesson 28	
29						Lesson 29	
30	Number Cubes				bills, coins	Lesson 30	
31	Number Cubes					Lesson 31	
32						Lesson 32	
33						Lesson 33	
34						Lesson 34	
35	Number Cubes					Lesson 35	
36	Number Cubes			base-10-blocks	bills, coins	Lesson 36	
37	Number Cubes					Lesson 37	
38	Number Cubes				bills, coins	Lesson 38	
39						Lesson 39	
40						Lesson 40	
41						Lesson 41	
42						Lesson 42	
43						Lesson 43	
44	Number Cubes					Lesson 44	

UNIT 1

Student Edition pages 1–2

Addition and Subtraction

INTRODUCING THE UNIT

Using the Student Pages To help students make the connection between what they learn in school and how it applies to the outside world, ask students to think of as many ways as they can that a farmer or rancher might use math. Then read aloud the paragraph on page 2.

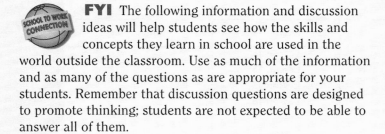

ACTIVITY Give students graph paper and pencils and ask them to draw a fence around a field that is a total of 20 units around the outside edge. Then encourage students to compare their fields and fences by asking questions such as: "How did you determine the size and shape of your field?" "Are all of the fenced shapes the same?" "Why are they different?" and "Why will 20 units fence all of these different shapes?"

SCHOOL TO WORK CONNECTION **FYI** The following information and discussion ideas will help students see how the skills and concepts they learn in school are used in the world outside the classroom. Use as much of the information and as many of the questions as are appropriate for your students. Remember that discussion questions are designed to promote thinking; students are not expected to be able to answer all of them.

Farming is one of the oldest occupations. Agriculture, as we know it, developed about 11,000 years ago in the Middle East, in an area called Mesopotamia between the Tigris and Euphrates rivers. People discovered that they could plant seeds to grow food and that they could capture and raise wild animals. They also learned to use river water to water their crops. "How do you think people discovered that they could grow food from plants?" "How would you plant seeds without tools?" "How would you know how many seeds to plant?" "How would you get water from a river to your crops?" "How would you figure out how many animals you need for food?"

About 5,000 years ago, the Egyptians learned to use animals to help with plowing. As providing food became easier, fewer people were needed for farming, so they could do other jobs, and cities began to develop. "How would you plow soil without a machine?" "How did animals make plowing easier and faster?"

UNIT 1

Addition and Subtraction

REVIEWING AND EXPANDING BASIC FACTS

- **fact families**
- **column addition**
- **perimeter**
- **graphing**

1

PROBLEM SOLVING

Junior Thinklab™*

Junior Thinklab™ provides a series of creative and logical problem-solving opportunities for individual students. The problems are designed to appeal to different cognitive abilities.

- ▶ Use Activity Cards 1–5 with this unit to reinforce ordering skills and concepts.
- ▶ Use Activity Cards 6–10 with this unit to reinforce classifying skills and concepts.
- ▶ Use Activity Cards 11–15 with this unit to reinforce perception and spatial relations skills and concepts.
- ▶ Use Activity Cards 16–20 with this unit to reinforce reasoning and deducing skills and concepts.
- ▶ Use Divergent Thinking Activity Sheets 1–5 with this unit to encourage creativity in art and in intellectual activity.

*available separately

SCHOOL TO WORK CONNECTION

Farmers use math . . .

Before a farmer or rancher puts up a fence, it is important to figure out how much fence to buy. The length of each side of a field is measured, and the lengths are added together. The fence keeps animals safe and also stops them from eating growing crops.

Farmers need to stay in one place most of the year in order take care of their crops. In the past, however, ranchers had to move around with their animals to find water and grazing land. In time, ranchers got plots of land large enough to feed their livestock, and they fenced their land to keep the animals from wandering away. "How do you think ranchers figure out how many cattle they can put on their land?" "What do they have to know to figure out how much their chicken feed will cost for a year?"

Math and science skills are very important in farming and ranching. For example, on today's dairy farms, farmers often use computers to keep records about their cows. "What are some things a farmer might want to record about cows?" "About growing wheat?" "What are some things farmers and ranchers have to think about to know whether they will make money?"

Although farmers don't have to go to college to learn farming, many farmers and ranchers do because they can learn a great deal in a short time. However, there is no substitute for practical experience.

COOPERATIVE LEARNING **Minds on Math** *Minds on Math* is a series of units covering problem solving, data collection, number sense, measurement, money, and geometry and spatial relations. Each unit provides a series of open-ended projects for individuals or small groups. These projects develop problem-solving and critical-thinking skills, utilize real-world materials, emphasize language, and integrate curriculum areas. Use projects from *Problems to Solve* to emphasize that there is more than one way to look at and solve any problem.

LITERATURE CONNECTION The books *The Apple Thief* and *Animal Orchestra* are fun ways to review numbers and counting. These books are part of the *Math Explorations and Applications* Literature Library*.

Home Connections You might want to send Home Connections Masters 33–34 to families the first week of school to introduce them to *Math Explorations and Applications.* Then use Masters 35–36 the following week to introduce this unit. Masters 35–36 provide family activities that apply skills and concepts presented in this unit.

*available separately

GAMES

THE ROLE OF GAMES

Games are an important component of the *Math Explorations and Applications* program. They offer students an opportunity to practice the mathematical skills to which they've been introduced and to develop logical reasoning as they use mathematical strategies. They make learning fun. Games also offer you another way to assess how well your students have learned each skill. There are two types of games presented in this program—Game Mats and Cube Games.

Game Mats

There are five Game Mats in Kindergarten, thirteen in levels 1–3, and fourteen in levels 4–6. In the Game Mat package, you receive 15 copies of each Game Mat, counters, place markers, Number Cubes, and money (not in Kindergarten). In addition, you have *A Guide for Using the Game Mats* and a color transparency for each Game Mat. Each game involves the use of several math skills including mathematical reasoning and probability. Many of the Game Mats are offered in a standard and a harder version.

Cube Games

These games, presented in the Student Edition in levels 3–6 and in the Teacher's Guide for K–2, reinforce basic math skills and involve mathematical reasoning.

USING THE GAMES

How Do I Know When to Choose a Game?

A lesson plan will prescribe a game, or it will suggest that you or your students select a game to play.

How Do I Know Which Game to Choose?

Check the Game Directory on page 405–407 of this Teacher's Guide. It lists the math focus of each Cube Game and each Game Mat so that you can give students the form of practice they need.

Do I Allow Students to Choose a Game?

So that students know which games they can choose from, keep a permanent bulletin board display of the games you've introduced. This display might be a simple list or a more elaborate presentation with game illustrations, rules, and materials. Put a group of students in charge of creating the display and keeping it up-to-date.

TIPS FOR TEACHING GAMES

After reading the rules for each game, which are provided in the lesson where the Cube Game is introduced or on each Game Mat, take the following steps:

- **Play the game yourself.** This will help you identify any difficulties your students might have.
- **Demonstrate how the game is played.** Making sure that everyone can see, say the rules aloud as you play another student or as two or more students play together. For the Game Mats, you may want to use the color overhead transparencies to demonstrate how each game is played.
- **Restate how the game is played.** Ask students to restate the object of the game and rules of the game in their own words to be sure everyone understands how to play.
- **Supervise students' play.** Be sure they get off to the right start.

Tips for Organizing Successful Game Sessions

- ◆ **Stress enjoyment rather than competition.** Emphasize sportsmanship, fair play, and taking turns.
- ◆ **In general, place students of the same ability together.** This way all students have a more equal chance of winning.
- ◆ **Change groupings from day to day.** Students can learn different things by playing with different partners.
- ◆ **Be sure students are challenged by a game.** Most Game Mats have a standard and a harder version. Some Cube Games suggest variations to the game.
- ◆ **Assign one referee for the day or one for each group.** Students sometimes get so absorbed in their own efforts that they do not follow the rules. A referee can monitor players' moves, keep track of scores, and in some games act as banker.
- ◆ **Make Game Mats accessible.** Store mats so that students can find and return them without your help. (You might want to laminate the mats.)

MENTAL MATH EXERCISES

Mental Math exercises offer an easy and practical technique for drilling students' math skills and assessing their performance. With these exercises students usually use either the Number Wheel (Levels 3–6) or Number Cubes (Levels K–6) to display their answers to your oral questions.

NUMBER WHEELS

Number Wheels have five wheels, each of which can be dialed to show any digit from 0 through 9. This allows students to make any integer from 0 through 99,999. To show the number 2047, for example, a student rotates the thousands wheel to show a 2, turns the hundreds wheel to show a 0, and so on. Different colors are used to identify each of the five wheels. On the back of the Number Wheels, the digits 0 through 9 are repeated with the addition of a decimal point.

NUMBER CUBES

Number Cubes allow students to make any integer from 0 through 100. In levels 3–6, students use the 0–5 (red) and 5–10 (blue) Number Cubes. To show the number 73, for example, a student should find the 7 face on the 5–10 cube and place that next to the 3 face on the 0–5 cube.

In Levels 1 and 2, each student should be given four cubes—two units cubes, 0–5 (red) and 5–10 (blue), and two tens cubes, 0–5 (yellow) and 5–10 (green). To show the number 43, for example, a student should find the 4 face on the 0–5 tens cube and place that next to the 3 face on the 0–5 units cube.

ADVANTAGES TO MENTAL MATH EXERCISES

- **Provide practice in mental computation**
- **Provide enjoyable, active drill**
- **Take only 5–10 minutes**
- **Allow full participation of the entire class**
- **Provide a basis for assessment**
- **Offer immediate feedback to you to students**
- **Ensure that students get their answers independently**
- **Protect students from embarrassment in front of their peers, because errors are not audible**

MENTAL MATH EXERCISES

HOW TO USE WHEELS AND CUBES

1. Present the class with a problem (orally or on the chalkboard) and say "Find."
2. Students determine the answer and dial it on their Number Wheels or position it on their Number Cubes.
3. Say "Hide."
4. Students hide their answers by holding their Wheels or Cubes against their chests.
5. Say "Show," when you see that most students have an answer.
6. Students hold up their Wheels or Cubes so you can see their responses.
7. Check students' responses.
8. Show and/or say the correct answer.
9. Move on to the next problem.

Tips for Using Number Wheels and Cubes

- **Add a "peek-to-be-sure" step.** This should occur between the "Hide" and "Show" steps of the procedure. It asks students who have already found answers to check them. This keeps them involved as they wait for the "Show" command.
- **Use good judgment to decide when to give the "Show" command.** Give students who are progressing toward a solution time enough to finish, but avoid prolonged waiting because this calls attention to slower students.
- **Encourage your students.** Mental Math exercises allow an active exchange between you and your students. Use this opportunity to give your students plenty of positive reinforcement.

Sometimes the problems in a Mental Math exercise will be complex enough to require paper and pencil. In these cases, have students show their answers to you as you walk around the room.

LESSON 1

Student Edition pages 3–4

Counting and Writing Numbers

LESSON PLANNER

Objectives

- ▶ to review counting numbers through 100
- ▶ to review writing the numbers 0 through 100
- ▶ to review the use of Number Cubes
- ▶ to introduce estimating numbers of objects

Context of the Lesson This is the first of five lessons reviewing counting and writing numbers. A new skill, estimating numbers, is also introduced in this lesson.

Materials	Program Resources
colored pencils	Number Cubes
	Practice Master 1
	Enrichment Master 1
	For extra practice: CD-ROM* Lesson 1

1 Warm-Up

5 MINUTES

Problem of the Day Write the following numbers on the chalkboard. Ask students to copy each number and write the number that comes before and after each in counting: 45 56 88 30. (44, 46; 55, 57; 87, 89; 29, 31)

MENTAL MATH Recite the following riddles. Ask students to write their answers to each riddle:

I am the number before 18. Who am I? (17)
I am the number after 79. Who am I? (80)
I am the number after 40. Who am I? (41)
I am the number before 50. Who am I? (49)

2 Teach

Using the Number Cubes The procedure for using the Number Cubes is described in detail on page 3A of this Teacher's Guide. It is important that students be familiar with the position of each number on the Number Cubes. Help students understand which cube to

LESSON 1

Name ______________________

Counting and Writing Numbers

Roll. Trace or write.

Where are the 3, 4, and 5?

Where are the 8, 9, and 10?

GAME Play the "Tracing and Writing Numbers" game.

Trace.

0	1	2	3	4	5	6	7	8	9	10

Trace.

0	1	2	3	4	5	6	7	8	9	10

Write.

NOTE TO HOME
Students trace and write the numbers from 0–10 as they play a game.

Why teach it at this time?

Because students tend to forget over the summer, the early lessons focus on reviewing addition facts. If this review is not a challenge to your students, you may emphasize the Thinking Story Book and other games and activities in these lessons.

Literature Connection You might want to read aloud *Yoshi 1, 2, 3* by Yoshi to reinforce lesson concepts.

RETEACHING

Have students count the number of students in the class and then estimate the number of noses, eyes, hands, feet, ears, and fingers they have. Talk about how they arrived at their estimates.

*available separately

◆ LESSON 1 Counting and Writing Numbers

COOPERATIVE LEARNING Do the "Estimating" activity.

6 Is your estimate reasonable? ____________

If you count the desks, you can estimate how many children are in the class.

Count. **Answers will depend on objects chosen.**

7 What objects did you count? ____________

8 How many? _____

Estimate.

9 What objects will you estimate? ____________

10 How many did you estimate? _____

Check your estimate.

11 How many objects did you count? _____

NOTE TO HOME
Students count and estimate, then check their estimates.

use in order to find a number and where that number is on the cube. Have students practice finding, hiding, and showing numbers using the Number Cubes. Ask students questions similar to those in *Mental Math.* Have them work together and explain how they got their answers.

Using the Student Pages Have pairs of students play the "Tracing and Writing Numbers" game on page 3 to practice writing the digits in numbers 0–100. You may wish to photocopy student page 3 so students will have more forms on which to work. Choose the level. Level 1 is tracing with arrows; level 2 is tracing without arrows; level 3 is writing. Then have players take turns rolling two Number Cubes and tracing or writing the number. If a number has already been traced or written, the player loses a turn. The first player to complete a row of numbers is the winner.

To complete the estimating activity on page 4, have students count a group of items, such as workbooks or shoes. Have them record the number on the page. Next, have students estimate a number of items related to the items counted. For example, if they counted students, they can estimate the number of desks. Have students record the estimates on the page. Then, have them check their estimates by counting, and record this number. Discuss with students the techniques they used to estimate.

3 Wrap-Up (5 MINUTES)

In Closing Ask students to explain how they figure out which number comes before or after a given number.

Performance Assessment Observe whether students know how to find, hide, and show the correct numbers at the appropriate time when doing the Number Cube activity.

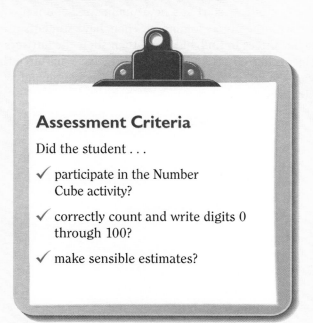

Assessment Criteria

Did the student . . .

✓ participate in the Number Cube activity?

✓ correctly count and write digits 0 through 100?

✓ make sensible estimates?

PRACTICE p. 1

LESSON 1 PRACTICE Name ____________

Trace.

11	12	13	14	15	16	17	18	19	20

Write.

11	12	13	14	15	16	17	18	19	20

Count desks or workbooks.

1 What things did you count? workbooks or desks

2 How many? 19 or 24

Estimate the other.

3 What things did you estimate? workbooks or desks

4 How many did you estimate? 18–25

Check your estimate.

5 What did you do to check your estimate? Students will probably count.

ENRICHMENT p. 1

LESSON 1 ENRICHMENT Name ____________

Four of the number tiles are out of place. Draw a circle around the misplaced number tiles. Write the correct number in that spot.

1	2	3	4	5
6	7 (9)	8	9 (7)	10
11	12 (13)	13 (12)	14	15
16	17	18	19	20

LESSON 2

Student Edition pages 5–6

More Counting and Writing

LESSON PLANNER

Objective

▶ to continue to review counting numbers through 100

Context of the Lesson This is the second of five lessons that review counting and writing numbers.

Materials	Program Resources
none	Number Cubes Reteaching Master Practice Master 2 Enrichment Master 2 For extra practice: CD-ROM* Lesson 2

1 Warm-Up

5 MINUTES

Problem of the Day Write the following pattern on the chalkboard and challenge students to finish it by writing the next four numbers: 73, 73, 72, 72, 71, ____, ____, ____, ____ (71, 70, 70, 69)

MENTAL MATH Have students count up in unison from different numbers between 1–100. For example, start at 78 and count up: 78, 79, 80. Then have them count down from a number. Stop them from time to time and let different students start at a new number and count up or down with the others joining in. Then, have students use Number Cubes to find, hide, and then show the answers to problems like 43 + 1 and 76 − 1. If they have mastered this, have them go on to problems that involve adding and subtracting 2.

LESSON 2

Name __________________________

More Counting and Writing

Count up or count down. Fill in the missing numbers.

1	5	6	7	8	9	10	11	12
2	0	1	2	3	4	5	6	7
3	20	21	22	23	24	25	26	27
4	76	77	78	79	80	81	82	83
5	39	38	37	36	35	34	33	32
6	63	62	61	60	59	58	57	56

NOTE TO HOME
Students name missing numbers from 0–100.

Real-World Connection Encourage students to think of "countdowns" that they have heard outside of school. They might have heard countdowns to space shuttle launches, countdowns of seconds until a New Year, or countdowns of Top-40 songs.

Literature Connection You might want to read aloud *Old Dame Counterpane* by Jane Yolen to reinforce lesson concepts.

RETEACHING p. 1

LESSON 2 RETEACHING Name ____________

Count up. Fill in the missing numbers.

1	2	3	4	5	6	7	8	9	10
11	12	13	14	15	16	17	18	19	20
21	22	23	24	25	26	27	28	29	30
31	32	33	34	35	36	37	38	39	40
41	42	43	44	45	46	47	48	49	50
51	52	53	54	55	56	57	58	59	60
61	62	63	64	65	66	67	68	69	70
71	72	73	74	75	76	77	78	79	80
81	82	83	84	85	86	87	88	89	90
91	92	93	94	95	96	97	98	99	100

Math Explorations and Applications Level 2 · 1

*available separately

◆ LESSON 2 More Counting and Writing

Take-Home Activity

GAME

Counting and Writing Numbers

Players: Two
Materials: Pen and paper for each player

RULES

First Round

Leader: Choose a starting number and an ending number between 0 and 100.

Leader: Count on from the starting number. Say and write one, two, or three numbers. Then stop.

Players: Take turns counting, saying, and writing the next three numbers.

Winner: The player who says and writes the ending number wins the first round.

More Rounds

The second player becomes the leader, then the third player, and so on.

NOTE TO HOME
Students count and write numbers between 1 and 100.

2 Teach

GAME **Using the Student Pages** Remind students to count up or down, as appropriate, before they begin each line on page 5. Check for wrong answers and for illegible or incorrectly written numbers. Then demonstrate the "Counting and Writing Numbers" game. Students can see how the game is played from the description on page 6.

3 Wrap-Up

5 MINUTES

In Closing Ask students to explain how they knew whether to count up or count down when they completed page 5 of their book.

ANALYZING ANSWERS Check to see whether students counted up when they should have been counting down or vice versa. Students should look at the numbers given and ask themselves, "Are the numbers going up or down?" before they write their answers.

ALTERNATIVE ASSESSMENT **Informal Assessment** Use students' answers to page 5 to informally assess their ability to count up and count down.

Assessment Criteria

Did the student . . .

✓ correctly complete 18 of the 23 items on page 5?

✓ show the correct cubes when playing the cube activity?

✓ correctly count up and write the numbers legibly when playing the "Counting and Writing Numbers" game?

PRACTICE p. 2

LESSON 2 PRACTICE Name ____________

Count up or down. Fill in the missing numbers.

1	14	15	16	17	18	19	20	21
2	30	31	32	33	34	35	36	37
3	42	43	44	45	46	47	48	49
4	58	59	60	61	62	63	64	65
5	73	74	75	76	77	78	79	80
6	93	94	95	96	97	98	99	100
7	12	11	10	9	8	7	6	5
8	84	83	82	81	80	79	78	77

2 • Math Explorations and Applications Level 2

ENRICHMENT p. 2

LESSON 2 ENRICHMENT Name ____________

Ring the numbers that are shown more than once.

1. Start at 1.
8 1 2 6 4 9 5 7 10 3 8

2. Start at 10.
10 17 18 12 13 12 19 14 11 15 16 12 13

3. Start at 25.
33 26 27 31 28 25 36 29 35 30 37 26 32 26 32 34

4. Start at 87.
96 90 95 94 87 91 92 88 97 94 96 89 93

2 • Math Explorations and Applications Level 2

THINKING STORIES

WHAT ARE THINKING STORIES?

Thinking Stories are short stories about common sense mathematical problems, many of which people face every day. Thinking Stories are designed to be read aloud to an entire class. Some Thinking Stories apply lesson concepts, and some introduce or pre-teach an upcoming lesson concept, but the majority of stories simply require students to use their mathematical knowledge and logical reasoning, because real life presents us with a variety of problems at the same time.

The same characters are used in all grade levels. The children in the stories are always the same age as the students at that grade level. Students become familiar with each character and how each one reacts to specific situations.

Tips for Using the Thinking Story Books (Levels 1–3)

- **Read the stories aloud.** Give students time to think about each question, but not so much time that they forget the point of the story.
- **Discuss the problems.** Ask your students how they arrived at their answers. Encourage debate. There are often many ways to solve a problem.
- **Encourage students to think carefully.** Speed should not be emphasized.
- **When possible, let students use Number Cubes.** This will encourage *all* students to respond.
- **Recognize sensible answers.** Even if a student gives an incorrect answer, he or she probably thought carefully about it and should be praised.
- **Encourage students to act out or use manipulatives to solve difficult problems.** This technique may help students organize their thinking.

Levels K–3

In Kindergarten, the Thinking Stories are found in the Teacher's Guide in each lesson. In levels 1–3, the Thinking Stories are presented in both the Teacher's Guide and in a separate book. Interspersed in each story are questions that will prompt your students to think ahead of the story characters. The questions might ask students to identify what is wrong with what a character has done or said, to anticipate what is going to happen as a result, or to think of other possibilities that the character hasn't considered. There are also many additional problems in the separate Thinking Story book (levels 1–3) that can be used at any time.

Levels 4–6

In levels 4–6, the Thinking Stories are presented in the Student Editions. After listening to the story as a class, students can reread the story, either by themselves or in small groups, and discuss the questions at the end.

WHAT ARE THE EXTRA STORY PROBLEMS IN LEVELS 1–3?

In the separate Thinking Story book, there are additional story problems that follow each story. They require students to use the same thinking skills that the story characters used. These problems can be used at any time.

WHAT MAKES THINKING STORIES AND STORY PROBLEMS UNIQUE?

The characters in the stories and problems have peculiarities that your students will come to know. Mr. Muddle, for example, easily forgets things. Ferdie jumps to conclusions without thinking. Mr. Breezy gives more information than is needed and, therefore, makes easy problems seem difficult. Ms. Eng, on the other hand, provides insufficient information to solve the questions and problems she poses. Your students will learn to recognize these peculiarities and avoid them in their own thinking. The stories and problems are filled with so many surprises that your students will be challenged as well as entertained.

WHEN SHOULD I USE THE STORIES AND PROBLEMS?

In Kindergarten, the problems are provided with each individual lesson in the Teacher's Guide. In levels 1–3, the Teacher's Guide will instruct you which of the 20 story selections to use and when to use them. In general, you will be directed to read one story about every five or six lessons. On days when no stories are read, the Teacher's Guide will suggest you read problems—usually three or four—to your students. If it has been a day or two since you read a particular story, you might want to read it again before presenting new story problems. Stories and problems become more difficult as the year progresses.

WHICH THINKING SKILLS ARE STRESSED IN THE STORIES AND PROBLEMS?

Math Skills

- Choosing which operation to use
- Recognizing relevant information
- Recognizing absurd or unreasonable answers
- Deciding when calculation isn't necessary
- Recognizing incorrect answers

Language Arts Skills

- Characterization
- Predicting what will happen in a story
- Making inferences
- Summarizing what has happened in a story
- Listening for details
- Drawing conclusions
- Evaluating information
- Recognizing cause-and-effect relationships
- Forming generalizations

LESSON 3

Student Edition pages 7–8

Counting and Regrouping Money

LESSON PLANNER

Objective

▶ to review counting and regrouping money

Context of the Lesson This is the third of five lessons reviewing counting and writing numbers.

Materials	Program Resources
play coins and bills*	"Yard Sale" Game Mats
	Thinking Story Book, pages 6–9
	Number Cubes
	Practice Master 3
	Enrichment Master 3
	For extra practice: CD-ROM* Lesson 3

1 Warm-Up

5 MINUTES

Problem of the Day Present the following problem to students: Megan has 34 dollars. She has some \$10 bills, some \$5 bills, and some \$1 bills. How many of each does she have? (two \$10 bills, two \$5 bills, four \$1 bills)

MENTAL MATH Have students add or subtract one and show the answers using their Number Cubes:

a. 79 − 1 = (78)
b. 68 + 1 = (69)
c. 27 + 1 = (28)
d. 43 − 1 = (42)
e. 17 + 1 = (18)
f. 81 − 1 = (80)
g. 52 + 1 = (53)
h. 30 + 1 = (31)
i. 99 − 1 = (98)
j. 73 + 1 = (74)

2 Teach

MENTAL MATH **Using the Student Pages** Be sure students know the meaning of the dollar (\$) and cent (¢) signs. Allow them to use play money to complete these pages. Students can correct their pages by counting in unison to arrive at each answer. For example: 10, 20, 30, 31, 32, 33, 34 = \$34.

LESSON 3

Name ____________________

Counting and Regrouping Money

Work these problems.

How much money?

1  \$ 34

2  \$ 42

3  \$ 57

4  \$ 32

NOTE TO HOME
Students review counting money amounts.

Literature Connection You might want to read aloud *Old Dame Counterpane* by Jane Yolen to reinforce lesson concepts.

CULTURAL DIVERSITY Invite students to bring foreign currency in to show the class. Have students find out how much each coin or bill might be worth in United States currency. Discuss whether the foreign currency can be counted the same way as the United States currency.

RETEACHING

Reteaching is not necessary at this time because regrouping money will be covered again in Lesson 36.

*available separately

◆ LESSON 3 Counting and Regrouping Money

Solve these problems.

How much money?

5  32 ¢

6  26 ¢

7  $ 27

8  $ 45

THINKING STORY

Talk about the Thinking Story "Measuring Bowser."

GAME

Play the "Yard Sale" game.

NOTE TO HOME
Students review counting money amounts.

PRACTICE p. 3

LESSON 3 PRACTICE Name ____________

How much money?

1  $ 49

2  58 ¢

3  $ 38

4  74 ¢

5  $ 36

6  24 ¢

ENRICHMENT p. 3

LESSON 3 ENRICHMENT Name ____________

Kendra wants to buy an apple, a banana, and a muffin. Look at the prices. Draw the coins Kendra could use to pay for each item.

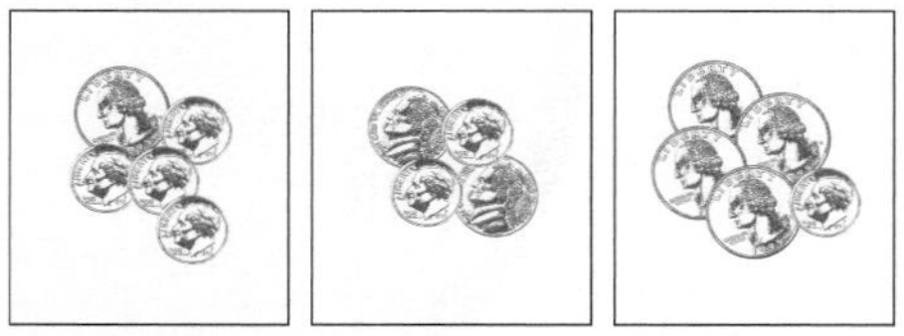

Answers will vary. Any coins that sum to 65¢ (for apples), 30¢ (for bananas), and $1.10 for muffins are acceptable.

Using the Thinking Story Read aloud "Measuring Bowser" on pages 6–9 of the Thinking Story Book. Stop and discuss the questions asked throughout the story. Mr. Breezy needs help weighing and measuring Bowser the dog. Portia and Manolita use logical thinking to find Bowser's weight, and Mr. Breezy has a tip for finding Bowser's height.

MATH JOURNAL

Have students write a paragraph explaining how Portia and Manolita worked together to solve the problem.

GAME

Introducing the "Yard Sale" Game Mats Demonstrate and then have students play the "Yard Sale" game to provide practice in changing money ($1 bills for $10 bills and $10 bills for $100 bills.) The "Harder Yard Sale" game is on the other side of the Game Mat. In the harder version students change $1, $5, $10, $20, and $50 bills for bills of denominations up to $100. Complete directions are on the Game Mats.

3 Wrap-Up

5 MINUTES

In Closing Ask students what bills they would use to make $57. (two twenties, one ten, one five, and two singles)

ANALYZING ANSWERS

Check to see whether students made errors by counting the wrong amounts. Have students count aloud to show you how they arrived at their answers. Correct errors by showing how they must first count by tens, then by fives, and then by ones when counting $10, $5, and $1 bills or dimes, nickels, and pennies.

ALTERNATIVE ASSESSMENT

Informal Assessment Have students show several amounts in play money: $27; $36; 79¢.

Assessment Criteria

Did the student . . .

✓ change money correctly in the "Yard Sale" game?

✓ add the total money amounts correctly on the pages?

✓ contribute to the Thinking Story discussion?

LOOKING AHEAD A calendar is needed for Lesson 4.

STORY 1

THINKING STORY

Measuring Bowser

"I could use some help," Mr. Breezy said.

Manolita and Portia said they'd be glad to help.

"It won't be as easy as it sounds," Mr. Breezy told them. "I need to find out some things about this dog, Bowser. First I want to know how much he weighs. There's a scale in the workroom. Tell me how many kilograms Bowser weighs, if you can find out."

Portia and Manolita thought that would be easy. They took Bowser and set him on the scale, but he jumped right off. They tried again, and again he jumped off before they could see how much he weighed. He was a very lively dog.

"This isn't as easy as we thought," said Manolita.

Do you have any idea what they could do? Hold him on the scale.

"I'll hold him on the scale and you read what it says," Portia suggested.

Portia had to press down hard on Bowser to keep him from jumping off.

"Twelve kilograms," Manolita read.

Do you think that is what Bowser weighs? no

Why not? Pressing down makes Bowser seem heavier than he really is.

"I'm not sure that's right," Manolita said. "The harder you press to hold him down, the more he seems to weigh. I think you're pushing the scale down. Let me try."

Manolita picked Bowser up and held him so that his paws just touched the scale.

"Two kilograms," Portia read. "I didn't think Bowser was that light."

Do you think 2 kilograms is the right weight? no

Why not? His whole weight isn't on the scale.

"I think you're holding him up so that his whole weight isn't on the scale," Portia said.

"That makes him seem lighter than he is. I have another idea."

Portia held Bowser in her arms and stood on the scale with him. The scale read 33 kilograms.

"Thirty-three kilograms!" Portia said. "This dog is a giant! Funny, he doesn't feel that heavy."

Do you think that is how much Bowser weighs? no

What is Portia weighing? She is weighing herself and Bowser.

The girls thought and thought. They waited, hoping Bowser would fall asleep so they could lay him on the scale. But Bowser kept jumping around, lively as ever. Finally Portia had an idea. She stood on the scale alone.

"I weigh 23 kilograms," she said.

How can that help them find out how much Bowser weighs? She'll know how much to subtract later.

If Portia weighs 23 kilograms and Portia and Bowser together weigh 33 kilograms, how much does Bowser weigh? 10 kg

◆ STORY 1 **Measuring Bowser**

"I get it, Portia," Manolita said. "If you weigh 23 kilograms and you and Bowser weigh 33 kilograms together, then Bowser must weigh 10 kilograms, because 23 and 10 make 33."

They rushed to tell Mr. Breezy, who was proud of the girls for being so clever. "Because you were so good at finding out how much Bowser weighs," he said, "perhaps you can find out how tall he is."

The girls thought that would be much easier. Manolita took a meterstick and stood it up beside Bowser's head while Portia held him still.

"I can't tell," Manolita said. "Sometimes the top of his head is about 40 centimeters high and sometimes it's only 30. He keeps bobbing his head around too much."

"Naughty Bowser!" Portia scolded. Bowser felt bad at being called naughty, and he hung his head low.

"Now I have it," Manolita said. "He's only 20 centimeters high."

Do you think that is right? no

Why not? Bowser is hanging his head, making him appear shorter.

"His head is lower than his back now," Manolita said. "That will never do. Here." Manolita walked over to the dog and said, "Sit, Bowser, sit!" Bowser obediently sat up on his hind legs and held very still.

"Now he's 50 centimeters high," Portia said. "I'll bet that's right."

Do you think it is? no

Why not? Bowser is sitting up, making him appear taller.

"I'm afraid that won't do either," Manolita said. "When he's sitting up that way we're measuring how long he is instead of how tall he is."

The girls had run out of ideas. They went to Mr. Breezy sadly and told him they had failed. "Bowser is a different height every time we measure him," Portia said. "He just won't hold his head in the same place all the time."

"That's the way dogs are," said Mr. Breezy. "That's why we usually measure their height at their shoulders instead of at their heads. Didn't I tell you that?"

. . . the end

LESSON 4

Student Edition pages 9–10

Numbers on the Calendar

LESSON PLANNER

Objectives

- to review reading a monthly calendar and provide students with an understanding of its structure
- to continue reviewing counting and writing numbers
- to review ordinal numbers

Context of the Lesson This is the fourth of five lessons that review counting and writing numbers.

Materials

calendar of current month

Program Resources

"Calendar" Game Mat
Number Cubes
Thinking Story Book, pages 10–11
Practice Master 4
Enrichment Master 4
For extra practice:
CD-ROM* Lesson 4

1 Warm-Up (5 MINUTES)

Problem of the Day Write this problem on the chalkboard: Mark is two years younger than Brad. Brad is one year older than José. José is 8 years old. How old is Mark? (7 years old)

MENTAL MATH Have students add or subtract 2 and reveal the answers on their Number Cubes.

a. 69 – 2 = (67)
b. 81 + 2 = (83)
c. 29 + 2 = (31)
d. 92 – 2 = (90)
e. 37 + 2 = (39)
f. 73 – 2 = (71)
g. 56 + 2 = (58)
h. 65 – 2 = (63)
i. 49 – 2 = (47)

LESSON 4

Name ______________________

Numbers on the Calendar

December has 31 days.

Fill in the missing numbers.

December						
Sunday	Monday	Tuesday	Wednesday	Thursday	Friday	Saturday
	1	2	3	4	5	6
7	8	9	10	11	12	13
14	15	16	17	18	19	20
21	22	23	24	25	26	27
28	29	30	31			

Write the answers.

1. What day is December 5? Friday
2. What day is December 12? Friday
3. What day is December 23? Tuesday
4. What day is December 17? Wednesday

NOTE TO HOME
Students fill in missing dates on a calendar and name specific days of the week.

Why teach it at this time?

The calendar is introduced in this lesson because it demonstrates a familiar and interesting application for counting and writing numbers. Presenting the calendar early in the year allows students' understanding to grow gradually through repeated use throughout the year.

Art Connection Have students work in groups to create monthly calendars for the remaining school year. Encourage students to decorate their calendars. Display each group's calendar during the appropriate month.

RETEACHING

Use a classroom calendar to point out holidays, birthdays, and other familiar events to the students. Have students identify the day and date of each highlighted event.

*available separately

◆ LESSON 4 Numbers on the Calendar

Use the Mixed Practice on page 365 after this lesson.

October has 31 days.

Fill in the missing numbers.

October						
Sunday	Monday	Tuesday	Wednesday	Thursday	Friday	Saturday
			1	2	3	4
5	6	7	8	9	10	11
12	13	14	15	16	17	18
19	20	21	22	23	24	25
26	27	28	29	30	31	

Write the day of the week.

5. October 1 **Wednesday**
6. October 2 **Thursday**
7. October 14 **Tuesday**
8. October 9 **Thursday**
9. October 17 **Friday**
10. October 16 **Thursday**
11. On October 7 Sam found out that he would have a test on October 14. How much time does Sam have to prepare? **7 days or 1 week**

GAME Play the "Calendar" game.

NOTE TO HOME
Students fill in missing dates on a calendar and name specific days of the week.

2 Teach

Demonstrate Use a current month calendar. Work with the class to discuss how to read the calendar. Ask questions such as: "On which day of the week is the first day of this month?" and "What date was a week before the tenth?" and "What day of the week will the first day of next month be?"

Using the Student Pages Before students work these pages, you might wish to explain why monthly calendars are not the same each year. Consider working page 9 with the class and having them work page 10 on their own. When finished, students can explain how they arrived at each answer.

Introducing the "Calendar" Game Mat Demonstrate and play the game. This Game Mat provides practice in using a monthly calendar. Complete directions are on the Game Mat.

Using the Thinking Story Present one or two new problems from those following "Measuring Bowser" on pages 10–11 of the Thinking Story Book.

3 Wrap-Up

5 MINUTES

In Closing Ask students the following question: If the first Friday in March is March 6, what date will the second Friday be?

ALTERNATIVE ASSESSMENT

Performance Assessment Have students draw a calendar for next month. Give them the first day and date. Observe which students can correctly draw the calendar.

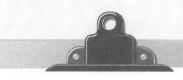

Assessment Criteria

Did the student . . .

✓ correctly answer nine of the 11 problems on pages 9–10?

✓ correctly identify the days when playing the "Calendar" game?

PRACTICE p. 4

LESSON 4 PRACTICE Name ______

Make a calendar. Fill in the name and numbers for this month. Answers will vary.

Sunday	Monday	Tuesday	Wednesday	Thursday	Friday	Saturday

1. On what day of the week does the third day of this month fall? ______
2. What day is one week before the fifteenth of this month? ______
3. What day is one week after the fifteenth of this month? ______

4 • Math Explorations and Applications Level 2

ENRICHMENT p. 4

LESSON 4 ENRICHMENT Name ______

1. In what year were you born? Answers will vary.
2. In what month were you born? ______

Make a calendar for the month and year you were born. Ask your teacher for a hint.

Sunday	Monday	Tuesday	Wednesday	Thursday	Friday	Saturday

3. On what day of the week were you born? ______

4 • Math Explorations and Applications Level 2

ASSESSMENT

This is the first Mastery Checkpoint at this grade level. Throughout each unit of each grade level, at benchmarks specified on the Mastery Checkpoint Chart, you are able to assess students' progress.

MASTERY CHECKPOINT CHARTS

The Mastery Checkpoint Chart contains a listing of the mastery objectives that are considered important for future progress in mathematics. These benchmarks appear on a chart in the Assessment Blackline Master Book on pages vii-viii. You can determine each student's mastery of specific objectives by his or her performance of the mastery objective in the lesson and/or by using the specific Mastery Checkpoint test provided in the Assessment Blackline Master Book. Those students who are having difficulty with a skill should receive extra help before continuing on in the unit. But an entire class should not be held up until all students learn the skill. Each lesson provides you with either a Reteaching Strategy or a Reteaching Master that will help you present the lesson concept in a slightly different way.

Tips on Using the Mastery Checkpoint Chart

- Fill in the names of all students in your class.
- For each checkpoint on the Mastery Checkpoint Chart, the Teacher's Guide gives opportunities to assess either by observation or by using the Student Edition page(s). Students can also be given the Assessment Blackline Master for that specific Checkpoint.
- Place a check mark (✓) in the appropriate column of the Mastery Checkpoint Chart beside the name of each student who demonstrates success on the objective in question.
- Pencil in a *P* in the appropriate column for each student who, in your judgment, grasps the necessary idea for accomplishing the objective but needs further practice to sharpen his or her skill. Assign extra practice to identified students.
- Pencil in a *T* for each student who has not grasped the necessary idea and therefore needs further teaching. Give extra teaching to identified students.
- Replace *T*s or *P*s with check marks when students demonstrate mastery of a skill.

ASSESSMENT OPPORTUNITIES IN THE PROGRAM

The *Math Explorations and Applications* program offers many opportunities to assess students' skills. Activities that students engage in on a daily basis, such as Mental Math exercises, games, response exercises, Thinking Story discussions, and Student Edition exercises allow you to steadily monitor individual progress.

In the Teacher's Guide

Each lesson in the Teacher's Guide provides at least two different assessment suggestions. One is Assessment Criteria, which gives you questions to ask yourself while you observe students playing a game, completing an activity, participating in a Thinking Story discussion, or working in cooperative groups. The additional suggestions include the following types of assessment:

- informal assessment (interviews, observation, and oral)
- formal assessment (tests, reviews, and checkpoints)
- self assessment
- alternative assessment (portfolio and performance)

In the Student Editions

A formal Mid-Unit Review as well as a Unit Review and a Unit Test are provided in the Student Edition in levels 1–6. The exception is Kindergarten, which has a Mid-Book Review and a Book Test. There are also self-assessments throughout the Student Editions in which students are asked to evaluate their own performance.

In the Assessment Blackline Masters

In the Assessment Blackline Master book there is a page for each Mastery Checkpoint, an additional Mid-Unit Review, and two Unit Tests, one in standardized format. Each unit also provides Performance Assessment activities and Portfolio Assessment suggestions. There is also additional information on the various alternative assessment options that are provided in this program and suggestions for grading these assessments using rubrics.

DAILY MONITORING

The following activities will help you assess your students' progress on a daily basis:

- **Cube Games and Game Mats**
  These allow you to watch students practice specific skills under conditions natural to them.
- **Mental Math Exercises**
  These exercises, which involve Number Wheels and Number Cubes, allow you to see everyone's responses, give immediate feedback, and involve the entire class.
- **Student Edition Exercises**
  These help you determine which skills your students can use on paper and which they need to practice.
- **Thinking Story Sessions**
  These help you determine whether or not your students are able to apply their knowledge of math concepts to everyday common sense problems.

LESSON 5

Student Edition pages 11–12

Writing Numbers

LESSON PLANNER

Objectives

- ✓ to evaluate students' ability to count and write numbers from 0–100
- ▶ to further review counting and writing numbers

Context of the Lesson This, the fifth of five lessons on counting and writing numbers, contains Mastery Checkpoints 1 and 2 for assessing the mastery of writing, counting, and sequencing numbers through 100.

Materials

craft sticks or unit cubes (optional)

Program Resources

Thinking Story Book, pages 10–11
Practice Master 5
Enrichment Master 5
Assessment Master
For extra practice:
CD-ROM* Lesson 5

1 Warm-Up (5 MINUTES)

PROBLEM SOLVING

Problem of the Day Write the following number series on the chalkboard and have students find and correct the mistake in each series.

a. 13, 14, 15, 18, 17, 18, 19, 20 (first 18 should be 16)
b. 80, 81, 78, 77, 76, 75, 74 (81 should be 79)
c. 27, 28, 29, 28, 31, 32, 33, 34 (second 28 should be 30)

MENTAL MATH Have students tell whether + or – belongs in each blank:

a. 79 _____ 1 = 80 (+) **b.** 40 _____ 2 = 38 (–)
c. 91 _____ 1 = 92 (+) **d.** 34 _____ 1 = 33 (–)
e. 19 _____ 2 = 21 (+) **f.** 88 _____ 2 = 90 (+)

LESSON 5

Name ______________________________

Writing Numbers

Count up or count down. Fill in the missing numbers.

1	3	4	5	6	7	8	9
2	22	21	20	19	18	17	16
3	100	99	98	97	96	95	94
4	54	53	52	51	50	49	48
5	28	29	30	31	32	33	34
6	36	37	38	39	40	41	42

NOTE TO HOME
Students fill in missing numbers before and after numbers between 0 and 100.

RETEACHING p. 2

LESSON 5 RETEACHING Name ______________________________

Fill in the missing numbers.

1. 4 __5__ 6
2. 18 __19__ 20
3. 70 __71__ 72
4. 27 __28__ __29__
5. 11 __12__ __13__
6. 39 __40__ __41__
7. __12__ 13 __14__
8. __43__ 44 __45__
9. __59__ 60 __61__ __62__ __63__ 64
10. __8__ __9__ 10 __11__ __12__ 13
11. __88__ __89__ 90 __91__ 92 __93__
12. __48__ __49__ 50 __51__ __52__ 53

1	2	3	4	5	6	7	8	9	10
11	12	13	14	15	16	17	18	19	20
21	22	23	24	25	26	27	28	29	30
31	32	33	34	35	36	37	38	39	40
41	42	43	44	45	46	47	48	49	50
51	52	53	54	55	56	57	58	59	60
61	62	63	64	65	66	67	68	69	70
71	73	73	74	75	76	77	78	79	80
81	82	83	84	85	86	87	88	89	90
91	92	93	94	95	96	97	98	99	100

PRACTICE p. 5

LESSON 5 PRACTICE Name ______________________________

Count up or down. Fill in the missing numbers.

1	48	49	50	51	52	53	54	55
2	15	14	13	12	11	10	9	8
3	62	63	64	65	66	67	68	69
4	31	30	29	28	27	26	25	24
5	7	6	5	4	3	2	1	0
6	93	94	95	96	97	98	99	100
7	52	53	54	55	56	57	58	59
8	74	73	72	71	70	69	68	67

*available separately

◆ **LESSON 5 Writing Numbers**

Mr. Gonzales is 34 years old.

7. How old will he be in two years? 36

8. How old will he be in three years? 37

9. Mark earned two dollars today. Now he has 85 dollars. How many dollars did he have yesterday? $83

10. A train going from Omaha to New York City had 73 cars. Two cars were removed in Chicago and one car was added in Pittsburgh. How many cars reached New York City? 72

11. An airplane holds 67 passengers, two pilots, and one attendant. How many people does it hold all together? 70

NOTE TO HOME
Students solve short word problems.

2 Teach

Using the Student Pages Have students complete page 11 on their own. Work the first problem on page 12 with students; then, have them complete the page independently. As they finish students can go on to a game. Give students a choice of games from among those already introduced: "Counting and Writing Numbers," "Yard Sale," or "Calendar."

Using the Thinking Story Present one or two problems from those following "Measuring Bowser" on pages 10–11 of the Thinking Story Book.

3 Wrap-Up

5 MINUTES

In Closing Talk about when students need to write or count numbers in their everyday lives. (Possible answers: counting money to buy toys, counting days on a calendar, finding out how many students are in a class)

Mastery Checkpoints 1 and 2

Use students' answers to page 11 or Assessment Masters 7 and 8 to assess their mastery of writing and counting numbers from 0–100 and of numerical sequences through 100. The results of this assessment may be recorded on the Mastery Checkpoint Chart.

ENRICHMENT p. 5

LESSON 5 ENRICHMENT Name ______

Write the Spanish words for the numbers from 1 to 20. Use the English-Spanish guide at the bottom to help you.

1 uno	2 dos
3 tres	4 cuatro
5 cinco	6 seis
7 siete	8 ocho
9 nueve	10 diez
11 once	12 doce
13 trece	14 catorce
15 quince	16 dieciseis
17 diecisiete	18 dieciocho
19 diecinueve	20 veinte

Alphabetical English to Spanish Guide

eight—ocho	nine—nueve	ten—diez
eighteen—dieciocho	nineteen—diecinueve	thirteen—trece
eleven—once	one—uno	three—tres
fifteen—quince	seven—siete	twelve—doce
five—cinco	seventeen—diecisiete	twenty—veinte
four—cuatro	six—seis	two—dos
fourteen—catorce	sixteen—dieciseis	

ASSESSMENT p. 2

UNIT 1 **Mastery Checkpoint 1** Writing numbers through 100 (Lesson 5)

Name ______

The student demonstrates mastery by writing well-formed numbers for all the items.

Count up or count down.
Fill in the missing numbers.

1	63	64	65	66	67	68	69
2	35	34	33	32	31	30	29
3	48	49	50	51	52	53	54
4	76	77	78	79	80	81	82
5	84	83	82	81	80	79	78
6	100	99	98	97	96	95	94
7	17	18	19	20	21	22	23
8	1	2	3	4	5	6	7

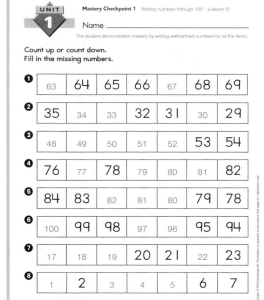

Assessment Criteria

Did the student . . .

- ✓ demonstrate ability to write and count numbers from 0–100?
- ✓ write all numbers legibly and with correct form on page 11?
- ✓ correctly identify at least 90% of the missing numbers in the sequences on page 11?
- ✓ correctly solve all of the word problems on page 12?

LESSON 6

Student Edition pages 13–14

Adding and Subtracting by Counting

LESSON PLANNER

Objective

- ▶ to review mental addition and subtraction of 0, 1, 2, and 3

Context of the Lesson This objective is continued in Lesson 7.

Materials	Program Resources
none	Number Cubes Thinking Story Book, pages 10–11 Practice Master 6 Enrichment Master 6 For extra practice: CD-ROM* Lesson 6

1 Warm-Up 5 MINUTES

Problem of the Day Write the following problem on the chalkboard: A garden has 32 rows. Rita plants two rows of flowers every night. How many rows does she have left to plant after three nights? (Students can subtract 6 from 32 or 2 from 32 three times to get 26 rows.)

MENTAL MATH Present the following problems and ask students to reply with their Number Cubes:

a. What is 1 less than 96? (95)

b. What is 3 more than 21? (24)

c. What is 0 more than 85? (85)

d. What is 2 more than 39? (41)

e. What is 2 less than 57? (55)

f. What is 1 more than 88? (89)

g. What is 3 less than 40? (37)

h. What is 0 less than 9? (9)

i. What is 1 less than 62? (61)

j. What is 3 more than 89? (92)

LESSON 6

Name ______________________________

Adding and Subtracting by Counting

Draw a ring around the answers.

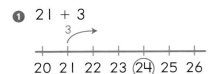

1. 21 + 3
   (arrow: 3)
   20 21 22 23 (24) 25 26

2. 21 − 3
   (arrow: 3)
   17 (18) 19 20 21 22 23

3. 21 − 2
   (arrow: 2)
   17 18 (19) 20 21 22 23

4. 19 + 2
   (arrow: 2)
   18 19 20 (21) 22 23 24

5. 30 + 2
   26 27 28 29 30 31 (32) 33 34

6. 30 − 2
   26 27 (28) 29 30 31 32

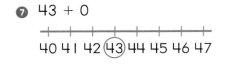

7. 43 + 0
   40 41 42 (43) 44 45 46 47

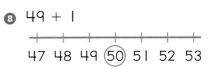

8. 49 + 1
   47 48 49 (50) 51 52 53

9. 51 − 2
   48 (49) 50 51 52 53 54 55

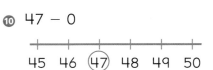

10. 47 − 0
    45 46 (47) 48 49 50

NOTE TO HOME
Students use number lines to add and subtract 0, 1, 2, or 3.

Literature Connection You might want to read aloud *Counting Our Way to Maine* by Maggie Smith to reinforce lesson concepts.

RETEACHING

COOPERATIVE LEARNING Have students work in small groups and use craft sticks to model and solve problems in which they must add and subtract 0, 1, 2, or 3.

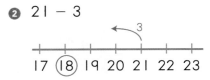

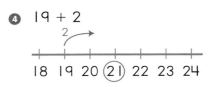

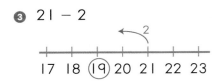

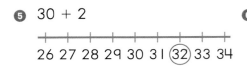

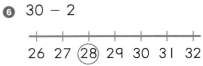

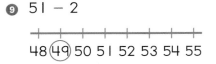

*available separately

◆ **LESSON 6** **Adding and Subtracting by Counting**

Solve these problems. Watch the signs.

25 26 27 28 29 30 31 32 33 34 35 35 36 37 38 39 40 41 42 43 44 45

11. 31 + 2 = 33
12. 40 − 1 = 39
13. 38 + 3 = 41
14. 30 − 1 = 29
15. 40 + 1 = 41
16. 29 + 2 = 31
17. 35 − 2 = 33
18. 37 − 1 = 36
19. 27 − 2 = 25
20. 36 + 2 = 38
21. 39 + 2 = 41
22. 42 + 3 = 45
23. 33 + 3 = 36
24. 42 − 3 = 39
25. 34 + 1 = 35
26. 32 − 3 = 29

NOTE TO HOME
Students add and subtract 0, 1, 2, or 3 using a number line.

PRACTICE p. 6

LESSON 6 PRACTICE Name ______

Solve. Watch the signs.

55 56 57 58 59 60 61 62 63 64 65 66 67 68 69 70 71 72 73 74 75

1. 58 + 3 = 61
2. 58 − 3 = 55
3. 60 − 2 = 58
4. 71 − 1 = 70
5. 62 + 2 = 64
6. 73 + 2 = 75
7. 57 − 1 = 56
8. 69 + 0 = 69
9. 56 + 3 = 59
10. 69 − 3 = 66
11. 73 − 1 = 72
12. 64 − 2 = 62
13. 57 + 1 = 58
14. 68 + 0 = 68
15. 65 − 3 = 62
16. 71 + 3 = 74

6 • *Math Explorations and Applications* Level 2

ENRICHMENT p. 6

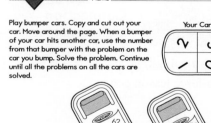

LESSON 6 ENRICHMENT Name ______

Play bumper cars. Copy and cut out your car. Move around the page. When a bumper of your car hits another car, use the number from that bumper with the problem on the car you bump. Solve the problem. Continue until all the problems on all the cars are solved.

Your Car

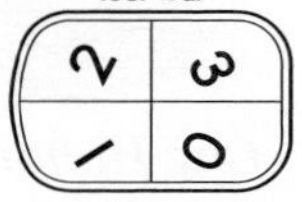

6 • *Math Explorations and Applications* Level 2

❷ Teach

Demonstrate Ask students what method they used to solve the Mental Math addition problems. Demonstrate this method using the last Mental Math problem. Write 89 on the chalkboard and count up three numbers: 89 → 90 → 91 → 92. Point out that the number you start with is not counted when counting up. Then practice mental subtraction by asking questions such as: "What's 2 less than 71?" (69) Confirm the answer by writing the given number and counting down to the left: 69 ← 70 ← 71.

Using the Student Pages Have students complete the problems using the number lines and arrows on page 13 first, and then go on to the rest of the page. Encourage students to solve the problems on page 14 mentally.

Using the Thinking Story Present one or two problems from those following "Measuring Bowser" on pages 10–11 of the Thinking Story Book.

❸ Wrap-Up

5 MINUTES

In Closing Ask students to explain the difference between adding two to a number and subtracting two from a number. (You have to count up two when you add and count down two when you subtract.)

ANALYZING ANSWERS

A common error students make when counting up or down is to count the number they start with. For example, to find 3 more than 21 they count "21, 22, 23" rather than "22, 23, 24." This will be obvious if students' incorrect answers are always one less for addition or one more for subtraction than the correct answer.

SELF ASSESSMENT

Have students correct their own answers on pages 13 and 14. Ask them to write on the top of each page *M* if they think they have mastered the material, or *N* if they think they need more practice.

Assessment Criteria

Did the student . . .

✓ add and subtract correctly without using a number line more than half the time?

✓ write numbers legibly?

LESSON 7

Student Edition page 15–16

Counting Up or Down

LESSON PLANNER

Objective

- to continue to review mental addition and subtraction of 0, 1, 2, and 3

Context of the Lesson This objective is continued from Lesson 6.

Materials	Program Resources
none	Number Cubes
	Thinking Story Book, pages 10–11
	Practice Master 7
	Enrichment Master 7
	For extra practice: CD-ROM* Lesson 7

1 Warm-Up

5 MINUTES

Problem of the Day Write the following problem on the chalkboard: Ellen is carrying a 10-pound bag of potatoes and two melons. Each melon weighs 2 pounds. How many pounds of food is she carrying? (14)

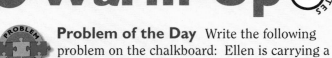

MENTAL MATH Have students find, hide, and show the answers to the following problems with their Number Cubes:

a. 96 – 0 = (96)	**b.** 21 – 3 = (18)
c. 85 + 1 = (86)	**d.** 41 + 2 = (43)
e. 55 – 0 = (55)	**f.** 89 – 3 = (86)
g. 37 – 1 = (36)	**h.** 61 + 2 = (63)
i. 76 + 3 = (79)	**j.** 68 + 0 = (68)
k. 27 – 1 = (26)	**l.** 43 + 3 = (46)
m. 17 – 0 = (17)	**n.** 58 + 2 = (60)

LESSON 7

Name ______________________________

Counting Up or Down

Draw a ring around the answers.

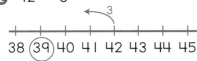

1. 53 + 2
   2 →
   51 52 53 54 (55) 56

2. 42 − 3
   ← 3
   38 (39) 40 41 42 43 44 45

3. 58 + 2
   2 →
   55 56 57 58 59 (60) 61 62

4. 15 + 1
   1 →
   12 13 14 15 (16) 17 18 19

5. 87 − 2
   83 84 (85) 86 87 88 89 90

6. 12 − 3
   8 (9) 10 11 12 13 14 15

7. 60 − 1
   56 57 58 (59) 60 61 62 63

8. 89 + 3
   86 87 88 89 90 91 (92) 93

9. 26 + 3
   23 24 25 26 27 28 (29) 30

10. 21 − 0
    18 19 20 (21) 22 23 24 25

NOTE TO HOME
Students review using number lines to add and subtract 0, 1, 2, or 3.

Literature Connection You might want to read aloud *From One to One Hundred* by Terri Sloat to reinforce lesson concepts.

ESL Meeting Individual Needs
You might want to read the problems on page 16 to students who are learning to speak English. Be sure they understand the meaning of clue words such as *spent*, *taller than*, and *gave*.

RETEACHING

Continue using the same reteaching strategy described in Lesson 6 for students who still need practice.

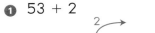

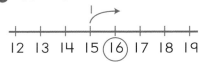

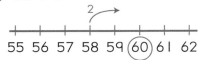

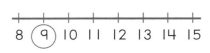

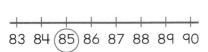

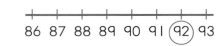

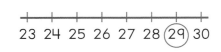

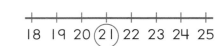

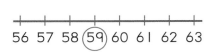

*available separately

◆ **LESSON 7** Counting Up or Down

Solve these problems. Watch the signs.

⑪ 87 + 2 = 89 ⑫ 88 + 3 = 91

⑬ 38 − 3 = 35 ⑭ 32 − 3 = 29

⑮ 48 + 0 = 48 ⑯ 11 − 2 = 9

ACT IT OUT

Use play money to act out the stories.
Write the answers.

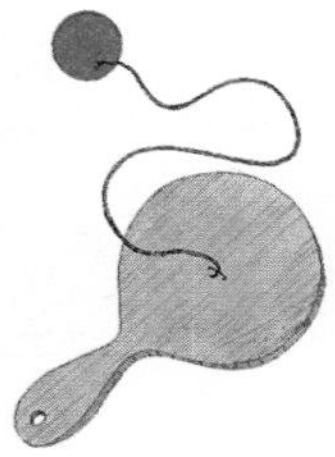

⑰ I had $43.
If I spend $2 for a toy,
how much money will I have? $ 41

⑱ José is 3 centimeters taller than Len.
Len is 97 centimeters tall.
How tall is José? 100 centimeters

⑲ I had 19¢.
If my sister gives me 3¢,
how much money will I have? 22 ¢

NOTE TO HOME
Students solve problems in which they must add or subtract 0, 1, 2, or 3.

❷ Teach

Using the Student Pages Have students complete pages 15–16 independently. Keep play money or counting objects, such as craft sticks or base-10 blocks, available for students to use to model the word problems on page 16. You might want to suggest that students draw pictures rather than use objects to model some of the problems.

Using the Thinking Story Present one or two new problems from those following "Measuring Bowser" on pages 10–11 of the Thinking Story Book.

❸ Wrap-Up

5 MINUTES

In Closing Ask students to make up a word problem in which they must add two in order to solve it.

ANALYZING ANSWERS

When checking students' answers to the word problems look for both computational errors and problem-solving weaknesses. For example, in computational errors students know that they have to add, but they add incorrectly. With problem-solving weaknesses, students do not know whether to add or subtract to solve the problem. Provide appropriate extra practice for students depending on which type of error they make.

ALTERNATIVE ASSESSMENT

Informal Assessment Check that students understand when to add and when to subtract when solving word problems.

Assessment Criteria

Did the student . . .

✓ answer 15 of 19 problems correctly?

✓ know when to add or subtract?

LOOKING AHEAD Materials for the "Frog Pond" Game Mat in Lesson 8 include flash cards, computer games, or a flannel board to show addition and subtraction sequences.

PRACTICE p. 7

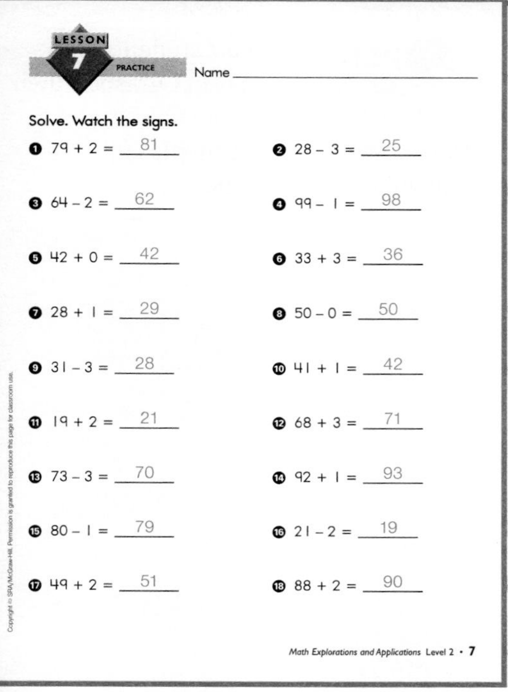

LESSON 7 PRACTICE Name ________

Solve. Watch the signs.

❶ 79 + 2 = 81 ❷ 28 − 3 = 25

❸ 64 − 2 = 62 ❹ 99 − 1 = 98

❺ 42 + 0 = 42 ❻ 33 + 3 = 36

❼ 28 + 1 = 29 ❽ 50 − 0 = 50

❾ 31 − 3 = 28 ❿ 41 + 1 = 42

⓫ 19 + 2 = 21 ⓬ 68 + 3 = 71

⓭ 73 − 3 = 70 ⓮ 92 + 1 = 93

⓯ 80 − 1 = 79 ⓰ 21 − 2 = 19

⓱ 49 + 2 = 51 ⓲ 88 + 2 = 90

Copyright © SRA/McGraw-Hill. Permission is granted to reproduce this page for classroom use.

Math Explorations and Applications Level 2 • 7

ENRICHMENT p. 7

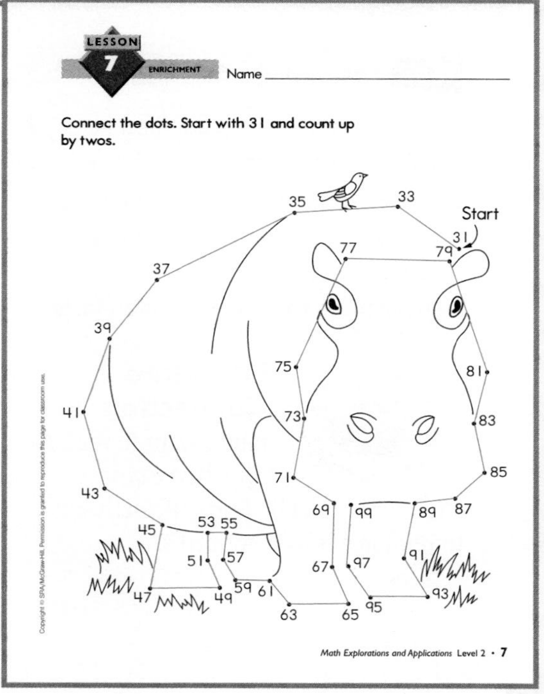

LESSON 7 ENRICHMENT Name ________

Connect the dots. Start with 31 and count up by twos.

Copyright © SRA/McGraw-Hill. Permission is granted to reproduce this page for classroom use.

Math Explorations and Applications Level 2 • 7

LESSON 8

Student Edition pages 17–18

Addition Facts

LESSON PLANNER

Objectives

- to review addition facts in which both addends are five or less, both addends are equal (doubles), and one addend is ten
- to provide practice for writing number sentences to solve addition word problems

Context of the Lesson This is the first of ten lessons reviewing addition facts.

Materials	Program Resources
calendar	"Frog Pond" Game Mats
flannel board (optional)	Number Cubes
	Thinking Story Book, pages 10–11
	Practice Master 8
	Enrichment Master 8
	For extra practice: CD-ROM* Lesson 8

1 Warm-Up (5 minutes)

Problem of the Day Have a calendar available for students to consult. Write the following question on the chalkboard: What is the date that is exactly ten days after your birthday?

MENTAL MATH Have students use their Number Cubes to respond to the following addition facts:

Each addend is 0, 1, or 2:

a. 96 + 0 = (96) **b.** 13 + 2 = (15)

c. 81 + 1 = (82) **d.** 27 + 0 = (27)

Each addend is equal to or less than 5:

a. 2 + 3 = (5) **b.** 5 + 4 = (9)

c. 4 + 3 = (7) **d.** 0 + 2 = (2)

One of the addends is 10:

a. 10 + 6 = (16) **b.** 2 + 10 = (12)

c. 8 + 10 = (18) **d.** 9 + 10 = (19)

PRACTICE

LESSON 8

Name ____________________

Addition Facts

Add.

1. 10 + 5 = 15
2. 4 + 4 = 8
3. 10 + 8 = 18
4. 5 + 5 = 10
5. 7 + 10 = 17
6. 3 + 3 = 6
7. 2 + 10 = 12
8. 4 + 3 = 7
9. 10 + 9 = 19
10. 6 + 10 = 16
11. 0 + 10 = 10
12. 5 + 4 = 9
13. 10 + 4 = 14
14. 3 + 10 = 13

GAME Play the "Frog Pond" game.

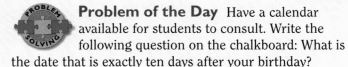

NOTE TO HOME
Students add and play a game using addition facts.

Why teach it at this time?

Students' responses to addition facts should become automatic and rapid to prepare for adding multidigit numbers. Therefore, it is recommended that students *not* use number lines or manipulatives to review addition facts.

Literature Connection You might want to read *I Spy Two Eyes: Numbers in Art* by Lucy Micklethwait to reinforce lesson concepts.

RETEACHING

COOPERATIVE LEARNING Pair students who haven't grasped their addition facts with more able students. Have them discuss strategies for remembering the facts.

*available separately

◆ **LESSON 8 Addition Facts**

Solve these problems

15. There are six oranges in each bag. How many oranges in both bags? 24

16. Seven children are on each team. How many on both teams? 14

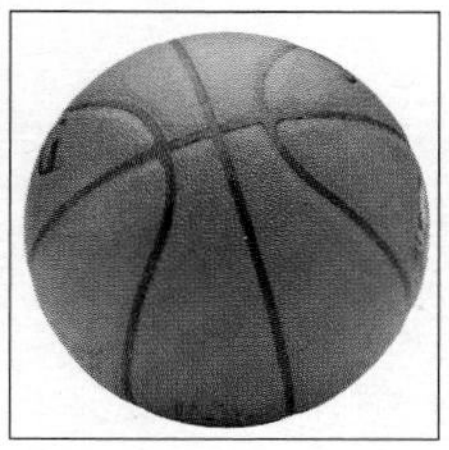

17. The ride can hold 12 people. Nine people are on the ride now. How many more can ride? 3

FANTASTIC FACT

Save energy—smile! It takes 20 muscles to frown, but only 14 to smile.

NOTE TO HOME
Students practice addition and subtraction.

PRACTICE p. 8

LESSON 18 PRACTICE Name ______

Subtract.

1. 10 − 8 = 2
2. 7 − 2 = 5
3. 6 − 0 = 6
4. 9 − 7 = 2
5. 10 − 2 = 8
6. 12 − 0 = 12
7. 9 − 2 = 7
8. 8 − 6 = 2

Add.

9. 6 + 6 = 12
10. 7 + 8 = 15
11. 4 + 9 = 13
12. 9 + 5 = 14
13. 10 + 6 = 16
14. 3 + 8 = 11
15. 7 + 10 = 17
16. 8 + 8 = 16

ENRICHMENT p. 8

LESSON 18 ENRICHMENT Name ______

How many ways can you make the difference.

Figure out the missing numbers. Complete the number sentence.

	First Number	Minus the Second Number	Difference
1	10 11 12	− 0 − 1 − 2	10
2	11 12 13	− 0 − 1 − 2	11
3	12 13 14	− 0 − 1 − 2	12
4	13 14 15	− 0 − 1 − 2	13
5	14 15 16	− 0 − 1 − 2	14

2 Teach

ACT IT OUT **"Modeling Addition Sentences" Activity** Have students act out addition sentences using objects. For example, to model 3 + 4 = ? students can take three crayons and four more crayons, put them together and count the total number.

Demonstrate Make up word problems for each kind of addition fact. Show students how to solve each problem by writing an addition number sentence. For example, for addends that are five or less: Leroy had $5. He earned $3 more. How much does he now have? (5 + 3 = 8) For doubles: Carlos has five apples. Maria has five apples. How many apples do they have all together? (5 + 5 = 10) For addends up to ten: There are ten books on one shelf and five on another. How many books are there all together? (10 + 5 = 15)

Using the Student Pages Have students complete pages 17 and 18 independently. Reteach as needed.

Using the Thinking Story Present one or two problems from those following "Measuring Bowser" on pages 10–11 of the Thinking Story Book.

GAME **Introducing the "Frog Pond" Game Mat** Demonstrate and then play the "Frog Pond" game, which provides practice in adding with two addends of ten or less. Complete directions are on the Game Mat.

3 Wrap-Up

5 MINUTES

In Closing Have students explain how they add doubles. Students should realize that they can use mental math.

ALTERNATIVE ASSESSMENT **Performance Assessment** Hold a math bee. Divide the class into two teams. Have players take turns solving addition facts. Give each student only a short time to answer. Each team's turn continues until an answer is missed. Note which students are having the most difficulty and which demonstrate mastery.

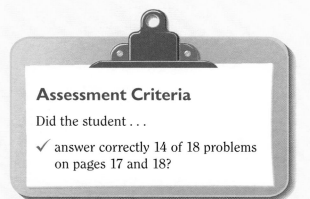

Assessment Criteria

Did the student . . .

✓ answer correctly 14 of 18 problems on pages 17 and 18?

LESSON 9

Student Edition pages 19–20

Double Addends to Ten

LESSON PLANNER

Objective

- ▶ to provide review of doubled addends to 10 + 10

Context of the Lesson This is the second of ten lessons of addition facts review.

Materials	Program Resources
audiocassette of doubles facts (optional)	Number Cubes
index cards	Reteaching Master
	Practice Master 9
	Enrichment Master 9
	For extra practice: CD-ROM* Lesson 9

1 Warm-Up (5 minutes)

Problem of the Day Write the following question on the chalkboard and ask students to solve it: What doubles fact has a sum whose digits add up to 3? (6 + 6 = 12)

MENTAL MATH Read the following addition facts aloud. Have students respond with their Number Cubes.

a. 4 + 4 = (8)
b. 3 + 5 = (8)
c. 5 + 5 = (10)
d. 6 + 3 = (9)
e. 4 + 2 = (6)
f. 4 + 5 = (9)
g. 2 + 7 = (9)
h. 3 + 3 = (6)
i. 2 + 8 = (10)

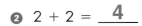

LESSON 9

Name ______________________

Double Addends to Ten

Add.

1. 4 + 4 = 8
2. 2 + 2 = 4

3. 3 + 3 = 6
4. 5 + 5 = 10
5. 9 + 9 = 18
6. 7 + 7 = 14
7. 8 + 8 = 16
8. 6 + 6 = 12
9. 0 + 0 = 0
10. 1 + 1 = 2

NOTE TO HOME
Students practice doubling numbers.

COOPERATIVE LEARNING Provide each student with several blank index cards. One student will draw doubles problems on his or her index cards; the other will write number sentences. Then students will switch sets and write the appropriate number sentences or draw the appropriate pictures on the backs of the cards.

RETEACHING p. 3

LESSON 9 RETEACHING Name ______________________

Doubles can help you add.

Look at the lesser number.

5 + 6 = 11   5 + 5 = 10

5 + 6 is almost like 5 + 5.
Six is one more than five.
Eleven is one more than ten.

2 + 3 = 5 (2 + 2 = 4 → add 1)

5 + 4 = 9 (4 + 4 = 8 → add 1)

Add.

1. 6 + 7 = 13   6 + 6 = 12
2. 9 + 8 = 17   8 + 8 = 16
3. 9 + 10 = 19   9 + 9 = 18
4. 8 + 7 = 15   8 + 8 = 16

*available separately

◆ **LESSON 9** Double Addends to Ten

Use the Mixed Practice on page 366 after this lesson.

Add.

11. 4 + 4 = **8**
12. 2 + 2 = **4**
13. 10 + 10 = **20**
14. 2 + 3 = **5**
15. 9 + 10 = **19**
16. 8 + 8 = **16**
17. 9 + 9 = **18**
18. 7 + 10 = **17**
19. 4 + 4 = **8**
20. 7 + 7 = **14**
21. 4 + 5 = **9**
22. 6 + 6 = **12**

	23	24	25	26	27
	5	5	6	3	9
	+ 5	+ 3	+ 4	+ 3	+ 1
	10	**8**	**10**	**6**	**10**

	28	29	30
	1	2	7
	+ 1	+ 4	+ 3
	2	**6**	**10**

NOTE TO HOME
Students practice addition facts.

PRACTICE p. 9

LESSON 9 PRACTICE Name ____________

Add.

1. 5 + 9 = 14
2. 9 + 3 = 12
3. 9 + 6 = 15
4. 4 + 9 = 13
5. 1 + 9 = 10
6. 9 + 2 = 11
7. 9 + 7 = 16
8. 9 + 9 = 18
9. 8 + 9 = 17
10. 9 + 10 = 19

	11	12	13	14
	9	2	5	3
	+ 8	+ 9	+ 9	+ 9
	17	11	14	12

	15	16	17	18
	9	9	0	1
	+ 4	+ 6	+ 9	+ 9
	13	15	9	10

Math Explorations and Applications Level 2 • 9

ENRICHMENT p. 9

LESSON 9 ENRICHMENT Name ____________

You need several sheets of scrap paper. Fold one sheet of paper in half. Draw four dots near the top of the page. Use your pencil to poke holes through each dot. Unfold the paper.

How many holes did you make? 8

Do the same thing with five, six, seven, eight, and nine dots. Use a new sheet of scrap paper each time. Fill the chart.

Number of Dots	Number of Holes
4	8
5	10
6	12
7	14
8	16
9	18

Math Explorations and Applications Level 2 • 9

2 Teach

Introducing the "Doubles" Activity To practice doubles to 5 + 5 have students use their Number Cubes to show answers to six basic facts: 0 + 0, 1 + 1 . . . 5 + 5. Repeat several times in different orders. Students who have difficulty can use their fingers to see the sums. Repeat the activity for sums for doubles from 6 + 6 through 10 + 10. If students are having difficulty, have them draw two squares on a sheet of paper and draw circles in each square that correspond to the doubles they are having trouble with. They can then count the circles. For example, 8 circles + 8 circles = 16 circles.

PROBLEM SOLVING

Using the Student Pages Have students work independently to complete these pages. Students can use the pictures on page 19 to help them get started.

3 Wrap-Up

5 MINUTES

In Closing Have students write as many doubles addition facts as they can in five minutes.

ALTERNATIVE ASSESSMENT

Informal Assessment Have students orally give the sums of doubles facts as quickly as they can.

Assessment Criteria

Did the student . . .

✓ correctly solve 8 of 10 problems on page 19?

✓ correctly solve 16 of 20 problems on page 20?

LEARNING STYLES

Meeting Individual Needs
Consider making a tape recording of doubles facts for auditory learners. They can say or write answers in place of or after completing pages 19 and 20.

LESSON 10

Student Edition pages 21–22

Addition Facts Review

LESSON PLANNER

Objective

- to provide review of nines addition facts by relating them to tens addition facts

Context of the Lesson This is the third of ten lessons of addition facts review.

Materials	Program Resources
craft sticks	Number Cubes
pennies or other counters (optional)	Practice Master 10
	Enrichment Master 10
	For extra practice: CD-ROM* Lesson 10

1 Warm-Up

5 MINUTES

Problem of the Day Write the following number patterns on the chalkboard and have students describe and complete them:

a. 0, 1, 3, 6, ____ (+1, +2, +3, +4; 10)

b. 19, 18, 16, 15, 13, ____ (−1, −2, −1, −2, −1; 12)

c. 1, 1, 2, 2, 2, 4, 3, 3, 6, 4, 4, 8, ____, ____, 10 (1 + 1 = 2, 2 + 2 = 4, 3 + 3 = 6, 4 + 4 = 8; 5, 5, 10)

MENTAL MATH Write the following problems on the chalkboard. Have students use Number Cubes to tell whether 0, 1, 2, or 3 belongs in each blank.

a. 32 + ____ = 33 (1) b. 50 − ____ = 48 (2)

c. 91 + ____ = 91 (0) d. 44 − ____ = 44 (0)

e. 10 − ____ = 7 (3) f. 29 + ____ = 30 (1)

GIFTED & TALENTED **Meeting Individual Needs**

Have students make up word problems that must be solved by adding 9 to a number. Then have them solve their own problems and give them to other students to solve.

LESSON 10

Name ______________________

Addition Facts Review

Add.

1. 10 + 7 = **17**
2. 10 + 10 = **20**
3. 9 + 7 = **16**
4. 10 + 9 = **19**
5. 10 + 5 = **15**
6. 4 + 10 = **14**
7. 9 + 5 = **14**
8. 4 + 9 = **13**
9. 8 + 10 = **18**
10. 6 + 10 = **16**
11. 8 + 9 = **17**
12. 6 + 9 = **15**
13. 3 + 10 = **13**
14. 10 + 2 = **12**
15. 1 + 10 = **11**
16. 10 + 0 = **10**

NOTE TO HOME
Students practice addition facts up to 20.

RETEACHING

Use base-10 materials to show students how adding 9 to a number is related to adding 10. Have them model 10 + 7 using craft sticks. Ask: What does this model show? (10 + 7 = 17) Show students how to use the sticks to show the related nines fact of 9 + 7 by taking one stick from the 10. They can see that if 10 + 7 = 17 then 9 + 7 must be 16. Repeat with other ten and nine facts.

*available separately

◆ **LESSON 10** Addition Facts Review

Add.

17. 5 + 9 = 14
18. 7 + 9 = 16
19. 5 + 5 = 10
20. 8 + 8 = 16
21. 9 + 9 = 18
22. 9 + 3 = 12
23. 9 + 8 = 17
24. 3 + 8 = 12

25. 6 + 6 = 12
26. 9 + 6 = 15
27. 3 + 5 = 8
28. 6 + 9 = 15
29. 2 + 9 = 11
30. 9 + 1 = 10
31. 2 + 6 = 8
32. 4 + 9 = 13

FANTASTIC FACT There are about 45,000 thunderstorms in the world every day.

NOTE TO HOME
Students practice addition facts up to 20.

PRACTICE p. 10

LESSON 10 PRACTICE Name ______

Add.

1. 5 + 5 = 10
2. 4 + 3 = 7
3. 2 + 2 = 4
4. 4 + 4 = 8
5. 5 + 6 = 11
6. 3 + 2 = 5
7. 4 + 5 = 9
8. 9 + 9 = 18
9. 6 + 7 = 13
10. 6 + 6 = 12
11. 8 + 8 = 16
12. 5 + 6 = 11
13. 3 + 3 = 6
14. 3 + 4 = 7
15. 7 + 7 = 14
16. 1 + 2 = 3
17. 8 + 9 = 17
18. 1 + 1 = 2

ENRICHMENT p. 10

LESSON 10 ENRICHMENT Name ______

Play Mathland.

Get some markers. Make playing cards with the addition facts to 20. On each card, write a different fact. Shuffle the cards. You may make extra cards, too.

Put the cards on the game. In turn, each player draws a card, solves the problem, and moves his or her marker to the answer on the board. The first person to the finish is the winner.

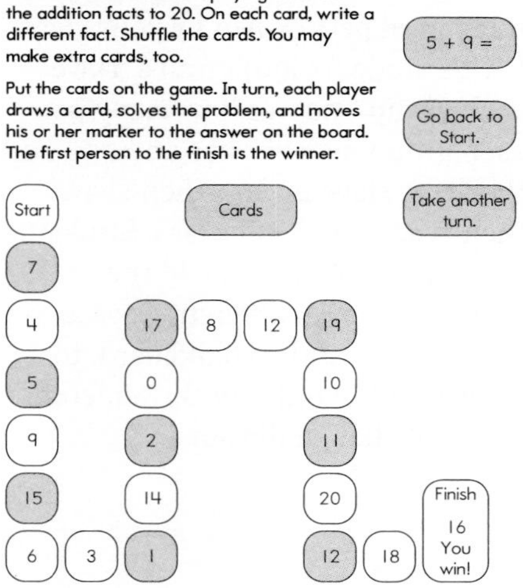

2 Teach

Demonstrate Have students use their Number Cubes to answer several tens facts such as 10 + 7 and 10 + 4. Then ask: How is 9 + 7 related to 10 + 7? (It is one less.) Then what is 9 + 7? (16) Repeat questions with several other facts such as 10 + 8 and 9 + 8. Finally, continue the practice without including the tens facts: 9 + 6 = ?, 9 + 3 = ?, etc.

Using the Student Pages Have students work independently to complete these pages. Then go over the answers with the class and have students correct any problems they got wrong.

3 Wrap-Up

5 MINUTES

In Closing Have students write a rule for adding 9 to any number. (The answer is always one less than 10 plus the number.)

Informal Assessment Use students' responses to pages 21 and 22 as an informal assessment of their mastery of addition facts.

ALTERNATIVE ASSESSMENT

Assessment Criteria

Did the student . . .

✓ correctly solve 13 of 16 problems on page 21?

✓ correctly solve 13 of 16 problems on page 22?

SPECIAL NEEDS

Meeting Individual Needs

Have students use pennies or other objects to count in order to model and complete the problems on these pages.

LESSON 11

Student Edition pages 23–24

Commutative Property

LESSON PLANNER

Objectives

- to provide review of the commutative property for addition
- to demonstrate how to apply the commutative property to make addition facts easier

Context of the Lesson This is the fourth of ten lessons of addition facts review. The commutative property is presented for the first time in this grade level.

Materials	Program Resources
calculators (optional)	Number Cubes
large cardboard box (optional)	Thinking Story Book, pages 12–15
	Practice Master 11
	Enrichment Master 11
	For extra practice: CD-ROM* Lesson 11

1 Warm-Up

5 MINUTES

Problem of the Day Write this problem on the chalkboard: Megan was three years old when her little brother, Keith, was born. How old will Megan be when she is twice as old as Keith? (6 years old)

MENTAL MATH Provide practice in addition facts and have students show answers with their Number Cubes.

a. 9 + 9 = (18)
b. 9 + 4 = (13)
c. 9 + 2 = (11)
d. 6 + 9 = (15)
e. 5 + 9 = (14)
f. 9 + 7 = (16)

2 Teach

Demonstrate Have two students face the class. Ask the first to hold up eight fingers and the second to hold up three. Have students explain what addition fact this shows. (8 + 3 = 11) Have students exchange places, still with their fingers up. Ask what fact this shows. (3 + 8 = 11) Ask how the two facts are related. (The numbers are in different order, but the sums are the same.) Repeat with several pairs of numbers.

LESSON 11

Name ______________________

Commutative Property

Add.

1. 10 + 3 = 13
2. 6 + 4 = 10
3. 3 + 10 = 13
4. 4 + 6 = 10
5. 8 + 3 = 11
6. 2 + 9 = 11
7. 3 + 8 = 11
8. 1 + 8 = 9
9. 1 + 10 = 11
10. 10 + 1 = 11
11. 8 + 5 = 13
12. 5 + 8 = 13
13. 9 + 4 = 13
14. 4 + 9 = 13
15. 7 + 6 = 13
16. 6 + 7 = 13

NOTE TO HOME
Students use the commutative property to help solve problems.

Social Studies Connection Have students find the total number of pets owned by your class. Divide students into groups. Have each group find out how many pets each group member has and add up the total. Have groups then share their results with the class. Students can use calculators to add the numbers several different ways as you do the sums at the chalkboard, to show that the order of the addends does not change the sum.

RETEACHING

Arrange ten students in groups of four and six. Have students write a number sentence showing how to add the group: 4 + 6 = 10. Have the groups exchange places. Students then write a new number sentence showing how to add groups in this order: 6 + 4 = 10. Ask students to explain what they showed. (Possible answer: It did not matter in which order the students stood, the total was always the same.)

*available separately

◆ LESSON 11 Commutative Property

What comes out?

17 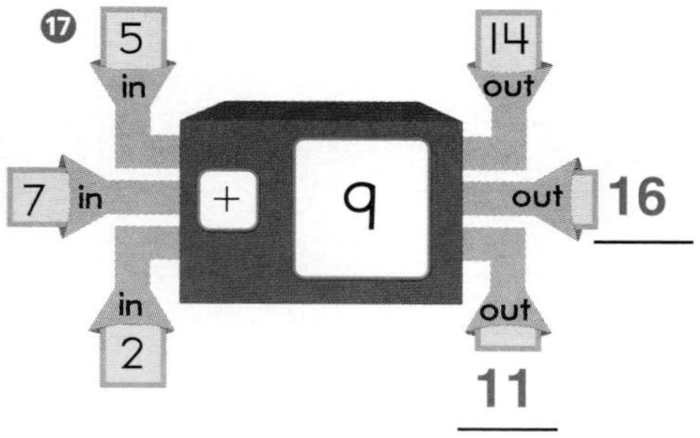

18 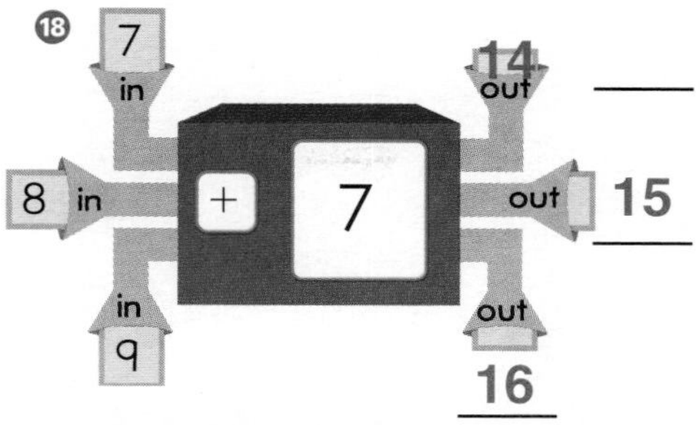

What went in?

19 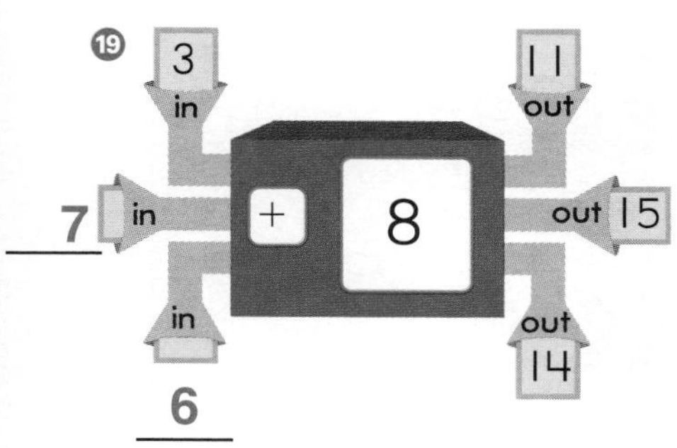

20 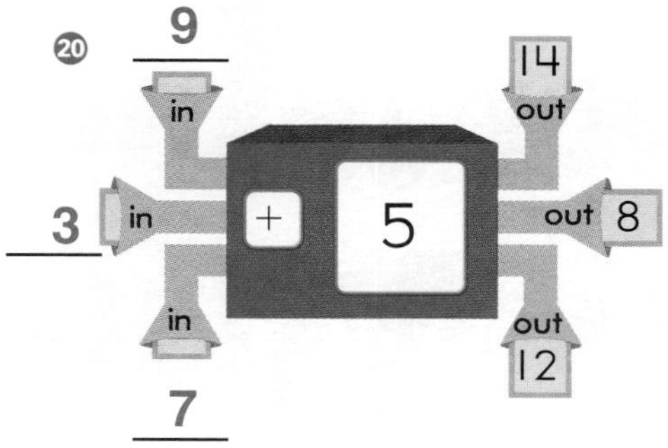

What is the rule?

21 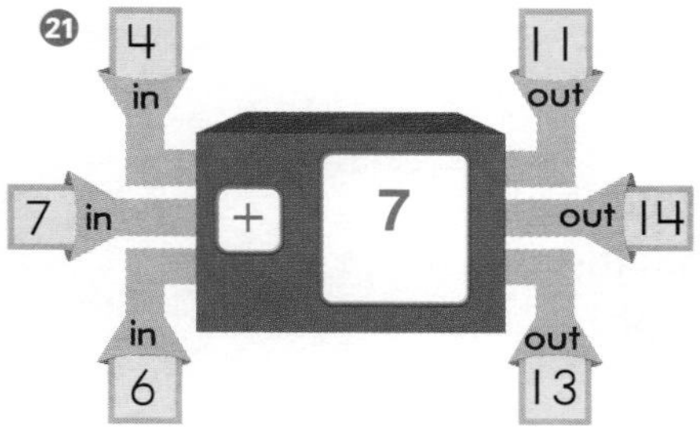

22 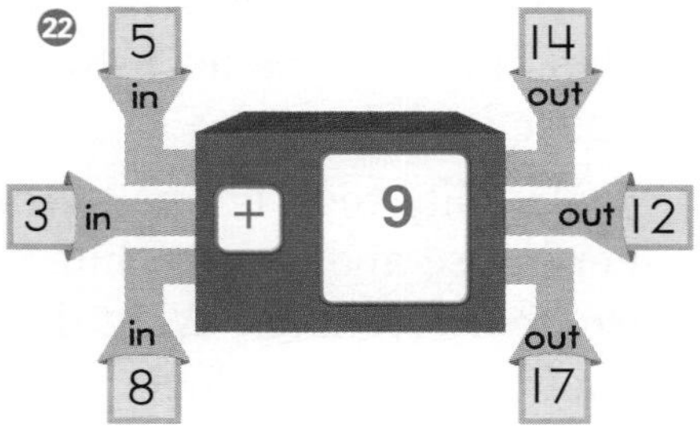

NOTE TO HOME
Students solve function problems.

PRACTICE p. 11

LESSON 11 PRACTICE Name ______

Add.

1. 3 + 2 = 5
2. 2 + 3 = 5
3. 5 + 4 = 9
4. 4 + 5 = 9
5. 7 + 8 = 15
6. 8 + 7 = 15
7. 6 + 7 = 13
8. 7 + 6 = 13
9. 9 + 6 = 15
10. 6 + 9 = 15
11. 8 + 5 = 13
12. 5 + 8 = 13
13. 6 + 5 = 11
14. 5 + 6 = 11
15. 8 + 9 = 17
16. 9 + 8 = 17
17. 4 + 7 = 11
18. 7 + 4 = 11
19. 0 + 2 = 2
20. 2 + 0 = 2

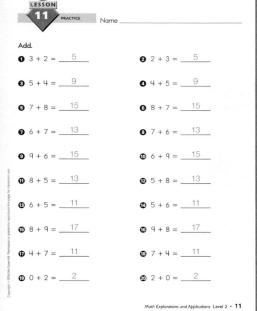

ENRICHMENT p. 11

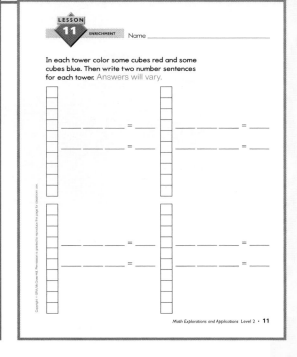

LESSON 11 ENRICHMENT Name ______

In each tower color some cubes red and some cubes blue. Then write two number sentences for each tower. Answers will vary.

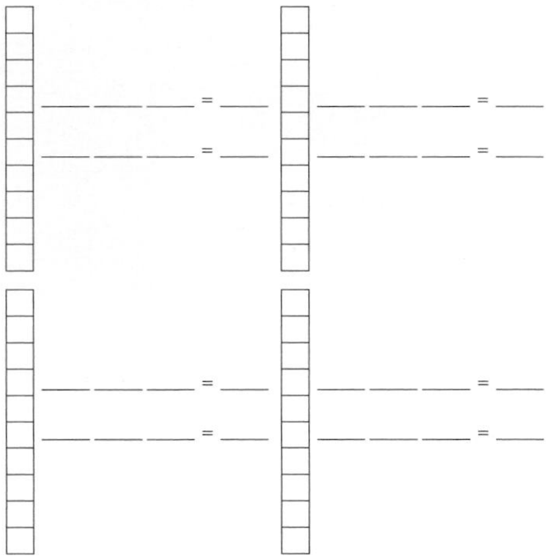

Introducing the "Function Machine" Activity

Have one student hide in a large cardboard box. Secretly work out a simple rule with this student, such as always adding 5 to a number. Have other students write numbers on slips of paper and put them into the "machine." The student inside the box crosses out the number and writes the new one by applying the rule. The other students try to figure out the rule.

Using the Student Pages Have students complete the pages independently.

Using the Thinking Story Read "The Amazing Number Machine Makes Mistakes" in the Thinking Story Book on pages 12–15 aloud to the class. Stop and discuss the questions asked throughout the story.

3 Wrap-Up

5 MINUTES

In Closing Ask students whether the order of two numbers that are added together will change their sum. (no) Ask how knowing this might help them with some addition facts. (If you know a fact like 9 + 2 = 11, then you already know the solution to 2 + 9.)

ALTERNATIVE ASSESSMENT

Informal Assessment Use students' answers to page 23 to informally assess their understanding of the commutative property.

Assessment Criteria

Did the student . . .

✓ participate in the Thinking Story discussion?

✓ use the commutative property to correctly answer 13 of 16 problems on page 23?

✓ correctly fill in 5 of 6 of the missing numbers on page 24?

✓ correctly identify both rules on page 24?

STORY 2

THINKING STORY

The Amazing Number Machine Makes Mistakes

Ferdie decided to have a surprise party for Portia. It would be an extra-surprising surprise party because her birthday wasn't until December, and he planned to have the party in May.

How many months early will the party be? seven

Ferdie knew it was seven months early, but once he got the idea he couldn't wait that long to have the party. The first person he invited was Manolita.

"That's a great idea, but you'll need some help to plan the party. I know just the machine for the job," said Manolita.

"Machine?" asked Ferdie. "What machine?"

"Didn't you know?" asked Manolita. "I've built an extra-special super-duper number machine that knows everything. Anything you want to know it can tell you. If you need to know anything about a party, it can tell you that too. Let's go to my house. I'll show it to you and we can get started."

"Let's stop and get Marcus," said Ferdie.

"He's not at home right now," said Manolita. "But he may stop by my house later."

Manolita took Ferdie to the basement of her house and showed him the Amazing Number Machine. "What do you want to know first?" she asked.

"Let's figure out how much food we need. I'm inviting 15 guests, and we need two cupcakes for each guest."

How many cupcakes do they need? thirty

"Oh Amazing Number Machine," said Manolita. "We will have 15 children at the party . . ."

"How many cupcakes do we need if each child will have two?" asked Ferdie.

After a moment, a deep voice came out of the machine. "Seventeen cupcakes," it said.

Was the machine right? no

Did the machine add 15 and 15? no

What did the machine do? It added 15 and 2.

"It hasn't been working very well lately," said Manolita. "It seems to have a bug in it."

"Let's try it again. Oh Amazing Number Machine," said Ferdie, "fifteen guests and two cupcakes for each guest."

The machine answered, "Thirteen cupcakes."

Did the machine add this time? no

What did the machine do? It subtracted 2 from 15.

"Your machine has more than a bug in it," said Ferdie. "I can figure it out faster myself. We need 30 cupcakes. But the next problem is harder. Cupcakes come in packages of six each. I think we need six packages."

"Wait," said the machine, "give me another chance."

Manolita started, "Oh Amazing Number Machine, Ferdie thinks we need six packages of cupcakes to get 30 cupcakes. There are six cupcakes in a package. Is he right?"

Is Ferdie right? no

How many packages of cupcakes do they need? five

The machine answered in an even deeper voice, "Ferdie is wrong. Six packages of cupcakes makes 12 cupcakes."

Is the machine right? no

What did it do? It added 6 and 6.

◆ STORY 2 The Amazing Number Machine Makes Mistakes

"That silly machine added 6 and 6," said Ferdie. "That's not the way to figure out how many packages we need."

How would you figure out how many packages they need? Answers may vary; possibilities include skip counting by 6s to get to 30 or finding what number times 6 equals 30.

"The machine is doing about as well as you are," said Manolita. "Let me figure it out. There are six cupcakes in a package. Six times 5 is 30. We need five packages of cupcakes."

Is Manolita right? yes

"I just remembered something," said Ferdie. "Two of my guests have measles. They won't be able to come to the party. I wonder how many guests will be there."

How many guests will be at the party? 13

How did you figure that out? Subtract 2 from 15.

6 X 5 = 30

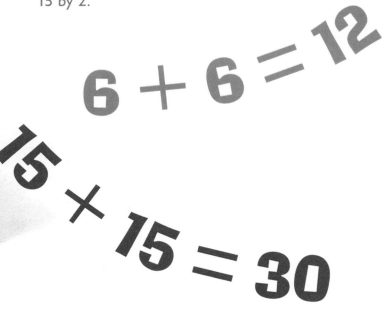

"Give me another chance," said the machine, "that's an easy one." Ferdie decided to give the machine just one more chance. "Oh Amazing Number Machine, if there are 15 guests and two can't come, how many guests will there be?"

"Thirty," answered the machine.

Did the machine subtract 2 from 15? no

What did it do? It multiplied 15 by 2.

6 + 6 = 12

15 + 15 = 30

Sanchez is at bat . . .

"I'll never trust that machine again!" said Ferdie. "It added 15 and 15. It should have subtracted 2 from 15. Anyone knows that if two guests get sick you have to subtract them from the party. There will be only 13 guests."

"I don't understand what has gotten into that machine," said Manolita. "There must be something wrong with it–listen."

The children were very quiet so that they could listen. Strange sounds were coming from inside the machine. They could hear wee voices talking and something that sounded like a crowd shouting in the distance.

"Let's give the machine one more chance," Manolita said. "Oh Amazing Number Machine, here is one more problem for you, and it's an easy one."

Do you have any idea what could be making noises like that? Someone is inside.

"Quiet!" said the machine. "Can't you hear that the bases are loaded and there is only one out?"

"I think I recognize that voice," Ferdie said. "Let me see what's going on here."

Ferdie lifted the lid off the machine. Inside he found Marcus holding a tiny radio to his ear. There was nothing else inside the machine.

How does the machine work? Marcus answers the questions.

"What's wrong with you today?" Manolita asked Marcus. "You always used to give good answers when you were inside the machine."

"Sorry," said Marcus. "I guess I was too busy trying to listen to a baseball game at the same time."

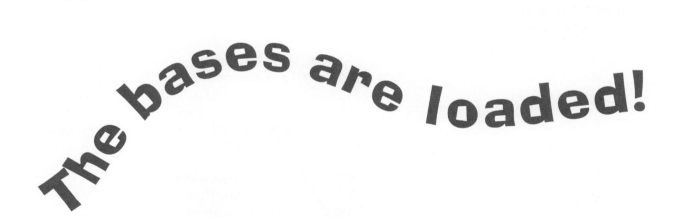

. . . the end

The bases are loaded!

LESSON 12

Student Edition pages 25–26

Reviewing Addition Facts

LESSON PLANNER

Objectives

- ▶ to reinforce students' knowledge of basic addition facts
- ▶ to identify areas of needed improvement in rapid and correct recall of the addition facts

Context of the Lesson This is the fifth of ten lessons on addition facts review.

Materials	Program Resources
none	Number Cubes
	Thinking Story Book, pages 16–17
	Practice Master 12
	Enrichment Master 12
	For extra practice: CD-ROM* Lesson 12

1 Warm-Up

5 MINUTES

Problem of the Day Write the following problem on the chalkboard: Hector is not allowed to watch television for 12 weekdays. If today is Tuesday, and this new rule begins today, what is the first weekday he can watch television again? (three Thursdays from today)

MENTAL MATH Have students add the following pairs of numbers, showing their answers with Number Cubes:

a. 5 + 6 = (11)	**b.** 7 + 8 = (15)
c. 4 + 5 = (9)	**d.** 9 + 10 = (19)
e. 8 + 9 = (17)	**f.** 2 + 3 = (5)
g. 6 + 7 = (13)	**h.** 5 + 7 = (12)
i. 2 + 4 = (6)	**j.** 8 + 10 = (18)
k. 6 + 8 = (14)	**l.** 7 + 9 = (16)
m. 4 + 6 = (10)	**n.** 3 + 5 = (8)

LESSON 12

Name ______________________

Reviewing Addition Facts

Add.

1. 7 + 8 = 15
2. 6 + 7 = 13
3. 9 + 8 = 17
4. 5 + 6 = 11
5. 5 + 7 = 12
6. 9 + 7 = 16
7. 8 + 10 = 18
8. 8 + 6 = 14
9. 9 + 5 = 14
10. 9 + 3 = 12
11. 7 + 9 = 16
12. 4 + 9 = 13
13. 8 + 4 = 12
14. 7 + 4 = 11
15. 6 + 9 = 15
16. 9 + 10 = 19
17. 10 + 10 = 20
18. 10 + 3 = 13

MATH JOURNAL Draw a ring around a problem on this page. Write in your Math Journal how you solved it.

NOTE TO HOME
Students review adding nine, adding doubles, doubles plus one, and doubles plus two.

Literature Connection You might want to read aloud *Counting Wildflowers* by Bruce McMillan to reinforce lesson concepts.

Physical Education Connection Have students think about a game, such as basketball, and how speedy addition skills could help them understand that game. Invite them to write a short paragraph about an interesting part of a game they saw, and how the score changed during that part of the game.

RETEACHING

Consider sending the "Addition Table" game, which is introduced in the next lesson, home with students who are having difficulty with their addition facts. Encourage them to play the game with family members.

*available separately

◆ LESSON 12 Reviewing Addition Facts

Add.

⑲ 3 + 5 = 8 ⑳ 8 + 3 = 11

㉑ 8 + 1 = 9 ㉒ 5 + 8 = 13

㉓ 2 + 8 = 10 ㉔ 8 + 2 = 10

㉕ 6 + 4 = 10 ㉖ 4 + 6 = 10

㉗ 3 + 7 = 10 ㉘ 4 + 7 = 11

㉙ 2 + 7 = 9 ㉚ 9 + 8 = 17

㉛ 4 + 9 = 13 ㉜ 6 + 2 = 8

㉝ 3 + 2 = 5 ㉞ 5 + 1 = 6

㉟ 7 + 1 = 8 ㊱ 7 + 3 = 10

FANTASTIC FACT

The sugarcane plant can grow to be 20 feet tall.

NOTE TO HOME
Students continue addition practice.

2 Teach

Demonstrate Show students how knowing doubles can help them mentally add other related facts. Use the following examples to demonstrate.

Knowing 8 + 8 = 16 helps you to figure out 8 + 9. Because 9 is 1 more than 8, the sum is 1 more than 16: 8 + 8 = 16, so 8 + 9 = 17.

Knowing 8 + 8 = 16 helps you to figure out 7 + 9. Because 7 is 1 less than 8 and 9 is 1 more, the sum is the same.

Knowing + 10 facts helps you to figure out + 9 facts. 9 + 6 is 1 less than 10 + 6: 10 + 6 = 16, so 9 + 6 = 15.

Using the Student Pages Have students complete pages 25 and 26 independently.

Using the Thinking Story Present one or two problems from those following "The Amazing Number Machine Makes Mistakes" on pages 16–17 of the Thinking Story Book.

3 Wrap-Up

5 MINUTES

In Closing Have students tell which strategy they would use to help them mentally add 8 + 6. (14)

ALTERNATIVE ASSESSMENT

Portfolio Assessment Have students write about one of their favorite addition strategies and give an example of how it is used. Have them include the explanation in their Math Portfolios.

PRACTICE p. 12

LESSON 12 PRACTICE Name ____________

Add.

❶ 8 + 9 = 17 ❷ 4 + 3 = 7

❸ 5 + 6 = 11 ❹ 4 + 5 = 9

❺ 10 + 9 = 19 ❻ 8 + 7 = 15

❼ 5 + 4 = 9 ❽ 9 + 5 = 14

❾ 6 + 7 = 13 ❿ 9 + 6 = 15

⓫ 9 + 8 = 17 ⓬ 7 + 6 = 13 ⓭ 5 + 8 = 13 ⓮ 3 + 4 = 7

⓯ 7 + 7 = 14 ⓰ 9 + 9 = 18 ⓱ 6 + 6 = 12 ⓲ 8 + 8 = 16

ENRICHMENT p. 12

LESSON 12 ENRICHMENT Name ____________

Fill the number dresser. What drawer does each problem go into? The answers to the problems tell you. Write each problem on the drawer that shows its answer.

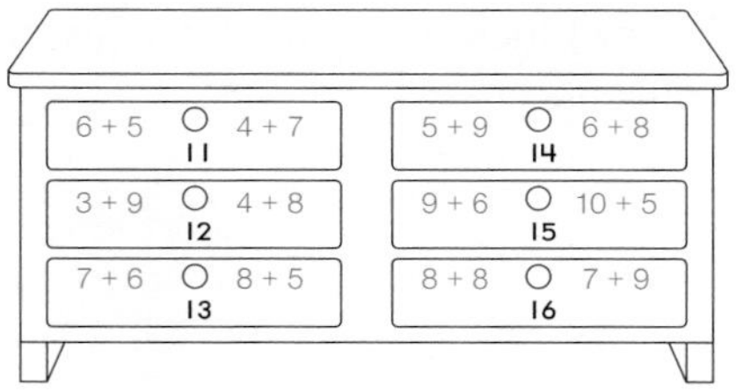
6 + 5
4 + 7
11
5 + 9
6 + 8
14
3 + 9
4 + 8
12
9 + 6
10 + 5
15
7 + 6
8 + 5
13
8 + 8
7 + 9
16

8 + 8 = ______	8 + 5 = ______	9 + 6 = ______
6 + 5 = ______	5 + 9 = ______	10 + 5 = ______
4 +7 = ______	7 + 9 = ______	3 + 9 = ______
4 + 8 = ______	6 + 8 = ______	7 + 6 = ______

Assessment Criteria

Did the student . . .

✓ use mental math to correctly answer at least 29 of 36 of the problems?

✓ use correct addition strategies?

LESSON 13

Student Edition pages 27–28

Addition Table

LESSON PLANNER

Objectives

- ▶ to review the use of an addition table
- ▶ to improve students' memorization of addition facts through 10 + 10

Context of the Lesson This is the sixth of ten lessons on addition facts review.

Materials

overhead projector (optional)

transparency of 10 + 10 addition table (optional)

Program Resources

"Addition Table" Game Mats

Number Cubes

Thinking Story Book, pages 16–17

Practice Master 13

Enrichment Master 13

For extra practice:
CD-ROM* Lesson 13

1 Warm-Up

5 MINUTES

Problem of the Day Write the following problem on the chalkboard: Tom is taller than Chris. Frank is shorter than Tom. Chris is the shortest. Write the names in order from shortest to tallest. (Chris, Frank, Tom)

MENTAL MATH Read the following problems aloud and have students answer with their Number Cubes:

a. 5 + 5 = (10)	**b.** 7 + 7 = (14)
c. 6 + 6 = (12)	**d.** 5 + 4 = (9)
e. 8 + 7 = (15)	**f.** 8 + 8 = (16)
g. 4 + 4 = (8)	**h.** 3 + 2 = (5)
i. 10 + 5 = (15)	**j.** 7 + 8 = (15)
k. 5 + 9 = (14)	**l.** 6 + 9 = (15)

PRACTICE

LESSON 13

Name ______________________

Addition Table

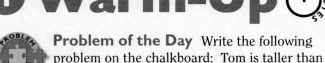

+	0	1	2	3	4	5	6	7	8	9	10
0	0	1	2	3	4	5	6	7	8	9	10
1	1	2	3	4	5	6	7	8	9	10	11
2	2	3	4	5	6	7	8	9	10	11	12
3	3	4	5	6	7	8	9	10	11	12	13
4	4	5	6	7	8	9	10	11	12	13	14
5	5	6	7	8	9	10	11	12	13	14	15
6	6	7	8	9	10	11	12	13	14	15	16
7	7	8	9	10	11	12	13	14	15	16	17
8	8	9	10	11	12	13	14	15	16	17	18
9	9	10	11	12	13	14	15	16	17	18	19
10	10	11	12	13	14	15	16	17	18	19	20

5 + 6 = 11

Add.

1. 3 + 9 = **12**
2. 6 + 5 = **11**
3. 8 + 5 = **13**
4. 4 + 7 = **11**
5. 3 + 6 = **9**
6. 8 + 8 = **16**
7. 7 + 7 = **14**
8. 6 + 6 = **12**
9. 9 + 9 = **18**
10. 5 + 5 = **10**

NOTE TO HOME
Students use an addition table to help them remember addition facts.

Literature Connection You might want to read aloud *Counting* by Henry Pluckrose to reinforce lesson concepts.

RETEACHING

Make copies of an addition table that is incomplete. Have students complete the table.

*available separately

◆ LESSON 13 Addition Table

Add.

⑪ 8 + 7 = 15
⑫ 7 + 8 = 15
⑬ 2 + 8 = 10
⑭ 9 + 4 = 13
⑮ 4 + 9 = 13
⑯ 8 + 2 = 10
⑰ 6 + 8 = 14
⑱ 8 + 6 = 14
⑲ 3 + 8 = 11
⑳ 8 + 3 = 11
㉑ 6 + 6 = 12
㉒ 5 + 9 = 14
㉓ 7 + 5 = 12
㉔ 7 + 4 = 11
㉕ 9 + 3 = 12
㉖ 3 + 9 = 12
㉗ 3 + 4 = 7
㉘ 5 + 2 = 7

GAME

Play the "Addition Table" game.

NOTE TO HOME
Students continue to practice and play a game reviewing addition facts.

PRACTICE p. 13

LESSON 13 PRACTICE Name ________

Add.

1. 4 + 9 = 13
2. 8 + 7 = 15
3. 6 + 6 = 12
4. 4 + 8 = 12
5. 2 + 9 = 11
6. 6 + 8 = 14
7. 8 + 2 = 10
8. 9 + 8 = 17
9. 6 + 7 = 13
10. 9 + 5 = 14
11. 3 + 8 = 11
12. 7 + 3 = 10
13. 5 + 4 = 9
14. 9 + 3 = 12
15. 5 + 7 = 12
16. 9 + 6 = 15

Math Explorations and Applications Level 2 • 13

ENRICHMENT p. 13

LESSON 13 ENRICHMENT Name ________

	1	2	3	4	5	6	7	8	9	10
1			A		B				C	
2			D	E	F	G	H		I	J
3	A	D			K		L			
4		E			M	N	O	P	Q	
5	B	F	K	M			R		S	
6		G		N			T	U	V	W
7		H	L	O	R	T			X	
8				P		U			Y	Z
9	C	I		Q	S	V	X	Y		
10		J				W		Z		

Use the code to write this number twister.
Then try to say it fast three times.

S	I	X		S	H	I	N	Y
9, 5	2, 9	7, 9		5, 9	7, 2	9, 2	4, 6	8, 9

S	E	A		S	H	E	L	L	S
5, 9	4, 2	3, 1		9, 5	2, 7	2, 4	7, 3	3, 7	9, 5

Make up your own twisters. Share them with a friend.

Math Explorations and Applications Level 2 • 13

2 Teach

Demonstrate Show students how to use the addition table on page 27. Demonstrate using the table to add 5 + 6. Repeat with several other sums, then have volunteers show how to use the table. You might want to have students use a ruler to keep their place along the columns and row.

Using the Student Pages Have students complete pages 27 and 28, using the addition table on page 27 whenever needed.

Using the Thinking Story Present one or two problems from those following the Thinking Story "The Amazing Number Machine Makes Mistakes" on pages 16–17 of the Thinking Story Book.

GAME **Introducing the "Addition Table" Game Mat** Demonstrate and then have students play the "Addition Table" game in pairs to practice using an addition table and adding two addends of 5 or less. A "Harder Addition Table" version has its own Game Mat. Complete directions for both games and variations are found on the Game Mats.

3 Wrap-Up

5 MINUTES

In Closing Give a sum and have volunteers name two addends shown on the addition table for that sum.

ALTERNATIVE ASSESSMENT

Informal Assessment Observe students to see whether they understand how to use an addition table to find sums.

Assessment Criteria

Did the student . . .

- ✓ find the correct sums using the addition table?
- ✓ solve 22 of 28 addition problems correctly?
- ✓ write numbers legibly?

LOOKING AHEAD An addition table drawn on a transparency or on the chalkboard will be needed in Lesson 14.

LESSON 14

Student Edition pages 29–30

Practicing Addition Facts

LESSON PLANNER

Objectives

- ▶ to identify addition facts and strategies students have mastered
- ▶ to provide practice with addition facts not mastered
- ▶ to provide practice in solving word problems

Context of the Lesson This is the seventh of ten lessons reviewing addition facts.

Materials	Program Resources
flash cards (optional)	"Harder Addition Table" Game Mat
overhead projector (optional)	Number Cubes
transparency of 10 + 10 addition table (optional)	Thinking Story Book, pages 16–17
	Reteaching Master
	Practice Master 14
	Enrichment Master 14
	For extra practice: CD-ROM* Lesson 14

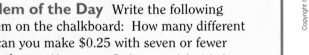

1 Warm-Up

5 MINUTES

Problem of the Day Write the following problem on the chalkboard: How many different ways can you make $0.25 with seven or fewer coins? Describe each way. (1 quarter; 2 dimes and 1 nickel; 1 dime and 3 nickels; 2 dimes and 5 pennies; 5 nickels; 2 dimes and 5 pennies)

MENTAL MATH Have students answer the following problems using their Number Cubes:

a. 6 + 3 = (9)	b. 3 + 5 = (8)
c. 7 + 3 = (10)	d. 4 + 6 = (10)
e. 7 + 4 = (11)	f. 10 + 10 = (20)
g. 8 + 3 = (11)	h. 5 + 1 = (6)
i. 8 + 4 = (12)	j. 3 + 6 = (9)
k. 9 + 9 = (18)	l. 3 + 0 = (3)
m. 8 + 5 = (13)	n. 4 + 2 = (6)

LESSON 14

Name ______________________

Practicing Addition Facts

Add.

1. 0 + 7 = 7
2. 3 + 6 = 9
3. 9 + 2 = 11
4. 4 + 8 = 12
5. 1 + 8 = 9
6. 7 + 4 = 11
7. 10 + 4 = 14
8. 3 + 7 = 10
9. 7 + 10 = 17
10. 5 + 8 = 13
11. 6 + 6 = 12
12. 8 + 3 = 11
13. 5 + 7 = 12
14. 4 + 7 = 11

15. 6 + 8 = 14
16. 3 + 8 = 11
17. 7 + 6 = 13
18. 9 + 9 = 18
19. 10 + 1 = 11

NOTE TO HOME
Students review and learn new addition facts.

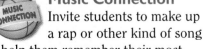

COOPERATIVE LEARNING Students who need practice learning addition facts can work in pairs using flash cards. Have partners take turns giving and solving problems.

Music Connection Invite students to make up a rap or other kind of song to help them remember their most difficult addition and subtraction facts.

Literature Connection You might want to read aloud *One Green Island* by Charlotte Hard to reinforce lesson concepts.

RETEACHING

Continue using the reteaching strategies used in lessons 12 and 13.

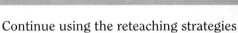

*available separately

◆ **LESSON 14 Practicing Addition Facts** **Use the Mixed Practice on page 367 after this lesson.**

Solve these problems.

⑳ I had four books. I got three more for my birthday.

Now I have 7 books.

A ball costs $7.
A bat costs $3.

㉑ How much do they cost all together? $10

㉒ How much do two bats cost? $6

㉓ How much do two balls cost? $14

㉔ The soccer team has won 12 games this season. If they win three more games this week, how many games will they have won so far? 15

NOTE TO HOME
Students solve word problems.

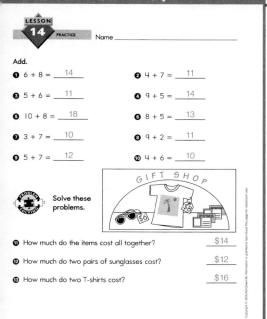

PRACTICE p. 14

LESSON 14 PRACTICE Name ____________

Add.

❶ 6 + 8 = 14	❷ 4 + 7 = 11
❸ 5 + 6 = 11	❹ 9 + 5 = 14
❺ 10 + 8 = 18	❻ 8 + 5 = 13
❼ 3 + 7 = 10	❽ 9 + 2 = 11
❾ 5 + 7 = 12	❿ 4 + 6 = 10

Solve these problems.

⓫ How much do the items cost all together? $14

⓬ How much do two pairs of sunglasses cost? $12

⓭ How much do two T-shirts cost? $16

14 • Math Explorations and Applications Level 2

ENRICHMENT p. 14

LESSON 14 ENRICHMENT Name ____________

Connect the dots. Start with 16 and count up by threes to 100. At 100, count down by fours till you get to 0.

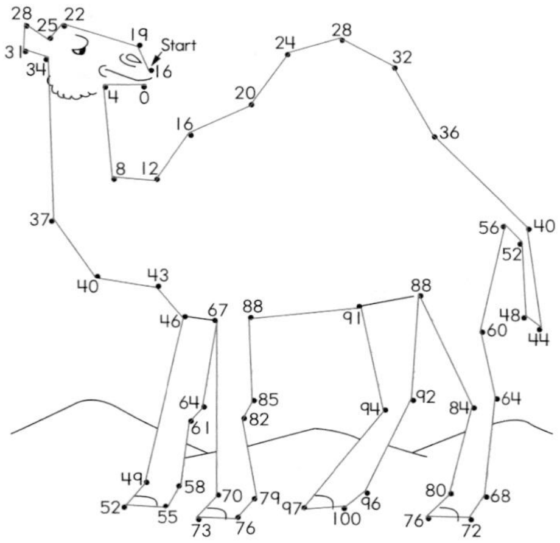

14 • Math Explorations and Applications Level 2

❷ Teach

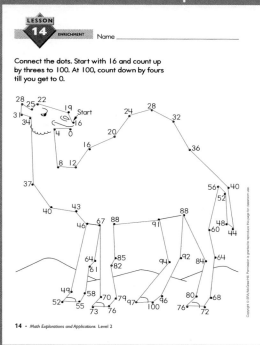

Demonstrate Display a 10 + 10 addition table on a transparency or on the chalkboard. Work with students to identify the facts they have mastered. Students should have mastered most of them. Cross off those rows and columns in which almost everyone knows the facts. Write on the chalkboard those facts students have not mastered.

Using the Student Pages Prepare students for the speed test in the next lesson by giving them three minutes to complete page 29. You might want to provide extra practice for those students who do not finish on time. Be sure everyone has finished page 29 before going on to page 30. Some students might need to draw pictures, act out, or use concrete objects to help them solve the word problems on page 30.

Using the Thinking Story Present one or two problems from those following "The Amazing Number Machine Makes Mistakes" on pages 16–17 of the Thinking Story Book.

GAME **Using the "Harder Addition Table" Game Mat** Play one of the parts of the "Harder Addition Table" game. If students are no longer challenged by this game, you might want to teach them the "Roll a 15" game, which is formally introduced in Lesson 18.

❸ Wrap-Up

5 MINUTES

In Closing Have students write three addition facts: one with 6, one with 7, and one with 8 as an addend.

ALTERNATIVE ASSESSMENT **Informal Assessment** Assess students by observing who was able to complete page 29 in three minutes or less with no mistakes.

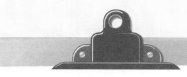

Assessment Criteria

Did the student . . .

✓ solve 15 of 19 addition problems quickly and correctly?

✓ solve all of the word problems correctly?

LESSON 15

Student Edition pages 31–32

Addition Fact Review

LESSON PLANNER

Objective

- to provide review of addition facts with sums from 1–10

Context of the Lesson This is the eighth of ten lessons of addition facts review.

Materials

base-10 materials (optional)

Program Resources

Number Cubes

Thinking Story Book, pages 16–17

Practice Master 15

Enrichment Master 15

For extra practice:
CD-ROM* Lesson 15

1 Warm-Up 5 MINUTES

Problem of the Day Write this problem on the chalkboard: Write as many number sentences as you can that show two numbers that add up to ten. (0 + 10, 10 + 0; 1 + 9, 9 + 1; 2 + 8, 8 + 2; 3 + 7, 7 + 3; 4 + 6, 6 + 4; 5 + 5; 11 ways)

MENTAL MATH Have students write two addends for each sum on the chalkboard, then ask other students to give alternative addends. (Answers vary. Possible answers are given.)

a. 7 (4 + 3) **b.** 9 (2 + 7) **c.** 4 (3 + 1)

d. 8 (6 + 2) **e.** 5 (3 + 2) **f.** 6 (5 + 1)

2 Teach

Using the Number Cubes Present several oral word problems in which students use addition facts. Have them find, hide, and show their solutions using the Number Cubes. For example: Six boys and seven girls are on a bus. How many children are there all together? (13); or, A red model car and a blue model car each cost $4. How much do they cost all together? ($8)

LESSON 15

Name ______________________

Addition Fact Review

ALGEBRA READINESS

What comes out?

1
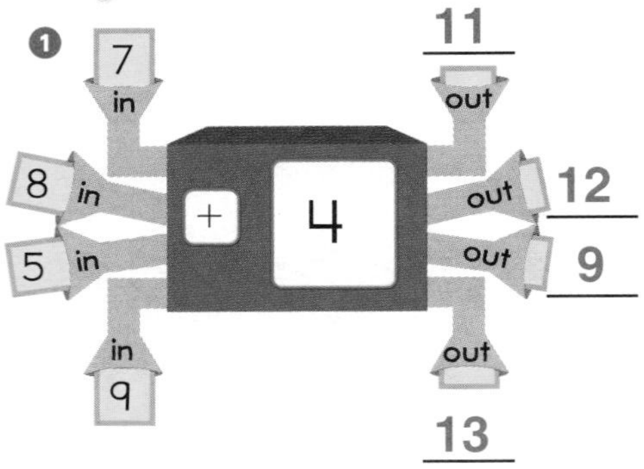

2
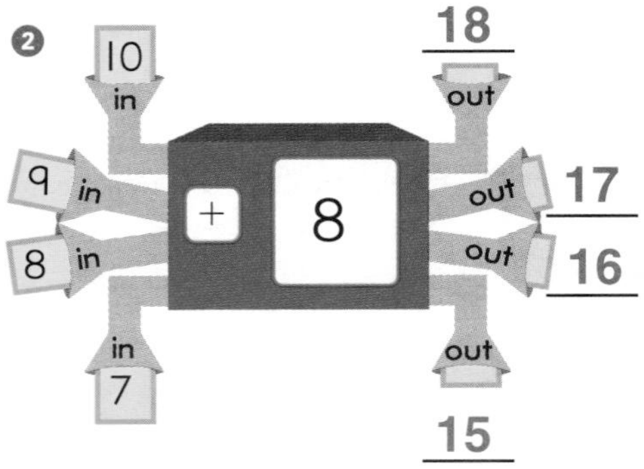

3
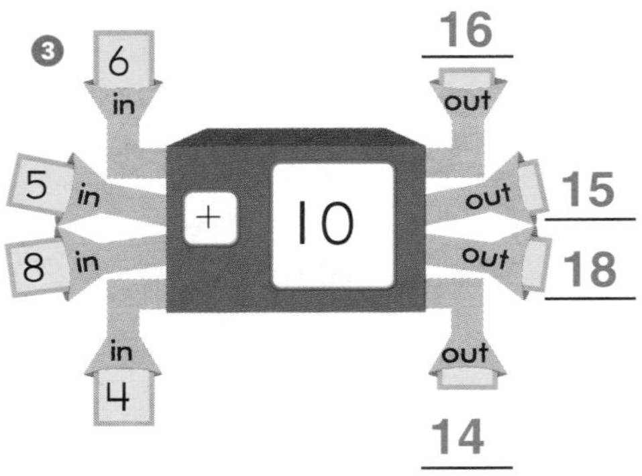

4
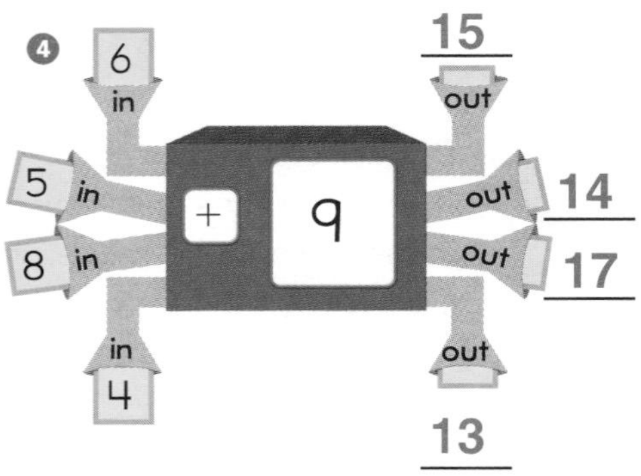

NOTE TO HOME
Students solve function problems.

RETEACHING

Have students make their own set of flash cards with addition facts on the front and answers on the back. Allow them to practice facts on their own with their cards whenever time permits.

*available separately

◆ LESSON 15 Addition Fact Review

Answer these questions.

5. How much does the red book cost? $ 7
6. How much do the red and blue books cost together? $ 11
7. How many books are there all together? 3
8. How much do the blue and yellow books cost together? $ 12
9. How much do the red and yellow books cost together? $ 15
10. How much do the three books cost together? $ 19

FANTASTIC FACT Most dollar bills wear out within two years.

NOTE TO HOME
Students solve word problems.

PRACTICE p. 15

LESSON 15 PRACTICE Name ____________

Add.

1. 4 + 4 = 8
2. 3 + 7 = 10
3. 6 + 2 = 8
4. 4 + 5 = 9
5. 1 + 6 = 7
6. 0 + 8 = 8
7. 7 + 2 = 9
8. 2 + 8 = 10
9. 6 + 3 = 9
10. 5 + 5 = 10
11. 3 + 4 = 7
12. 5 + 3 = 8
13. 6 + 4 = 10
14. 3 + 3 = 6
15. 0 + 7 = 7
16. 2 + 5 = 7
17. 8 + 1 = 9
18. 7 + 3 = 10

ENRICHMENT p. 15

LESSON 15 ENRICHMENT Name ____________

Fill in the blank squares with a number or a sign to make correct number sentences up and down and sideways.

5	+	5	=	10
+				–
3	+ or –	0	=	3
=				=
8	–	1	=	7
+				–
2	+ or –	0	=	2
=				=
10	–	5	=	5

Using the Student Pages Discuss the first function machine on page 31. Have students explain what the rule means. (Add 4 to each number on the left.) Then have students complete both pages independently. When they are finished, have them share and compare their methods and answers.

Using the Thinking Story Present one or two new questions from those following "The Amazing Number Machine Makes Mistakes" on pages 16–17 of the Thinking Story Book.

3 Wrap-Up (5 MINUTES)

In Closing Have students write sums from 1–10 in which 3 is one of the addends. (0 + 3 = 3; 1 + 3 = 4; 2 + 3 = 5; 3 + 3 = 6; 4 + 3 = 7; 5 + 3 = 8; 6 + 3 = 9; and 7 + 3 = 10)

SELF ASSESSMENT Have students list any facts with sums between 1 and 10 that they still have not mastered.

Assessment Criteria

Did the student . . .

✓ correctly solve 14 of 16 addition facts on page 31?

✓ correctly solve all of the word problems on page 32?

LOOKING AHEAD Lesson 17 will require a watch or clock with a second hand.

LEARNING STYLES

Meeting Individual Needs

Allow visual learners to practice addition facts by reading problems and writing answers. Allow auditory learners to practice addition by giving them problems orally and allowing them to answer orally as well. Kinesthetic learners can practice by making models of addition facts with sums up to 10 using concrete objects such as base-10 blocks, coins, or counters.

LESSON 16

Student Edition pages 33–34

Addition Checkpoint

LESSON PLANNER

Objectives

- ▶ to provide practice with addition in a realistic situation
- ▶ to demonstrate how to compare numbers in a realistic situation
- ▶ to provide practice in solving realistic word problems

Context of the Lesson This is the ninth of ten lessons of addition facts review.

Materials	**Program Resources**
play money*	Thinking Story Book, pages 16–17
	Practice Master 16
	Enrichment Master 16
	For extra practice: CD-ROM* Lesson 16

1 Warm-Up

5 MINUTES

Problem of the Day Write the following problem on the chalkboard: How many different ways can you write problems with two addends, both less than 10, that equal the sum of 15? (four ways: 6 + 9, 9 + 6, 7 + 8, 8 + 7)

MENTAL MATH Have students write two addends for each sum on the chalkboard and ask other students to write two alternative addends. (Answers vary. Possible answers are given.)

a. 17 (9 + 8) **b.** 12 (7 + 5)

c. 15 (8 + 7) **d.** 11 (6 + 5)

e. 16 (8 + 8) **f.** 13 (6 + 7)

SPECIAL NEEDS

Meeting Individual Needs

Some students might need to use play money to help them act out the problems on pages 33–34. Have these students work in small groups to model and discuss the problems as they complete them.

LESSON 16

Name ____________________

Addition Checkpoint

Answers these questions.

1. How much does the toy clock cost? $ 9
2. How much do the clock and balloon cost? $ 10
3. How much do the doll and clock cost? $ 17
4. How much do the clock and doll cost? $ 17
5. How much do the clock and tea set cost? $ 17
6. How much do the balloon and tea set cost? $ 9
7. How much do the tea set and doll cost? $ 16

NOTE TO HOME
Students solve word problems to review addition facts up to 20.

RETEACHING

Have students make their own set of flash cards with problems on front and answers on back for sums from 11–20. Allow them to practice facts on their own with their cards whenever time permits. They can combine these flash cards with those they made for sums up to 10 and practice all of their addition facts.

*available separately

◆ **LESSON 16** Addition Checkpoint

Answers these questions.

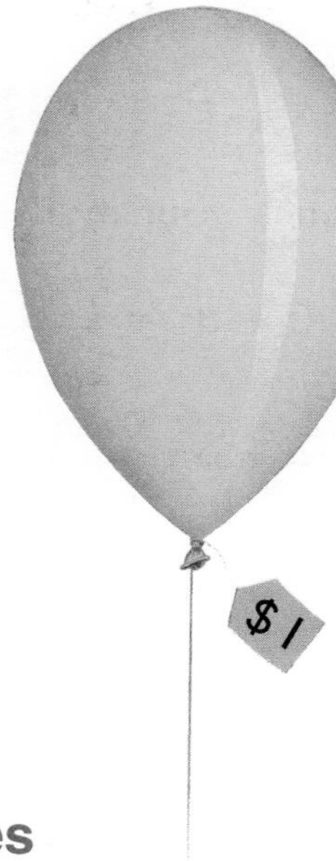

I have $17.

8 Can I buy the clock? **yes**

9 Can I buy the clock and tea set? **yes**

10 Can I buy the clock, tea set, and balloon? **no**

11 Which three things can I buy? **tea set, doll, balloon**

12 Can I buy two dolls? **yes**

13 Can I buy two clocks? **no**

14 Can I buy two tea sets? **yes**

15 Can I buy two balloons? **yes**

NOTE TO HOME
Students solve word problems to review addition facts up to 20.

2 Teach

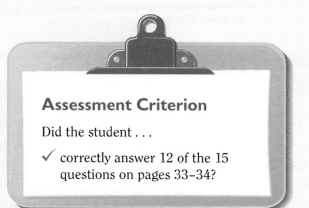

Demonstrate Draw two price tags from page 33 on the chalkboard: doll, $8; and clock, $9. Have a volunteer write a number sentence he or she would use to find the total cost of the doll and clock. ($8 + $9 = $17) Then show students a $20 bill. Ask how they can tell whether they can pay for two clocks with the $20 bill. Students should understand that they must first add the cost of two clocks ($9 + $9 = $18) and then compare the total cost with the amount they have. Because $20 is greater than $18, they can buy the two clocks.

Using the Student Pages Have students look at the pictures on the top of pages 33 and 34. Be sure they understand the price of each item by asking students to tell you how much certain items cost based on the illustration. Then have students work individually or in small groups to answer the questions. When finished, have students share and compare their methods and answers.

Using the Thinking Story Present one or two new problems from those following "The Amazing Number Machine Makes Mistakes" on pages 16–17 of the Thinking Story Book.

3 Wrap-Up

5 MINUTES

In Closing Have students explain why problem 4 on page 34 can have more than one correct answer.

SELF ASSESSMENT

Have students list any facts with sums between 11 and 20 that they still have not mastered.

Assessment Criterion

Did the student . . .

✓ correctly answer 12 of the 15 questions on pages 33–34?

LOOKING AHEAD Lesson 17 will require a watch or clock with a second hand.

PRACTICE p. 16

LESSON 16 PRACTICE Name ____________

Add.

1 8 + 4 = 12
2 7 + 7 = 14
3 6 + 5 = 11
4 9 + 5 = 14
5 10 + 10 = 20
6 3 + 8 = 11
7 7 + 6 = 13
8 2 + 10 = 12
9 6 + 6 = 12
10 8 + 5 = 13
11 7 + 4 = 11
12 8 + 9 = 17
13 10 + 4 = 14
14 9 + 9 = 18
15 9 + 7 = 16
16 7 + 5 = 12
17 8 + 6 = 14
18 4 + 7 = 11

ENRICHMENT p. 16

LESSON 16 ENRICHMENT Name ____________

Help Rachel get to the mailbox.

(house)			30		63			7	53
75	20		51		8		29		42
	83	19	0	33		49	62	18	(mailbox)
26	12		28	6	7	10	21	22	84
9		13		35			34	14	44
40			25	56	23	77	16		49
15	31	82	75	27	45	24	66	37	6
	2		68		19				17
3		36	4			5		32	

Solve a problem. Color the box with the answer number. When you've finished all the problems, you will see the path from Rachel's house to her mailbox.

1 11 + 2 = 13
2 10 + 6 = 16
3 20 + 7 = 27
4 17 + 2 = 19
5 16 + 8 = 24
6 19 + 3 = 21
7 10 + 4 = 14
8 13 + 5 = 18
9 14 + 5 = 19
10 18 + 7 = 25
11 11 + 1 = 12
12 15 + 5 = 20

LESSON 17

Student Edition pages 35–36

Additional Practice

LESSON PLANNER

Objectives

- ✓ to identify facts students have and have not mastered
- ▶ to reinforce students' knowledge of basic addition facts

Context of the Lesson This is the last of ten lessons that review addition facts and provide items for monitoring individual progress. Mastery Checkpoint 3 in this lesson assesses students' mastery of basic addition facts.

Materials

watch or clock with second hand

Program Resources

Number Cubes
Reteaching Master
Practice Master 17
Enrichment Master 17
Assessment Master
For extra practice:
CD-ROM* Lesson 17

1 Warm-Up

5 MINUTES

Problem of the Day Write the following problem on the chalkboard: Which two numbers meet both of the following rules?

- ▶ They are only one number apart from each other.
- ▶ Their sum is two digits which when added together equal 6. (8, 7)

MENTAL MATH Write the following addition facts on the chalkboard and have students use Number Cubes to respond.

a. 2 + 3 = (5)
b. 2 + 9 = (11)
c. 4 + 2 = (6)
d. 2 + 7 = (9)
e. 10 + 2 = (12)
f. 8 + 2 = (10)
g. 1 + 9 = (10)
h. 9 + 3 = (12)
i. 5 + 9 = (14)
j. 7 + 9 = (16)
k. 9 + 9 = (18)
l. 10 + 9 = (19)

LESSON 17

Name ____________________

Additional Practice

Check your math skills.

1. 0 + 8 = 8
2. 9 + 9 = 18
3. 6 + 6 = 12
4. 3 + 7 = 10
5. 7 + 6 = 13
6. 6 + 8 = 14
7. 9 + 2 = 11
8. 1 + 5 = 6
9. 3 + 6 = 9
10. 10 + 10 = 20
11. 8 + 8 = 16
12. 7 + 2 = 9
13. 7 + 9 = 16
14. 2 + 9 = 11
15. 10 + 4 = 14
16. 9 + 8 = 17
17. 6 + 9 = 15
18. 8 + 4 = 12

Number correct [ ]

NOTE TO HOME
Students check their knowledge of addition facts.

RETEACHING p. 4

LESSON 17 RETEACHING Name ____________________

Example:

  7
+ 2

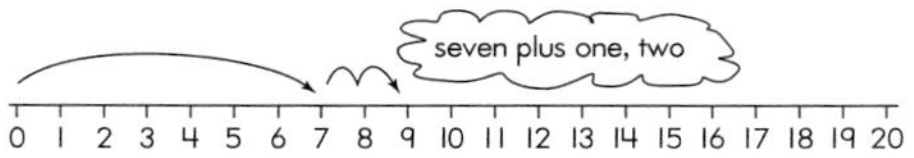

Use the number line to help you find the answers to these problems.

1. 4 + 4 = 8
2. 5 + 8 = 13
3. 10 + 7 = 17
4. 9 + 6 = 15
5. 9 + 4 = 13
6. 7 + 7 = 14
7. 5 + 8 = 13
8. 8 + 8 = 16
9. 7 + 4 = 11
10. 4 + 5 = 9
11. 6 + 6 = 12
12. 7 + 8 = 15
13. 5 + 3 = 8
14. 9 + 9 = 18
15. 3 + 8 = 11
16. 10 + 10 = 20

PRACTICE p. 17

LESSON 17 PRACTICE Name ____________________

Check your math skills.

1. 5 + 7 = 12
2. 9 + 3 = 12
3. 4 + 6 = 10
4. 7 + 7 = 14
5. 8 + 9 = 17
6. 4 + 9 = 13
7. 8 + 3 = 11
8. 6 + 5 = 11
9. 9 + 6 = 15
10. 8 + 7 = 15
11. 4 + 8 = 12
12. 5 + 9 = 14
13. 10 + 7 = 17
14. 2 + 10 = 12
15. 2 + 8 = 10
16. 8 + 6 = 14
17. 5 + 6 = 11
18. 7 + 8 = 15

Number correct [ ]

*available separately

◆ LESSON 17 Additional Practice

Answer these questions.

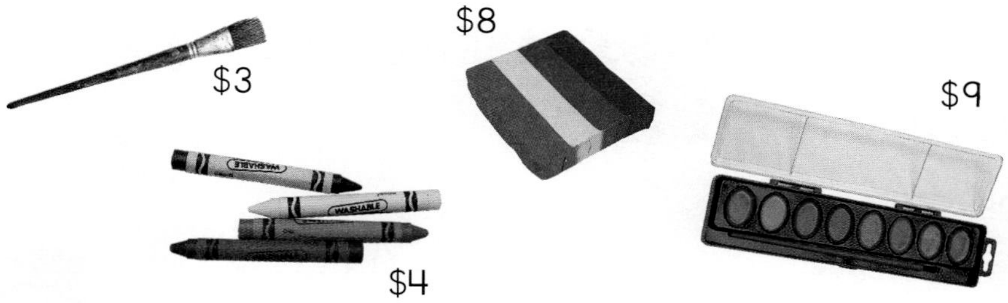

⓳ How much do two paintbrushes cost? $ 6

⓴ How much do two boxes of crayons cost? $ 8

㉑ How much do two packs of clay cost? $ 16

㉒ How much do a set of paints and another paintbrush cost together? $ 12

㉓ How much do a box of crayons and a pack of clay cost together? $ 12

㉔ How much do all the things cost together? $ 24

㉕ How much do crayons and paints cost together? $ 13

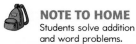

NOTE TO HOME
Students solve addition and word problems.

❷ Teach

Demonstrate Explain to students that they will take a speed test on the addition facts. Explain that you will review facts with them as a class and then they will work with partners to prepare for the test. Provide oral drill on all basic addition facts. Then have students work in pairs using oral drill or flash cards.

Using the Student Pages Allow students about three minutes to complete page 35 independently. Then have students correct their papers as you call out the answers. Have them write the number of correct answers in the box at the bottom of the page. Then direct them to copy the problems they got wrong and use them to study for the next speed test they will be taking in a few days. Have students then complete page 36 independently, but do not time them. Discuss the answers when they are finished.

❸ Wrap-Up

5 MINUTES

In Closing Ask students to choose three addition facts they have the most difficulty with. Take a survey to see whether others have difficulty with the same facts. Discuss strategies they can use to help remember these facts.

Mastery Checkpoint 3

At this time, most students should demonstrate mastery of basic addition facts. Use the results of the speed test students completed on page 35 or Assessment Masters 9 and 10 to assess students' knowledge of basic addition facts. You might want to record the results on the Mastery Checkpoint Chart.

ENRICHMENT p. 17

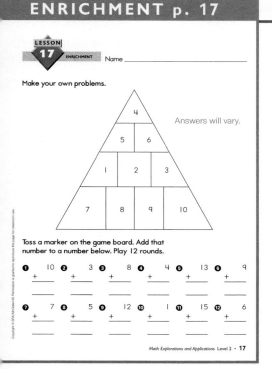

LESSON 17 ENRICHMENT Name ______

Make your own problems.

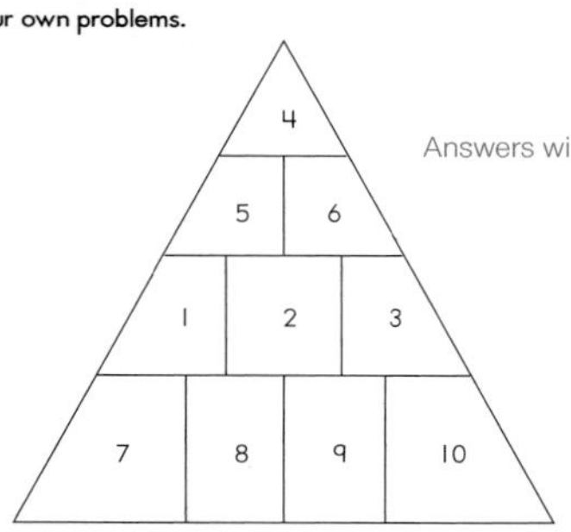

Answers will vary.

Toss a marker on the game board. Add that number to a number below. Play 12 rounds.

❶ 10 + ❷ 3 + ❸ 8 + ❹ 4 + ❺ 13 + ❻ 9 +

❼ 7 + ❽ 5 + ❾ 12 + ❿ 1 + ⓫ 15 + ⓬ 6 +

Math Explorations and Applications Level 2 • 17

ASSESSMENT p. 4

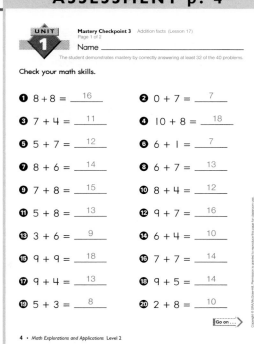

UNIT 1 **Mastery Checkpoint 3** Addition facts (Lesson 17)
Page 1 of 2
Name ______
The student demonstrates mastery by correctly answering at least 32 of the 40 problems.

Check your math skills.

❶ 8 + 8 = 16	❷ 0 + 7 = 7
❸ 7 + 4 = 11	❹ 10 + 8 = 18
❺ 5 + 7 = 12	❻ 6 + 1 = 7
❼ 8 + 6 = 14	❽ 6 + 7 = 13
❾ 7 + 8 = 15	❿ 8 + 4 = 12
⓫ 5 + 8 = 13	⓬ 9 + 7 = 16
⓭ 3 + 6 = 9	⓮ 6 + 4 = 10
⓯ 9 + 9 = 18	⓰ 7 + 7 = 14
⓱ 9 + 4 = 13	⓲ 9 + 5 = 14
⓳ 5 + 3 = 8	⓴ 2 + 8 = 10

Go on . . .

4 • Math Explorations and Applications Level 2

Assessment Criteria

Did the student . . .

✓ demonstrate ability in basic addition facts by completing the speed test within three minutes?

✓ correctly solve 15 of 18 problems on page 35?

✓ correctly solve 5 of 7 word problems on page 36?

LESSON 18

Student Edition pages 37–38

Subtraction Involving 0, 1, and 2

LESSON PLANNER

Objectives

- ▶ to review subtraction facts in which the subtrahend is 0, 1, or 2
- ▶ to review subtraction facts in which the difference is 0, 1, or 2
- ▶ to provide further practice for mastery of addition facts

Context of the Lesson This is the first of 11 lessons focusing on review of subtraction facts.

Materials	Program Resources
none	Number Cubes
	Thinking Story Book, pages 16–17
	Practice Master 18
	Enrichment Master 18
	For extra practice: CD-ROM* Lesson 18

1 Warm-Up (5 MINUTES)

Problem of the Day Write the following problem on the chalkboard: Max has ten baseball cards. Carol has three cards and Kim has four. How many more cards does Max have than Carol and Kim together? (three more)

MENTAL MATH Have students answer the following using their Number Cubes:

a. 9 – 0 = (9)	**b.** 12 – 0 = (12)
c. 5 – 0 = (5)	**d.** 8 – 1 = (7)
e. 11 – 1 = (10)	**f.** 4 – 1 = (3)
g. 6 – 2 = (4)	**h.** 14 – 2 = (12)
i. 10 – 2 = (8)	**j.** 9 – 9 = (0)
k. 10 – 10 = (0)	**l.** 8 – 8 = (0)
m. 12 – 11 = (1)	**n.** 9 – 8 = (1)
o. 10 – 9 = (1)	**p.** 12 – 10 = (2)
q. 8 – 6 = (2)	**r.** 5 – 3 = (2)

LESSON 18

Name ______________________

Subtraction Involving 0, 1, and 2

Subtract.

❶ 8 – 8 = 0	❷ 13 – 13 = 0
❸ 9 – 9 = 0	❹ 9 – 0 = 9
❺ 8 – 7 = 1	❻ 10 – 10 = 0
❼ 8 – 6 = 2	❽ 9 – 2 = 7
❾ 10 – 9 = 1	❿ 9 – 7 = 2
⓫ 10 – 1 = 9	⓬ 9 – 8 = 1
⓭ 14 – 0 = 14	⓮ 5 – 3 = 2

⓯	⓰	⓱	⓲	⓳
7	10	9	8	6
– 2	– 2	– 1	– 2	– 5
5	8	8	6	1

NOTE TO HOME
Students review subtraction facts involving 0, 1, and 2.

RETEACHING

Because this is the first of many lessons on subtraction, reteaching is not essential at this time.

Literature Connection You might want to read aloud *Ten Sly Piranhas* by William Wise to reinforce lesson concepts.

*available separately

◆ **LESSON 18 Subtraction Involving 0, 1, and 2**

Solve the problems.

⑳ 8 + 5 = **13** ㉑ 3 + 7 = **10**

㉒ 4 + 7 = **11** ㉓ 6 + 4 = **10**

㉔ 6 + 9 = **15** ㉕ 5 + 5 = **10**

㉖ 10 + 7 = **17** ㉗ 9 + 5 = **14**

㉘ 5 + 7 = **12** ㉙ 9 + 9 = **18**

㉚ 4 − 4 = **0** ㉛ 10 − 8 = **2** ㉜ 4 + 8 = **12** ㉝ 7 − 6 = **1**

㉞ 7 − 0 = **7** ㉟ 6 − 1 = **5** ㊱ 5 − 2 = **3** ㊲ 4 − 3 = **1**

GAME Play the "Roll a 15" game.

NOTE TO HOME
Students review addition facts.

❷ Teach

Demonstrate Use the Mental Math problems to illustrate the following concepts:

Subtracting 0 (Problems a–c: Answer is always the number you subtracted from.)

Subtracting 1 (Problems d–f: Answer is always 1 less than the number you subtracted from.)

Subtracting 2 (Problems g–i: Answer is always 2 less.)

Subtracting a number from itself (Problems j–l: Answer is always 0.)

Subtracting a number 1 less than the given number (Problems m–o: Answer is always 1.)

Subtracting a number 2 less than the given number (Problems p–r: Answer is always 2.)

Using the Student Pages Have students complete pages 37 and 38. Correct the answers as a class.

Introducing the "Roll a 15" Game Demonstrate and then have students play this game to practice adding 2, 3, or 4 numbers between 0–10 in sequence. Players take turns rolling all four Number Cubes, one at a time, trying to get as close to 15 as possible. A player may stop after any roll. The player whose score is closest to 15 wins the round. The winner of a round rolls first in the next round.

Using the Thinking Story Present one or two new problems from those following "The Amazing Number Machine Makes Mistakes" on pages 16–17 of the Thinking Story Book.

PRACTICE p. 18

LESSON 18 PRACTICE Name ______

Subtract.

❶ 10 − 8 = 2 ❷ 7 − 2 = 5

❸ 6 − 0 = 6 ❹ 9 − 7 = 2

❺ 10 − 2 = 8 ❻ 12 − 0 = 12

❼ 9 − 2 = 7 ❽ 8 − 6 = 2

Add.

❾ 6 + 6 = 12 ❿ 7 + 8 = 15

⓫ 4 + 9 = 13 ⓬ 9 + 5 = 14

⓭ 10 + 6 = 16 ⓮ 3 + 8 = 11

⓯ 7 + 10 = 17 ⓰ 8 + 8 = 16

ENRICHMENT p. 18

LESSON 18 ENRICHMENT Name ______

How many ways can you make the difference.

Figure out the missing numbers. Complete the number sentence.

	First Number	Minus the Second Number	Difference
❶	10 11 12	− 0 − 1 − 2	10
❷	11 12 13	− 0 − 1 − 2	11
❸	12 13 14	− 0 − 1 − 2	12
❹	13 14 15	− 0 − 1 − 2	13
❺	14 15 16	− 0 − 1 − 2	14

❸ Wrap-Up

5 MINUTES

In Closing Ask students to explain the strategies they used to subtract numbers on page 37.

ALTERNATIVE ASSESSMENT

Informal Assessment Observe which students are able to complete page 38 quickly and accurately.

Assessment Criterion

Did the student . . .

✓ correctly answer 30 of 37 problems on pages 37 and 38?

LESSON 19

Student Edition pages 39–40

Missing Addends

LESSON PLANNER

Objective

▶ to provide review in supplying missing addends

Context of the Lesson This is the second of 11 lessons focusing on review of subtraction facts.

Materials

- double-pan balance (optional)
- tape
- two sets of 11 slips of paper numbered from 0–10

Program Resources

- Number Cubes
- Practice Master 19
- Enrichment Master 19

For extra practice:
CD-ROM* Lesson 19

1 Warm-Up

5 MINUTES

Problem of the Day Write the following problem on the chalkboard: Yesterday there were 15 cookies in the jar. Today there are 7. How many cookies were eaten? (8)

MENTAL MATH Write the following missing-addend problems on the chalkboard and have students use Number Cubes to show the missing addend.

a. 5 + □ = 10 (5)
b. 3 + □ = 13 (10)
c. 9 + □ = 15 (6)
d. □ + 8 = 16 (8)
e. □ + 7 = 15 (8)
f. □ + 4 = 14 (10)

2 Teach

Demonstrate Write the following problem on the chalkboard: 4 + 6 = 11. Ask: Is this correct? (No) Erase the 6 and ask students to tell what number belongs in the blank: 4 + ____ = 11. (7) Repeat with several other addition facts such as ____ + 7 = 10 and 6 + ____ = 12. Students should realize that they can use the addition facts they know to help them find the missing addends. Then have students find, hide, and show their answers with Number Cubes to additional missing-addend problems.

LESSON 19

Name ______________________

Missing Addends

ALGEBRA READINESS

Solve these problems.

1. 3 + [5] = 8
2. 7 + [7] = 14
3. [3] + 5 = 8
4. 4 + [10] = 14
5. 9 + [6] = 15
6. [4] + 10 = 14
7. 8 + [7] = 15
8. 8 + [8] = 16
9. 4 + [7] = 11
10. [9] + 9 = 18
11. [3] + 8 = 11
12. 10 + [5] = 15

COOPERATIVE LEARNING Do the "Missing Addend Puzzle" activity.

NOTE TO HOME
Students find missing addends in addition sentences.

RETEACHING

Have one student place a numbered weight on each side of the balance of a double-pan balance scale. Have a second student tell how many and where additional numbered weights must be placed on the scale to balance it.

Why teach it at this time?

In this lesson students practice naming missing addends to prepare them for Lesson 21 in which the relationship between missing-addend problems and subtraction will be taught.

Literature Connection Read *Amelia's Nine Lives* by Lorna Balian to reinforce lesson concepts.

*available separately

◆ LESSON 19 Missing Addends

Take-Home Activity

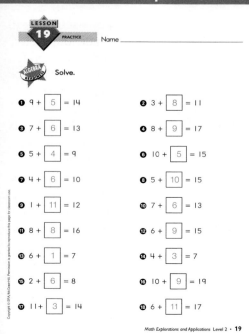

GAME

Missing Numbers

Players: Two or more
Materials: Two 0–5 Number Cubes and two 5–10 Number Cubes

RULES

Leader: The leader secretly rolls any two cubes and shows one to the other player. Then the leader tells the player the sum.

Players: The player figures out the number that is hidden.

I played the game with

______________________________.

Use the Mixed Practice on page 368 after this lesson.

NOTE TO HOME
Students solve missing addend problems.

PRACTICE p. 19

LESSON 19 PRACTICE Name ____________

Solve.

1. 9 + 5 = 14
2. 3 + 8 = 11
3. 7 + 6 = 13
4. 8 + 9 = 17
5. 5 + 4 = 9
6. 10 + 5 = 15
7. 4 + 6 = 10
8. 5 + 10 = 15
9. 1 + 11 = 12
10. 7 + 6 = 13
11. 8 + 8 = 16
12. 6 + 9 = 15
13. 6 + 1 = 7
14. 4 + 3 = 7
15. 2 + 6 = 8
16. 10 + 9 = 19
17. 11 + 3 = 14
18. 6 + 11 = 17

ENRICHMENT p. 19

LESSON 19 ENRICHMENT Name ____________

Color the sections of each target having numbers that add up to the center number. The first one has been done for you.

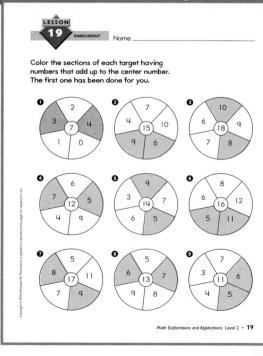

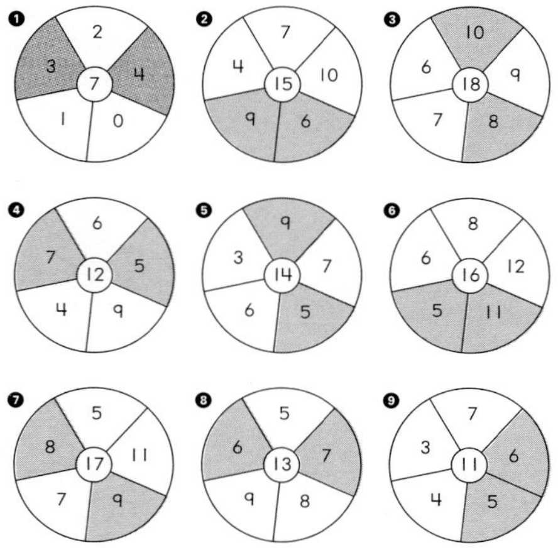

Introducing the "Missing Addend Puzzle" Activity Tape a number (between 0–10) on the back of each of two students. After the players look at each other's number, have a volunteer from the class tell the sum of the numbers. Each player must then figure out what number is on his or her own back. Repeat with different pairs of students.

PROBLEM SOLVING **Using the Student Pages** Have students complete page 39 independently. You might want to work a couple of problems with the class. Then correct the answers with the class.

GAME **Introducing the "Missing Number" Game** Demonstrate and then play the "Missing Number" game on page 40 to provide practice in solving missing-addend problems with addends of 10 or less.

3 Wrap-Up

5 MINUTES

In Closing Ask students to explain how knowing addition facts can help them find missing addends.

SELF ASSESSMENT Ask students to tell you whether they think they need extra help at this point.

Assessment Criteria

Did the student . . .

✓ correctly find the missing addends during the demonstration and Number Cube activity?

✓ correctly identify 10 of the 12 missing addends on page 39?

✓ correctly identify the numbers in the "Missing Number" activity?

LESSON 20

Student Edition pages 41–42

Functions

LESSON PLANNER

Objectives

- ▶ to provide practice in addition and subtraction facts
- ▶ to demonstrate patterns using function machines

Context of the Lesson This is the third of 11 lessons that review subtraction facts.

Materials	Program Resources
craft sticks	Number Cubes Practice Master 20 Enrichment Master 20 For extra practice: CD-ROM* Lesson 20

1 Warm-Up (5 MINUTES)

Problem of the Day Write the following number patterns on the chalkboard and have students describe and complete them.

a. 87, 86, 84, 83, 81, 80, _____ _____ (−1, −2, −1, −2; 78, 77)

b. 21, 24, 27, 30, _____ _____ (+3; 33, 36)

c. 47, 57, 67, 77, _____ _____ (+10; 87, 97)

MENTAL MATH Write the following problems on the chalkboard and have students give the answers orally using mental math.

a. 9 + 2 = _____ + 9 (2)

b. 6 + 7 = 7 + _____ (6)

c. 4 + 7 = _____ + 4 (7)

d. 5 + 9 = _____ + 5 (9)

e. 8 + _____ = 7 + 8 (7)

f. 3 + _____ = 8 + 3 (8)

LESSON 20

Name ______________________________

Functions

What went in?

1
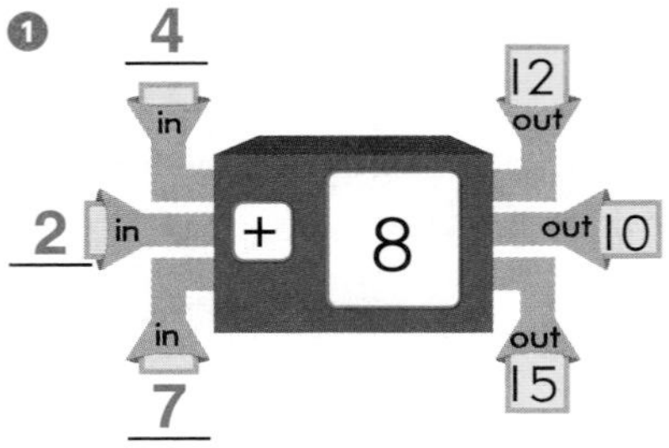

2
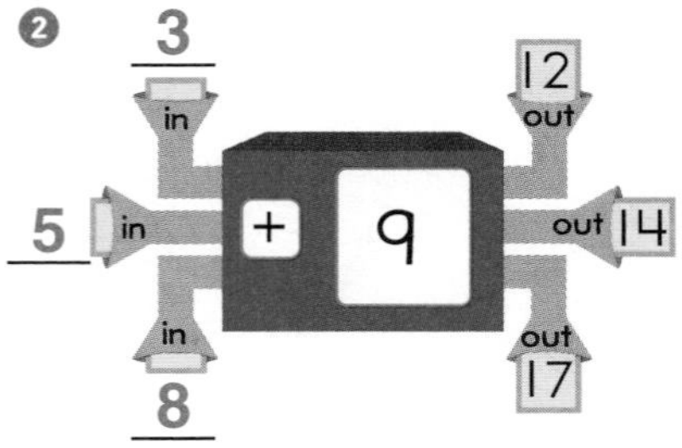

What's the rule?

3
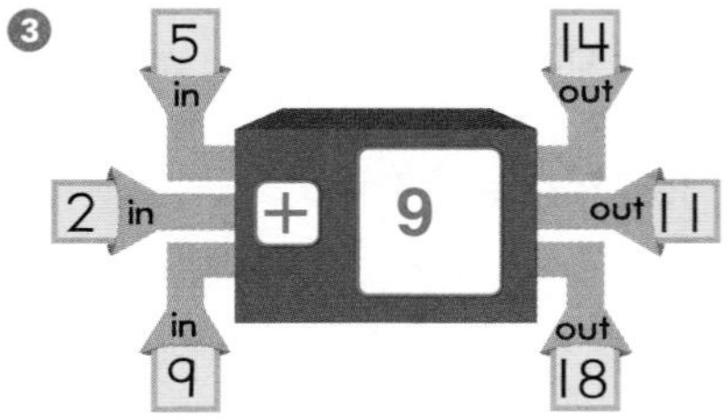

4
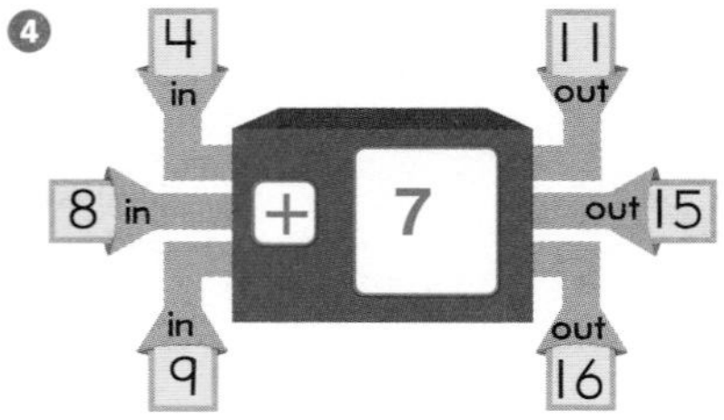

What comes out?

5
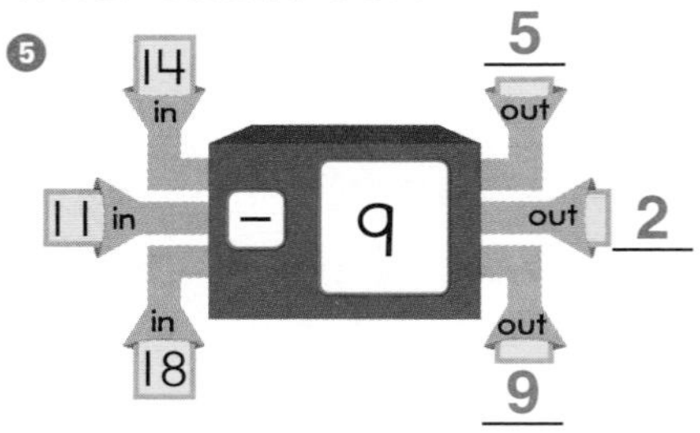

6
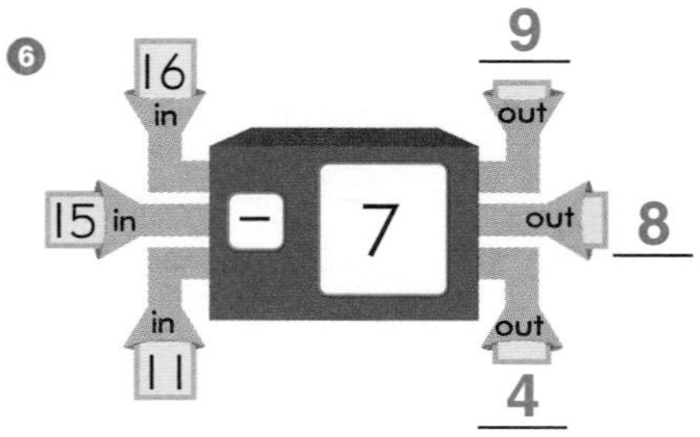

NOTE TO HOME
Students solve function problems involving addition and subtraction.

RETEACHING

Act out function machines using base-10 materials. For example, hide four craft sticks in a box. Show students six craft sticks. Put the six craft sticks in the box. Then show students all ten craft sticks. Have them tell how many craft sticks were in the box before you added the six. Repeat for subtraction by showing ten craft sticks. Then without showing students how many craft sticks you take away, put four in the box. Show them the six remaining and ask how many are in the box.

*available separately

◆ **LESSON 20 Functions**

Solve these problems.

7. 2 + [9] = 11
8. 5 + [9] = 14
9. [8] + 3 = 11
10. [8] + 6 = 14
11. 4 + [7] = 11
12. 7 + [7] = 14
13. [6] + 5 = 11
14. 10 + [4] = 14
15. 6 + [5] = 11
16. [4] + 10 = 14
17. [4] + 7 = 11
18. 14 − 10 = [4]
19. 11 − 4 = [7]
20. 14 − 4 = [10]
21. 11 − 9 = [2]
22. 14 − 6 = [8]
23. 11 − 2 = [9]
24. 14 − 8 = [6]
25. 11 − 6 = [5]
26. 14 − 7 = [7]

Talk about any patterns you see.

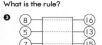

NOTE TO HOME
Students practice addition and subtraction facts.

❷ Teach

Using the "Function Machine" Activity Remind students of the function machine they worked with in Lesson 11. Explain that function machines can subtract as well as add. Consider doing the activity from Lesson 11 again, but having the student in the box make up a subtraction rule instead of an addition rule. Discuss what happens if the rule is "subtract 3" and someone puts in a 2. Students should understand that the "machine" cannot do the subtraction in this case.

PROBLEM SOLVING

Using the Student Pages Have students complete pages 41 and 42 independently. When discussing patterns on page 42, students should notice that the −9 and −7 machines are the +9 and +7 machines working backwards.

❸ Wrap-Up

5 MINUTES

In Closing Explain to students you have a function machine whose rule is −3. Have them identify the rule for a function machine that works backwards from your machine. (+3) Then have students describe any patterns they used to help them solve the problems on pages 41 and 42.

ALTERNATIVE ASSESSMENT

Informal Assessment Use students' answers to pages 41 and 42 to informally assess their understanding of addition and subtraction facts and the commutative property.

PRACTICE p. 20

LESSON 20 PRACTICE Name ______

What went in?

1. (9) (4) (7) → +7 → (16) (11) (14)
2. (5) (8) (2) → +5 → (10) (13) (7)

What is the rule?

3. (8) (5) (7) → (16) (13) (15)
The rule is +8.
4. (7) (5) (9) → (13) (11) (15)
The rule is +6.
5. (16) (13) (15) → (8) (5) (7)
The rule is −8.
6. (13) (11) (15) → (7) (5) (9)
The rule is −6.

Solve.

7. 6 + [9] = 15
8. 15 − 8 = 7
9. [5] + 10 = 15
10. 15 − 6 = 9
11. 9 + [6] = 15
12. 15 − 9 = 6

20 • *Math Explorations and Applications* Level 2

ENRICHMENT p. 20

LESSON 20 ENRICHMENT Name ______

There is a number in the center of each design. Some of the pairs of numbers add up to the center number. Some of the pairs of numbers are wrong.

Color triangles with the wrong addends blue. Then color the rest of the patterns any way you like, using any colors except blue.

The blue triangles are given.

12, 3; 9, 4

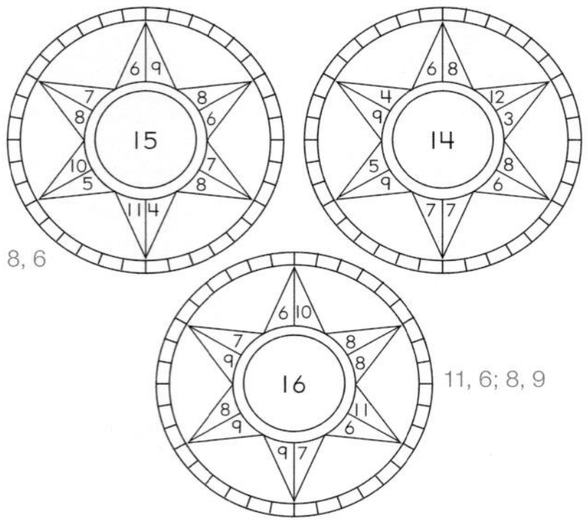

8, 6

11, 6; 8, 9

20 • *Math Explorations and Applications* Level 2

Assessment Criteria

Did the student . . .

✓ correctly solve 4 of the 6 problems on page 41?

✓ correctly solve 16 of the 20 problems on page 42?

LEARNING STYLES

Meeting Individual Needs
Kinesthetic learners might need to use base-10 materials to help them complete page 41.

UNIT 1

Student Edition pages 43–44

Mid-Unit Review

The Mid-Unit Review pinpoints troublesome skill areas for students, allowing plenty of time for additional practice and reteaching before the unit ends. If students did not do well on the Mid-Unit Review and have completed additional practice, you might want to use the Mid-Unit Review provided on pages 8–10 in the Assessment Master Book.

Using the Student Pages Have students complete problems 1–24 on pages 43 and 44 on their own. You might treat this review as a formal assessment of students' skills and have students complete this review as a timed test. See suggestions on page 44.

UNIT 1

Name ______________________

Mid-Unit Review

Count up or down. Fill in the missing numbers.

1	7	8	9	10	11	12	13	
2	31	32	33	34	35	36	37	38
3	47	46	45	44	43	42	41	40
4	52	51	50	49	48	47	46	45

Add or subtract. Watch the signs.

5. 24 + 2 = 26
6. 35 + 3 = 38
7. 29 − 1 = 28
8. 49 + 2 = 51
9. 42 − 3 = 39
10. 30 − 1 = 29

Solve these problems.

11. There are five children on a team. How many children are on two teams? 10

NOTE TO HOME
Students review unit skill and concepts.

A hat costs $4. Gloves cost $6.

⑫ How much do a hat and gloves cost together? $ 10

⑬ How much do two hats cost? $ 8

⑭ How much do two pairs of gloves cost? $ 12

Add.

⑮ 3 + 7 = 10

⑯ 0 + 9 = 9

⑰ 6 + 5 = 11

⑱ 8 + 4 = 12

Solve these problems.

⑲ 3 + [9] = 12

⑳ 4 + [8] = 12

㉑ [7] + 5 = 12

㉒ [6] + 6 = 12

Solve these problems.

㉓ Jamal had 12¢. He gave his sister 5¢. How much does he have left? 7 ¢

㉔ Rita had four fish. Then she got five more. How many fish does she have now? 9

NOTE TO HOME
Students review unit skill and concepts.

ASSESSMENT p. 8

UNIT 1 Mid-Unit Review (Use after Lesson 20.) Page 1 of 3

Name ______

The student demonstrates mastery by correctly answering at least 24 of the 30 problems.

Count up or down.

1. 15 16 17 18 19 20 21
2. 23 22 21 20 19 18 17
3. 45 46 47 48 49 50 51
4. 29 28 27 26 25 24
5. 63 64 65 66 67 68
6. 32 31 30 29 28 27

How many cents?

7. = 33¢
8. = 70¢
9. = 60¢
10. = 50¢

Go on...

8 • *Math Explorations and Applications* Level 2

Timed Test Throughout the Teacher's Guide there are suggestions for sets of exercises to be completed as a "timed test." This usually occurs on pages of basic facts where the focus is on speedy recall. It gives each student a chance to improve as the year goes on. Invite students to keep their scores or the pages in their Math Journals or keep the actual pages in their Math Portfolios so that they can track their improvement.

Here are some suggestions for giving timed tests:

- Have all students start at the same time.
- Write 0 on the chalkboard as you tell them to start; after one minute erase the 0 and write 1; after two minutes write 2; and so on. Have students write that number at the tops of their papers when they finish the test so they know how long they took to complete the test.
- Grade the papers yourself or have students correct their own papers as you call out the answers. Encourage the students to brainstorm ways to improve their times on future tests.

Home Connections You may want to send home Home Connections Masters 37–38 which provide additional activities families can complete together. These activities apply the skills being presented in this unit.

Unit Project This would be a good time to assign the address and phone book project on pages 98a and 98b. Students may begin working on the project in cooperative groups in their free time as you work through the unit. The Unit Project is a good opportunity for students to experience completing a long-term project, practice recognizing and writing numerals from 0 to 20, and discover that numbers are used by measuring, counting, ordering, quantifying, and labeling.

LESSON 21

Student Edition pages 45–46

Missing Addends and Subtraction

LESSON PLANNER

Objectives

- ▶ to provide review of missing-addend problems and to demonstrate how they are related to subtraction
- ▶ to provide review of the inverse relationship between addition and subtraction, and to demonstrate how knowledge of addition facts can help students recall subtraction facts
- ▶ to provide practice of addition facts

Context of the Lesson This is the fourth of 11 lessons focusing on review of subtraction facts.

Materials	Program Resources
none	Number Cubes
	Thinking Story Book, pages 18–21
	Reteaching Master
	Practice Master 21
	Enrichment Master 21
	For extra practice: CD-ROM* Lesson 21

1 Warm-Up

5 MINUTES

Problem of the Day Write the following problem on the chalkboard: There are 15 children in the band. There are three more boys than girls. How many girls are in the band? (6)

MENTAL MATH Write the following pairs of problems on the chalkboard, and have students use Number Cubes to show the missing addends.

a. 7 + □ = 13 (6) 13 – 7 = _____ (6)

b. 6 + □ = 12 (6) 12 – 6 = _____ (6)

c. □ + 3 = 10 (7) 10 – 3 = _____ (7)

d. □ + 8 = 18 (10) 18 – 8 = _____ (10)

e. 15 + □ = 19 (4) 19 – 15 = _____ (4)

f. 3 + □ = 20 (17) 20 – 3 = _____ (17)

LESSON 21

Name ______________________

Missing Addends and Subtraction

ALGEBRA READINESS

Find the missing numbers.

1. [5] + 5 = 10
   10 − 5 = 5

2. [1] + 7 = 8
   8 − 7 = 1

3. 6 + [10] = 16
   16 − 6 = 10

4. [8] + 7 = 15
   15 − 7 = 8

5. [7] + 7 = 14
   14 − 7 = 7

6. [8] + 4 = 12
   12 − 4 = 8

7. 5 + [9] = 14
   14 − 5 = 9

8. [4] + 9 = 13
   13 − 9 = 4

THINKING STORY

Talk about the Thinking Story "Mr. Muddle Takes a Test."

NOTE TO HOME
Students review finding missing addends and use answers to complete subtraction sentences.

LITERATURE CONNECTION

Literature Connection Read *Mouse Count* by Ellen Stoll Walsh to reinforce lesson concepts.

RETEACHING p. 5

LESSON 21 RETEACHING Name ______________________

5 + __6__ = 11

Shade five cubes in one color. In a new color continue shading until 11 cubes have been shaded. How many cubes have been shaded in the second color?

Solve these problems the same way.

1. 3 + __5__ = 8   8 − 3 = 5
2. __6__ + 9 = 15   15 − 9 = 6
3. 7 + __5__ = 12   12 − 7 = 5
4. __8__ + 6 = 14   14 − 6 = 8

Solve these problems. Then copy and cut out the problems and match them with the addition problems above.

12 − 7 = 5	14 − 6 = 8	8 − 3 = 5	15 − 9 = 6

*available separately

◆ **LESSON 21 Missing Addends and Subtraction**

Find the answer.

9. The plate and pitcher cost $17. How much does the plate cost? $ 10
10. If you have $10 can you buy a cup and a pitcher? no
11. How much do the bowl and pitcher cost together? $ 19
12. How much do the pitcher and cup cost together? $ 14
13. The pitcher and saucer cost $14. How much does the saucer cost? $ 4

NOTE TO HOME
Students solve addition problems with a missing addend.

❷ Teach

Demonstrate Provide students with examples of word problems that show the relationship among addition, missing addends, and subtraction. For example: There are eight people in a room. Six more come in. How many in all? (addition) 8 + 6 = ____ (14) Some people are in a room. Six more come in. Now there are 14. How many people were there to start with? (missing addend and subtraction) ____ + 6 = 14 (8) or 14 − 6 = ____ (8) Then provide other pairs of related equations, such as: ____ + 5 = 13 (8) and 13 − 5 = ____ (8).

Using the Student Pages Have students complete page 45 independently. Then discuss the relationship between each pair of problems. Have students complete page 46. Discuss how they decided what number sentence to use to solve each problem.

Using the Thinking Story Read the story "Mr. Muddle Takes a Test" on Thinking Story Book pages 18–21 aloud to the class.

❸ Wrap-Up

5 MINUTES

In Closing Write the following addition problems on the chalkboard. Have students give a related subtraction equation for each.

a. 8 + 7 = 15 (15 − 8 = 7 or 15 − 7 = 8)
b. 6 + 7 = 13 (13 − 7 = 6 or 13 − 6 = 7)
c. 4 + 9 = 13 (13 − 9 = 4 or 13 − 4 = 9)

ALTERNATIVE ASSESSMENT

Performance Assessment Have students make a drawing to show each of the following equations: 3 + 8 = 11 and 11 − 3 = 8.

Assessment Criteria

Did the student . . .

✓ correctly solve the word problems in the demonstration?

✓ correctly solve 14 of the 16 problems on page 45?

✓ correctly solve 4 of the 5 word problems on page 46?

PRACTICE p. 21

LESSON 21 PRACTICE Name ____

ALGEBRA READINESS Solve.

1. [2] + 9 = 11; 11 − 9 = 2
2. [9] + 5 = 14; 14 − 5 = 9
3. 7 + [5] = 12; 12 − 7 = 5
4. 6 + [10] = 16; 16 − 6 = 10
5. 8 + [5] = 13; 13 − 8 = 5
6. 2 + [5] = 7; 7 − 2 = 5
7. 4 + [8] = 12; 12 − 4 = 8
8. [13] + 2 = 15; 15 − 2 = 13
9. [8] + 8 = 16; 16 − 8 = 8
10. 6 + [5] = 11; 11 − 6 = 5

Math Explorations and Applications Level 2 • 21

ENRICHMENT p. 21

LESSON 21 ENRICHMENT Name ____

Draw the path that Ramon followed.

Ramon stood on the square marked START. He moved three spaces to the left. Then he moved five spaces down. He moved four spaces left, then three down. Ramon moved four spaces right. He moved seven spaces up. Then he moved left five and down three. He moved eight spaces right. He moved up three and left one.

On what space is Ramon? 71

73	74	75	76	77	78	79	80	start
64	65	66	67	68	69	70	71	72
55	56	57	58	59	60	61	62	63
46	47	48	49	50	51	52	53	54
37	38	39	40	41	42	43	44	45
28	29	30	31	32	33	34	35	36
19	20	21	22	23	24	25	26	27
10	11	12	13	14	15	16	17	18
1	2	3	4	5	6	7	8	9

Math Explorations and Applications Level 2 • 21

STORY 3

THINKING STORY

Mr. Muddle Takes A Test

"I can't understand it," Mr. Muddle said. "I'm not spending any more than I used to, and yet I seem to be running out of money."

"Are you still earning as much money as you used to?" Mr. Eng asked him.

"Well, no," said Mr. Muddle. "As a matter of fact, ever since I stopped working, I haven't been earning any money at all. I wonder if that could have anything to do with my problem."

What does not working have to do with Mr. Muddle's problem?
He's still spending the same amount he used to, but he is not earning any money.

"From the sound of it, you won't have any money at all in a little while unless you get a job and start earning some more," Mr. Eng told him. "Mrs. Breezy works for an employment agency. Maybe she could help you find a job."

The next time he thought of it, Mr. Muddle went down to the office where Mrs. Breezy worked.

"What kind of job are you looking for?" Mrs. Breezy asked.

"One that will pay me some money," Mr. Muddle said. "I find that I am running out of money, and so I would like to earn some more."

"Many people have that problem," Mrs. Breezy said, "but I was wondering what particular kind of work you are good at. What kind of work have you done in the past?"

"Oh, all kinds of work," Mr. Muddle said, "but I can't remember exactly."

"Well," said Mrs. Breezy, "I think the thing to do would be to give you some tests to find out what you do best."

"Good," said Mr. Muddle. "I like tests."

"First we'll see how you are at arithmetic," Mrs. Breezy said. "If I have five apples and eat two of them, how many apples do I have left?"

"That's easy," said Mr. Muddle. "Five apples."

What do you think the answer was supposed to be? three

"Perhaps you didn't hear the question," Mrs. Breezy said. "I said I have five apples and eat two of them."

"Exactly," said Mr. Muddle. "Then you have five apples—three on the outside and two on the inside."

"I think that's enough arithmetic," Mrs. Breezy said. "Let's try some different questions. How many days are there in a week?"

"Which week?" Mr. Muddle asked.

Does it matter which week? no

Why not? There are always seven days in a week.

◆ STORY 3 Mr. Muddle Takes a Test

"Any week," Mrs. Breezy said. "They all have the same number of days."

"I just want to make sure I get this one right," Mr. Muddle said. "Do you mean a week starting on Sunday or starting on Monday?"

Does it make a difference? no

Why not? No matter where you start counting, there are still seven days in a week.

"You can start on any day you like," Mrs. Breezy said. "The question is just how many days will it take to make a whole week?"

"Then I would say, on the average, more or less, about seven," Mr. Muddle answered.

Is there anything wrong with Mr. Muddle's answer? The answer, seven days, is an exact number, not an average or an approximation.

"Actually," said Mrs. Breezy, "a week is always just seven days, but we'll count your answer right. Now for a harder question: How many eggs are in a dozen?"

"How many eggs . . . in a dozen?"

"You're going to ask what kind of eggs, right?" Mrs. Breezy said.

"You've read my mind exactly," Mr. Muddle said.

"Well," she said, "the answer is any kind of eggs. It doesn't matter."

Why doesn't it matter? A dozen is another name for 12. It relates to the number of items, not the kind of items.

"You mean I can have any kind of eggs I want?" said Mr. Muddle. "Good. How about pigeon eggs?"

"That's just fine," Mrs. Breezy said.

"The only trouble is," Mr. Muddle said, "I don't think I've ever seen a dozen pigeon eggs. So you can't expect me to know how many pigeon eggs there are in a dozen."

Have you ever seen a dozen pigeon eggs? Allow several students to answer.

Do you know how many pigeon eggs there are in a dozen? 12

How can you know even if you've never seen a dozen pigeon eggs? A dozen is another name for 12. It doesn't matter what type of items are being counted.

"A dozen is a dozen, no matter what it is a dozen of," Mrs. Breezy said. "Do you know how many that is?"

"Give me a hint," said Mr. Muddle.

"All right. It's the same as the number of fingers on your hands, plus two."

"Two what?"

"Two fingers!"

"You mean to say that a dozen pigeon eggs is 12 fingers?" said Mr. Muddle. "I find that hard to believe."

What does Mrs. Breezy really mean? She means that the number 12, or one dozen, is the same quantity as 10 plus 2.

Mrs. Breezy explained patiently, "I mean that the number of pigeon eggs in a dozen is the same as the number of fingers on your hands, plus 2. That number is 12. I guess there isn't any point in asking you more questions."

"Did I pass the test?" Mr. Muddle asked.

"Let's put it this way," Mrs. Breezy said. "I don't think the test is going to help us much in finding you a job. But I'll be looking around for a job that's right for you, and I'll let you know."

"Thank you very much," said Mr. Muddle. "I've learned a lot from you. I've learned that there are 12 days in a week and seven eggs in a dozen. I won't forget it."

What's wrong with what Mr. Muddle said? He reversed the numbers. He should have said that there are seven days in a week and 12 eggs in a dozen.

. . . the end

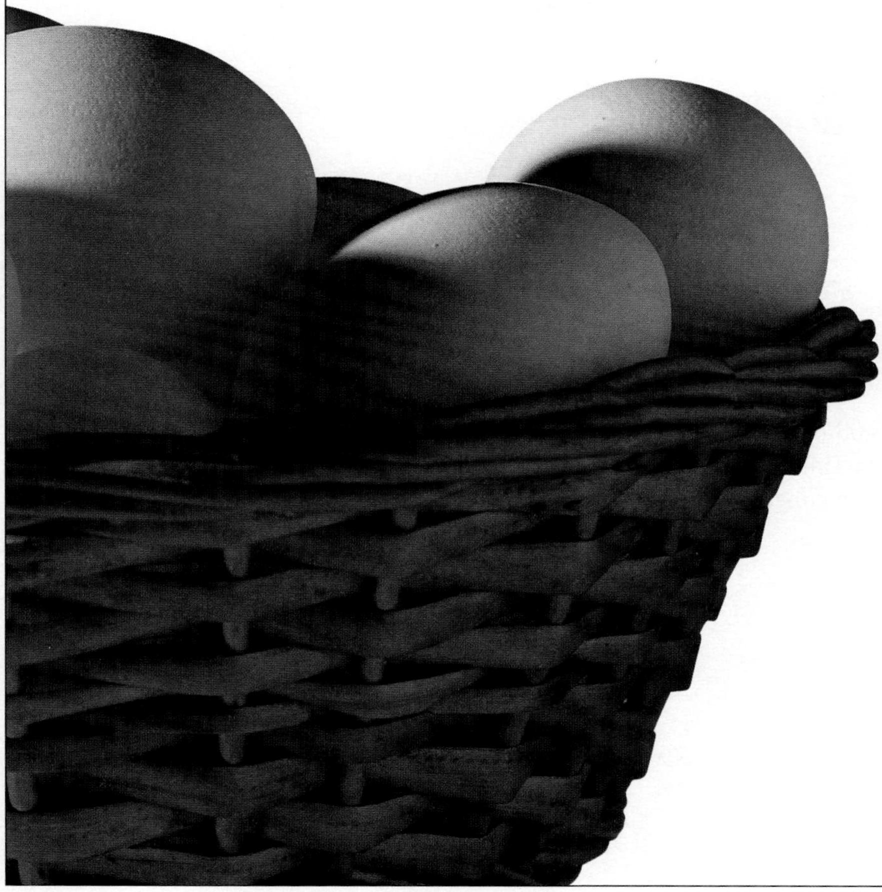

LESSON 22

Student Edition pages 47–48

Using an Addition Table to Subtract

LESSON PLANNER

Objectives

- to introduce the addition table for subtraction
- to provide practice in addition and subtraction facts
- to reinforce the inverse relationship between addition and subtraction

Context of the Lesson This is the fifth of 11 lessons focusing on review of subtraction facts.

Materials

overhead projector (optional)

transparency of 10 + 10 addition table (optional)

Program Resources

Number Cubes

Practice Master 22

Enrichment Master 22

For extra practice:

CD-ROM* Lesson 22

1 Warm-Up

5 MINUTES

Problem of the Day Present the following problem to the class: Ari bought a $5 book and a $3 comic. He paid with a $10 bill. How much change should he get back? ($2)

MENTAL MATH Present the following problems and have students show the answers using their Number Cubes.

a. 16 – 8 = (8) **b.** 7 – 4 = (3) **c.** 17 – 10 = (7)

d. 16 – 9 = (7) **e.** 9 – 6 = (3) **f.** 14 – 7 = (7)

g. 12 – 9 = (3) **h.** 10 – 7 = (3) **i.** 19 – 9 = (10)

2 Teach

Demonstrate Display an addition table with an overhead projector or use the one on page 47. Demonstrate how to use the table to solve subtraction problems. Work with students to solve 17 – 9: Place a finger on the 9 column and run it down to 17. Find the number of that row to get the solution. (8) Practice several similar problems with students.

LESSON 22

Name ______________________

Using an Addition Table to Subtract

17 − 9 = 8

+	0	1	2	3	4	5	6	7	8	9	10
0	0	1	2	3	4	5	6	7	8	9	10
1	1	2	3	4	5	6	7	8	9	10	11
2	2	3	4	5	6	7	8	9	10	11	12
3	3	4	5	6	7	8	9	10	11	12	13
4	4	5	6	7	8	9	10	11	12	13	14
5	5	6	7	8	9	10	11	12	13	14	15
6	6	7	8	9	10	11	12	13	14	15	16
7	7	8	9	10	11	12	13	14	15	16	17
8	8	9	10	11	12	13	14	15	16	17	18
9	9	10	11	12	13	14	15	16	17	18	19
10	10	11	12	13	14	15	16	17	18	19	20

Find the answers in the addition table.

1. 17 − 8 = 9
2. 13 − 6 = 7
3. 6 − 4 = 2
4. 9 − 5 = 4
5. 15 − 5 = 10
6. 11 − 2 = 9
7. 9 − 3 = 6
8. 16 − 7 = 9

GAME Play the "Roll 20 to 5" game.

NOTE TO HOME
Students learn how to use an addition table for subtraction.

Literature Connection Read "Caledonia and the Calculator" on pages 62–63 of *Play Ball: Sports Math* from Time-Life Inc. to reinforce lesson concepts.

RETEACHING

Have students work in small groups. Provide practice using the addition table to solve pairs of related equations such as: 7 + 6 = (13) and 13 – 7 = (6). Encourage them to explain how they solved each problem.

*available separately

◆ LESSON 22 Using an Addition Table to Subtract

ALGEBRA READINESS

Find the missing numbers.

⑨ 8 + __9__ = 17 ⑩ 11 − 3 = __8__

⑪ 8 + __3__ = 11 ⑫ 11 − 8 = __3__

⑬ 17 − 8 = __9__ ⑭ 17 − 9 = __8__

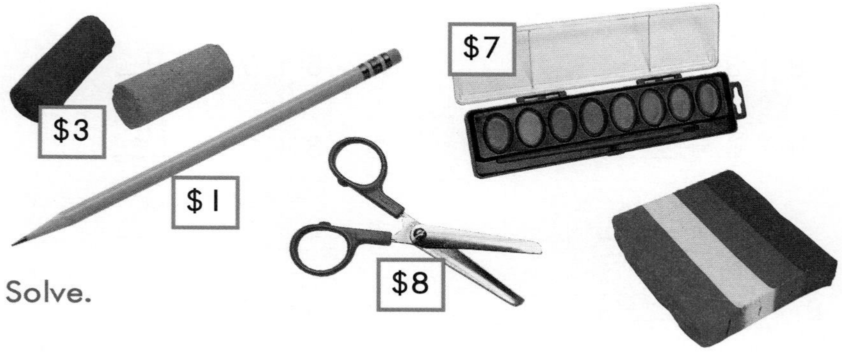

Solve.

⑮ If you have $15, can you buy both the chalk and the paint set? $__yes__

⑯ The paint set and scissors cost $15 together. If you have $21, how much money will you get back? $__6__

⑰ Two packs of clay cost $12. How much does one pack of clay cost? $__6__

NOTE TO HOME
Students practice addition and subtraction in number sentences and word problems.

Using the Student Pages Have students complete page 47 independently. Discuss the word problems on page 48 with the class. Have students explain what information they are *given,* what they need to *find out,* and *how* they will solve each problem. Then have students solve the problems on their own.

Introducing the "Roll 20 to 5" Game

Have students play the "Roll 20 to 5" game to provide practice in subtracting 10 or less from numbers through 20. Students play in pairs with two 0–5 and two 5–10 Number Cubes. Player 1 rolls one of the four cubes and subtracts that number from 20. He or she then rolls each of the three remaining cubes in turn, trying to get a difference as close to 5 as possible. A player may stop after one, two, three, or four rolls. Then player 2 takes a turn. The player closest to 5 wins the round. Variations: After deciding in advance how many and which of the four cubes to roll, each player rolls the cubes at once and then subtracts the total from 20. More than two players can play.

3 Wrap-Up

5 MINUTES

In Closing Ask volunteers to explain how to use the addition table to solve subtraction problems. Then ask, "Why can you use an addition table to find subtraction facts?" (because addition is the inverse, or opposite, of subtraction)

ALTERNATIVE ASSESSMENT

Informal Assessment Use students' answers to pages 47–48 as an informal assessment of their understanding of subtraction facts and their relationship to addition.

PRACTICE p. 22

LESSON 22 PRACTICE Name ____________________

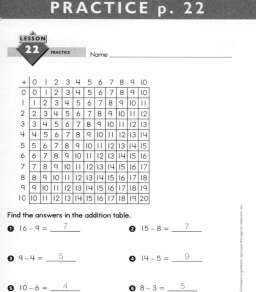

+	0	1	2	3	4	5	6	7	8	9	10
0	0	1	2	3	4	5	6	7	8	9	10
1	1	2	3	4	5	6	7	8	9	10	11
2	2	3	4	5	6	7	8	9	10	11	12
3	3	4	5	6	7	8	9	10	11	12	13
4	4	5	6	7	8	9	10	11	12	13	14
5	5	6	7	8	9	10	11	12	13	14	15
6	6	7	8	9	10	11	12	13	14	15	16
7	7	8	9	10	11	12	13	14	15	16	17
8	8	9	10	11	12	13	14	15	16	17	18
9	9	10	11	12	13	14	15	16	17	18	19
10	10	11	12	13	14	15	16	17	18	19	20

Find the answers in the addition table.

❶ 16 − 9 = __7__ ❷ 15 − 8 = __7__

❸ 9 − 4 = __5__ ❹ 14 − 5 = __9__

❺ 10 − 6 = __4__ ❻ 8 − 3 = __5__

❼ 12 − 5 = __7__ ❽ 18 − 9 = __9__

22 • *Math Explorations and Applications* Level 2

ENRICHMENT p. 22

LESSON 22 ENRICHMENT Name ____________________

Add with two rulers. Here's how.

3 + 9 = ?

Line up two rulers.

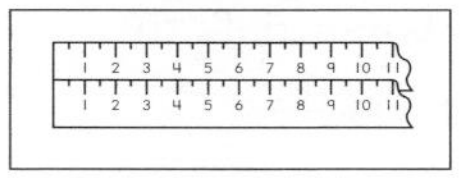

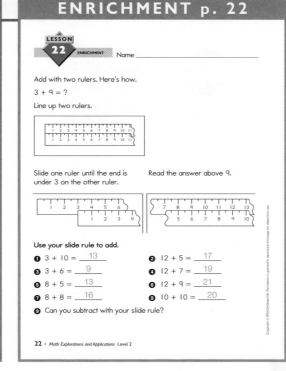

Slide one ruler until the end is under 3 on the other ruler.

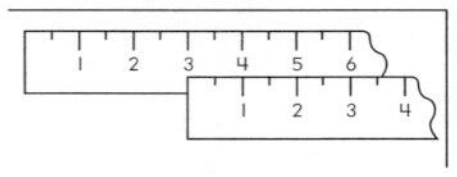

Read the answer above 9.

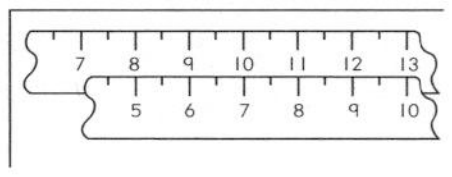

Use your slide rule to add.

❶ 3 + 10 = __13__ ❷ 12 + 5 = __17__

❸ 3 + 6 = __9__ ❹ 12 + 7 = __19__

❺ 8 + 5 = __13__ ❻ 12 + 9 = __21__

❼ 8 + 8 = __16__ ❽ 10 + 10 = __20__

❾ Can you subtract with your slide rule?

22 • *Math Explorations and Applications* Level 2

Assessment Criteria

Did the student . . .

✓ correctly solve six of the eight subtraction problems on page 47?

✓ correctly solve four of the six problems on page 48?

✓ correctly solve the word problems on page 48?

LESSON 23

Student Edition pages 49–50

Adding and Subtracting

LESSON PLANNER

Objectives

- ▶ to check students' understanding of addition facts
- ▶ to review subtraction facts with a subtrahend of 10 or 9
- ▶ to review subtraction facts with a difference of 10 or 9

Context of the Lesson This is the sixth of 11 lessons focusing on review of subtraction facts.

Materials	Program Resources
base-10 blocks (optional)	Number Cubes
	Thinking Story Book, pages 22–23
	Practice Master 23
	Enrichment Master 23
	For extra practice: CD-ROM* Lesson 23

1 Warm-Up

5 MINUTES

Problem of the Day Write the following problem on the chalkboard: It took Matt one hour to get to the mall from his house. He shopped for three hours and left the mall at noon. What time had he left his house to go to the mall? (8:00 A.M.)

MENTAL MATH Have students answer the following questions using their Number Cubes:

a. 6 + 3 = (9)
b. 5 + 8 = (13)
c. 3 + 7 = (10)
d. 4 + 8 = (12)
e. 3 + 8 = (11)
f. 9 + 6 = (15)
g. 7 + 9 = (16)
h. 8 + 9 = (17)
i. 5 + 9 = (14)
j. 3 + 6 = (9)
k. 7 + 4 = (11)
l. 9 + 9 = (18)
m. 7 + 7 = (14)

PRACTICE

LESSON 23

Name ______________________

Adding and Subtracting

Check your math skills.

1. 7 + 0 = 7
2. 2 + 7 = 9
3. 5 + 5 = 10
4. 8 + 5 = 13
5. 6 + 5 = 11
6. 1 + 7 = 8
7. 8 + 3 = 11
8. 3 + 3 = 6
9. 4 + 6 = 10
10. 8 + 2 = 10
11. 9 + 9 = 18
12. 2 + 6 = 8
13. 8 + 10 = 18
14. 9 + 7 = 16
15. 7 + 4 = 11
16. 8 + 3 = 11
17. 5 + 9 = 14
18. 7 + 5 = 12
19. 8 + 8 = 16
20. 3 + 9 = 12

Number correct ☐

NOTE TO HOME
Students check their accuracy with addition facts.

Literature Connection You might want to read aloud *Ten Little Animals* by Laura Jane Coats to reinforce lesson concepts.

RETEACHING

COOPERATIVE LEARNING Have students work in small groups to practice subtraction facts using base-10 units or other manipulatives.

*available separately

◆ **LESSON 23** Adding and Subtracting

Use the Mixed Practice on page 369 after this lesson.

Subtract.

21 18 − 10 = 8
22 17 − 7 = 10
23 13 − 10 = 3
24 14 − 4 = 10
25 11 − 10 = 1
26 12 − 2 = 10
27 16 − 9 = 7
28 16 − 7 = 9
29 14 − 9 = 5
30 15 − 6 = 9

31 18 − 9 = 9
32 15 − 5 = 10
33 13 − 4 = 9
34 19 − 10 = 9

35 19 − 9 = 10
36 16 − 6 = 10
37 20 − 10 = 10

NOTE TO HOME
Students review subtraction facts involving 9 and 10.

2 Teach

Using the Student Pages Have students complete page 49 independently. Give them about three minutes to finish. All students should stop when you call time. Then have students correct their papers as you call out the right answers. Have them enter the number of correct answers in the box at the bottom of the page.

Present the following demonstration before having students complete page 50 on their own.

Demonstrate Present and discuss the following subtraction strategies at the chalkboard:

Subtracting 10 leaves the number in the ones place. Examples: 17 - 10 = 7; 16 - 10 = 6

Subtracting the ones leaves 10. Examples: 17 - 7 = 10; 16 - 6 = 10

Subtracting 9 leaves 1 more than the number in the ones place. Examples: 17 - 9 = 8; 16 - 9 = 7

Subtracting 1 more than the number in the ones place leaves 9. Examples: 17 - 8 = 9; 16 - 7 = 9

Using the Thinking Story Present one or two problems from those following "Mr. Muddle Takes a Test" on pages 22–23 of the Thinking Story Book.

3 Wrap-Up

5 MINUTES

In Closing Ask students to describe the subtraction strategies they learned in this lesson.

SELF ASSESSMENT

Have students compare their score on page 49 with their scores for Lesson 17.

PRACTICE p. 23

LESSON 23 PRACTICE Name ____

Check your math skills.

1 6 + 2 = 8
2 3 + 9 = 12
3 5 + 8 = 13
4 5 + 10 = 15
5 2 + 9 = 11
6 9 + 4 = 13
7 9 + 5 = 14
8 6 + 7 = 13
9 10 + 6 = 16
10 8 + 6 = 14
11 7 + 5 = 12
12 3 + 7 = 10
13 3 + 8 = 11
14 8 + 1 = 9
15 1 + 9 = 10
16 4 + 7 = 11
17 1 + 10 = 11
18 7 + 7 = 14

Number correct ☐

ENRICHMENT p. 23

LESSON 23 ENRICHMENT Name ____

Use the money to help you solve the problems.

David was in charge of the cash box for the school book sale. Before the sale started he had two ten-dollar bills, two five-dollar bills, and five one-dollar bills in the box. After each problem write and solve the number sentence.

1 Kim bought one book that cost $11. He gave David a $20 bill. How much change did he get back?
$20 − $11 = $9

2 Sari bought one book for $8 and one book for $7. She gave David two bills and did not get any money back. How much did Sari spend?
$8 + $7 = $15

3 Ms. Trent bought one book for $6 and two books for $4 each. She paid with two $10 bills. How much change did she get back? $6 + $4 = 10
$20 − $4 = $6

4 How much money does David have in the cash box now?
$35 + $11 + $15 + $14 = $75

Assessment Criteria

Did the student . . .

✓ quickly and correctly answer 16 of 20 problems on page 49?

✓ correctly answer 13 of 17 problems on page 50?

LESSON 24

Student Edition pages 51–52

Subtraction Facts

LESSON PLANNER

Objectives

- ▶ to identify subtraction facts that students have and have not mastered
- ▶ to reinforce subtraction facts that have been mastered
- ▶ to encourage students to begin to memorize remaining subtraction facts

Context of the Lesson This is the seventh of 11 lessons focusing on the review of subtraction facts.

Materials	Program Resources
10 + 10 addition table on overhead transparency or chalkboard	"Space" Game Mat
	Number Cubes
	Thinking Story Book, pages 22–23
	Reteaching Master
	Practice Master 24
	Enrichment Master 24
	For extra practice: CD-ROM* Lesson 24

1 Warm-Up

5 MINUTES

Problem of the Day Present the following problem to the class: Len is 2 centimeters shorter than Rico. Rico is 2 centimeters shorter than Pam. Pam is 92 centimeters tall. How tall is Len? (88 cm)

MENTAL MATH Write the following subtraction facts on the chalkboard and have students use Number Cubes to show the answers.

a. 9 – 0 = (9)
b. 7 – 6 = (1)
c. 12 – 0 = (12)
d. 5 – 4 = (1)
e. 8 – 1 = (7)
f. 6 – 2 = (4)

LESSON 24

Name ______

Subtraction Facts

Subtract.

1. 8 – 5 = 3
2. 9 – 5 = 4
3. 7 – 3 = 4
4. 9 – 9 = 0
5. 9 – 4 = 5
6. 8 – 0 = 8
7. 6 – 3 = 3
8. 9 – 6 = 3

9. 9 – 3 = 6	10. 9 – 2 = 7	11. 7 – 4 = 3	12. 5 – 1 = 4	13. 8 – 3 = 5
14. 7 – 6 = 1	15. 6 – 1 = 5	16. 9 – 1 = 8	17. 6 – 0 = 6	18. 5 – 2 = 3

GAME Play the "Space" game.

NOTE TO HOME
Students review and learn new subtraction facts.

RETEACHING p. 6

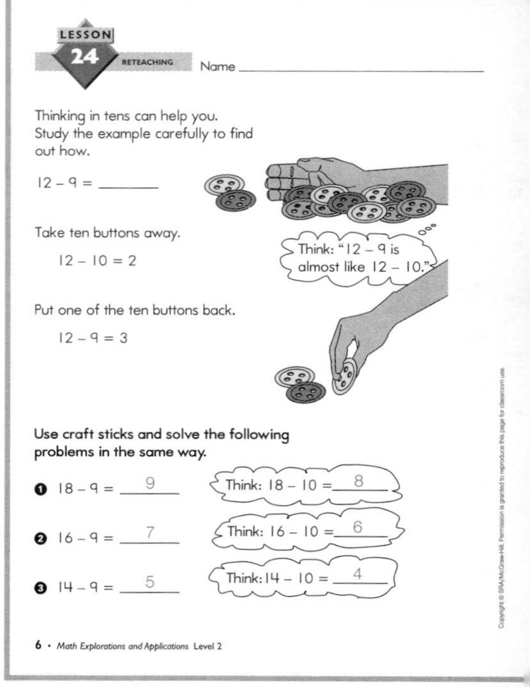
LESSON 24 RETEACHING Name ______

Thinking in tens can help you.
Study the example carefully to find out how.

12 – 9 = ______

Take ten buttons away.
12 – 10 = 2

Think: "12 – 9 is almost like 12 – 10."

Put one of the ten buttons back.
12 – 9 = 3

Use craft sticks and solve the following problems in the same way.

1. 18 – 9 = 9 Think: 18 – 10 = 8
2. 16 – 9 = 7 Think: 16 – 10 = 6
3. 14 – 9 = 5 Think: 14 – 10 = 4

6 • Math Explorations and Applications Level 2

Why teach it at this time?

Because of the inverse relationship between addition and subtraction, students who have mastered their addition facts should know all of the subtraction facts as well. However, because some young students will still have difficulty with subtraction facts, further practice is presented over the next several lessons.

Literature Connection Read "How Do Octopi Eat Pizza Pie?" on pages 6–7 of *Pizza Math* from Time-Life Inc. to reinforce lesson concepts.

*available separately

◆ **LESSON 24** Subtraction Facts

Subtract.

⑲ 18 − 9 = 9   ⑳ 15 − 8 = 7

㉑ 18 − 10 = 8   ㉒ 14 − 7 = 7

㉓ 16 − 6 = 10   ㉔ 12 − 6 = 6

㉕ 16 − 7 = 9   ㉖ 12 − 7 = 5

㉗ 16 − 8 = 8   ㉘ 12 − 8 = 4

Solve.

㉙ Peggy has 12 marbles. If she loses eight of them, how many will she have? 4

㉚ Carla had ten marbles. She won some more. She has 15 marbles now. How many did she win? 5

㉛ Isaac has ten marbles. If he wins seven more, how many will he have? 17

NOTE TO HOME
Students practice addition and subtraction number sentences.

PRACTICE p. 24

LESSON 24 PRACTICE Name ____________

Subtract.

❶ 8 − 6 = 2   ❷ 10 − 5 = 5

❸ 9 − 4 = 5   ❹ 7 − 5 = 2

❺ 9 − 9 = 0   ❻ 9 − 2 = 7

❼ 8 − 7 = 1   ❽ 6 − 3 = 3

❾ 9 − 8 = 1   ❿ 9 − 5 = 4

⓫ 8 − 0 = 8   ⓬ 9 − 6 = 3   ⓭ 6 − 1 = 5   ⓮ 7 − 4 = 3

⓯ 9 − 2 = 7   ⓰ 8 − 4 = 4   ⓱ 7 − 6 = 1   ⓲ 8 − 2 = 6

ENRICHMENT p. 24

LESSON 24 ENRICHMENT Name ____________

Write the number sentences. For each number below roll a 5–10 Number Cube. Subtract that amount to get the remainder. Then roll a 0–5 Number Cube. Subtract that amount from the remainder.

19 Answers will vary.

16

20

15

21

17

18

14

❷ Teach

Demonstrate As you did in Lesson 13, display a 10 + 10 addition table. This time, work with the class to cross off the sums corresponding to the subtraction facts that students already know. By this point these should include the first three rows, last two rows, first three columns, and last two columns of the addition table. Then list the subtraction facts that are left on the chalkboard and practice them together with the class. Have students use their Number Cubes to show answers to the facts in the demonstration.

Using the Student Pages Have students work independently on page 51 as quickly as they can. Correct this page before students go on to page 52, which most students should also be able to complete on their own. Provide individual help to those who need it.

Introducing the "Space" Game Mat Demonstrate and play the game, which provides practice in solving addition and missing-addend problems with sums of ten or less. Complete instructions are on the Game Mat.

Using the Thinking Story Present one or two new problems from those following "Mr. Muddle Takes a Test" on pages 22–23 of the Thinking Story Book.

❸ Wrap-Up

5 MINUTES

In Closing Ask volunteers to make up their own word problems that involve subtraction.

SELF ASSESSMENT

Have students make their own 10 + 10 addition tables or make copies for them. Have them cross off all of the sums related to the subtraction facts they have mastered.

Assessment Criteria

Did the student . . .

✓ correctly solve 14 of 18 subtraction fact problems on page 51?

✓ correctly solve 10 of 13 problems on page 52?

✓ correctly identify the numbers under the counters when playing the "Space" game?

LESSON 25

Student Edition pages 53–54

Reviewing Subtraction Facts

LESSON PLANNER

Objectives

- to continue to review known subtraction facts
- to provide practice for beginning the memorization of subtraction facts with a minuend of 10, 11, or 12

Context of the Lesson This is the eighth of 11 lessons focusing on review of subtraction facts.

Materials	Program Resources
transparency or chalkboard copy of 10 + 10 addition table	Number Cubes Thinking Story Book, pages 22–23 Practice Master 25 Enrichment Master 25 For extra practice: CD-ROM* Lesson 25

1 Warm-Up (5 MINUTES)

Problem of the Day Write this problem on the chalkboard: Toni had ten basketball trading cards. She gave some to her little brother. Now she has four left. How many cards did she give to her little brother? (6)

MENTAL MATH Have students answer the following questions with their Number Cubes:

a.	10 – 7 = (3)	b.	12 – 2 = (10)
c.	5 + 6 = (11)	d.	9 – 8 = (1)
e.	10 – 5 = (5)	f.	6 – 6 = (0)
g.	7 – 6 = (1)	h.	5 + 7 = (12)
i.	11 – 8 = (3)	j.	8 – 6 = (2)
k.	11 – 4 = (7)	l.	5 + 9 = (14)
m.	2 + 3 = (5)	n.	12 – 7 = (5)
o.	11 – 9 = (2)	p.	12 – 8 = (4)
q.	3 + 10 = (13)	r.	12 – 4 = (8)

LESSON 25

Name ______________________

Reviewing Subtraction Facts

Subtract.

1. 12 − 7 = 5
2. 12 − 5 = 7
3. 12 − 4 = 8
4. 11 − 4 = 7
5. 11 − 8 = 3
6. 10 − 3 = 7
7. 10 − 6 = 4
8. 12 − 10 = 2
9. 12 − 6 = 6
10. 10 − 10 = 0
11. 11 − 9 = 2
12. 11 − 5 = 6
13. 12 − 8 = 4
14. 10 − 5 = 5
15. 10 − 4 = 6
16. 11 − 3 = 8
17. 11 − 10 = 1
18. 12 − 1 = 11
19. 11 − 6 = 5
20. 12 − 2 = 10

NOTE TO HOME
Students review subtraction facts.

Language Arts Connection Invite students to write a funny story in which the main character has to find ten things in one day. Have students state what the ten things are, why the character has to find them, and how many more are left to find after each discovery.

Literature Connection You might want to read aloud *1 + 1 Take Away Two!* by Michael Bernstein to reinforce lesson concepts.

RETEACHING

Give students a choice of games from among those previously introduced or assign games based on the skills in which students need the most help.

*available separately

◆ LESSON 25 Reviewing Subtraction Facts

Subtract.

(21) 11 − 7 = 4
(22) 11 − 1 = 10
(23) 10 − 4 = 6
(24) 12 − 12 = 0
(25) 10 − 7 = 3
(26) 11 − 0 = 11
(27) 8 − 3 = 5
(28) 9 − 1 = 8
(29) 9 − 0 = 9
(30) 8 − 7 = 1

(31) 7 − 4 = 3
(32) 10 − 5 = 5
(33) 12 − 6 = 6
(34) 8 − 4 = 4
(35) 12 − 3 = 9

(36) 10 − 1 = 9
(37) 12 − 7 = 5
(38) 6 − 3 = 3
(39) 10 − 6 = 4
(40) 11 − 5 = 6

NOTE TO HOME
Students practice and review subtraction facts.

PRACTICE p. 25

LESSON 25 PRACTICE Name ______

Subtract.

1. 12 − 0 = 12
2. 10 − 5 = 5
3. 11 − 7 = 4
4. 10 − 4 = 6
5. 9 − 3 = 6
6. 11 − 0 = 11
7. 12 − 1 = 11
8. 9 − 9 = 0
9. 10 − 8 = 2
10. 12 − 6 = 6
11. 9 − 8 = 1
12. 10 − 2 = 8
13. 12 − 8 = 4
14. 11 − 10 = 1
15. 10 − 4 = 6
16. 12 − 6 = 6
17. 12 − 7 = 5
18. 11 − 3 = 8

ENRICHMENT p. 25

LESSON 25 ENRICHMENT Name ______

Circle some of each kind of animal. These animals will be taken to another farm.

Write number problems that tell each story. Tell how many animals there were together, how many will go to another farm, and how many will stay behind.

Answers will vary, but students' equations should agree with the number of each animal they circled.

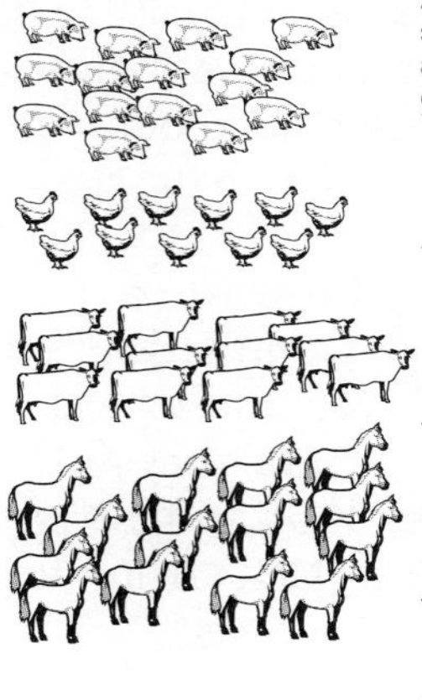

2 Teach

Demonstrate Display the addition table used in previous lessons with all of the facts crossed off except for the last 16. Show students the facts with minuends of 10, 11, and 12 on the table. List these facts on the chalkboard and practice them with the class: 10 - 7; 10 - 6; 10 - 5; 10 - 4; 10 - 3; 11 - 8; 11 - 7; 11 - 6; 11 - 5; 11 - 4; 11 - 3; 12 - 8; 12 - 7; 12 - 6; 12 - 5; 12 - 4.

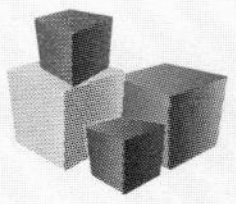

Using the Number Cubes Have students use their Number Cubes to review the 16 facts left in the demonstration. Cross off the new subtraction facts the group has learned. The only numbers that should remain at this point are 13 in row five; 13 and 14 in row six; 13, 14, 15 in row seven; and 13, 14, 15, and 16 in row eight.

Using the Student Pages Students should be able to complete pages 53 and 54 quickly without counting. Correct the answers as a class.

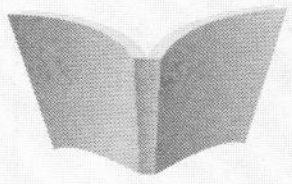

Using the Thinking Story Present four new problems from those following "Mr. Muddle Takes a Test" on pages 22–23 of the Thinking Story Book. Consider having students use their Number Cubes to show numerical answers.

3 Wrap-Up

5 MINUTES

PROBLEM SOLVING

In Closing Ask volunteers to make up their own word problems involving subtraction.

SELF ASSESSMENT

Have students make their own 10 + 10 addition tables, or make copies for them, and have them cross off all of the sums related to the subtraction facts they have mastered.

Assessment Criterion

Did the student . . .

✓ correctly and quickly answer 32 of 40 subtraction fact problems?

LESSON 26

Student Edition pages 55–56

Practicing Subtraction Facts

LESSON PLANNER

Objectives

- ▶ to continue to provide review of known subtraction facts
- ▶ to encourage students to begin memorizing subtraction facts with a minuend of 13, 14, 15, or 16

Context of the Lesson This is the ninth of 11 lessons focusing on review of subtraction facts.

Materials	Program Resources
counters	Number Cubes
flash cards	Practice Master 26
overhead projector (optional)	Enrichment Master 26
transparency of 10 + 10 addition table (optional)	For extra practice: CD-ROM* Lesson 26

1 Warm-Up

5 MINUTES

Problem of the Day Present this problem to the class: Little Milly made a tower 12 blocks high. Some blocks fell off the top of the tower. Now the tower is 7 blocks high. How many blocks fell off? (5)

MENTAL MATH Present the following subtraction facts and have students use Number Cubes to show the answers.

a. 13 – 6 = (7)	**b.** 15 – 8 = (7)	**c.** 11 – 7 = (4)
d. 10 – 6 = (4)	**e.** 12 – 7 = (5)	**f.** 8 – 3 = (5)
g. 9 – 0 = (9)	**h.** 13 – 8 = (5)	

2 Teach

Demonstrate Display the addition table with all of the facts crossed off except for the last ten. Show students the facts with minuends of 13, 14, 15, and 16 on the table. List these facts on the chalkboard and practice them with the

LESSON 26

Name ____________________

Practicing Subtraction Facts

Subtract.

1. 13 − 8 = 5	2. 16 − 8 = 8
3. 15 − 7 = 8	4. 14 − 7 = 7
5. 14 − 6 = 8	6. 13 − 5 = 8
7. 14 − 4 = 10	8. 14 − 8 = 6
9. 15 − 8 = 7	10. 14 − 9 = 5
11. 15 − 10 = 5	12. 13 − 7 = 6
13. 13 − 6 = 7	14. 13 − 3 = 10
15. 13 − 9 = 4	16. 14 − 5 = 9

GAME Play the "What's the Problem?" game.

NOTE TO HOME
Students practice subtraction facts including those involving 13, 14, 15, and 16.

Social Studies Connection Have groups survey the number of boys and girls in several other classes in your school. They may use models, such as base-10 units, to find out how many more boys or girls there are in each class. Groups can present their findings to the class.

Literature Connection Invite students to read "How Many Are Left?" on pages 30–31 of *My First Number Book* by Marie Heinst to reinforce lesson concepts.

RETEACHING

Provide or have students make flash cards with subtraction facts and have them work in pairs to review the facts using the flash cards. Encourage students to answer quickly. If they know a fact "by sight," they can remove that card from their set.

*available separately

◆ **LESSON 26** Practicing Subtraction Facts

Answer these questions.

⑰ I had $14. I bought a book. Now I have $6. Which book did I buy? the red book

⑱ I had $14. I bought a book. Now I have $7. Which book did I buy? either the green book or the blue book

⑲ I had $14. I bought two books. I still have $2. Which two books did I buy?

either the blue book and yellow book or the yellow book and green book

⑳ Can I buy the green and blue books if I have $14? yes

㉑ Can I buy the green and red books if I have $14? no

NOTE TO HOME
Students solve money problems.

PRACTICE p. 26

LESSON 26 PRACTICE Name ______

Subtract.

1. 14 − 5 = 9
2. 15 − 8 = 7
3. 13 − 4 = 9
4. 14 − 9 = 5
5. 16 − 8 = 8
6. 15 − 7 = 8
7. 16 − 10 = 6
8. 13 − 9 = 4
9. 14 − 8 = 6
10. 14 − 7 = 7
11. 15 − 5 = 10
12. 16 − 9 = 7
13. 14 − 4 = 10
14. 13 − 6 = 7
15. 13 − 8 = 5
16. 16 − 7 = 9
17. 15 − 9 = 6
18. 13 − 9 = 4

26 • Math Explorations and Applications Level 2

ENRICHMENT p. 26

LESSON 26 ENRICHMENT Name ______

Cut out the number squares below. Fold them. Mix them up and then choose one at a time. Subtract each number you choose from a number listed. Write and solve the number sentences. Answers will vary.

1. 13 − ___ = ___
2. 12 − ___ = ___
3. 15 − ___ = ___
4. 9 − ___ = ___
5. 14 − ___ = ___
6. 10 − ___ = ___
7. 16 − ___ = ___
8. 18 − ___ = ___

13	8	11	7
9	6	12	5

26 • Math Explorations and Applications Level 2

class: 13 − 5; 13 − 6; 13 − 7; 13 − 8; 14 − 8; 14 − 7; 14 − 6; 15 − 8; 15 − 7; 16 − 8.

Using the Number Cubes Have students use their Number Cubes to review the tens facts, as well as other known subtraction and addition facts. When they finish, cross off the last ten subtraction facts on the addition table.

Using the Student Pages Students should be able to complete pages 55 and 56 independently. Correct both pages with the class.

Introducing the "What's the Problem?" Game Demonstrate the "What's the Problem?" game, which provides practice solving addition and subtraction fact problems. Students play in pairs using pencil and paper and 25 counters. Player 1 says and writes a number between 0 and 20 to complete the sentence: "My answer is _____." Player 2 writes three addition and/or subtraction problems that give the answer that player 1 identified. If correct, player 2 wins the round. If not, player 1 wins.

3 Wrap-Up

5 MINUTES

In Closing Ask volunteers to share the strategies they used to solve the problems on page 55.

ALTERNATIVE ASSESSMENT

Informal Assessment Observe students as they work on this lesson to see which students have mastered and which students are still having difficulty solving subtraction facts. Note whether students need more practice in computing or in problem-solving skills.

Assessment Criteria

Did the student . . .

✓ correctly solve 13 of 16 subtraction fact problems on page 55?

✓ correctly solve all of the word problems on page 56?

✓ write accurate addition and subtraction sentences when playing the "What's the Problem?" game?

LESSON 27

Student Edition pages 57–58

More Subtraction Practice

LESSON PLANNER

Objectives

- ▶ to review all of the basic subtraction facts
- ▶ to provide practice with subtraction word problems

Context of the Lesson This is the tenth of 11 lessons focusing on review of subtraction facts.

Materials	Program Resources
play money (optional)	Number Cubes
	Thinking Story Book, pages 24–27
	Reteaching Master
	Practice Master 27
	Enrichment Master 27
	For extra practice: CD-ROM* Lesson 27

1 Warm-Up

5 MINUTES

Problem of the Day Write the following problem and incorrect solution on the chalkboard. Have students read the problem, copy the solution, circle the mistake, and then write the correct solution.

Problem: There are ten marbles in a bag. Eight are blue. The rest are red. How many are red?

Solution: 10 + 8 = 18. 18 are red. (Students should circle the + sign and 18; they should rewrite the solution as 10 − 8 = 2. Two are red.)

MENTAL MATH Have students solve the following problems using their Number Cubes:

a. 8 − 2 = (6)	b. 16 − 7 = (9)
c. 15 − 5 = (10)	d. 13 − 5 = (8)
e. 8 − 8 = (0)	f. 17 − 10 = (7)
g. 15 − 9 = (6)	h. 11 − 7 = (4)
i. 7 − 2 = (5)	j. 9 − 0 = (9)
k. 17 − 8 = (9)	l. 9 − 3 = (6)

PRACTICE

LESSON 27

Name ________________

More Subtraction Practice

Subtract.

1. 12 − 7 = 5
2. 17 − 10 = 7
3. 14 − 7 = 7
4. 15 − 9 = 6
5. 13 − 8 = 5
6. 14 − 10 = 4
7. 10 − 6 = 4
8. 11 − 2 = 9
9. 9 − 2 = 7
10. 10 − 7 = 3
11. 6 − 1 = 5
12. 8 − 4 = 4
13. 5 − 3 = 2
14. 11 − 5 = 6
15. 18 − 8 = 10
16. 7 − 6 = 1
17. 18 − 9 = 9
18. 4 − 4 = 0
19. 16 − 7 = 9
20. 11 − 6 = 5

NOTE TO HOME
Students review all basic subtraction facts.

RETEACHING p. 7

LESSON 27 RETEACHING Name ________________

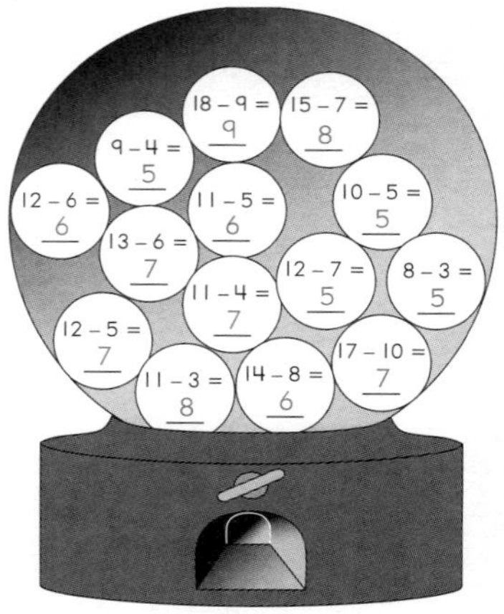

Solve the problems. Use the answers to help you color the gum balls. Color them this way.

5 — red 6 — blue
7 — green 8 — yellow 9 — orange

Math Explorations and Applications Level 2 • 7

GIFTED & TALENTED

Meeting Individual Needs

Have students make up a new monetary system for a fictional country. Students might consider how much things cost in their new country when devising their system. Encourage them to create stories about any people shown on the face of the money.

*available separately

◆ **LESSON 27** More Subtraction Practice

Work these problems.

$7

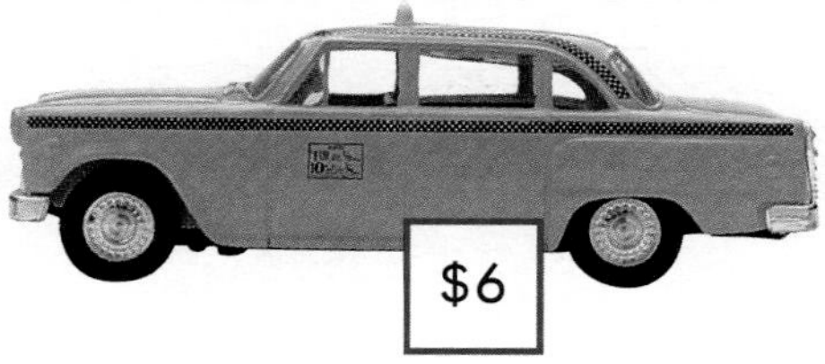

$6

$2

Kaya has $10.

21. Suppose she buys the ball. How much change will she get? $ 3
22. How much change if she buys the car? $ 4
23. How much change if she buys the marbles? $ 8
24. Does Kaya have enough money to buy the ball and the car? no
25. Does she have enough money to buy the ball and the marbles? yes

THINKING STORY

Talk about the Thinking Story "Ferdie Knows the Rules."

NOTE TO HOME
Students solve word problems.

❷ Teach

COOPERATIVE LEARNING **Demonstrate** Write these subtraction word problems on the chalkboard. Have students work in pairs to find the equation and answer for each problem:

a. I had 20¢. I spent 6¢. How much do I have left? (14¢)

b. There are 12 chairs at the table, but only eight children are sitting. How many empty chairs are there? (4)

c. I was told to read 15 pages. I have read nine. How many do I have left? (6)

Using the Student Pages Have students complete pages 57 and 58. Explain that page 57 is practice for the speed test they will take in the next lesson. Consider writing on the chalkboard each minute that elapses so students can assess how fast they are going.

Using the Thinking Story Read aloud "Ferdie Knows the Rules" on pages 24–27 of the Thinking Story Book. Stop and discuss the questions asked throughout the story.

MATH JOURNAL Here students write about a rule that applies correctly to one situation, but will not work in different circumstances.

❸ Wrap-Up

5 MINUTES

In Closing Ask students to write three subtraction facts, and then write a related addition fact for each. For example, 12 - 7 = 5, 5 + 7 = 12.

SELF ASSESSMENT Have students determine whether they need more practice before the speed test in the next lesson by answering the following questions: Did I finish page 57 in less than three minutes? Did I get all the answers correct?

Assessment Criteria

Did the student . . .

✓ correctly and quickly solve 16 of 20 subtraction fact problems on page 57?

✓ correctly solve all of the word problems on page 58?

✓ contribute to the Thinking Story discussion?

PRACTICE p. 27

LESSON 27 PRACTICE Name ____________

Subtract.

1. 9 − 8 = 1
2. 11 − 7 = 4
3. 16 − 9 = 7
4. 13 − 5 = 8
5. 8 − 8 = 0
6. 9 − 5 = 4
7. 12 − 10 = 2
8. 13 − 8 = 5
9. 8 − 7 = 1
10. 10 − 6 = 4

PROBLEM SOLVING Solve these problems.

Alex has $15.

11. Suppose he buys a hat. How much change will he get? $6
12. How much change will he get if he buys the gloves? $8
13. How much change will he get if he buys the belt? $10
14. Does Alex have enough money to buy the belt and the socks? yes
15. Does Alex have enough money to buy the hat and the gloves? no

ENRICHMENT p. 27

LESSON 27 ENRICHMENT Name ____________

Use the clues to figure out the number riddles.

1. Our difference is eight. One of us is one more than ten. Who are we? 11 and 3
2. Neither of us is greater than 17. Our difference is 17. Who are we? 17 and 0
3. Our difference is 12. We are both less than 15. Neither of us is 14 or 0. Who are we? 13 and 1
4. Our difference is 11. Our sum is 19. Who are we? 15 and 4
5. Our sum is 18. Our difference is less than one. Who are we? 9 and 9

STORY 4

THINKING STORY

Ferdie Knows the Rules

In school Ferdie learned many rules. For instance, he learned the rule that when you add 0 to a number the number stays the same. He learned the rule that when you are writing a sentence you should always start it with a capital letter. Ferdie decided that rules were a good thing, and he began using rules all the time. He even started telling Portia rules that she should follow.

Do you know any other good rules? Are rules always a good thing? Answers will vary; encourage students to identify what they consider to be both "good" and "bad" rules.

One day Portia was going to take a book over to Marcus's house. As she started out the front door of their apartment building, Ferdie stopped her, saying, "That's not the way to get to Marcus's house. There's a rule for that. The rule is, 'The quickest way to get from one place to another is in a straight line.'"

Is that always a good rule? Can you think of any times when it wouldn't be? when something you want to get to is on the other side of a wall, for example

"Marcus's house is in back of our building," Ferdie said. "So the quickest way to get there is to go straight out the back door, straight across our backyard, straight across Marcus's backyard, and right up to his back door. That's what the rule tells you to do, and the rule is always right."

"I think I'd better go out the front door and along the sidewalk," said Portia. She knew that it had rained a lot during the night.

Why does Portia want to use the sidewalk? to avoid the wet or muddy yard

Both backyards were full of mud, and there was even a small stream running between Marcus's house and the apartment building where Ferdie and Portia lived. "Have you been outside today?" Portia asked. "I don't have to go outside," argued Ferdie. "The sidewalk is not a straight line, and my rule is the best rule."

"Maybe sometimes," said Portia, "but I don't think your rule will work this time."

"Never mind," snapped Ferdie. "I'll prove it to you. We'll have a race. I'll go my way and you go yours. We'll see who gets there first."

Is Ferdie's rule best this time? no

What do you think will happen? Answers may vary; possibilities include that Ferdie will get stuck in the mud.

◆ STORY 4 Ferdie Knows the Rules

"Get ready, get set, go!" said Ferdie, as he headed out the back door. Portia went out the front door and ran along the sidewalk. Ferdie dragged through the mud and water, muttering to himself, "I have to take the shortest way, and this must be it."

By the time Ferdie reached Marcus's house, Portia was already inside talking to Marcus and his father. "I can't let you in the house like that, Ferdie," said Mrs. Breezy. "You're all muddy."

"That's all right," said Ferdie. "I'll wait out here."

As Portia came out, Ferdie called to her. "Come on, Portia. Let's walk home along the sidewalk."

As they were walking home, Ferdie said, "Maybe my rule about the straight line works only when it's not muddy. But I know another rule that works all the time. The rule is, 'When you get more, you always add.'"

Can you think of any times when the rule wouldn't work? Encourage students to think of times when they "got more" to see whether Ferdie's rule holds true.

Portia thought about Ferdie's rule for a long time. Finally she said, "I think that's a pretty good rule, Ferdie, but I wonder if it works for my classroom. There used to be five empty desks in my room. Then two more children came into the class. How many empty desks do you think there are now?"

"That's easy," said Ferdie. "You said you got two more children, so that means you add. Five and two make seven. Now there are seven empty desks."

Is Ferdie right? no

How many empty desks are there now? three

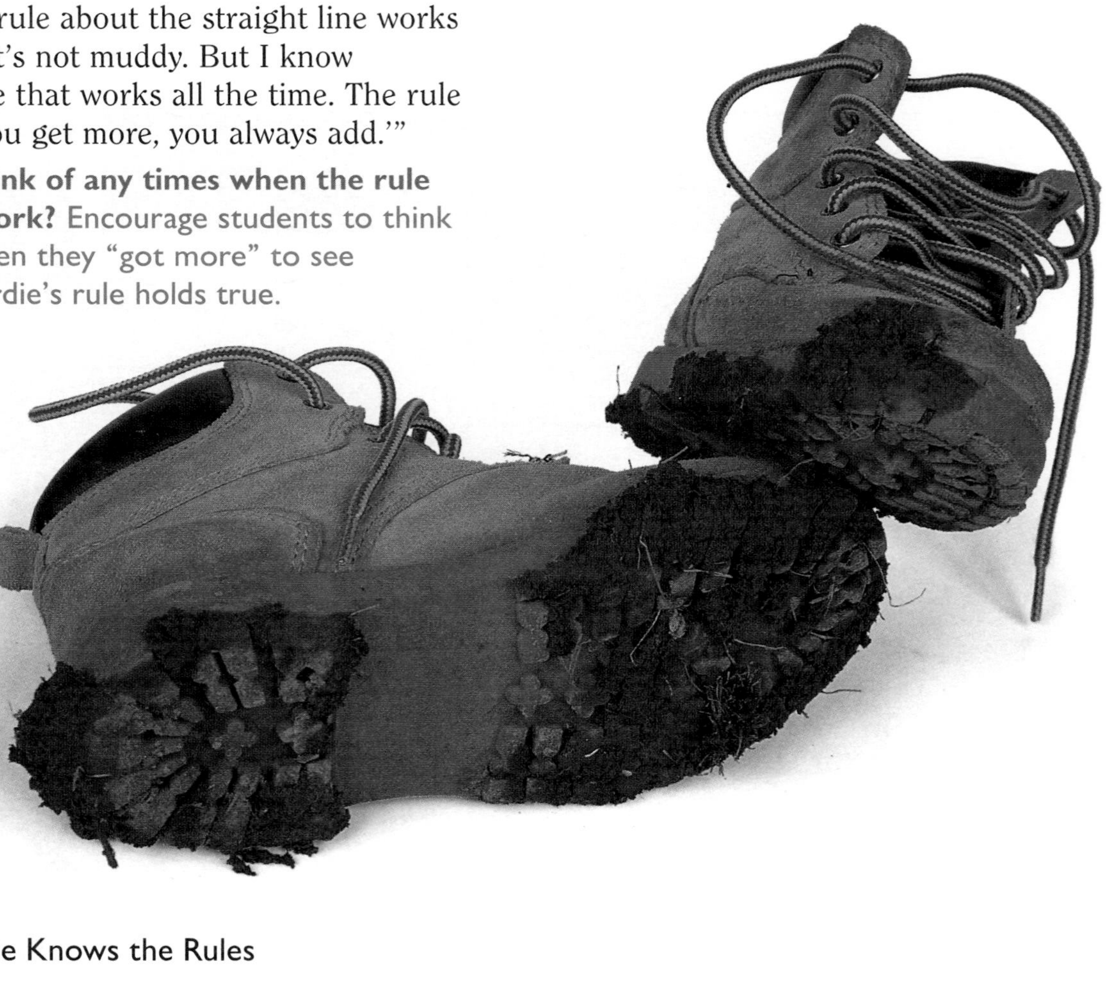

"But there are only three empty desks now," Portia said. "There used to be five empty desks, but the new children took two of them, so now there are only three."

"That's not fair!" Ferdie said. "You didn't tell me that they took two of them. When you take away, then you subtract. That's another rule. If you had told it to me the right way, I would have used the right rule and I would have gotten the right answer."

Portia was beginning to have fun now with her brother's rules. "Is that another rule that works all the time," she asked, "that when you take away you subtract?"

"All the time," Ferdie said, although he was beginning to look a bit worried.

"Then try it on this," Portia said. "There used to be three crayons missing from my crayon box. Then someone I know took away two crayons. How many crayons do you think are missing now? I suppose you'll tell me just one!"

Why does Portia think Ferdie will say that only one crayon is missing? She knows that he will subtract, and 3 − 2 = 1.

"Don't worry," said Ferdie. "You'll get all five crayons back, even if it doesn't fit with the rule."

How do you suppose Ferdie knew there were five crayons missing? He probably had them because he said that Portia would get them back.

. . . the end

LESSON 28

Student Edition pages 59–60

Subtraction Checkpoint

LESSON PLANNER

Objectives

✓ to assess students' mastery of basic subtraction facts

▶ to provide reinforcement in basic subtraction facts

Context of the Lesson This lesson, the last of 11 lessons reviewing subtraction facts, contains Mastery Checkpoint 4 for assessing mastery of basic subtraction facts.

Materials

- art supplies (optional)
- flash cards
- overhead projector
- transparency with 10 + 10 addition table
- watch or clock with a second hand

Program Resources

- Number Cubes
- Thinking Story Book, pages 28–29
- Practice Master 28
- Enrichment Master 28
- Assessment Master

For extra practice:
CD-ROM* Lesson 28

1 Warm-Up

5 MINUTES

Problem of the Day Write the following problem on the chalkboard: Mr. Ito's cat weighs 11 pounds. The cat used to weigh 9 pounds. How much weight did the cat gain? (2 lbs)

MENTAL MATH Present the following problems and have students show their answers using Number Cubes.

a. 5 + 6 = (11) **b.** 3 + 4 = (7)

c. 17 – 8 = (9) **d.** 8 + 3 = (11)

e. 6 + 8 = (14) **f.** 11 – 8 = (3)

g. 13 – 7 = (6) **h.** 7 + 8 = (15)

LESSON 28

Name ____________________

Subtraction Checkpoint

Check your math skills.

❶ 20 − 10 = 10 ❷ 9 − 0 = 9

❸ 17 − 9 = 8 ❹ 15 − 8 = 7

❺ 16 − 7 = 9 ❻ 12 − 6 = 6

❼ 14 − 4 = 10 ❽ 11 − 10 = 1

❾ 8 − 1 = 7 ❿ 15 − 5 = 10

⓫ 18 − 9 = 9 ⓬ 11 − 7 = 4

⓭ 16 − 8 = 8 ⓮ 9 − 6 = 3

⓯ 13 − 10 = 3 ⓰ 10 − 3 = 7

⓱ 12 − 8 = 4 ⓲ 10 − 5 = 5

Number correct ☐

NOTE TO HOME
Students check their knowledge of subtraction facts.

RETEACHING

Continue to provide practice through appropriate games such as "Roll 20 to 5" and "What's the Problem?" Encourage students to take home directions for the games and play them with parents or other family members.

PRACTICE p. 28

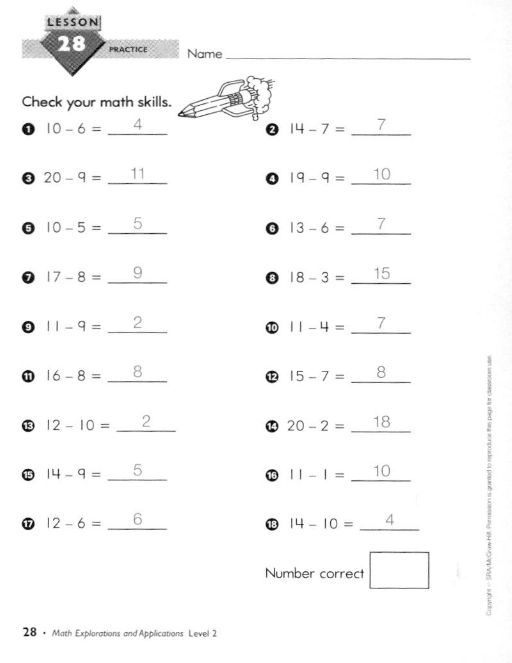
LESSON 28 PRACTICE Name ____________________

Check your math skills.

❶ 10 – 6 = 4 ❷ 14 – 7 = 7

❸ 20 – 9 = 11 ❹ 19 – 9 = 10

❺ 10 – 5 = 5 ❻ 13 – 6 = 7

❼ 17 – 8 = 9 ❽ 18 – 3 = 15

❾ 11 – 9 = 2 ❿ 11 – 4 = 7

⓫ 16 – 8 = 8 ⓬ 15 – 7 = 8

⓭ 12 – 10 = 2 ⓮ 20 – 2 = 18

⓯ 14 – 9 = 5 ⓰ 11 – 1 = 10

⓱ 12 – 6 = 6 ⓲ 14 – 10 = 4

Number correct ☐

Copyright © SRA/McGraw-Hill. Permission is granted to reproduce this page for classroom use.

28 • *Math Explorations and Applications* Level 2

*available separately

◆ LESSON 28 Subtraction Checkpoint

Use the Mixed Practice on page 370 after this lesson.

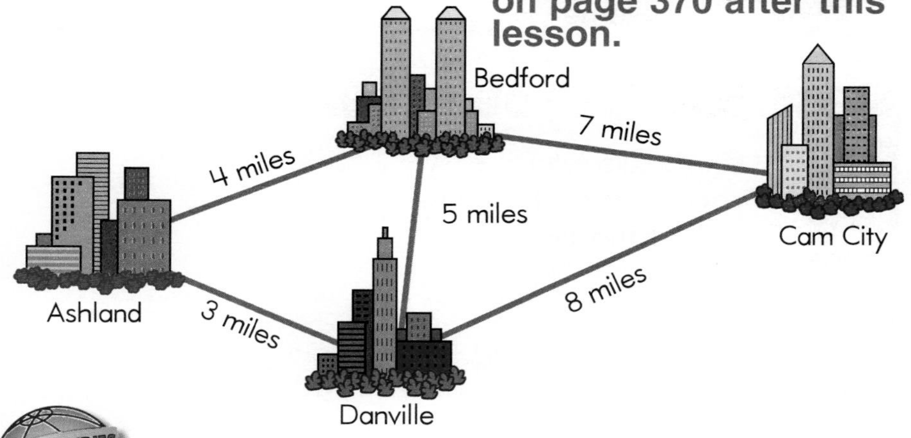

SOCIAL STUDIES CONNECTION

Use the map to answer the questions.

⑲ How far is it from Danville to Cam City? **8 miles**

⑳ How much farther is it from Danville to Cam City than from Danville to Bedford? **3 miles**

㉑ Jill drove from Danville to Cam City to Bedford. How far was that? **15 miles**

㉒ Katie drove from Danville to Ashland to Bedford. How far was that? **7 miles**

㉓ Who drove farther? **Jill**

How much farther? **8 miles**

㉔ Jason drove from Danville to Bedford directly. How much farther did Jill drive than Jason? **10 miles**

NOTE TO HOME
Students solve addition and subtraction word problems.

ENRICHMENT p. 28

LESSON 28 ENRICHMENT Name ____________

Add to the addition table. Fill in the chart.

+	10	11	12	13	14	15	16	17	18	19	20
0	10	11	12	13	14	15	16	17	18	19	20
1	11	12	13	14	15	16	17	18	19	20	21
2	12	13	14	15	16	17	18	19	20	21	22
3	13	14	15	16	17	18	19	20	21	22	23
4	14	15	16	17	18	19	20	21	22	23	24
5	15	16	17	18	19	20	21	22	23	24	25
6	16	17	18	19	20	21	22	23	24	25	26
7	17	18	19	20	21	22	23	24	25	26	27
8	18	19	20	21	22	23	24	25	26	27	28
9	19	20	21	22	23	24	25	26	27	28	29
10	20	21	22	23	24	25	26	27	28	29	30

Use the chart to find the answers to these problems.

❶ 20 + 5 = 25 ❷ 18 − 7 = 11 ❸ 28 − 9 = 19

❹ 16 − 4 = 12 ❺ 11 + 6 = 17 ❻ 14 + 7 = 21

28 • *Math Explorations and Applications* Level 2

ASSESSMENT p. 6

UNIT 1 **Mastery Checkpoint 4** Subtraction facts (Lesson 30)
Page 1 of 2
Name ____________
The student demonstrates mastery by correctly answering at least 32 of the 40 problems.

Check your math skills.

❶ 14 − 3 = 11 ❷ 12 − 4 = 8

❸ 9 − 7 = 2 ❹ 10 − 9 = 1

❺ 11 − 2 = 9 ❻ 15 − 5 = 10

❼ 15 − 7 = 8 ❽ 14 − 7 = 7

❾ 12 − 8 = 4 ❿ 13 − 6 = 7

⓫ 17 − 9 = 8 ⓬ 17 − 8 = 9

⓭ 20 − 10 = 10 ⓮ 11 − 0 = 11

⓯ 16 − 8 = 8 ⓰ 10 − 1 = 9

⓱ 12 − 5 = 7 ⓲ 16 − 6 = 10

⓳ 13 − 4 = 9 ⓴ 16 − 5 = 11

Go on . . .

6 • *Math Explorations and Applications* Level 2

❷ Teach

Demonstrate Explain that students will take a speed test on subtraction facts. Allow students to prepare for the test by practicing with flash cards and Number Cubes. Then provide oral drill on the basic facts. Display the addition table on an overhead projector and review each fact.

Using the Student Pages Allow four minutes for students to complete page 59 independently. Have students correct their own papers by circling incorrect answers and writing in the correct answers. Have them write the number that were correct in the box at the bottom of the page. Students can complete page 60 independently at their own rate.

Using the Thinking Story Present one or two new problems from those following "Ferdie Knows the Rules" on pages 28–29 of the Thinking Story Book.

❸ Wrap-Up

5 MINUTES

In Closing Ask students to explain how addition and subtraction are related.

ANALYZING ANSWERS

Provide practice when students are making more errors in computation (page 59) or in problem solving (page 60).

Mastery Checkpoint 4

At this time, most students should be proficient in basic subtraction facts. You may use page 59 or Assessment Masters 13 and 14 to assess students' mastery of subtraction facts. You may want to record the results on the Mastery Checkpoint Chart.

Assessment Criteria

Did the student . . .

✓ correctly solve 15 or more problems in four minutes on page 59?

✓ correctly solve 4 of 6 word problems on page 60?

LESSON 29

Student Edition pages 61–62

Using a Calculator

LESSON PLANNER

Objectives

- to introduce students to calculators
- to provide practice in addition and subtraction
- to provide practice in finding missing symbols in an equation

Context of the Lesson This is the first calculator activity lesson.

Materials	Program Resources
calculators	Practice Master 29
	Enrichment Master 29
	For extra practice: CD-ROM* Lesson 29

1 Warm-Up

5 MINUTES

Problem of the Day Write the following problem on the chalkboard: One year has 365 days. There are 35 days left in the year. How can you find out how many days have passed since the beginning of the year? (330)

MENTAL MATH Present the following facts and have students use Number Cubes to show answers.

a. 7 + 4 = (11) **b.** 8 + 7 = (15)
c. 9 + 3 = (12) **d.** 14 – 6 = (8)
e. 12 – 7 = (5) **f.** 11 – 7 = (4)

2 Teach

Demonstrate Pass out calculators and work with students as they practice using their calculators to solve simple addition and subtraction problems, such as 7 + 3 and 8 – 2. Allow students time to experiment. Suggest they do the following: Press c (clear), then + 1 = (the display should show 1) and then repeatedly press the = key. The display should then show 2, 3, 4 . . . .

LESSON 29

Name ______________________

Using a Calculator

Using a calculator is easy.
Practice. Push the keys.
Look at the display.

1 + 8 = ?

Push 1
Push +
Push 8
Push =
What is your answer? 9
Push C to clear the display.

8 − 1 = ?

Push 8
Push −
Push 1
Push =
What is your answer? 7
Push C to clear the display.

Practice using your calculator.

1. 4 + 8 = 12
2. 8 + 8 + 9 = 25
3. 4 + 7 = 11
4. 3 + 6 + 5 = 14
5. 5 + 6 = 11
6. 2 + 4 + 7 = 13
7. 8 − 7 = 1
8. 16 − 9 = 7

NOTE TO HOME
Students practice addition and subtraction on a calculator.

Why teach it this way?

To help students understand and become competent with a calculator, time is allowed for them to experiment with their calculators. Students have the opportunity to ask and answer specific questions about using a calculator.

RETEACHING

Provide extra practice solving simple addition and subtraction problems, such as 3 + 5 and 9 – 6, with calculators. Instruct students to take their time, to place the calculator flat on the desk, and to press the keys carefully. They should look at the display after they press each key to be sure it shows the numbers they expect.

*available separately

◆ LESSON 29 Using a Calculator

Practice using your calculator. Work the problems. Then check them with a classmate.

Push (C) to clear the display after every problem.

9. 4 + 8 = **12**
10. 9 − 6 = **3**
11. 7 + 7 = **14**
12. 1 0 − 6 = **4**
13. 1 3 − 5 = **8**
14. 2 7 − 4 = **23**
15. 2 6 + 7 = **33**
16. 6 2 + 4 = **66**
17. 1 7 + 8 = **25**
18. 1 4 + 3 + 8 = **25**
19. 2 7 − 3 − 2 = **22**
20. 4 9 − 8 − 5 = **36**

NOTE TO HOME
Students practice using a calculator.

COOPERATIVE LEARNING Allow students to work in small groups and use their calculators to solve subtraction and addition problems. Have group members predict what the display will read before they press the = sign. They then press = to check their predictions. Next, have all group members enter the same number. A leader writes down a second number. The other members try to figure out how to change the first number to the second without pressing the clear key. For example, all press 8. The leader writes down 4. Everyone else must figure out that they can key in −4 = to change the 8 to a 4.

Using the Student Pages Because this is the first formal calculator activity, you might want to work with the class to complete these pages.

3 Wrap-Up

5 MINUTES

In Closing Ask students to share anything interesting they learned about the calculator. Encourage them to explain what different keys on the calculator do.

ALTERNATIVE ASSESSMENT

Performance Assessment Observe how students use calculators. Check that they know when to press = to get an answer.

Assessment Criteria

Did the student . . .

- ✓ press the correct keys to solve addition and subtraction problems?
- ✓ press the keys in the correct order?
- ✓ correctly use the calculator to solve the problems on pages 61 and 62?

PRACTICE p. 29

LESSON 29 PRACTICE Name ____________

First give your answer. Then do the problem with the calculator and compare.

1. 6 + 8 = 14 My answer; 14 Calculator answer
2. 15 − 9 = 6 My answer; 6 Calculator answer
3. 16 − 7 = 9 My answer; 9 Calculator answer
4. 5 + 6 = 11 My answer; 11 Calculator answer
5. 9 + 6 = 15 My answer; 15 Calculator answer

Fill in the missing numbers and signs. Use your calculator to check your answers.

6. 65 + 3 = [68]
7. 65 [−] 2 = 63
8. 54 [+] [4] = 58
9. 11 [−] [6] = 5
10. 18 [−] [5] = 13
11. 49 + 2 = [51]

Math Explorations and Applications Level 2 • 29

ENRICHMENT p. 29

LESSON 29 ENRICHMENT Name ____________

Let's get fancy! Try these problems. Write your answers in the display windows.

Remember to push (C) to clear the display after each problem.

1. 2 2 + 5 − 5 + 6 = [28]
2. 4 6 − 1 8 + 3 − 2 = [29]
3. 2 7 + 8 + 9 − 4 = [40]
4. 9 + 2 6 − 4 − 3 = [28]
5. Pretend that you are at the grocery store. Use your calculator to keep track of what things cost. First you get three oranges that cost 15 cents each. Then you get one package of gum that costs 25 cents. You change your mind and put one orange back and get a pear that costs 27 cents. How much money will you spend? 82 cents
6. You are sorting crayon pieces. First you make a pile of eight red pieces. Then you make a pile of nine blue pieces. You have a pile of four yellow pieces and a pile of two purple pieces. Your friend wants some crayons, so you give her one of each color. How many crayons do you have left? 19

Math Explorations and Applications Level 2 • 29

LESSON 30

Student Edition pages 63–64

Addition and Subtraction

LESSON PLANNER

Objectives

- to provide practice with addition and subtraction facts
- to provide practice in solving mixed addition and subtraction problems
- to provide practice in solving word problems

Context of the Lesson These objectives are continued in the next lesson.

Materials	Program Resources
play money or base-10 units (optional)	Number Cubes Thinking Story Book, pages 28–29 Practice Master 30 Enrichment Master 30 For extra practice: CD-ROM* Lesson 30

1 Warm-Up (5 minutes)

Problem of the Day Write this problem on the chalkboard: Mark, Tara, and Hector are standing in a line. How many different ways can they line up? (Six ways: Mark, Tara, Hector; Mark, Hector, Tara; Tara, Mark, Hector; Tara, Hector, Mark; Hector, Mark, Tara; and Hector, Tara, Mark)

MENTAL MATH Have students answer these questions using their Number Cubes:

a. 4 + 5 = (9)	**b.** 7 – 3 = (4)
c. 10 – 6 = (4)	**d.** 4 + 7 = (11)
e. 4 + 2 = (6)	**f.** 11 – 5 = (6)
g. 6 + 4 = (10)	**h.** 6 + 6 = (12)
i. 7 + 2 = (9)	**j.** 13 – 6 = (7)
k. 5 + 4 = (9)	**l.** 10 – 5 = (5)

LESSON 30

Name ____________________

Addition and Subtraction

Work these problems. Watch the signs.

1. 8 + 4 = 12	2. 12 – 8 = 4	3. 4 + 8 = 12	4. 12 – 4 = 8	5. 9 – 3 = 6
6. 9 + 9 = 18	7. 8 + 6 = 14	8. 7 – 4 = 3	9. 14 – 6 = 8	10. 11 – 3 = 8
11. 8 + 3 = 11	12. 7 + 4 = 11	13. 6 + 8 = 14	14. 14 – 7 = 7	
15. 11 – 4 = 7	16. 3 + 8 = 11	17. 6 + 9 = 15	18. 3 + 7 = 10	

NOTE TO HOME
Students practice addition and subtraction facts mixed together.

Social Studies Connection Have students work in groups of four to play store. They can create and act out math problems related to buying and selling items priced under $1.00. Students can take turns being the cashier while others are shoppers.

Literature Connection You might want to read aloud *The M&M's Brand Chocolate Candies Counting Book* by Barbara Barbieri McGrath to reinforce lesson concepts.

RETEACHING

Present the word problems below. Have students go through the problems by first writing A (for addition) or S (for subtraction) next to each one to indicate the operation they will use. Discuss why they chose each operation; then have them find the answers.

There are seven days in a week. How many days are there in two weeks? (A: 7 + 7 = 14)

There are five school days in a week. How many school days are there in two weeks? (A: 5 + 5 = 10)

In two weeks how many days are there that aren't school days? (S: 7 – 5 = 2, and A: 2 + 2 = 4)

*available separately

◆ **LESSON 30** Addition and Subtraction

Solve these problems.

⑲ Mike has 20¢. A pencil costs 9¢.
Can Mike buy two pencils? yes
Can he buy three pencils? no

⑳ Lisa had seven baseball cards.
She gave two of them away.
How many does she have now? 5

㉑ Paco has a $10 bill.
He buys a book for $4.
How much change
does he get? $ 6

㉒ Mrs. Simon has a $5 bill and a $10 bill. The hat she wants to buy costs $12. Does she have enough money?
yes

NOTE TO HOME
Students solve word problems involving addition and subtraction.

PRACTICE p. 30

LESSON 30 PRACTICE Name ____________

Solve. Watch the signs.

1. 9 + 5 = 14
2. 18 − 9 = 9
3. 4 + 9 = 13
4. 15 − 5 = 10
5. 13 − 4 = 9
6. 20 − 3 = 17
7. 7 + 6 = 13
8. 2 + 10 = 12
9. 6 + 6 = 12
10. 16 − 2 = 14
11. 9 − 3 = 6
12. 8 + 7 = 15
13. 11 − 3 = 8
14. 5 + 6 = 11
15. 14 − 5 = 9
16. 9 + 7 = 16

30 • *Math Explorations and Applications* Level 2

ENRICHMENT p. 30

LESSON 30 ENRICHMENT Name ____________

Someone solved these problems. The answers are right but the signs are missing. Fill in the missing signs.

1. 6 + 7 = 13
2. 9 − 4 = 5
3. 8 + 11 = 19
4. 13 − 5 = 8
5. 11 − 3 = 8
6. 7 + 8 = 15
7. 5 + 3 = 8
8. 10 + 6 = 16
9. 12 − 6 = 6
10. 7 + 3 = 10
11. 14 − 1 = 13
12. 11 − 2 = 9
13. 10 + 3 = 13
14. 6 + 8 = 14
15. 12 − 6 = 6
16. 9 + 8 = 17

30 • *Math Explorations and Applications* Level 2

❷ Teach

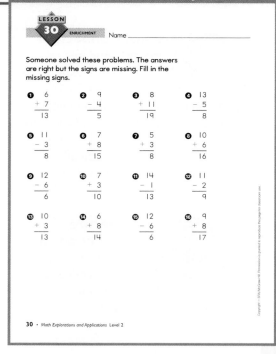

Demonstrate Present oral word problems to the students. Have them identify the operation they will use (addition or subtraction) before they solve the problems. You might want to use money or base-10 units to model solutions to some of the problems. Example: I have $10 to buy a birthday present for my cousin. The toy store has a football that costs $6 and a toy airplane that costs $3. How much would I have left if I bought the football? (subtraction; $4) How much would I have left if I bought the airplane? (subtraction; $7) How much would I have left if I bought both? (addition, subtraction; $1)

Using the Student Pages Before assigning the pages, direct students to look carefully at the sign for each problem. You might want to provide materials such as play money and base-10 units for students to model the word problems on page 64.

Using the Thinking Story Present one or two new problems from those following "Ferdie Knows the Rules" on pages 28–29 of the Thinking Story Book.

❸ Wrap-Up

5 MINUTES

In Closing Have students make up a word problem involving addition and one involving subtraction. Have them trade their problems with their classmates.

ALTERNATIVE ASSESSMENT

Informal Assessment Check students' answers to the questions on pages 63–64 to see who is still having problems with addition, subtraction, or both.

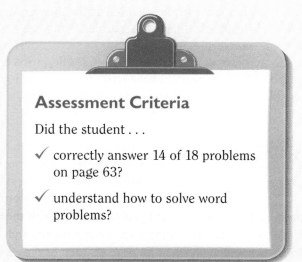

Assessment Criteria

Did the student . . .

✓ correctly answer 14 of 18 problems on page 63?

✓ understand how to solve word problems?

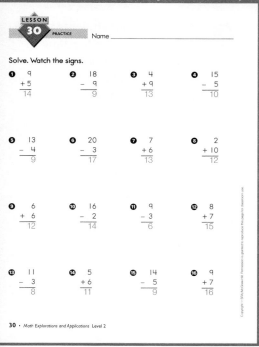

LESSON 31

Student Edition pages 65–66

Applying Addition and Subtraction

LESSON PLANNER

Objectives

- to provide practice with addition and subtraction facts
- to provide practice solving word problems

Context of the Lesson These objectives are continued from the previous lesson.

Materials	Program Resources
flash cards, subtraction (optional)	Number Cubes Thinking Story Book, pages 28–29 Practice Master 31 Enrichment Master 31 For extra practice: CD-ROM* Lesson 31

1 Warm-Up 5 MINUTES

Problem of the Day Write this problem on the chalkboard. How many different three-digit numbers can you make from the digits 1, 2, and 3? What are they? (six different numbers: 123, 132, 213, 232, 321, 312)

MENTAL MATH As in the previous lesson, present students with oral word problems. Have them identify the arithmetic operation as well as the answer for each problem. For example: I have ten marbles. Ming has eight. How many more do I have than Ming? (Subtract; 2) How many do we have all together? (Add; 18) If Ming wins five of my marbles how many will I have left? (Subtract; 5) How many will Ming have? (Add; 13)

GIFTED & TALENTED **Meeting Individual Needs** Have partners choose two problems from page 65 and make up word problems to go with them. Have them trade problems with other students and figure out which problem on page 65 each of the new word problems matches.

LESSON 31

Name ______________________

Applying Addition and Subtraction

Work these problems. Watch the signs.

1. $8 - 7 = 1$
2. $8 + 7 = 15$
3. $14 - 5 = 9$
4. $20 - 10 = 10$
5. $13 + 5 = 18$
6. $6 + 7 = 13$
7. $0 + 9 = 9$
8. $17 - 8 = 9$
9. $8 + 4 = 12$
10. $9 - 3 = 6$
11. $1 + 3 =$ 4
12. $3 + 6 =$ 9
13. $13 - 4 =$ 9
14. $10 + 5 =$ 15
15. $9 + 4 =$ 13
16. $15 - 7 =$ 8
17. $14 - 9 =$ 5
18. $12 - 8 =$ 4

NOTE TO HOME
Students practice addition and subtraction facts.

Science Connection Work with students to devise a science experiment that will require use of the basic addition and/or subtraction facts. For example: if you add 1 liter of red water to 1 liter of blue water, how many liters of water will you have all together? (2) What color will it be? (purple)

Literature Connection You might want to read aloud *Number One, Number Fun* by Kay Chorao to reinforce lesson concepts.

RETEACHING

COOPERATIVE LEARNING Pair students who need reteaching to work together with subtraction flash cards. Or, assign a game that has already been introduced that provides practice with subtraction facts.

*available separately

◆ LESSON 31 Applying Addition and Subtraction

Solve these problems.

19. Andrew had nine apples. He picked seven more apples. How many apples does he have now? 16

20. Andrew used eight of the 16 apples to make a pie. How many apples does he have left? 8

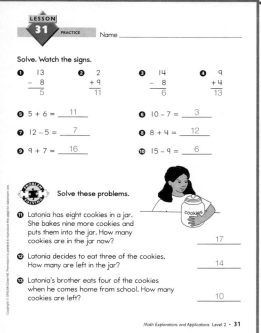

21. Suppose Andrew eats three of those apples. How many will be left? 5

22. If Andrew gives two of these to apples to Brant and three to Bren, how many will be left? 0

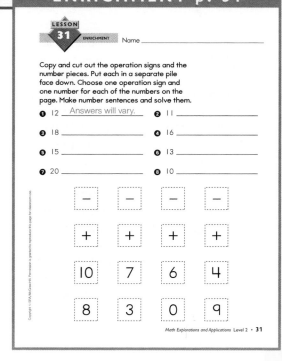

NOTE TO HOME
Students solve mixed word problems.

PRACTICE p. 31

LESSON 31 PRACTICE Name ____________

Solve. Watch the signs.

1. 13 − 8 = 5
2. 2 + 9 = 11
3. 14 − 8 = 6
4. 9 + 4 = 13
5. 5 + 6 = 11
6. 10 − 7 = 3
7. 12 − 5 = 7
8. 8 + 4 = 12
9. 9 + 7 = 16
10. 15 − 9 = 6

PROBLEM SOLVING Solve these problems.

11. Latonia has eight cookies in a jar. She bakes nine more cookies and puts them into the jar. How many cookies are in the jar now? 17
12. Latonia decides to eat three of the cookies. How many are left in the jar? 14
13. Latonia's brother eats four of the cookies when he comes home from school. How many cookies are left? 10

Math Explorations and Applications Level 2 • 31

ENRICHMENT p. 31

LESSON 31 ENRICHMENT Name ____________

Copy and cut out the operation signs and the number pieces. Put each in a separate pile face down. Choose one operation sign and one number for each of the numbers on the page. Make number sentences and solve them.

1. 12 Answers will vary.
2. 11 ________
3. 18 ________
4. 16 ________
5. 15 ________
6. 13 ________
7. 20 ________
8. 10 ________

−	−	−	−
+	+	+	+
10	7	6	4
8	3	0	9

Math Explorations and Applications Level 2 • 31

② Teach

Using the Number Cubes Have students find, hide, and show their answers to addition and subtraction problems. Be sure to break up the mixed problems so that students can solve each problem. For example: 6 + 3 = (9), 9 − 7 = (2), 2 + 3 = (5), 5 − 5 = (0).

Using the Student Pages Remind students to pay attention to the signs before they begin page 65. Encourage students who need them to use concrete objects or draw pictures to help them solve the word problems on page 66. Work individually with students having difficulty reading or solving the word problems.

Using the Thinking Story Present one or two new problems from those following "Ferdie Knows the Rules" on pages 28–29 of the Thinking Story Book.

③ Wrap-Up

In Closing Ask students what word clues they use in deciding whether to add or subtract to solve word problems. (Some students may suggest clue words such as "How many are left" for subtraction and "all together" for addition.)

ALTERNATIVE ASSESSMENT

Informal Assessment Check students' answers to the questions to see who needs more practice with basic addition and/or subtraction facts.

Assessment Criteria

Did the student . . .

✓ correctly answer 14 of 18 addition and subtraction problems?

✓ correctly answer all of the word problems on page 66?

LOOKING AHEAD You will need a large supply of craft sticks and rubber bands or other base-10 materials for Lesson 33.

LESSON 32

Student Edition pages 67–68

Adding and Subtracting Three Numbers

LESSON PLANNER

Objectives

- ▶ to introduce addition and subtraction of three numbers
- ▶ to introduce column addition of one-digit numbers
- ▶ to review basic addition and subtraction facts

Context of the Lesson Column addition is introduced here and continued in Lesson 92.

Materials	Program Resources
none	Number Cubes
	Reteaching Master
	Practice Master 32
	Enrichment Master 32
	For extra practice: CD-ROM* Lesson 32

1 Warm-Up

5 MINUTES

Problem of the Day Write the following problem on the chalkboard: Joe started out with 12 pencils. He gave three away in school. He bought four more after school. How many pencils does he have now? (13)

MENTAL MATH Have students solve the following chain calculations. Be sure to explain how these problems are related:

a. 6 + 4 = (10), 10 – 7 = (3), 3 + 6 = (9), 9 – 8 = (1)

b. 8 – 3 = (5), 5 + 3 = (8), 8 – 4 = (4), 4 – 3 = (1)

c. 1 + 3 = (4), 4 + 3 = (7), 7 – 3 = (4), 4 + 0 = (4)

2 Teach

Demonstrate Display the following problem on the chalkboard: 4 + 6 + 7 = _____. Have students solve it and explain their method. Students could add 4 + 6 = 10, then 10 + 7 = 17. Or, they could add 7 + 6 = 13 and 13 + 4 = 17. Point out that any order will work in addition problems. Then display: 14 – 8 + 2 = _____. Again, ask students to

LESSON 32

Name ______________________

Adding and Subtracting Three Numbers

Work these problems. Watch the signs.

1. 5 + 5 + 4 = __14__   Think: 5 + 5 = 10; 10 + 4 = 14

5	10
+ 5	+
+ 4	4
14	

2. 11 – 4 + 4 = __11__
3. 10 – 8 + 7 = __9__
4. 5 + 5 + 5 = __15__
5. 4 + 8 – 2 = __10__
6. 16 – 0 – 8 = __8__

7	8	9	10	11
4	8	5	7	6
5	2	5	3	5
+ 9	+ 7	+ 5	+ 8	+ 8
18	17	15	18	19

12	13	14	15	16
6	9	4	3	2
3	0	5	3	7
+ 9	+ 5	+ 6	+ 3	+ 4
18	14	15	9	13

NOTE TO HOME
Students add and subtract three numbers.

CULTURAL DIVERSITY Review with students for whom English is a second language the different words that can be used for addition and subtraction, such as *take away, plus,* and *minus.* Also, invite them to teach the class how to count to ten in their first language.

Literature Connection You might want to read aloud "How Does Gus Count People on the Bus?" in *Look Both Ways: City Math* by Time-Life, Inc. to reinforce lesson concepts.

RETEACHING p. 8

LESSON 32 RETEACHING Name ______________________

When adding more than two numbers, it is helpful to work the problem in parts.

Example 1:
5 + 3 + 7 = ?

First add 5 + 3. Then add 7 to that answer.

8
+ 7
15

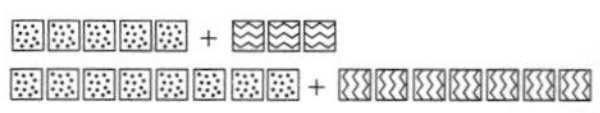

Example 2:
10 – 5 + 9 = ?

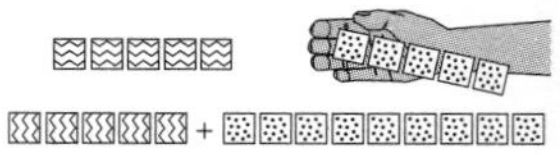

First subtract 10 – 5. Then add 9 to that answer.

5
+ 9
14

Add.

1. 6 + 2 + 4 = __12__
   6 + 2 = __8__
   + 4
   __12__
2. 8 + 5 + 1 = __14__
   8 + 5 = __13__
   + 1
   __14__
3. 12 – 4 + 7 = __15__
   12 – 4 = __8__
   + 7
   __15__
4. 16 + 4 – 9 = __11__
   16 + 4 = __20__
   – 9
   __11__

*available separately

◆ LESSON 32 Adding and Subtracting Three Numbers

Solve these problems.

17. How much money for three crayons? 9 ¢

18. for two checkers and one crayon? 19 ¢

19. for four marbles? 16 ¢

20. for two crayons and one marble? 10 ¢

21. for one crayon, one checker, and one marble? 15 ¢

22. Jason has 15¢. Can he buy two crayons and two marbles? yes

GAME Play the "Roll a Number Sentence" game.

NOTE TO HOME
Students solve word problems.

solve the problem. Demonstrate that order does make a difference in subtraction. To get the correct answer, the problem must be solved from left to right: 14 − 8 = 6, then 6 + 2 = 8. Finally, show students how to add a column of three one-digit numbers.

Using the Student Pages Have students complete pages 67–68 independently.

SPECIAL NEEDS

Meeting Individual Needs

Students having trouble solving the problems on page 67 might find it helpful to write subtotals. For example: 5 + 5 = 10 + 4 = 14

GAME **Introducing the "Roll a Number Sentence" Game** Demonstrate and play the "Roll a Number Sentence" game to provide practice in chain calculations for addition and subtraction. Players will need two 0–5 Number Cubes. Players take turns rolling both cubes and making a number sentence in one of three ways: add the two numbers rolled plus the lesser number again; add the two numbers rolled plus the greater number again; double the greater number and subtract the lesser number. The player with the greatest answer wins the round.

3 Wrap-Up 5 MINUTES

In Closing Have students solve this problem, going from right to left: 7 + 13 + 4 − 7 = (23). Then have them do it correctly, from left to right (17). Have them explain the difference.

ALTERNATIVE ASSESSMENT

Informal Assessment Observe which students have difficulty solving the problems on pages 67–68. Note which kinds of problems give them the most trouble.

Assessment Criteria

Did the student . . .

✓ solve the addition and subtraction facts?

✓ understand the different strategies for solving addition and subtraction chain calculations?

✓ solve word problems correctly?

✓ understand column addition of one-digit numbers?

PRACTICE p. 32

LESSON 32 PRACTICE Name ______

Solve. Watch the signs.

1. 5 + 3 − 4 = 4	2. 2 + 5 + 7 = 14
3. 7 + 2 + 2 = 11	4. 16 − 2 − 4 = 10
5. 10 − 4 + 6 = 12	6. 13 + 5 − 2 = 16
7. 18 − 9 + 9 = 18	8. 11 − 2 + 7 = 16
9. 10 + 10 − 5 = 15	10. 4 − 3 + 7 = 8
11. 11 + 2 − 3 = 10	12. 1 + 7 − 8 = 0
13. 19 − 10 + 1 = 10	14. 3 + 8 − 6 = 5
15. 12 − 6 + 0 = 6	16. 8 − 3 + 10 = 15
17. 15 − 5 + 10 = 20	18. 10 − 5 − 5 = 0

32 • *Math Explorations and Applications* Level 2

ENRICHMENT p. 32

LESSON 32 ENRICHMENT Name ______

The chart below lists some presidents, their political parties, and how many years they served. Use the information to answer the questions.

President	Years in Office	Party
Franklin Roosevelt	12	Democratic
Harry Truman	8	Democratic
Dwight Eisenhower	8	Republican
John Kennedy	3	Democratic
Lyndon Johnson	5	Democratic
Richard Nixon	5	Republican
Gerald Ford	3	Republican
Jimmy Carter	4	Democratic
Ronald Reagan	8	Republican
George Bush	4	Republican

1. How many years did Roosevelt and Truman hold office all together? 20
2. George Bush served as Ronald Reagan's vice-president before he was elected president in 1988. How many years was Bush vice-president and president all together? 12
3. How many years was a Democrat president? 32
4. How many years was a Republican president? 28

32 • *Math Explorations and Applications* Level 2

LESSON 33

Student Edition pages 69–70

Pictographs

LESSON PLANNER

Objectives

- to demonstrate how to read a pictograph
- to demonstrate how to draw a map based on conclusions drawn from a pictograph

Context of the Lesson This is the first of three lessons on graphing.

Materials	**Program Resources**
none	Practice Master 33
	Enrichment Master 33
	For extra practice: CD-ROM* Lesson 33

1 Warm-Up

5 MINUTES

Problem of the Day Present the following problem to the class orally: Del has 12 model cars. His sister, Maria, has nine. Del gives Maria four of his cars. How many more cars does Maria now have than Del? (5 more)

MENTAL MATH Write the following missing-operations problems on the chalkboard and have students tell which operation sign belongs in each blank.

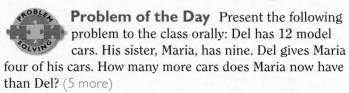

a. 4 _____ 8 = 12 (+) **b.** 9 _____ 4 = 13 (+)

c. 8 _____ 2 = 6 (−) **d.** 14 _____ 8 = 6 (−)

e. 8 _____ 4 = 12 (+) **f.** 12 _____ 0 = 12 (− or +)

LESSON 33

Name ______________________

Pictographs

Each figure stands for ten children.

Ms. Allen's class

Ms. Beck's class

Mr. Carl's class

Answer these questions.

1. How many children are in Ms. Allen's class? 40
2. How many children are in Ms. Beck's class? 30
3. How many children are in Mr. Carl's class? 50
4. How many more children are in Mr. Carl's class than in Ms. Beck's class? 20
5. How many children are in Ms. Allen's class and Ms. Beck's class all together? 70
6. Mr. Dixon's class has 20 children. Draw a pictograph to show that.

NOTE TO HOME
Students read pictographs.

RETEACHING

Work with the class to make a pictograph showing students' favorite colors. Agree on a symbol to stand for each vote. Ask a volunteer to count the votes and fill in the correct number of symbols for each color listed.

Science Connection Have students keep track of rainy days for four weeks. At the end of the fourth week, work together with the class to share and compute results. Display the results on a table. Then have students work in groups to convert the data from the table into pictographs.

*available separately

◆ **LESSON 33** Pictographs

Use the Mixed Practice on page 371 after this lesson.

Each (barrel) stands for ten gallons of gas used on a trip between two towns.

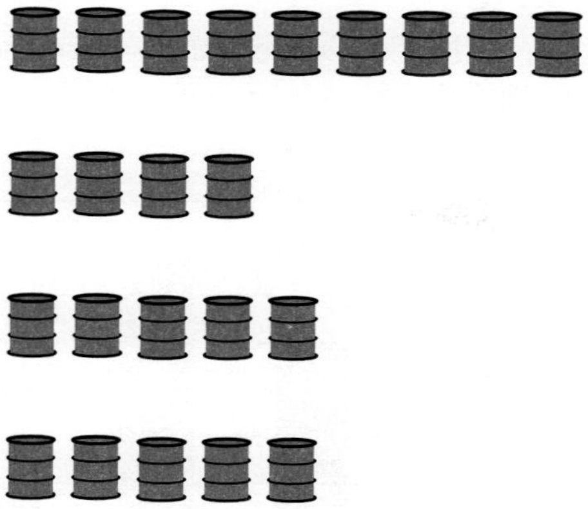

7. How many gallons are used on a trip from Albright to Trent? **90**
8. How many gallons are used on a trip from Albright to Wayne? **40**
9. How many gallons are used on a trip from Trent to Newtown? **50**
10. How many gallons are used on a trip from Newtown to Wayne? **50**

SOCIAL STUDIES CONNECTION

11. On a sheet of paper, draw a map that shows where Albright, Trent, Wayne, and Newtown might be. Compare your map with others.

NOTE TO HOME
Students read pictographs.

❷ Teach

Using the Student Pages Use the pictograph at the top of page 69 to discuss what a pictograph is and how to read it. Explain that each figure on this pictograph stands for ten children. Ask how many children are in Ms. Allen's class. Encourage students to explain how they arrived at their answer. Be sure students understand that because each figure stands for ten children they should count by tens for each figure. Repeat the discussion and explanation for the pictograph on page 70. Have students work in pairs to complete the pages. When correcting their answers, point out that the last question on page 70 can have many answers. Check that the distances on students' maps are proportionate to the number of gallons of gas used to travel between towns. Have pairs share and compare their maps when finished.

❸ Wrap-Up

5 MINUTES

In Closing Ask how students decided how far the towns should be from each other on their maps. Discuss whether the maps should all look alike and why.

ALTERNATIVE ASSESSMENT

Performance Assessment Have students make a pictograph showing how many boys and girls are in the class.

PRACTICE p. 33

LESSON 33 PRACTICE Name ______

Each (flower) stands for ten flower bulbs that were planted.

1. How many flower bulbs did Lidia plant? 80
2. How many flower bulbs did Courtney plant? 50
3. How many flower bulbs did Lucy plant? 70
4. How many flower bulbs did Tammy plant? 30
5. How many more flower bulbs did Lucy plant than Tammy? 40
6. How many flower bulbs did Courtney and Tammy plant all together? On a separate sheet of paper draw a pictograph to show this. 80 Check students' pictographs.

Rod, Stan, Mike, Dan and Jim play basketball for the Warriors. Each (ball) stands for ten points that each player scored.

7. Jim scored 20 points. On a separate sheet of paper draw a pictograph to show this. Check students' pictographs.
8. How many points did the Warriors score all together? 110

Math Explorations and Applications Level 2 • 33

ENRICHMENT p. 33

LESSON 33 ENRICHMENT Name ______

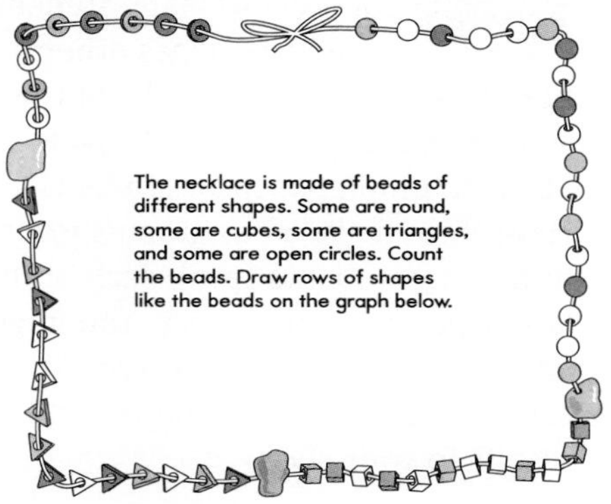

The necklace is made of beads of different shapes. Some are round, some are cubes, some are triangles, and some are open circles. Count the beads. Draw rows of shapes like the beads on the graph below.

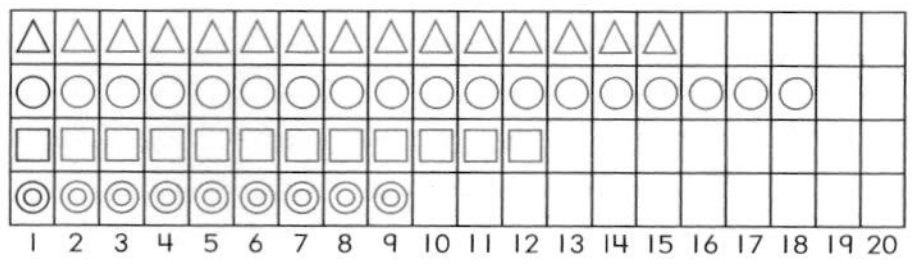

Math Explorations and Applications Level 2 • 33

Assessment Criteria

Did the student . . .

✓ correctly answer all of the questions on page 69?

✓ correctly answer all of the questions on page 70?

✓ draw accurate maps based on the pictograph on page 70?

LESSON 34

Student Edition pages 71–72

Vertical Bar Graphs

LESSON PLANNER

Objectives

- ▶ to explain to students how to read a bar graph
- ▶ to have students make bar graphs from given data

Context of the Lesson This is the second of three lessons on graphing.

Materials	**Program Resources**
1" graph paper (optional)	Practice Master 34 Enrichment Master 34 For extra practice: CD-ROM* Lesson 34

1 Warm-Up

5 MINUTES

Problem of the Day Write the following patterns on the chalkboard. Have students copy and complete them, and then discuss their answers.

a. 51, 50, 49, 41, 40, 39, 31, 30, 29, ____, ____, ____ (21, 20, 19)

b. 12, 13, 24, 25, 36, 37, ____, ____ (48, 49)

MENTAL MATH Write the following columns on the chalkboard. Have students explain whether each equation in Column A is less than, greater than, or equal to each corresponding number in Column B.

	Column A	Column B	
a.	12 – 8	4	(equal)
b.	13 – 7	5	(greater than)
c.	6 + 9	16	(less than)
d.	14 – 6	8	(equal)

LESSON 34

Name ____________________

Vertical Bar Graphs

Jenni, Ryan, Ladonna, Daniel, and Adam made a bar graph showing how many books they read.

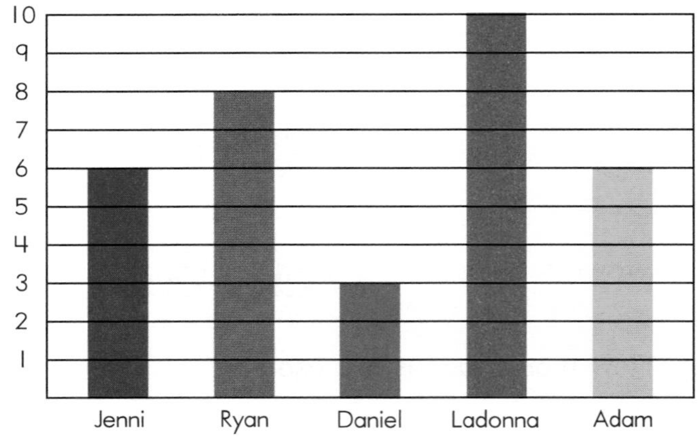

Find the answers.

1. Who has read the most books? Ladonna
   How many? 10
2. Who has read the fewest books? Daniel
   How many? 3
3. How many books has Jenni read? 6
4. How many books has Adam read? 6
5. How many books has Ryan read? 8

NOTE TO HOME
Students read vertical bar graphs.

CULTURAL DIVERSITY Work with the class to survey how many students speak languages other than English. List the results of the survey on the chalkboard. Provide one-inch graph paper for students. Have them make a bar graph showing how many students speak each of the languages from the survey. You might have groups of students survey other classes, make a graph, and report the results to your class.

RETEACHING

Display a vertical bar graph with numbers but without any labels. Discuss with the class what the labels could possibly be. For example, display the following:

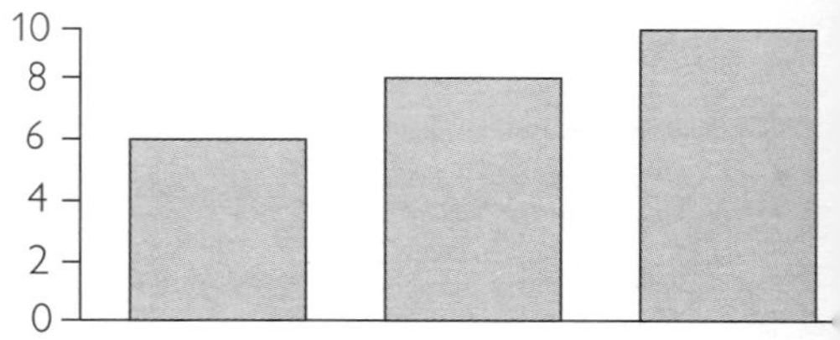

Ask: What could the numbers stand for? What could each bar stand for?

*available separately

◆ **LESSON 34** Vertical Bar Graphs

Nora read seven books. Jordan read nine books. Baxter has not read any books. Ian read five books and Teresa read ten books.

Complete the bar graph.

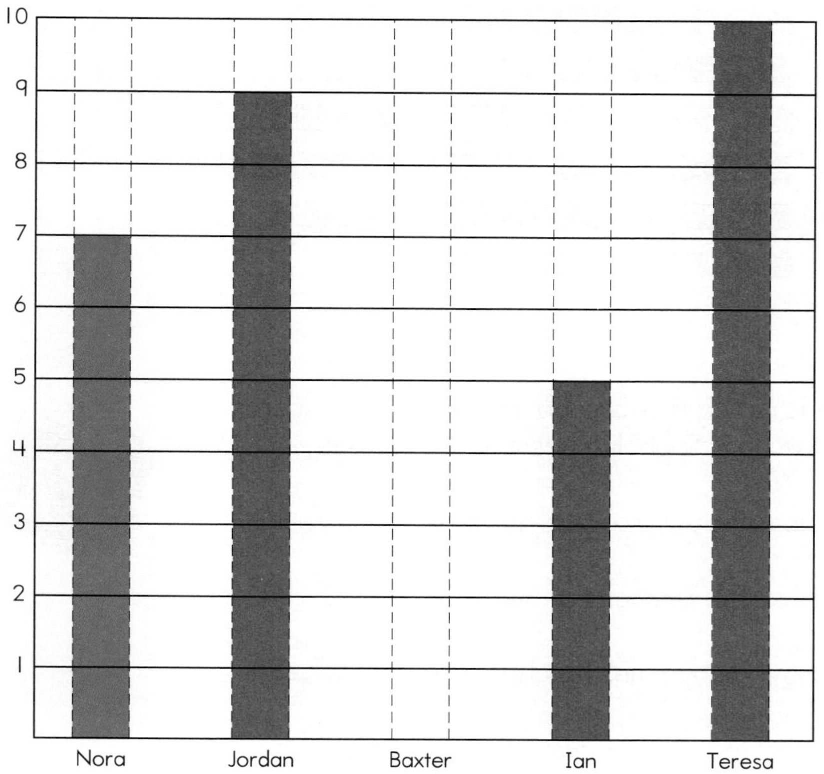

FANTASTIC FACT

"The Tale of Peter Rabbit" by Beatrix Potter is the best-selling children's book of all time.

NOTE TO HOME
Students read vertical bar graphs.

2 Teach

COOPERATIVE LEARNING **Using the Student Pages** Use the graph on the top of page 71 to discuss what a bar graph is and how to read it. Explain that the names of five people are listed along the bottom and that the "bars" above those names show how many books each person has read. Ask students what they think the numbers on the side of the graph mean. Ask students how many books Daniel has read and how many books Ladonna has read. (10, 3) Encourage them to explain how they arrived at their answers. Have students then work in small groups to complete pages 71–72. As they complete the graph on page 72, be sure members agree in advance how far each bar should be drawn.

3 Wrap-Up

5 MINUTES

In Closing Have groups share and compare their bar graphs on page 72. Encourage them to explain how they arrived at where each bar would stop.

ALTERNATIVE ASSESSMENT **Informal Assessment** Use students' answers and graphs from pages 71 and 72 to informally assess their understanding of bar graphs.

PRACTICE p. 34

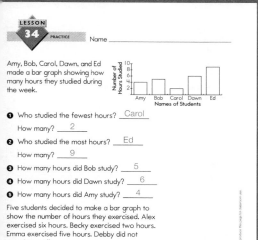

LESSON 34 PRACTICE Name ______

Amy, Bob, Carol, Dawn, and Ed made a bar graph showing how many hours they studied during the week.

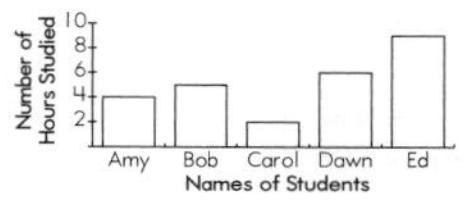

1. Who studied the fewest hours? Carol
   How many? 2
2. Who studied the most hours? Ed
   How many? 9
3. How many hours did Bob study? 5
4. How many hours did Dawn study? 6
5. How many hours did Amy study? 4

Five students decided to make a bar graph to show the number of hours they exercised. Alex exercised six hours. Becky exercised two hours. Emma exercised five hours. Debby did not exercise at all.

6. Complete the bar graph. Check students' bar graphs.

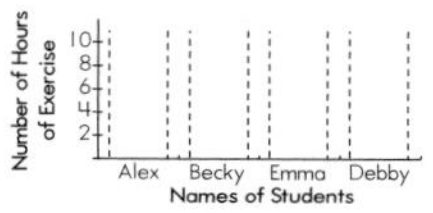

34 • Math Explorations and Applications Level 2

ENRICHMENT p. 34

LESSON 34 ENRICHMENT Name ______

Put a box of crayons (or jelly beans) into a dish. Then put the same colors together. Draw a bar graph to show how many of each color you have. Answers will vary.

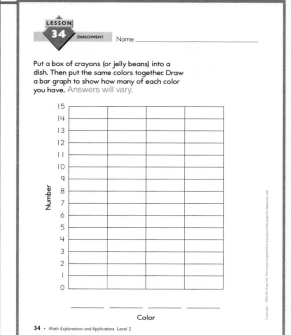

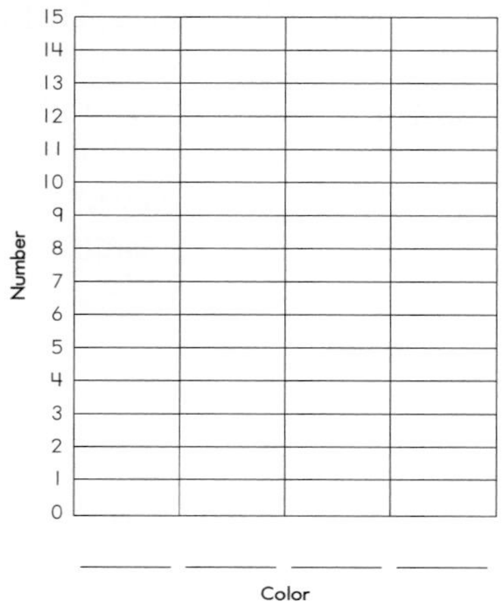

34 • Math Explorations and Applications Level 2

Assessment Criteria

Did the student . . .

✓ correctly answer all of the questions on page 71?

✓ correctly complete the bar graph on page 72?

LESSON 35

Student Edition pages 73–74

Horizontal Bar Graphs

LESSON PLANNER

Objectives

- to provide practice in reading horizontal bar graphs
- to demonstrate how to generate data and record the results on a horizontal bar graph

Context of the Lesson This is the third of three lessons on graphing.

Materials	Program Resources
none	Number Cubes
	Reteaching Master
	Practice Master 35
	Enrichment Master 35
	For extra practice: CD-ROM* Lesson 35

1 Warm-Up

5 MINUTES

Problem of the Day Present the following problem to the class: How many different ways could you make 50 cents by using five or fewer coins? What are the ways? (5 ways: 1 50-cent piece; 2 quarters; 1 quarter, 2 dimes, 1 nickel; 1 quarter, 1 dime, 3 nickels; 5 dimes)

MENTAL MATH Write the following columns on the chalkboard. Have students tell whether each equation in Column A is less than, greater than, or equal to each corresponding number in Column B.

	Column A	Column B
a.	16 − 9	6 (greater than)
b.	7 + 8	15 (equal)
c.	6 + 5	12 (less than)
d.	13 − 7	8 (less than)

LESSON 35

Name ____________

Horizontal Bar Graphs

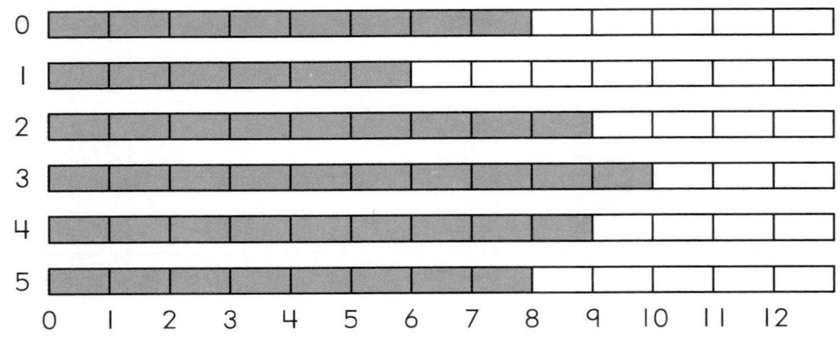

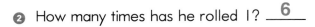

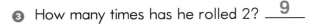

Ben is rolling a 0–5 cube. He is keeping records on the bar graph. He has rolled 50 times.

1. How many times has he rolled 0? 8
2. How many times has he rolled 1? 6
3. How many times has he rolled 2? 9
4. How many times has he rolled 3? 10
5. How many times has he rolled 4? 9
6. How many times has he rolled 5? 8

NOTE TO HOME
Students read horizontal bar graphs.

Literature Connection Work with students to take a survey of their favorite stories or books. Display the results on a chart on the chalkboard. Have students make a horizontal bar graph showing the results. Some students might enjoy surveying other classes and showing the results on graphs.

RETEACHING p. 9

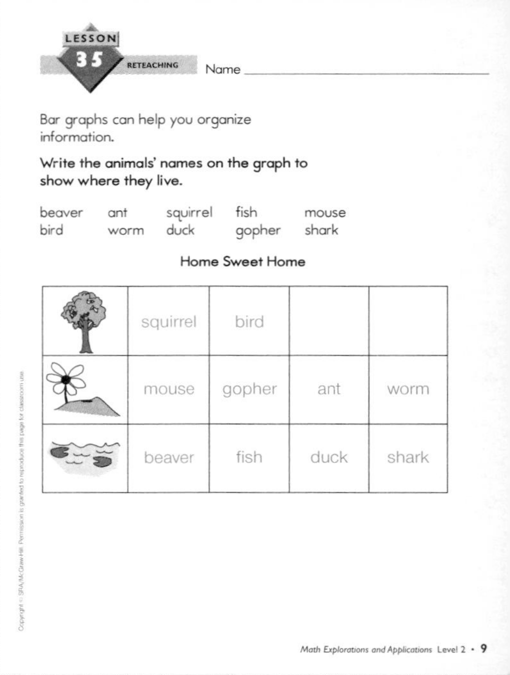

LESSON 35 RETEACHING Name ____________

Bar graphs can help you organize information.

Write the animals' names on the graph to show where they live.

beaver bird ant worm squirrel duck fish gopher mouse shark

Home Sweet Home

(tree)	squirrel	bird		
(ground)	mouse	gopher	ant	worm
(water)	beaver	fish	duck	shark

Math Explorations and Applications Level 2 • 9

*available separately

◆ LESSON 35 Horizontal Bar Graphs

COOPERATIVE LEARNING

Work with another student.

Roll the 0–5 cube. Keep records on the bar graph. Stop when one number has been rolled ten times.

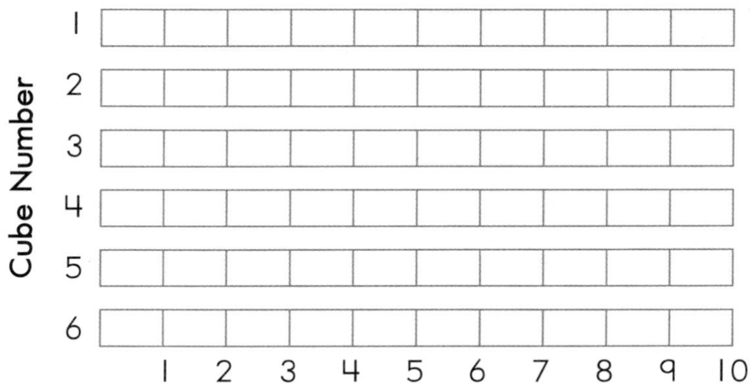

Roll a 5–10 cube. Keep records. Stop when a number has been rolled ten times.

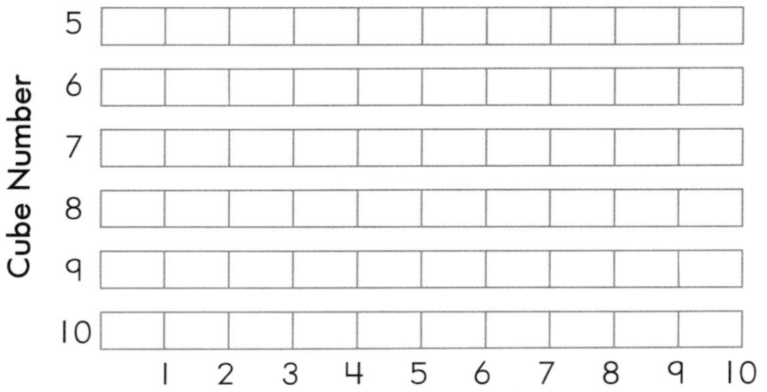

NOTE TO HOME
Students record data on a horizontal bar graph.

PRACTICE p. 35

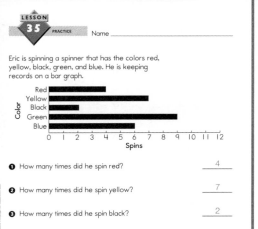

LESSON 35 PRACTICE Name ______

Eric is spinning a spinner that has the colors red, yellow, black, green, and blue. He is keeping records on a bar graph.

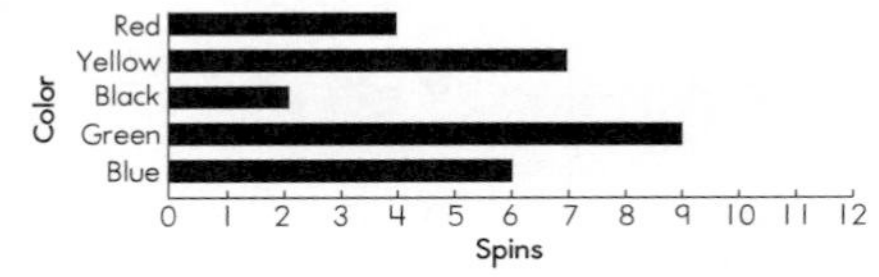

1. How many times did he spin red? 4
2. How many times did he spin yellow? 7
3. How many times did he spin black? 2
4. How many times did he spin green? 9
5. How many times did he spin blue? 6
6. How many times did he spin the spinner all together? 28

Math Explorations and Applications Level 2 • 35

ENRICHMENT p. 35

LESSON 35 ENRICHMENT Name ______

Choose 20 people you know. Ask them for their birth months. Make a graph that shows how many people were born in each month. Starting from the left, fill in a box for each person born in each month. Answers will vary.

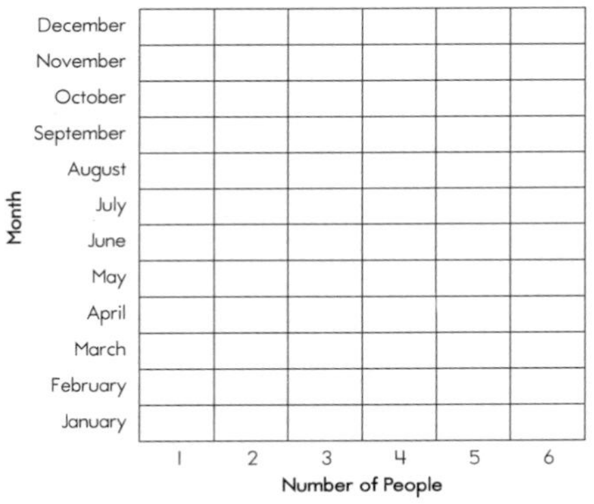

Math Explorations and Applications Level 2 • 35

2 Teach

Using the Student Pages Use the bar graph on page 73 to begin a discussion about what horizontal bar graphs are and how to read them. Ask how this graph differs from the others students have worked on so far. (Possible answer: This time the number of times something has happened is written along the top and bottom, and the label telling what is happening is shown on the bottom.) Discuss how to read the graph to find out how many times Ben has rolled a 0. Be sure students understand that they must first find the 0 on the left side of the graph, and then see how many numbers to the right the bar ends on. Have students complete page 73 independently and then work in pairs to complete page 74. When finished, have pairs share and compare their graphs.

3 Wrap-Up

5 MINUTES

In Closing Discuss whether all students got the same results on their bar graphs that they made on page 74. Ask: If we did this experiment again, would you expect to draw the same bar graph? Why or why not?

ALTERNATIVE ASSESSMENT

Informal Assessment Use students' answers for pages 73 and 74 to informally assess their understanding of horizontal bar graphs.

Assessment Criteria

Did the student . . .

✓ correctly answer all of the questions on page 73?

✓ correctly roll the cube and record the data on a horizontal bar graph on page 74?

LESSON 36

Student Edition pages 75–76

Place Value—Base Ten

LESSON PLANNER

Objectives

- ▶ to review counting the tens and ones in numbers less than 100
- ▶ to review counting money ($1, $5, $10 bills and pennies, nickels, and dimes)
- ✓ to assess student mastery of word problems

Context of the Lesson This is the first of three lessons that review base-10 numeration. It also contains Mastery Checkpoint 5 for assessing mastery of word problems.

Materials

craft sticks (loose and in bundles of ten) or other base-10 materials

play money

Program Resources

Thinking Story Book, pages 30–33
Practice Master 36
Enrichment Master 36
Assessment Master
For extra practice:
CD-ROM* Lesson 36

1 Warm-Up

5 MINUTES

Problem of the Day Write the following problem on the chalkboard: Keith has two quarters and two nickels. Kendra has one quarter and five nickels. Who has more money? How can you tell? (Keith, because he has 60 cents. Kendra only has 50 cents.)

MENTAL MATH Have students tell which problem in each pair yields the greater number:

a. 18 − 9 or 9 + 1 (9 + 1)
b. 4 + 7 or 2 + 8 (4 + 7)
c. 12 − 4 or 2 + 5 (12 − 4)
d. 7 + 8 or 4 + 9 (7 + 8)
e. 11 − 9 or 8 − 2 (8 − 2)
f. 6 + 6 or 15 − 7 (6 + 6)

2 Teach

MENTAL MATH **Demonstrate** Show ten craft sticks bound with a rubber band. Ask: "How many sticks do you think there are?" Count and confirm answers. Hold up four bundles of ten sticks in one hand and three single sticks in the other. Ask: "How many sticks all together?" (43) Ask students how they arrived at their answer. Repeat for several other numbers less than 100. Then ask: "How

LESSON 36

Name ______________________

Place Value—Base Ten

How many sticks? Write your answers.

1. 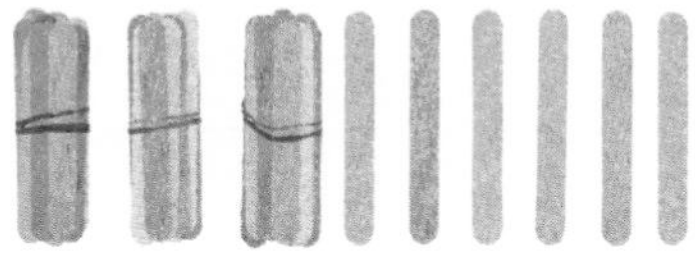 36
2. 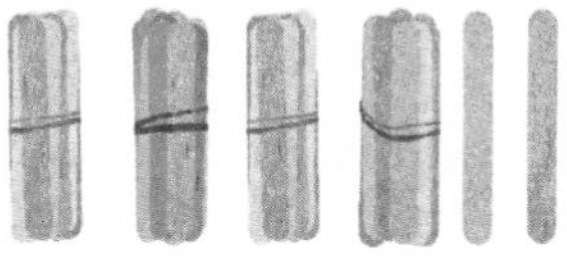 42
3. 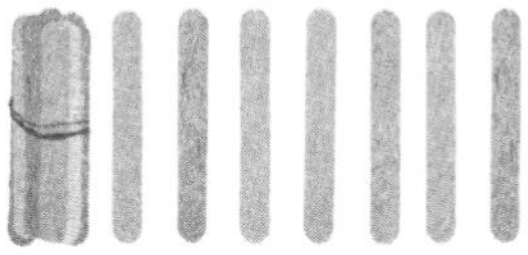 17
4. 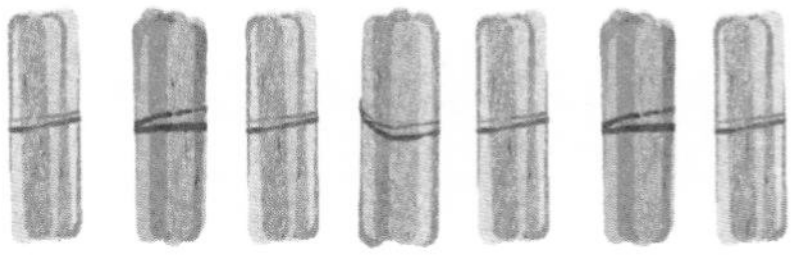 70
5. 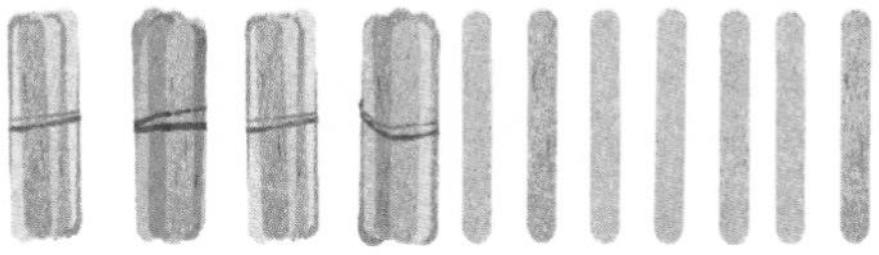 47
6. 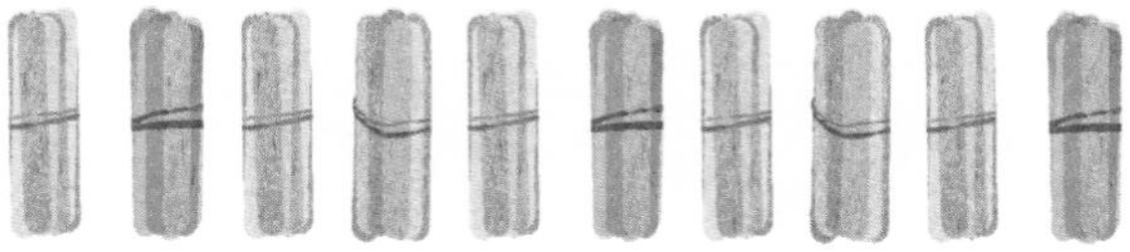 100

NOTE TO HOME
Students count tens and ones.

RETEACHING

MENTAL MATH Use base-10 rods and units to make models that show place value in numbers less than 100. Have students tell how many each model stands for.

PRACTICE p. 36

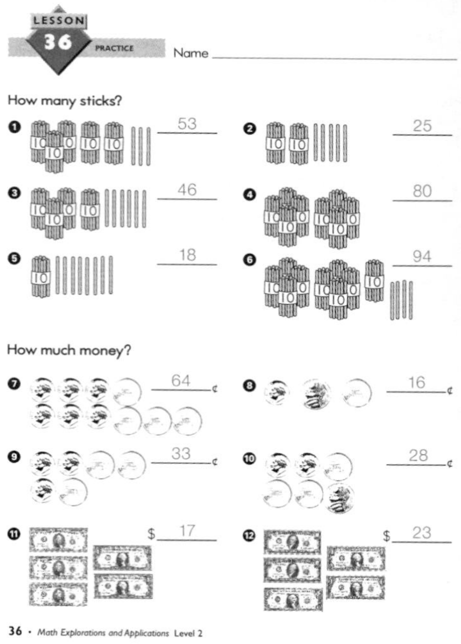
LESSON 36 PRACTICE Name ______

How many sticks?

1. 53
2. 25
3. 46
4. 80
5. 18
6. 94

How much money?

7. 64¢
8. 16¢
9. 33¢
10. 28¢
11. $ 17
12. $ 23

36 • Math Explorations and Applications Level 2

*available separately

◆ LESSON 36 Place Value—Base Ten

How much money? Write your answers.

7

32¢

8

55¢

9

18¢

10

52¢

11

$34

THINKING STORY Talk about the Thinking Story "Portia's Rules."

GAME Play the "Get to 100 by Tens or Ones" game.

NOTE TO HOME
Students review counting money.

many bundles of ten sticks and how many single sticks do I need to show 57 sticks?" Help students to understand the tens and ones place in each number.

Using the Student Pages Work the first problem on page 75 with students, explaining how you arrive at the answer. Then have students complete the remaining problems on these pages independently.

Introducing the "Get to 100 by Tens or Ones" Game Demonstrate and play this game to provide practice in mentally adding sets of numbers through 100. Students will need 20 play $10 bills, 20 play $1 bills, and paper and pencils. Players take turns placing one bill in the playing area. Each player keeps a running total of the amount. The first player to reach $100 or more is the winner of the round.

Using the Thinking Story Read aloud "Portia's Rules" on pages 30–33 of the Thinking Story Book. Stop and discuss the questions asked throughout the story. Remind students that Portia is baking without adult supervision because this is a story, and that in real life, baking requires adult assistance.

Mastery Checkpoint 5

At this time most students will be able to work word problems. You may use Assessment Master 15 to assess students' mastery of word problems. You may want to record the results on the Mastery Checkpoint Chart.

ENRICHMENT p. 36

LESSON 36 ENRICHMENT Name ____________

A full box has eight glasses in it. Write how many glasses are on each table. Show your work.

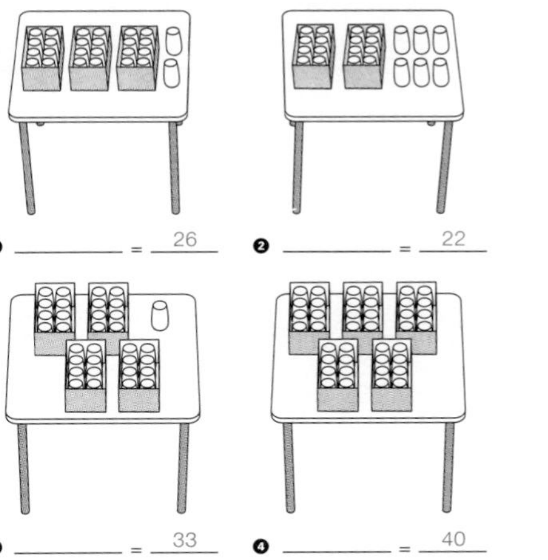

1 ______ = 26
2 ______ = 22
3 ______ = 33
4 ______ = 40

Copyright © SRA/McGraw-Hill. Permission is granted to reproduce this page for classroom use.

36 • Math Explorations and Applications Level 2

ASSESSMENT p. 11

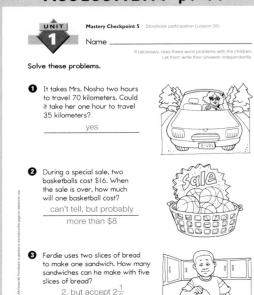

UNIT 1 Mastery Checkpoint 5 Storybook participation (Lesson 36)

Name ____________

If necessary, read these word problems with the children. Let them write their answers independently.

Solve these problems.

1 It takes Mrs. Nosho two hours to travel 70 kilometers. Could it take her one hour to travel 35 kilometers?
yes

2 During a special sale, two basketballs cost $16. When the sale is over, how much will one basketball cost?
can't tell, but probably more than $8

3 Ferdie uses two slices of bread to make one sandwich. How many sandwiches can he make with five slices of bread?
2, but accept $2\frac{1}{2}$

Copyright © SRA/McGraw-Hill. Permission is granted to reproduce this page for classroom use.

Math Explorations and Applications Level 2 • 11

3 Wrap-Up

5 MINUTES

In Closing Have students write numbers for the following: 6 tens and 4 ones (64); 8 ones (8); 4 tens (40); 10 tens (100).

SELF ASSESSMENT Have students circle and correct any incorrect answers on pages 75–76.

Assessment Criteria

Did the student . . .

✓ correctly count tens and ones?

✓ understand the relationship between tens and ones?

✓ correctly count money?

STORY 5

THINKING STORY

Portia's Rules

Portia likes to use rules, just like her brother, Ferdie. But Portia knows that when you think of a rule you should test it to make sure it works.

One day Portia noticed that her coat was size 7. "That's interesting," she thought. "I'm seven years old and my coat is size 7. Maybe that's a rule."

What rule might Portia be thinking of? that a person's coat size is the same as the person's age

Is that a good rule? no

Why not? Ask students to think of situations where Portia's rule does not hold.

But Portia knew that she would have to test her rule to make sure it was a good one.

How could Portia test her rule? Encourage students to identify methods Portia could use to test her rule.

First she asked her friend Wendy about her age and her coat size. Wendy was five years old and she wore a size five coat.

Has Portia done enough to prove her rule? no

What else could she do? Encourage students to think of other things Portia should do in order to prove her rule.

"Maybe my rule only works for children," thought Portia. The first grown-up she met was Mr. Mudancia. "Do you mind telling me how old you are, Mr. Mudancia?" she asked.

"I'm 40 years old," he answered.

"Do you wear a size 40 coat?"

"Why, yes, I do," he answered. "That's odd, isn't it?"

"Not at all," answered Portia. "It's a good rule."

Is it a good rule? Why does Mr. Mudancia think that it's odd? Mr. Mudancia thought it odd that his size and age matched. This is a sign of an unusual situation, rather than a universal one.

Just then, Fred Flurry walked up to them. "How old are you?" asked Portia.

"I'm 25," answered Fred. Portia was puzzled. Fred seemed to be the same size as Mr. Mudancia. But she decided to stick with her rule.

"You wear a size 25 coat, don't you?"

Does Portia's rule work? no

Why not? Fred's age and size do not match.

◆ STORY 5 Portia's Rules

"No, I don't," answered Fred. "I wear a size 40–about the same size as Mr. Mudancia."

Portia was disappointed. "Thanks," she said. "I guess I'll have to find a new rule."

As Portia passed the bakery, she noticed cookies were on sale, 12 for 50¢. "I only have 25¢," she told the baker. "How many cookies can I buy?"

"It takes half as much money to get half as many cookies," answered the baker. "That's an easy rule to remember."

How many cookies could Portia buy? six

"That means I can buy six cookies," said Portia. "And you've given me a new rule. It takes half as much to get half as many."

Is that exactly what the baker said? no

What did Portia leave out? It takes half as much money to get half as many cookies.

"Maybe that rule works best with cookies," thought Portia, as she hurried home. "I think I'll bake some of my own."

Portia found a recipe for 24 cookies. "I only want 12 cookies. That's half as many, so I'll use just half as much of everything."

She used only half as much flour as the recipe said, half as much butter, and half as much sugar.

Is Portia doing the right thing so far to make half as much? yes

Portia mixed in half as much of everything as the recipe said, and she ended up with some nice-looking cookie dough. She used the dough to form 12 cookies. Then it was time to bake them. The recipe said to bake them for ten minutes at 400 degrees Fahrenheit. "I guess I'd better stick to the rule," Portia said. "It's worked fine so far."

What do you think Portia will do? Use half as much time and temperature.

She set the oven at half the temperature.

How many degrees is that? 200° F

She baked them for only half as long as the recipe said.

How many minutes did she leave them in the oven? five

What do you think she found when she took them out? The cookies were not done.

What could she do to make them better? Raise the oven temperature and bake the cookies longer.

"I think we can still save them," her mother said. "We'll just have to bake them longer in a hotter oven. Whatever made you put them in an oven at only 200 degrees? Didn't you have a recipe?"

"Yes," said Portia, "but I only wanted half as many cookies, so I used only half as much of everything–half as much flour, half as much butter, half as much temperature, half as much time."

"It's a good rule, Portia, but it doesn't work for everything," her mother said. "It takes just as long to bake 12 cookies as it does 24."

"How can you ever tell when the rule fits and when it doesn't?" Portia asked.

"You just have to think and learn," her mother said. "After your cookies are baked, I think we'll have time to run down to the store and buy a watermelon to have with dinner. On second thought, let's just get half a watermelon. That should take us only half as long, right?"

"I see what you mean," said Portia.

Do you think her mother was joking? Why? Portia's mom was probably joking in order to point out Portia's earlier thinking error.

. . . the end

LESSON 37

Student Edition pages 77–78

Place Value—Using Money

LESSON PLANNER

Objectives

- to review counting the tens and ones in numbers less than 100 (base-10 numeration)
- to review using tally marks to record data
- to review using coins to make given amounts of money

Context of the Lesson This is the second of three lessons that review base-10 numeration.

Materials	Program Resources
none	Number Cubes
	Thinking Story Book, pages 34–35
	Practice Master 37
	Enrichment Master 37
	For extra practice: CD-ROM* Lesson 37

1 Warm-Up

5 MINUTES

Problem of the Day Write the following problem on the chalkboard: How many ways can you make $20 with a combination of $10 and $5 bills? Describe each way. (two ways: two $10 bills; one $10 bill and two $5 bills)

MENTAL MATH Have students tell which amount in each pair is greater:

a. 47¢ or 39¢ (47¢)

b. 97¢ or $1 ($1)

c. 55¢ or 49¢ (55¢)

d. two dimes or three nickels (two dimes)

e. seven $1 bills or one $10 bill (one $10 bill)

f. nine pennies or two nickels (two nickels)

PRACTICE

LESSON 37

Name ______________________

Place Value—Using Money

Show each amount with coins. Draw as few coins as you can.

1. 37¢ — 25, 10, 1, 1
2. 65¢ — 50, 10, 5
3. 82¢ — 50, 25, 5, 1, 1
4. 17¢ — 10, 5, 1, 1
5. 34¢ — 25, 5, 1, 1, 1, 1

NOTE TO HOME
Students show which coins make given amounts of money.

Art Connection Divide students into four groups. Assign a coin value to each group: 25 cents, 10 cents, 5 cents, or 1 cent. Have each group design a coin for its value that shows the amount on the front. Have them make and cut out several copies of the coin. Then have each group combine with another group to create an addition or subtraction problem using their coins.

Literature Connection You might want to read aloud *What comes in 2's, 3's, and 4's?* by Suzanne Akern to reinforce lesson concepts.

RETEACHING

COOPERATIVE LEARNING Have students work in groups. Have them lay out coins for specific amounts of money. For example, 37 cents can be shown with three dimes, one nickel, and two pennies. Have them check their coins as you explain and show how each amount can be made.

*available separately

◆ **LESSON 37** Place Value—Using Money

Use the Mixed Practice on page 372 after this lesson.

Draw coins to make 30¢. Try to do it with

6. 2 coins — 25, 5
7. 3 coins — 10, 10, 10
8. 4 coins — 10, 10, 5, 5
9. 5 coins — 10, 5, 5, 5, 5
10. 6 coins — 5, 5, 5, 5, 5, 5
11. Can you do it with 7 coins? no

NOTE TO HOME
Students show the same money amount in different ways.

PRACTICE p. 37

LESSON 37 PRACTICE Name ____________

Show each amount with as few coins as you can.

1. 26¢ — 25¢, 1¢
2. 18¢ — 10¢, 5¢, 1¢, 1¢, 1¢
3. 35¢ — 25¢, 10¢
4. 11¢ — 10¢, 1¢
5. 46¢ — 25¢, 10¢, 10¢, 1¢
6. 52¢ — 25¢, 25¢, 1¢, 1¢

ENRICHMENT p. 37

LESSON 37 ENRICHMENT Name ____________

Think of a question about the months of the year.

Write your question here. ____________

Ask about 50 people.

Month	Tally	Total
January		
February		
March		
April		
May		
June		
July		
August		
September		
October		
November		
December		

Which month had the most responses? If you asked 50 more people, would you expect about the same results? Answers will vary.

2 Teach

Demonstrate Review the use of tally marks. Explain that tally marks can help us keep track of the number of times something happens or the number of items we have. Draw tally marks in groups of five with the fifth one crossing the other four. Ask students how many tally marks you have drawn on the board.

COOPERATIVE LEARNING **Using the Student Pages** Provide play coins for students to use. Demonstrate and discuss how to solve the first problem on page 77. Students may work in pairs and experiment with coin combinations to complete pages 77–78.

Using the Thinking Story Present two or three problems from those following "Portia's Rules" on pages 34–35 of the Thinking Story Book.

GAME **Introducing the "Pennies, Nickels, and Dimes" Game** Demonstrate and play the game to provide practice making change. You need about 25 play pennies, 25 nickels, 15 dimes, and a 0–5 Number Cube. Place coins in a central pile. Each player in turn rolls a cube and takes that many pennies from the bank. Players trade pennies for nickels and dimes. The first player to have five nickels and five dimes is the winner.

3 Wrap-Up

5 MINUTES

In Closing Have students write the name of each coin and its value. Then have them create problems involving money like those in the Mental Math exercise.

ALTERNATIVE ASSESSMENT **Performance Assessment** Ask each student to show you a given amount of play money. Note any students who have difficulty with the task.

Assessment Criteria

Did the student . . .

✓ draw the correct coins and amounts on pages 77 and 78?

✓ correctly compute tally marks?

LESSON 38

Student Edition pages 79–80

Counting by Tens

LESSON PLANNER

Objectives

- ▶ to provide review and extend students' knowledge of base-10 numeration
- ▶ to demonstrate how to use patterns to add and subtract multiples of ten

Context of the Lesson This is the third of three lessons that review base-10 numeration.

Materials	Program Resources
index cards (optional)	Number Cubes
play money (optional)	Thinking Story Book, pages 34–35
	Reteaching Master
	Practice Master 38
	Enrichment Master 38
	For extra practice: CD-ROM* Lesson 38

1 Warm-Up

5 MINUTES

PROBLEM SOLVING **Problem of the Day** Present the following problem to the class orally: There are 20 red and 40 blue crayons in box one. There are 50 blue crayons in box two. Which box has more crayons? How many more? (box 1; 10 more)

MENTAL MATH Present the following problems and have students use mental math to solve them.

- **a.** 30 + 50 = (80)
- **b.** 90 – 40 = (50)
- **c.** 70 – 10 = (60)
- **d.** 80 + 70 = (150)
- **e.** 140 – 70 = (70)
- **f.** 70 + 50 = (120)
- **g.** 10 + 70 = (80)
- **h.** 150 – 70 = (80)

2 Teach

Demonstrate Have students count from 1–20 as you list the numbers in one column on the chalkboard. Have them count by tens as you write the numbers from 10–200 beside their corresponding unit numbers. Next, ask how much 2 + 3 is. (5) Then ask what 2 tens + 3 tens are. (5 tens) Ask what 20 + 30 equals. (50)

LESSON 38

Name ______________________

Counting by Tens

Solve using mental math.

1. 10 + 0 = 10
2. 10 + 10 = 20
3. 10 + 10 + 10 = 30
4. 20 + 10 = 30
5. 10 + 10 + 10 + 10 = 40
6. 30 + 10 = 40
7. 10 + 10 + 10 + 10 + 10 = 50
8. 40 + 10 = 50
9. 10 + 10 + 10 + 10 + 10 + 10 = 60
10. 50 + 10 = 60
11. 10 + 10 + 10 + 10 + 10 + 10 + 10 = 70
12. 60 + 10 = 70

NOTE TO HOME
Students add tens.

Literature Connection Invite students to read *Count* by Denise Fleming to reinforce lesson concepts.

RETEACHING p. 10

LESSON 38 RETEACHING Name ______________

Fill in the missing numbers on the number lines.

1. 0, 1, 2, 3, 4, 5, 6, 7, 8
2. 0, 10, 20, 30, 40, 50, 60, 70, 80

Write the numbers.

3. 4 tens = 40
4. 7 tens = 70
5. 5 tens = 50
6. 9 tens = 90

Solve these problems using your sticks.

7. 7 + 2 = 9
8. 70 + 20 = 90

Solve.

9. 5 + 4 = 9
10. 50 + 40 = 90
11. 3 + 7 = 10
12. 30 + 70 = 100

10 • Math Explorations and Applications Level 2

*available separately

◆ **LESSON 38 Counting by Tens**

Work these problems. Watch the signs.

⑬ 3 + 5 = 8 ⑭ 30 + 50 = 80

⑮ 5 + 2 = 7 ⑯ 50 + 20 = 70

⑰ 8 + 7 = 15 ⑱ 80 + 70 = 150

⑲ 9 − 3 = 6 ⑳ 90 − 30 = 60

㉑ 13 − 6 = 7 ㉒ 130 − 60 = 70

㉓ 8 + 4 = 12 ㉔ 80 + 40 = 120 ㉕ 7 − 3 = 4 ㉖ 70 − 30 = 40

GAME Play the "Roll a Number" game.

FANTASTIC FACT Try to write this number—one centillion. A centillion is 1 followed by 308 zeros.

NOTE TO HOME
Students add and subtract.

PRACTICE p. 38

LESSON 38 PRACTICE Name ____

Add.

1. 2 + 6 = 8
2. 20 + 60 = 80
3. 4 + 3 = 7
4. 40 + 30 = 70
5. 8 + 8 = 16
6. 80 + 80 = 160
7. 9 + 2 = 11
8. 90 + 20 = 110

Subtract.

9. 6 − 3 = 3
10. 60 − 30 = 30
11. 9 − 5 = 4
12. 90 − 50 = 40
13. 13 − 4 = 9
14. 130 − 40 = 90
15. 12 − 6 = 6
16. 120 − 60 = 60

38 • Math Explorations and Applications Level 2

ENRICHMENT p. 38

LESSON 38 ENRICHMENT Name ____

Kip made a number helper that looked like the ancient abacus used for adding and subtracting. He had two rows of nine rings each. The left row stood for tens. The right row stood for ones. He moved the rings to show numbers.

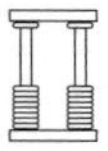

1 ten and 1 one = 11

Which number is shown in each picture?

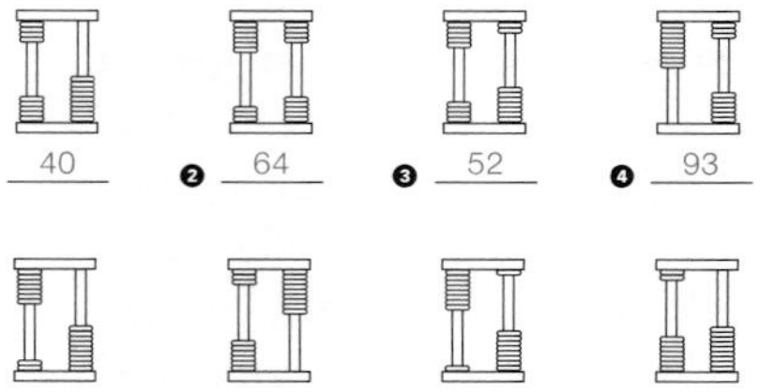

1. 40
2. 64
3. 52
4. 93
5. 70
6. 39
7. 81
8. 20

9. What is the largest number Kip can show with his abacus? 99

38 • Math Explorations and Applications Level 2

Repeat with several similar examples. Ask whether anyone sees a pattern. Students should notice that to write a number of tens in customary form, they write the number with a zero after it. This is also true for adding and subtracting tens: Add or subtract the two numbers to get the number of tens in the answer, and then write a zero after the number.

Using the Student Pages Have students complete pages 79 and 80 independently. Point out that the exercises on page 80 are presented in pairs: There is a tens problem with each units problem.

Introducing the "Roll a Number" Game Students can play the "Roll a Number" game in small groups, using paper, pencils, and a 0–5 Number Cube. Each player draws two blanks to represent a two-digit number: ____ ____. Player 1 rolls the cube twice, calling out each number, and other players write the digits on the lines. The players with the greatest two-digit number win. Players take turns rolling the cube for each round. Variation: students try to make the greatest three- or four-digit number.

Using the Thinking Story Present three problems from those following the story "Portia's Rules" on pages 34–35 of the Thinking Story Book.

3 Wrap-Up (5 MINUTES)

In Closing Ask students to explain how adding and subtracting units is related to adding and subtracting tens.

Performance Assessment See which students can count from 0 to 200 by tens either orally or in writing.

Assessment Criteria

Did the student . . .

✓ correctly count by tens?

✓ correctly solve 10 of 12 problems on page 79?

✓ correctly solve 11 of 14 problems on page 80?

LOOKING AHEAD You will need a centimeter ruler for each student in Lesson 39.

LESSON 39

Student Edition pages 81–82

Measuring Length—Centimeters

LESSON PLANNER

Objectives

- ▶ to review length measurement
- ▶ to introduce the centimeter as a standard metric unit of length

Context of the Lesson This is the first of five lessons on measurement.

Materials	Program Resources
centimeter ruler	Practice Master 39
	Enrichment Master 39
	For extra practice: CD-ROM* Lesson 39

1 Warm-Up 5 MINUTES

Problem of the Day Write the following problem on the chalkboard: Which is greater, 4 tens and 5 ones or 5 tens and 4 ones? How can you tell? (5 tens and 4 ones is greater, because there are more tens, or because 54 is greater than 45.)

MENTAL MATH Have students write each in standard form:

a. 6 tens + 5 ones = (65)
b. 10 tens = (100)
c. 3 tens + 9 ones = (39)
d. 5 tens + 4 tens = (90)
e. 6 tens + 2 tens = (80)
f. 9 ones = (9)
g. 9 tens = (90)
h. 12 ones + 5 ones = (17)

2 Teach

Demonstrate Explain that standard units of measurement are agreed to by most people and they do not vary. Distribute centimeter rulers as you explain that the centimeter is a standard unit of length in the metric system. Choose one or two objects, such as a chalkboard eraser or pencil, to measure. Show students how to place the ruler to measure each object. Have students choose and measure the length of several more objects on their own.

LESSON 39

Name ______________________

Measuring Length—Centimeters

The centimeter is a unit of length.

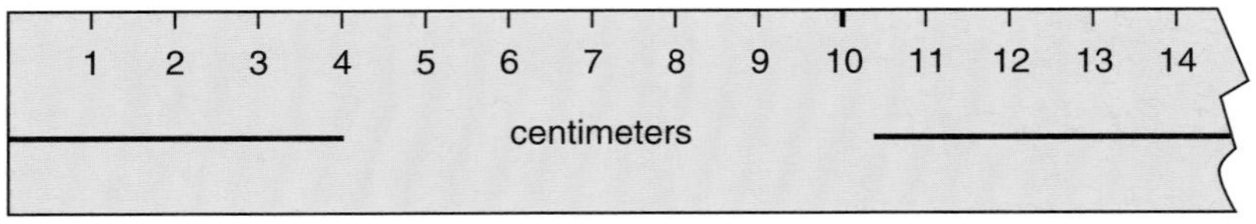

This pencil is 14 centimeters long.

This nail is 8 centimeters long.

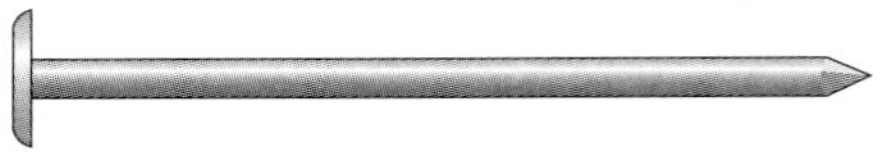

How long are these? Use your centimeter ruler. Write your answers.

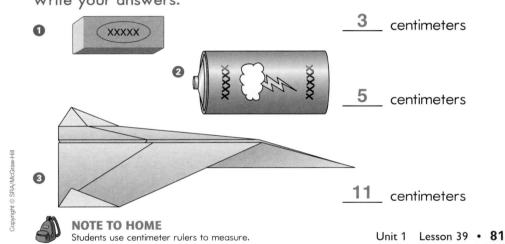

❶ 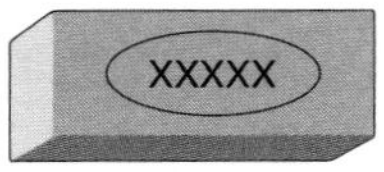

3 centimeters

❷ 

5 centimeters

❸ 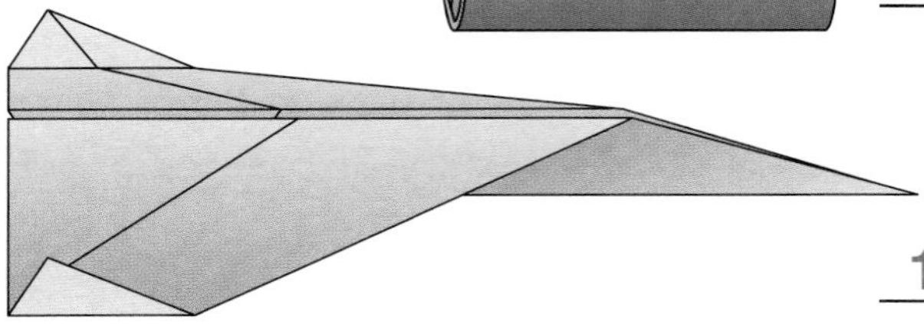

11 centimeters

NOTE TO HOME
Students use centimeter rulers to measure.

Why teach it this way?

Both the metric and customary systems of measure are introduced and used throughout this grade. Children are encouraged to think in both systems without being asked to convert from one system to the other.

Science Connection Divide students into groups. Have each group plant a corn or green bean seed in a small pot. Have groups measure their plants each week using centimeter rulers. Have them record the growth on a table and then show the completed data (after about a month) on a bar graph. Display the graphs on a bulletin board.

RETEACHING

Draw several line segments on a sheet of paper. Make copies and give one to each student. Have students estimate the length of each line segment. Have them write their estimate next to the lines and then measure each and write the exact length in centimeters. Discuss the students' estimates.

*available separately

◆ LESSON 39 Measuring Length—Centimeters

Add the measures of the sides to find the perimeter.

4
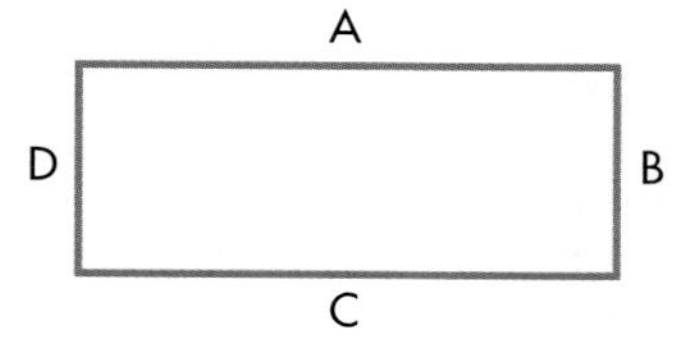

Side	Centimeters
A	5
B	2
C	5
D	2
Perimeter	14

5
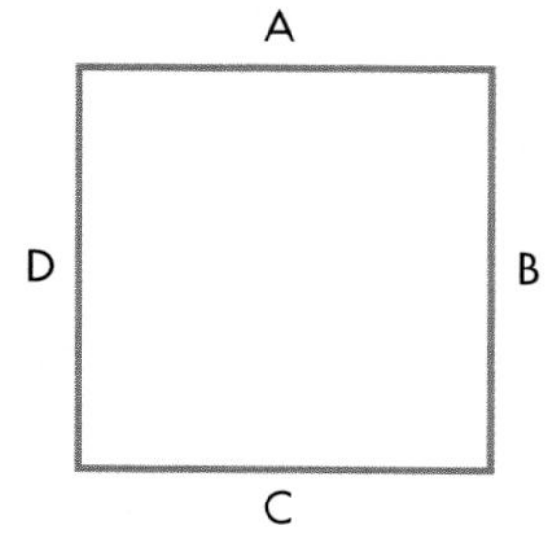

Side	Centimeters
A	4
B	4
C	4
D	4
Perimeter	16

6
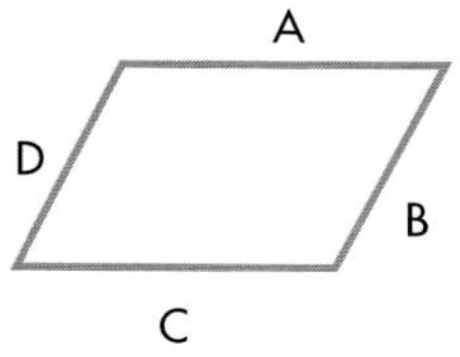

Side	Centimeters
A	3
B	2
C	3
D	2
Perimeter	10

FANTASTIC FACT The world's longest bicycle held 35 people. It was nearly 67 feet long.

NOTE TO HOME
Students measure perimeter.

PRACTICE p. 39

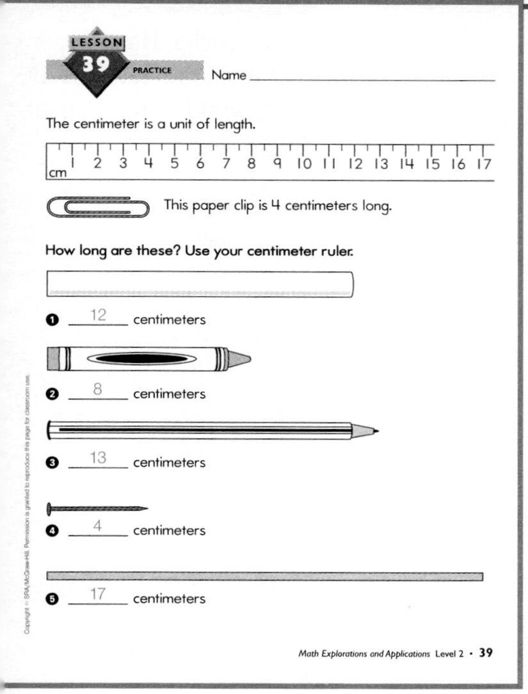
LESSON 39 PRACTICE Name ____________

The centimeter is a unit of length.

cm 1 2 3 4 5 6 7 8 9 10 11 12 13 14 15 16 17

This paper clip is 4 centimeters long.

How long are these? Use your centimeter ruler.

1. 12 centimeters
2. 8 centimeters
3. 13 centimeters
4. 4 centimeters
5. 17 centimeters

Copyright © SRA/McGraw-Hill. Permission is granted to reproduce this page for classroom use.

Math Explorations and Applications Level 2 • 39

ENRICHMENT p. 39

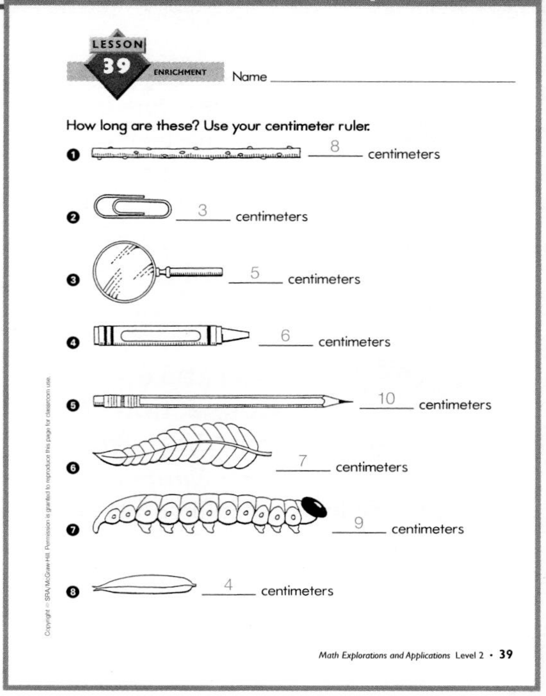
LESSON 39 ENRICHMENT Name ____________

How long are these? Use your centimeter ruler.

1. 8 centimeters
2. 3 centimeters
3. 5 centimeters
4. 6 centimeters
5. 10 centimeters
6. 7 centimeters
7. 9 centimeters
8. 4 centimeters

Copyright © SRA/McGraw-Hill. Permission is granted to reproduce this page for classroom use.

Math Explorations and Applications Level 2 • 39

Using the Student Pages On page 81 have everyone measure the pencil and the nail. Discuss and agree upon the answers before students write them. Then have students measure the other objects on page 81 independently and write their answers on the appropriate lines. On page 82, have students figure the perimeter measurements.

3 Wrap-Up

5 MINUTES

In Closing Have students explain how they use a centimeter ruler to measure length.

ALTERNATIVE ASSESSMENT

Performance Assessment Have students use a centimeter ruler to draw a line segment that is 10 cm long. Check students' drawings.

Assessment Criteria

Did the student . . .

✓ put the zero end of the ruler at one end of the object measured?

✓ read the number at the other end of the object measured?

✓ correctly calculate the perimeter of each figure on page 82?

LOOKING AHEAD In Lesson 40 you will need a meterstick for each child.

LESSON 40

Student Edition pages 83–84

Measurement—Meters and Centimeters

LESSON PLANNER

Objectives

- ▶ to introduce the meter as a standard unit of measure
- ▶ to demonstrate the relationship between centimeters and meters
- ▶ to provide experience in measuring length using metric units

Context of the Lesson This is the second of six lessons on measurement.

Materials	Program Resources
metersticks	Practice Master 40
	Enrichment Master 40
	For extra practice: CD-ROM* Lesson 40

1 Warm-Up

5 MINUTES

Problem of the Day Present this problem to the class orally: Henry bought two pens that cost 50 cents each. Aiko bought one pen for 80 cents. Who spent more money? How much more? (Henry spent 20¢ more.)

MENTAL MATH Present the following problems and have students give the answers quickly.

a. 50 + 30 = (80) **b.** 80 + 70 = (150)

c. 60 + 70 = (130) **d.** 120 – 50 = (70)

e. 140 – 90 = (50) **f.** 110 – 50 = (60)

LESSON 40

Name ______________________

Measurement—Meters and Centimeters

The meter and the centimeter are units of length. There are 100 centimeters in 1 meter.

Meter can be written as **m**

Centimeter can be written as **cm**

COOPERATIVE LEARNING Do the "Measuring" activity.

Find three objects in the classroom that are about 1 meter long. Write how many centimeters long they are. **Answers will vary.**

	Object	Centimeters
❶	______________	______
❷	______________	______
❸	______________	______

1 meter = 100 centimeters

❹ 2 m = **200** cm ❺ 4 m = **400** cm

❻ 3 m = **300** cm ❼ 6 m = **600** cm

NOTE TO HOME
Students learn to measure in centimeters and meters.

Health Connection Have students work in pairs. Have partners measure each other's height in centimeters using a meterstick. Then have partners share and compare results and discuss whether everyone's answers make sense.

Literature Connection Read aloud *Much Bigger Than Martin* by Steven Kellogg to reinforce lesson concepts.

RETEACHING

Hold up several metersticks. Have students tell how many centimeters they would cover if placed end to end. Repeat with other numbers of metersticks.

*available separately

◆ LESSON 40 Measurement—Meters and Centimeters

Measure.

Try to find something that is about 2 meters long or 2 meters high. Measure to see how many centimeters each is. **Answers will vary.**

	Object	Centimeters
8	________	____
9	________	____
10	________	____
11	________	____

Fill in the blanks.

12	7 m = **700** cm	13	10 m = **100** cm
14	**5** m = 500 cm	15	**4** m = 400 cm
16	**8** m = 800 cm	17	**1** m = 100 cm
18	**9** m = 900 cm	19	**6** m = 600 cm

NOTE TO HOME
Students estimate and measure in centimeters.

PRACTICE p. 40

LESSON 40 PRACTICE Name ________

The meter and centimeter are units of length.
There are 100 centimeters in 1 meter.

1. Find some objects at home that are about 1 meter long. Use a meterstick or centimeter ruler to measure them. Write how many centimeters long they are. Answers will vary.

Objects	Centimeters
________	________
________	________
________	________
________	________
________	________

Change meters to centimeters.

2. 6 m = 600 centimeters
3. 8 m = 800 centimeters
4. 2 m = 200 centimeters
5. 10 m = 1000 centimeters
6. 7 m = 700 centimeters
7. 1 m = 100 centimeters

ENRICHMENT p. 40

LESSON 40 ENRICHMENT Name ________

To wrap her package, Zoe needs ribbon. She can use small pieces, but they must add up to exactly 1 meter. Use your centimeter ruler to decide which pieces she could use. Color those pieces.

17 cm
16 cm
12 cm
11 cm
15 cm
14 cm
13 cm
3 cm
4 cm
5 cm
8 cm
7 cm
9 cm
2 cm
6 cm
10 cm

Answers will vary. Ribbons should be of lengths that add up to 100. For example, students may color ribbons measuring 17, 16, 15, 14, 13, 12, 11, and 2 cm.

2 Teach

Demonstrate Display a meterstick and tell students that there are 100 centimeters in one meter. Ask them how many centimeters there are in two meters. (200) Describe and demonstrate how to measure the length of various objects using the meterstick. Focus on objects that are about one meter long. Demonstrate how they can measure each object to the nearest meter or, to be more exact, to the nearest centimeter.

COOPERATIVE LEARNING **Using the Student Pages** You might want to work on page 83 as a class. Then divide students into small groups to complete page 84. When finished, have groups share and compare their findings. Guide students to see that all of their answers on page 83 and the bottom of 84 are multiples of 10.

3 Wrap-Up

5 MINUTES

In Closing Have students describe how they can convert meters to centimeters. (Add two zeros to the number.)

ALTERNATIVE ASSESSMENT **Performance Assessment** Have students use a meterstick to draw a line segment that is 89 centimeters long. Check students' drawings.

Assessment Criteria

Did the student . . .

✓ put the zero end of the meterstick at one end of each object to be measured?

✓ accurately read the number at the other end of each object to be measured?

✓ correctly convert meters to centimeters on pages 83 and 84?

LOOKING AHEAD You will need an inch ruler and a centimeter ruler for each student in Lesson 41.

LESSON 41

Student Edition pages 85–86

Measuring Length—Inches

LESSON PLANNER

Objectives

- ▶ to introduce the inch as a standard unit of length
- ▶ to provide experience in measuring length in inches
- ▶ to make students aware of the two systems of measurement: customary and metric

Context of the Lesson This is the third of six lessons on measurement.

Materials	Program Resources
inch and centimeter rulers	Practice Master 41 Enrichment Master 41 For extra practice: CD-ROM* Lesson 41

1 Warm-Up

5 MINUTES

Problem of the Day Write the following problem on the chalkboard: Maia is 140 centimeters tall. Is she taller or shorter than a meter? By how much? (40 cm taller)

MENTAL MATH Write the following problems on the chalkboard and have students tell how many centimeters each equals. Remind them of the meaning of the abbreviations.

a. 3 m + 4 m = _____ cm (700)

b. 200 cm + 1 m = _____ cm (300)

c. 5 m + 4 m = _____ cm (900)

d. 700 cm + 200 cm = _____ cm (900)

e. 1 m + 5 m = _____ cm (600)

f. 4 m + 40 cm = _____ cm (440)

LESSON 41

Name ______________________________

Measuring Length—Inches

The inch is another unit of length.

This pencil is 5 inches long.

How long are these? Use an inch ruler. Write your answers.

1.  __2__ inches

2.  __3__ inches

3.  __4__ inches

NOTE TO HOME
Students use an inch ruler to measure.

Language Arts Connection Have students work in pairs to make pen pal cards to send to another class. Provide construction paper and inch rulers for each pair of students. Have students measure and cut out cards 9 inches long and 5 inches wide. Then have each pair of students write a friendly message to students in another class. Send the cards and wait for responses.

Literature Connection Read *Length* by Henry Pluckrose to reinforce lesson concepts.

RETEACHING

Have students draw and label three line segments: 4 inches, 8 inches, and 12 inches. Have them then exchange and check each others' drawings.

*available separately

◆ **LESSON 41** Measuring Length—Inches

Answers will vary.

A foot is 12 inches long.

Find some things in your classroom that are about a foot long. Measure them and tell how many inches long they are.

Object	Inches
❹ ________________	________
❺ ________________	________
❻ ________________	________
❼ ________________	________

Find things that are about 2 feet long. Measure. How many inches long are they?

Object	Inches
❽ ________________	________
❾ ________________	________

NOTE TO HOME
Students estimate and measure in inches.

PRACTICE p. 41

LESSON 41 PRACTICE Name ____________

The inch is a unit of length.

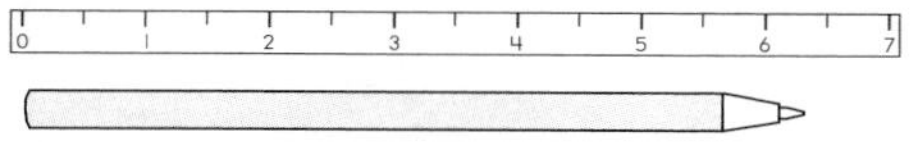

This pen is 6 inches long.

How long are these? Use an inch ruler.

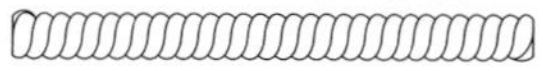

❶ 4 inches

❷ 5 inches

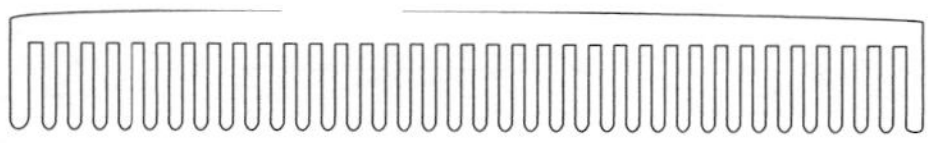

❸ 7 inches

❹ 3 inches

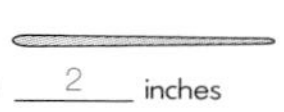

❺ 2 inches

Math Explorations and Applications Level 2 • 41

ENRICHMENT p. 41

LESSON 41 ENRICHMENT Name ____________

You can find rectangles everywhere. Look at floor tiles, wall tiles, bricks, and blocks. How many different size rectangles can you find in your school or home?

Use an inch ruler to find how long and wide they are. Write the name of the rectangle. Then write how wide it is and how long it is.

Kind of Rectangle	How Wide?	How Long?
Answers will vary.		

Math Explorations and Applications Level 2 • 41

❷ Teach

Demonstrate Display an inch ruler and demonstrate how to measure in inches and have students measure the length of various objects using their inch rulers. Discuss the two standard systems of measurement used in the United States. Point out that students have learned how to measure in metric units when measuring centimeters and meters and in customary units when measuring in inches.

Introducing the "Measuring" Activity Provide both inch and centimeter rulers for each student. Have them measure one object using both rulers. Discuss students' measurements and point out that because centimeters are smaller than inches, the number of centimeters will always be greater than the corresponding number of inches.

COOPERATIVE LEARNING **Using the Student Pages** You might want to complete page 85 as a class. Have students work in small groups to complete page 86. Then have groups share and compare their findings.

❸ Wrap-Up (5 MINUTES)

In Closing Have students name all the units of length that they have learned about so far in this program. (inch, foot, centimeter, and meter)

ALTERNATIVE ASSESSMENT **Performance Assessment** Have students use a ruler to draw a line segment 5 inches long. Check students' drawings.

Assessment Criteria

Did the student . . .

✓ put the zero end of the inch ruler at one end of each object to be measured?

✓ accurately read the number at the other end of each object to be measured?

✓ correctly measure all pictures and objects on pages 85 and 86?

LESSON 42

Student Edition pages 87–88

Measurement—Yards, Feet, and Inches

LESSON PLANNER

Objectives

- to introduce feet and yards
- to demonstrate how to convert yards to feet and to inches
- to provide practice in measuring length in inches, feet, and yards

Context of the Lesson This is the fourth of six lessons on measurement.

Materials	Program Resources
inch ruler and yardstick	Thinking Story Book, pages 36–39
posterboard (optional)	Reteaching Master
	Practice Master 42
	Enrichment Master 42
	For extra practice: CD-ROM* Lesson 42

1 Warm-Up (5 MINUTES)

Problem of the Day Write this problem on the chalkboard: You need to cover a table that is 24 inches wide and 52 inches long with colored paper. You have a piece of paper 36 inches wide and 96 inches long. What will you do to exactly cover the tabletop? (Possible answer: Cut the 36"-side down by 12" and cut the 96"-side down by 44".)

MENTAL MATH Have students add or subtract to find the answers to the following problems.

a. 30 + 60 = (90) **b.** 40 + 80 = (120) **c.** 120 − 50 = (70)

d. 130 − 40 = (90) **e.** 70 + 70 = (140) **f.** 150 − 90 = (60)

LESSON 42

Name ______________________

Measurement—Yards, Feet, and Inches

The inch and the foot are units of length.
There are 12 inches in 1 foot.

The yard is also a unit of length. There are 3 feet or 36 inches in 1 yard.

Yard can be written as **yd**
Feet or foot can be written as **ft** and inches as **in**

How many? Use a ruler to count if you need to.

1. 1 yard = __3__ feet = __36__ inches
2. 2 yards = __6__ feet = __72__ inches

NOTE TO HOME
Students learn how to convert yards and feet to inches.

Literature Connection Read *How Big Is a Foot?* by Rolf Myller to reinforce lesson concepts.

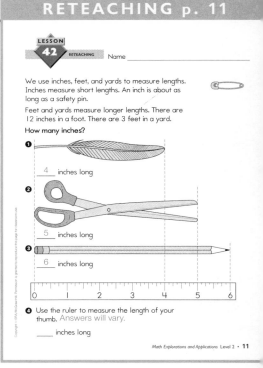

RETEACHING p. 11

LESSON 42 RETEACHING Name ______________________

We use inches, feet, and yards to measure lengths. Inches measure short lengths. An inch is about as long as a safety pin.

Feet and yards measure longer lengths. There are 12 inches in a foot. There are 3 feet in a yard.

How many inches?

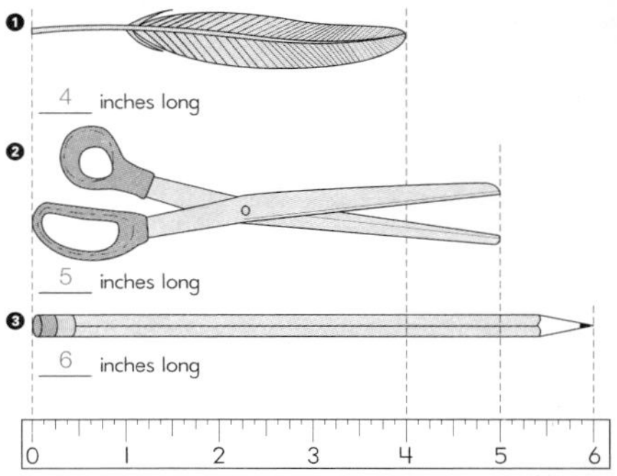

1. __4__ inches long
2. __5__ inches long
3. __6__ inches long
4. Use the ruler to measure the length of your thumb. Answers will vary.

____ inches long

Math Explorations and Applications Level 2 • 11

*available separately

◆ **LESSON 42 Measurement—Yards, Feet, and Inches**

COOPERATIVE LEARNING

Find some things in your classroom that are about 1 yard long. Measure them. How many inches long are they?

	Object	Inches
3	______	______
4	______	______
5	______	______
6	______	______

Complete the following. Use a ruler to count if you need to.

7. 1 foot = 12 inches
8. __5__ feet = 60 inches
9. __2__ feet = 24 inches
10. __10__ feet = 120 inches
11. 4 feet = __48__ inches
12. 6 feet = __72__ inches

THINKING STORY

Talk about the Thinking Story "Paint Up, Fix Up, Measure Up."

NOTE TO HOME
Students estimate and measure in yards, feet, and inches.

PRACTICE p. 42

LESSON 42 PRACTICE Name ______

The inch and the foot are units of length.
There are 12 inches in 1 foot.

0 1 2 3 4 5 6 7 8 9 10 11 12

The yard is also a unit of length.
There are 3 feet in 1 yard.
There are 36 inches in 1 yard.

0 1 2 3 4 5 6 7 8 9 10 11 12 13 14 15 16 17 18 19 20 21 22 23 24 25 26 27 28 29 30 31 32 33 34 35 36

1 yard = 3 feet = 36 inches

How many?

1. 3 yards = __9__ feet = __108__ inches
2. 2 yards = __6__ feet = __72__ inches
3. 4 yards = __12__ feet = __144__ inches
4. Which is longer, 2 feet or 20 inches? __2 feet__
5. Which is longer, 1 yard or 40 inches? __40 inches__

ENRICHMENT p. 42

LESSON 42 ENRICHMENT Name ______

Look around a room in your home. Choose five objects of different lengths that you can measure. List each object on the lines below. After it, list its size in yards, feet, and inches.

Object	Yards	Feet	Inches
Answers will vary.			

2 Teach

Demonstrate Discuss customary units of length. Explain and demonstrate to students, using a ruler and yardstick, that there are 12 inches in one foot, 3 feet in one yard, and 36 inches in one yard.

COOPERATIVE LEARNING **Using the Student Pages** You might want to complete page 87 as a class. Then have students work in groups to complete page 88. When finished, have groups share and compare their findings.

Using the Thinking Story Read "Paint Up, Fix Up, Measure Up" on Thinking Story Book pages 36–39 aloud to the class. Stop and discuss the questions asked throughout the story.

3 Wrap-Up

5 MINUTES

In Closing Have students tell how many inches are in a foot and yard and how many feet are in a yard.

ALTERNATIVE ASSESSMENT **Informal Assessment** Use students' work on pages 87 and 88 to informally assess their understanding of customary units of length.

Assessment Criteria

Did the student . . .

- ✓ participate in the discussion of the Thinking Story?
- ✓ correctly tell how many inches are in a foot?
- ✓ correctly tell how many feet are in a yard?
- ✓ correctly measure all objects on page 88?

LOOKING AHEAD Students will need centimeter rulers for Lesson 43.

STORY 6

THINKING STORY

Paint Up, Fix Up, Measure Up

Mr. Muddle's house gets more and more broken down every year. The longer he waits to repair things, the more he forgets the things that need to be repaired.

Last spring he remembered that his house needed painting, but he soon forgot that it had four sides. He stopped painting after only one side was finished.

How many sides were left unpainted? three

In the summer Mr. Muddle noticed that three sides of his house were still unpainted. All four sides of his house are the same size, and he remembered buying 10 gallons of paint to paint one side.

How much paint will he need to finish painting his house? 30 gallons

Mr. Muddle went to the paint store and bought 10 gallons of paint so he could finish the house.

Will he have enough paint? no

How much of the house will he be able to paint with 10 gallons? one side

How much of the house will still need to be painted? two sides

When he had used the 10 gallons of paint, Mr. Muddle was surprised to find that only one more side of his house was painted and that two sides still needed paint. He went back to the paint store, but he couldn't remember how much paint he needed.

How much more paint does Mr. Muddle need? 20 gallons

Mr. Muddle decided to go home and check before buying any more paint.

When he got home, he noticed that he needed a new screen for the back door. "I might as well take care of that right now," he thought. He carefully measured the screen and found that it was 80 centimeters wide and 200 centimeters high.

Suggest that the students draw a picture of the screen and write the dimensions along the edges.

◆ STORY 6 Paint Up, Fix Up, Measure Up

Mr. Muddle wrote down the measurements so that he wouldn't forget them. When he got to the hardware store, he found that the only screening they sold was 100 centimeters wide.

What should Mr. Muddle do? How long a piece of screening should he buy? 200 cm

At first Mr. Muddle thought he would buy a piece 200 centimeters long. "That would be the right length," he thought, "but it would be too wide." Then he had an idea. "Since this screening is 20 centimeters too wide," he thought, "I'll get it 20 centimeters shorter to make up for it."

How long a piece of screening will Mr. Muddle buy? 180 cm; Suggest that the students draw a picture of the piece of screening Mr. Muddle bought and write the dimensions.

Mr. Muddle bought a piece of screening that was 180 centimeters long and, of course, it was 100 centimeters wide. When he returned home and tried to put it into the door frame, he was surprised to find that it didn't fit.

What was wrong with it? It was too wide and too short.

The screen stuck out on the sides and didn't reach up to the top. "I guess I could cut some off the sides to make it fit," Mr. Muddle thought. "But my metal-cutting scissors are broken. Besides, I don't know any way to make it longer at the top. I guess I'll just have to put it on the way it is and hope the flies don't notice that something is wrong."

What do you think the flies will find out? They can get in at the top.

Mr. Muddle was surprised to find that so many flies were getting in through his back door. "I have this nice new screen to keep them out," he said, "but they all keep coming in through the top part of the door that isn't covered. Those flies don't seem to appreciate all the work I've done."

. . . the end

LESSON 43

Student Edition pages 89–90

Estimating Length

LESSON PLANNER

Objective

▶ to provide practice in estimating and measuring length in metric units

Context of the Lesson This is the fifth of six lessons on measurement. This lesson contains Mastery Checkpoint 6 for assessing mastery of basic measurement concepts.

Materials	**Program Resources**
centimeter rulers	Thinking Story Book, pages 40–41
	Practice Master 43
	Enrichment Master 43
	Assessment Master
	For extra practice: CD-ROM* Lesson 43

Note: This lesson may take more than one day.

1 Warm-Up (5 MINUTES)

Problem of the Day Draw the following figure on the chalkboard. Have students copy the figure and then tell how many rectangles there are. (9 including the squares which are also rectangles)

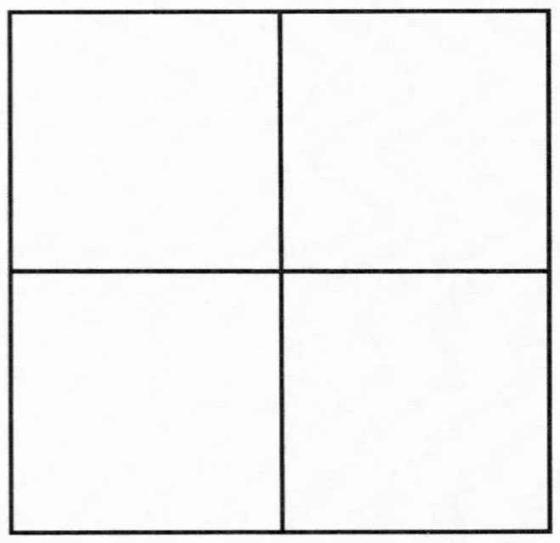

MENTAL MATH Have students use their hands to show how long they think the following units of measure are, then show them the correct measurements.

a. meter **b.** centimeter

c. millimeter **d.** inch

e. foot **f.** yard

LESSON 43

Name ______________________

Estimating Length

First estimate the length of each object in centimeters. Then measure to check. Write your answers. **Estimates will vary.**

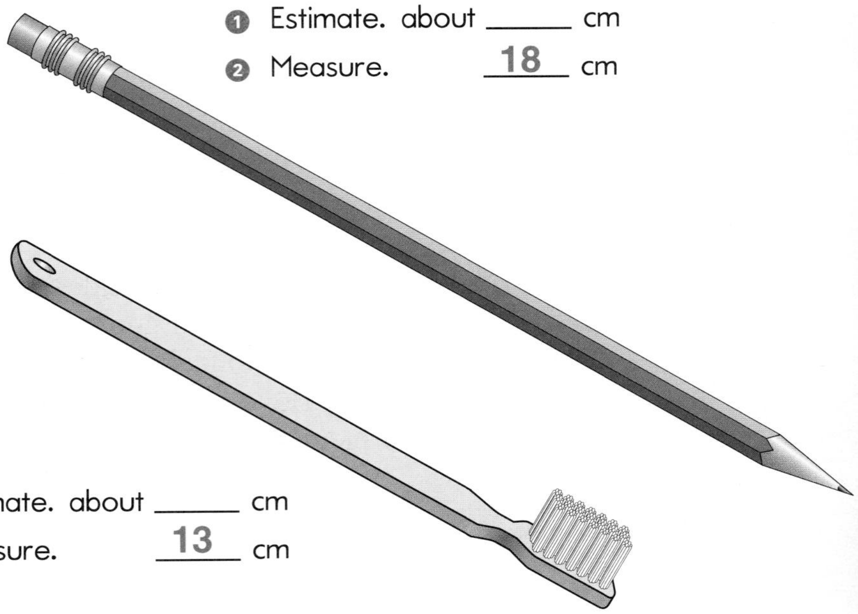

❶ Estimate. about ______ cm

❷ Measure. 18 cm

❸ Estimate. about ______ cm

❹ Measure. 13 cm

❺ Estimate. about ______ cm

Measure. 8 cm

NOTE TO HOME
Students estimate how long, then measure to check their estimates.

RETEACHING

Take advantage of any classroom activities that lend themselves to practice in estimating and measuring. For example, during physical education, have students first estimate how far they can throw, then throw and make a second estimate, and finally measure.

PRACTICE p. 43

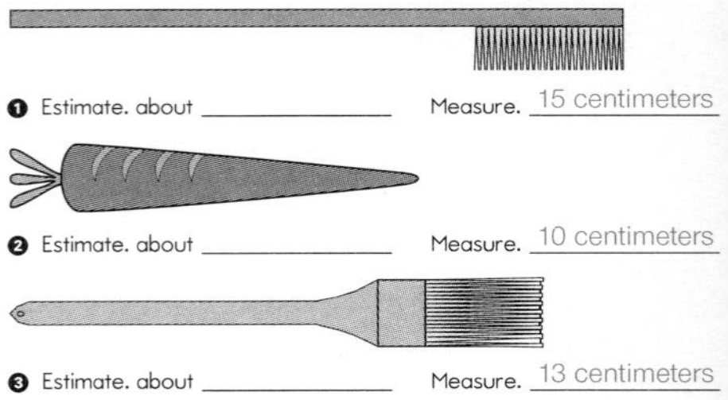

LESSON 43 PRACTICE Name ______________

First estimate the length of each object in centimeters. Then measure to check. Estimates will vary.

❶ Estimate. about ______ Measure. 15 centimeters

❷ Estimate. about ______ Measure. 10 centimeters

❸ Estimate. about ______ Measure. 13 centimeters

How long? Unit: centimeters or inches.
Fill in the table.

Objects	Estimate Length	Measure Length	Difference
Book	Estimates will vary.		Differences will vary.
Pencil			
Desk			

Math Explorations and Applications Level 2 • 43

*available separately

◆ LESSON 43 Estimating Length

Use the Mixed Practice on page 373 after this lesson.

COOPERATIVE LEARNING Do the "Measuring Length" activity.

6 How long? Unit ______

Objects	Estimate Length	Measure Length	Difference

FANTASTIC FACT A kangaroo can leap over 25 feet in a single hop.

NOTE TO HOME
Students estimate length, measure objects, and record their findings.

ENRICHMENT p. 43

LESSON 43 ENRICHMENT Name ____________

After each length below, write the names of three objects that you think will be about that length. Then measure each object with an inch ruler. Write the actual length of each object.

Length	Object	Actual Length
6 inches	Answers will vary.	
10 inches		
16 inches		
30 inches		

Math Explorations and Applications Level 2 • 43

ASSESSMENT p. 12

UNIT 1 **Mastery Checkpoint 6** Measuring length and weight (Lesson 43)
Page 1 of 2

Name ____________

The student demonstrates mastery by accurately measuring length and weight of at least 15 objects.

How long?

Objects	Estimate Length	Measure Length	Difference
Answers will vary.			

Go on . . .

12 • *Math Explorations and Applications* Level 2

2 Teach

Using the Student Pages Have students complete page 89 individually. Be sure they write both the number and unit of length for each answer. Discuss methods and answers before going on to the activity on page 90.

COOPERATIVE LEARNING Students can work in groups to complete the "Measuring Length" activity on page 90. You might want to complete the first line in the chart with the class to demonstrate what they should do. Then provide a collection of objects for each group to measure as they complete the rest of the chart. When they are finished, have the groups share and compare their methods and results.

Using the Thinking Story Present one or two new problems from those following "Paint Up, Fix Up, Measure Up" on pages 40–41 of the Thinking Story Book.

3 Wrap-Up

5 MINUTES

In Closing Have students describe how they estimate an object's length.

ANALYZING ANSWERS Observe whether students are making errors in measuring. Check to see that they always place the zero on the ruler at the beginning of the object they are measuring and that they measure to the nearest centimeter at the end of the object.

Mastery Checkpoint 6

At this point, most students will be proficient at measuring weight and length. You may use Assessment Masters 16 and 17 to assess students' mastery of measurement. You might want to record the results on the Mastery Checkpoint Chart.

Assessment Criteria

Did the student . . .

✓ make sensible estimates of length?

✓ measure objects accurately?

LESSON 44

Student Edition pages 91–92

Measurement—Perimeters

LESSON PLANNER

Objectives

- to provide practice in finding the perimeter of objects
- to provide practice in measuring in both customary and metric systems
- to demonstrate that when converting from a larger to a smaller unit of measure, the number of units will be greater

Context of the Lesson This is the last of six lessons on measurement.

Materials

inch and centimeter rulers

Program Resources

Number Cubes

Thinking Story Book, pages 40–41

Practice Master 44

Enrichment Master 44

For extra practice:
CD-ROM* Lesson 44

1 Warm-Up 5 MINUTES

Problem of the Day Write the following problem on the chalkboard: Karen has a table that is 40 inches wide. Her tablecloth is 50 inches wide. How much of the tablecloth can hang equally over each side? (5″ on each side)

MENTAL MATH Present the following problems and have students use Number Cubes to show answers.

a. 13 – 6 = (7)
b. 9 + 5 = (14)
c. 7 + 8 = (15)
d. 14 – 8 = (6)
e. 15 – 7 = (8)
f. 5 + 8 = (13)
g. 4 + 7 = (11)
h. 6 + 6 = (12)
i. 14 – 9 = (5)
j. 12 – 9 = (3)
k. 4 + 6 = (10)
l. 13 – 7 = (6)

LESSON 44

Name ______________________

Measurement—Perimeters

Find the perimeter.

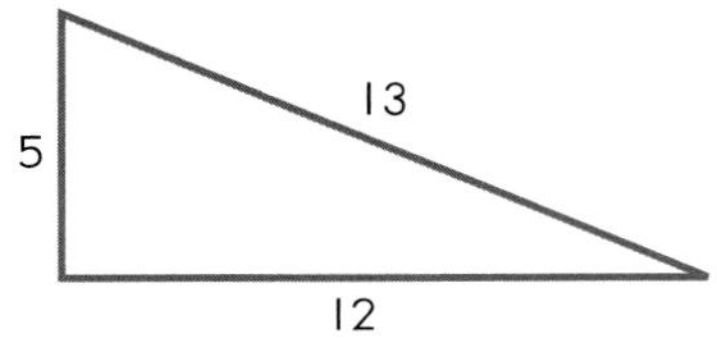

1. perimeter = 30

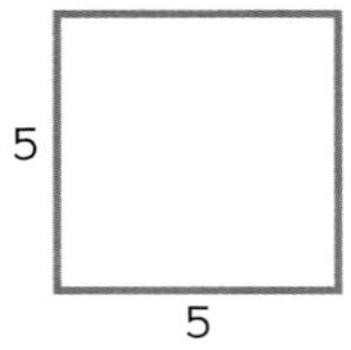

2. perimeter = 20

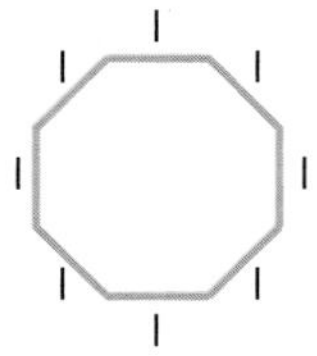

3. perimeter = 8

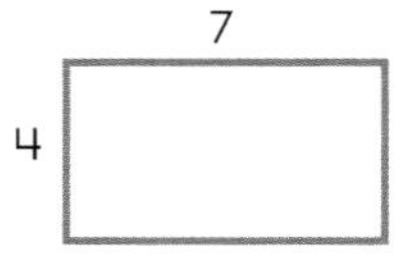

4. perimeter = 22

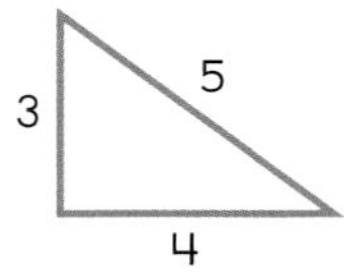

5. perimeter = 12

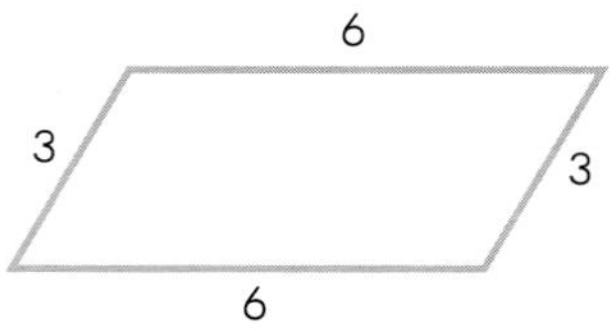

6. perimeter = 18

NOTE TO HOME
Students find the perimeter of figures.

Art Connection Have groups of students find the perimeter of different bulletin boards in your classroom or hallway. Then have them design borders that will fit around the perimeters of the bulletin boards.

RETEACHING

Have students use their inch rulers to draw the following figures and then measure the perimeter of each in inches and centimeters:

a. rectangle: length 3 inches, width 2 inches
b. triangle: three sides, 4 inches each
c. square: each side 3 inches

*available separately

◆ **LESSON 44 Measurement—Perimeters**

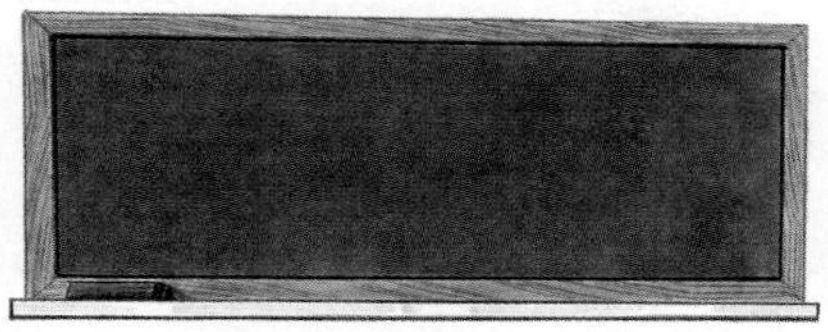

COOPERATIVE LEARNING Work with another student.

Measure some objects in your classroom, such as your book, your chair, or a chalkboard. Tell what the perimeter of each object is both in centimeters and in inches. **Answers will vary.**

	Object	Perimeter in centimeters	Perimeter in inches
7	______	______	______
8	______	______	______
9	______	______	______
10	______	______	______
11	______	______	______
12	______	______	______

13. Which is greater, the number of inches in the perimeter or the number of centimeters in the perimeter? **the number of centimeters**

14. Which is longer, an inch or a centimeter? **an inch**

NOTE TO HOME
Students measure objects and find the perimeter.

2 Teach

Using the Student Pages Discuss and name the figures on page 91. (triangle, rectangle, square, octagon, parallelogram) Define *perimeter* for students by explaining it is the distance around a figure. Ask students how they would find the distance around a figure. Explain that to find the perimeter of each figure they will have to add the lengths of each side. Have students complete page 91 individually and then work with a partner to complete page 92. When students finish, have pairs compare and share their results. Discuss students' answers to questions 13 and 14. Have them explain why there are more centimeters than inches when measuring the same object.

Using the Thinking Story Present one or two new problems from those following the story "Paint Up, Fix Up, Measure Up" on pages 40–41 of the Thinking Story Book.

3 Wrap-Up

5 MINUTES

In Closing Have students write a definition for *perimeter.*

SELF ASSESSMENT

Have students correct their own pages as you provide the correct answers. Ask them to draw a "smiley face" on the top of the pages they assess as good work and a "sad face" if they are not happy with their work.

PRACTICE p. 44

LESSON 44 PRACTICE Name ______

Measure each side. Then write how long it is.

1.

Side	Centimeters
A	5
B	5
C	5
D	5

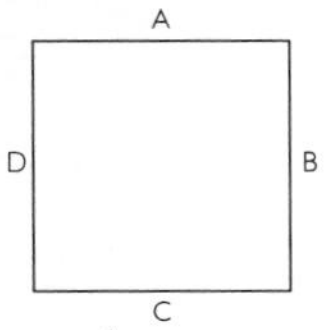

2.

Side	Centimeters
A	4
B	5
C	4
D	5

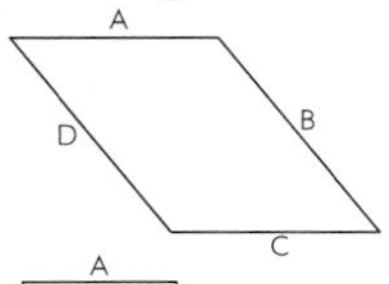

3.

Side	Centimeters
A	3
B	2
C	3
D	2

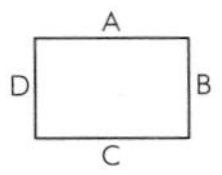

4.

Side	Centimeters
A	2
B	2
C	3
D	3

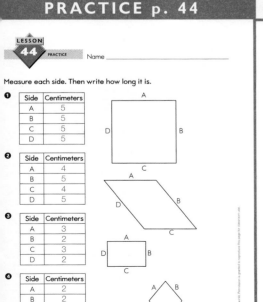

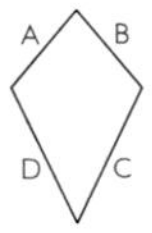

44 • Math Explorations and Applications Level 2

ENRICHMENT p. 44

LESSON 44 ENRICHMENT Name ______

Choose four books from your bookshelf. Place the books face up on a table. Use a centimeter ruler to measure the books. Fill in a chart below for each book, with *S* for the side measurement, *T* for the top, *C* for the length between opposite corners, and *Th* for thickness.

1. Book A

Space Measured	Centimeters
S	
T	
C	
Th	

2. Book B

Space Measured	Centimeters
S	
T	
C	
Th	

3. Book C

Space Measured	Centimeters
S	
T	
C	
Th	

4. Book D

Space Measured	Centimeters
S	
T	
C	
Th	

44 • Math Explorations and Applications Level 2

Assessment Criteria

Did the student . . .

✓ correctly answer five of the six problems on page 91?

✓ correctly measure five of the six objects in centimeters and inches on page 92?

✓ correctly answer the last two questions on page 92?

LESSON 45

Student Edition pages 93–96

Unit 1 Test

Using the Student Pages The Unit Test on Student Edition pages 93 through 96 provides an opportunity to formally evaluate your students' proficiency with skills and concepts developed in this unit. It is similar in content and format to the Unit Review. Students who did well on the Unit Review might not need to take this test. Students who did not do well on the Unit Review should be provided with additional practice opportunities, such as the Mixed Practice pages, before taking the Unit Test. For further evaluation, you might want to have these students also take the Unit Test in multiple choice format, provided on pages 83–94 in the Assessment Master Book.

LESSON 45

Name ____________________

Unit 1 Test

Check your math skills. Count up or count down. Fill in the missing numbers.

1	4	5	6	7	8	9	10	11
2	36	37	38	39	40	41	42	43
3	43	42	41	40	39	38	37	36
4	21	20	19	18	17	16	15	14

Work these problems. Watch the signs.

5. 8 + 6 = 14
6. 9 + 7 = 16
7. 3 + 8 = 11
8. 7 + 9 = 16
9. 14 − 4 = 10
10. 10 + 8 = 18
11. 15 − 7 = 8
12. 8 + 8 = 16
13. 9 + 3 = 12
14. 13 − 4 = 9

NOTE TO HOME
This test checks unit skills and concepts.

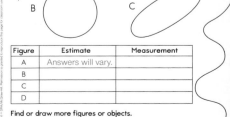

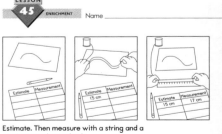

ENRICHMENT p. 45

LESSON 45 ENRICHMENT Name ____________________

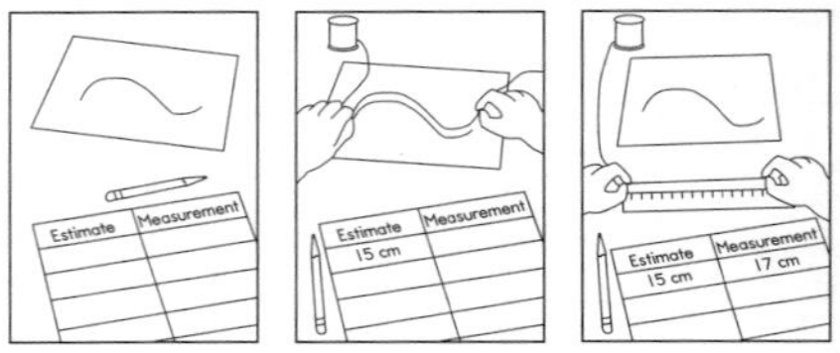

Estimate. Then measure with a string and a centimeter ruler to check.

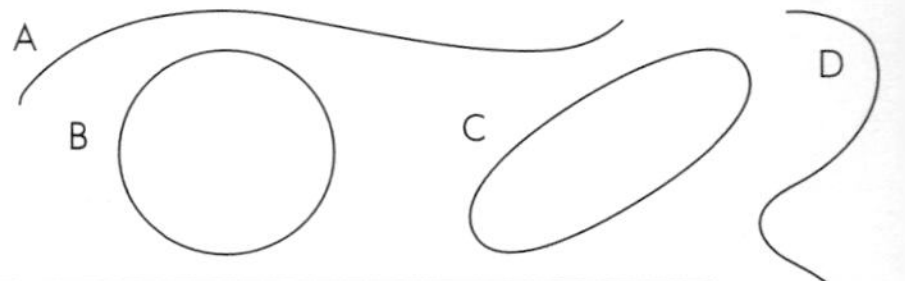

Figure	Estimate	Measurement
A	Answers will vary.	
B		
C		
D		

Find or draw more figures or objects. Estimate. Then measure.

◆ LESSON 45 Unit 1 Test

Solve these problems. Watch the signs.

⑮ 20 − 10 = **10**　⑯ 50 + 20 = **70**

⑰ 30 + 40 = **70**　⑱ 80 − 50 = **30**

⑲ 54 + 3 = **57**　⑳ 54 − 3 = **51**

㉑ 65 − 3 = **62**　㉒ 76 + 3 = **79**

㉓ 47 + 2 = **49**　㉔ 88 − 1 = **87**

㉕ 66 + 1 = **67**　㉖ 51 + 2 = **53**

㉗ 74 − 3 = **71**　㉘ 38 + 1 = **39**

㉙ 8 + 7 + 3 = **18**

㉚ 6 + 4 + 5 = **15**

㉛ 4 + 4 + 4 = **12**

㉜ 9 + 0 + 7 = **16**

FANTASTIC FACT: A skunk can spray you from ten feet away.

NOTE TO HOME
This test checks unit skills and concept.

PRACTICE p. 45

LESSON 45 PRACTICE　Name ____________

Solve. Watch the signs.

❶ 6 + 5 = 11　❷ 20 − 10 = 10

❸ 7 + 8 = 15　❹ 8 + 5 = 13

❺ 13 − 2 = 11　❻ 2 + 9 = 11

❼ 10 + 9 = 19　❽ 17 − 10 = 7

❾ 15 − 8 = 7　❿ 9 + 8 = 17

⓫ 4 + 7 = 11　⓬ 11 − 6 = 5

⓭ 3 + 9 = 12　⓮ 8 + 8 = 16

⓯ 14 − 7 = 7　⓰ 12 − 10 = 2

⓱ 16 − 2 = 14　⓲ 5 + 7 = 12

Math Explorations and Applications Level 2 • 45

ASSESSMENT p. 14

UNIT 1　**Unit 1 Test** (Use after Lesson 45.)　Page 1 of 6

Name ____________

The student demonstrates mastery by correctly answering at least 40 of the 50 problems.

Count up or count down.
Fill in the missing numbers.

❶

25	26	27	28	29	30	31	32

❷

44	43	42	41	40	39	38	37

Solve. Watch the signs.

❸ 7 + 5 = 12　❹ 9 + 6 = 15

❺ 15 − 5 = 10　❻ 10 + 9 = 19

❼ 16 − 9 = 7　❽ 7 + 7 = 14　❾ 9 + 5 = 14　❿ 15 − 6 = 9　⓫ 13 − 9 = 4

Go on . . .

14 • *Math Explorations and Applications* Level 2

◆ LESSON 45 Unit 1 Test

Name ______________________

How much money? Write your answers.

33  41 ¢

34  17 ¢

35  $ 26

ALGEBRA READINESS

Solve these problems.

36 3 + [5] = 8

37 5 + [6] = 11

38 [6] + 7 = 13

39 [8] + 8 = 16

40 The toy train is __9__ cm long.

NOTE TO HOME
This test checks unit skills and concept.

PROBLEM SOLVING

Solve these problems.

41 Lonnie had seven strawberries. He picked five more. How many strawberries does he have now? **12**

42 Eric has $15. He buys a hat for $6. How much money does he have left? $ **9**

43 Theresa has 12¢. Stickers cost 5¢ each. Can Theresa buy two stickers? **yes**

44 Janell had 15 marbles. She lost some of them. How many does Janell have now? ______ **not enough information given**

45 Suzanne has five magazines. Her sister buys her two more. How many does Suzanne have now? **7**

NOTE TO HOME
This test checks unit skills and concepts.

LESSON 46

Student Edition pages 97–98

Extending the Unit

LESSON PLANNER

Objective

- to provide remediation instruction and enrichment activities

Context of the Lesson This is the first remediation and enrichment lesson in this book. The next will be at the end of Unit 2.

Materials	Program Resources
none	Practice Master 46
	Enrichment Master 46
	For extra practice: CD-ROM* Lesson 46

1 Warm-Up

5 MINUTES

Problem of the Day Write the following problem on the chalkboard: Al, Beth, and Darnell are standing in line. How many different ways could they be standing in line? (6)

MENTAL MATH Have students use mental math to add.

a. 20 + 50 = (70)

b. 30 + 80 = (110)

c. 40 + 50 = (90)

d. 10 + 90 = (100)

e. 70 + 50 = (120)

2 Teach

Using the Student Pages Students who need remediation can do activities, play games, and complete extra practice in skills diagnosed in Lesson 45. Enrichment activities for students who have finished remediation or do not need it are included on student pages 97 and 98. Page 98 can be done with a calculator by students who have mastered basic addition and subtraction facts.

LESSON 46

Name ______________________________

Extending the Unit

GAME Play the "Dot-Square" game.

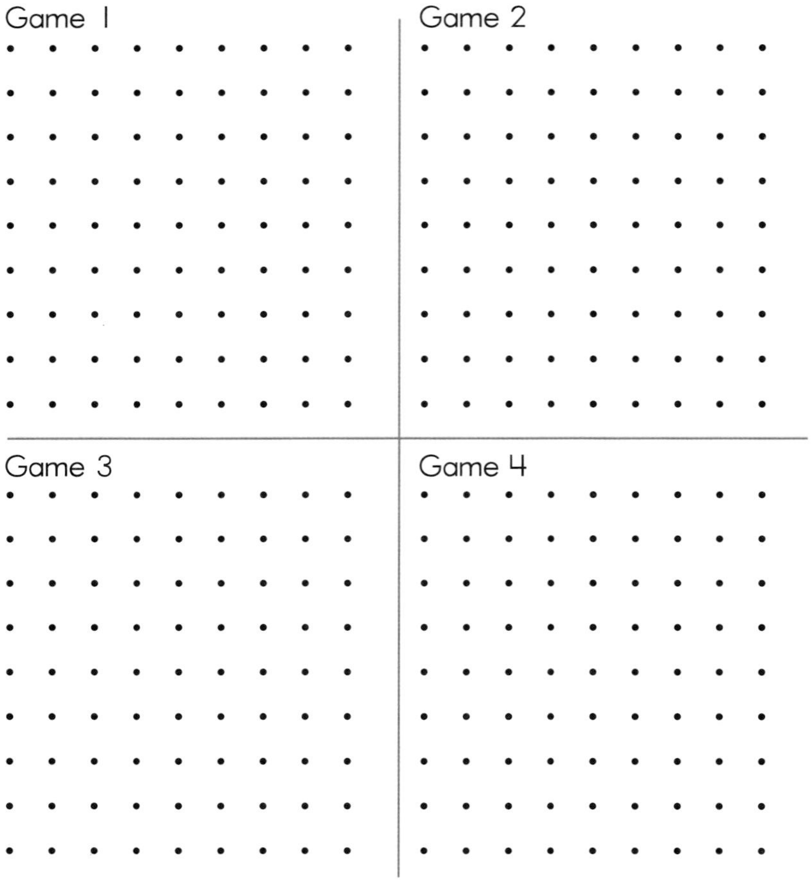

NOTE TO HOME
Students play a game in which they try to make as many squares as possible.

COOPERATIVE LEARNING Allow students who do not need remediation to work with those who do to play games that were introduced previously in this unit.

RETEACHING

Use play money to reteach addition and subtraction to those students who need remediation. Have students work in small groups, using play money or other base-10 materials to model and solve problems involving adding and subtracting ones and tens.

*available separately

◆ **LESSON 46** Extending the Unit

Use the Mixed Practice on page 374 after this lesson.

Solve these problems.

❶ 3 + 4 = 7	❷ 30 + 40 = 70	❸ 9 − 5 = 4	❹ 90 − 50 = 40
❺ 5 + 4 = 9	❻ 50 + 40 = 90	❼ 80 − 30 = 50	❽ 60 + 30 = 90
❾ 90 − 10 = 80	❿ 9 − 9 = 0	⓫ 90 − 90 = 0	⓬ 40 + 20 = 60
⓭ 7 + 4 = 11	⓮ 10 + 40 = 50	⓯ 17 − 9 = 8	⓰ 80 − 70 = 10
⓱ 8 + 7 = 15	⓲ 18 + 70 = 88	⓳ 60 + 6 = 66	⓴ 40 + 12 = 52

NOTE TO HOME
Students add and subtract.

PRACTICE p. 46

LESSON 46 PRACTICE Name ____________

Solve. Watch the signs.

❶ 62 + 2 = 64	❷ 37 − 3 = 34
❸ 71 − 1 = 70	❹ 94 − 1 = 93
❺ 86 + 3 = 89	❻ 68 + 2 = 70
❼ 91 + 2 = 93	❽ 34 − 1 = 33
❾ 84 − 2 = 82	❿ 28 + 3 = 31
⓫ 52 − 3 = 49	⓬ 59 + 1 = 60
⓭ 48 + 1 = 49	⓮ 77 − 2 = 75
⓯ 99 − 2 = 97	⓰ 63 − 2 = 61
⓱ 39 + 2 = 41	⓲ 20 + 3 = 23

46 • Math Explorations and Applications Level 2

ENRICHMENT p. 46

LESSON 46 ENRICHMENT Name ____________

Which line is longer? Measure to check.

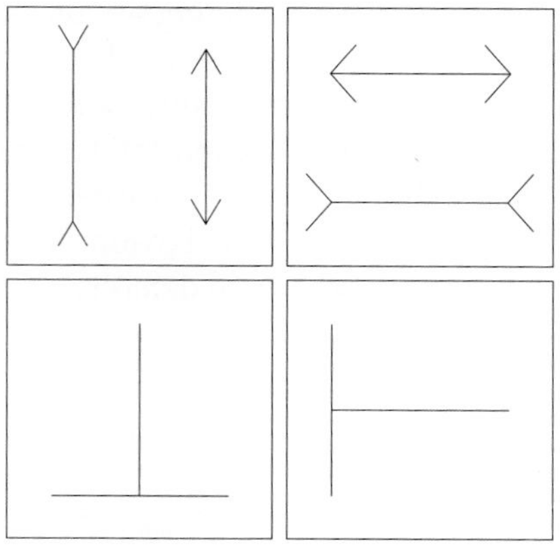

Each pair of lines is the same length.

46 • Math Explorations and Applications Level 2

GAME **Introducing the "Dot-Square" Game** Space for four of these games is provided on page 97. Two players play this game to develop geometric intuition. Player 1 connects 2 adjacent dots with a vertical or horizontal line in Game 1. Player 2 then takes a turn and does the same. A player who draws a line that completes a square writes his or her initials in the square. Play continues until all squares in the Game 1 section are finished. The player whose initials are in more squares wins.

❸ Wrap-Up (5 MINUTES)

In Closing Have students explain any strategies they used in playing the "Dot-Square" game.

ALTERNATIVE ASSESSMENT

Performance Assessment Observe students play the "Dot-Square" game to informally assess who is developing geometric intuition.

Assessment Criteria

Did the student . . .

✓ use strategies to complete squares in the "Dot-Square" game?

✓ correctly complete 16 of 20 problems on page 98?

Student Edition pages 98a–98b

Wrap-Up

PRESENTING THE PROJECT

Project Objectives

- to introduce students to the methods of completing a long-term project
- to present the concepts that numbers are used for measuring, counting, ordering, quantifying, and labeling
- to provide practice in the recognition and writing of numerals from 0 to 20

Materials

index cards or notepaper

paper

Yellow Pages phone book

Students write names of businesses and their phone numbers on index cards, each business on a different card. Students might also want to include emergency and nonemergency numbers for hospitals, police and fire departments, and ambulances.

This is a fun project to incorporate in a social studies unit on community. If your students have built a fictitious community or a map or model of their own community, they can make a Yellow Pages for it. If students have not created a community, you might make that part of this project. Students can design and lay out their community or town. It is standard practice in all media to list fictitious numbers with the prefix 555. You might want to consider having your students use that prefix in their phone books instead of a real prefix.

Encourage students to figure out the best way to arrange the entries in their phone book. Help them think about the pros and cons of listing the numbers in sequence, by area of town, alphabetically, by type of business, or perhaps in a combination of these.

Challenge students to figure out how phone numbers are assigned, why each phone has a different number, and why there are a limited number of prefixes in each community.

If there are only ten numerals and we use seven in a phone number, how many ways can phone numbers be arranged so that no two phones in an area code have the same number?

Invite students to "play" with the numbers in their phone books. They can arrange the numbers from greatest to least. They can total the digits in phone numbers or try finding three phone numbers whose digits produce the same sum.

Wrapping Up the Project Have students compile the individual numbers into a book. Periodically ask quick questions that send the children to their phone book. For example, you might say, "If our sink is leaking, who should we call to fix it? Find the phone number of a plumber" or "I found this phone number written on a slip of paper. Can you find out whose number it is?"

What Is a Math Project? Math projects in *Math Explorations and Applications* are real-world problem-solving activities in which students use many different mathematics skills. These mathematics projects are not word problems that focus on one skill area; rather, students must draw from all that they already know about mathematics to complete them. They offer students freedom to problem-solve on their own or ask teachers and classmates to help them with the necessary mathematics skills.

Why Use Projects in Mathematics? Projects give students a reason to learn mathematics. They provide students a direct route to mathematics literacy and are a powerful way for students to apply math concepts in real-world situations. As with the problems and projects people face in their daily lives, the problem solver has to make decisions as to which skills to use to complete the project. These projects are suggestions only; you and your students may wish to generate and to implement your own ideas as different math skills are explored and used.

Creating a Project Environment Projects invite students to explore and experiment. When students begin a project, you may want to arrange the classroom furniture to be more conducive to group work. Students will be better able to focus on the project if resources are readily available in the classroom, so you may wish to gather materials ahead of time.

The Teacher's Role During a project, the teacher's role is to serve as a guide rather than an informational source by asking questions that encourage students to think about the problem and use their problem-solving skills. This will encourage students to generate more questions to explore in the project. For these projects you are not expected to know all the answers or be able to solve all the problems but rather to model good problem-solving and investigative behaviors. Treat every student question as an opportunity to demonstrate how to approach a problem and pursue the answer.

Grouping Projects can be completed by individual students, but students often learn more by working together. Ideally, cooperative group projects mix students of different ability levels so that all students learn from each other and have a chance to succeed.

Successful group work does not just happen. Groups need to establish expectations of the roles and responsibilities of every member of the group. Encourage group members to take specific roles that ensure that everyone makes an overall contribution to the project by inviting students to assign a specific role to each group member.

When to Assess the Project Assessment should occur throughout all stages of a project.

- **Before a project,** assess to find out what students already know and what their needs, interests, and experiences are.
- **During a project,** assess to check progress, provide assistance, or modify activities, if necessary.
- **After a project,** assess to find out what students learned, evaluate the quality of the learning, and gauge the effectiveness of the project approach.

What to Assess In the project approach to mathematics, students have the opportunity to demonstrate a variety of competencies. Teachers can choose to evaluate students on any or all of the following:

- **Basic skills** include reading, writing, arithmetic and mathematics, speaking, and listening.
- **Thinking skills** include thinking creatively, making decisions, solving problems, thinking visually, and reasoning.
- **Interpersonal skills** include individual responsibility, self-esteem, ability to work in a group, self-management, and integrity.

How to Assess Record and use information in ways that you determine will be helpful to you and your students. Below are some ideas for routine forms of assessment that can provide regular feedback.

- **Observations** can take the form of watching, listening, discussing, questioning, challenging, or answering students' questions.
- **Checklists** can help you focus on specific aspects of your students' learning and behavior.
- **Interviews** of individuals, pairs, or small groups can provide valuable insights into students' thoughts about a project and the project approach, as well as how students view themselves and others.
- **Group assessment** can focus on how well all members of the group fulfill their roles, enabling the group to function successfully.
- **Student self-assessment** provides an opportunity to understand your students' perception of their own strengths, problems, and work habits, as well as their perception of the value of the project.
- **Portfolio assessment** can be accomplished by collecting samples of students' work on this project and throughout the unit.

Literature Connection You might want to read *Sea Squares* by Joy N. Hulme to your class to extend the lesson on the counting and ordering of numbers.

Technology Connection The software *Talking Classroom* from Orange Cherry (IIGS, for grades K–12) provides further exploration with how numbers are used all around us.

UNIT 2

Two-Digit Addition and Subtraction

RENAMING AND REGROUPING

OVERVIEW

In this unit students learn the algorithm for adding and subtracting two-digit numbers. The emphasis is on place value and on applying these skills to realistic problems. Students also learn to tell time. Students are introduced to fractions and make a connection between fractions and geometry. Then, students identify planes and solids and consider concepts of congruence and symmetry. Students also identify and complete patterns and function tables. In addition, they collect data and learn to read a thermometer.

Integrated Topics in This Unit Include:

- reading a graph
- modeling tens and ones
- adding two-digit numbers, with and without renaming
- applying addition
- subtracting two-digit numbers, with and without regrouping
- applying subtraction
- telling time to the hour, half hour, and quarter hour
- identifying quarters, halves, thirds, fifths, and other fractions
- relating fractions, geometry, and time
- identifying plane shapes
- identifying congruent shapes
- recognizing and drawing lines of symmetry
- identifying solid shapes
- identifying and completing patterns
- completing function tables
- collecting data
- measuring temperature

FRACTIONS

ADDING AND SUBTRACTING TWO-DIGIT NUMBERS

"By emphasizing underlying concepts, using physical materials to model procedures, linking the manipulation of materials to the steps of the procedures, and developing thinking patterns, teachers can help children master basic facts and algorithms and understand their usefulness and relevance to daily situations."

—NCTM Curriculum and Evaluation Standards for School Mathematics

GAMES

Motivating Mixed Practice

Games provide **basic math skills** practice in cooperative groups and develop **mathematical reasoning.**

Dot-Square Game	Lesson 46	page 98
Make 10 Bingo Game	Lesson 50	page 108
Get to 100 with the 5–10 Cube Game	Lesson 51	page 110
Four-Cube Addition Game	Lesson 53	page 114
Harder Yard Sale Game	Lesson 57	page 122
Add or Subtract a Ten Game	Lesson 58	page 124
Three-Cube Subtraction Game	Lesson 59	page 126
Three-Cube Subtraction Game	Lesson 60	page 128
Four-Cube Subtraction Game	Lesson 62	page 132
Roll a Problem Game	Lesson 67	page 142
Roll a Problem Game	Lesson 69	page 147
Time Game	Lesson 70	page 150
Choice of Game	Lesson 71	page 153
Harder Time Game	Lesson 72	page 156
Fraction Game	Lesson 75	page 165

THINKING STORIES

Integrated Problem Solving

Thinking Stories provide opportunities for students to work in **cooperative groups** and develop **logical reasoning skills** while they integrate reading skills with mathematics.

Ms. Arthur's Budget, Part 1	Lesson 51	pages 42–47
Ms. Arthur's Budget, Part 2	Lesson 60	pages 48–53
Plenty of Time	Lesson 68	pages 54–59
Take a Chance	Lesson 73	pages 60–65
Half a Job	Lesson 77	pages 66–71
The Ten-Minute Wonder	Lesson 86	pages 72–77

Story Summaries In "Ms. Arthur's Budget" students will use their mathematics skills to gain a basic understanding of financial responsibility.

In "Plenty of Time," students will use their mathematics skills to learn about time and will develop an understanding of congruent figures.

In "Take a Chance," students will use their logic and mathematics skills to reach a basic understanding of parts of a whole and probability.

"Half a Job" focuses on fractions as Mr. Muddle paints the room.

In "The Ten-Minute Wonder," Trixie finds several ways to speed up her errands for Mr. Breezy's dog training school.

PROJECT

Making Connections

The Unit Project establishes more real-world connections. Students work in **cooperative groups** to solve problems and communicate their findings.

In the Unit Project, students prepare a graph of weather information. Students may begin this project any time after Lesson 68.

Students will use their mathematics skills to learn about time and will develop an understanding of congruent figures.

UNIT 2

Two-Digit Addition and Subtraction Lesson Plans

	LESSON		PACING	PRIMARY OBJECTIVES	FEATURE	RESOURCES	NCTM STANDARDS
47	Graphs	101–102	1 day	to provide practice in reading a graph on a grid		Practice Master 47 Enrichment Master 47	2, 4, 5, 11
48	Place Value	103–104	1 day	to demonstrate how to convert numbers that are in nonstandard form to standard form		Practice Master 48 Enrichment Master 48	2, 3, 4, 7
49	Adding Tens and Ones	105–106	1 day	to provide practice in adding two-digit numbers with large addends		Reteaching Master Practice Master 49 Enrichment Master 49	4, 7, 8
50	Adding Two-Digit Numbers	107–108	1 day	to provide practice for adding two two-digit numbers	Game	Practice Master 50 Enrichment Master 50	4, 7, 8
51	Two-Digit Numbers	109–110	1 day	to provide continued practice in solving problems involving the sum of two-digit numbers	Game	Practice Master 51 Enrichment Master 51	1, 2, 3, 4, 8
52	Adding with Renaming	111–112	1 day	to provide practice in using an algorithm for adding two two-digit numbers	Thinking Story	Reteaching Master Practice Master 52 Enrichment Master 52	4, 7, 8
53	Two-Digit Addition	113–114	1 day	to provide practice solving realistic problems involving two-digit addition	Thinking Story	Practice Master 53 Enrichment Master 53	1, 2, 3, 4, 8, 10
54	More Two-Digit Addition	115–116	1 day	to provide practice in adding two two-digit numbers	Thinking Story	Practice Master 54 Enrichment Master 54	1, 2, 3, 4, 8
55	Practicing Two-Digit Addition	117–118	1 day	✓ to assess mastery of adding two two-digit numbers		Reteaching Master Practice Master 55 Enrichment Master 55 Assessment Master p.23	1, 2, 3, 4, 8
56	Keeping Sharp	119–120	1 day	to review basic subtraction facts	Thinking Story	Practice Master 56 Enrichment Master 56	1, 2, 3, 4, 8
57	Renaming Tens as Ones	121–122	1 day	to provide practice in converting numbers in standard form to a form that can be used in two-digit subtraction algorithms	Thinking Story Game	Practice Master 57 Enrichment Master 57	7, 8
58	Subtracting Multiples of Ten	123–124	1 day	to introduce subtraction with multiples of ten	Thinking Story Game	Practice Master 58 Enrichment Master 58	7, 8
59	Subtracting Two-Digit Numbers from Multiples of Ten	125–126	1 day	to provide practice in subtraction of two-digit numbers from multiples of ten	Thinking Story	Reteaching Master Practice Master 59 Enrichment Master 59	8
60	Two-Digit Subtraction	127–128	1 day	to demonstrate how to subtract two-digit numbers from two-digit numbers that are multiples of ten	Thinking Story	Practice Master 60 Enrichment Master 60	1, 2, 3, 4, 8
61	Subtracting Two-Digit Numbers	129–130	1 day	to provide practice in subtracting two-digit numbers	Thinking Story	Practice Master 61 Enrichment Master 61	8
62	Practicing Two-Digit Subtraction	131–132	1 day	to provide reinforcement and review of two-digit subtraction	Game	Reteaching Master Practice Master 62 Enrichment Master 62	8
63	Applying Subtraction	133–134	1 day	to provide practice subtracting two-digit numbers	Thinking Story	Practice Master 63 Enrichment Master 63	1, 2, 3, 4, 8
64	Subtracting with Money	135–136	1 day	to provide practice in subtracting two two-digit numbers		Practice Master 64 Enrichment Master 64	1, 2, 3, 4, 7, 8
65	Checking Subtraction	137–138	1 day	to provide practice using addition to check two-digit subtraction problems	Thinking Story	Reteaching Master Practice Master 65 Enrichment Master 65	1, 2, 3, 4, 8
66	Subtraction Check	139–140	1 day	to assess the students' mastery of subtracting two two-digit numbers		Practice Master 66 Enrichment Master 66 Assessment Master p. 24	1, 2, 3, 4, 8
67	Addition and Subtraction	141–142	1 day	to provide practice with two-digit addition and subtraction		Practice Master 67 Enrichment Master 67	1, 2, 3, 4, 8

LESSON		PACING	PRIMARY OBJECTIVES	FEATURE	RESOURCES	NCTM STANDARDS
68	Practice Adding and Subtracting 143–144	1 day	to provide practice solving mixed two-digit addition and subtraction problems	Thinking Story	Reteaching Master Practice Master 68 Enrichment Master 68	1, 2, 3, 4, 8
	Mid-Unit Review 145–146				Assessment Master pp. 25–26	
69	Check Your Adding and Subtracting 147–148	1 day	to assess students' ability to know whether to add or subtract to solve a word problem	Thinking Story, Game	Practice Master 69 Enrichment Master 69 Assessment Master pp. 27–29	1, 2, 3, 4, 7, 8
70	Telling Time—Hour and Half Hour........ 149–150	1 day	to review telling time to the nearest half hour	Thinking Story, Game	Practice Master 70 Enrichment Master 70	2, 4, 10
71	Telling Time—Quarter Hour 151–154	1 day	to introduce telling time to the quarter hour		Reteaching Master Practice Master 71 Enrichment Master 71	2, 4, 10
72	Telling Time—Halves and Quarters........ 155–156	1 day	to provide practice for telling time to the quarter hour	Thinking Story, Game	Practice Master 72 Enrichment Master 72	2, 4, 10
73	Fractions—Halves and Quarters........ 157–158	1 day	to introduce halves and quarters	Thinking Story	Practice Master 73 Enrichment Master 73	6, 12
74	Halves, Quarters, and Thirds........ 159–162	1 day	to provide practice identifying and showing halves and quarters	Thinking Story	Reteaching Master Practice Master 74 Enrichment Master 74	6, 12
75	Fifths and Other Fractions........ 163–166	1 day	to review and assess students' understanding of halves, thirds, fourths, and fifths	Game	Practice Master 75 Enrichment Master 75 Assessment Master p. 30	6, 12
76	Fractions and Geometry... 167–168	1 day	to provide practice in relating fractions to geometry and telling time	Thinking Story, Game	Practice Master 76 Enrichment Master 76	1, 2, 3, 4, 9, 10, 12
77	Fractions........ 169–170	1 day	to provide practice identifying fractional parts	Thinking Story	Practice Master 77 Enrichment Master 77	2, 4, 9, 12
78	Fractions of Numbers...... 171–172	1 day	to provide practice identifying fractional parts	Thinking Story	Reteaching Master Practice Master 78 Enrichment Master 78	2, 4, 6, 12
79	Geometrical Shapes—Plane Figures 173–174	1 day	to review definitions of some two-dimensional shapes	Thinking Story	Practice Master 79 Enrichment Master 79	9
80	Congruent Shapes........ 175–176	1 day	to help students develop and understanding of congruency	Thinking Story, Game	Practice Master 80 Enrichment Master 80	9
81	Symmetry 177–178	1 day	to help students recognize and draw lines of symmetry	Thinking Story	Practice Master 81 Enrichment Master 81	9
82	Geometric Shapes—Solid Figures........ 179–180	1 day	to review names of solid figures		Reteaching Master Practice Master 82 Enrichment Master 82	9
83	More Congruency........ 181–182	1 day	to review and assess students' understanding of	Game	Practice Master 83 Enrichment Master 83 Assessment Master pp. 31–32	1, 2, 3, 4, 8, 9
84	Patterns 183–184	1 day	to provide practice with identifying and completing patterns		Practice Master 84 Enrichment Master 84	13
85	Function Tables 185–186	1 day	to provide further practice with identifying inputs, outputs, and rules in function machines		Practice Master 85 Enrichment Master 85	3, 13
86	Collecting Data........ 187–188	1 day	to introduce reading charts that use tally marks	Thinking Story	Reteaching Master Practice Master 86 Enrichment Master 86	11
87	Measurement—Thermometers........ 189–190	1 day	to demonstrate how to read thermometers	Thinking Story	Practice Master 87 Enrichment Master 87	4, 10
88	Unit Review 191–194	1 day	to review two-digit addition and subtraction			
89	Unit Test 195–198	1 day	to review two-digit addition and subtraction		Assessment Master pp. 33–38	
90	Extending the Unit........ 199–200	1 day	to review two-digit addition and subtraction	Project		

UNIT CONNECTIONS

INTERVENTION STRATEGIES

In this Teacher's Guide there will be specific strategies suggested for students with individual needs—ESL, Gifted and Talented, Special Needs, Learning Styles, and At Risk. These strategies will be provided at the point of use. Here are the icons to look for and the types of strategies that will accompany them:

ESL

English as a Second Language
These strategies, designed for students who do not fluently speak the English language, will suggest meaningful ways to present the lesson concepts and vocabulary.

GIFTED & TALENTED

Gifted and Talented
Strategies to enrich and extend the lesson will offer further challenges to students who have easily mastered the concepts already presented.

SPECIAL NEEDS

Special Needs
Students who are physically challenged or who have learning disabilities might require alternative ways to complete activities, record answers, use manipulatives, and so on. The strategies labeled with this icon will offer helpful methods of presenting lesson concepts to these students.

LEARNING STYLES

Learning Styles
Each student has a unique learning style. The strategies labeled with this icon address a variety of learning modalities, such as tactile/kinesthetic, visual, and auditory.

AT RISK

At Risk
These strategies highlight the relevancy of math skills and concepts to the world outside the classroom. They are directed toward students who appear to be at risk of dropping out of school before graduation.

TECHNOLOGY CONNECTIONS

The following materials, designed to reinforce and extend lesson concepts, will be referred to throughout this Teacher's Guide. It might be helpful to order the software and video or check it out of the school media center or local community library.

TECHNOLOGY CONNECTION

Look for this Technology Connection *icon.*

- *Mighty Math Carnival Countdown* from Edmark, Mac, IBM, for grades K–2 (software)
- *Talking Clock* from Orange Cherry, Mac, IBM, for grades K–3 (software)
- *KidsMath* from GreatWav, Mac, IBM, for grades K–4 (software)
- *Math Mystery Theatre: Fraction Freaks* from EdCon/Imperial International, VHS, for grades 2–8 (video)
- *Interactive Math Journey* from The Learning Company, Mac, IBM, for grades 1–3 (software)
- *Troggle Trouble* from MECC, Mac, IBM, for grades 1–6 (software)

CROSS-CURRICULAR CONNECTIONS

This Teacher's Guide offers specific suggestions for connecting the math skills and concepts presented in the unit with other subject areas and with real-world situations. These strategies will be provided at the point of use.

Look for these icons:

- Geography
- Health
- Social Studies
- Music
- Science
- Math
- Art
- Physical Education
- Language Arts

LITERATURE CONNECTIONS

Relevant fiction and nonfiction books are suggested throughout the Teacher's Guide at the point where they could be used to introduce, reinforce, or extend specific lesson concepts. You might want to locate these books in your school or your local community library.

Look for this **Literature Connection** *icon.*

- *A Chair for My Mother* by Vera B. Williams, Greenwillow Books, 1982
- *Anno's Math Games II* by Mitsumasa Anno, Philomel Books, 1989
- *The Stopwatch* by David Lloyd, Lippincott, 1986
- *Look Both Ways: City Math,* pp. 62–63 "Calculate It!," Time-Life for Children, 1992
- *Doctor DeSoto* by William Steig, Farrar, Straus, and Giroux, 1982
- *Mathematical Games for One or Two* by Mannis Charosh, pp. 30–33, T. Crowell, 1972
- *The Case of the Missing Zebra Stripes: Zoo Math,* pp. 62–63 "Calculator Code," Time-Life for Children, 1992
- *A Nice Walk in the Jungle* by Nan Bodsworth, Viking Kestrel, 1989
- *Alexander, Who Used to be Rich Last Sunday* by Judith Viorst, Atheneum, 1978
- *Play Ball: Sports Math,* pp. 55–57 "Speeds of Racers," Time-Life for Children, 1993
- *Ming Lo Moves a Mountain* by Arnold Lobel, Scholastic, 1982
- *17 Kings and 42 Elephants* by Margaret Mahy, Dial Books for Young Readers, 1987
- *How Many Teeth?* by Paul Showers, HarperCollins, 1991
- *Six Sleepy Sheep* by Jeffie Ross Gordon, Caroline House, 1991
- *Counting Jennie* by Helena Clare Pittman, Carolrhoda Books, 1994
- *Arithmetic* by Carl Sandburg, Harcourt Brace Jovanovich, 1993
- *Arithmetricks* by Edward H. Julius, Wiley, 1995
- *Ten Brothers with Camels* by Gladys T. Cretan, Golden Press, 1975
- *Counting* by Lakshmi Hewavisenti pp. 14–15 "Four in a Line," Gloucester Press, 1991
- *P. Bear's New Year's Eve Party* by Paul Owen Lewis, Beyond Word Pub, 1989
- *The Boy Who Stopped Time* by Anthony Taber, M.K. McElderry Books, 1993

ASSESSMENT OPPORTUNITIES AT-A-GLANCE

LESSON	PORTFOLIO	PERFORMANCE	FORMAL	SELF	INFORMAL	MULTIPLE CHOICE	MASTERY CHECKPOINTS	ANALYZING ANSWERS
47					✓			
48					✓			
49		✓						
50	✓							
51					✓			
52				✓				
53		✓						
54				✓				
55			✓				✓	
56				✓				
57					✓			
58		✓						
59		✓						
60		✓						✓
61		✓						
62					✓			
63					✓			
64	✓							
65					✓			
66			✓				✓	
67					✓			
68				✓				
Mid-Unit Review			✓					
69			✓				✓	
70					✓			
71	✓							
72					✓			
73					✓			
74		✓						
75			✓				✓	
76					✓			
77								
78	✓							
79	✓							
80					✓			
81	✓							
82					✓			
83							✓	
84		✓	✓					
85					✓			
86	✓							
87					✓			
Unit Review/ Unit Test			✓		✓			

ASSESSMENT OPTIONS

PORTFOLIO ASSESSMENT

Throughout this Teacher's Guide are suggested activities in which students draw pictures, make graphs, write about mathematics, and so on. Keep students' work to assess growth of understanding as the year progresses.

Lessons 50, 64, 71, 78, 79, 81, and 86

PERFORMANCE ASSESSMENT

Performance assessment items focus on evaluating how students think and work as they solve problems. Opportunities for performance assessment can be found throughout the unit. Rubrics and guides for assessment are in the front of the Assessment Masters book.

Lessons 49, 53, 58, 59, 60, 61, 74, and 84

FORMAL ASSESSMENT

A Mid-Unit Review and a Unit Test help assess students' understanding of concepts, skills, and problem solving. The *Math Explorations and Applications* CD-ROM Test Generator can create additional unit tests at three ability levels. Also, Mastery Checkpoints are provided periodically throughout the unit.

Lessons 55, 66, 69, 75, 83, Mid-Unit Test. Unit Review, and Unit Test

SELF ASSESSMENT

Throughout the program students evaluate math skills through self-assessment activities.

Lessons 52, 54, 56, and 68

INFORMAL ASSESSMENT

A variety of assessment suggestions are provided, including interviews, oral questions or presentations, and debates. Also, each lesson includes Assessment Criteria–a list of questions about each student's progress, understanding, and participation.

Lessons 47, 48, 51, 57, 62, 63, 65, 67, 70, 72, 73, 76, 77, 80, 82, and 87

MULTIPLE-CHOICE TESTS (STANDARDIZED FORMAT)

Each unit includes a Unit Test in standardized format, presenting students with an opportunity to practice taking a test in this format.

MASTERY CHECKPOINTS

Mastery Checkpoints are provided throughout the unit to assess student proficiency in specific skills. Checkpoints reference appropriate Assessment Masters and other assessment options. Results of these evaluations can be recorded on the Mastery Checkpoint Chart.

Lesson 55, 66, 69, 75, and 83

ANALYZING ANSWERS

Analyzing Answers suggests possible sources of student error and offers teaching strategies for addressing difficulties.

Lesson 60

Look for these icons:

> ***"Observing, questioning, and listening are the primary sources of evidence for assessment that is continual, recursive, and integrated with instruction."***
>
> *—NCTM Assessment Standards*

ASSESSING INDIVIDUAL PROGRESS

WHAT TO EXPECT FROM STUDENTS AS THEY COMPLETE THIS UNIT

TWO-DIGIT ADDITION

At this time most students should demonstrate mastery of adding two two-digit numbers. Use Student Edition page 117 or Assessment Master page 23 to assess students' mastery.

TWO-DIGIT SUBTRACTION

At about this time most of the students should demonstrate mastery of two-digit subtraction by correctly solving 12 out of 16 problems on page 139. You might want to use Assessment Master page 24 as well to assess mastery.

MIXED TWO-DIGIT ADDITION AND SUBTRACTION

Use Assessment Master 27–29 to check students' ability to decide whether to add or subtract in a particular situation and to check their ability to add and subtract correctly.

SIMPLE FRACTIONS

Students should understand the concepts of halves, thirds, fourths, and fifths as applied to fractional areas. Consider using Assessment Master page 30 to assess students' understanding.

CONGRUENCY

Use students' answers to pages 181–182 and the questions asked during the demonstration to assess their ability to distinguish congruent objects from noncongruent objects and their understanding of how to check for congruency by tracing or placing one object on top of another. You might also wish to use Assessment Master pages 31 and 32.

UNIT 2

PROGRAM RESOURCES

THESE ADDITIONAL COMPONENTS OF *MATH EXPLORATIONS AND APPLICATIONS* CAN BE PURCHASED SEPARATELY FROM SRA/MCGRAW-HILL.

LESSON	BASIC MANIPULATIVE KIT	GAME MAT PACKAGE	TEACHER KIT	OPTIONAL MANIPULATIVE KIT	OVERHEAD MANIPULATIVE KIT	*MATH EXPLORATIONS AND APPLICATIONS* CD-ROM	LITERATURE LIBRARY
47						Lesson 47	
48	Number Cubes			base-10 blocks		Lesson 48	
49				base-10 blocks		Lesson 49	
50	Number Cubes			base-10 blocks		Lesson 50	
51	Number Cubes			base-10 blocks		Lesson 51	
52	Number Cubes					Lesson 52	
53	Number Cubes			base-10 blocks		Lesson 53	
54	Number Cubes					Lesson 54	
55	Number Cubes					Lesson 55	
56	Number Cubes					Lesson 56	
57	Number Cubes	Harder Yard Sale Games		base-10 blocks	bills, coins	Lesson 57	
58	Number Cubes			base-10 blocks		Lesson 58	
59	Number Cubes			base-10 blocks		Lesson 59	
60				base-10 blocks	bills, coins	Lesson 60	
61	Number Cubes			base-10 blocks		Lesson 61	
62	Number Cubes			base-10 blocks		Lesson 62	
63	Number Cubes					Lesson 63	
64	Number Cubes					Lesson 64	
65	Number Cubes					Lesson 65	
66	Number Cubes			base-10 blocks		Lesson 66	
67	Number Cubes					Lesson 67	
68	Number Cubes					Lesson 68	
69	Number Cubes					Lesson 69	
70	Number Cubes	Time Game	clock	clock face		Lesson 70	
71				clock face		Lesson 71	
72		Harder Time Game	clock	clock face		Lesson 72	
73	Number Cubes				bills, coins	Lesson 73	
74	Number Cubes					Lesson 74	
75	Number Cubes					Lesson 75	
76				clock face		Lesson 76	Half a Slice of Bread and Butter
77	Number Cubes					Lesson 77	
78	Number Cubes			base-10 blocks	bills, coins	Lesson 78	
79						Lesson 79	
80	Number Cubes					Lesson 80	
81	Number Cubes					Lesson 81	
82	Number Cubes					Lesson 82	
83					bills, coins	Lesson 83	
84							
85	Number Cubes						
86							Marti and the Mango
87	Number Cubes						

UNIT 2

Student Edition pages 99–100

Two-Digit Addition and Subtraction

INTRODUCING THE UNIT

Using the Student Pages To help students make the connection between what they learn in school and how it applies to the outside world, ask the students why it is important for a tile layer to know math. Then read aloud the paragraph on page 100.

ACTIVITY Give the students drawing paper, pencils, markers or crayons, and graph paper and challenge them to design a mosaic. Then invite students to compare their designs by asking questions such as: "How are your mosaics alike and different?" "What shapes did you use?" "What colors did you use?" "How did you figure out how big your mosaic should be?" "How will you figure out how many tiles you need of each color and shape?" and "What will you do if you have to make your mosaic large enough to cover the top of a table?" As a challenge, you might suggest that students make "shopping lists" of individual tiles in their mosaics, charting the number of each size, shape, and color.

SCHOOL TO WORK CONNECTION

FYI The following information and discussion ideas will help students see how the skills and concepts they learn in school are used in the world outside the classroom. Use as much of the information and as many of the questions as are appropriate for your students. Remember, discussion questions are designed to promote thinking; students are not expected to be able to answer all of them.

Making designs with tiles has been a popular art form for thousands of years. Mosaic is the art of making beautiful pictures or patterns with hundreds or thousands of tiny pieces of pottery, glass, or jewels. It is used to decorate everything from churches to garden walls to table tops. The ancient Romans were famous for their intricate mosaics, but the art reached its height in the city of Byzantium in the fifth century. A church, called Haigia Sofia and now a Muslim mosque, was built near the end of the fifth century and still stands. The dome of the mosque is covered in mosaic. The work took generations to complete because each tile is no bigger than a postage stamp and

UNIT 2

Two-Digit Addition and Subtraction

RENAMING AND REGROUPING

- time
- fractions
- congruent figures
- symmetry
- money

99

PROBLEM SOLVING

Junior Thinklab™*

Junior Thinklab™ provides a series of creative and logical problem-solving opportunities for individual students. The problems are designed to appeal to different cognitive abilities.

- Use Activity Cards 21–25 with this unit to reinforce ordering skills and concepts.
- Use Activity Cards 26–30 with this unit to reinforce classifying skills and concepts.
- Use Activity Cards 31–35 with this unit to reinforce perception and spatial relations skills and concepts.
- Use Activity Cards 36–40 with this unit to reinforce reasoning and deducing skills and concepts.
- Use Divergent Thinking Activity Sheets 6–10 with this unit to encourage creativity in art and in intellectual activity.

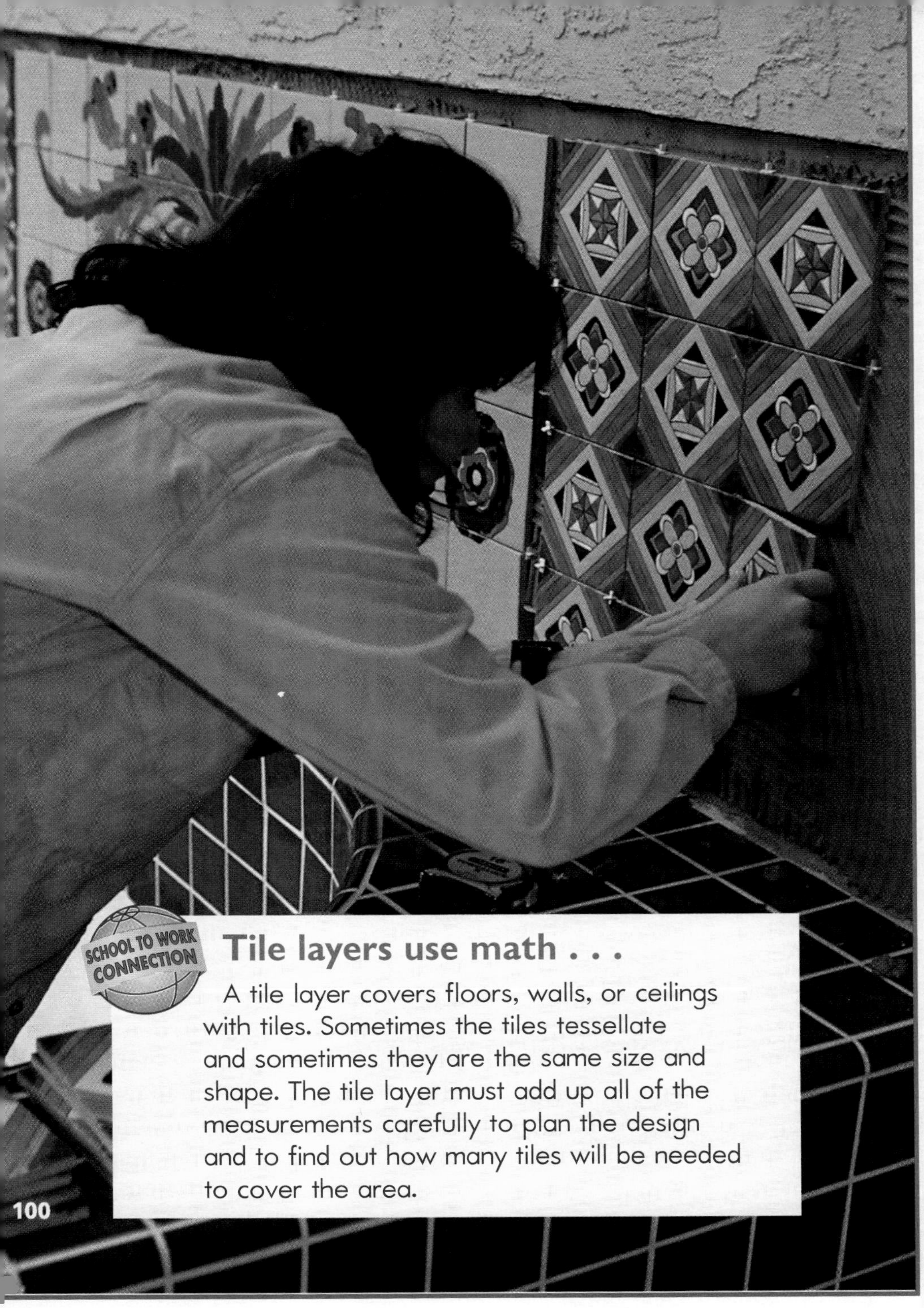

SCHOOL TO WORK CONNECTION

Tile layers use math . . .

A tile layer covers floors, walls, or ceilings with tiles. Sometimes the tiles tessellate and sometimes they are the same size and shape. The tile layer must add up all of the measurements carefully to plan the design and to find out how many tiles will be needed to cover the area.

100

there are millions of tiles. "How do you think you would plan a mosaic large enough to cover the floor of your classroom?" "How would you figure out what tiles you would need?" "How would you decide who would do the work and what they would do?" "How long do you think it would take the class to do the work?"

Laying tile, whether as an art form or as a profession, requires the utmost care and planning. Just as any pattern can be reduced to a mathematical equation, so making patterns in tiles requires careful calculation and execution. Once the design is established, it must be carried out with precision. This means calculating the size, shape, and number of tiles that go in each place and working out carefully the resources. "If you were going to put one color of new tile on your kitchen or bathroom floor, how would you decide how much tile you need?" "If you were going to use two colors of tile, what would you need to know in order to buy the right amount of tile?" "How would you figure out how much the tile would cost?"

COOPERATIVE LEARNING **Minds on Math** *Minds on Math* is a series of units covering problem solving, data collection, number sense, measurement, money, and geometry and spatial relations. Each unit provides a series of open-ended projects for individuals or small groups. These projects develop problem-solving and critical-thinking skills, utilize real-world materials, emphasize language, and integrate curriculum areas. Use projects from *Problems to Solve* to emphasize that there is more than one way to look at and solve any problem.

LITERATURE CONNECTION The books *Squeeze In* and *Two More* are charming ways to look at adding. These books are part of *the Math Explorations and Applications* Literature Library*.

Home Connections You may want to send Home Connections Masters 39–40 to families to provide additional activities for them to do together. These activities apply skills and concepts presented in this unit.

*available separately

LESSON 47

Student Edition pages 101–102

Graphs

LESSON PLANNER

Objectives

- ▶ to provide practice in reading a graph on a grid
- ▶ to explain how to draw conclusions from data on a graph

Context of the Lesson This lesson focuses on how grids can be used to record and organize data.

Materials	Program Resources
outdoor thermometer (optional)	Practice Master 47
overhead projector	Enrichment Master 47
	For extra practice: CD-ROM* Lesson 47

1 Warm-Up

5 MINUTES

Problem of the Day Present this problem to the class: The white table is 48 inches tall. The blue table is 48 centimeters tall. How can you tell which table is higher without measuring? (The white table is taller: 1" is longer than 1 cm so 48" is longer, or taller, than 48 cm.)

MENTAL MATH Write these problems on the chalkboard and have students fill in the blanks.

a. 12 inches = _____ feet (1)

b. 1 yard = _____ feet (3)

c. 1 yard = _____ inches (36)

d. 200 centimeters = _____ meters (2)

e. 1 meter = _____ centimeters (100)

f. 2 feet = _____ inches (24)

LESSON 47

Name ______________________

Graphs

We use graphs to help record and organize information.

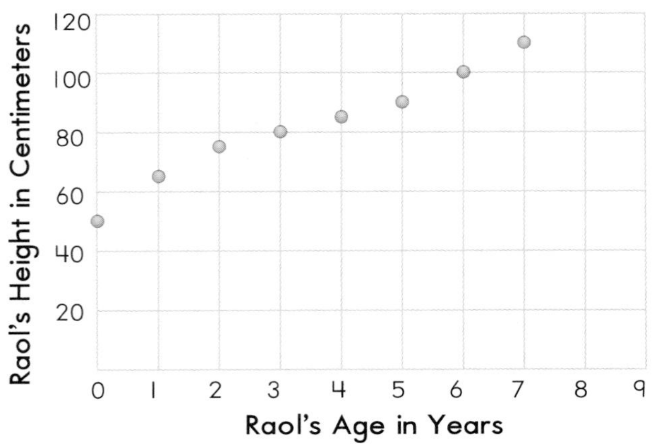

Use the graph to answer the questions.

1. How tall was Raol when he was three years old? 80 cm

2. About how old was Raol when he was 100 cm tall? 6

3. How tall was Raol when he was born? 50 cm

4. How tall was Raol when he was seven years old? 110 cm

NOTE TO HOME
Students read a graph.

Science Connection Provide an outdoor thermometer. Have students work in groups to keep track of the daily temperature outside at a specific time of day for two weeks. Have them record the data and then show it on a grid. When finished, groups can share and compare their grids.

RETEACHING

Display the grids on pages 101–102, or similar data, using an overhead projector. Have students show how to answer specific questions based on the data. Encourage students to point to the exact places on the grid as they find each answer.

*available separately

◆ **LESSON 47** Graphs

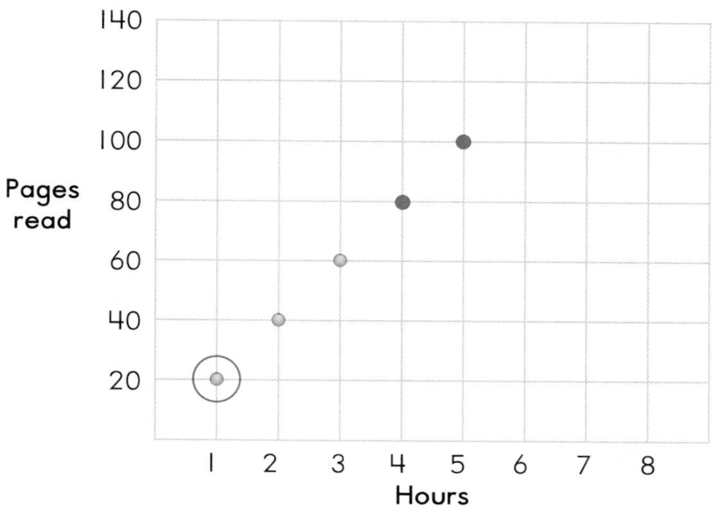

Use the graph to answer the questions.

Andrew is reading a book. After one hour, he had read 20 pages. He kept track on a graph.

5. Do you see the point that shows one hour and 20 pages? Ring it.
6. How many pages did he read in two hours? **40**
7. How many pages did he read in three hours? **60**
8. When do you think he will have read about 100 pages? **5 hours**
9. Put a point on the graph for five hours and 100 pages.
10. Put a point on the graph for four hours and the number of pages you think he might have read then.

NOTE TO HOME
Students read a grid and estimate.

PRACTICE p. 47

LESSON 47 PRACTICE Name ____________

Use the graph to answer the questions.

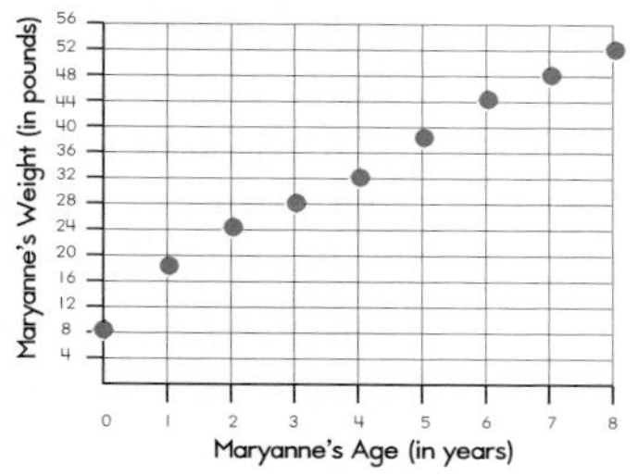

1. How much did Maryanne weigh when she was two years old? 24 pounds
2. About how old was Maryanne when she weighed 48 pounds? 7 years old
3. How much did Maryanne weigh when she was born? 8 pounds
4. How much did Maryanne weigh when she was six years old? 44 pounds

Math Explorations and Applications Level 2 • **47**

ENRICHMENT p. 47

LESSON 47 ENRICHMENT Name ____________

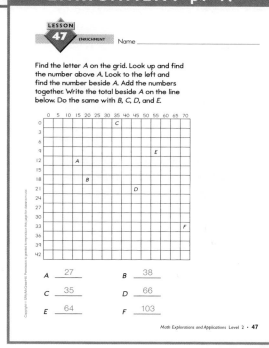

Find the letter *A* on the grid. Look up and find the number above *A*. Look to the left and find the number beside *A*. Add the numbers together. Write the total beside *A* on the line below. Do the same with *B*, *C*, *D*, and *E*.

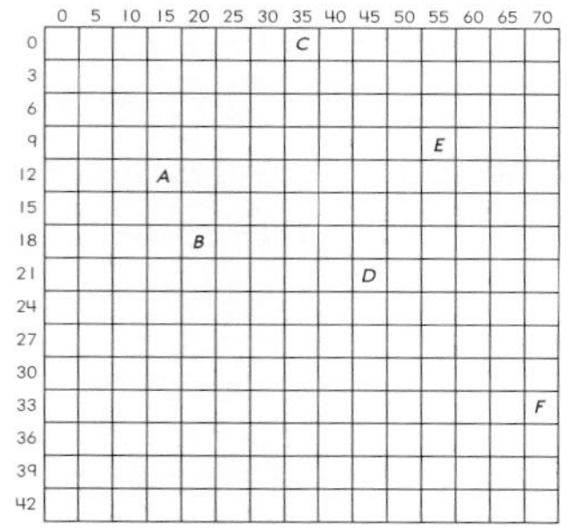

A 27 *B* 38

C 35 *D* 66

E 64 *F* 103

Math Explorations and Applications Level 2 • **47**

2 Teach

Using the Student Pages Have students look at the graph on page 101. Explain that the numbers at the bottom of the graph tell Raol's age and the numbers along the left side tell how tall he was at each age. Ask volunteers to explain how they can use the graph to tell how tall Raol was at one, four, and six years of age. Be sure students understand how to read the graph, and then have them complete pages 101–102 independently. When students finish, have them share and explain their methods and answers. Discuss their answers to questions 8 and 10 on page 102. Guide students to see that although they cannot be sure their answers are exact, they are reasonable based on the information given in the graph.

3 Wrap-Up

5 MINUTES

In Closing Ask students to explain the relationship between a bar graph and this kind of graph. (This graph has a point where the top of the bar would be on a bar graph.)

ALTERNATIVE ASSESSMENT

Informal Assessment Use students' responses to pages 101–102 to informally assess their ability to read data on grids.

Assessment Criteria

Did the student . . .

✓ correctly answer at least eight of ten questions on pages 101–102?

✓ recognize the relationship between the graph in this lesson and bar graphs?

✓ recognize the reasonableness of answers to questions 8 and 10 on page 102?

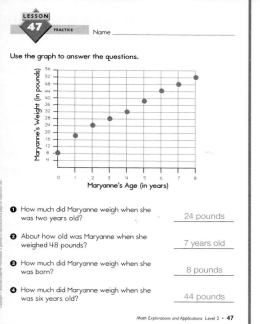

LESSON 48

Student Edition pages 103–104

Place Value

LESSON PLANNER

Objectives

- ▶ to demonstrate how to convert numbers that are in nonstandard form to standard form
- ▶ to demonstrate counting groups of ten and single units

Context of the Lesson This lesson prepares students to add two-digit numbers.

Materials	Program Resources
base-10 materials*	Number Cubes
craft sticks	Practice Master 48
	Enrichment Master 48
	For extra practice: CD-ROM* Lesson 48

1 Warm-Up

5 MINUTES

Problem of the Day Write the following problem on the chalkboard: What is a two-digit number in which the sum of its digits is 15 and the difference is 3? (96 or 69)

MENTAL MATH Present the following problems and have students use Number Cubes to show the answers.

a. 15 – 9 = (6) b. 4 + 8 = (12)

c. 13 – 8 = (5) d. 7 + 7 = (14)

e. 14 – 9 = (5) f. 10 + 8 = (18)

LESSON 48

Name ______________________

Place Value

2 tens and 14 = 34

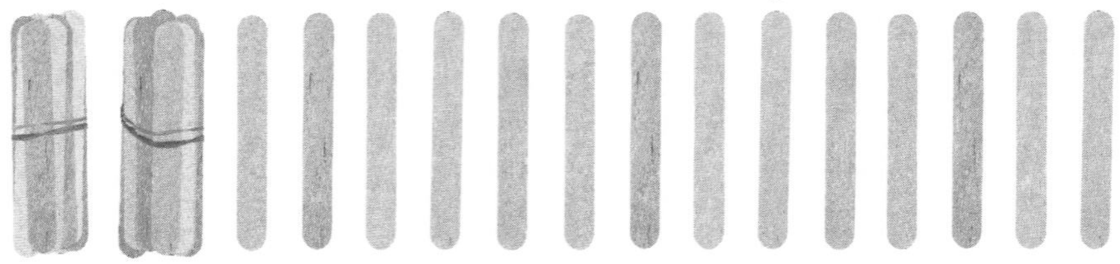

Use sticks to help.
Write the standard name for each of these.

1. 5 tens and 7 = 57
2. 3 tens and 12 = 42
3. 2 tens and 8 = 28
4. 2 tens and 13 = 33
5. 4 tens and 18 = 58
6. 8 tens and 0 = 80
7. 6 tens and 8 = 68
8. 5 tens and 10 = 60
9. 8 tens and 19 = 99
10. 0 tens and 8 = 8
11. 1 ten and 8 = 18
12. 1 ten and 14 = 24
13. 0 tens and 17 = 17
14. 3 tens and 15 = 45
15. 7 tens and 16 = 86
16. 4 tens and 18 = 58

NOTE TO HOME
Students use bundles of sticks to help them write numbers in standard form.

Why teach it at this time?

In the next several lessons, students will learn to add two-digit numbers. In order to understand how and when to regroup, they will need to recognize and know how to trade ten ones for one ten. This lesson provides isolated practice in this skill before students apply it.

RETEACHING

Write the following on the chalkboard: _____ tens and _____. Write the numbers from 1–19 on slips of paper. Place 1–9 in box one and 10–19 in box two. Have one student pick a number out of box one and write it in the first blank and a number from box two and write it in the second blank. Have another student rewrite the number in standard form. Replace the slips of paper and repeat until students understand how to write numbers in standard form.

*available separately

◆ LESSON 48 Place Value

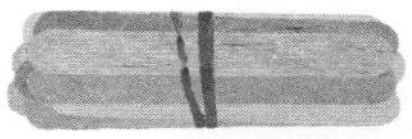

Each bundle has ten sticks. How many sticks in each picture?

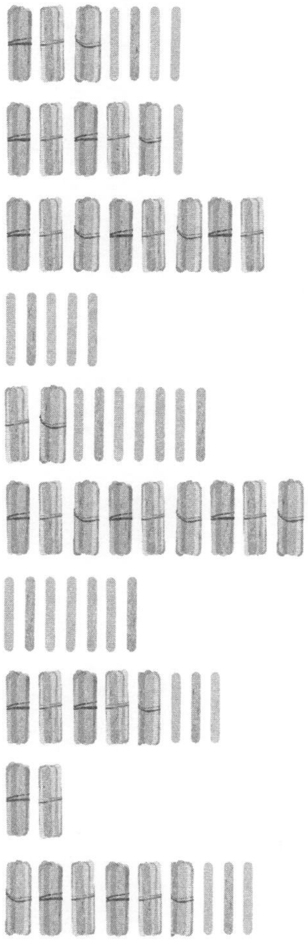

17. 34
18. 51
19. 80
20. 5
21. 27
22. 90
23. 7
24. 53
25. 20
26. 63

NOTE TO HOME
Students count using groups of ten.

PRACTICE p. 48

LESSON 48 PRACTICE Name ____________

Write the standard name for each of these.

1. 4 tens and 9 = 49
2. 8 tens and 4 = 84
3. 6 tens and 12 = 72
4. 6 tens and 16 = 76
5. 7 tens and 0 = 70
6. 2 tens and 17 = 37
7. 3 tens and 14 = 44
8. 9 tens and 5 = 95
9. 1 ten and 18 = 28
10. 1 ten and 13 = 23
11. 8 tens and 10 = 90
12. 0 tens and 19 = 19
13. 5 tens and 15 = 65
14. 4 tens and 11 = 51
15. 0 tens and 11 = 11
16. 7 tens and 10 = 80
17. 2 tens and 13 = 33
18. 3 tens and 12 = 42
19. 9 tens and 7 = 97
20. 6 tens and 0 = 60
21. 8 tens and 17 = 97
22. 5 tens and 19 = 69
23. 1 ten and 12 = 22
24. 6 tens and 9 = 69
25. 3 tens and 6 = 36
26. 1 ten and 15 = 25

48 • *Math Explorations and Applications* Level 2

ENRICHMENT p. 48

LESSON 48 ENRICHMENT Name ____________

Many thousands of years ago Egyptians used pictures for numbers.

A stroke shaped / meant 1.
An arch shaped Ω meant 10.

Write the modern numbers that match the Egyptian symbols below.

1. /// 3
2. ΩΩ 20
3. ΩΩΩ/// 33
4. ΩΩΩΩ 40
5. ΩΩΩ/// ΩΩΩ/// 66
6. //// ΩΩΩΩΩ//// 58
7. ΩΩΩΩ/ ΩΩΩΩ/ 82
8. ΩΩΩΩ// ΩΩΩ/ 73
9. ///// Ω//// 19
10. ΩΩΩΩΩ//// ΩΩΩΩ//// 98
11. ΩΩ// 22
12. ΩΩΩΩ/// 43

48 • *Math Explorations and Applications* Level 2

2 Teach

Demonstrate Display two bunches of ten sticks and 15 single sticks. Explain that you have two bunches of ten and 15 more. Ask students how many that is. (35) Ask how you can show the same number with more bundles of ten. (Bundle 10 of the 15 sticks and show 3 bundles of 10 and 5 single sticks.) Repeat for several more similar examples, such as five tens and 13 = 63; eight tens and 10 = 90.

MATH MANIPULATIVES **Using the Student Pages** Have students use base-10 materials and work in groups to complete these pages. Students who finish early can play the "Yard Sale" game introduced in Lesson 3.

3 Wrap-Up

5 MINUTES

In Closing Ask students to explain the procedure they used to write the standard name for their answers on page 103. (They should realize that whenever there were more than 10 units they took 10 from the units and added it to the tens.)

ALTERNATIVE ASSESSMENT **Informal Assessment** Use students' responses to pages 103–104 to informally assess their understanding of writing numbers in standard form and counting groups of tens.

Assessment Criteria

Did the student . . .

✓ correctly solve at least 13 of 16 problems on page 103?

✓ correctly count at least eight of ten sets of sticks on page 104?

LESSON 49

Student Edition pages 105–106

Adding Tens and Ones

LESSON PLANNER

Objectives

- ▶ to provide practice in adding two-digit numbers with large addends
- ▶ to provide practice with recognizing situations that require addition

Context of the Lesson This is the introductory lesson of seven lessons on two-digit addition.

Materials	Program Resources
craft sticks (loose and in bundles of ten) or other base-10 materials*	Reteaching Master Practice Master 49 Enrichment Master 49 For extra practice: CD-ROM* Lesson 49

1 Warm-Up 5 MINUTES

Problem of the Day Write the following problem on the chalkboard: There are 130 animals in a shelter: 80 are dogs, 10 are rabbits, and the rest are cats. How many are cats? (40)

MENTAL MATH Have students add and respond in unison:

a. 1 ten + 13 = (23)

b. 2 tens + 32 = (52)

c. 3 tens + 21 = (51)

d. 4 tens + 14 = (54)

e. 6 tens + 7 = (67)

f. 5 tens + 31 = (81)

LESSON 49

Name ______________________

Adding Tens and Ones

Use sticks or other objects to solve these problems.

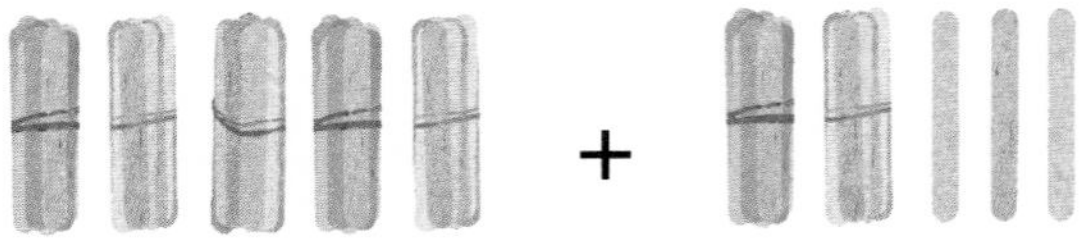

1. 50 sticks + 23 sticks = 73 sticks

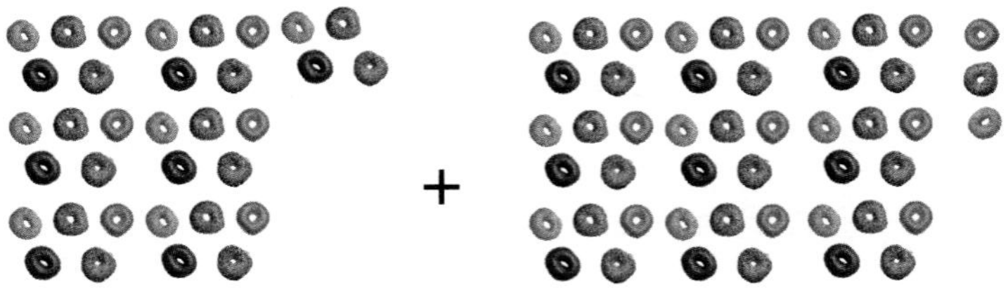

2. 34 bagels + 48 bagels = 82 bagels

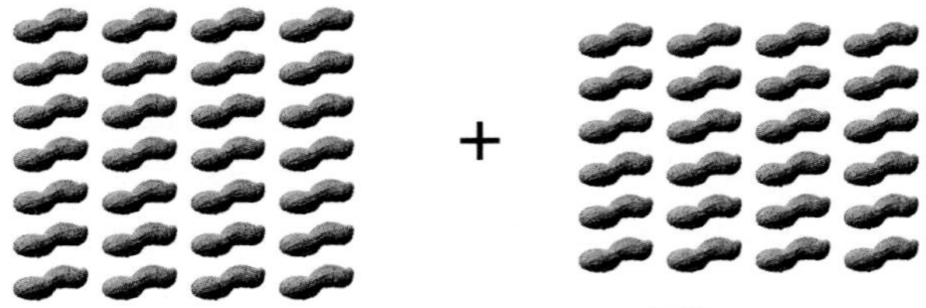

3. 28 peanuts + 24 peanuts = 52 peanuts

NOTE TO HOME
Students use models to help them add tens and ones.

Language Arts Connection Encourage students write a brief story about a friendly animal. The story must include three numbers greater than ten, and these numbers should either be added or subtracted from each other.

Literature Connection You might want to read aloud *Anno's Math Games II* by Mitsumasa Anno to reinforce lesson concepts.

RETEACHING p. 12

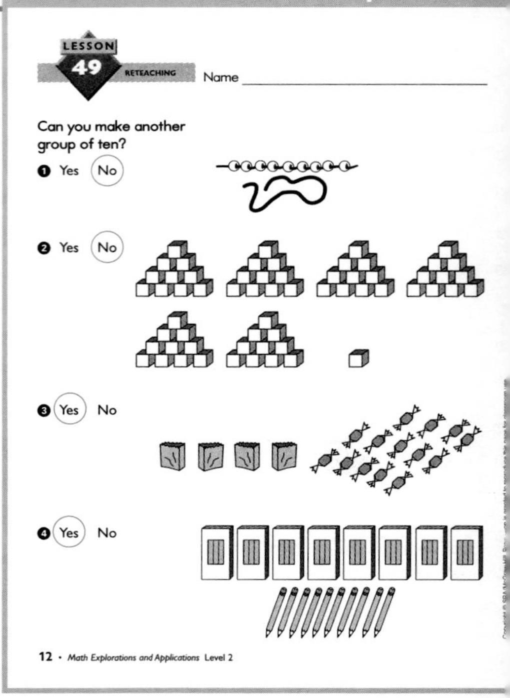
LESSON 49 RETEACHING Name ______________________

Can you make another group of ten?

1. Yes (No)
2. Yes (No)
3. (Yes) No
4. (Yes) No

12 • *Math Explorations and Applications* Level 2

*available separately

◆ LESSON 49 Adding Tens and Ones

How much?

4 34¢ + 22¢ = 56 ¢

5 51¢ + 16¢ = 67 ¢

Use sticks or other objects to solve these problems.

6 17 + 18 = 35

7 26 + 37 = 63

8 82 + 17 = 99

9 13 + 68 = 81

10 26 + 37 = 63

11 53 + 42 = 95

12 16 + 69 = 85

13 41 + 28 = 69

14 23 + 15 = 38

15 39 + 13 = 52

16 39 + 14 = 53

17 13 + 21 = 34

18 46 + 22 = 68

19 11 + 45 = 56

NOTE TO HOME
Students continue using models to help them add tens and ones.

2 Teach

MENTAL MATH **Demonstrate** Use craft sticks or other base-10 materials to show students how to add two 2-digit numbers. Count out four bundles of ten sticks and eight single sticks. Have students tell how many sticks there are (48). Take three more bundles of ten and five more single sticks. Have students discuss how to find out how many there are all together. Guide students to see that they now have seven tens and 13 single sticks. Ask whether they can make another bundle of ten from the 13. Show how, if necessary, and then have students count the total number of tens and ones (83). Point out that this shows that 48 + 35 = 83. Repeat the demonstration and discussion for several more problems such as: 23 + 41 = (64) and 26 + 44 = (70).

Using the Student Pages Allow students to use base-10 materials to complete pages 105 and 106. When finished, have them share their methods and correct their answers.

3 Wrap-Up

5 MINUTES

In Closing Have students tell how many tens and how many units they would use to add 16 + 27. (4 tens and 3 units)

ALTERNATIVE ASSESSMENT

Performance Assessment Observe how students use models to add. Check to see whether they understand that they must make as many bundles of ten as they can to write the answer in standard form.

PRACTICE p. 49

LESSON 49 PRACTICE Name ____________

Use sticks or other objects to solve.

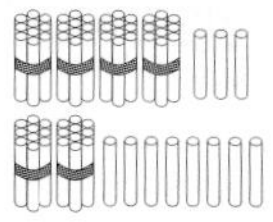

1 43 sticks + 28 sticks = 71 sticks

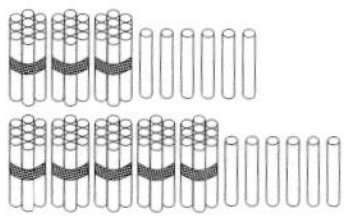

2 36 sticks + 56 sticks = 92 sticks

Solve.

3 38 + 18 = 56

4 21 + 45 = 66

5 16 + 39 = 55

6 13 + 44 = 57

7 17 + 29 = 46

8 15 + 27 = 42

9 42 + 46 = 88

10 13 + 58 = 71

11 15 + 16 = 31

12 24 + 29 = 53

ENRICHMENT p. 49

LESSON 49 ENRICHMENT Name ____________

There are four judges for the diving contest. Each judge has a red flag, a blue flag, and a green flag. After each diver takes a turn, the judges hold up a flag to show the score. The red flag means 25 points, the blue means 15 points, and the green means 10 points.

Add up the score for each diver.

Peter	one red, two blue, one green	65
Hiro	two red, two greens	70
Cal	one red, three greens	55
Shaneel	two red, one blue, one green	75
Marco	four blue	60
Keesha	one red, three blue	70
Quinn	three red, one green	85

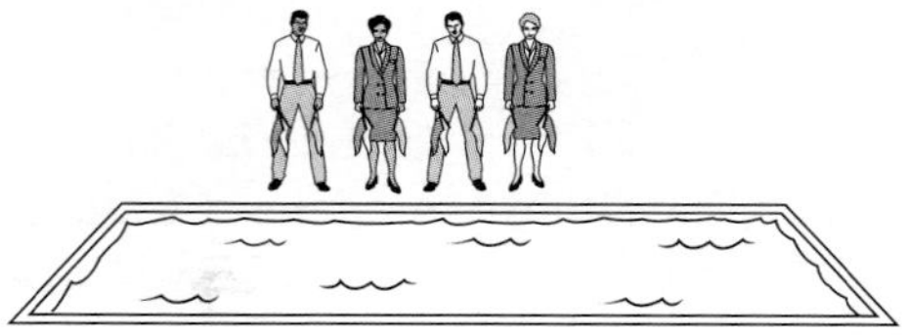

Assessment Criteria

Did the student . . .

✓ compute the correct number of tens?

✓ compute the correct number of units?

✓ correctly regroup units to tens?

✓ correctly solve 15 of 19 problems on pages 107 and 108?

LESSON 50

Student Edition pages 107–108

Adding Two-Digit Numbers

LESSON PLANNER

Objectives

- ▶ to provide practice for adding two 2-digit numbers with sums equal to a multiple of ten
- ▶ to provide more practice in recognizing situations that require addition

Context of the Lesson This is the second of seven lessons on two-digit addition.

Materials	Program Resources
base-10 materials*	Number Cubes
	Practice Master 50
	Enrichment Master 50
	For extra practice: CD-ROM* Lesson 50

1 Warm-Up

5 MINUTES

Problem of the Day Write the following problem on the chalkboard: Brad's bedtime is three hours after he finishes dinner. He takes one hour to eat dinner. Brad's dinner is served at 5 P.M. What time is his bed time? (9 P.M.)

MENTAL MATH Have students use their Number Cubes to answer the following problems:

a.	13 – 7 = (6)	b.	3 + 7 = (10)
c.	19 – 9 = (10)	d.	16 – 9 = (7)
e.	1 + 9 = (10)	f.	14 – 2 = (12)
g.	10 – 8 = (2)	h.	11 – 9 = (2)
i.	20 – 10 = (10)	j.	15 – 11 = (4)
k.	7 + 10 = (17)	l.	13 + 12 = (25)

PRACTICE

LESSON 50

Name ______________________

Adding Two-Digit Numbers

Use sticks or other objects to solve these problems.

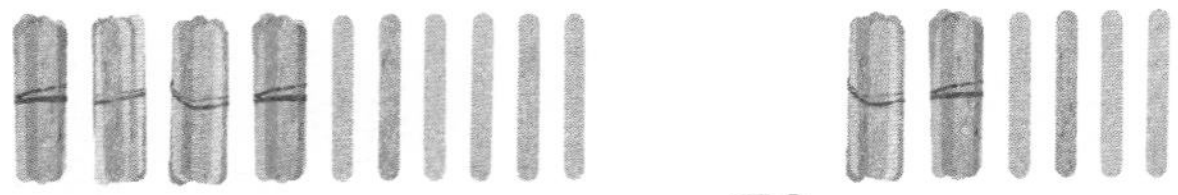

1. 46 sticks + 24 sticks = __70__ sticks

2. 27 dollars + 23 dollars = __50__ dollars

3. 25¢ + 15¢ = __40__ ¢

GAME Play the "Make 10 Bingo" game.

NOTE TO HOME
Students add two-digit numbers whose sums are multiples of ten.

COOPERATIVE LEARNING Have students work in groups of three. Ask one member to make up a two-digit addition problem and show it to another. Have that student model the problem using base-10 materials. Have the other student try to figure out the problem by watching how it is modeled. Then group members can switch roles and repeat several times.

Literature Connection You might want to read aloud *The Stopwatch* by David Lloyd to reinforce lesson concepts.

RETEACHING

Demonstrate how to solve other two-digit addition problems with sums that are multiples of tens. Have students say the steps of addition while you do them.

*available separately

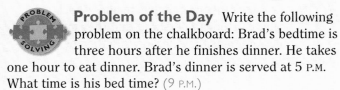

◆ **LESSON 50** **Adding Two-Digit Numbers**

Use sticks to add.

31 + 19 = **50**

Write what you did.

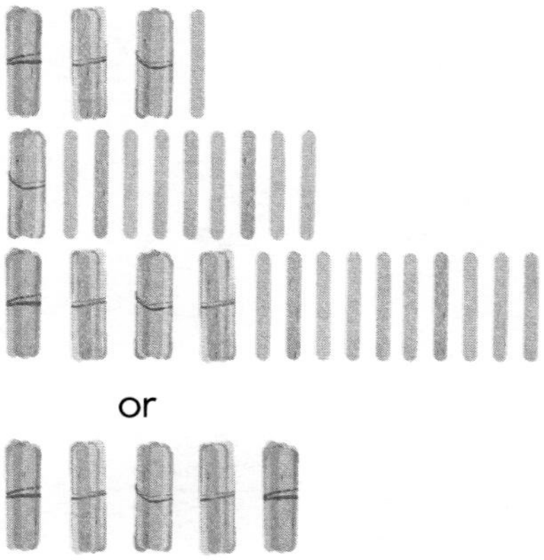

3 tens and 1
+ 1 ten and 9
4 tens and 10

or

5 tens and 0

4. 14 + 36 = **50**
1 ten and 4
+ 3 tens and 6
4 tens and **10** or **5** tens and **0**

5. 17 + 13 = **30**
1 ten and 7
+ 1 ten and 3
2 tens and **10** or **3** tens and **0**

6. 24 + 56 = **80**
2 tens and 4
+ 5 tens and 6
2 tens and **10** or **8** tens and **0**

NOTE TO HOME
Students continue using models to understand adding two-digit numbers.

PRACTICE p. 50

LESSON 50 PRACTICE Name ____________

Use sticks to add. Write what you did.

1. 24 + 46 = 70
2 tens and 4
+ 4 tens and 6
6 tens and 10
or
7 tens and 0

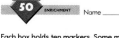

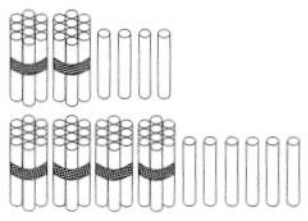

2. 19 + 41 = 60
1 tens and 9
4 tens and 1
5 tens and 10
or
6 tens and 0

3. 48 + 32 = 80
4 tens and 8
3 tens and 2
7 tens and 10
or
8 tens and 0

4. 77 + 13 = 90
7 tens and 7
1 tens and 3
8 tens and 10
or
9 tens and 0

ENRICHMENT p. 50

LESSON 50 ENRICHMENT Name ____________

Each box holds ten markers. Some markers are not in boxes. Ring the markers that will make the total number on the right.

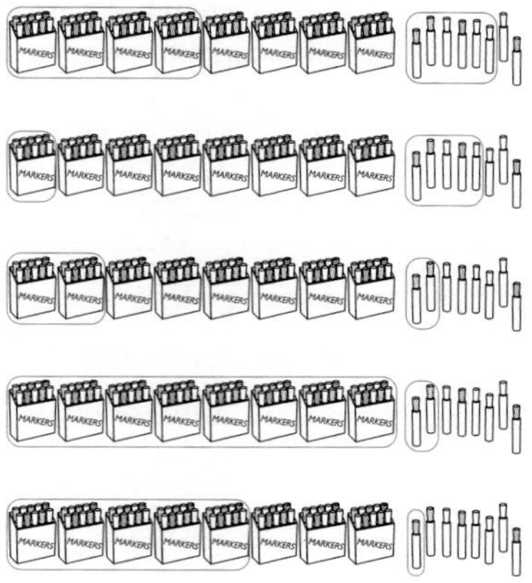

2 Teach

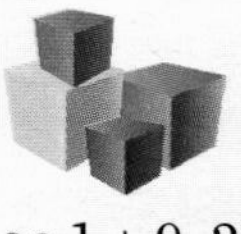

Using the Number Cubes Provide students with practice in single-digit addition facts, emphasizing those with sums of 10, such as 1 + 9, 2 + 8, and 6 + 4. Include some subtraction facts. Students should respond using Number Cubes.

Demonstrate Work with the class using base-10 materials to find solutions to problems in which the sum of the units is 10. Each problem should have a sum that is a multiple of 10 and is equal to or less than 100. Present problems similar to the following: Juan had $17. He earned $13 more. How much money does he now have? ($30)

Introducing the "Make 10 Bingo" Game Demonstrate and play this game to provide practice in finding pairs of addends to make 10. This game is similar to Bingo. You will need a chalkboard or pencil and paper and a 0–5 and a 5–10 Number Cube. Each player writes a row of any five numbers from 0 through 10. The leader rolls the two Number Cubes. Players decide whether either of these two numbers can be added to any of their five numbers to make ten. The player who is first to complete all five sums is the winner. To vary the game, extend the range of numbers or subtract instead of add.

Using the Student Pages Allow students to use base-10 materials to complete pages 107 and 108. You might want to do the first problem on page 108 with the class.

3 Wrap-Up

5 MINUTES

In Closing Have students name single-digit addition facts with sums of 10.

Portfolio Assessment Ask students to write an explanation of how to recognize that a number is a multiple of ten and to place their writing in their Math Portfolios.

Assessment Criteria

Did the student . . .

✓ compute the correct number of tens?

✓ understand why the sums had no units?

✓ correctly solve all six problems?

LESSON 51

Student Edition pages 109–110

Two-Digit Numbers

LESSON PLANNER

Objective

▶ to provide continued practice in solving problems involving the sum of two 2-digit numbers

Context of the Lesson This is the third of seven lessons on two-digit addition.

Materials	**Program Resources**
base-10 materials*	Thinking Story Book, pages 42–45
	Number Cubes
	Practice Master 51
	Enrichment Master 51
	For extra practice: CD-ROM* Lesson 51

1 Warm-Up

5 MINUTES

Problem of the Day Write the following problem on the chalkboard: A bookcase is 2 m tall. A chest of drawers is 300 cm tall. Which is taller? How can you tell? (the chest of drawers, because the bookcase is only 200 cm tall)

MENTAL MATH Tell students you have $50. Ask them whether you have enough money to buy the following items. Have them answer in unison.

a. a vase for $40 and a carpet for $5? (yes)

b. a shirt for $20 and a computer game for $31? (no)

c. a comic book for $1 and popcorn for $1? (yes)

2 Teach

MENTAL MATH **Demonstrate** Work with the class using base-10 materials to find solutions to two-digit addition problems, some of which require regrouping and some of which do not. Each problem should have a sum that is equal to or less than 100. Present word problems and written problems similar to the following: One class has 25 students and another has 28 students. How many students are in both classes? (53)

LESSON 51

Name ____________________

Two-Digit Numbers

Use sticks to add.

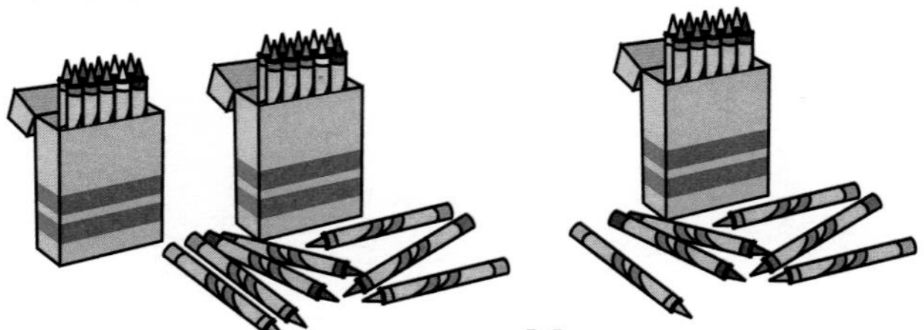

❶ 27 crayons + 16 crayons = 43 crayons

❷ 40 checkers + 32 checkers = 72 checkers

❸ 35 paper clips + 35 paper clips = 70 paper clips

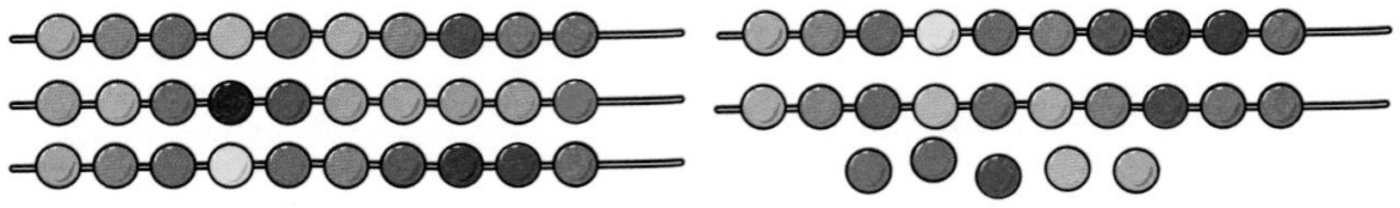

❹ 30 beads + 25 beads = 55 beads

NOTE TO HOME
Students practice solving problems by adding two-digit numbers.

Art Connection Have students make their own base-10 units using only things found around the house. Encourage students to recycle things that would have otherwise been thrown away.

Literature Connection You might want to read aloud "Calculate It!" in *Look Both Ways* by Time-Life, Inc. to reinforce lesson concepts.

RETEACHING

Continue using base-10 materials when working with students who are still having trouble adding two-digit numbers.

*available separately

◆ LESSON 51 Two-Digit Numbers

Use the Mixed Practice on page 375 after this lesson.

Use sticks to add.

28 + 35 = 63

Write what you did.

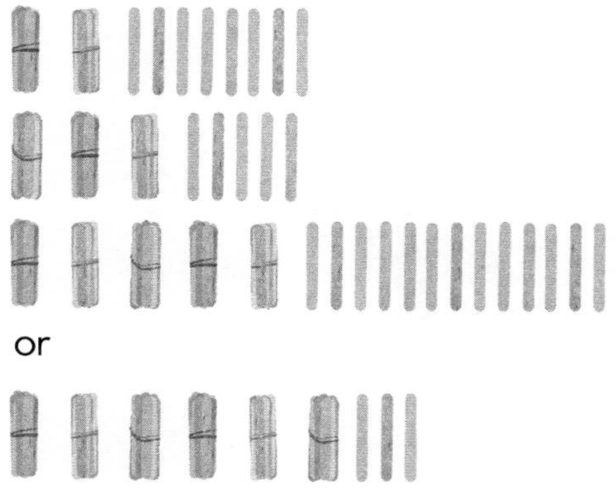

2 tens and 8

+ 3 tens and 5

5 tens and 13

or

6 tens and 3

5. 23 + 31 = 54 — 2 tens and 8; 3 tens and 5; 5 tens and 13 or 6 tens and 3

6. 44 + 56 = 100 — 4 tens and 4; 5 tens and 6; 9 tens and 10 or 10 tens and 0

GAME: Play the "Get to 100 with the 5–10 Cube" game.

THINKING STORY: Talk about the Thinking Story "Ms. Arthur's Budget, Part 1."

NOTE TO HOME
Students practice and play a game where they must add two-digit numbers.

Introducing the "Get to 100 with the 5–10 Cube" Game Demonstrate and play this game to provide practice in adding one-digit numbers to two-digit numbers. Students will need paper and pencil and a 5–10 Number Cube. Each player in turn rolls the cube and writes the number on his or her paper. In subsequent turns, each player rolls the cube and adds the number to the total he or she rolled in previous turns. The first player to reach or go beyond 100 is the winner. For an easier game, use the 0–5 Number Cube and a lower total. For a more difficult game, use more than one cube and/or a higher total.

Using the Student Pages Allow students to use base-10 materials to complete pages 109 and 110 if they wish. You might want to have students rewrite the problems on page 109 in vertical form before working them out.

Using the Thinking Story Read aloud "Ms. Arthur's Budget, Part 1" on pages 42–45 of the Thinking Story Book. Stop and discuss the questions asked throughout the story.

3 Wrap-Up

5 MINUTES

In Closing Ask students to explain how they know when they have to regroup ten units into one ten when adding two-digit numbers. Students should understand that they must do this every time the units add up to ten or more.

ALTERNATIVE ASSESSMENT

Informal Assessment As students play the "Get to 100 with the 5–10 Cube" game, observe students who have been having trouble with addition to make sure they are adding their rolls correctly.

Assessment Criteria

Did the student . . .

✓ add tens and units to get the correct answer?

✓ regroup when necessary?

PRACTICE p. 51

LESSON 51 PRACTICE Name ______

Use sticks to add. Write what you did.

1. 44 + 21 = 65 — 4 tens and 4; + 2 tens and 1; 6 tens and 5
2. 61 + 29 = 90 — 6 tens and 1; 2 tens and 9; 9 tens and 0
3. 53 + 12 = 65 — 5 tens and 3; 1 tens and 2; 6 tens and 5
4. 29 + 10 = 39 — 2 tens and 9; 1 tens and 0; 3 tens and 9
5. 40 + 38 = 78 — 4 tens and 0; 3 tens and 8; 7 tens and 8

Math Explorations and Applications Level 2 • 51

ENRICHMENT p. 51

LESSON 51 ENRICHMENT Name ______

Each girl may choose two T-shirts with numbers that add up to the number on her sign. Draw a line from each girl to the T-shirts she may choose.

Math Explorations and Applications Level 2 • 51

STORY 7

THINKING STORY

Ms. Arthur's Budget

Part 1

[Before beginning this story, write Ms. Arthur's budget on the chalkboard or a large piece of paper and cover it. Then uncover it when you get to the appropriate part of the story.]

Ferdie, Portia, Manolita, Marcus, and Willy saw a great new software game at the shopping mall. They even had a chance to try it out.

"I wish we could have that game in school," said Willy. "With that game we would really be able to practice our math facts."

Can you think of software programs that give practice with math facts? Answers will vary, but most students will have had experience with software that gives basic fact practice.

"We'll buy the program," said Ferdie. "How much is it?"

"That will be 40 dollars plus two dollars tax," the clerk replied.

"But we don't have 42 dollars," Portia answered.

"Can you change the price a little?" asked Manolita. "That way we may be able to afford it."

"No," said the clerk, "our store has a one price policy. If you want the software, you'll have to pay the full price."

The next day the children decided to ask

Ms. Arthur, their teacher, if she could get the software for them. “I’m sorry,” she replied, “but that software is not in my classroom budget.”

What do you think a classroom budget is?
Using the context of the story, students may be able to tell that a budget has to do with money.

“My budget is simply a list of things I will buy and how much they cost,” added Ms. Arthur. “It helps me keep track of how much money I spend. At the beginning of each year I prepare a budget, and Ms. Sullivan, the principal, approves it. It’s too bad you didn’t ask me last week.”

Why do you think Ms. Arthur said “It’s too bad you didn’t ask me last week?”
Probably her budget was approved last week.

Portia wanted to know how much money was in the budget. Marcus wanted to know what things were going to be bought. Ms. Arthur agreed to show the students her classroom budget. She wrote this on the chalkboard.

[Show the budget.]

MS. ARTHUR’S BUDGET

ITEM	DOLLARS	
	Budget	Spent
Storybooks	135	150
Puzzles	40	42
Math games	75	100
Software	50	0
Total	300	292

◆ STORY 7 Ms. Arthur's Budget, *Part 1*

"You see," said Ms. Arthur, "each year I am given 300 dollars to buy materials for my class. I prepare a list of things I need and about what they will cost. Then I ask Ms. Sullivan to approve it."

"But you have 50 dollars to spend on software," shouted Ferdie. "Where is it?"

Is Ferdie right? Yes and no. Yes, because Ms. Arthur hasn't bought any software even though she had it in her budget. No, because she overspent on other things and has only eight dollars left in her budget.

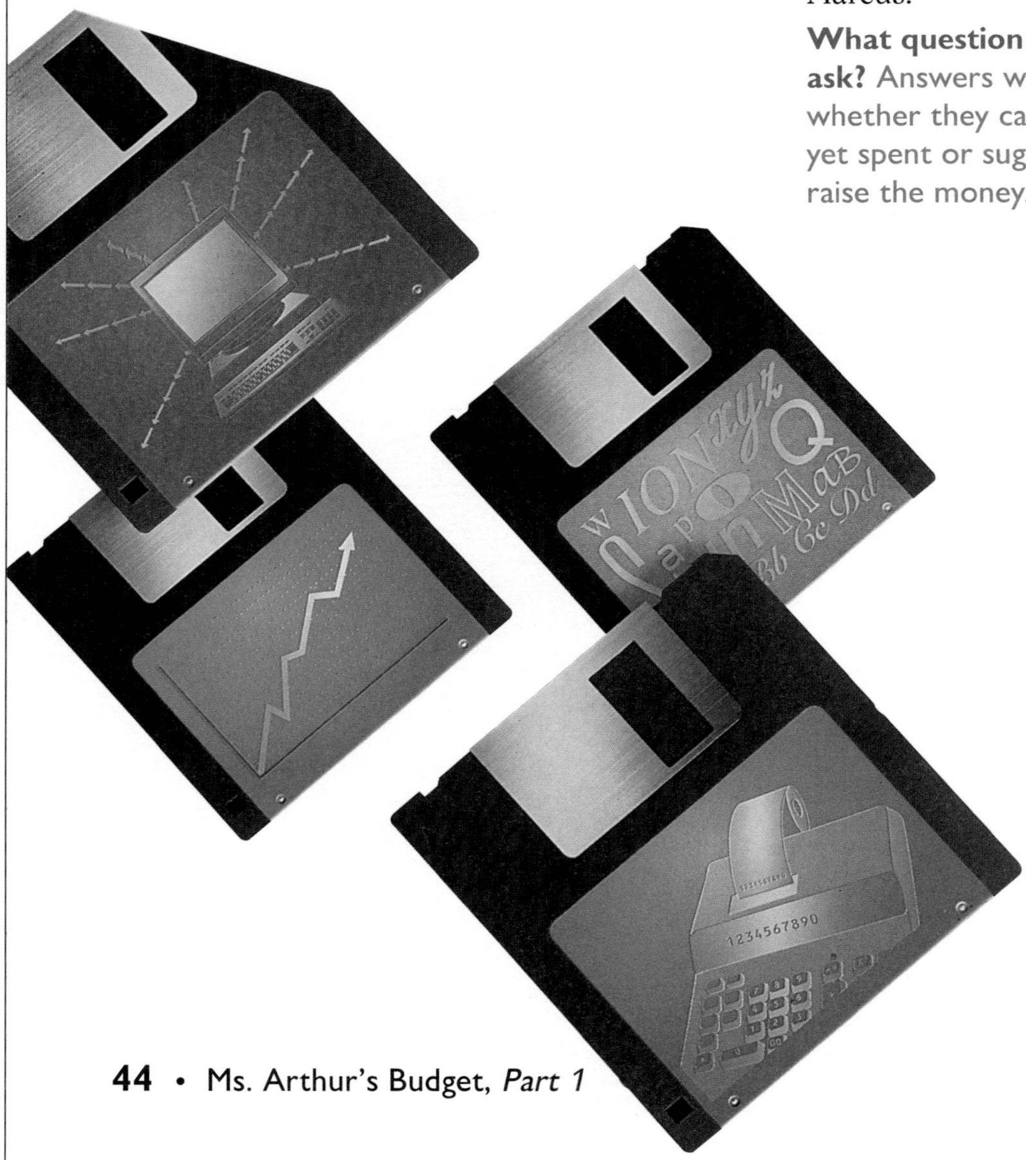

"That's right," said Ms. Arthur. "I have 50 dollars budgeted for software, but unfortunately I spent more money than I thought I would on other things. I have very little money left."

How much money is left in Ms. Arthur's budget? $8

How much did she overspend on storybooks? $15

How much did she overspend on math games? $25

"I have a question, Ms. Arthur," said Marcus.

What question do you think Marcus will ask? Answers will vary; Marcus may ask whether they can use the eight dollars not yet spent or suggest a way the class could raise the money.

"Can we use the eight dollars that is not yet spent for the software?" Marcus asked.

"Why yes," said Ms. Arthur, "but that's not enough money," she added.

How much more will the students need? $34

"We still need 34 dollars," said Portia. "We'll never be able to buy the software this year," she added.

"I have an idea," said Manolita. "Let's ask Ms. Sullivan to change the budget a little. That way we'll have enough money."

Does Manolita have a good idea? Yes and no. It's possible that Ms. Sullivan will have extra money, but it is not a good idea to overspend a budget.

What are some other ways of getting the money? Allow discussion. Other good ways are to work, ask the parent organization to contribute, take up a collection, and so on.

. . . to be continued

LESSON 52

Student Edition pages 111–112

Adding with Renaming

LESSON PLANNER

Objectives

- ▶ to provide practice in using an algorithm for adding two 2-digit numbers
- ▶ to continue to provide experience in recognizing addition situations

Context of the Lesson This is the fourth of seven lessons on two-digit addition.

Materials	Program Resources
none	Number Cubes
	Thinking Story Book, pages 46–47
	Reteaching Master
	Practice Master 52
	Enrichment Master 52
	For extra practice: CD-ROM* Lesson 52

1 Warm-Up (5 MINUTES)

Problem of the Day Write the following problem on the chalkboard: Suppose you buy a pencil for 10 cents and an eraser for 20 cents. If you pay for them with two quarters how much change will you get? (20 cents)

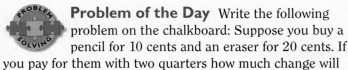

MENTAL MATH Have students add or subtract and answer the following problems with their Number Cubes:

a. 30 + 40 = (70) **b.** 60 + 70 = (130)

c. 50 + 50 = (100) **d.** 120 – 60 = (60)

e. 110 – 70 = (40) **f.** 100 – 40 = (60)

SPECIAL NEEDS **Meeting Individual Needs**

Have small groups of students model addition problems using base-10 materials. Help them keep a written record in the form of an algorithm as they complete each step.

LESSON 52

Name ____________________

Adding with Renaming

Add.

34 + 58 = ?

3 tens and 4 34

+ 5 tens and 8 + 58

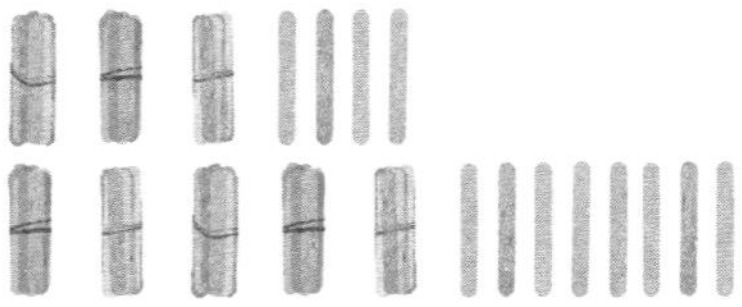

1 ten 1

3 tens and 4 34

+ 5 tens and 8 + 58

2 2

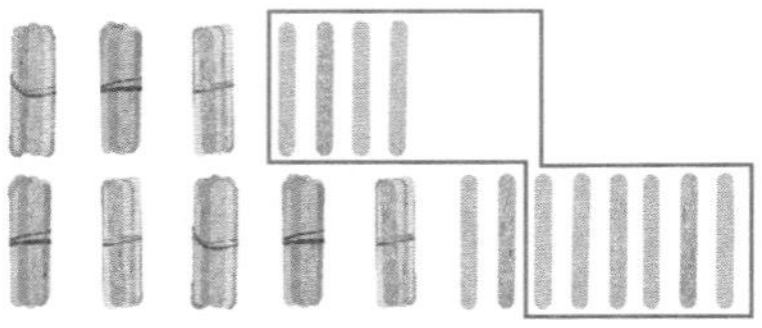

1 ten 1

3 tens and 4 34

+ 5 tens and 8 + 58

9 tens and 2 92

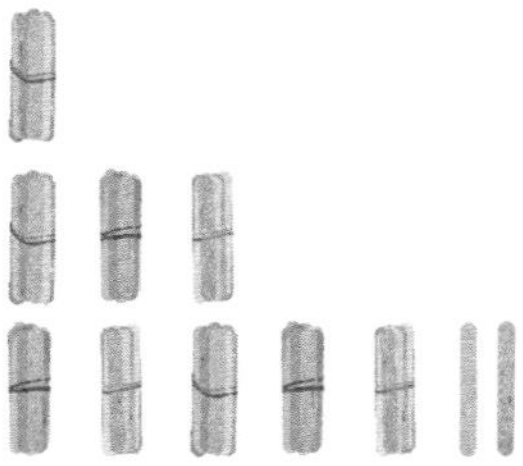

NOTE TO HOME
Students learn a standard procedure for adding two-digit numbers.

Literature Connection You might want to read aloud "Construct Perfect Magic" in *Math Wizardry for Kids* by Margaret Kerda and Phyllis S. Williams to reinforce lesson concepts.

RETEACHING p. 13

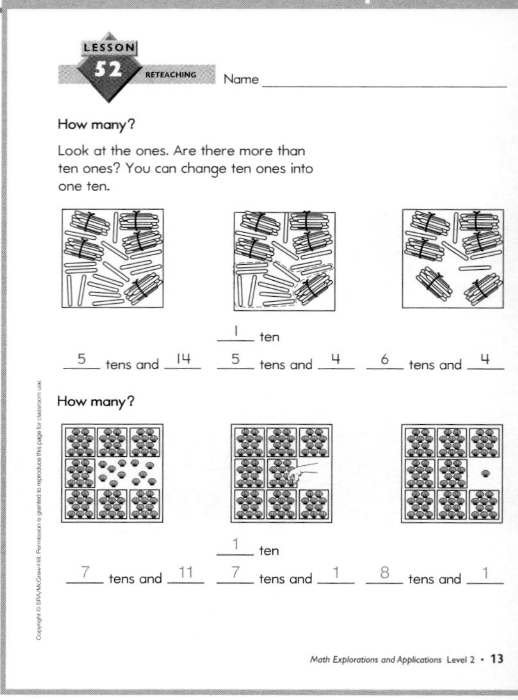
LESSON 52 RETEACHING Name

How many?

Look at the ones. Are there more than ten ones? You can change ten ones into one ten.

5 tens and 14 | 1 ten 5 tens and 4 | 6 tens and 4

How many?

7 tens and 11 | 1 ten 7 tens and 1 | 8 tens and 1

Math Explorations and Applications Level 2 • 13

*available separately

◆ **LESSON 52** Adding with Renaming

Add. Write your answers.

❶ 89 + 7 = 96	❷ 19 + 46 = 65	❸ 15 + 15 = 30	❹ 25 + 25 = 50
❺ 45 + 45 = 90	❻ 94 + 6 = 100	❼ 0 + 73 = 73	❽ 30 + 57 = 87
❾ 89 + 1 = 90	❿ 89 + 10 = 99	⓫ 27 + 36 = 63	⓬ 24 + 55 = 79
⓭ 36 + 6 = 42	⓮ 36 + 16 = 52	⓯ 59 + 9 = 68	⓰ 59 + 29 = 88

FANTASTIC FACT

Did you know that it takes nearly two days for your body to digest a meal?

NOTE TO HOME
Students solve addition problems with regrouping.

PRACTICE p. 52

LESSON 52 PRACTICE Name ______

Add.

❶ 76 + 14 = 90	❷ 79 + 12 = 91	❸ 68 + 14 = 82	❹ 17 + 15 = 32
❺ 27 + 35 = 62	❻ 14 + 56 = 70	❼ 33 + 14 = 47	❽ 49 + 26 = 75
❾ 39 + 43 = 82	❿ 26 + 57 = 83	⓫ 72 + 18 = 90	⓬ 64 + 17 = 81
⓭ 60 + 37 = 97	⓮ 81 + 18 = 99	⓯ 76 + 19 = 95	⓰ 25 + 38 = 63

52 • *Math Explorations and Applications* Level 2

ENRICHMENT p. 52

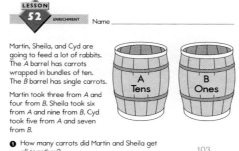

LESSON 52 ENRICHMENT Name ______

Martin, Sheila, and Cyd are going to feed a lot of rabbits. The *A* barrel has carrots wrapped in bundles of ten. The *B* barrel has single carrots.

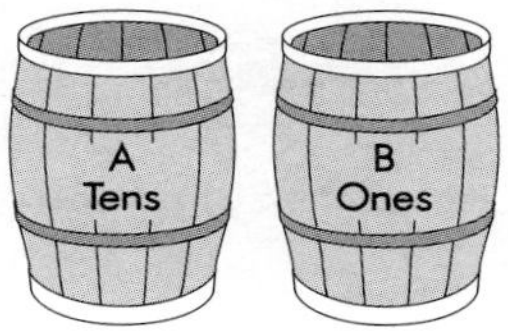

Martin took three from *A* and four from *B*. Sheila took six from *A* and nine from *B*. Cyd took five from *A* and seven from *B*.

1. How many carrots did Martin and Sheila get all together? 103
2. How many carrots did Martin and Cyd get? 91
3. How many carrots did Sheila and Cyd get? 126
4. The rabbit keeper checked the barrels when the children had gone home. There were 58 carrots left. How many carrots were there before the three children fed the rabbits? 218

52 • *Math Explorations and Applications* Level 2

❷ Teach

Demonstrate Write the following problems on the chalkboard:

34	3 tens and 4
+58	+5 tens and 8
(92)	(8 tens and 12)

Discuss how the problems are alike. Have a volunteer solve either of the problems and explain the method. Focus on why the 12 in the ones column is regrouped by placing the 2 in the ones column and the 1 in the tens. Present several similar problems, and encourage students to explain each step in their solution.

Using the Student Pages Discuss the algorithm on page 111. Show how the 12 single sticks were regrouped into 1 ten and 2 single sticks. Show students how each step of the modeled problem on the left reflects each step in the algorithm on the right. Encourage students to refer to this page as they complete page 112 on their own. Help students who are having difficulty.

Using the Thinking Story Present one or two new problems from those following "Ms. Arthur's Budget, Part 1" on pages 46–47 of the Thinking Story Book.

❸ Wrap-Up

5 MINUTES

In Closing Ask students whether they always have to regroup units to the tens when they add two 2-digit numbers. Have them give an example to support their answer. (No, when the sum of the units is less than 10 you do not have to regroup; example: 32 + 23 = 55)

SELF ASSESSMENT

When students have finished page 112, read aloud the correct answers. Have students correct any incorrect answers and write the number of problems they got right on the top of their page.

Assessment Criteria

Did the student . . .

✓ correctly add the units?

✓ regroup when necessary?

✓ correctly solve 13 of 16 problems on page 112?

LESSON 53

Student Edition pages 113–114

Two-Digit Addition

LESSON PLANNER

Objectives

- to provide practice solving realistic problems involving two-digit addition
- to provide practice adding two 2-digit numbers

Context of the Lesson This is the fifth of seven lessons leading to the mastery of two-digit addition.

Materials	Program Resources
base-10 materials*	Number Cubes
	Thinking Story Book, pages 46–47
	Practice Master 53
	Enrichment Master 53
	For extra practice: CD-ROM* Lesson 53

1 Warm-Up

5 MINUTES

Problem of the Day Present this problem to the class: Keith is three years older than Kendra. He is three years younger than Max. Max is twice as old as Mark, who is nine. How old are Keith, Kendra, and Max? (15, 12, 18)

MENTAL MATH Present the following problems and have students respond quickly.

a. 20 + 40 = (60) b. 70 + 40 = (110) c. 80 + 80 = (160)

d. 140 – 90 = (50) e. 70 – 40 = (30) f. 130 – 70 = (60)

2 Teach

Demonstrate Present students with several word problems similar to those below. Discuss how to solve each.

- It is 38 kilometers from here to City A. It is 57 kilometers from City A to City B. How many kilometers will you drive if you go from here to City A and then to City B? (95) From here to City A and back here again? (76)
- Tuan has $1.00. He sees four packs of stickers at 38¢, 59¢, 26¢, and 34¢. Which can he buy? (He can buy the 59¢ pack and 1 of any other; or 1, 2, or 3 of any but the 59¢ pack.)

LESSON 53

Name ______________________

Two-Digit Addition

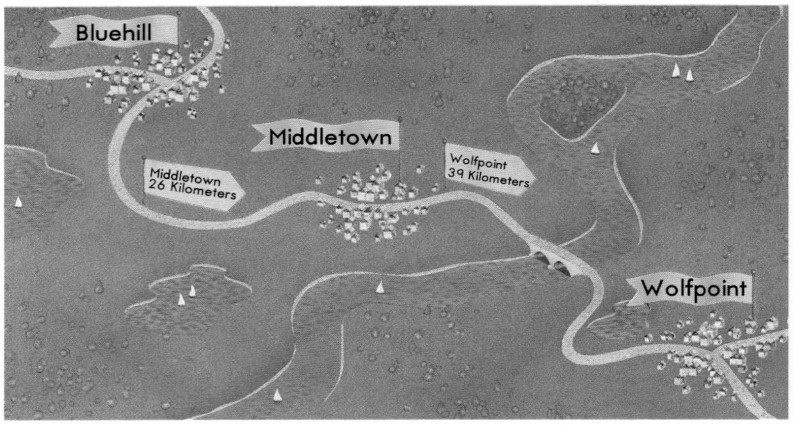

GEOGRAPHY CONNECTION

Use the map to answer the questions.

1. How far is it from Bluehill to Middletown to Wolf Point?
   26 kilometers + 39 kilometers = 65 kilometers

2. How far is it from Wolfpoint to Middletown to Bluehill?
   39 kilometers + 26 kilometers = 65 kilometers

3. How far is it from Bluehill to Middletown and back to Bluehill?
   26 kilometers + 26 kilometers = 52 kilometers

NOTE TO HOME
Students solve word problems.

Literature Connection Read *Doctor DeSoto* by William Steig to students to reinforce lesson concepts.

LEARNING STYLES

Meeting Individual Needs

If students have difficulty reading the map, read it and discuss it before students begin working. Make sure that students can understand the meaning of the numbers on the map.

RETEACHING

List a set of three two-digit problems on the chalkboard: 78 + 24 (102); 33 + 25 (58); 67 + 36 (103). Before working with the class to solve the problems, have students circle any examples they think require regrouping. Discuss how they knew and what they will do. Then solve all of the examples with the class.

*available separately

◆ LESSON 53 Two-Digit Addition

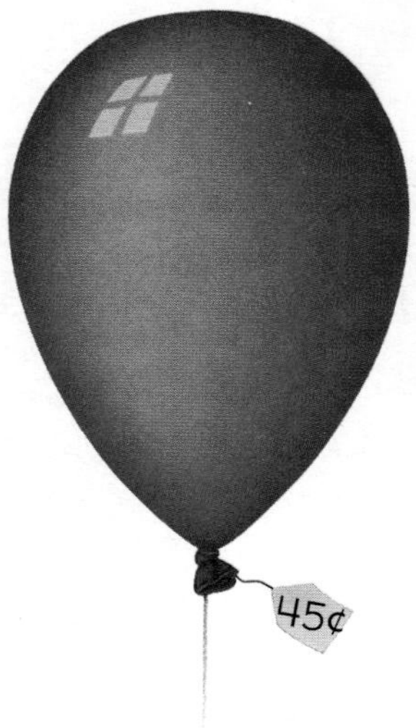

Solve the problems.

4. How much do the pen and pencil cost together? 41 ¢

5. How much do the toy soldier and balloon cost together? 93 ¢

6. How much do the doll and pen cost together? 92 ¢

7. How much do two pens cost? 58 ¢

8. How much do two pencils cost? 24 ¢

9. How much do two toy soldiers cost? 96 ¢

10. I have one dollar (100 cents). Can I buy the toy soldier and the doll? no

11. What is the greatest number of different things I can buy for one dollar? 3

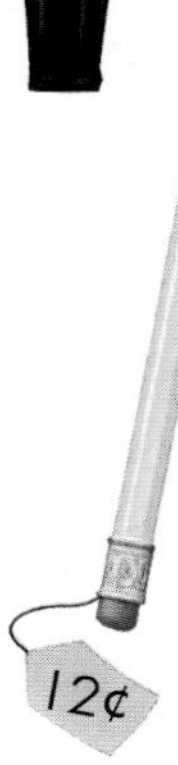

NOTE TO HOME
Students solve word problems.

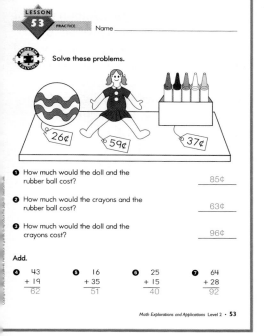

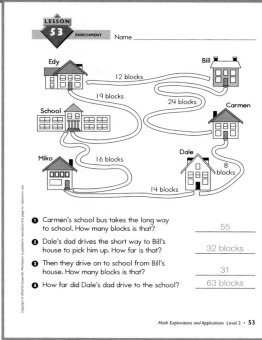

PRACTICE p. 53

LESSON 53 PRACTICE Name ____________

Solve these problems.

1. How much would the doll and the rubber ball cost? 85¢
2. How much would the crayons and the rubber ball cost? 63¢
3. How much would the doll and the crayons cost? 96¢

Add.

4. 43 + 19 = 62
5. 16 + 35 = 51
6. 25 + 15 = 40
7. 64 + 28 = 92

Math Explorations and Applications Level 2 • 53

ENRICHMENT p. 53

LESSON 53 ENRICHMENT Name ____________

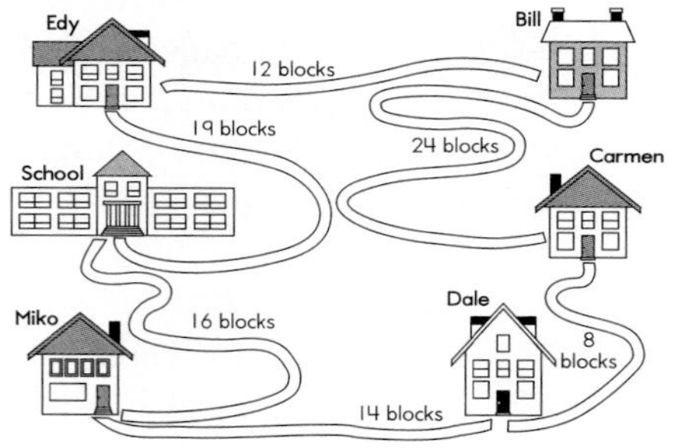

1. Carmen's school bus takes the long way to school. How many blocks is that? 55
2. Dale's dad drives the short way to Bill's house to pick him up. How far is that? 32 blocks
3. Then they drive on to school from Bill's house. How many blocks is that? 31
4. How far did Dale's dad drive to the school? 63 blocks

Math Explorations and Applications Level 2 • 53

Using the Student Pages Allow students to use base-10 materials, if necessary, to complete pages 113–114 independently. When students finish, discuss their methods and solutions.

Introducing the "Four-Cube Addition" Game Demonstrate the game, which provides practice in adding two 2-digit numbers. Students play in twos or threes, using pencils, paper, and Number Cubes. Players take turns rolling all four cubes, then grouping them to form two 2-digit numbers. Then they add the numbers to find the sum. If a 10 is rolled in either units or tens, the player rolls again until another number comes up. The player with the highest correct sum wins. You can play the "Easier Four-Cube Addition" game by having students use base-10 materials, such as craft sticks, to find the sum of the two numbers rolled.

Using the Thinking Story Present one or two of the problems following the story "Ms. Arthur's Budget, Part 1" on pages 46–47 of the Thinking Story Book.

3 Wrap-Up (5 MINUTES)

In Closing Ask students how they know when to regroup the ones column when adding two 2-digit numbers. (When the ones add up to 10 or more, they must regroup.)

Performance Assessment (ALTERNATIVE ASSESSMENT) Observe students during the "Four-Cube Addition" game to see whether they add each sum accurately.

Assessment Criteria

Did the student . . .

✓ correctly solve all three problems on page 113?

✓ correctly solve six of eight problems on page 114?

✓ find the correct sums when playing the "Four-Cube Addition" game?

LESSON 54

Student Edition pages 115–116

More Two-Digit Addition

LESSON PLANNER

Objectives

- ▶ to provide practice in adding two 2-digit numbers
- ▶ to provide practice in solving realistic problems involving two-digit addition

Context of the Lesson This is the sixth of seven lessons leading to the mastery of two-digit addition.

Materials	**Program Resources**
maps of the state (optional)	Number Cubes Thinking Story Book, pages 46–47 Practice Master 54 Enrichment Master 54 For extra practice: CD-ROM* Lesson 54

1 Warm-Up

5 MINUTES

Problem of the Day Write this problem on the chalkboard: Tomorrow is not a weekday. Today is not a weekend day. What day is today? (Friday)

MENTAL MATH Write the following equations with missing relations signs on the chalkboard. Have students fill in the blanks with <, >, or =.

a. 7 + 4 _____ 10 (>)

b. 12 − 7 _____ 5 (=)

c. 6 + 7 _____ 3 + 9 (>)

d. 15 − 8 _____ 12 − 5 (=)

e. 12 − 6 _____ 7 + 4 (<)

f. 3 + 3 _____ 11 − 7 (>)

LESSON 54

Name ______________________________

More Two-Digit Addition

Add. Write the answers.

❶ 78 + 1 = 79	❷ 78 + 10 = 88	❸ 43 + 7 = 50	❹ 43 + 17 = 60
❺ 62 + 21 = 83	❻ 34 + 46 = 80	❼ 34 + 47 = 81	❽ 62 + 20 = 82
❾ 28 + 17 = 45	❿ 63 + 37 = 100	⓫ 22 + 44 = 66	⓬ 39 + 18 = 57
⓭ 25 + 25 = 50	⓮ 39 + 49 = 88	⓯ 43 + 21 = 64	⓰ 43 + 11 = 54
⓱ 40 + 37 = 77	⓲ 53 + 21 = 74	⓳ 53 + 20 = 73	⓴ 42 + 36 = 78

NOTE TO HOME
Students practice adding two-digit numbers with and without regrouping.

Literature Connection Read aloud pages 30–33 of *Mathematical Games for One or Two* by Mannis Charosh to reinforce lesson concepts.

Social Studies Connection Have students work in small groups. Provide a simple map of your state for each group. Have groups choose a place they would like to visit that is between 20 and 50 miles from your town. Have them calculate the distance they would travel to and from the location they choose and explain why they chose that place.

RETEACHING

Begin by writing simple addition facts on the chalkboard. Do not move on to harder ones until everyone can solve the simple problems. Then move on to more complex problems. Continue until everyone can solve two 2-digit addition problems in a row. You might want to follow this sequence: 4 + 9 (13; one digit + one digit); 12 + 3 (15; two digits + one digit); 14 + 12 (26; two digits + two digits, no regrouping); 16 + 7 (23; two digits + one digit with regrouping); and finally 16 + 17 (33; two digits + two digits with regrouping).

*available separately

◆ **LESSON 54** More Two-Digit Addition

Solve the problems.

Bus Schedule

From Granville	Leaves	Arrives	Round Trip Price
to Allentown	2:17 PM	8:32 PM	$32
to Choirville	6:54 AM	11:43 AM	$24
to Middlebury	7:02 AM	4:38 PM	$48
to Park City	11:50 AM	1:20 PM	$9
to Danville	12:43 PM	9:47 PM	$53

21. How much will it cost to take trips to both Park City and Allentown? $ **41**
22. How much will it cost to take trips to both Middlebury and Allentown? $ **80**
23. How much will it cost to take trips to both Danville and Choirville? $ **77**
24. What time does the bus leave for Middlebury? **7:02 A.M.**

MATH JOURNAL

Which city do you think is closest to Granville? Explain your answer in your Math Journal.

NOTE TO HOME
Students practice ~~addition and~~ reading a table.

❷ Teach

Using the Number Cubes Write two-digit addition problems on the chalkboard one at a time, and have students use pencil and paper to solve them. Be sure all sums are 100 or less; for example 27 + 34 (61) and 46 + 31 (77). Have students find, hide, and show their answer using their Number Cubes.

Using the Student Pages Have students work independently to complete page 115. Help those students who are still having difficulty adding two-digit numbers. Work page 116 with the class. Discuss what a schedule is and help students read it. As you complete each problem, have students explain how they arrived at the answer.

Using the Thinking Story Present one or two problems from those following "Ms. Arthur's Budget, Part 1" on pages 46–47 of the Thinking Story Book.

❸ Wrap-Up

5 MINUTES

In Closing Have students make up their own word problem using the bus schedule on page 116.

SELF ASSESSMENT

Conduct brief interviews with students. Ask them whether they feel they understand how to add two-digit numbers. Encourage students who do not understand this skill to explain where they are having difficulty.

PRACTICE p. 54

LESSON 54 PRACTICE Name ____

Add.

1. 48 + 6 = 54	2. 18 + 32 = 50	3. 20 + 65 = 85
4. 33 + 49 = 82	5. 66 + 34 = 100	6. 28 + 63 = 91
7. 29 + 19 = 48	8. 12 + 55 = 67	9. 72 + 13 = 85
10. 83 + 7 = 90	11. 29 + 29 = 58	12. 35 + 15 = 50
13. 44 + 18 = 62	14. 16 + 19 = 35	15. 76 + 17 = 93

54 • Math Explorations and Applications Level 2

ENRICHMENT p. 54

LESSON 54 ENRICHMENT Name ____

The chart shows how many kilometers each person ran. Look at the chart. Write and solve the number sentence for each question.

Name	Kilometers
Joe	46
Stacy	31
Misha	25
Tyler	51
Carrie	37

1. How many kilometers did Tyler and Carrie run all together? 51 + 37 = 88
2. How many kilometers did Joe and Misha run all together? 46 + 25 = 71
3. How many kilometers did Stacy and Tyler run all together? 31 + 51 = 82
4. Which runner ran more than two times farther than which other runner? Tyler ran more than two times farther than Misha.
5. Which two runners ran less than 60 kilometers all together? Stacy and Misha

54 • Math Explorations and Applications Level 2

Assessment Criteria

Did the student . . .

✓ correctly solve 17 of 20 problems on page 115?

✓ demonstrate understanding of how to read a bus schedule?

✓ contribute to solving the problems on page 116?

LESSON 55

Student Edition pages 117–118

Practicing Two-Digit Addition

LESSON PLANNER

Objective

✓ to assess mastery of adding two 2-digit numbers

Context of the Lesson This, the last of seven lessons focusing on adding two 2-digit numbers, contains Mastery Checkpoint 7 for assessing mastery of adding two 2-digit numbers.

Materials	Program Resources
none	Number Cubes
	Reteaching Master
	Practice Master 55
	Enrichment Master 55
	Assessment Master
	For extra practice: CD-ROM* Lesson 55

1 Warm-Up

5 MINUTES

Problem of the Day Write the following problem on the chalkboard: Suppose you have 89¢. Can you buy a 47¢ pen and a 39¢ pencil? Why or why not? (Yes; 47 + 39 = 86, so there is enough money.)

MENTAL MATH Write the following sets of numbers on the chalkboard and have students rewrite each set of numbers in order from least to greatest.

a. 12, 85, 29, 44, 9 (9, 12, 29, 44, 85)

b. 76, 67, 92, 29, 13, 9, 55, 60 (9, 13, 29, 55, 60, 67, 76, 92)

2 Teach

Demonstrate Explain that students will be given a test on two-digit addition. Help them prepare for the test in one of the following ways: Have them work with partners to practice; have them play the "Four-Cube Addition" game; or, work with the class to solve two-digit addition problems you write on the chalkboard.

LESSON 55

Name ______________________________

Practicing Two-Digit Addition

How well can you add? Write the answers.

❶	❷	❸	❹
56	34	28	25
+ 28	+ 27	+ 41	+ 25
84	**81**	**69**	**50**

❺	❻	❼	❽
34	61	37	43
+ 55	+ 29	+ 58	+ 7
89	**90**	**95**	**50**

❾	❿	⓫	⓬
75	82	8	28
+ 19	+ 7	+ 49	+ 27
94	**89**	**57**	**55**

⓭	⓮	⓯	⓰
26	28	43	35
+ 54	+ 25	+ 26	+ 44
80	**53**	**69**	**79**

⓱	⓲	⓳	⓴
52	63	49	44
+ 21	+ 18	+ 20	+ 44
73	**81**	**69**	**88**

Number correct ☐

NOTE TO HOME
Students check their skill with two-digit addition.

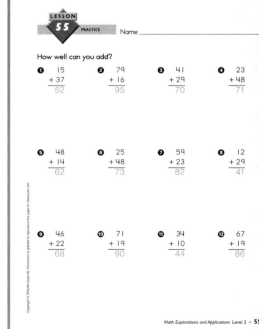

RETEACHING p. 14

LESSON 55 RETEACHING Name ______________________

Example:

Add. 3 tens and 9
+ 2 tens and 5

Step 1 Add the ones.	Step 2 Rewrite.	Step 3 Add the tens.
	1 ten	1 ten
3 tens and 9	3 tens and 9	3 tens and 9
+ 2 tens and 5	+ 2 tens and 5	+ 2 tens and 5
14	4	6 tens and 4

Add.

❶ 1 ten
4 tens and 6
+ 3 tens and 8
8 tens and 4

❷ 1 ten
1 ten and 5
+ 5 tens and 5
7 tens and 0

❸ 1 ten
3 tens and 5 → 35
+ 2 tens and 7   + 27
6 tens and 2   62

❹ 1 ten
4 tens and 4 → 44
+ 1 ten and 8   + 18
6 tens and 2   62

❺ 56
+ 37
93

❻ 12
+ 78
90

PRACTICE p. 55

LESSON 55 PRACTICE Name ______________________

How well can you add?

❶	❷	❸	❹
15	79	41	23
+ 37	+ 16	+ 29	+ 48
52	95	70	71

❺	❻	❼	❽
48	25	59	12
+ 14	+ 48	+ 23	+ 29
62	73	82	41

❾	❿	⓫	⓬
46	71	34	67
+ 22	+ 19	+ 10	+ 19
68	90	44	86

*available separately

◆ **LESSON 55** Practicing Two-Digit Addition

Players throw darts. If the sum equals 96, the player wins a teddy bear.

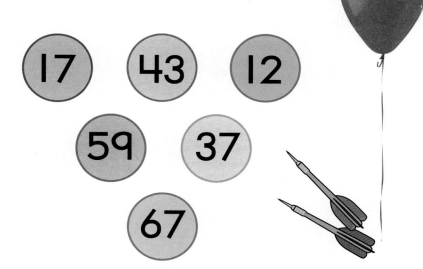

17 43 12

59 37

67

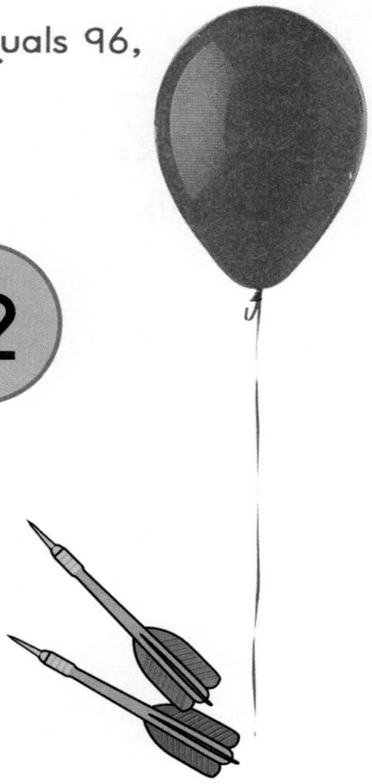

96 WINS!

21. Which pair of numbers totals 96? **59 and 37**

22. Can you make 96 by adding three of the numbers? **yes**

23. If so, which three? **67, 17, and 12**

24. Are there other ways to make 96 by using some numbers more than once? **yes (eight 12s)**

NOTE TO HOME
Students solve two-digit word problems.

ENRICHMENT p. 55

LESSON 55 ENRICHMENT Name ____________

Write the numbers to complete the problems.

1. 53 + 35 = 88
2. 34 + 14 = 48
3. 55 + 11 = 66
4. 16 + 48 = 64
5. 29 + 5 = 34
6. 72 + 9 = 81
7. 80 + 16 = 96
8. 67 + 24 = 91
9. 18 + 13 = 31
10. 58 + 21 = 79
11. 48 + 15 = 63
12. 32 + 9 = 41

Math Explorations and Applications Level 2 • 55

ASSESSMENT p. 20

UNIT 2 **Mastery Checkpoint 7** Two-digit addition (Lesson 55)

Name ____________

The student demonstrates mastery by correctly answering at least 13 of the 16 problems.

How well can you add?

1. 38 + 23 = 61
2. 30 + 57 = 87
3. 54 + 7 = 61
4. 17 + 17 = 34
5. 24 + 36 = 60
6. 24 + 39 = 63
7. 43 + 29 = 72
8. 75 + 16 = 91
9. 28 + 45 = 73
10. 59 + 9 = 68
11. 85 + 12 = 97
12. 93 + 6 = 99
13. 47 + 38 = 85
14. 36 + 16 = 52
15. 19 + 42 = 61
16. 56 + 24 = 80

20 • *Math Explorations and Applications* Level 2

Using the Student Pages Have students work independently to complete the test on page 117. Do not time students. When everyone is finished with this page, have them correct their answers and write the number that were correct at the bottom of the page. Work on page 118 with the class.

3 Wrap-Up (5 MINUTES)

In Closing Have students make up their own word problem that involves adding two 2-digit numbers. Have them solve their problems and then exchange them and solve a classmate's problem.

Mastery Checkpoint 7

At this time, most students should demonstrate mastery of adding two 2-digit numbers. Use page 117 or Assessment Master 23 to assess students' mastery. The results of this assessment may be added to the Mastery Checkpoint Chart.

Assessment Criteria

Did the student . . .

✓ correctly solve 16 of 20 problems on page 117?

✓ correctly answer questions while working with the class on page 118?

GIFTED & TALENTED — Meeting Individual Needs

Before completing page 118 with the class, consider assigning it to your gifted and talented students to complete with a partner. Then have these students share their methods and answers as you work with the rest of the class to complete the page.

LESSON 56

Student Edition pages 119–120

Keeping Sharp

LESSON PLANNER

Objectives

- ▶ to review basic subtraction facts
- ▶ to provide practice solving realistic word problems

Context of the Lesson This lesson includes a speed test in subtraction. Students can compare their scores with those from the last subtraction speed test.

Materials	Program Resources
stopwatch or clock with a second hand	Number Cubes Thinking Story Book, pages 46–47 Practice Master 56 Enrichment Master 56 For extra practice: CD-ROM* Lesson 56

1 Warm-Up

5 MINUTES

Problem of the Day Write the following problem on the chalkboard: There are 60 tickets left for the game. On Monday, 25 were sold. On Tuesday, 15 were sold. How many are left? (20)

MENTAL MATH Have students show their answers to the following subtraction problems using their Number Cubes:

a. 13 – 5 = (8)	**b.** 14 – 7 = (7)
c. 15 – 8 = (7)	**d.** 17 – 8 = (9)
e. 16 – 8 = (8)	**f.** 11 – 6 = (5)
g. 15 – 7 = (8)	**h.** 16 – 9 = (7)
i. 14 – 9 = (5)	**j.** 13 – 8 = (5)
k. 12 – 6 = (6)	**l.** 13 – 6 = (7)
m. 13 – 7 = (6)	**n.** 14 – 8 = (6)
o. 18 – 9 = (9)	**p.** 14 – 6 = (8)

LESSON 56

Name ______________________________

Keeping Sharp

Check your math skills.

❶ 8 − 5 = 3	❷ 10 − 4 = 6	❸ 13 − 7 = 6	❹ 16 − 6 = 10
❺ 12 − 7 = 5	❻ 14 − 9 = 5	❼ 15 − 8 = 7	❽ 18 − 10 = 8
❾ 7 − 3 = 4	❿ 10 − 6 = 4	⓫ 17 − 8 = 9	⓬ 16 − 8 = 8
⓭ 15 − 9 = 6	⓮ 14 − 8 = 6	⓯ 13 − 5 = 8	⓰ 9 − 3 = 6
⓱ 14 − 7 = 7	⓲ 12 − 6 = 6	⓳ 14 − 4 = 10	⓴ 6 − 2 = 4

Number correct ☐

NOTE TO HOME
Students check their subtraction skills.

Literature Connection Read aloud or invite students to read *A Nice Walk in the Jungle* by Nan Bodsworth to reinforce lesson concepts.

RETEACHING

Provide further practice for subtraction by presenting students with oral word problems. Have them use pencil and paper to find the answers. Present a word problem, have students solve it, then invite volunteers to give the solution. Discuss whether the solution is correct and why. Word problems should be similar to the following: I had 12 eggs and broke four. Now how many do I have? (8)

*available separately

◆ **LESSON 56** Keeping Sharp

Use the Mixed Practice on page 376 after this lesson.

Solve these problems.

21 Rosa had $17.
She spent $9.
How much money does she have now? $ **8**

22 Sam had 30 pennies.
He traded them for dimes.
How many dimes did he get? **3**

23 Petra planted ten bean seeds.
Eight of them sprouted.
How many didn't sprout? **2**

24 Casey had 29 soda cans.
She collected 18 more.
How many did she have together? **47**

NOTE TO HOME
Students solve word problems.

2 Teach

COOPERATIVE LEARNING Have students work in pairs or small groups, testing each other on subtraction facts.

Using the Student Pages Give students four minutes to complete page 119. Have students correct their papers and write their scores at the bottom of the page. Students who score less than 14 might need further subtraction fact review. After the speed test, have students work independently to complete the word problems on page 120.

Using the Thinking Story Present one or two new problems from those following "Ms. Arthur's Budget, Part 1" on pages 46–47 of the Thinking Story Book.

3 Wrap-Up

5 MINUTES

In Closing Have students make up a word problem that can be solved by subtraction. Have them solve their problems, then exchange problems with a classmate to solve.

SELF ASSESSMENT Students can use their scores to assess their mastery of subtraction facts. Have students make and use flashcards for any facts they missed on the speed test.

Assessment Criteria

Did the student . . .

✓ correctly and quickly complete 16 of the 20 problems on page 119?

✓ correctly solve the word problems on page 20?

ESL **Meeting Individual Needs**

You might want to read and explain some of the words in the word problems on page 120 to students who are just learning English. Be sure they understand what they must find in order to solve each problem.

PRACTICE p. 56

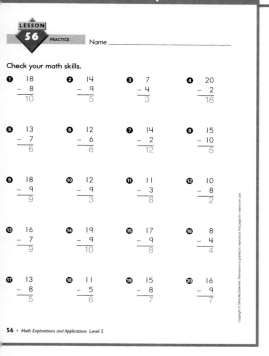

LESSON 56 PRACTICE Name ______

Check your math skills.

1. 18 − 8 = 10	2. 14 − 9 = 5	3. 7 − 4 = 3	4. 20 − 2 = 18
5. 13 − 7 = 6	6. 12 − 6 = 6	7. 14 − 2 = 12	8. 15 − 10 = 5
9. 18 − 9 = 9	10. 12 − 9 = 3	11. 11 − 3 = 8	12. 10 − 8 = 2
13. 16 − 7 = 9	14. 19 − 9 = 10	15. 17 − 9 = 8	16. 8 − 4 = 4
17. 13 − 8 = 5	18. 11 − 5 = 6	19. 15 − 8 = 7	20. 16 − 9 = 7

56 • Math Explorations and Applications Level 2

ENRICHMENT p. 56

LESSON 56 ENRICHMENT Name ______

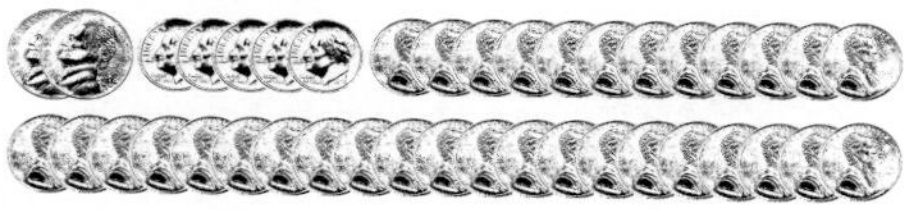

Solve these problems.

1. Bret gathered coins from his dresser drawer. He found five dimes, two nickels, and 33 pennies. How much money did he find? 93 cents
2. He traded most of his pennies for dimes. How many dimes did he get? 3
3. Bret kept 70 cents and gave the rest to his little sister. How much did he give her? 23 cents
4. He took his 70 cents to the store where he bought a 15-cent whistle and a 30-cent marker. How much money did he have left? 25 cents
5. Bret and Dan wanted to share a pack of game cards that cost 50 cents. Each of them would pay the same amount. Did Bret have enough money left to pay his share of the game cards? How much was that? yes; 25 cents
6. Bret's sister bought a pretty stamp for 22 cents. How much money did she have left? 1 cent

56 • Math Explorations and Applications Level 2

LESSON 57

Student Edition pages 121–122

Renaming Tens as Ones

LESSON PLANNER

Objective

- to provide practice in converting numbers in standard form to a form that can be used in two-digit subtraction algorithms

Context of the Lesson This lesson is the only one of its type used in preparation for learning two-digit subtraction.

Materials

play money* and other base-10 materials*

Program Resources

"Yard Sale" Game Mats

Number Cubes

Thinking Story Book, pages 46–47

Practice Master 57

Enrichment Master 57

For extra practice:
CD-ROM* Lesson 57

1 Warm-Up 5 MINUTES

Problem of the Day Write the following problem on the chalkboard: I have five coins. They equal 40 cents. What coins do I have? (three dimes and two nickels)

MENTAL MATH Have students subtract and answer using their Number Cubes:

a. 5 + 4 = (9)	**b.** 9 + 6 = (15)
c. 7 + 4 = (11)	**d.** 19 – 10 = (9)
e. 7 – 6 = (1)	**f.** 8 + 9 = (17)
g. 8 – 5 = (3)	**h.** 6 + 5 = (11)
i. 16 – 10 = (6)	**j.** 6 + 4 = (10)
k. 15 – 10 = (5)	**l.** 7 + 10 = (17)
m. 6 + 0 = (6)	**n.** 7 + 2 = (9)
o. 10 – 8 = (2)	**p.** 17 – 10 = (7)

LESSON 57

Name ______________________

Renaming Tens as Ones

Rewrite to show one fewer ten.

55 = 4 tens and 15

1. 63 = __5__ tens and __13__

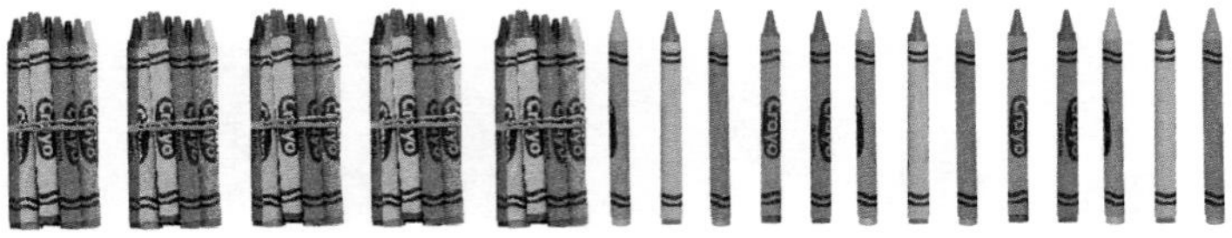

2. 49 = __3__ tens and __19__

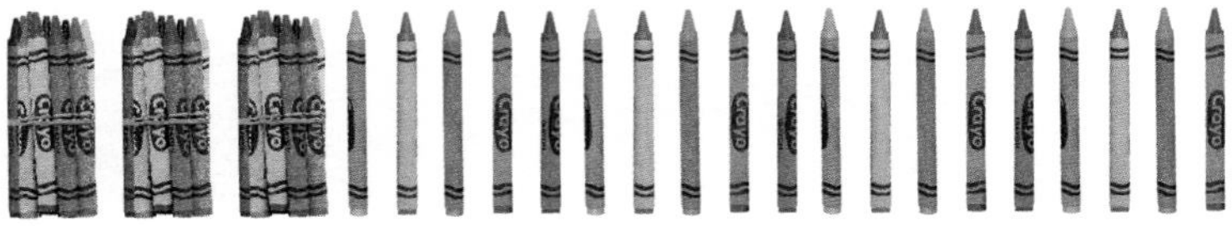

3. 38 = __2__ tens and __18__

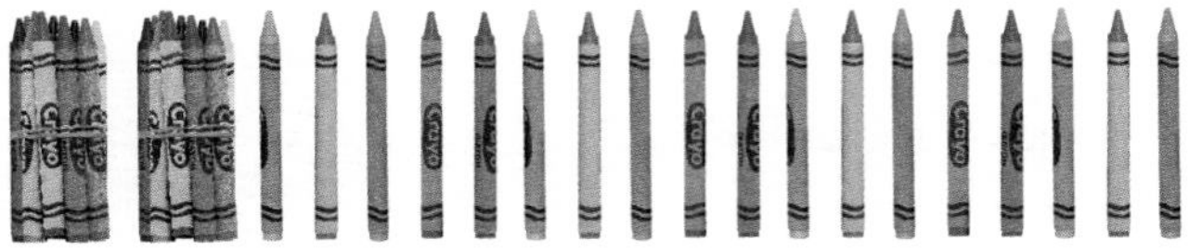

NOTE TO HOME
Students begin learning how to rewrite numbers for subtraction.

Literature Connection Read aloud or invite students to read *Alexander, Who Used to Be Rich Last Sunday* by Judith Viorst to reinforce lesson concepts.

LEARNING STYLES

Meeting Individual Needs

Have auditory learners tell what they must do to rewrite numbers to show more ones. Have them say each step as they write it on paper.

RETEACHING

Use alternative base-10 materials to demonstrate making more ones. If you used money in the original demonstration, show how to change the numbers using craft sticks. For example, show four bunches of ten sticks and five singles. Ask students how to show more singles. Remove the rubber band from one bunch. Count the groups of ten and singles now. (three tens and 15 singles)

*available separately

◆ LESSON 57 Renaming Tens as Ones

Rewrite each number to show one fewer ten.

❹ 43 = 3 tens and 13

❺ 60 = 5 tens and 10

❻ 22 = 1 tens and 12

❼ 100 = 9 tens and 10

❽ 36 = 2 tens and 16

❾ 89 = 7 tens and 19

❿ 15 = 0 tens and 15

⓫ 56 = 4 tens and 16

⓬ 78 = 6 tens and 18

⓭ 97 = 8 tens and 17

⓮ 46 = 3 tens and 16

⓯ 61 = 5 tens and 11

⓰ 50 = 4 tens and 10

⓱ 14 = 0 tens and 14

⓲ 48 = 3 tens and 18

⓳ 37 = 2 tens and 17

NOTE TO HOME
Students practice rewriting numbers for subtraction.

PRACTICE p. 57

LESSON 57 PRACTICE Name ____________

Rewrite each number to show more ones.

❶ 37 = 2 tens and 17 ❷ 70 = 6 tens and 10

❸ 26 = 1 tens and 16 ❹ 45 = 3 tens and 15

❺ 71 = 6 tens and 11 ❻ 29 = 1 tens and 19

❼ 18 = 0 tens and 18 ❽ 77 = 6 tens and 17

❾ 42 = 3 tens and 12 ❿ 51 = 4 tens and 11

⓫ 88 = 7 tens and 18 ⓬ 82 = 7 tens and 12

⓭ 53 = 4 tens and 13 ⓮ 16 = 0 tens and 16

⓯ 65 = 5 tens and 15 ⓰ 33 = 2 tens and 13

⓱ 94 = 8 tens and 14 ⓲ 99 = 8 tens and 19

Math Explorations and Applications Level 2 • 57

ENRICHMENT p. 57

LESSON 57 ENRICHMENT Name ____________

Each shelf at the bakery has bags with ten rolls in them. Some rolls are not in bags. Above the rolls are numbers that tell how many rolls are on that shelf. Fill in the blanks or draw the missing rolls to make each shelf correct.

❶ 62 = 6 tens and 2 more

❷ 47 = 3 tens and 17 more

❸ 78 = 6 tens and 18 more

❹ 51 = 4 bags and 11 more

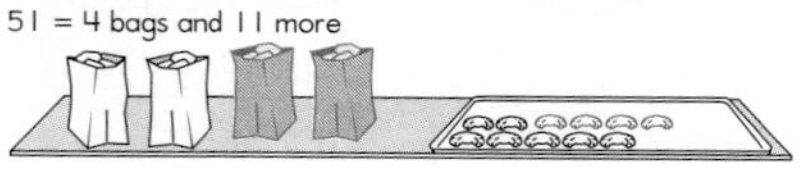

❺ 33 = 2 bags and 13 more

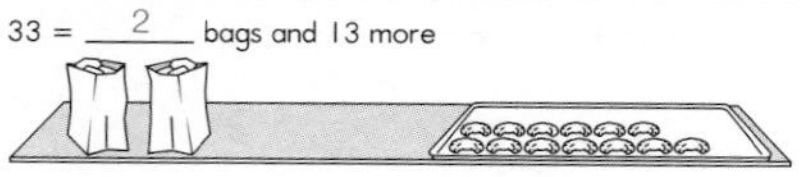

Math Explorations and Applications Level 2 • 57

❷ Teach

Demonstrate Hold up two \$10 bills and six \$1 bills. Have students tell how much money you have. (\$26) Ask them how you can have at least ten \$1 bills and still have the same amount of money. Guide students to see that you can exchange one \$10 bill for ten \$1 bills. Write the following exchange on the chalkboard: 26 = 1 ten and 16. Present several similar problems: 38 = (2) tens and (18); 51 = (4) tens and (11); 60 = (5) tens and (10); 13 = (0) tens and (13).

Using the Student Pages Have students work independently to complete pages 121 and 122. Provide individual help to those students who are having difficulty by asking them questions as they work on each problem. For example, ask: "What will you do to the tens?" "What will you do to the ones set?"

Using the Thinking Story Present one or two problems from those following the story "Ms. Arthur's Budget, Part 1" on pages 46–47 of the Thinking Story Book.

Introducing the "Yard Sale" Game Mats Demonstrate and play this game in which students change \$100 and \$10 bills for bills of smaller denominations. You may wish to play the harder variation with students who need more of a challenge. Complete directions are on the Game Mat.

❸ Wrap-Up

5 MINUTES

In Closing Have students write in their Math Journals an explanation of how to rewrite a two-digit number to show more ones. (Students should recognize the pattern that they always take 1 ten away from the tens and add it to the ones.)

Informal Assessment Observe which students quickly complete page 122. Notice which students still have not learned the pattern for rewriting numbers to show more ones.

Assessment Criteria

Did the student . . .

✓ always take away one ten?

✓ add the ten to the ones?

LESSON 58

Student Edition pages 123–124

Subtracting Multiples of Ten

LESSON PLANNER

Objective

▶ to introduce subtraction with multiples of ten

Context of the Lesson This is the first of nine lessons on subtracting two-digit numbers.

Materials

base-10 materials*

Program Resources

Number Cubes

Thinking Story Book, pages 46–47

Practice Master 58

Enrichment Master 58

For extra practice:
CD-ROM* Lesson 58

1 Warm-Up

5 MINUTES

Problem of the Day Write the following problem on the chalkboard: There are 17 bottles of juice left on the store shelf. Eight are grape. The rest are orange. How many are orange? (9)

MENTAL MATH Have students subtract and answer using their Number Cubes:

a. 80 – 80 = (0) **b.** 90 – 20 = (70)

c. 50 – 30 = (20) **d.** 80 – 60 = (20)

e. 90 – 70 = (20) **f.** 80 – 70 = (10)

g. 90 – 90 = (0) **h.** 70 – 20 = (50)

i. 10 – 10 = (0) **j.** 90 – 10 = (80)

2 Teach

Demonstrate Write the problem 70 – 20 on the chalkboard. Show students how to solve it using base-10 materials such as craft sticks. Show seven bunches of ten sticks. Take away two bunches. Show that there are five bunches of ten sticks, or 50, left. Present several more problems subtracting multiples of ten and written vertically, such as:

$$\begin{array}{r} 60 \\ -\ 40 \\ \hline (20) \end{array}$$

LESSON 58

Name ____________________

Subtracting Multiples of Ten

Solve these problems.

1. Mika had 80¢.
She spent 50¢. Now she has __30__ ¢.

2. Jerry has 50¢.
The cherries cost 80¢. He needs __30__ ¢.

3. 30 − 10 = __20__

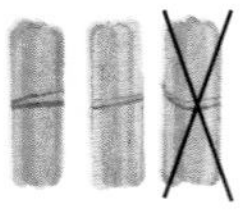

4. 80 − 20 = __60__

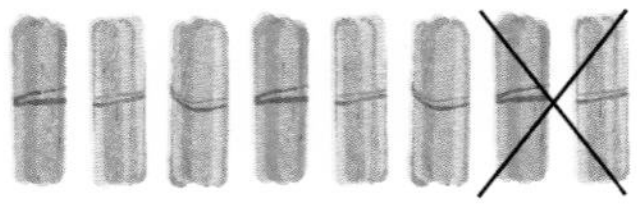

NOTE TO HOME
Students subtract multiples of ten.

COOPERATIVE LEARNING Have students work in pairs. One student should write a subtraction fact in units. The other should solve the problem and then write the same problem as multiples of ten. The first student then solves the new problem. Partners switch roles and repeat.

Literature Connection Read aloud or invite students to read "Speeds of Racers" in *Play Ball: Sports Math* by Time-Life, Inc. to reinforce lesson concepts.

RETEACHING

List the following subtraction facts on the chalkboard:

9 – 2 = (7) 10 – 3 = (7)
7 – 5 = (2) 8 – 2 = (6)
10 – 5 = (5)

Have students copy and complete them. Then have students rewrite each fact as a multiple of ten with the solution.

(90 – 20 = 70) (100 – 30 = 70)
(70 – 50 = 20) (80 – 20 = 60)
(100 – 50 = 50)

*available separately

◆ LESSON 58 Subtracting Multiples of Ten

Use sticks or other objects to subtract.

⑤ $\begin{array}{r}60\\-30\\\hline 30\end{array}$	⑥ $\begin{array}{r}80\\-40\\\hline 40\end{array}$	⑦ $\begin{array}{r}100\\-50\\\hline 50\end{array}$	⑧ $\begin{array}{r}70\\-20\\\hline 50\end{array}$
⑨ $\begin{array}{r}100\\-30\\\hline 70\end{array}$	⑩ $\begin{array}{r}40\\-0\\\hline 40\end{array}$	⑪ $\begin{array}{r}20\\-10\\\hline 10\end{array}$	⑫ $\begin{array}{r}60\\-10\\\hline 50\end{array}$
⑬ $\begin{array}{r}90\\-20\\\hline 70\end{array}$	⑭ $\begin{array}{r}80\\-70\\\hline 10\end{array}$	⑮ $\begin{array}{r}80\\-10\\\hline 70\end{array}$	⑯ $\begin{array}{r}50\\-30\\\hline 20\end{array}$
⑰ $\begin{array}{r}80\\-20\\\hline 60\end{array}$	⑱ $\begin{array}{r}30\\-30\\\hline 0\end{array}$	⑲ $\begin{array}{r}20\\-10\\\hline 10\end{array}$	⑳ $\begin{array}{r}80\\-30\\\hline 50\end{array}$
㉑ $\begin{array}{r}50\\-10\\\hline 40\end{array}$	㉒ $\begin{array}{r}40\\-10\\\hline 30\end{array}$	㉓ $\begin{array}{r}70\\-0\\\hline 70\end{array}$	㉔ $\begin{array}{r}10\\-0\\\hline 10\end{array}$

Play the "Add or Subtract a Ten" game.

NOTE TO HOME
Students subtract multiples of ten.

PRACTICE p. 58

LESSON 58 PRACTICE Name ______

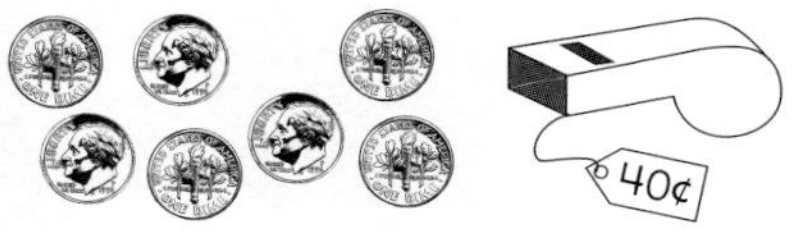

❶ Alexi had 70¢. He spent 40¢. Now he has 30 ¢.

❷ Brittany has 40¢. This necklace costs 70¢. She needs 30 ¢.

Use sticks or other objects to subtract.

❸ 80 – 60 = 20 ❹ 40 – 10 = 30

❺ 70 – 20 = 50 ❻ 90 – 40 = 50

❼ 60 – 0 = 60 ❽ 90 – 60 = 30

ENRICHMENT p. 58

LESSON 58 ENRICHMENT Name ______

Solve these problems.

❶ June baked a cake for her mother's birthday. Her mother is 40 years old. June has ten candles. How many more does she need to make 40? 30 candles

❷ June put pink roses and blue roses on her mother's cake. She counts 50 in all. She counts 30 pink roses. How many roses are blue? 20

❸ There will be 20 people at the party. June can cut this big cake into 30 pieces. How many pieces will be left over if each person has one piece? 10

❹ Everyone can have lemonade, too. June had 40 lemons. She used ten to make the lemonade. How many are left? 30 lemons

❺ All the people at the party can sit down at two tables. The big table seats 12 people. How many can sit at the smaller table? 8 people

Using the Number Cubes Have students use only the two tens cubes to solve problems in which they must subtract multiples of ten. Present problems on the chalkboard, orally, and as word problems.

Introducing the "Add or Subtract a Ten" Game Demonstrate and play this game in which students add or subtract multiples of 10 between 0 and 100. The lead player decides whether to use addition or subtraction, rolls a Number Cube, and either adds the multiple of 10 to 0 (addition) or subtracts the multiple of 10 from 100 (subtraction). The second player rolls the cube and either adds or subtracts the multiple from the leader's total. Play continues until the first person gets to 100 or more or to 0 or less. Variations include extending the range of numbers and using a 5–10 tens Number Cube instead of a 0–5 cube.

Using the Student Pages Have students complete pages 123–124 independently. Allow those who need them to use base-10 materials.

Using the Thinking Story Present one or two new problems from those following the story "Ms. Arthur's Budget, Part 1" on pages 46–47 of the Thinking Story Book.

❸ Wrap-Up

In Closing Ask students how subtracting two-digit multiples of ten is the same as subtracting ones. Ask them how it is different.

Performance Assessment Observe students' ability to subtract multiples of ten as they play the "Add or Subtract a Ten" game.

Assessment Criteria

Did the student . . .

✓ subtract horizontal problems correctly?

✓ subtract vertical problems correctly?

LESSON 59

Student Edition pages 125–126

Subtracting Two-Digit Numbers from Multiples of Ten

LESSON PLANNER

Objective

- ▶ to provide practice of subtraction of two-digit numbers from multiples of ten

Context of Lesson This is the second of nine lessons on subtracting two-digit numbers.

Materials

- craft sticks or other base-10 materials
- rubber bands

Program Resources

- Number Cubes
- Thinking Story Book, pages 46–47
- Reteaching Master
- Practice Master 59
- Enrichment Master 59
- For extra practice: CD-ROM* Lesson 59

1 Warm-Up (5 MINUTES)

Problem of the Day Write the following problem on the chalkboard: Megan wants a key chain that costs 90 cents. So far she has saved 60 cents. How much more money must she save? (30 cents more)

MENTAL MATH Have students subtract and answer using their Number Cubes:

a. 80 – 30 = (50)
b. 70 – 30 = (40)
c. 60 – 60 = (0)
d. 50 – 10 = (40)
e. 20 – 10 = (10)
f. 90 – 60 = (30)
g. 40 – 20 = (20)
h. 10 – 10 = (0)
i. 90 – 80 = (10)

LESSON 59

Name ______________________

Subtracting Two-Digit Numbers from Multiples of Ten

60 – 37 = __?__

60	6 tens and 0
– 37	– 3 tens and 7

5 10	5 10
~~6~~ ~~0~~	~~6~~ tens and ~~0~~
– 3 7	– 3 tens and 7

5 10	5 10
~~6~~ ~~0~~	~~6~~ tens and ~~0~~
– 3 7	– 3 tens and 7
2 3	2 tens and 3

NOTE TO HOME
Students use sticks to regroup when subtracting.

Why teach it this way?

To reinforce the concept of subtraction in this lesson, problems that require regrouping are deliberately mixed with those that do not. This helps to avoid the common error of subtracting the smaller number from the greater number in the units column in problems such as 53 – 26.

Literature Connection Read aloud or invite students to read *Ming Lo Moves a Mountain* by Arnold Lobel to reinforce lesson concepts.

RETEACHING p. 15

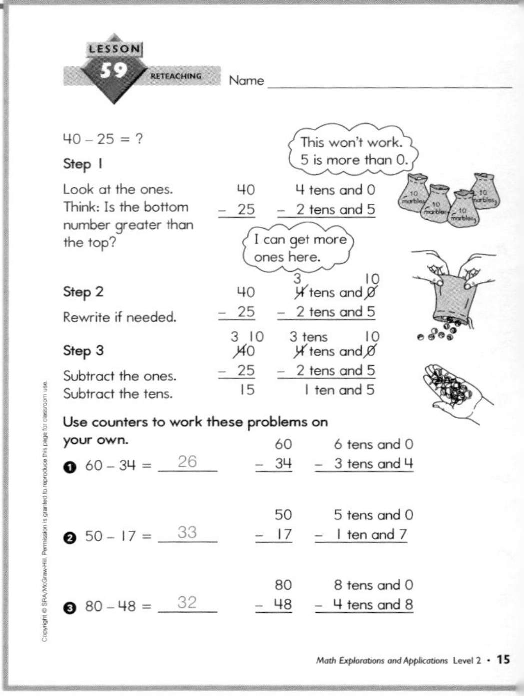
LESSON 59 RETEACHING Name ______________________

40 – 25 = ?

Step 1
Look at the ones. Think: Is the bottom number greater than the top?

40 − 25 | 4 tens and 0 − 2 tens and 5

Step 2
Rewrite if needed.

40 − 25 | 3 10: ~~4~~ tens and ~~0~~ − 2 tens and 5

Step 3
Subtract the ones. Subtract the tens.

3 10: ~~4~~0 − 25 = 15 | 3 tens 10: ~~4~~ tens and ~~0~~ − 2 tens and 5 = 1 ten and 5

Use counters to work these problems on your own.

1. 60 – 34 = 26 | 60 − 34 | 6 tens and 0 − 3 tens and 4
2. 50 – 17 = 33 | 50 − 17 | 5 tens and 0 − 1 ten and 7
3. 80 – 48 = 32 | 80 − 48 | 8 tens and 0 − 4 tens and 8

Math Explorations and Applications Level 2 • 15

*available separately

◆ LESSON 59 Subtracting Two-Digit Numbers from Multiples of Ten

Subtract. Use sticks to help. Record what you did.

❶ 90 − 48 = __?__

9 tens and 0	8 tens and 10 (9 and 0 crossed out)	8 10
− 4 tens and 8	− 4 tens and 8	90
		− 48
		42

❷ 100 − 54 = __?__

10 tens and 0	9 tens and 10 (10 and 0 crossed out)	9 10
− 5 tens and 4	− 5 tens and 4	100
		− 54
		46

❸ 80 − 30 =

8 tens and **0**	80
− **3** tens and **0**	− 30
	50

❹ 70 − 48 =

6 ... **10**	
7 tens and **0**	70
− **4** tens and **8**	− 48
	22

NOTE TO HOME
Students subtract with regrouping.

PRACTICE p. 59

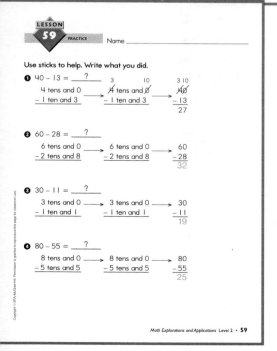

LESSON 59 PRACTICE Name ______________

Use sticks to help. Write what you did.

❶ 40 − 13 = __?__

4 tens and 0 / − 1 ten and 3 → 3 tens and 10 (4 and 0 crossed out) / − 1 ten and 3 → 3 10 / 40 / − 13 / 27

❷ 60 − 28 = __?__

6 tens and 0 / − 2 tens and 8 → 6 tens and 0 / − 2 tens and 8 → 60 / − 28 / 32

❸ 30 − 11 = __?__

3 tens and 0 / − 1 ten and 1 → 3 tens and 0 / − 1 ten and 1 → 30 / − 11 / 19

❹ 80 − 55 = __?__

8 tens and 0 / − 5 tens and 5 → 8 tens and 0 / − 5 tens and 5 → 80 / − 55 / 25

ENRICHMENT p. 59

LESSON 59 ENRICHMENT Name ______________

Play with a friend. Toss a marker onto the gameboard. Write the number in one of your friend's problems below. Your friend works the problem. Then your friend takes a turn and writes a number in one of your problems for you to work. Continue until all of the problems are solved.

4 tens | 5 tens | 2 tens | 3 tens | 1 ten | 8 tens

Player 1		Player 2	
63 +	=	29 +	=
17 +	=	43 +	=
56 +	=	38 +	=
65 +	=	12 +	=
93 −	=	42 −	=
75 −	=	86 −	=
44 −	=	62 −	=

❷ Teach

MATH MANIPULATIVES **Demonstrate** Write the problem 80−47 on the chalkboard. Model the problem with eight bunches of ten craft sticks. Guide students to see that you must remove a rubber band from one bunch of ten to be able to take away 47 sticks. Show and explain what you did by rewriting the problem on the chalkboard like this:

7 10		
8 tens and 0 (crossed out)	→	7 tens and 10
− 4 tens and 7		− 4 tens and 7
		(3 tens and 3)

Have students give the answer. (33) Then show how to write the problem as an algorithm:

$$\begin{array}{r} 7\ 10 \\ \not{8}\not{0} \\ -\ 47 \\ \hline 33 \end{array}$$

Repeat, discuss, and solve several similar problems and their algorithms.

Using the Student Pages Work with the class to complete page 125 and the first problem on page 126. Have students use base-10 materials to complete the rest of the page.

Using the Thinking Story Present one or two new problems from those following the story "Ms. Arthur's Budget, Part 1" on pages 46–47 of the Thinking Story Book.

❸ Wrap-Up

5 MINUTES

In Closing Have students describe how they would subtract 27 from 70.

ALTERNATIVE ASSESSMENT **Performance Assessment** Observe how students use models as they subtract. Check to see that they understand when they must unbundle tens.

Assessment Criteria

Did the student . . .

✓ correctly change the ten?

✓ correctly add the ten to the ones?

✓ correctly subtract the numbers?

LESSON 60

Student Edition pages 127–128

Two-Digit Subtraction

LESSON PLANNER

Objective

▶ to demonstrate how to subtract two-digit numbers from two-digit numbers that are multiples of ten

Context of the Lesson This is the third of nine lessons focusing on subtracting two-digit numbers.

Materials

base-10 materials*

play money*

newspaper weather forecast (optional)

Program Resources

Number Cubes

Thinking Story Book, pages 48–51

Practice Master 60

Enrichment Master 60

For extra practice: CD-ROM* Lesson 60

1 Warm-Up (5 MINUTES)

Problem of the Day Present this problem: Jenna studies one hour for each subject. At 4:20 P.M. she starts studying for math and science. Will she be finished in time to watch her favorite television program at 7:30 P.M. if she takes an hour for dinner? How can you tell? (Yes, because she will eat and study for 3 hours, until 7:20 P.M.)

MENTAL MATH Present the following subtraction problems. Have students use Number Cubes to respond.

a. 100 – 30 = (70) **b.** 80 – 40 = (40)

c. 120 – 60 = (60) **d.** 90 – 50 = (40)

2 Teach

Demonstrate Write the problem 80 – 47 on the chalkboard. First demonstrate how to use craft sticks to solve the problem. Show eight bunches of ten. Rewrite the problem on the chalkboard to show that you cannot take away the 47 sticks:

8 tens and 0
– 4 tens and 7

LESSON 60

Name ____________________

Two-Digit Subtraction

Solve these problems.

❶ 40 − 27 = **13**

❷ 100 − 93 = **7**

❸ 74 − 13 = **61**

❹ 55 − 10 = **45**

❺ 60 − 28 = **32**

❻ 70 − 19 = **51**

❼ 36 − 27 = **9**

❽ 84 − 26 = **58**

❾ Michael had 80¢. He spent 46¢. He has **34** ¢ left.

❿ Yoshie had 50¢. She spent 25¢. She has **25** ¢ left.

⓫ Ashley had 90¢. She spent 50¢. She has **40** ¢ left.

⓬ Debra had 46¢. She spent 25¢. She has **21** ¢ left.

⓭ Ivan had 40¢. He spent 37¢. He has **3** ¢ left.

⓮ Rob had 75¢. He spent 39¢. He has **36** ¢ left.

THINKING STORY

Talk about the Thinking Story "Ms. Arthur's Budget, Part 2."

NOTE TO HOME
Students work subtraction and word problems.

Science Connection Provide photocopies of your newspaper's weather section. Have students work in groups to compare the weather in the city where they live to the weather in four other cities. Groups can then share their results with the class.

RETEACHING

Teach the problems the same way as in the demonstration, but use play money instead of base-10 materials to model each problem.

*available separately

Take-Home Activity

Three-Cube Subtraction

Players: Two or more

Materials: One 0–5 cube and one 5–10 tens cube and paper and pencil

RULES

Leader: Roll all three cubes and make a two-digit number from the numbers shown. Subtract the number shown on the 5–10 tens cube.

Players: Each of the other players does the same thing.

Winner: The person who has the greatest difference wins the round.

I played the game with

______________________________.

NOTE TO HOME
Students subtract two-digit numbers.

Ask students what you might do. Then remove a rubber band from one of the bunches. Demonstrate that taking the band off one bunch of ten makes the problem look like this:

8 tens and 0	→	7 tens and 10	7 10 ~~80~~
−4 tens and 7	→	−4 tens and 7	− 47
		3 tens and 3	33

Demonstrate that now you can take away the 47 sticks. Ask for the answer (33) and display three tens and three. Repeat with several similar problems.

Using the Student Pages Have students work independently on page 127. Students may use base-10 materials. Ask students to check their solutions with classmates and correct answers when necessary.

Introducing the "Three-Cube Subtraction" Game Demonstrate the game for students to play. This game provides practice in subtracting 2-digit numbers from 2-digit multiples of ten. Directions are on page 128.

Using the Thinking Story Read "Ms. Arthur's Budget, Part 2" on Thinking Story Book pages 48–51 aloud to the class. Stop and discuss the questions asked throughout the story.

3 Wrap-Up

5 MINUTES

In Closing Have students tell which problems on page 127 did not involve regrouping and why. (Problems 3, 4, 11, and 12. The second addend in each problem is equal to or smaller than the first addend.)

Assessment Criteria

Did the student . . .

✓ correctly solve 11 of 14 problems on page 127?

✓ correctly solve problems in the "Three-Cube Subtraction" game?

Performance Assessment Observe students as they play the "Three-Cube Subtraction" game to see whether they accurately solve each problem they create.

ALTERNATIVE ASSESSMENT

PRACTICE p. 60

LESSON 60 PRACTICE Name ______________

Subtract.

1. 80 − 24 = 56
2. 50 − 18 = 32
3. 40 − 32 = 8
4. 60 − 43 = 17
5. 70 − 17 = 53
6. 90 − 36 = 54

Solve these problems.

7. Scott had 70¢. He spent 35¢. He has 35 ¢ left.
8. Jhan had 60¢. She spent 19¢. She has 41 ¢ left.
9. Patrick had 40¢. He spent 26¢. He has 14 ¢ left.
10. Brady had 80¢. He spent 74¢. He has 6 ¢ left.
11. Amber had 30¢. She spent 20¢. She has 10 ¢ left.
12. Colleen had 50¢. She spent 25¢. She has 25 ¢ left.

60 • Math Explorations and Applications Level 2

ENRICHMENT p. 60

LESSON 60 ENRICHMENT Name ______________

Brad, Terry, Pam, and Ciulo want some comics.

1. Terry has $2. He wants to buy two different comics, but he needs to have 25¢ left for the bus. Can he buy two comics? yes
2. Which comics can he buy? Big Zap and Green Grunge, Big Zap and Captain Mongo, or Big Zap and Meteor Mutant
3. Pam has 92¢. She bought the Big Zap comic. How much did she have left? 17¢
4. Ciulo bought the Captain Mongo comic. He has 26¢ left. How much did he have before he bought the comic? $1.25
5. Brad bought the Meteor Mutant comic and the Captain Mongo comic. He has one penny left. How much did Brad have when he got to the store? $2.00

60 • Math Explorations and Applications Level 2

STORY 8

THINKING STORY

Ms. Arthur's Budget

Part 2

[You will need to refer to the budget discussed in Part 1 of this story. Students should be able to see the budget written on the chalkboard or on large paper.]

The children in Ms. Arthur's class decided to ask Ms. Sullivan, the principal, whether she could get the money they needed to buy the software. They appointed Ferdie, Manolita, and Marcus to meet with her.

"Good morning students. I understand you asked to meet with me," said Ms. Sullivan.

"That's right," answered Ferdie. "All of the children in Ms. Arthur's class asked us to represent them. We came to ask you to put a bit more money in Ms. Arthur's budget. We want to buy a great new software program and Ms. Arthur only has eight dollars left in her budget."

"It's educational," added Manolita.

Do you remember how much the software costs? $42

How much more money do the students need? $34

"We need 34 more dollars," Manolita explained. "Ms. Arthur's budget is 300 dollars and we'd like you to change it a little."

By how much does Manolita want the budget changed? She wants the budget changed from 300 dollars to 334 dollars.

"I see that you need 34 more dollars," answered Ms. Sullivan, "and I know that the software will help very much with learning arithmetic, but I have already prepared my budget and I'm afraid that I won't be able to help you. Perhaps you can raise the money some other way."

"But you must have a very large budget, and we only need 34 dollars," moaned Ferdie.

Why does Ferdie think Ms. Sullivan has a very big budget? Her budget includes money for all the teachers in the school.

"It's true that I have a larger budget," replied Ms. Sullivan, "but I must provide money for all of the teachers."

"How much do you budget for each teacher?" asked Manolita.

"I give the first-, second-, and third-grade teachers the same amount of money," replied Ms. Sullivan.

How much do you think each first-, second-, and third-grade teacher gets? $300

"Each of the three teachers gets 300 dollars," said Ms. Sullivan. "And I budget a little more for the fourth-, fifth-, and sixth-grade teachers," she added.

Is that fair? Why or why not? It's fair and not fair. It's fair because upper grade materials, such as books, usually cost a bit more. It's unfair because the amount spent on each class or child should be about the same.

"How much do you budget for the fourth-, fifth-, and sixth-grade teachers?" asked Manolita.

"I put 350 dollars in their budgets," replied Ms. Sullivan. "There are three teachers, and that's really all I can afford. My total budget for all of the teachers in first through sixth grades is only 2000 dollars."

How many teachers are there all together in first through sixth grades? six; one at each grade

School Budget	
First Grade	$300
Second Grade	$300
Third Grade	$300
Fourth Grade	$350
Fifth Grade	$350
Sixth Grade	$350

◆ STORY 8 Ms. Arthur's Budget, *Part 2*

"I think you have enough money in your budget to help us buy the software," said Marcus.

Why did Marcus say that? Probably because he realized that Ms. Sullivan budgeted 300 dollars for each of the primary teachers or 900 dollars all together, and 350 dollars for each of the upper grade-teachers or 1050 dollars all together. That means she budgeted 900 + 1050 dollars or 1950 dollars. She still has 50 dollars that is not budgeted in her 2000 dollar budget.

"That's right," Ferdie and Manolita chimed in. "You have 50 dollars left in your budget that hasn't been set aside for something else."

Are the children correct? Yes—see the explanation in the last question.

"You budgeted 900 dollars for the first-, second-, and third-grade teachers, and 1050 dollars for the fourth-, fifth-, and sixth-grade teachers. That's 1950 dollars all together," said Manolita. "You still have fifty dollars left," added Ferdie. "Can we have it?"

"That's very good figuring," said Ms. Sullivan. "I guess I do have fifty dollars left. I had forgotten about that. But let's not be too hasty. It wouldn't be fair to give Ms. Arthur more money than the first- and third-grade teachers."

Would that be fair? probably not

"Too bad," said Ferdie. "Budgeting just doesn't seem to work."

Is Ferdie right? Not really; budgeting helps you spend money wisely and fairly, and helps prevent you from spending more than you should.

"Ms. Sullivan, I have an idea," said Marcus. "All of the children in the school use the computer room and . . ."

What do you think Marcus is going to say? Most likely he's going to suggest that the fifty dollars be used to buy the software for the computer room. That way all of the students can use the software. Some students might argue that sixth graders won't be interested in second-grade software. Others might argue that some sixth graders need practice with basic facts.

"Why don't you buy the software for the computer room?" asked Marcus. "That way all of the students will be able to use the software."

"What a good idea," replied Ms. Sullivan. "I think I'll take your advice and do just that. Thank you for coming to discuss this important matter with me."

"I guess budgets are not so bad after all," said Ferdie.

. . . the end

LESSON 61

Student Edition pages 129–130

Subtracting Two-Digit Numbers

LESSON PLANNER

Objective

▶ to provide practice in subtracting two-digit numbers

Context of the Lesson This is the fourth of nine lessons on subtracting two-digit numbers.

Materials	**Program Resources**
base-10 materials*	Number Cubes
	Thinking Story Book, pages 52–53
	Practice Master 61
	Enrichment Master 61
	For extra practice: CD-ROM* Lesson 61

1 Warm-Up

5 MINUTES

Problem of the Day Write the following problem on the chalkboard: There are 40 children waiting in line at the movies. If 23 are girls, how many are boys? (17)

MENTAL MATH Have students add and subtract, using their Number Cubes to show their answer:

a. 13 – 6 = (7) **b.** 16 – 8 = (8) **c.** 13 – 9 = (4)
d. 6 + 7 = (13) **e.** 15 – 8 = (7) **f.** 9 + 6 = (15)
g. 7 + 4 = (11) **h.** 15 – 7 = (8) **i.** 12 – 7 = (5)
j. 6 + 5 = (11)

2 Teach

Demonstrate Write the problem 53 - 25 on the chalkboard. Model the problem with five bunches of ten sticks and three single sticks. Guide students to see that you must remove a rubber band from one bunch of ten to be able to take away 25 sticks. Show and explain what you did by rewriting the problem on the chalkboard like this:

```
 4          13
 5 tens and 3  →  4 tens and 13
-2 tens and 5    -2 tens and  5
```


LESSON 61

Name ____________________

Subtracting Two-Digit Numbers

Subtract. Use sticks to help.

53 − 25 = __?__

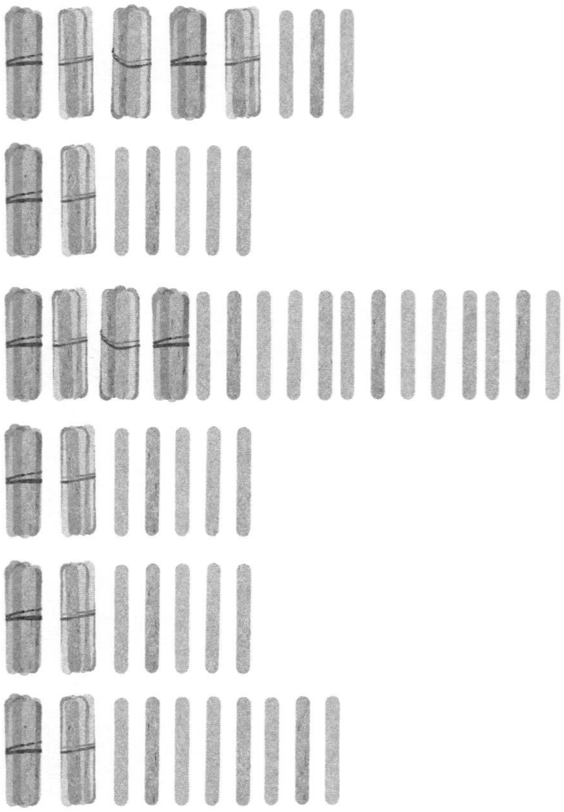

```
  53      5 tens and 3
− 25    − 2 tens and 5

 4 13    4          13
 5  3    5 tens and  3
− 2  5  − 2 tens and 5

 4 13
 5  3    5 tens and 3
− 2  5  − 2 tens and 5
          2 tens and 8
```


NOTE TO HOME
Students subtract two-digit numbers.

RETEACHING

Demonstrate other subtraction situations that can be solved using the original algorithm you demonstrated: 53 - 25. For example, give 53 sticks to one student and 25 to another. Discuss and have students show how to find out how many more sticks the student with 53 sticks has than the student with 25 sticks. Or, show students that you have 25 sticks. Ask, "How can I find out how many more I would need to make 53 sticks?"

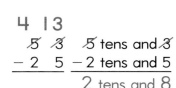

GIFTED & TALENTED **Meeting Individual Needs**

Write the following problem as a model on the chalkboard: Students study math each day for 45 minutes. If they have studied math for 27 minutes so far, how much longer will they study math today? (18 minutes) Invite pairs of students to use the problem as a model and write five similar problems. Keep the problems and answers in a folder for other students to solve.

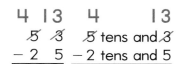

*available separately

◆ LESSON 61 Subtracting Two-Digit Numbers

Use the Mixed Practice on page 377 after this lesson.

Subtract. Use sticks to help.
Record what you did.

❶ 22 − 13 = ?

	1 (2 crossed out) tens and	12 (2 crossed out)	22
−	1 tens and	3	− 13
			9

❷ 50 − 25 = ?

	4 (5 crossed out) tens and	10 (0 crossed out)	50
−	2 tens and	5	− 25
			25

❸ 44 − 29 = ?

	3 (4 crossed out) tens and	14 (4 crossed out)	44
−	2 tens and	9	− 29
			15

❹ 83 − 73 = 10

❺ 100 − 25 = 75

❻ 17 − 17 = 0

❼ 49 − 29 = 20

❽ 27 − 13 = 14

❾ 63 − 37 = 26

❿ 18 − 9 = 9

⓫ 36 − 18 = 18

NOTE TO HOME
Students practice subtraction with two-digit numbers.

Have students give the answer (28). Then show how to write the problem as an algorithm:

```
 4 13
 5̸ 3̸
-2  5
 2  8
```

Repeat, discuss, and solve several similar problems and their algorithms.

Using the Student Pages Work with the class to complete page 129 and the first problem on page 130. Have students use base-10 materials to complete the rest of the page.

Using the Thinking Story Present one or two new problems from those following "Ms. Arthur's Budget, Part 2" on pages 52–53 of the Thinking Story Book.

3 Wrap-Up (5 MINUTES)

In Closing Have students describe how they would subtract 27 from 54.

ALTERNATIVE ASSESSMENT

Performance Assessment Observe students as they work to see whether they understand when they must unbundle tens.

Assessment Criterion

Did the student . . .

✓ correctly solve nine of 11 problems on page 130?

PRACTICE p. 61

LESSON 61 PRACTICE Name ____________

44 − 19 = ?

44	4 tens and 4 ones
− 19	− 1 ten and 9 ones

3 14 (44 crossed out)	3 (4 crossed out) tens and 14 (4 crossed out) ones
− 19	− 1 ten and 9 ones
	2 tens and 5 ones

Use sticks to subtract. Write what you did.

❶ 33 − 18 = 15
❷ 22 − 9 = 13
❸ 54 − 27 = 27
❹ 21 − 21 = 0
❺ 46 − 15 = 31
❻ 36 − 26 = 10
❼ 84 − 29 = 55
❽ 32 − 12 = 20
❾ 100 − 47 = 53

Math Explorations and Applications Level 2 • 61

ENRICHMENT p. 61

LESSON 61 ENRICHMENT Name ____________

The map shows some cities in the western United States. Under the name of each city is its average temperature for the month of July.

Study the map. Then answer the questions.

❶ How many degrees warmer is it in Las Vegas than in Salt Lake City? 12

❷ How many degrees warmer is it in Boise than in Portland? 7

❸ Which two cities shown have the closest temperatures in July? Los Angeles, Boise

How close are the temperatures? 1 degree

❹ How much of a difference is there between the warmest and the coolest cities shown on the map? 30 degrees

Math Explorations and Applications Level 2 • 61

LESSON 62

Student Edition pages 131–132

Practicing Two-Digit Subtraction

LESSON PLANNER

Objective

- to provide reinforcement and review of two-digit subtraction

Context of the Lesson This is the fifth of nine lessons on subtracting two-digit numbers.

Materials	Program Resources
base-10 materials*	Number Cubes
	Thinking Story Book, pages 52–53
	Reteaching Master
	Practice Master 62
	Enrichment Master 62
	For extra practice: CD-ROM* Lesson 62

1 Warm-Up

5 MINUTES

Problem of the Day Write the following problem on the chalkboard: You spend \$0.42 on an apple and a quarter for a sticker. You pay with \$0.75. How much change do you get back? (\$0.08)

MENTAL MATH Have students add and subtract, using their Number Cubes to respond:

a. 6 + 6 = (12)
b. 16 − 9 = (7)
c. 14 − 5 = (9)
d. 14 − 7 = (7)
e. 4 + 8 = (12)
f. 11 − 3 = (8)
g. 6 + 9 = (15)

2 Teach

Demonstrate Write the following problem on the chalkboard:

$$\begin{array}{r} 43 \\ -28 \\ \hline (15) \end{array}$$

LESSON 62

Name ______________________

Practicing Two-Digit Subtraction

Remember.

$$\begin{array}{r} 83 \\ -\ 25 \\ \hline \end{array} \qquad \begin{array}{r} {}^{7}\not{8}\ {}^{13}\not{3} \\ -\ 2\ 5 \\ \hline \end{array} \qquad \begin{array}{r} {}^{7}\not{8}\ {}^{13}\not{3} \\ -\ 2\ 5 \\ \hline 5\ 8 \end{array}$$

Subtract. Write your answers.

❶ 70 − 43 = 27	❷ 72 + 43 = 29	❸ 74 − 43 = 31	❹ 68 − 39 = 29
❺ 81 − 26 = 55	❻ 47 + 23 = 24	❼ 45 − 25 = 20	❽ 33 − 17 = 16
❾ 64 − 17 = 47	❿ 38 − 35 = 3	⓫ 41 − 20 = 21	⓬ 46 − 29 = 17

NOTE TO HOME
Students practice subtraction of two-digit numbers.

Literature Connection Read aloud or invite students to read *How Many Teeth?* by Paul Showers to reinforce lesson concepts.

RETEACHING p. 16

LESSON 62 RETEACHING Name ______________________

52 − 26 = ?

Step 1

Look at the ones.
Think: Is the bottom greater than the top?

52 − 26 | 5 tens and 2 − 2 tens and 6

Step 2

Think: Take one ten from five tens. Make it four tens. Give ten to the two ones. Make it a 12.

4 12 / ~~5~~2 − 26 | 4 tens 12 / ~~5~~ tens and ~~2~~ − 2 tens and 6

Step 3

Subtract the ones.
Subtract the tens.

4 12 / ~~5~~2 − 26 = 26 | 4 tens 12 / ~~5~~ tens and ~~2~~ − 2 tens and 6 = 2 tens and 6

Use craft sticks or peanuts to solve these problems.

❶ 70 − 13 = 57 ❷ 96 − 39 = 57 ❸ 48 − 25 = 23 ❹ 61 − 44 = 17

*available separately

◆ LESSON 62 Practicing Two-Digit Subtraction

PROBLEM SOLVING

Solve these problems.

13 David had 63¢. He spent 28¢.
Now he has **35** ¢.

14 Yori has 43¢. She needs 62¢.
She needs **19** ¢ more.

15 Jacob has 43¢. Emily has 39¢.
Who has more? **Jacob**
How much more? **4** ¢

16 Lani has 78¢. Tina has 92¢.
Who has more? **Tina**
How much more? **14** ¢

GAME

Play the "Four-Cube Subtraction" game.

NOTE TO HOME
Students solve word problems and play a subtraction game.

PRACTICE p. 62

LESSON 62 PRACTICE Name ____________

Subtract.

1. 46 − 17 = 29	2. 25 − 18 = 7	3. 61 − 12 = 49	4. 42 − 23 = 19
5. 89 − 22 = 67	6. 97 − 58 = 39	7. 46 − 16 = 30	8. 84 − 37 = 47
9. 60 − 45 = 15	10. 31 − 18 = 13	11. 52 − 24 = 28	12. 76 − 58 = 18
13. 77 − 47 = 30	14. 83 − 59 = 24	15. 90 − 39 = 51	16. 29 − 12 = 17

62 • *Math Explorations and Applications* Level 2

ENRICHMENT p. 62

LESSON 62 ENRICHMENT Name ____________

Play tic-tac-toe with a friend. Choose a problem. Add or subtract. If your answer is correct, mark *X* or *O* in your box.

26 + 11 = 37	72 − 43 = 29	45 − 20 = 25
34 − 21 = 13	44 + 15 = 59	56 − 34 = 22
78 − 22 = 56	48 + 23 = 71	56 − 38 = 18

76 + 14 = 90	46 − 18 = 28	17 − 15 = 2
86 − 71 = 15	29 + 33 = 62	25 − 14 = 11
94 − 36 = 58	57 + 12 = 69	66 − 44 = 22

Make your own tic-tac-toe game and play it with a friend.

62 • *Math Explorations and Applications* Level 2

Show students how to use craft sticks and pencil and paper to solve the problem. Show four bunches of ten sticks and three single sticks. Point to the 43 in the algorithm. Explain that to take away 28 you need to unwrap one bunch. Show this in the algorithm by crossing out the 4 and changing it to 3 tens and changing 3 to 13 ones. Take away the 28 sticks. Complete the algorithm, then count the remaining sticks. (15) Present several more examples with and without regrouping. Have students solve them along with you.

GAME **Introducing the "Four-Cube Subtraction" Game** Demonstrate and play this game to provide practice in subtracting two-digit numbers. Students will need paper and pencil and Number Cubes (0–5, 5–10 units, and 0–5, 5–10 tens). In turn the players roll all four cubes and group them to form two 2-digit numbers; then they subtract the numbers. In each round, the player with the *least* answer wins. This strategy requires students to use regrouping.

MATH MANIPULATIVES **Using the Student Pages** Discuss the sample problem on page 131 with students. Then have students complete both pages independently. Keep base-10 materials available for those who need them. When students finish, present the correct answers and have them check their own work.

Using the Thinking Story Present one or two new problems from those following "Ms. Arthur's Budget, Part 2" on pages 52–53 of the Thinking Story Book.

3 Wrap-Up

5 MINUTES

In Closing Ask students how they decide whether or not they have to change a ten to ten ones when subtracting two-digit numbers.

ALTERNATIVE ASSESSMENT **Informal Assessment** Observe students as they complete pages 131 and 132. Check to see which students still need to use base-10 materials to subtract and which students can subtract using pencil and paper only.

Assessment Criteria

Did the student . . .

✓ correctly solve ten of the 12 algorithms on page 131?

✓ correctly solve all of the word problems on page 132?

Student Edition pages 133–134

Applying Subtraction

LESSON PLANNER

Objectives

- to provide practice subtracting two-digit numbers
- provide practice using subtraction to solve realistic problems

Context of the Lesson This is the sixth of nine lessons that focuses on subtracting two-digit numbers.

Materials	Program Resources
centimeter ruler	Number Cubes
gram scale	Thinking Story Book, pages 52–53
2 jars of water	Practice Master 63
	Enrichment Master 63
	For extra practice: CD-ROM* Lesson 63

1 Warm-Up

5 MINUTES

Problem of the Day Write the following problem on the chalkboard: Sandy is 56 inches tall. Her sister is 4 feet and 4 inches tall. Who is taller? By how much? (Sandy is 4 in. taller than her sister.)

MENTAL MATH Have students add or subtract, using their Number Cubes to respond.

a. 110 – 50 = (60) **b.** 90 + 40 = (130)

c. 120 – 80 = (40) **d.** 60 + 50 = (110)

LESSON 63

Name ______________________

Applying Subtraction

Solve these problems.

1. 73 − 48 = **25**	2. 63 − 37 = **26**	3. 52 − 22 = **30**	4. 49 − 27 = **22**
5. 50 − 25 = **25**	6. 66 − 57 = **9**	7. 88 − 44 = **44**	8. 32 − 18 = **14**

9. This chair was 94 cm high. Matt cut 4 cm off each leg.

Now how high is the chair? **90** cm

10. Beth is 93 cm tall. Her brother Daniel is 86 cm tall.

Who is taller? **Beth**

How much taller? **7** cm

NOTE TO HOME
Students solve subtraction and word problems.

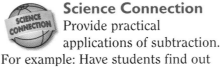

Science Connection Provide practical applications of subtraction. For example: Have students find out which classroom in your school uses the most chalk. They can measure the chalk in each classroom at the beginning of the day and at the end of the day. Have them measure by length, weight, or number of pieces; collect and organize the data; and then use subtraction to see which classroom used more chalk.

Literature Connection Read aloud *Six Sleepy Sheep* by Jeffie Ross Gordon to reinforce lesson concepts.

RETEACHING

Divide students into groups based on their needs in the following skills:

1. Knowing subtraction facts
2. Knowing when to regroup
3. Knowing how to regroup

Provide examples that focus on each group's particular need.

*available separately

◆ **LESSON 63** Applying Subtraction

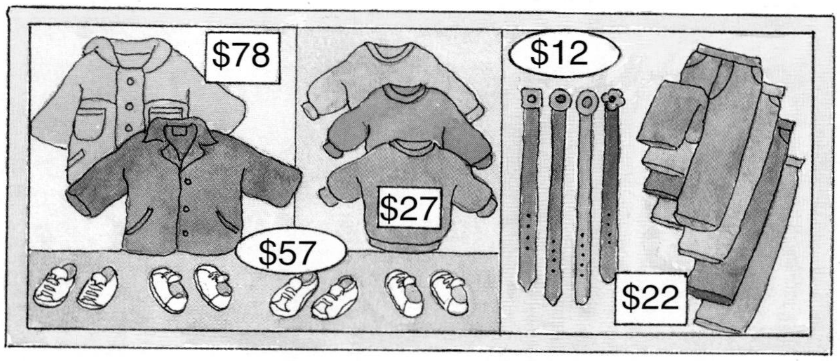

Solve these problems.

⓫ Natalie had $76. She bought shoes. She now has $ 19 .

⓬ Rachel bought a shirt. She gave the clerk two $20 bills. How much change did she get? $ 13

⓭ Simon has $90. He wants to buy a jacket and slacks. Can he? no

⓮ Stan has a $50 bill. He buys slacks and a belt. How much change should he get? $ 16

⓯ Tyrone bought a shirt, slacks, and a belt. He gave the clerk four $20 bills. How much change should he get? $ 19

NOTE TO HOME
Students solve word problems involving money.

PRACTICE p. 63

LESSON 63 PRACTICE Name ____________

Solve.

❶ 60 − 55 = 5
❷ 46 − 29 = 17
❸ 66 − 33 = 33
❹ 36 − 18 = 18
❺ 37 − 29 = 8
❻ 42 − 22 = 20
❼ 59 − 47 = 12
❽ 53 − 35 = 18

Solve these problems.

❾ Rosario had a piece of rope 35 centimeters long. He cut off a 17-centimeter piece. Now how long is the rope? 18 cm

❿ My dog Max is 41 centimeters tall. My cat Ginger is 24 centimeters tall. Which is taller? Max How much taller? 17 cm

Math Explorations and Applications Level 2 • 63

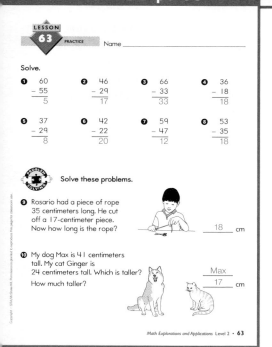

ENRICHMENT p. 63

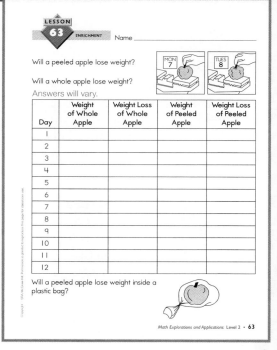

LESSON 63 ENRICHMENT Name ____________

Will a peeled apple lose weight?

Will a whole apple lose weight?

Answers will vary.

Day	Weight of Whole Apple	Weight Loss of Whole Apple	Weight of Peeled Apple	Weight Loss of Peeled Apple
1				
2				
3				
4				
5				
6				
7				
8				
9				
10				
11				
12				

Will a peeled apple lose weight inside a plastic bag?

Math Explorations and Applications Level 2 • 63

❷ Teach

Demonstrate Weigh an opened jar of water in grams. Reweigh it each day for the next five days. Do the same for a closed jar of water of the same size. Keep a record of both jars on a table similar to the following. Discuss the difference in weight between the two jars and reasons for it.

Day	Weight of Open jar	Weight Loss	Weight of Closed Jar	Weight Loss
1	94 g	0 g	94	0 g
2	92 g	2 g	94	0 g

Using the Student Pages Have students complete the problems at the top of page 133 independently, then work with the class to complete the word problems. Then have students work in pairs to complete page 134. When they finish, have partners share and compare their methods and answers with the rest of the class.

Using the Thinking Story Present one or two new problems from those following "Ms. Arthur's Budget, Part 2" on pages 52–53 of the Thinking Story Book.

❸ Wrap-Up (5 MINUTES)

In Closing Have students describe a situation in their own life in which they had to subtract, such as a game or sport.

ALTERNATIVE ASSESSMENT

Informal Assessment Use students' answers to pages 133 and 134 to assess their understanding of subtraction of two-digit numbers.

Assessment Criteria

Did the student . . .

✓ correctly solve eight of ten problems on page 133?

✓ correctly solve five of six problems on page 134?

LESSON 64

Student Edition pages 135–136

Subtracting with Money

LESSON PLANNER

Objectives

- ▶ to provide practice in subtracting two 2-digit numbers
- ▶ to demonstrate how to use subtraction to solve realistic problems

Context of the Lesson This is the seventh of nine lessons focusing on subtracting two-digit numbers.

Materials	Program Resources
none	Number Cubes
	Practice Master 64
	Enrichment Master 64
	For extra practice:
	CD-ROM* Lesson 64

1 Warm-Up (5 MINUTES)

Problem of the Day Write the following problem on the chalkboard: Depika has 47¢ in one pocket and 28¢ in another. Her sister has two quarters and two dimes. Who has more money? How much more? (Depika; 5¢ more)

MENTAL MATH Write the following equations on the chalkboard and have students show how to fill in the blanks with their Number Cubes.

a. 9 + 2 = _____ + 9 (2)

b. 70 + _____ = 80 + 70 (80)

c. 6 + _____ = 7 + 6 (7)

d. 8 + 8 = _____ + 8 (8)

e. _____ + 70 = 70 + 40 (40)

LESSON 64

Name ______________________

Subtracting with Money

Marta has $50. Enrique has $32.

1. Can Enrique buy the bicycle? **no**

2. Could Marta and Enrique buy the bicycle together? **yes**

3. If Marta and Enrique buy the bicycle together, how much money will they have left? $ **13**

4. If Marta buys the kite, how much money will she have left? $ **41**

5. If Enrique buys the baseball and bat, how much money will he have left? $_____

He can't buy them. He needs $3 more.

NOTE TO HOME
Students solve word problems involving money.

Real-World Connection Have students use a clock to time the number of minutes they work on each of two different subjects during the school day. Have students identify which subject they worked on longer and use subtraction to tell how much longer.

Literature Connection Read *Counting Jennie* by Helena Clare Pittman to reinforce lesson concepts.

RETEACHING

Creating word problems is not considered essential at this time. However, if students are still having difficulty in subtracting two-digit numbers, you might review this skill with them or assign appropriate Enrichment activities.

*available separately

◆ **LESSON 64 Subtracting with Money**

Lisa said "I have 90¢."

Martin said "I have 95¢."

Look at the picture. Make up some problems. Then solve them.

Examples: Who has more money? How much more? Can Lisa buy a baseball card? Can Lisa and Martin together buy the video?

THINKING STORY

Talk about the Thinking Story "Take a Chance."

NOTE TO HOME
Students make up and solve word problems.

❷ Teach

Using the Student Pages Have students work on pages 135 and 136 independently. Then have students take turns presenting their problems to the class as everyone else solves them and discusses the solution. When they finish the problems, students can play the "Four Cube Subtraction" game that was introduced in Lesson 62.

❸ Wrap-Up

5 MINUTES

In Closing Present several word problems orally and have students show thumbs up if they would subtract to solve the problem or thumbs down if they would not.

ALTERNATIVE ASSESSMENT

Portfolio Assessment Have students write their favorite word problem and its solution in their Math Portfolios.

Assessment Criteria

Did the student . . .

✓ correctly answer all five questions on page 135?

✓ make up word problems that involve subtraction in the solution on page 136?

PRACTICE p. 64

LESSON 64 PRACTICE Name ____________

Solve these problems.

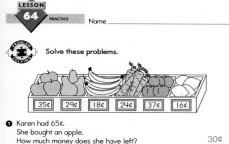

❶ Karen had 65¢.
She bought an apple.
How much money does she have left? 30¢
Can she buy a carrot with the money she has left? yes

❷ Frank had 53¢. He bought a pear.
How much money does he have left? 24¢
Can he buy a tomato with the money he has left? no

❸ Karen's brother had 25¢. He bought a banana.
How much money does he have left? 7¢
Can he buy a lemon with the money he has left? no

64 • Math Explorations and Applications Level 2

ENRICHMENT p. 64

LESSON 64 ENRICHMENT Name ____________

Pretend that Jane, Randa, and Kim are going to the fruit store. Decide how much money each girl has. Write some problems. Then solve them.

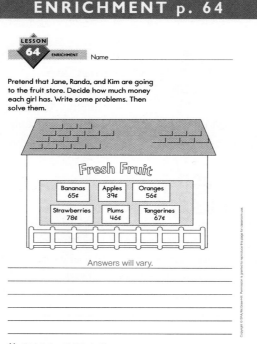

Answers will vary.

64 • Math Explorations and Applications Level 2

LESSON 65

Student Edition pages 137–138

Checking Subtraction

LESSON PLANNER

Objectives

- to provide practice using addition to check two-digit subtraction problems
- to provide experience solving subtraction word problems

Context of the Lesson This is the eighth of nine lessons on subtracting two-digit numbers.

Materials	Program Resources
none	Number Cubes
	Thinking Story Book, pages 52–53
	Reteaching Master
	Practice Master 65
	Enrichment Master 65
	For extra practice: CD-ROM* Lesson 65

1 Warm-Up

5 MINUTES

Problem of the Day Write the following problem on the chalkboard: Mr. Martinez is 63 years old. His brother is 17 years younger. How old is his brother? (46 years old)

MENTAL MATH Have students add or subtract, using their Number Cubes to respond:

a. 9 + 8 = (17)
b. 3 + 4 = (7)
c. 53 + 20 = (73)
d. 16 – 8 = (8)
e. 20 – 10 = (10)
f. 13 – 6 = (7)
g. 9 – 5 = (4)

2 Teach

Demonstrate Write a subtraction problem with the wrong solution on the chalkboard:

72 – 39 = 34 (33)

Guide students to see that if the solution were correct, 39 + 34 would equal 72. Have students find the correct answer and then show how they can use addition to check that they are right. (72 – 39 = 33 and 39 + 33 = 72)

LESSON 65

Name ______________________

Checking Subtraction

Ring each wrong answer.
(Six of the answers are wrong.)

1. 017 17 – 8 9	2. 84 – 27 57	3. 61 – 34 26	4. 70 – 43 27
5. 29 – 23 52	6. 40 – 32 18	7. 100 – 70 30	8. 45 – 25 18
9. 64 – 35 38	10. 75 – 25 50	11. 85 – 73 12	12. 83 – 25 58
13. 87 – 38 49	14. 76 – 35 35	15. 92 – 13 79	16. 70 – 43 27

NOTE TO HOME
Students check answers to subtraction problems.

Literature Connection Read aloud the poem "Arithmetic" by Carl Sandburg to reinforce lesson concepts.

LEARNING STYLES

Meeting Individual Needs

Provide visual and kinesthetic learners with a choice of games from among those already introduced.

RETEACHING p. 17

LESSON 65 RETEACHING Name ______________________

Study the picture below. Make up some problems to go with it.

Answers will vary. Possible answers:
How many carrot plants are in two rows? 9 + 9 = 18;
If the rabbit ate four carrots from one full row, how many are left in the row? 9 – 4 = 5

*available separately

◆ LESSON 65 Checking Subtraction

Solve these problems.

17 Arnold bought film for 12 pictures.
He has already taken three pictures.
How many more can he take? 9

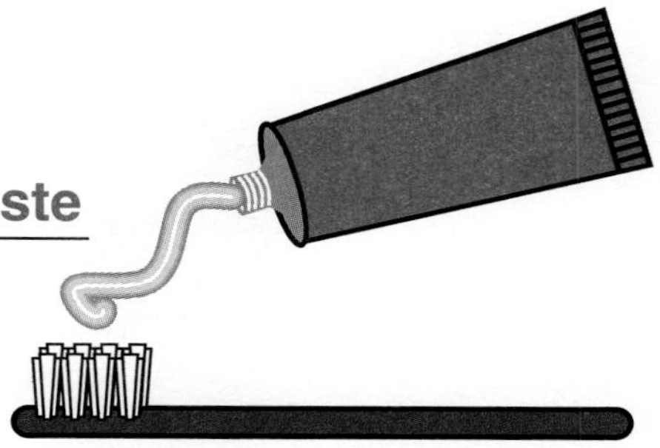

18 Toothpaste costs 84¢.
The toothbrush costs 79¢.
Which costs more? toothpaste
How much more? 5 ¢

19 Rosa has 95¢. Janet has 59¢.
Who has more? Rosa
How much more? 36 ¢

20 Sara had 73 football cards.
She gave some away.
Now she has 45 cards.
How many did she give away? 28

NOTE TO HOME
Students solve subtraction word problems.

Present several similar examples. Include some with correct solutions and some in which the solution is greater than the minuend. Discuss how students can check the accuracy of the solutions using mental math or addition.

Using the Student Pages Have students complete pages 137 and 138 independently.

Using the Thinking Story Present one or two new problems from those following the story "Ms. Arthur's Budget, Part 2" on pages 52–53 of the Thinking Story Book.

3 Wrap-Up 5 MINUTES

In Closing Have students explain how they can use addition to find out whether their answers to subtraction problems are correct.

ANALYZING ANSWERS

Check students' solutions to the word problems. Errors made by using the wrong operation indicate a weakness in problem-solving skills. Errors in subtraction indicate a weakness in computational skills.

ALTERNATIVE ASSESSMENT

Informal Assessment Have students correct their pages as you read the answers. Check to see which students did not find all six mistakes on page 137 or did not correctly solve the problems on page 138.

Assessment Criteria

Did the student . . .

✓ find at least five of the six subtraction mistakes on page 137?

✓ correctly answer all of the word problems on page 138?

ESL

Meeting Individual Needs

You might want to read the word problems aloud to students who are just learning English. Encourage them to use the pictures to help them understand the problems.

PRACTICE p. 65

LESSON 65 PRACTICE Name ____________

Ring each wrong answer.

1 48 − 26 = 22
2 18 − 9 = 9
3 50 − 15 = (45)
4 33 − 19 = 14
5 62 − 34 = (18)
6 28 − 13 = 15
7 29 − 19 = 10
8 78 − 59 = 19
9 72 − 13 = (69)

Solve this problem.

10 Karim had 35 marbles.
He gave some to his cousin.
Now he has 16 marbles.
How many did he give to his cousin? 19

ENRICHMENT p. 65

LESSON 65 PRACTICE Name ____________

Ring each wrong answer.

1 48 − 26 = 22
2 18 − 9 = 9
3 50 − 15 = (45)
4 33 − 19 = 14
5 62 − 34 = (18)
6 28 − 13 = 15
7 29 − 19 = 10
8 78 − 59 = 19
9 72 − 13 = (69)

Solve this problem.

10 Karim had 35 marbles.
He gave some to his cousin.
Now he has 16 marbles.
How many did he give to his cousin? 19

LESSON 66

Student Edition pages 139–140

Subtraction Check

LESSON PLANNER

Objective

✓ to assess students' mastery of subtracting two 2-digit numbers

Context of the Lesson This is the last of nine lessons focusing on subtracting two-digit numbers. This lesson also contains the eighth Mastery Checkpoint, which assesses mastery of two-digit subtraction.

Materials	Program Resources
base-10 materials*	Number Cubes
metersticks (optional)	Practice Master 66
	Enrichment Master 66
	Assessment Master
	For extra practice: CD-ROM* Lesson 66

1 Warm-Up (5 MINUTES)

Problem of the Day Write this problem on the chalkboard: A train travels at 65 miles per hour. It leaves Milleville at 9:05 A.M. It arrives at Hopewell Village at 11:05 A.M. How far is it from Milleville to Hopewell Village? (130 miles)

MENTAL MATH Have students do the following subtraction problems, using their Number Cubes to respond.

a. 12 – 7 = (5) **b.** 140 – 60 = (80)

c. 13 – 9 = (4) **d.** 150 – 90 = (60)

e. 11 – 7 = (4) **f.** 120 – 80 = (40)

LESSON 66

Name ____________________

Subtraction Check

How well can you subtract? Write your answers.

1. 56 − 29 = 27
2. 83 − 27 = 56
3. 46 − 23 = 23
4. 38 − 35 = 3
5. 84 − 30 = 54
6. 27 − 19 = 8
7. 75 − 25 = 50
8. 26 − 7 = 19
9. 64 − 38 = 26
10. 50 − 35 = 15
11. 46 − 8 = 38
12. 63 − 17 = 46
13. 97 − 34 = 63
14. 61 − 56 = 5
15. 74 − 42 = 32
16. 86 − 29 = 57

Number correct ☐

NOTE TO HOME
Students show their mastery of two-digit subtraction.

RETEACHING

If more than twenty percent of your students miss more than three problems, use games, base-10 materials, and further practice over the next several days to reinforce the skills needed to solve two-digit subtraction problems. After extra practice, give another test to those students who did not achieve mastery in the first.

PRACTICE p. 66

LESSON 66 PRACTICE Name ____________________

How well can you subtract?

1. 27 − 16 = 11
2. 45 − 27 = 18
3. 74 − 28 = 46
4. 33 − 19 = 14
5. 60 − 26 = 34
6. 37 − 10 = 27
7. 52 − 12 = 40
8. 86 − 37 = 49
9. 25 − 15 = 10
10. 48 − 19 = 29
11. 53 − 26 = 27
12. 81 − 14 = 67

Number correct ☐

66 • Math Explorations and Applications Level 2

*available separately

◆ **LESSON 66** Subtraction Check

Use the Mixed Practice on page 378 after this lesson.

17. Mitsu is 93 cm tall. David is 78 cm tall.
Who is taller? **Mitsu**
How much taller? **15** cm

18. Aaron weighs 76 pounds. Paige weighs 54 pounds.
Who is heavier? **Aaron**
How much heavier? **22** pounds

19. Rob can run 300 yards in 57 seconds. Clarence can run 300 yards in 48 seconds.
Who is faster? **Clarence**
How much faster? **9** seconds

20. Mr. Han is 73 years old. Ms. Clay is 48 years old.
Who is older? **Mr. Han**
How much older? **25** years

21. Dani is 15 years old.
How much older is Mr. Han than Dani? **58** years

22. How much older is Ms. Clay than Dani? **33** years

NOTE TO HOME
Students solve word problems.

❷ Teach

Demonstrate Explain that students will be given a test on two-digit subtraction. Help students prepare for the test in one of the following ways:

- ▶ Have them work with partners to practice together.
- ▶ Have them play the "Four-Cube Subtraction" game.
- ▶ Work with the entire class to solve two-digit subtraction problems that you write on the chalkboard.

Using the Student Pages Have students work independently to complete the test on page 139. Do not time students. When everyone is finished with this page, have them correct their answers and write the number that were correct at the bottom of the page. Have students then work in pairs to complete page 140 and then share and compare answers.

❸ Wrap-Up (5 MINUTES)

In Closing Have students make up their own word problems involving subtracting two 2-digit numbers. Have them solve their problems, then exchange with and solve a classmate's.

Mastery Checkpoint 8

At about this time most students should demonstrate mastery of two-digit subtraction by correctly solving 12 out of 16 problems on page 139. You might want to use Assessment Master 24 as well to assess mastery. The results of this assessment may be recorded on the Mastery Checkpoint Chart.

ENRICHMENT p. 66

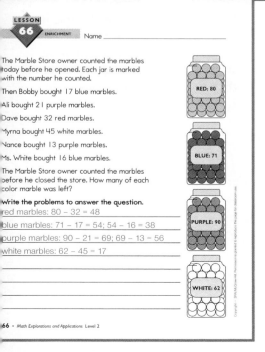

LESSON 66 ENRICHMENT Name ____________

The Marble Store owner counted the marbles today before he opened. Each jar is marked with the number he counted.

Then Bobby bought 17 blue marbles.

Ali bought 21 purple marbles.

Dave bought 32 red marbles.

Myrna bought 45 white marbles.

Nance bought 13 purple marbles.

Ms. White bought 16 blue marbles.

The Marble Store owner counted the marbles before he closed the store. How many of each color marble was left?

Write the problems to answer the question.

red marbles: 80 – 32 = 48

blue marbles: 71 – 17 = 54; 54 – 16 = 38

purple marbles: 90 – 21 = 69; 69 – 13 = 56

white marbles: 62 – 45 = 17

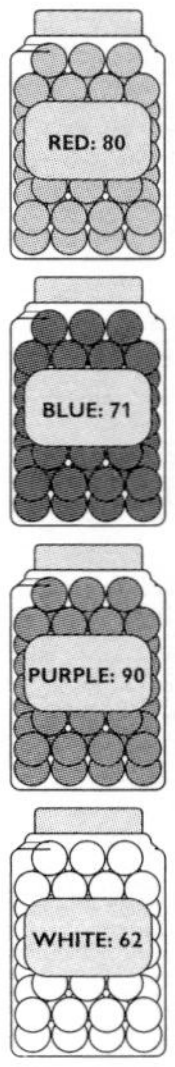

ASSESSMENT p. 21

UNIT 2 **Mastery Checkpoint 8** Two-digit subtraction (Lesson 66)

Name ____________

The student demonstrates mastery by correctly answering at least 13 of the 16 problems.

How well can you subtract?

❶ 23 – 17 = 6	❷ 75 – 25 = 50	❸ 42 – 25 = 17	❹ 65 – 9 = 56
❺ 22 – 12 = 10	❻ 92 – 13 = 79	❼ 50 – 34 = 16	❽ 73 – 28 = 45
❾ 80 – 31 = 49	❿ 87 – 8 = 79	⓫ 92 – 3 = 89	⓬ 37 – 19 = 18
⓭ 26 – 18 = 8	⓮ 72 – 43 = 29	⓯ 58 – 22 = 36	⓰ 29 – 20 = 9

Assessment Criteria

Did the student . . .

- ✓ correctly solve 13 of 16 problems on page 139?
- ✓ correctly answer eight of ten questions on page 140?

LESSON 67

Student Edition pages 141–142

Addition and Subtraction

LESSON PLANNER

Objective

- ▶ to provide practice with two-digit addition and subtraction

Context of the Lesson This is the first lesson that reviews both two-digit addition and subtraction problems.

Materials	Program Resources
none	Number Cubes
	Practice Master 67
	Enrichment Master 67
	For extra practice: CD-ROM* Lesson 67

1 Warm-Up

5 MINUTES

Problem of the Day Write the following problem on the chalkboard: A house has six windows in front and the same number in back. There are half as many windows on each side as there are in back. How many windows does the house have? (18)

MENTAL MATH Have students add or subtract the following using mental math.

a. 15 − 8 = (7)	b. 7 + 9 = (16)	c. 5 + 4 = (9)
d. 12 − 9 = (3)	e. 6 + 6 = (12)	f. 4 + 8 = (12)

2 Teach

Using the Student Pages Have students work independently to complete pages 141–142, being sure they note whether they should add or subtract before they do any calculations. When they finish, correct the pages together with the class.

GAME Introducing the "Roll a Problem" Game This game provides practice in adding and subtracting two-digit numbers and using intuitive notions of probability. You can play this game in small groups or as a class. Each player first draws lines to represent a two-digit addition or subtraction problem, as shown on the next page.

LESSON 67

Name ____________________

Addition and Subtraction

Solve these problems. Watch the signs.

1. 87 − 43 = **44**
2. 66 + 33 = **99**
3. 66 − 33 = **33**
4. 81 − 39 = **42**
5. 50 + 25 = **75**
6. 50 − 25 = **25**
7. 64 + 27 = **91**
8. 18 + 18 = **36**
9. 41 − 23 = **18**
10. 56 − 36 = **20**
11. 37 + 29 = **66**
12. 47 − 23 = **24**
13. 51 + 26 = **77**
14. 27 + 29 = **56**
15. 43 − 28 = **15**

GAME Play the "Roll a Problem" game.

NOTE TO HOME
Students practice and play a game to review addition and subtraction.

Literature Connection Read aloud *Arithmetricks* by Edward H. Julius to reinforce lesson concepts.

RETEACHING

Play the "Roll a Problem" game first with only addition problems. Do not move on to subtraction until most students have mastered the addition; then go on to play the game with subtraction problems.

*available separately

◆ **LESSON 67** **Addition and Subtraction**

16 Mr. Moe lives 64 miles from Malltown.
Ms. Harris lives 37 miles from Malltown.
Who lives farther from Malltown? **Mr. Moe**
How much farther? **27** miles

17 Ms. Ali lives at 83 Malvista Drive.
Ms. Hamad lives at 98 Malvista Drive.
How far apart are their houses? **not enough information given**

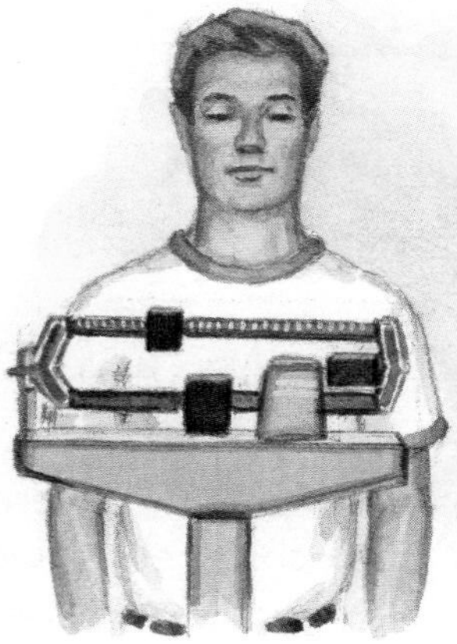

Mr. Moe weighs 82 kilograms.
Mr. Harris weighs 54 kilograms.
Ms. Ali weighs 49 kg.
Ms. Hamad weighs 73 kg.

18 How much more does Mr. Moe weigh than Ms. Ali? **33** kg

19 How much more does Mr. Moe weigh than Ms. Hamad? **9** kg

20 How much more does Ms. Hamad weigh than Ms. Ali? **24** kg

21 How much more does Mr. Harris weigh than Ms. Ali? **5** kg

NOTE TO HOME
Students practice word problems.

PRACTICE p. 67

LESSON 67 PRACTICE Name ____________

Solve. Watch the signs.

1 63 + 27 = 90	2 49 − 27 = 22	3 53 − 19 = 34	4 22 + 39 = 61
5 78 − 24 = 54	6 30 + 48 = 78	7 71 − 27 = 44	8 83 − 47 = 36
9 11 + 65 = 76	10 26 + 46 = 72	11 58 − 29 = 29	12 52 + 18 = 70
13 98 − 66 = 32	14 42 + 48 = 90	15 35 + 26 = 61	16 94 − 68 = 26

ENRICHMENT p. 67

LESSON 67 ENRICHMENT Name ____________

The printer ran out of ink so these problems do not have signs or answers. Help by writing the signs and answers.

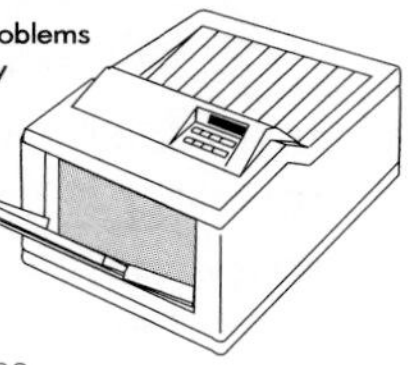

1. 97 − 46 = 51 or + 143
2. 38 − 29 = 9 or + 67
3. 55 − 14 = 41 or + 69
4. 78 − 37 = 41 or + 115
5. 46 + 51 = 97
6. 82 − 75 = 7 or + 157
7. 19 − 13 = 6 or + 32
8. 66 − 21 = 45 or + 87
9. 71 − 29 = 42 or + 100

____ ____

+ or − ____ ____

____ ____

Player 1 then rolls the cube four times, calling out each number. The players write each number on any line that does not have a number on it, before the next number is rolled. Players add or subtract their numbers after the fourth roll. The player with the largest sum wins. In subtraction, any player with a subtrahend greater than a minuend automatically loses. Variations: Alternate use of 0–5 cubes and 5–10 cubes, discounting any 10 that is rolled; or make the smallest sum or greatest difference count as the winner.

3 Wrap-Up

5 MINUTES

In Closing Explain to students that you have 53¢ in one pocket and 47¢ in the other. Have them make up an addition problem and a subtraction problem about this information.

ALTERNATIVE ASSESSMENT

Informal Assessment As students finish pages 141 and 142, note who is having difficulty with addition and subtraction.

Assessment Criteria

Did the student . . .

✓ correctly solve 12 of 15 problems on page 141?

✓ correctly solve four of six problems page 142?

✓ correctly formulate and solve problems created in the "Roll a Problem" game?

LEARNING STYLES

Meeting Individual Needs

As you review students' answers to page 142, have auditory learners explain their thinking orally about how they solved each problem. Encourage them to explain how they decided whether to add or subtract to solve each problem.

LESSON 68

Student Edition pages 143–144

Practice Adding and Subtracting

LESSON PLANNER

Objective

- ▶ to provide practice solving mixed two-digit addition and subtraction problems

Context of the Lesson This is the second of three lessons that reviews two-digit addition and subtraction together.

Materials	Program Resources
none	Number Cubes
	Thinking Story Book, pages 54–57
	Reteaching Master
	Practice Master 68
	Enrichment Master 68
	For extra practice: CD-ROM* Lesson 68

1 Warm-Up (5 minutes)

Problem of the Day Write the following problem on the chalkboard: Molly saved two ten-dollar bills and three dollar bills. She bought a $14 video game. How many ten-dollar bills does she have left? How many dollar bills? (no tens, 9 ones)

MENTAL MATH Have students add and subtract, using their Number Cubes to respond:

a. 6 + 5 = (11) **b.** 16 – 7 = (9)

c. 17 – 8 = (9) **d.** 6 + 8 = (14)

e. 7 + 3 = (10) **f.** 14 – 9 = (5)

g. 11 – 3 = (8) **h.** 18 – 9 = (9)

i. 8 + 5 = (13) **j.** 10 – 4 = (6)

LESSON 68

Name ____________________

Practice Adding and Subtracting

Solve these problems. Watch the signs.

1. 43 + 25 = 68
2. 37 − 36 = 1
3. 64 − 38 = 26
4. 18 + 47 = 65

5. Jessica has 19¢. If she earns 75¢, how much will she have? 94 ¢

6. There are 27 children in the class. Each child needs two pencils. How many pencils are needed? 54

7. Kareem had 37¢. He spent 15¢. Now he has 22 ¢.

8. Cindy has 82¢. If she spends 16¢, how much will she have? 66 ¢

NOTE TO HOME
Students practice solving word problems.

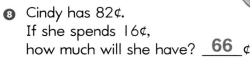

Language Arts Connection Have students work in pairs. Invite each pair of students to make up a story about a creature from outer space. Have them end their story with a word problem about the creature that involves either addition or subtraction. Partners can then share and compare stories and problems with other pairs.

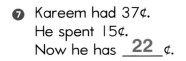

Literature Connection Read aloud or invite students to read *Ten Brothers with Camels* by Gladys T. Cretan to reinforce learning concepts.

RETEACHING p. 18

LESSON 68 RETEACHING Name ____________________

A problem gives facts and asks a question.

Ring the facts.
Underline the question.

Mom bought 12 cookies.
Alex ate four cookies.
How many cookies were left?
12 – 4 = ______

Ring the facts. Underline the questions.
Solve the problems.

1. Dan has 45¢. He buys a 32¢ stamp. How much does he have left?
45¢ – 32¢ = 13¢

2. There are 11 books on the table. The librarian put seven more books there. How many are there all together?
11 + 7 = 18 books

3. Karen planted 14 plants. Nina gave her eight more. How many plants are there all together?
14 + 8 = 22

4. Greg weighs 65 pounds. Panyia weighs 48 pounds. How much more does Greg weigh?
65 – 48 = 17 pounds

18 • *Math Explorations and Applications* Level 2

*available separately

◆ **LESSON 68** Practice Adding and Subtracting

Solve these problems.

9 Mr. Lin has $90.

Can he buy the jacket and pants? **no**

Can he buy the jacket and hat? **yes**

Can he buy the pants and hat? **yes**

10 There are 17 children in the library. Each child has two books.

How many books do they have all together? **34**

11 There are 25 dogs in Mr. Breezy's training school. Each dog has one tail.

How many tails do they have all together? **25**

THINKING STORY

Talk about the Thinking Story "Plenty of Time."

NOTE TO HOME
Students solve word problems.

2 Teach

Demonstrate Present students with oral word problems such as those on pages 143 and 144 involving both addition and subtraction. After students write down the information they need, allow time for them to solve the problem. Discuss the methods and solutions for each problem before going on to the next. Observe whether students are making errors in choosing the correct operation or doing the calculations.

Using the Student Pages Have students complete both pages independently. When they finish, present the correct answers so they can check their own papers. Discuss how they decided whether to add or subtract for each problem. Note that the solution to the third problem on page 143 does not require addition or subtraction.

Using the Thinking Story Read the story "Plenty of Time" on pages 54–57 of the Thinking Story Book. Stop and discuss the questions asked throughout the story.

3 Wrap-Up

5 MINUTES

In Closing Ask students to make up a problem in which they must add to solve it. Then have them make up one in which they must subtract.

SELF ASSESSMENT

After students correct their papers, have them evaluate their own performance and decide whether their skills are shiny or rusty.

PRACTICE p. 68

LESSON 68 PRACTICE Name ______

Solve. Watch the signs.

1. 43 − 19 = 24
2. 26 + 35 = 61
3. 45 + 15 = 60
4. 64 − 38 = 26

PROBLEM SOLVING Solve these problems.

Terence has $45.

5. Can he buy the basketball and soccer ball? yes
6. Can he buy the skates and soccer ball? no
7. Can he buy the basketball and skates? yes

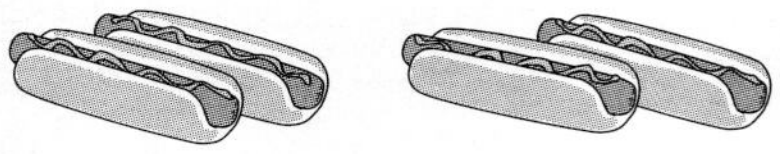

8. There are 26 children in the second-grade class. Each child eats two hot dogs for lunch. How many hot dogs are eaten all together? 52

ENRICHMENT p. 68

LESSON 68 ENRICHMENT Name ______

1. Class A and Class B are going to the museum. Class A has 34 students, and Class B has 27 students. How many students are going to the museum? 61
2. The museum opened in 1991. How many years has the museum been open? Answers will vary.
3. One room had 17 pictures of horses. There were three horses in five of those pictures. The rest showed only one horse each. How many horses were there all together? 27
4. One room has 46 pictures of the ocean. There are flying birds painted in 28 of the pictures. How many pictures show no birds at all? 18
5. The leader passed out two lists to each of the 23 children who went into the Spanish art room. How many lists were passed out? 46
6. It is 1:45 P.M. The buses will come back to get the students at 2:30 P.M. How many minutes do they have left? 45

Assessment Criteria

Did the student . . .

- ✓ correctly solve the four problems at the top of page 143?
- ✓ choose the correct operation to solve five of the seven word problems on pages 143–144?
- ✓ solve correctly five of the seven word problems on pages 143–144?

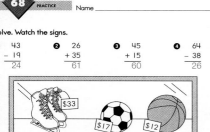

STORY 9

THINKING STORY

Plenty of Time

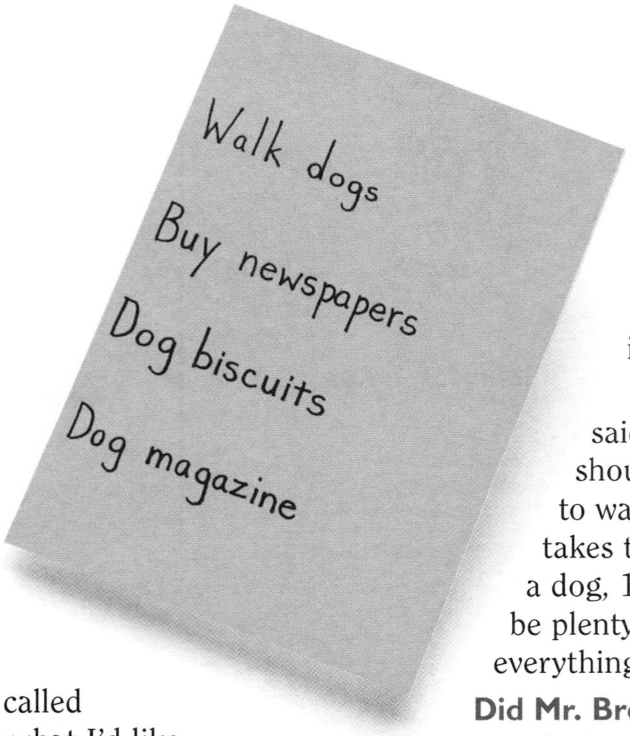

Trixie runs errands at Mr. Breezy's training school for dogs. Mr. Breezy is always in a hurry. He thinks that Trixie should be in a hurry too. Trixie tries to hurry, but she and Mr. Breezy have very different ideas about time.

One morning Mr. Breezy called Trixie into his office. "Here's what I'd like you to do, Trixie. First I'd like you to walk each dog around the block three times. Each dog likes to walk alone. So you need to walk all ten dogs, one at a time. Then would you please go to the drugstore and buy me a newspaper?"

"Sure," said Trixie. "I'll be back in about an hour."

"About an hour!" said Mr. Breezy. "That should be enough time to walk ten turtles. If it takes ten minutes to walk a dog, 15 minutes ought to be plenty of time to do everything."

Did Mr. Breezy give Trixie enough time to do the errands? no

How can you tell? It takes ten minutes for each dog, and there are ten dogs. That will take at least 100 minutes, or one hour and 40 minutes.

Trixie ran each dog around the block, ran to buy a newspaper, then ran back to the school. She was out of breath when she got back. She had been running for more than an hour and a half.

How much time did Mr. Breezy think the errands would take? 15 minutes

Why did it take Trixie so much longer? because she walked each dog individually

"Did you get lost?" Mr. Breezy asked Trixie when she got back.

"No," said Trixie, huffing and puffing. "I think you forgot–there are ten dogs, so I had to run around the block 30 times and then get a newspaper."

"Then you must be tired," said Mr. Breezy. "I'll make this next errand much easier. First walk to the grocery store. That should take ten minutes, even if you walk slowly. Then buy a large box of dog biscuits. That will take another ten minutes. So the whole trip should take you only 20 minutes."

What did Mr. Breezy forget to count? walking back from the grocery store

How long should the trip really take? 30 minutes

When Trixie returned from the grocery store, Mr. Breezy said, "You'll be happy to hear about the next job I have for you. It has only one part to it. You just need to get a dog magazine at the newsstand on the corner."

"About how long will that take?" asked Trixie.

"An hour," he answered.

Is Mr. Breezy right? No; it won't take that long.

Why not? The corner is not far away.

How long should it take? five or ten minutes

◆ STORY 9 Plenty of Time

Trixie bought the magazine and returned in five minutes. "You were really quick this time," said Mr Breezy. "It's getting near lunchtime. Luckily there are only five more things that need to be done."

Trixie groaned to herself. She knew that meant she was going to miss lunch.

"Now the first thing," said Mr. Breezy, "is that Bowser is acting like a very sad dog these days, and I'd like you to take him over to the park and let him run around for 15 minutes."

Trixie wrote "15 minutes" on a sheet of paper so she would remember.

"And while Bowser is running around, I'd like you to keep saying 'nice doggie' and things like that to him to make him feel better."

"That's another 15 minutes," Trixie thought sadly, writing it down.

Will that really take 15 more minutes? no
Why not? It's done at the same time Bowser is running around.

"I also want you to notice carefully what the weather is like," Mr. Breezy said, "because I'm trying to decide whether to play golf this afternoon."

"Five more minutes," Trixie thought, writing it down.

"And I want you to breathe deeply and run around a little yourself," Mr. Breezy added. "You're looking a bit run-down, and I think it will do you good."

Trixie wrote "ten minutes" on the sheet of paper.

"And finally I want you to keep an eye on Bowser all the time and see that he doesn't get into any trouble."

"How long will that take?" Trixie asked.

"About 15 minutes," Mr. Breezy said.

Trixie looked at the numbers she had written down: 15, 15, 5, 10, and 15. She added them up.

About how much will those numbers add up to? Can anyone figure it out exactly?
60 minutes

"Sixty minutes," Trixie said unhappily. "A whole hour!"

Should all these things take an hour to do? no

Why not? They can all be done at the same time.

Trixie took Bowser to the park and let him run around. She had to run quite a bit so as to stay close enough to keep an eye on Bowser and so that Bowser could hear her saying "nice doggie" and things like that. At the end of 15 minutes Trixie was breathing hard from running around so much, but she felt good because it was such a bright, sunny day. "Now what's the next thing I have to do?" she asked herself, trying to remember all the things Mr. Breezy had told her.

What chores does Trixie have left to do? none

How much time has she spent? 15 minutes

Why did the chores take so little time? She did them all at the same time.

Trixie realized that she had already done all the things Mr. Breezy had asked her to do and that it had taken only 15 minutes instead of an hour. "Sometimes I'm so fast I surprise myself," she said happily.

. . . the end

UNIT 2

Student Edition pages 145–146

Mid-Unit Review

The Mid-Unit Review pinpoints troublesome skill areas for students, allowing plenty of time for additional practice and reteaching before the unit ends. If students did not do well on the Mid-Unit Review and have completed additional practice, you might want to use the Mid-Unit Review provided on pages 22–23 in the Assessment Master Book.

Using the Student Pages Have students complete problems 1–34 on pages 145 and 146 on their own. You might treat this review as a formal assessment of students' skills and have students complete this review as a timed test. See suggestions on page 44.

UNIT 2

Name ____________________

Mid-Unit Review

Write the standard name for each of these.

1. 4 tens and 9 = **49**
2. 6 tens and 0 = **60**
3. 5 tens and 16 = **66**
4. 0 tens and 19 = **19**

Add.

5. 37 + 6 = **43**
6. 16 + 25 = **41**
7. 75 + 20 = **95**
8. 28 + 48 = **76**
9. 59 + 21 = **80**
10. 0 + 47 = **47**
11. 63 + 24 = **87**
12. 35 + 9 = **44**

Solve this problem.

13. Bob has 32 toy cars. His brother has 29 toy cars. How many cars to they have together? **61**

Subtract.

14. 40 − 10 = **30**
15. 80 − 30 = **50**
16. 90 − 42 = **48**
17. 100 − 67 = **33**
18. 82 − 37 = **45**
19. 75 − 45 = **30**
20. 54 − 22 = **32**
21. 68 − 53 = **15**

NOTE TO HOME
Students review unit skills and concepts.

◆ UNIT 2 Mid-Unit Review

Solve these problems.

22. May had 65¢. She spent 25¢.
How much does she have now? **40** ¢

23. Jose needs \$72. He has \$46.
How much more does he need? \$**26**

Work these problems. Watch the signs.

24. $\begin{array}{r} 42 \\ -\ 27 \\ \hline \mathbf{15} \end{array}$ 25. $\begin{array}{r} 56 \\ +\ 24 \\ \hline \mathbf{80} \end{array}$ 26. $\begin{array}{r} 39 \\ +\ 30 \\ \hline \mathbf{69} \end{array}$ 27. $\begin{array}{r} 83 \\ -\ 78 \\ \hline \mathbf{5} \end{array}$

28. $\begin{array}{r} 79 \\ -\ 15 \\ \hline \mathbf{64} \end{array}$ 29. $\begin{array}{r} 51 \\ +\ 44 \\ \hline \mathbf{95} \end{array}$ 30. $\begin{array}{r} 93 \\ -\ 66 \\ \hline \mathbf{27} \end{array}$ 31. $\begin{array}{r} 48 \\ +\ 36 \\ \hline \mathbf{84} \end{array}$

32. 18 − 11 = **7** 33. 21 − 11 = **10**

Solve these problems.

34. Janell has 25 blue cars and
36 red cars.
How many more red cars
than blue cars does she have? **11**

34. Elissa got \$25 for her birthday. She
earned \$7 more raking leaves.
How much did she have all together? \$**32**

NOTE TO HOME
Students review unit skills and concepts.

Home Connections You may want to send home Home Connections Masters 41–42 which provide additional activities families can complete together. These activities apply the skills being presented in this unit.

Unit Project This would be a good time to assign the "weather information project on pages 200a and 200b. Students may begin working on the project in cooperative groups in their free time as you work through the unit. The Unit Project is a good opportunity for students to practice collecting, organizing, displaying, and interpreting visually represented information, develop appropriate methods of collecting information, demonstrate individual techniques for collecting, organizing, and displaying information, and represent information in a variety of forms.

ASSESSMENT p. 22

UNIT 2 **Mid-Unit Review** (Use after Lesson 68.) Page 1 of 3

Name ______________________

The student demonstrates mastery by correctly answering at least 32 of the 40 problems.

Solve. Watch the signs.

1. 12 − 5 = 7
2. 17 − 8 = 9
3. 9 + 7 = 16
4. 14 − 6 = 8
5. 4 + 7 = 11
6. 8 + 7 = 15
7. 11 − 4 = 7
8. 6 + 8 = 14
9. 19 − 10 = 9
10. 13 − 5 = 8
11. 20 + 20 = 40
12. 70 + 70 = 140

Solve.

13. $\begin{array}{r} 9 \\ +\ 8 \\ \hline 17 \end{array}$ 14. $\begin{array}{r} 6 \\ +\ 7 \\ \hline 13 \end{array}$ 15. $\begin{array}{r} 8 \\ +\ 5 \\ \hline 13 \end{array}$ 16. $\begin{array}{r} 37 \\ +\ 53 \\ \hline 90 \end{array}$

Go on . . .

22 • *Math Explorations and Applications* Level 2

LESSON 69

Student Edition pages 147–148

Check Your Adding and Subtracting

LESSON PLANNER

Objectives

- ▶ to assess students' ability to know whether to add or subtract to solve a word problem
- ✓ to assess students' ability to solve addition and subtraction problems

Context of the Lesson This is the last of three lessons on two-digit addition and subtraction. It also contains Mastery Checkpoint 9 for assessing two-digit addition and subtraction skills.

Materials	Program Resources
none	Number Cubes
	Thinking Story Book, pages 58–59
	Practice Master 69
	Enrichment Master 69
	Assessment Master
	For extra practice: CD-ROM* Lesson 69

1 Warm-Up

5 MINUTES

Problem of the Day Present the following problem to the students: Julio ran 16 miles on Monday and 15 miles on Tuesday. Maria ran 2 more miles than Julio on both days. How many miles did Maria run all together? (35 miles)

MENTAL MATH Have students add and subtract mentally, using their Number Cubes to respond:

- a. 10 – 6 = (4)
- b. 7 – 6 = (1)
- c. 13 – 8 = (5)
- d. 9 – 6 = (3)
- e. 8 – 5 = (3)
- f. 5 – 3 = (2)
- g. 6 – 4 = (2)

2 Teach

GAME **Using the "Roll a Problem" Game** Have students play this game, which was introduced in Lesson 67. Be sure each student plays at least one subtraction and one addition variation of the game.

LESSON 69

Name ______________________

Check Your Adding and Subtracting

Solve these problems. Watch the signs.

1. $53 + 28 = 81$
2. $53 - 28 = 25$
3. $47 - 24 = 23$
4. $66 + 27 = 93$
5. $36 + 22 = 58$
6. $83 - 39 = 44$
7. $44 + 39 = 83$
8. $17 + 59 = 76$

PROBLEM SOLVING

Aaron has 27¢. Tanya has 35¢.

9. Who has more money? **Tanya**
10. How much more? **8** ¢
11. Together, how much do Tanya and Aaron have? **62** ¢

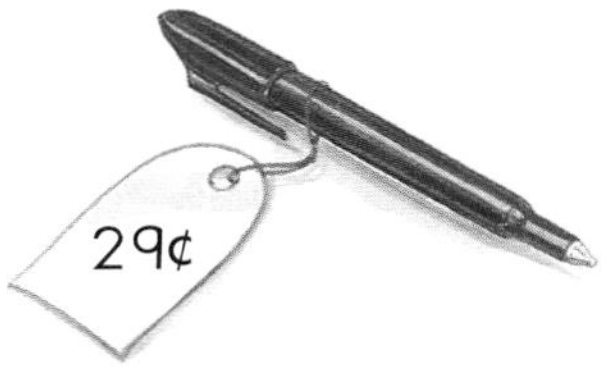

12. How much more does the comic book cost than the pen? **69** ¢

NOTE TO HOME
Students solve addition and subtraction problems.

RETEACHING

To help students who are still having difficulty determining whether to add or subtract to solve specific word problems, provide practice with problems that have small numbers. For example, present students with simple oral problems such as the following, and have them tell whether they will add or subtract to solve them:

I have five cents. I find two cents more. How much do I have? (add)

I had ten cents. I lost three cents. How much do I have? (subtract)

PRACTICE p. 69

LESSON 69 PRACTICE Name ______________

Solve. Watch the signs.

1. $68 - 23 = 45$
2. $46 + 17 = 63$
3. $25 + 29 = 54$
4. $53 - 19 = 34$
5. $26 + 65 = 91$
6. $75 - 48 = 27$

Solve these problems.

7. Gwen needs 64¢. She already has 37¢. How much more does she need? 27¢

8. How much more does the popcorn cost than the can of soda pop? 26¢

Math Explorations and Applications Level 2 • 69

*available separately

◆ LESSON 69 Check Your Adding and Subtracting

Solve these problems.

⑬ This corn plant is 81 centimeters tall. One week ago it was 69 centimeters tall. How much did it grow last week? __12__ cm

⑭ Juan has a $10 bill. How much change will he get if he buys the globe? $__4__

⑮ How much for two oranges? __78__ ¢

⑯ How much for one orange and one apple? __49__ ¢

⑰ Anita needs 75¢. She already has 50¢. How much more does she need? __25__ ¢

MATH JOURNAL: How are adding and subtracting alike and different? Write about it in your Math Journal.

NOTE TO HOME
Students solve word problems.

Using the Student Pages

Using the Student Pages Explain to students that pages 147–148 provide a way to check to see how well they can solve addition and subtraction problems. Have students complete both pages independently. When students finish, present the correct answers so they can check their own papers.

Using the Thinking Story Present one or two new problems from those following "Plenty of Time" on pages 58–59 of the Thinking Story Book.

③ Wrap-Up (5 MINUTES)

In Closing Ask students to explain and show how addition and subtraction are related. (Students should realize that addition is the opposite of subtraction. They can show this with craft sticks or show that they can add to check answers in subtraction.)

Mastery Checkpoint 9

Use Assessment Masters 27–29 to check students' ability to decide whether to add or subtract in a particular situation and to check their ability to add and subtract correctly. You may want to record the students' scores on the Mastery Checkpoint Chart.

Assessment Criteria

Did the student . . .

- ✓ correctly solve at least six of the eight problems at the top of page 147?
- ✓ use the appropriate operation in at least seven of the nine word problems on pages 147–148?

LOOKING AHEAD You will need a toy clock face or chalkboard clock faces beginning in Lesson 70.

ENRICHMENT p. 69

LESSON 69 ENRICHMENT Name ____________

Copy and cut out the numbers in Group A. Do the same for Group B. Place the numbers in two piles face down. Pick one number from Group A. Write it on the line. Flip a coin. Put + for heads or – for tails. Then pick a number from Group B and write it on the line. Solve the number sentence you made. Repeat until you have used all the numbers.

Answers will vary. However, number sentences should include the numbers from the two groups shown on the page, and answers should reflect correct addition or subtraction among those numbers.

Group A

74	67	51	59	70	62

Group B

19	26	11	17	10	22

Math Explorations and Applications Level 2 • 69

ASSESSMENT p. 25

UNIT 2 **Mastery Checkpoint 9** Addition and subtraction applications (Lesson 69)
Page 1 of 4

Name ____________

The student demonstrates mastery by correctly answering at least 21 of the 26 problems.

Solve these problems.

There are 29 students in Ms. Oliver's second-grade classroom. There are 35 desks and 35 chairs in the classroom.

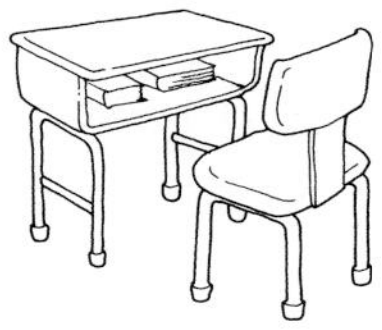

❶ Does each student have a desk and a chair?
yes

❷ How many desks will be empty if all the students are present?
6

Annie has five crayons. She has 32¢.

❸ How many crayons does Annie have?
5

Go on . . .

Math Explorations and Applications Level 2 • 25

LESSON 70

Student Edition pages 149–150

Telling Time—Hour and Half Hour

LESSON PLANNER

Objective

▶ to review telling time to the nearest half hour

Context of the Lesson This is the first of three lessons on telling time. The topic is reintroduced in Lesson 93. A brief introduction was provided in level 1.

Materials	Program Resources
clock face	"Time" Game Mat
toy analog clock	Number Cubes
	Thinking Story Book, pages 58–59
	Practice Master 70
	Enrichment Master 70
	For extra practice: CD-ROM* Lesson 70

1 Warm-Up (5 MINUTES)

PROBLEM SOLVING **Problem of the Day** Have students copy and complete the following patterns:

12, 15, 18, ___, ___, ___ (21, 24, 27)

33, 32, 30, 27, 23, ___, ___, ___ (18, 12, 5)

MENTAL MATH Have students add and subtract mentally, using Numbers Cubes to respond:

a. 14 – 6 = (8) **b.** 3 + 3 = (6) **c.** 10 – 8 = (2)

d. 8 – 3 = (5) **e.** 6 + 5 = (11) **f.** 10 – 7 = (3)

g. 15 – 7 = (8) **h.** 8 + 8 = (16) **i.** 14 – 6 = (8)

LEARNING STYLES **Meeting Individual Needs**

Allow kinesthetic learners to practice showing various times to the hour and half hour using a toy analog clock.

LESSON 70

Name __________________________

Telling Time—Hour and Half Hour

What time is it? Write your answers.

7 o'clock or 7:00

30 minutes after 7 o'clock or 7:30

1.  8 : 30
2.  11 : 00
3.  2 : 30
4.  6 : 30
5.  5 : 00
6.  5 : 30
7.  12 : 30
8.  9 : 00

NOTE TO HOME
Students review telling time to the nearest half hour.

Why teach it at this time?

This is the first lesson on telling time in this grade level. Although some students will remember what they learned in level 1 or will have learned to tell time at home, many will not know how to tell time at all. Although mastery is not expected, the next three lessons will provide an opportunity for these students to learn to tell time.

Literature Connection Read aloud or invite students to read *P. Bear's New Year's Eve Party* by Paul Owen Lewis to reinforce lesson concepts.

RETEACHING

Display a working analog clock in the classroom. Ask students what time it is at various times during the day when the clock shows hours and half hours. For example, ask them at 10:00, 11:30, and 12:00 to tell what time it is.

*available separately

◆ **LESSON 70** Telling Time—Hour and Half Hour

Show the time.

Use the Mixed Practice on page 379 after this lesson.

9 4:00

10 10:30

11 1:30

12 6:00

13 7:30

14 three-thirty | 3 : 30

15 five o'clock | 5 : 00

Play the "Time" game.

NOTE TO HOME
Students review time and play a game involving telling time.

PRACTICE p. 70

LESSON 70 PRACTICE Name ______

What time is it?

1 7:30
2 4:30
3 10:00
4 1:30
5 7:00
6 2:00

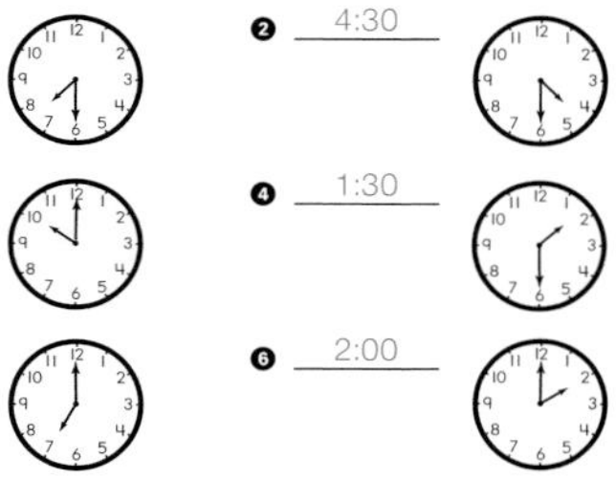

Draw the hands.

7 12:00 8 5:30 9 6:30
10 1:00 11 3:00 12 10:30

70 • *Math Explorations and Applications* Level 2

ENRICHMENT p. 70

LESSON 70 ENRICHMENT Name ______

1 Amanda must set the alarm clock to wake her for dance class. The class starts at 9:00 A.M. Amanda needs $1\frac{1}{2}$ hours to get to class. Draw the hands to show how late she can sleep.

2 Amanda's new dance teacher forgot to stop her class on time. The class started at 9:00 A.M. It lasted for 1 hour 40 minutes. Draw the hands to show what time the class ended.

3 Amanda walked past a store and saw three clocks. Each of the clocks had only the number 12 on it. Each had a different time. Tell what time was on each of the three clocks.

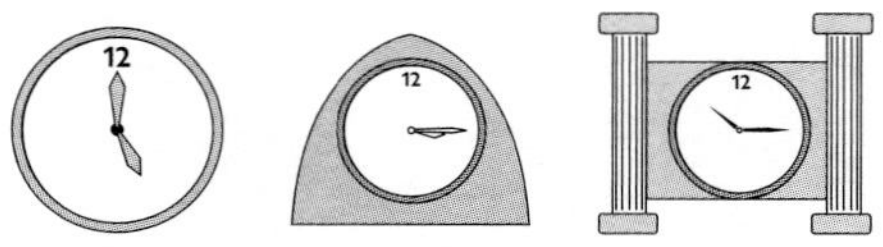

a. 5:00 b. 3:15 c. 10:15

70 • *Math Explorations and Applications* Level 2

2 Teach

Demonstrate Display a clock set to a time on the hour, such as 3:00. Discuss what time the clock shows and where the hour and minute hands are. Do the same for a half-hour time such as 3:30. Discuss the different ways this can be read: half past three, 30 minutes after three, or three-thirty. Finally, show the time using only the hour hand. Show the hour hand pointing directly to the 3. Explain that this is where the hour hand is when it is three o'clock. Then show the hand between 3 and 4. Explain that this is where the hour hand is when it is 3:30. Show several different times with both hands and have students tell what they are usually doing at those times.

Using the Student Pages Have students complete pages 149–150 independently. You might wish to work together to complete the first exercise on each page.

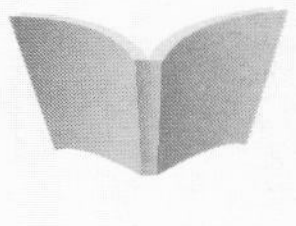

Using the Thinking Story Present one or two new problems from those following "Plenty of Time" on pages 58–59 of the Thinking Story Book.

Introducing the "Time" Game Mat Demonstrate and play this game to provide practice in telling time to the hour and half hour. Complete directions are on the game.

3 Wrap-Up

In Closing Ask students where the minute hand is when it is 30 minutes after seven and where it is when it is seven o'clock.

Informal Assessment Observe which students can correctly name the time shown on the clock when playing the "Time" Game Mat.

Assessment Criteria

Did the student . . .

✓ correctly write the time shown on six of the eight clocks on page 149?

✓ correctly indicate the time on at least five of the seven times indicated on page 150?

✓ correctly name the time shown on the clock when playing the "Time" game?

LESSON 71

Student Edition pages 151–154

Telling Time—Quarter Hour

LESSON PLANNER

Objective

▶ to introduce telling time to the quarter hour

Context of the Lesson This is the second of three lessons on telling time. It provides an introduction to fractions (quarter hours), which will be introduced in following lessons.

Materials

clock face with movable hands

Program Resources

Reteaching Master
Practice Master 71
Enrichment Master 71
For extra practice:
CD-ROM* Lesson 71

1 Warm-Up

5 MINUTES

Problem of the Day Write this problem on the chalkboard: It takes one student ten minutes to eat one sandwich. How long will it take two students to each eat a sandwich at the same time? Explain your reasoning. (10 minutes, because they are doing it at the same time)

MENTAL MATH Write the following on the chalkboard and have students fill in the blanks.

a. 600 cm = 6 _____ (meters)
b. 36 inches = 3 _____ (feet)
c. 12 inches = 1 _____ (foot)
d. 36 inches = 1 _____ (yard)
e. 3 feet = 1 _____ (yard)
f. 2 meters = 200 _____ (cm)

LESSON 71

Name ______________________________

Telling Time—Quarter Hour

What time is it?

15 minutes after 7 o'clock
or quarter after 7 o'clock

15 minutes before 8 o'clock
or quarter to 8 o'clock

❶ 
quarter after ____
half past ____
quarter to ____
3 o'clock

❷ 
quarter after ____
half past 5
quarter to ____
____ o'clock

❸ 

quarter after ____
half past 3
quarter to ____
____ o'clock

❹ 
quarter after 10
half past ____
quarter to ____
____ o'clock

❺ 
quarter after ____
half past ____
quarter to 10
____ o'clock

❻ 

quarter after ____
half past ____
quarter to ____
12 o'clock

NOTE TO HOME
Students tell time to the quarter hour.

Literature Connection Read aloud *The Boy Who Stopped Time* by Anthony Taber to reinforce lesson concepts.

*available separately

◆ **LESSON 71** Telling Time—Quarter Hour

What time is it?

7 
quarter after ____
half past ____
quarter to ____
_7_ o'clock

8 
quarter after _3_
half past ____
quarter to ____
____ o'clock

9 
quarter after ____
half past ____
quarter to _6_
____ o'clock

10 
quarter after ____
half past _2_
quarter to ____
____ o'clock

11 
quarter after ____
half past ____
quarter to ____
_1_ o'clock

12 
quarter after _6_
half past ____
quarter to ____
____ o'clock

13 10:30
quarter after ____
half past _10_
quarter to ____
____ o'clock

14 
quarter after ____
half past ____
quarter to _1_
____ o'clock

No wonder we get tired of left over turkey! Americans eat 50 million (50,000,000) turkeys on Thanksgiving.

NOTE TO HOME
Students practice telling time to the quarter hour.

2 Teach

Demonstrate Display or draw a clock on the chalkboard and review several time problems involving the hour and half hour. Then show students a clock without a minute hand and with the hour hand set between 3 and 4 (closer to the 3). Ask what time they think the clock shows. Encourage students to see that it is somewhere between 3 and 4 o'clock, but closer to 3 o'clock. Next, draw the minute hand pointing to the 3 and ask students to use one of the following phrases to tell the time: quarter after ____; half past ____; quarter to ____; or ____ o'clock.

If students are having difficulty with this terminology, ask them to visualize a mouse running around the clock. Ask the following questions to show that the clock can be divided into quarters:

- ▶ If the mouse starts at 12 and runs all the way around, where does it stop? (12)
- ▶ If the mouse starts at 12 and runs halfway around, where does it stop? (6)
- ▶ If it runs a quarter of the way around, where does it stop? (3 or 9, depending on which way)
- ▶ If it runs in the same direction as the hands of the clock move, where does it stop at one quarter of the way? (3) halfway? (6) three quarters of the way? (9)

For practice, have students tell different times for quarter hours that volunteers show on the clock. Be sure they use the terminology introduced in the beginning of the demonstration: *quarter after, half past, quarter to,* and *o'clock*.

Using the Student Pages Do page 151 with the class. Discuss each example and have students explain how they know each answer is correct. For instance, students should mention that they can tell what the hour is by noticing where the hour hand is pointing, and that the minute hand shows them whether it is a quarter after, quarter to, half-past, or on the hour.

Have students complete page 152 on their own. Correct this page together before having students continue.

◆ LESSON 71 Telling Time—Quarter Hour

Teach

Using the Student Pages Work the first two problems on page 153 with the class. Point out that students should use the same words as they did on pages 151 and 152 to tell what time it is. Then have students complete the remaining problems on this page and page 154 independently. When finished, they can share and correct their answers. You may also wish to have students choose and play a game from among those they have learned so far.

◆ LESSON 71 Telling Time—Quarter Hour

Name ______________________

What time is it?

15 4 : 15

16 8 : 15

17 5 : 00

18 11 : 45

19 6 : 45

20 9 : 00

21 9 : 30

22 12 : 30

NOTE TO HOME
Students tell time.

Art Connection Have students make a collection of clock faces by drawing the faces of watches and clocks they see at home and at school. This will help students internalize the position of the numbers on a clock, and to observe the variety of clocks in their lives. Display students' clocks on a classroom bulletin board entitled "The Many Faces of Time."

RETEACHING p. 19

LESSON 71 RETEACHING Name ______________________

When the hour hand points to 4 and the minute hand points to 12, or straight up, it is 4:00.

When the hour hand is between 4 and 5 and the minute hand points to 6, or straight down, it is 4:30, or half-past four.

When the hour hand is near 4 and the minute hand points to 3, it is 4:15, or a quarter after four.

When the hour hand is between 4 and 5 and the minute hand points to 9, it is 4:45, or a quarter to five.

Show half past 3.

Show a quarter past 7.

Show a quarter to 3.

◆ LESSON 71 Telling Time—Quarter Hour

Sharpen your skills.

Solve these problems. Watch the signs.

㉓ 34 + 34 = **68**

㉔ 34 − 34 = **0**

㉕ 83 − 17 = **66**

㉖ 52 − 27 = **25**

㉗ 83 + 17 = **100**

㉘ 67 − 37 = **30**

㉙ 42 + 56 = **98**

㉚ 60 − 43 = **17**

㉛ 29 + 53 = **82**

㉜ 66 − 38 = **28**

㉝ 24 − 17 = **7**

㉞ 84 − 20 = **64**

㉟ 39 − 18 = **21**

㊱ 65 − 49 = **16**

㊲ 43 + 16 = **59**

㊳ 52 + 24 = **76**

㊴ 76 − 35 = **41**

㊵ 14 + 77 = **91**

NOTE TO HOME
Students review adding and subtracting two-digit numbers.

PRACTICE p. 71

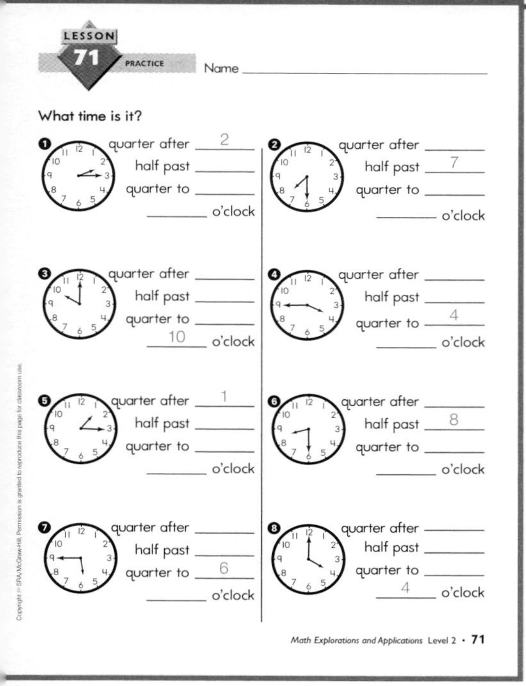

LESSON 71 PRACTICE Name ______

What time is it?

1. quarter after 2 / half past ___ / quarter to ___ / ___ o'clock
2. quarter after ___ / half past 7 / quarter to ___ / ___ o'clock
3. quarter after ___ / half past ___ / quarter to ___ / 10 o'clock
4. quarter after ___ / half past ___ / quarter to 4 / ___ o'clock
5. quarter after 1 / half past ___ / quarter to ___ / ___ o'clock
6. quarter after ___ / half past 8 / quarter to ___ / ___ o'clock
7. quarter after ___ / half past ___ / quarter to 6 / ___ o'clock
8. quarter after ___ / half past ___ / quarter to ___ / 4 o'clock

Math Explorations and Applications Level 2 • **71**

ENRICHMENT p. 71

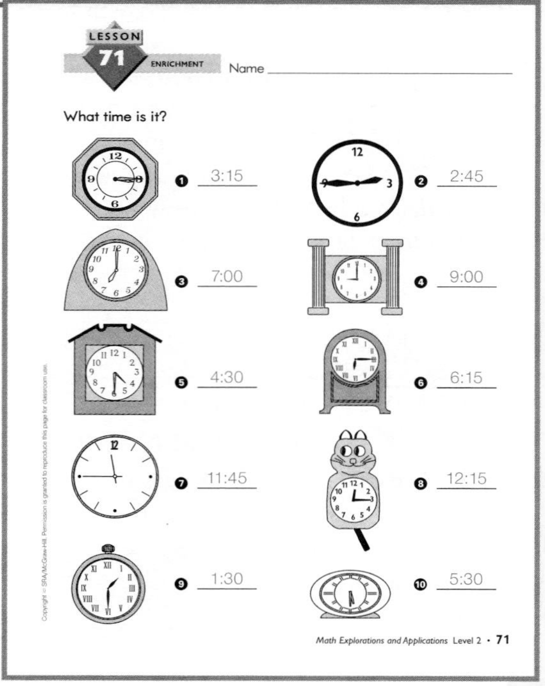

LESSON 71 ENRICHMENT Name ______

What time is it?

1. 3:15
2. 2:45
3. 7:00
4. 9:00
5. 4:30
6. 6:15
7. 11:45
8. 12:15
9. 1:30
10. 5:30

Math Explorations and Applications Level 2 • **71**

③ Wrap-Up (5 MINUTES)

In Closing Have students name a time that is a quarter to or quarter after an hour and tell what they usually do at that time.

ALTERNATIVE ASSESSMENT

Portfolio Assessment Have students draw a clock face on a sheet of paper and show a time they do a specific task, such as wake up, go to school, or eat dinner. Have them write about the task and the time at the bottom of their picture and save the pictures in their Math Portfolios.

Assessment Criteria

Did the student . . .

✓ participate in the discussion and completion of page 151?

✓ correctly solve six of eight problems on page 152?

✓ correctly solve six of eight problems they did on their own on page 153?

✓ correctly solve 15 of 18 problems on page 154?

LESSON 72

Student Edition pages 155–156

Telling Time—Halves and Quarters

LESSON PLANNER

Objective

▶ to provide practice for telling time to the quarter hour expressed as a number of minutes after the hour

Context of the Lesson This is last of three lessons on telling time. The topic is reintroduced in Lesson 93.

Materials	Program Resources
clock face	"Harder Time" Game Mat
toy clock	Thinking Story Book, pages 58–59
	Practice Master 72
	Enrichment Master 72
	For extra practice: CD-ROM* Lesson 72

1 Warm-Up (5 MINUTES)

Problem of the Day Explain to students that Mario wants to buy a $26 shirt and a $17 hat. He has $40. Ask students if he has enough money to buy both items. How can they tell? (No, 26 + 17 = 43. He needs $43 but has only $40.)

MENTAL MATH Set the clock face at the following positions and have students tell the time:

a. 10:00 **b.** 7:45 **c.** 6:15

d. 11:45 **e.** 4:00 **f.** 9:30

2 Teach

Demonstrate Display a clock that shows individual minutes. If none is available, have students use a clock on page 155. Have students count the number of minutes between the 12 and the 1. (5) Ask them to go on to count the number of minutes between the 12 and the 3, the 12 and the 6, and the 12 and the 9. (15, 30, 45) Guide students to realize that when the big hand is on the 3 it means it is 15 minutes after whatever hour the small hand is pointing to. Practice several examples using the toy clock. For example, show 3:15, 4:30, and 5:45, and have students tell the time.

LESSON 72

Name ______________________

Telling Time—Halves and Quarters

What time is it?

1  1 : 15

2  4 : 45

3  1 : 30

4  6 : 00

5  1 : 45

6  12 : 15

7  2 : 00

8  12 : 30

9  4 : 30

10  9 : 45

NOTE TO HOME
Students learn to tell time to the half and quarter hour.

Literature Connection Read aloud or invite students to read *Muledred* by Kathryn Brown to reinforce lesson concepts.

LEARNING STYLES

Meeting Individual Needs

Allow kinesthetic learners to practice showing time to the quarter hour using a toy analog clock.

RETEACHING

Display a working analog clock in the classroom. Ask students what time it is at various quarter hour times during the day, for example, 9:15, 10:30, and 11:45.

*available separately

◆ LESSON 72 Telling Time—Halves and Quarters

Draw the hands to show the time.

11 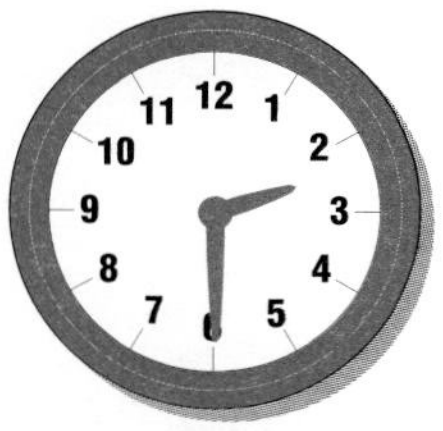

2:30

12 
2:45

13 
3:00

14 
5:15

15 
7:00

16 
7:45

17 
11:15

18 
8:30

Play the "Harder Time" game.

NOTE TO HOME
Students show time on a clock and play a game.

PRACTICE p. 72

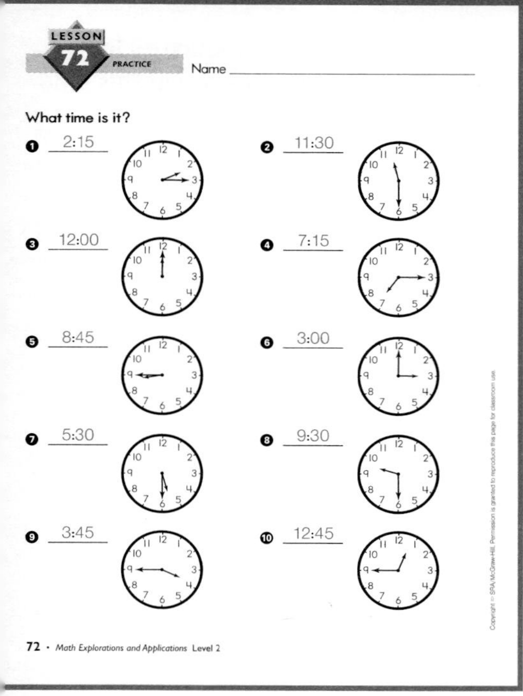
LESSON 72 PRACTICE Name

What time is it?

1. 2:15
2. 11:30
3. 12:00
4. 7:15
5. 8:45
6. 3:00
7. 5:30
8. 9:30
9. 3:45
10. 12:45

72 • Math Explorations and Applications Level 2

ENRICHMENT p. 72

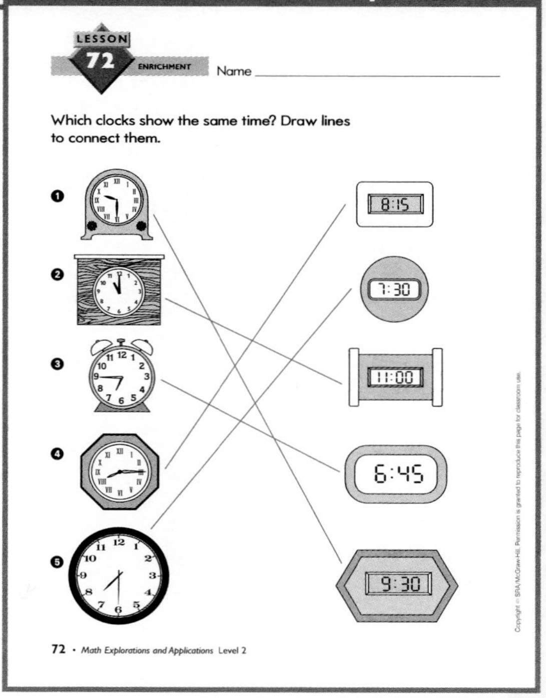
LESSON 72 ENRICHMENT Name

Which clocks show the same time? Draw lines to connect them.

1
2
3
4
5

8:15
7:30
11:00
6:45
9:30

72 • Math Explorations and Applications Level 2

Using the Student Pages Have students complete pages 155–156 independently. You might wish to do the first exercise on each page together.

Using the Thinking Story Present one or two questions from those following "Plenty of Time" on pages 58–59 of the Thinking Story Book.

Introducing the "Harder Time" Game Mat Demonstrate and play this game to provide practice in telling time to the hour, half hour, and quarter hour. The basic game was introduced in Lesson 70. Complete directions are on the Game Mat.

3 Wrap-Up

In Closing Ask students where the minute hand is when it is 15 minutes after the hour (on the 3), 30 minutes after the hour (on the 6), and 45 minutes after the hour (on the 9).

Informal Assessment Observe which students can correctly name the time shown on the clock when playing the "Harder Time" game.

Assessment Criteria

Did the student . . .

✓ accurately identify the time shown on eight of ten clocks on page 155?

✓ accurately draw hands on six of eight clocks on page 156?

✓ correctly name the time shown on the clock when playing the "Harder Time" game?

Meeting Individual Needs

For students who are having difficulty telling time, start with a clock that only has an hour hand. Have them tell the hours as you point the hand to different numbers. Do the same with a clock that only has a minute hand. After students can identify the number of minutes after each quarter hour, work with a clock that has both hands.

LESSON 73

Student Edition pages 157–158

Fractions—Halves and Quarters

LESSON PLANNER

Objective

▶ to introduce halves and quarters

Context of the Lesson This is the first of six lessons on fractions. This concept was briefly introduced in level 1.

Materials	Program Resources
crayons (optional)	Number Cubes
play money*	Thinking Story Book, pages 60–63
	Practice Master 73
	Enrichment Master 73
	For extra practice: CD-ROM* Lesson 73

1 Warm-Up

5 MINUTES

Problem of the Day Present the following problem to the class: What is the fewest number of coins you can use to make 43 cents? What are they? (six; a quarter, dime, nickel, three pennies)

MENTAL MATH Have students add or subtract, using their Number Cubes to respond:

a. 40 + 50 = (90) **b.** 70 + 60 = (130) **c.** 80 + 90 = (170)

d. 130 − 80 = (50) **e.** 150 − 60 = (90) **f.** 120 − 70 = (50)

2 Teach

MATH MANIPULATIVES Have students fold a sheet of paper in half lengthwise. Ask students: How many halves are there? (two) Are they equal? (yes)

Have students then fold the paper again widthwise and open it. Explain that each of the four sections they see is called a quarter. Ask students how many quarters there are in one half (two) and in the whole sheet. (four) You might also wish to use play money to show students that a quarter means a quarter of a dollar, and also that there are four quarters in a whole dollar and two half-dollars in a whole dollar.

LESSON 73

Name ____________________________

Fractions—Halves and Quarters

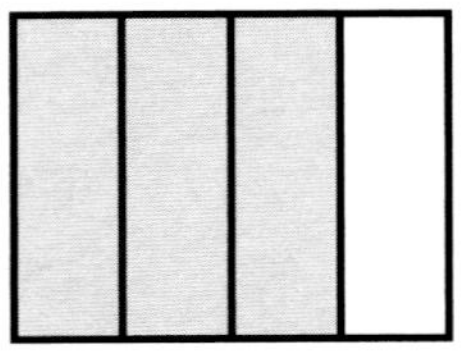

Answers are examples only.

Color one half $(\frac{1}{2})$.

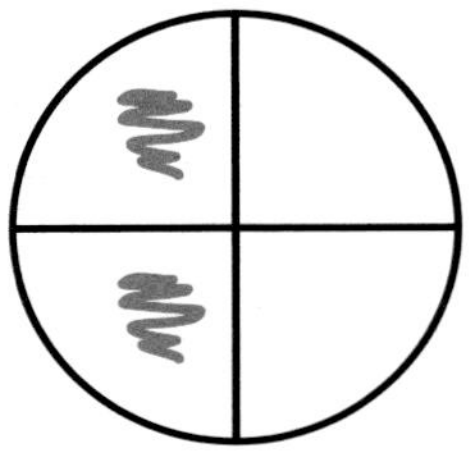

Color one quarter $(\frac{1}{4})$.

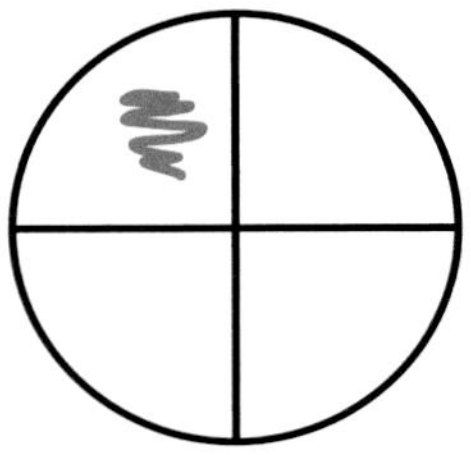

Color two quarters $(\frac{2}{4})$.

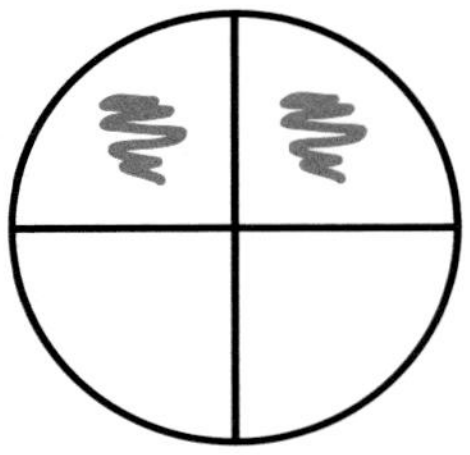

Color three quarters $(\frac{3}{4})$.

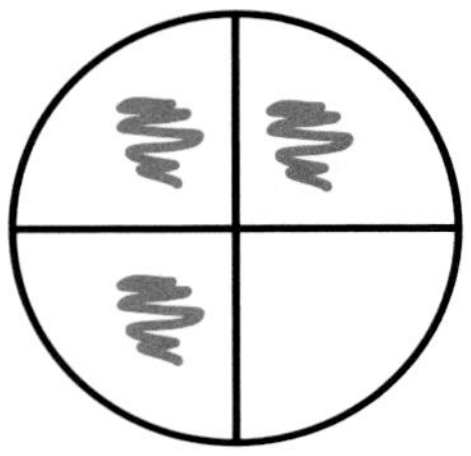

THINKING STORY

Talk about the Thinking Story "Take a Chance."

NOTE TO HOME
Students identify halves and quarters.

Literature Connection To learn more about fractions, students can read *Eating Fractions* by Bruce McMillan.

RETEACHING

Because this is an introductory lesson, reteaching is not necessary at this time.

*available separately

◆ **LESSON 73** Fractions—Halves and Quarters

Use the Mixed Practice on page 380 after this lesson.

Solve these problems.

❶ Lani has a quarter (25¢).
Kevin has a quarter (25¢).
How much money
do they have all together? **50¢**

❷ Mel has a quarter (25¢).
Carla has a quarter (25¢).
How much money
do they have all together? **50¢**

❸ How much money do Lani, Kevin, Mel, and Carla have all together? **$1.00 or 100¢**

Watch the signs.

❹ 64 + 23 = **87**	❺ 75 − 63 = **12**	❻ 87 + 12 = **99**	❼ 87 + 13 = **100**	❽ 29 + 37 = **66**
❾ 46 − 37 = **9**	❿ 50 − 25 = **25**	⓫ 50 + 25 = **75**	⓬ 75 + 25 = **100**	⓭ 18 + 63 = **81**

NOTE TO HOME
Students review adding and subtracting two-digit numbers.

PRACTICE p. 73

LESSON 73 PRACTICE Name

❶ Color one quarter.
❷ Color two quarters.
❸ Color one half.
❹ Color three quarters.

Allie, Mario, Carie, and Dave each have a quarter (25¢).

❺ How much money do Allie and Mario have all together? 50¢

❻ How much money do Allie, Mario, and Carie have all together? 75¢

❼ How much money do Allie, Mario, Carie, and Dave have all together? $1 or 100¢

Math Explorations and Applications Level 2 • 73

ENRICHMENT p. 73

LESSON 73 ENRICHMENT Name

Color one quarter of the circle yellow.
Color one quarter of the circle blue.
Color one half of the circle green.
Put red dots on two quarters of the circle.
Draw purple stripes on one half of the circle.

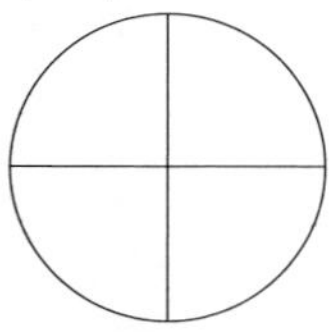

Color one half of the rectangle green.
Color one half of the rectangle blue.
Draw yellow stripes on three quarters of the rectangle.
Draw yellow stripes on one quarter of the rectangle.

Math Explorations and Applications Level 2 • 73

Using the Student Pages Have students complete page 157 first. When they finish, have them discuss and share their answers. Point out that there is more than one correct way to show the fractions. Have students then complete page 158 independently.

Using the Thinking Story Read aloud the story "Take a Chance" on pages 60–63 of the Thinking Story Book. Stop and discuss the questions. In the story, all the children in Ms. Arthur's class want to visit Mr. Eng's thumbtack factory, but only five can visit each week. The class decides on a fair way to choose who will go the first week, but Ferdie has other ideas. In the end, Ferdie sees why his way was unfair, and five children are chosen fairly.

MATH JOURNAL

Invite students to write a paragraph describing what the children saw at Mr. Eng's factory.

3 Wrap-Up

5 MINUTES

MATH JOURNAL

In Closing Have students draw models to show the following fractions: $\frac{1}{2}$, $\frac{1}{4}$, and $\frac{3}{4}$.

ALTERNATIVE ASSESSMENT

Informal Assessment Use students' answers to page 158 to informally assess which students understand the meaning of $\frac{1}{2}$, $\frac{1}{4}$, and $\frac{3}{4}$.

Assessment Criteria

Did the student . . .

✓ correctly color in the fractional parts on page 157?

✓ solve word problems correctly on page 158?

✓ correctly add and subtract eight of ten problems at the bottom of page 158?

✓ participate in the discussion of the Thinking Story?

STORY 10

THINKING STORY

Take a Chance

One day Ms. Arthur announced to her class, "I have good news for you. Mr. Eng has invited all of you to visit his famous thumbtack factory."

All the children cheered. They all wanted to see this factory, which was known for producing the world's most beautiful thumbtacks.

"But," said Ms. Arthur, "it's a very small factory and Mr. Eng can take only five children at a time. We have to decide which children can go this week. The rest of you can go other weeks." Everyone's hand went up. All the children wanted to go the first week.

"I see you all want to go this week," Ms. Arthur said. "We'll have to work out a fair way of deciding which children get to go."

What are some fair ways to decide? Answers may vary; possibilities include drawing names out of a can or hat.

"I know a fair way," said Ferdie. "Let's have a race around the schoolyard. The five children who run the fastest should be the ones who get to go."

"I like that idea too," said Marcus.

Do you think that is a fair way to decide? no

Can you think of a reason that Ferdie and Marcus would like that idea? They are probably fast runners.

"That's not a fair way," said Manolita. "Ferdie and Marcus want to do it that way because they know they're the fastest runners and they'll be sure to get to go first."

Who do you think one of the winners would be if they did it that way? Ferdie or Marcus

Ms. Arthur said, "I believe a fair way is one that gives everyone an equal chance of being picked."

Can you think of a way that would give every child in the class an equal chance of being picked? Answers may vary; possibilities include drawing names out of a can or hat.

Finally the class decided that the fairest way would be for all the children to write their names on slips of paper, put the slips into a box and mix them up, and then draw five names. So Ms. Arthur passed out slips of paper (all the same size), and the children wrote their names on them. Then she went around and collected the slips in a box. Then she mixed up the slips, held the box above Willy's head, and asked him to take out five slips.

"That's not fair," one of the children said. "Willy will be sure to pull out his own name."

Is that true? no

Why or why not? He can't see inside the box.

"I can't see what the names are," Willy said. "So there isn't any way I can be sure to get my own name–though I wish there were."

Willy carefully drew five slips from the box and handed them to Ms. Arthur. Looking at the slips of paper one by one, she said, "The five lucky children are Ivan, ...Ferdie, ...Willy, ...Sumi, ...and Ferdie!"

There were angry shouts from all over the room that Ferdie had cheated.

"No, I didn't," said Ferdie. "I'm just lucky, I guess."

Could it be just luck that Ferdie's name was drawn twice? no

How could it have happened? He must have put more than one slip of paper into the box.

"We'll have to look into this matter," said Ms. Arthur, sounding a bit angry. She dumped the slips of paper onto a table and spread them out.

"This is very strange," she said. "Every other child's name is here just once, but there are ten slips of paper with Ferdie's name on them. Ferdie, what do you have to say for yourself?"

"I was at the end of the row," Ferdie said, "and there were ten pieces of paper left when they got to me, so I just wrote my name on all of them. I don't see anything wrong with that."

Do you see anything wrong with it? He had a greater chance of being picked than the other students.

"Remember," Ms. Arthur said, "that a fair way is one that gives every child an equal chance. Did you all have an equal chance of winning?"

Did they? no

Can you explain why Ferdie had more of a chance to win than the others? His name is on ten slips of paper; the other students only have one each.

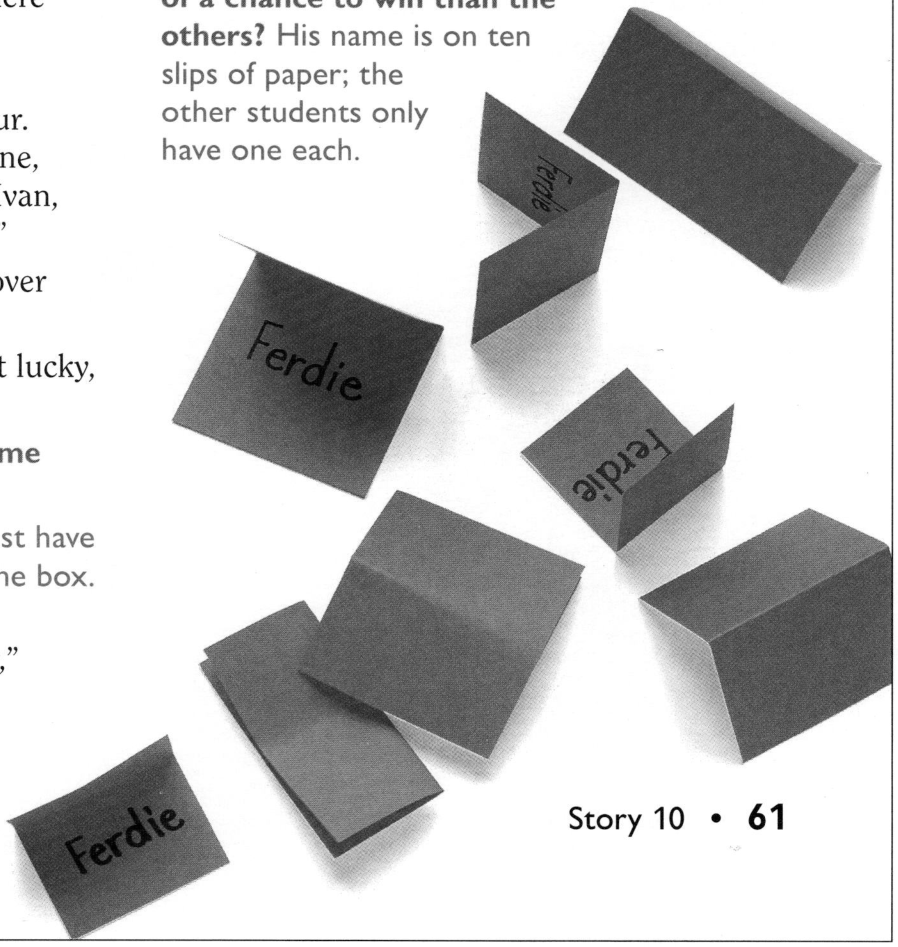

◆ STORY 10 Take a Chance

"We all had an equal chance except Ferdie," Manolita said. "He had lots more chances to win than the rest of us because lots of the pieces of paper had his name on them."

Ferdie looked sad. "I didn't think about that," he said. "I just wanted to be sure I still had a chance in case my name got stuck on the bottom of the box or something. I'm sorry."

"We've learned something about fair choosing," Ms. Arthur said, "and I believe you weren't trying to cheat, Ferdie. But we still have the problem of choosing the names fairly now."

"That's easy," Ferdie said. "Just put the names back into the box, all but mine, and pull out another name. That way we'll pick the last person fair and square."

Does that sound like a fair way to finish the choosing? no

Why or why not? Ferdie's name was not picked fairly.

Most of the children thought that was a fair way, but not Manolita. "That means that Ferdie gets to go," she said, "because his name is already one of the first four. But if he had done it right, like the rest of us, maybe his name wouldn't have been picked. Maybe my name would have been picked instead."

What do you think of Manolita's argument?

It makes sense.

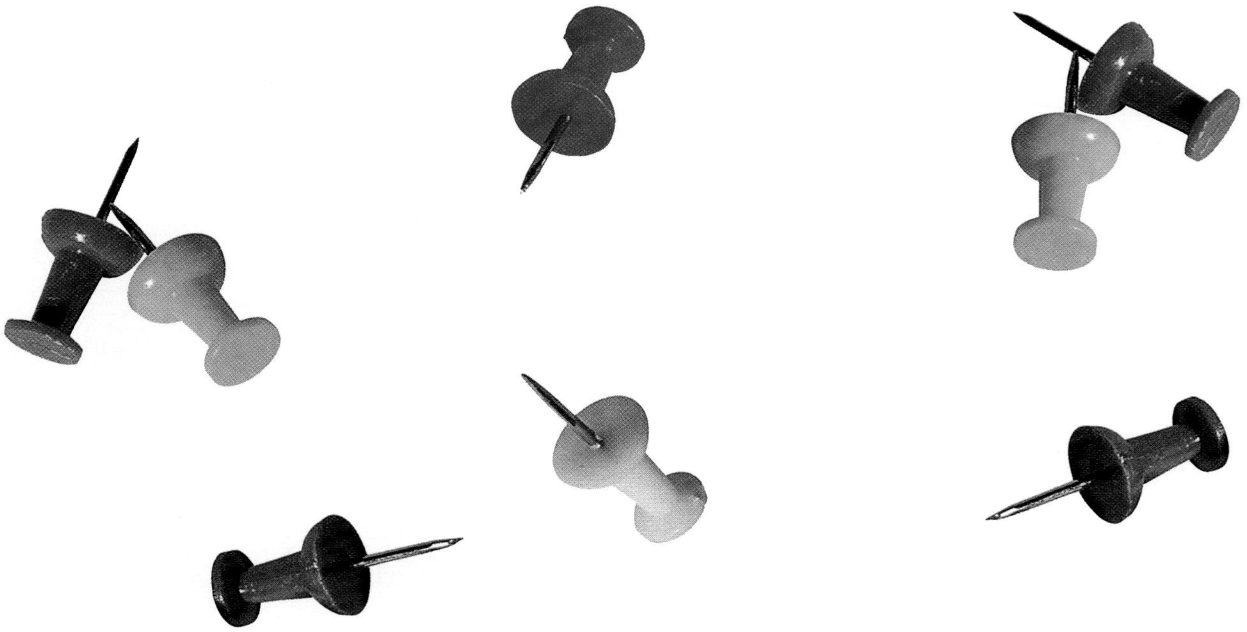

"That's good thinking, Manolita," said Ms. Arthur. "I'm afraid that Ferdie had an unfair advantage when his name was picked both times. So the way we'll handle it is that Ivan, Willy, and Sumi get to go, and then we'll draw two more names to decide who the other two will be."

"Then I won't have any chance at all!" Ferdie wailed.

Why does Ferdie think he won't have any chance? He thinks his name won't be in the box.

"Yes, you will," said Ms. Arthur, as she dropped one of the slips with Ferdie's name on it into the box and mixed it in with the others. "You won't have as good a chance as the others, because they all had a chance against Ivan, Willy, and Sumi. But you still have a chance."

Willy drew two more names. They were Susan and Mario.

"Don't feel bad," Manolita said to Ferdie. "You might get to go to the thumbtack factory next week."

. . . the end

[Note: There are some aspects of this story that you won't want to go into with the children but that you might want to be aware of. Ferdie did not have ten times the chance of being chosen just because he put his name in ten times. The probabilities depend on the size of the class; and for a class of normal size, Ferdie would have about five times the chance of being chosen that the other children had. The way it worked out at the end, he had only two fifths the chance of being chosen because the others had a chance on five draws, whereas he had a chance on only two. Ms. Arthur could have done the whole drawing over again, with each child's name in the box once, but that would have been upsetting to Ivan, Willy, and Sumi, who had been chosen fairly the first time.]

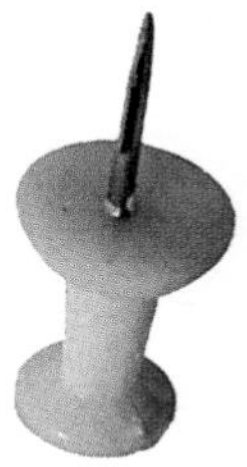

LESSON 74

Student Edition pages 159–162

Halves, Quarters, and Thirds

LESSON PLANNER

Objectives

- to provide practice identifying and showing halves and quarters
- to introduce thirds

Context of the Lesson This is the second of six lessons on fractions.

Materials
none

Program Resources
Number Cubes
Thinking Story Book, pages 64–65
Reteaching Master
Practice Master 74
Enrichment Master 74
For extra practice:
CD-ROM* Lesson 74

1 Warm-Up 5 MINUTES

Problem of the Day Write the following problem on the chalkboard: How can you make 45¢ using exactly five coins? (1 quarter and 4 nickels or 4 dimes and 1 nickel)

MENTAL MATH Have students add the following coins and express the results in cents:

a. a quarter and a dime (35¢)
b. two dimes and three nickels (35¢)
c. two quarters and four pennies (54¢)
d. a nickel and seven pennies (12¢)
e. a quarter, a dime, and two nickels (45¢)
f. three dimes, three nickels, three pennies (48¢)

LESSON 74

Name ______________________

Halves, Quarters, and Thirds

Answers are examples only.

Color one half ($\frac{1}{2}$) of each figure.

1 

2 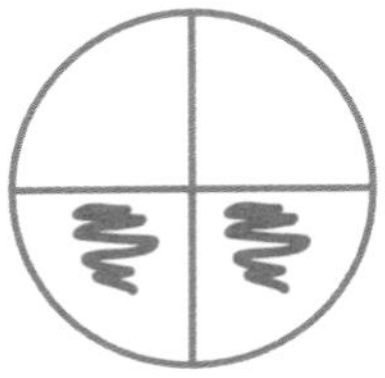

Color one quarter (one fourth or $\frac{1}{4}$) of each figure.

3 

4 

Color two quarters (two fourths or $\frac{2}{4}$) of each figure.

5 

6 

7 How many quarters in one half ($\frac{1}{2}$)? 2

NOTE TO HOME
Students practice identifying functional parts ($\frac{1}{2}$, $\frac{1}{4}$, and $\frac{2}{4}$).

Literature Connection Read *Give Me Half!* by Stuart J. Murphy to students to reinforce lesson concepts.

*available separately

◆ **LESSON 74 Halves, Quarters, and Thirds**

Answers are examples only.

Color one third ($\frac{1}{3}$) of each figure.

8 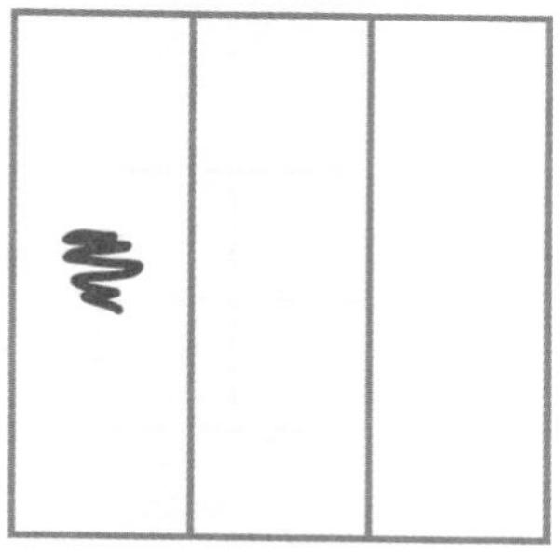

9 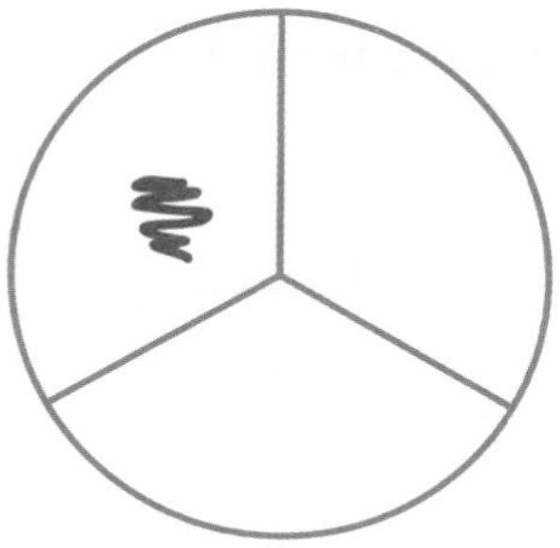

Color two thirds ($\frac{2}{3}$) of each figure.

10 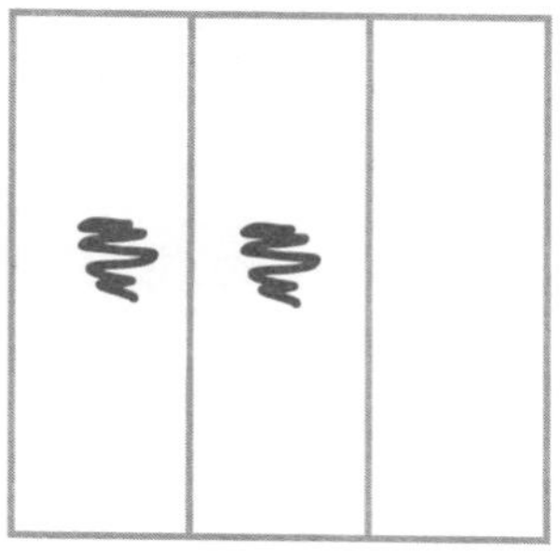

11 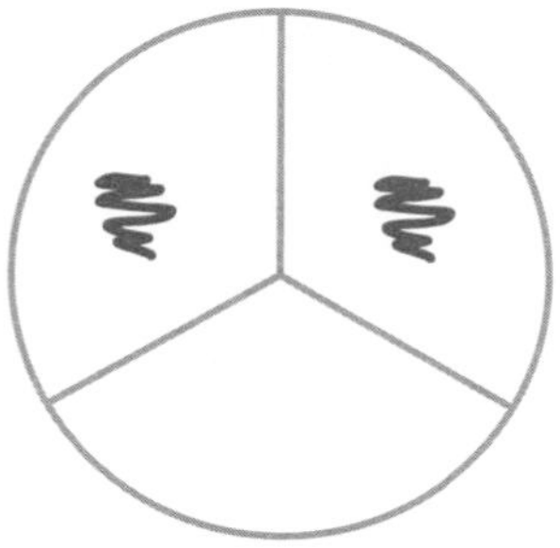

Color three quarters ($\frac{3}{4}$) of each figure.

12 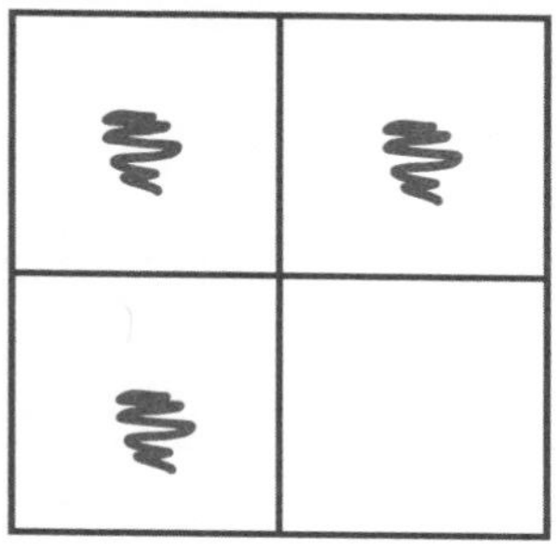

13 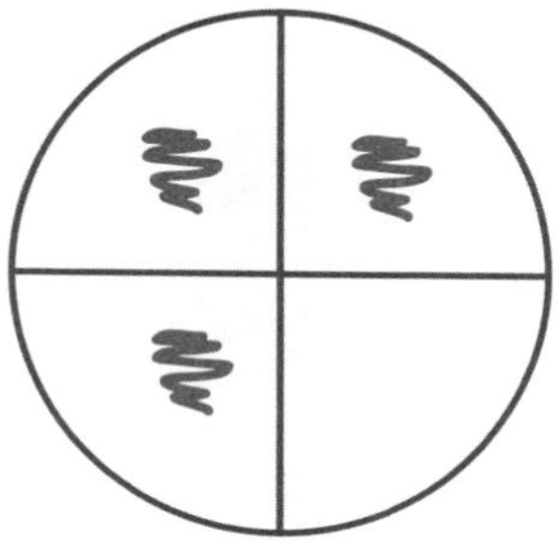

NOTE TO HOME
Students identify functional parts ($\frac{1}{3}$, $\frac{2}{3}$, and $\frac{3}{4}$).

2 Teach

Demonstrate Review the fractions students have learned by asking: When you divide a shape into two equal parts, what is each part called? (half) What are four equal parts called? (quarters) Then draw a rectangle on the chalkboard and ask volunteers to divide it into halves and then quarters.

Draw another rectangle and challenge students to divide it into thirds—three equal parts. Ask students to draw several more rectangles, divide them into thirds, and shade one third and two thirds as many ways as they can.

Draw several circles and have students divide them into halves and quarters and shade one, two, three, and four quarters as many ways as they can.

Choose a shaded shape and ask: How many parts are shaded? Write the number on the chalkboard under the shape. Then ask: How many parts are there all together? Draw a fraction line and write that number under it. Ask the students: What does this fraction tell us? (The bottom number tells how many parts all together; the top numbers tell how many parts of the whole.) You might want to use the terms *numerator* and *denominator*. Help students write the fractions for each shape they shaded.

Using the Student Pages Work page 159 together. Discuss each problem by comparing the shaded parts and how the fractions are written. Then have students work in small groups to complete page 160. Have groups discuss the possible answers to each problem.

◆ LESSON 74 Halves, Quarters, and Thirds

Teach

Using the Student Pages Continue to have the groups work together to complete pages 161–162. Then have the groups share their answers.

Using the Thinking Story Present one or two new problems from those following "Take a Chance" on pages 64–65 of the Thinking Story Book.

> *. . . if we want students to be really good at a particular skill, or if we want them to really remember and understand a concept, we must arrange for them to practice.*
>
> –Stephen S. Willoughby,
> *Mathematics Education for a Changing World*

◆ LESSON 74

Name ____________________

Answers are examples only.

Color one quarter $\left(\frac{1}{4}\right)$ four different ways.

14

Color two thirds $\left(\frac{2}{3}\right)$ three different ways.

15

Color two quarters $\left(\frac{2}{4}\right)$ six different ways.

16

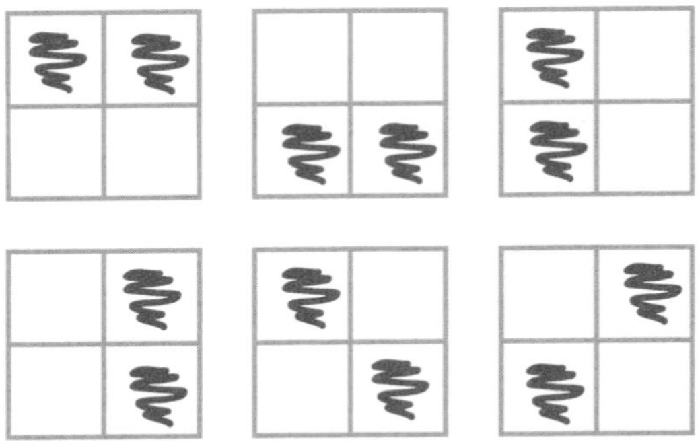

NOTE TO HOME
Students color functional parts $\left(\frac{1}{4}, \frac{2}{3}, \text{and } \frac{2}{4}\right)$ different ways.

RETEACHING p. 20

LESSON 74 RETEACHING Name ____________________

Step 1

Using sheets of construction paper, cut out three circles.
Label one of the circles **whole**.

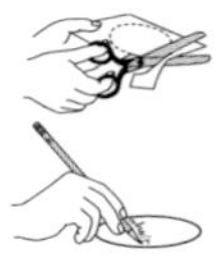

Step 2

Fold a second circle in half and label each part **half**.
Cut along the fold.

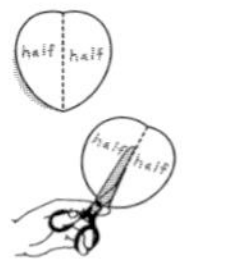

Step 3

Fold a third circle in half and in half again.
Label each of the parts **quarter**.
Cut along the folds.

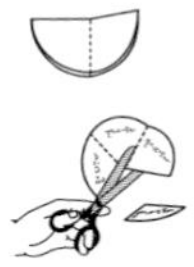

Step 4

Glue each of these circles on another sheet of construction paper.

20 • *Math Explorations and Applications* Level 2

*available separately

◆ **LESSON 74** Fractions

Answers are examples only.

Color $\frac{2}{3}$ in three different ways.

17 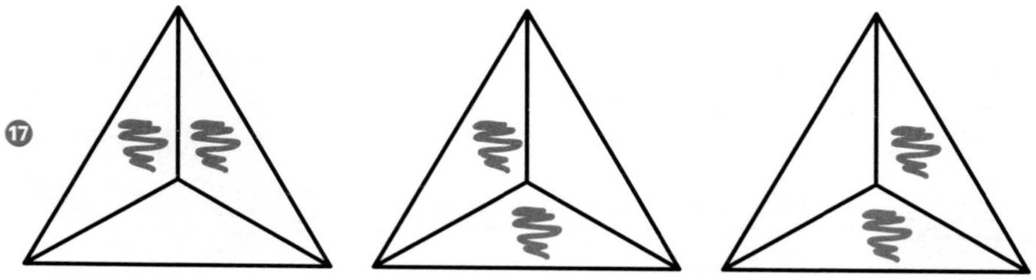

Color $\frac{2}{5}$ in six different ways.

18 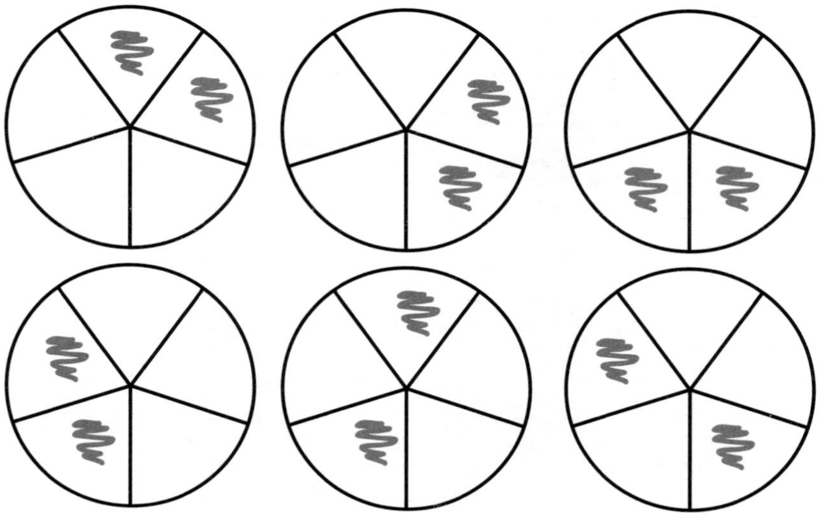

FANTASTIC FACT You can tell how old a fish is by counting the rings on its scales.

NOTE TO HOME
Students color fractional parts.

PRACTICE p. 74

LESSON 74 PRACTICE Name ____________

1. Color two quarters (two fourths) of each figure.

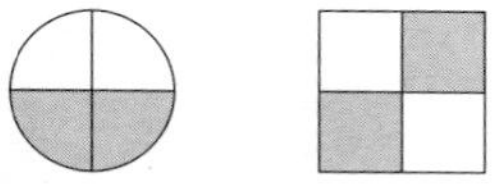

2. Color two thirds of each figure.

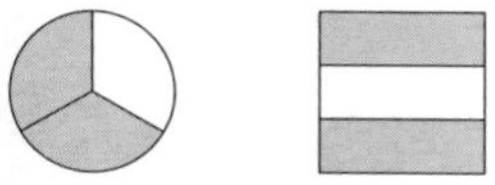

Shaded areas may vary.

3. Color three quarters (three fourths) of each figure.

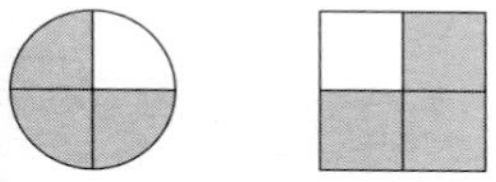

4. Color one third of each figure.

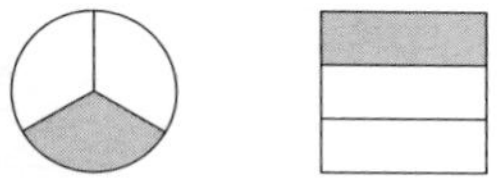

74 • *Math Explorations and Applications* Level 2

ENRICHMENT p. 74

LESSON 74 ENRICHMENT Name ____________

Draw lines to divide the circle into equal parts.

Draw the first line from the top of the circle to the bottom. Go through the dot in the center.

Draw the second line from the left edge of the circle to the right edge. Go through the dot in the center.

You have four equal parts. Figure out how to make eight equal parts. How many equal parts can you make?

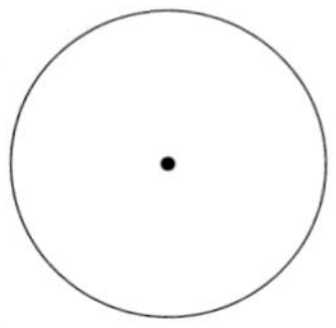

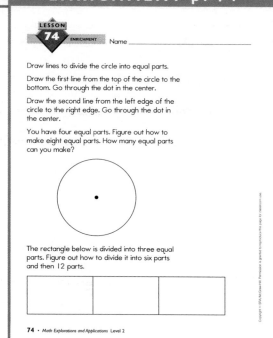

The rectangle below is divided into three equal parts. Figure out how to divide it into six parts and then 12 parts.

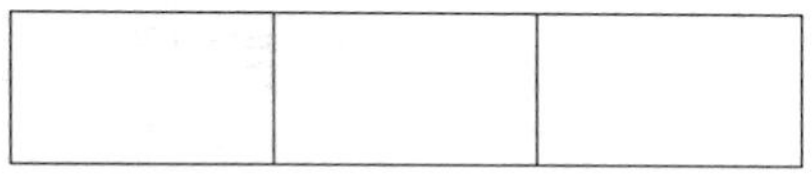

74 • *Math Explorations and Applications* Level 2

③ Wrap-Up (5 MINUTES)

In Closing Have students draw a square and divide it into quarters. Have them write the fraction $\frac{1}{4}$, then shade $\frac{1}{4}$, and tell what the numerator and denominator stand for in the picture they drew.

ALTERNATIVE ASSESSMENT

Performance Assessment Use students' pictures of squares and the explanations they gave above to assess their understanding of fractions so far.

Assessment Criteria

Did the student . . .

✓ demonstrate understanding of fractional parts during the demonstration?

✓ correctly shade 28 of 35 shapes on pages 160–162?

LEARNING STYLES

Meeting Individual Needs
Encourage kinesthetic learners to use pattern blocks to make models of halves, quarters, and thirds. For example, have them put two triangles together to show how they can each represent half of a rectangle.

LESSON 75

Student Edition pages 163–166

Fifths and Other Fractions

LESSON PLANNER

Objectives

- ▶ to introduce fifths
- ▶ to review halves, thirds, and fourths

Context of the Lesson This is the third of six lessons on fractions. This lesson also contains Mastery Checkpoint 10 to assess students' understanding of simple fractions.

Materials	Program Resources
crayons	"Fraction" Game Mat
	Number Cubes
	Practice Master 75
	Enrichment Master 75
	Assessment Master
	For extra practice: CD-ROM* Lesson 75

1 Warm-Up

5 MINUTES

Problem of the Day Write the following problem on the chalkboard: There are 40 buttons in a box. There are 23 red ones. The rest are blue. How many more red buttons than blue buttons are there? (six more red)

MENTAL MATH Have students add or subtract, using their Number Cubes to respond:

a. 6 + 6 = (12) **b.** 3 + 4 = (7)
c. 11 − 7 = (4) **d.** 9 + 4 = (13)
e. 6 − 3 = (3) **f.** 10 − 5 = (5)

LEARNING STYLES

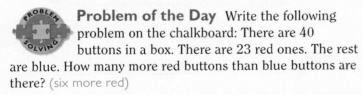

Meeting Individual Needs

Kinesthetic learners might benefit from working with pattern blocks to identify fractional parts. Work in small groups. Make circles of rectangles that are made up of halves, fourths, and fifths. Have students take pieces away from each shape that represent fractions such as $\frac{1}{2}$, $\frac{1}{3}$, $\frac{2}{3}$, $\frac{1}{5}$, and $\frac{2}{5}$.

LESSON 75

Name ______________________________

Fifths and Other Fractions

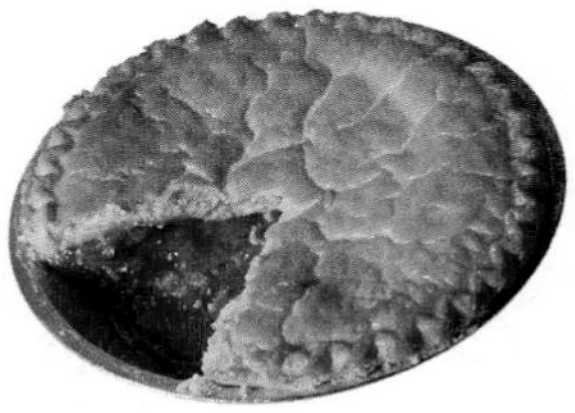

GAME Play the "Fraction" game.

Listen to the directions.

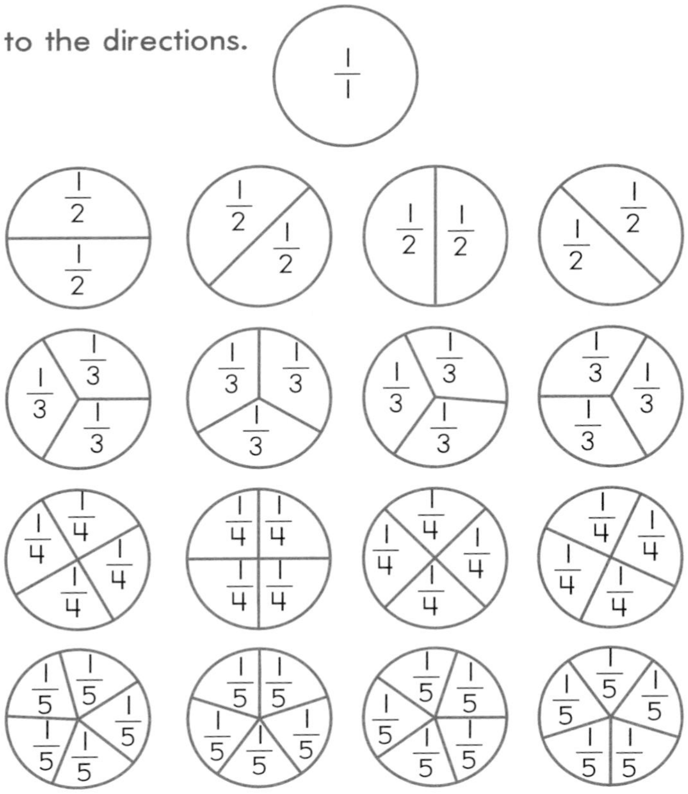

NOTE TO HOME
Students play a game in which they must identify fractional parts.

Literature Connection To learn more about fractions, students can read *Fraction Action* by Loreen Leedy.

*available separately

◆ **LESSON 75** Fifths and Other Fractions

Answers are examples only.

Color one fifth $\left(\frac{1}{5}\right)$.

❶

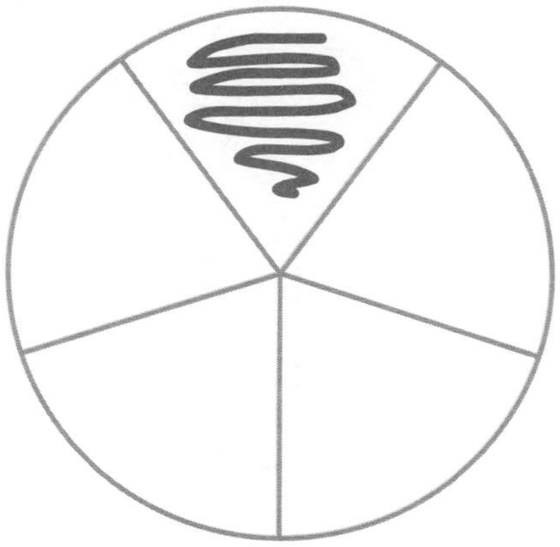

Color three fifths $\left(\frac{3}{5}\right)$.

❷

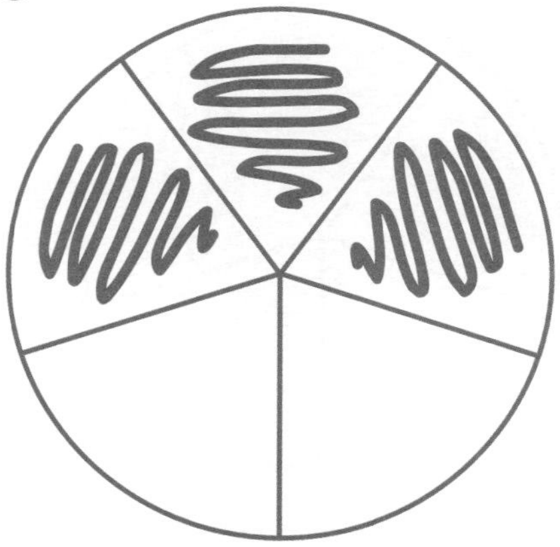

Color two fifths $\left(\frac{2}{5}\right)$.

❸

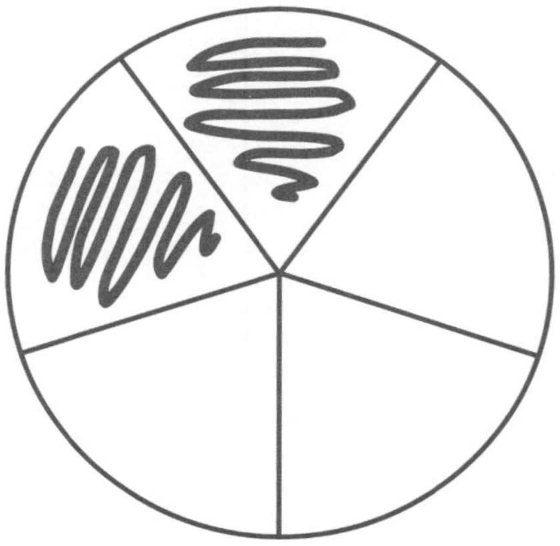

Color four fifths $\left(\frac{4}{5}\right)$.

❹

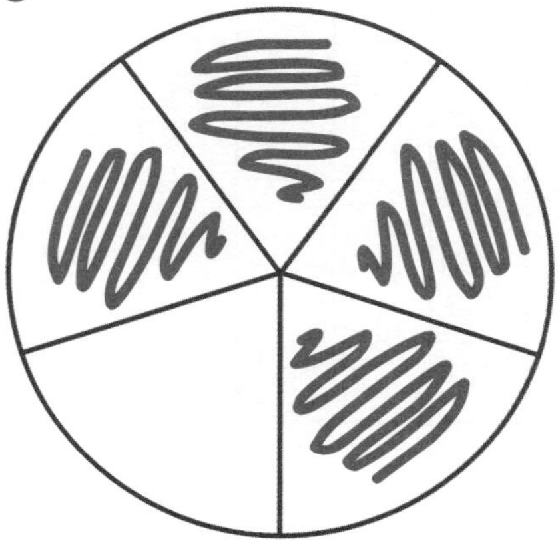

NOTE TO HOME
Students identify functional parts ($\frac{1}{5}$, $\frac{2}{5}$, and $\frac{3}{5}$).

❷ Teach

Demonstrate Draw a rectangle on the chalkboard. Ask students how you can divide it into fifths. Try students' suggestions until you have divided it correctly. Next have a volunteer shade $\frac{1}{5}$ of the rectangle. Have other students show other ways $\frac{1}{5}$ can be shaded. Repeat for $\frac{2}{5}$ and then $\frac{5}{5}$. Students should understand that they can shade $\frac{1}{5}$ and $\frac{2}{5}$ different ways, but $\frac{5}{5}$ can be shaded only one way. Demonstrate various ways $\frac{1}{5}$ and $\frac{2}{5}$ can be shaded. (There are five ways for $\frac{1}{5}$ to be shaded, but ten ways for $\frac{2}{5}$.)

Using the Student Pages Have students complete page 163 by playing the "Fraction" game, which provides practice in recognizing fractional areas and in recognizing when more than $\frac{1}{2}$ of a circle has been labeled. Students may then complete pages 164–165 on their own. Before they begin, remind them that there is more than one correct answer for each fractional part. You might wish to do the first circle with them. Point out that no matter which part is colored in, as long as it is only one part, the answer is correct.

◆ LESSON 75 **Fifths and Other Fractions**

Teach

Using the Student Pages Page 166 is a review of using addition to check subtraction. Consider doing the first problem on this page with the class. Point out that students can use addition to check the answer: Because 10 + 7 = 17 and not 18, they can see that 18 – 7 cannot be 10. As students finish, have them correct each answer they circled.

Introducing the "Fraction" Game Mat Demonstrate and play this game to provide practice in recognizing fractional areas and recognizing when more than $\frac{1}{2}$ circle has been labeled. The game can be played using page 163 or using the "Fraction" Game Mat. Complete instructions are on the Game Mat.

Rather than giving up on those children who have serious difficulties or are different from typical successful mathematics students in other ways, we must do a better job of helping them. We must be alert to differences among children whenever they occur. We must have high expectations for all children, and we must give them the necessary help to live up to those high expectations. All children can and should learn mathematics.

—Stephen S. Willoughby,
Mathematics Education for a Changing World

◆ LESSON 75 Fifths and Other Fractions
Name ______________________

Color four fifths ($\frac{4}{5}$).

5
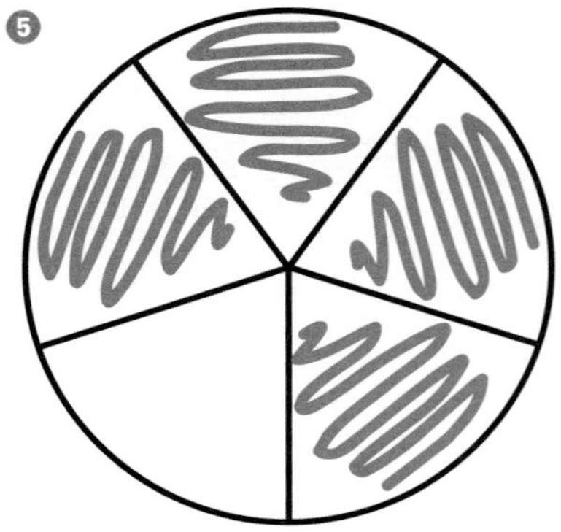

Color three fifths ($\frac{3}{5}$).

6
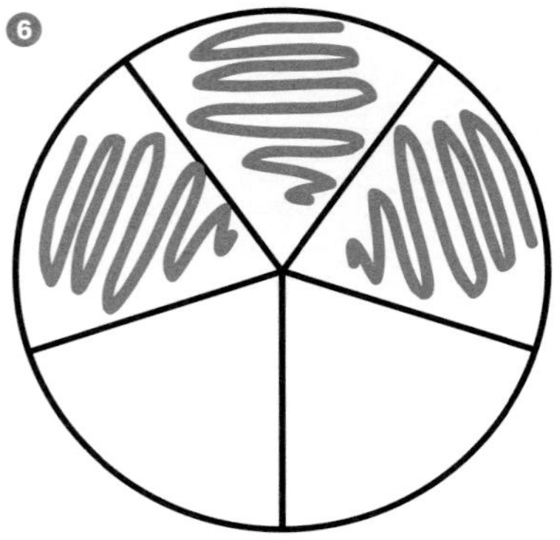

Color one fifth ($\frac{1}{5}$).

7

Color two fifths ($\frac{2}{5}$).

8
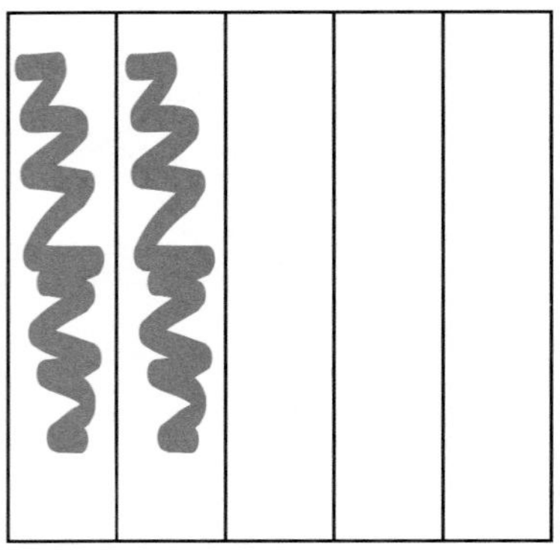

Answers are examples only.

NOTE TO HOME
Students continue to identify functional parts ($\frac{1}{5}$, $\frac{2}{5}$, $\frac{3}{5}$ and $\frac{4}{5}$).

RETEACHING

Make copies and distribute a sheet of paper that has several rectangles divided into fifths. Give students red, blue, and green crayons. Have them color in the rectangles by giving them directions such as: Color $\frac{1}{5}$ of the first rectangle red. Color $\frac{2}{5}$ of it blue. Color another $\frac{1}{5}$ green. How many fifths are not colored in? ($\frac{1}{5}$) Repeat similar directions with remaining rectangles.

PRACTICE p. 75

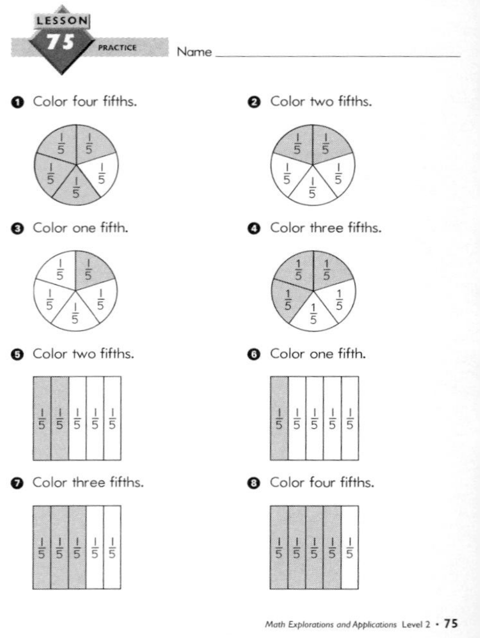
LESSON 75 PRACTICE Name ______________________

1 Color four fifths.

2 Color two fifths.

3 Color one fifth.

4 Color three fifths.

5 Color two fifths.

6 Color one fifth.

7 Color three fifths.

8 Color four fifths.

Copyright © SRA/McGraw-Hill. Permission is granted to reproduce this page for classroom use.

Math Explorations and Applications Level 2 • 75

◆ **LESSON 75** Subtraction Checkup

Ring each wrong answer.
(Eight of the answers are wrong.)

9. 18 − 7 = (10) **11**
10. 14 − 7 = (8) **7**
11. 17 − 7 = 10
12. 7 − 7 = (15) **0**
13. 16 − 9 = 7
14. 13 − 8 = 5
15. 16 − 10 = 6

16. 15 − 9 = (8) **6**
17. 15 − 5 = 10
18. 15 − 7 = (7) **8**
19. 12 − 9 = (4) **3**
20. 14 − 9 = 5
21. 11 − 7 = (5) **4**
22. 14 − 6 = (7) **8**
23. 12 − 6 = 6

NOTE TO HOME
Students identify incorrect answers to subtraction problems.

ENRICHMENT p. 75

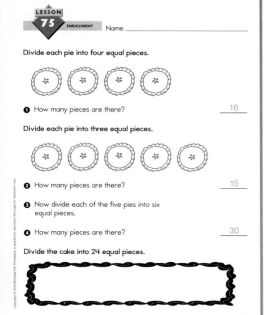

LESSON 75 ENRICHMENT Name ____________

Divide each pie into four equal pieces.

1. How many pieces are there? 16

Divide each pie into three equal pieces.

2. How many pieces are there? 15
3. Now divide each of the five pies into six equal pieces.
4. How many pieces are there? 30

Divide the cake into 24 equal pieces.

ASSESSMENT p. 29

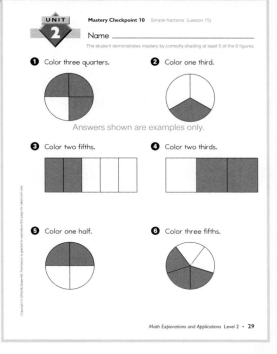

UNIT 2 **Mastery Checkpoint 10** Simple fractions (Lesson 75)

Name ____________

The student demonstrates mastery by correctly shading at least 5 of the 6 figures.

1. Color three quarters.

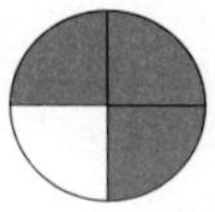

2. Color one third.

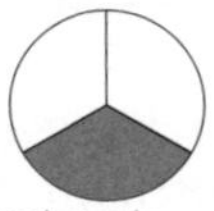

Answers shown are examples only.

3. Color two fifths.

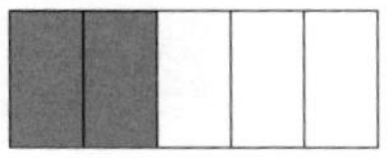

4. Color two thirds.

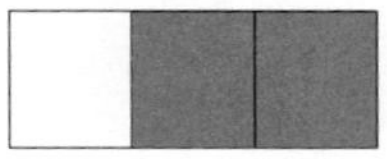

5. Color one half.

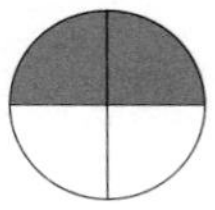

6. Color three fifths.

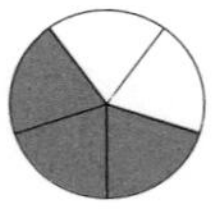

3 Wrap-Up 5 MINUTES

In Closing Have students write an explanation of what $\frac{1}{5}$ means in their Math Journals.

Mastery Checkpoint 10

Students should understand the concepts of halves, thirds, fourths, and fifths. Consider using Assessment Master 30 to assess students' understanding. You might want to record the results on the Mastery Checkpoint Chart.

Assessment Criteria

Did the student . . .

- ✓ color in the correct number of parts when playing the "Fraction" game?
- ✓ correctly color in fractional parts of six out of eight figures on pages 164 and 165?
- ✓ find six of the eight mistakes on page 166?

LESSON 76

Student Edition pages 167–168

Fractions and Geometry

LESSON PLANNER

Objectives

- ▶ to provide experience with fractions
- ▶ to provide practice in relating fractions to geometry and telling time

Context of the Lesson This is the fourth of six lessons on fractions.

Materials	Program Resources
clock face	"Fraction" Game Mat
crayons	Thinking Story Book, pages 64–65
ruler	Practice Master 76
scissors	Enrichment Master 76
	For extra practice: CD-ROM* Lesson 76

1 Warm-Up

5 MINUTES

Problem of the Day Present the following problem orally to students: Carlos drew a circle. He drew lines to make four equal parts on the circle. He colored in three of the parts. Did he color in more than half of the circle? How can you tell? (Yes, because two out of four is half, so three out of four is more than half.)

MENTAL MATH Set a clock at the following positions and have the children reply in one of four ways: "quarter after _____," "half past _____," "quarter to _____," or "_____ o' clock."

a.	3:00 (three o'clock)	**b.**	10:30 (half past ten)
c.	6:45 (quarter to seven)	**d.**	1:00 (one o'clock)
e.	2:15 (quarter after two)	**f.**	12:00 (twelve o'clock)
g.	8:30 (half past eight)	**h.**	5:15 (quarter after five)

SPECIAL NEEDS

Meeting Individual Needs

Students with special needs might need individual help as they complete pages 167 and 168 and as they play the "Fraction" game. To reinforce their understanding, have students say out loud the name of each fraction in each activity they do.

LESSON 76

Name ______________________________

Fractions and Geometry

Answers shown are examples only.

Color one quarter $\left(\frac{1}{4}\right)$.

1 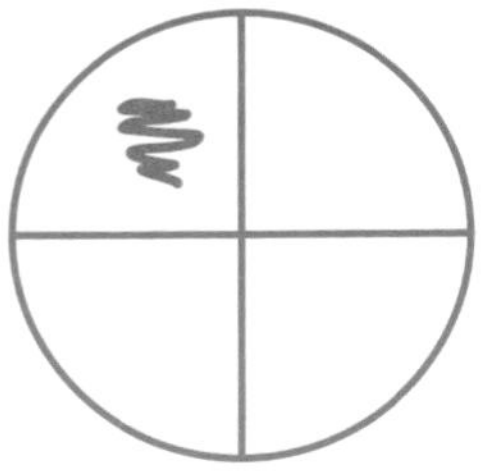

Color two quarters $\left(\frac{2}{4}\right)$.

2 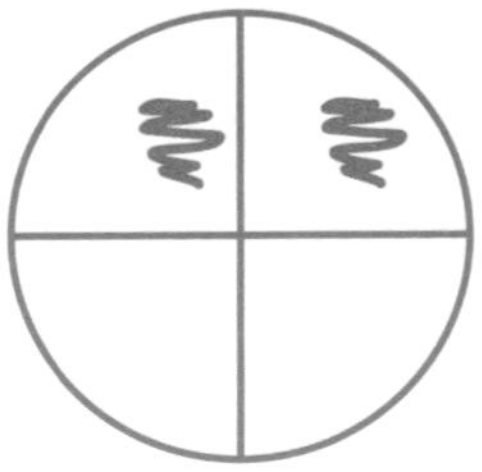

Color three quarters $\left(\frac{3}{4}\right)$.

3 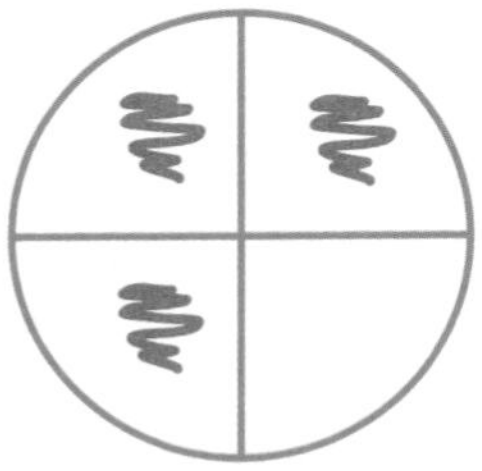

Color four quarters $\left(\frac{4}{4}\right)$.

4 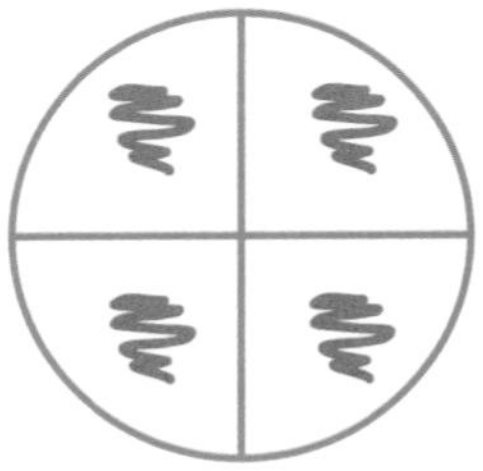

Color one quarter $\left(\frac{1}{4}\right)$ of the clock face.

5 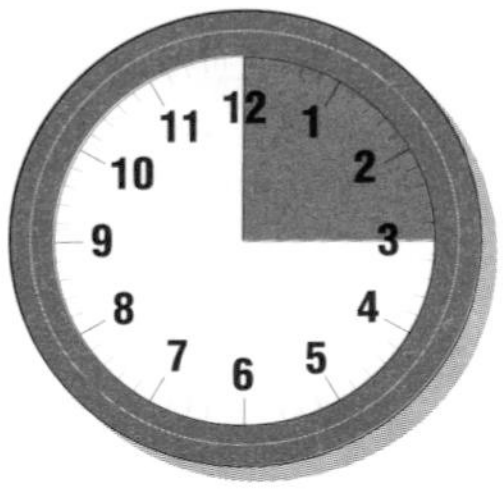

Color one half $\left(\frac{1}{2}\right)$ of the clock face.

6 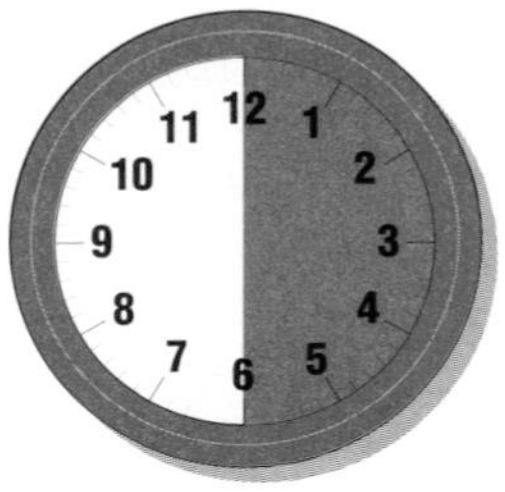

NOTE TO HOME
Students practice identifying fractional parts.

Literature Connection Read aloud or invite students to read *Fractions Are Parts of Things* by J. Richard Dennis to reinforce lesson concepts.

RETEACHING

Because fractions are continued in the next two lessons, reteaching is not necessary at this time.

*available separately

◆ **LESSON 76** Fractions and Geometry

Make a dot where you think the center of the clock is. Then cut out the clock. Fold it in half. Then fold it in quarters. Was your dot in the center of the clock?

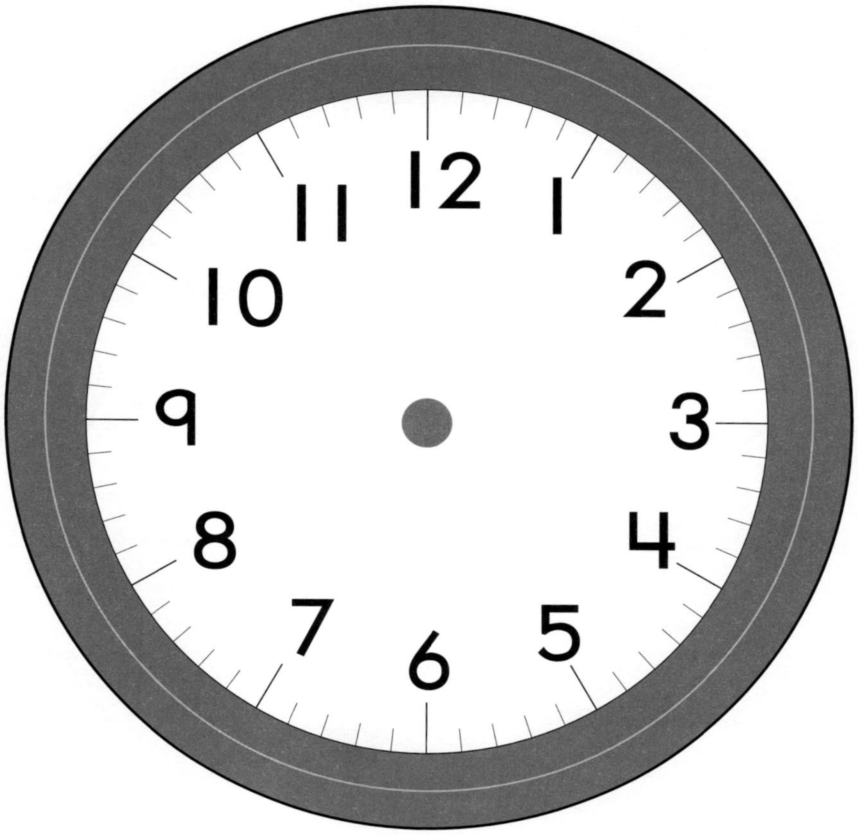

NOTE TO HOME
Students use the clock to learn about circles.

PRACTICE p. 76

LESSON 76 PRACTICE Name ____________

❶ Color four quarters.

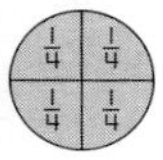

❷ Color two quarters.

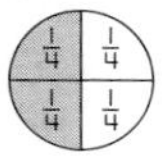

❸ Color one quarter.

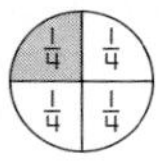

❹ Color three quarters.

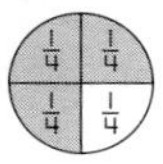

❺ Color three quarters of the clock face.

❻ Color one quarter of the clock face.

ENRICHMENT p. 76

LESSON 76 ENRICHMENT Name ____________

If you can get from Start to Finish, you get the pot of gold. To get there you may step only on the shaded fractions of each shape in the walk. Here are the rules:

1. Color $\frac{2}{3}$ of each circle.
2. Color $\frac{2}{4}$ of each square.

The shaded fractions of each shape must touch each other. Answers will vary. Possible answer given.

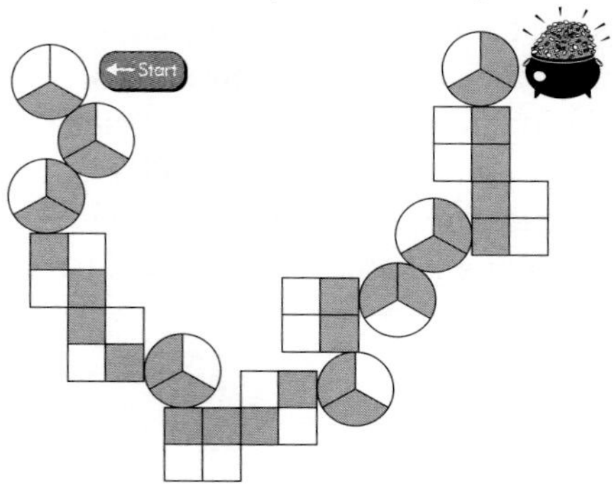

❷ Teach

Demonstrate Display a clock face. Discuss the relationship between quarter and half hours to the fractions one quarter and one half. Ask students to tell why a quarter hour might be called "quarter" hour. Show how much space on the clock is covered in a quarter hour. Repeat for half hour. Guide students to see that $\frac{1}{4}$ of the circle is covered for each quarter hour and $\frac{1}{2}$ is covered for each half hour.

Using the Student Pages Assign page 167. Instruct students to use their rulers to complete the last two problems. Remind them of the aforementioned demonstration with the clock face. Point out that there is more than one correct answer for each problem on this page except for one. (Color four quarters.) After discussing and correcting this page, assign page 168, which involves cutting out a clock. When students finish, have them draw hands on the clock face to show a quarter after two. Check students' clocks.

Using the Thinking Story Present one or two new problems from those following "Take a Chance" on pages 64–65 of the Thinking Story Book.

GAME **Using the "Fraction" Game Mat** Have students continue to play the "Fraction" game.

❸ Wrap-Up

5 MINUTES

In Closing Ask students to name items that they can divide into quarters. Students might suggest such things as a dollar, a loaf of bread, or a sheet of paper.

ALTERNATIVE ASSESSMENT

Informal Assessment Informally assess students' understanding of fractions by asking them as they are playing the "Fraction" game whether it seems too easy, just right, or too hard to play.

Assessment Criteria

Did the student . . .

✓ correctly color in three of the four fractional parts on page 167?

✓ correctly color in the fractional parts on the two clocks on page 167?

✓ correctly fold the clock on page 168 in half and then in quarters?

LESSON 77

Student Edition pages 169–170

Fractions

LESSON PLANNER

Objective

- to provide practice identifying fractional parts

Context of the Lesson This is the fifth of six lessons on fractions.

Materials	Program Resources
none	Number Cubes
	Thinking Story Book, pages 66–69
	Enrichment Master 77
	Practice Master 77
	For extra practice: CD-ROM* Lesson 77

1 Warm-Up

5 MINUTES

Problem of the Day Write this problem on the chalkboard: Bill is not older than Rudy. Doris is younger than Bill. Write their names in order from youngest to oldest. (Doris, Bill, Rudy)

MENTAL MATH Have students add or subtract the following problems, using their Number Cubes to respond.

a. 13 – 9 = (4) **b.** 15 – 7 = (8)

c. 7 + 4 = (11) **d.** 12 – 5 = (7)

e. 9 + 9 = (18) **f.** 6 + 5 = (11)

2 Teach

Demonstrate Model several problems similar to those on pages 169 and 170 for students to work together before assigning the pages. For example, draw three different rectangles on the chalkboard and shade in $\frac{1}{3}$, $\frac{1}{2}$, and $\frac{1}{4}$. Have volunteers write the fractional part that is shaded in each.

LESSON 77

Name ______________________

Fractions

What fraction is shaded?

1 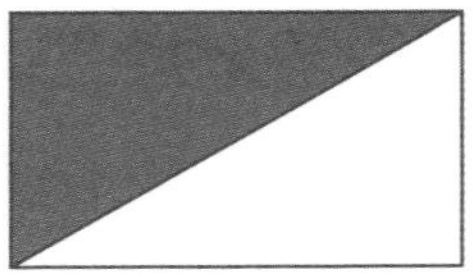

$\frac{1}{2}$

2 

$\frac{1}{2}$

3 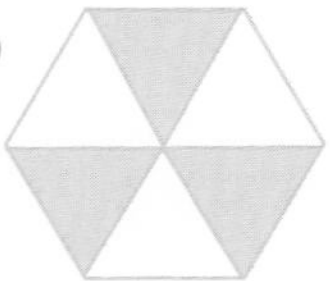

$\frac{3}{6}$ (or $\frac{1}{2}$)

4 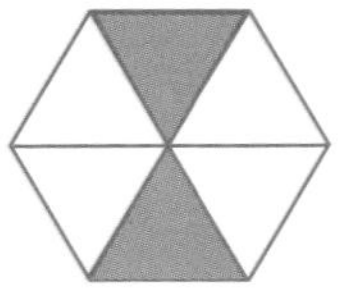

$\frac{2}{6}$ (or $\frac{1}{3}$)

5 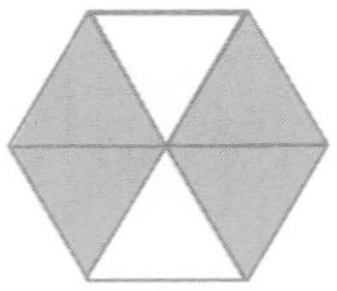

$\frac{4}{6}$ (or $\frac{2}{3}$)

6 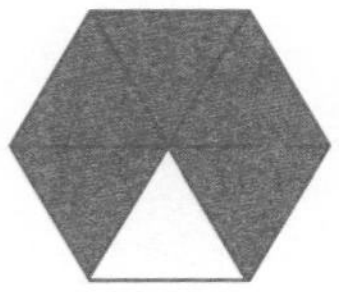

$\frac{5}{6}$

7 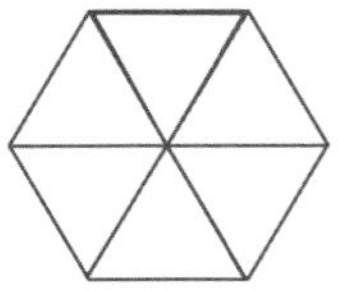

$\frac{0}{6}$ (or 0)

8 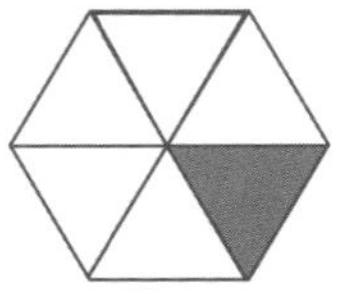

$\frac{1}{6}$

9 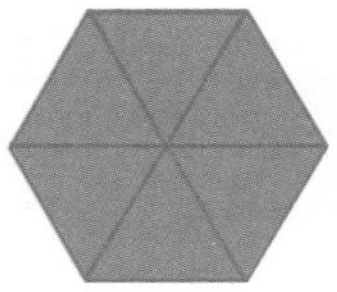

$\frac{6}{6}$ (or 1)

NOTE TO HOME
Students identify fractional parts.

Real-World Connection Have a pizza party. Order real ones, or make "pizzas" by dividing large cardboard circles into eighths. First, discuss how many pizzas you will need for your class. Ask questions such as: What part of a pizza will each student eat: $\frac{1}{8}$? $\frac{1}{4}$? $\frac{1}{2}$? How can we decide how many pizzas to order? After giving out the pizza slices, discuss the fractional parts each student eats and the fractional parts that are left over.

RETEACHING

Draw models of fractions using different colors. For example, display a circle that is divided into six equal parts. Color two parts red, one blue, and three yellow. Ask: What part is red? ($\frac{2}{6}$ or $\frac{1}{3}$) blue? ($\frac{1}{6}$) yellow? ($\frac{3}{6}$ or $\frac{1}{2}$) Remind students that the denominator, or bottom number, tells how many parts in all and the numerator, or top number, tells how many parts are shaded.

*available separately

◆ LESSON 77 Fractions

Use the Mixed Practice on page 381 after this lesson.

What fraction is shaded?

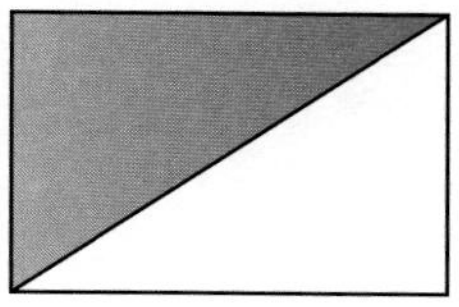

⑩ ____ $\frac{1}{2}$

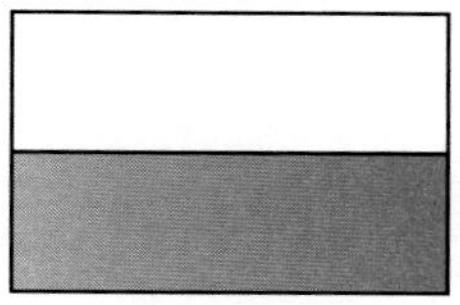

⑪ ____ $\frac{1}{2}$

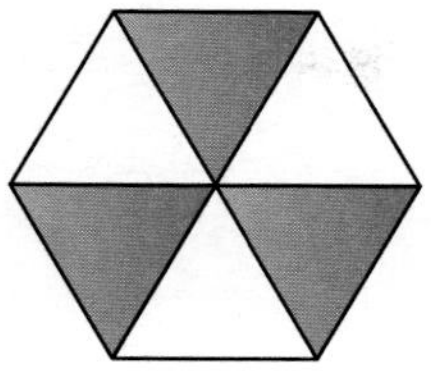

⑫ ____ $\frac{3}{6}$

⑬ ____ $\frac{2}{6}$

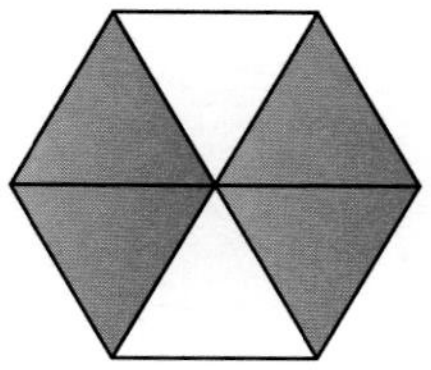

⑭ ____ $\frac{4}{6}$

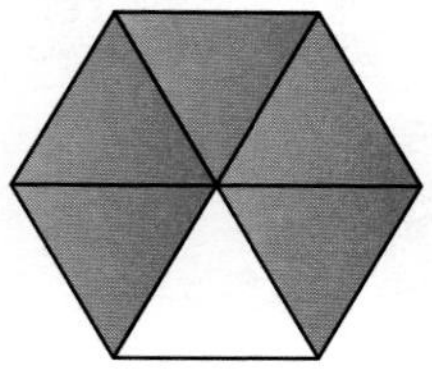

⑮ ____ $\frac{5}{6}$

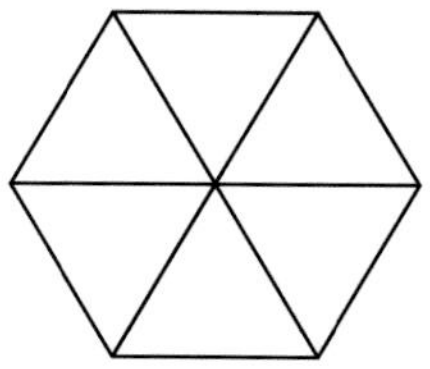

⑯ ____ $\frac{0}{6}$

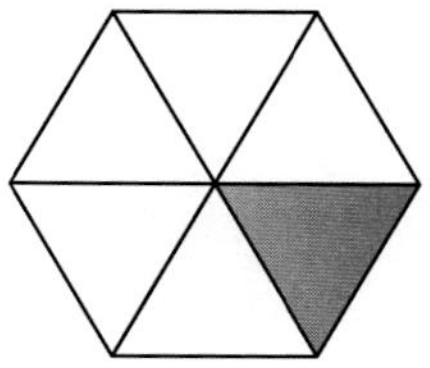

⑰ ____ $\frac{1}{6}$

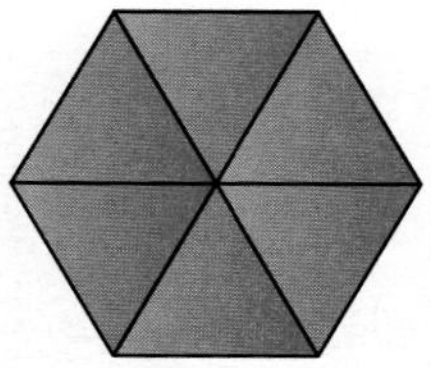

⑱ ____ $\frac{6}{6}$

THINKING STORY

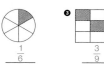

Talk about the Thinking Story "Half a Job."

NOTE TO HOME
Students identify fractional parts.

PRACTICE p. 77

LESSON 77 PRACTICE Name ____________

What fraction is shaded?

❶ 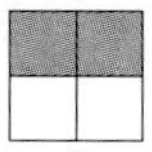 $\frac{2}{4}$

❷ 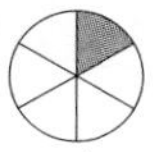 $\frac{1}{6}$

❸ 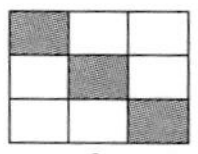 $\frac{3}{9}$

❹ 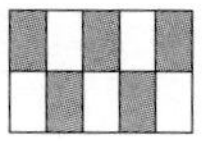 $\frac{5}{10}$

❺  $\frac{1}{2}$

❻ 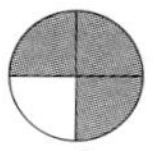 $\frac{3}{4}$

❼ 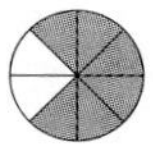 $\frac{6}{8}$

❽ 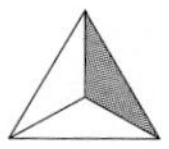 $\frac{1}{3}$

❾ 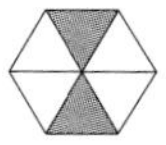 $\frac{2}{6}$

❿ 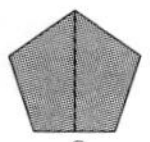 $\frac{2}{2}$

⓫ 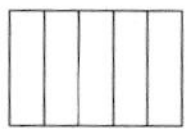 $\frac{0}{5}$

⓬ 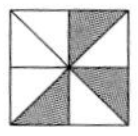 $\frac{3}{8}$

ENRICHMENT p. 77

LESSON 77 ENRICHMENT Name ____________

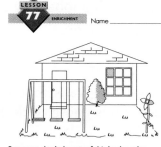

Someone shaded parts of this backyard to show fractions. Can you tell what they are?

❶ What fraction does the shading on the window show? $\frac{1}{9}$

❷ What fraction does the shading on the flower show? $\frac{1}{4}$

❸ What fraction does the shading on the bush show? $\frac{1}{2}$

❹ What fraction of the swings is shaded? $\frac{1}{3}$

❺ Use a pencil or crayon to add shading. Tell how you changed a fraction. Answers will vary.

Using the Student Pages Have students work independently to complete pages 169 and 170. Then have students discuss how they arrived at their answers.

Using the Thinking Story Read aloud the story "Half a Job" on Thinking Story Book pages 66–69. Stop and discuss the questions asked throughout the story.

❸ Wrap-Up

5 MINUTES

In Closing Draw 12 circles on the chalkboard. Ask how many you should circle to show $\frac{1}{2}$ (6); $\frac{1}{3}$ (4); and $\frac{1}{4}$ (3). Have students explain how they arrived at their answers.

ALTERNATIVE ASSESSMENT

Informal Assessment Use students' answers to pages 169 and 170 to informally assess their ability to name fractional parts.

Assessment Criteria

Did the student . . .

✓ correctly answer seven of nine problems on page 169?

✓ correctly answer seven of nine problems on page 170?

✓ participate in the Thinking Story discussion?

STORY 11

THINKING STORY

Half a Job

Year by year, things grew worse in Mr. Muddle's house. "Everything needs to be fixed, everything needs to be painted," he groaned. "There's so much work to be done that I can't get started."

"I'll tell you how I handle problems like that," said Ms. Eng. "When a job is so big that I don't feel like starting it, I just do half the job each day. That way it isn't so hard."

How long does it take Ms. Eng to do the job? two days

"Half the job each day," said Mr. Muddle. "That sounds like an excellent idea. I'm going to try it. I think I'll start today with painting the walls in this room."

"Good luck," said Ms. Eng. "I'll be back in a week, and I expect I'll find this house in much better shape if you follow my advice and do half a job every day."

Mr. Muddle got out paint, brushes, and a roller, and he started painting the walls in that room.

How many walls should he paint the first day if he is going to do half the job? two

Mr. Muddle figured that half of 4 is 2. And so the first day he painted two walls.

The next day Mr. Muddle got out his painting materials again and was ready to start work. "Now, what was it Ms. Eng told me to do?" he asked himself. "Ah, yes, I remember. Do half the job each day. There are two walls that need painting, so if I do half the job today, that means I paint one wall." Mr. Muddle painted one of the walls.

Do you think that is what Ms. Eng meant? no

What should Mr. Muddle have done instead? do the other half of the job by painting both walls

The next day Mr. Muddle said, "This idea of doing only half the job each day really makes life easy. It didn't take me very long at all to do my painting yesterday, and today it should take even less time."

How many walls are left to be painted in the room? one

How much do you think Mr. Muddle will paint today? probably half of the wall

Mr. Muddle noticed that only one wall in the room needed painting. Because the rule was to do half a job each day, he painted only half the wall that day.

How many walls has Mr. Muddle painted so far? three and a half

How much painting is there still left to do? half a wall

Do you think Mr. Muddle will finish the room the next day? no

Why or why not? If he does half of the remaining half wall, he will still have one fourth of the wall left to paint.

The next day Mr. Muddle had a very easy job. There was only half a wall left to paint. So his job was to paint half a wall. But he remembered that he was supposed to do only half the job that day.

How much did Mr. Muddle paint that day? one fourth of the wall

How much of the last wall is still not painted? one fourth

About how wide would a fourth of the wall in an ordinary room be? maybe one meter

◆ STORY 11 Half a Job

By the next day there was only a strip of wall left to be painted, and it took Mr. Muddle just a few minutes to paint half of it. Every day the strip of wall that was unpainted grew narrower. Every day Mr. Muddle painted only half of what was left.

Do you think Mr. Muddle will ever finish painting the wall? no

Why or why not? He'll keep painting only half of what's left.

Ms. Eng stopped by to see how Mr. Muddle was coming with his work on the house. "What have you been doing?" she asked.

"Just painting the walls in this one room," said Mr. Muddle.

"That's strange," said Ms. Eng. "I thought that job would take you only two days."

Why did Ms. Eng think it would take only two days to paint the room? She thought he would paint one half the room one day and the other half of the room the second day.

"You've done a beautiful job of painting this room," said Ms. Eng, "but you seem to have missed a little strip on this wall."

Why is there still a little strip that isn't painted? It's the half left over from what he painted the day before.

"I haven't missed it," said Mr. Muddle. "I'm still working on it. I'm following your good advice and doing half a job each day. For a while the work kept getting easier and easier because every day I had less to paint. But now it's getting harder. The strip is so narrow that it's very difficult to paint only half of it. I have to go very slowly, because if I'm not careful I'll make a mistake and paint the whole strip at once."

What would happen if Mr. Muddle painted the whole strip at once? He'd finish painting the room.

"I'm afraid I didn't explain my idea well enough," said Ms. Eng. "I meant that you should do half the job the first day and the rest of it the next day. That way you do the whole job in two days."

"That's a hard rule to follow," Mr. Muddle said. "You have to remember what the whole job is. It's easier for me if I just look each day and see what needs to be done and then do half of it."

"Then I think you'd better just forget about my advice and try to do a whole job in one day," said Ms. Eng. "Otherwise it will take you forever to finish one job."

Why would it take Mr. Muddle forever to finish? He would always leave half of what there was yet to do.

. . . the end

LESSON 78

Student Edition pages 171–172

Fractions of Numbers

LESSON PLANNER

Objectives

- ▶ to provide practice identifying fractional parts
- ▶ to provide practice identifying a fraction of a number

Context of the Lesson This is the last of six lessons on fractions.

Materials	**Program Resources**
base-10 materials*	Number Cubes
play money*	Thinking Story Book, pages 70–71
	Reteaching Master
	Practice Master 78
	Enrichment Master 78
	For extra practice: CD-ROM* Lesson 78

1 Warm-Up

5 MINUTES

Problem of the Day Write this problem on the chalkboard: There are 20 students in second grade. There are 12 in the chorus and 15 in the band. Eight belong to both. How many do not belong to either chorus or band? (1)

MENTAL MATH Have students add or subtract the following using their Number Cubes to respond.

a. 120 – 40 = (80) **b.** 150 – 60 = (90) **c.** 30 + 90 = (120)

d. 20 + 80 = (100) **e.** 130 – 60 = (70) **f.** 60 + 80 = (140)

2 Teach

Demonstrate Use play money to show how to find a fractional part of a number. Ask: How many cents is a quarter worth? (25) a dollar? (100) How many quarters are equal to one dollar? (4) Then write the following on the chalkboard: $\frac{1}{4}$ of 100 = _____ (25). Remind students that the denominator of a fraction stands for the total number of parts and the numerator tells how many equal parts there are. Show four quarters and explain that if 100 cents is divided into four equal parts, each one of those parts equals 25 cents. Therefore, one of four equal parts or $\frac{1}{4}$ of 100 = 25. Repeat by showing half dollars to find $\frac{1}{2}$ of 100 (50) and ten dimes to show $\frac{1}{10}$ of 100 (10).

LESSON 78

Name ______________________

Fractions of Numbers

Complete the chart. Use your punchout coins to help you.

	Make this amount.	Use this kind of coin.	How many coins?
1	$1	nickel	20
2	$1	quarter	4
3	$1	dime	10
4	50¢	quarter	2
5	50¢	dime	5
6	50¢	nickel	10

7 How much is $\frac{1}{4}$ of $1? __25__¢

8 How much is $\frac{1}{2}$ of $1? __50__¢

NOTE TO HOME
Students use coins to make different money amounts.

Literature Connection Read aloud *The Half-Birthday* by Charlotte Pomerantz to reinforce lesson concepts.

RETEACHING p. 21

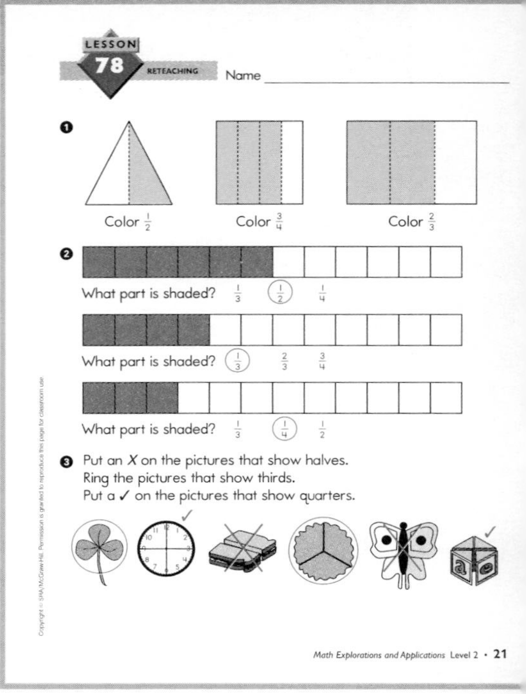

LESSON 78 RETEACHING
Name
Color $\frac{1}{2}$
Color $\frac{3}{4}$
Color $\frac{2}{3}$
What part is shaded? $\frac{1}{3}$ $\frac{1}{2}$ $\frac{1}{4}$
What part is shaded? $\frac{1}{3}$ $\frac{2}{3}$ $\frac{3}{4}$
What part is shaded? $\frac{1}{3}$ $\frac{1}{4}$ $\frac{1}{2}$
Put an X on the pictures that show halves.
Ring the pictures that show thirds.
Put a ✓ on the pictures that show quarters.
Math Explorations and Applications Level 2 • 21

*available separately

◆ LESSON 78 Fractions of Numbers

Find the answers. You may use sticks or other objects to help.

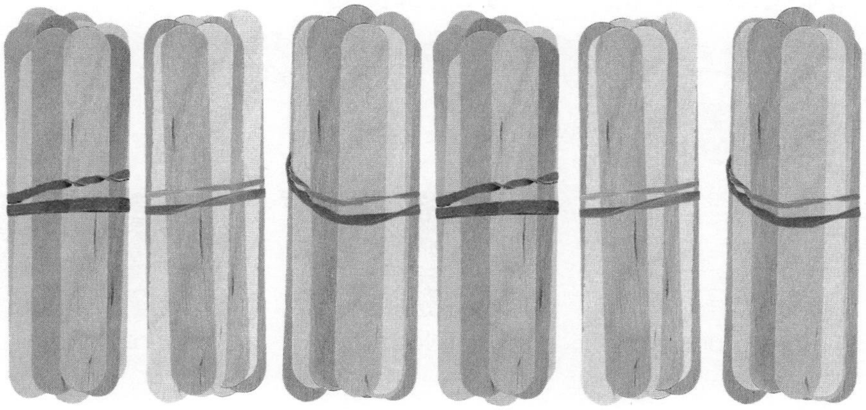

9. $\frac{1}{4}$ of 60 = 15
10. $\frac{2}{4}$ of 60 = 30
11. $\frac{3}{4}$ of 60 = 45
12. $\frac{4}{4}$ of 60 = 60
13. $\frac{1}{2}$ of 60 = 30
14. $\frac{2}{2}$ of 60 = 60
15. $\frac{1}{2}$ of 100 = 50
16. $\frac{2}{2}$ of 100 = 100

NOTE TO HOME
Students solve fraction of number problems.

PRACTICE p. 78

LESSON 78 PRACTICE Name ____________

Complete this chart. Use play coins to help you.

Make this amount.	Use this kind of coin.	How many coins?
30¢	dime	3
50¢	dime	5
50¢	quarter	2
50¢	nickel	10
$1	dime	10
$1	quarter	4

Try to find the answers. You may use sticks and other objects to help.

1. $\frac{1}{3}$ of 30 = 10
2. $\frac{1}{5}$ of 50 = 10
3. $\frac{1}{2}$ of 50 = 25
4. $\frac{1}{10}$ of 50 = 5
5. $\frac{1}{10}$ of 100 = 10
6. $\frac{1}{4}$ of 100 = 25
7. $\frac{2}{3}$ of 30 = 20
8. $\frac{3}{3}$ of 30 = 30
9. $\frac{1}{4}$ of 60 = 15
10. $\frac{1}{2}$ of 60 = 30

78 • *Math Explorations and Applications* Level 2

ENRICHMENT p. 78

LESSON 78 ENRICHMENT Name ____________

Can you make 10¢ with one coin? With two coins? With three coins?

Show how to make these amounts. Write *no* for the combinations that cannot be made.

Make This Amount	Use Exactly One Coin	Use Exactly Two Coins	Use Exactly Three Coins	Use Exactly Four Coins
10¢	one dime	two nickels	no	no
15¢	no	one nickel, one dime	three nickels	no
21¢	no	no	two dimes, one penny	two nickels, one dime, one penny
25¢	one quarter	no	two dimes, one nickel	one dime, three nickels
36¢	no	no	one quarter, one dime, one penny	one quarter, two nickels, one penny

Make up your own coin puzzles. Give them to a friend.

78 • *Math Explorations and Applications* Level 2

Using the Student Pages Divide students into groups. Have groups use craft sticks or other base-10 materials to model the first two problems on page 172 with you. Have students gather 60 sticks on their desks. Ask: How many groups must we divide them into for problem 9? (four) How can you tell? (The denominator is 4.) Have students work together until they discover how to divide the sticks equally. Students should find there are 15 sticks in each group of four.

Have groups complete the rest of page 172 and page 171 on their own, using play money if needed. When finished, have groups compare answers.

Using the Thinking Story Present one or two new problems from those following "Half a Job" on pages 70–71 of the Thinking Story Book.

3 Wrap-Up (5 MINUTES)

In Closing Draw 24 circles on the chalkboard. Ask how many you should circle to show $\frac{1}{2}$ (12); $\frac{1}{3}$ (8); and $\frac{1}{4}$ (6). Have students explain how they arrived at their answers.

ALTERNATIVE ASSESSMENT

Portfolio Assessment Have students draw the 24 circles and show each fractional part as discussed in the closing activity. Check their drawings and have students save them in their Math Portfolios.

Assessment Criteria

Did the student . . .

✓ correctly answer six of the eight problems on page 171?

✓ correctly answer four of the remaining six problems?

SPECIAL NEEDS

Meeting Individual Needs
Provide more help with base-10 materials and simple examples. For example, have them work only with $\frac{1}{2}$ of numbers such as 6, 8, and 10. Display 6 sticks. Ask: How can you show two equal groups? (Divide them into 3 and 3.) How many in each group? (3) Then what is $\frac{1}{2}$ of 6? (3) Repeat for $\frac{1}{2}$ of 8, $\frac{1}{2}$ of 10, and so on.

LESSON 79

Student Edition pages 173–174

Geometric Shapes—Plane Figures

LESSON PLANNER

Objectives

- ▶ to review definitions of some two-dimensional shapes: right triangle, parallelogram, rectangle, and square
- ▶ to provide opportunities to create two-dimensional shapes by cutting other figures

Context of the Lesson This is the first of five lessons on geometry concepts.

Materials	Program Resources
scissors	Thinking Story Book, pages 70–71
	Practice Master 79
	Enrichment Master 79
	For extra practice: CD-ROM* Lesson 79

1 Warm-Up 5 MINUTES

Problem of the Day Write the following problem on the chalkboard: Use the numbers 0–5 only once to fill in the blanks:

a. ____ + ____ = 7 (3, 4)

b. ____ – ____ = 3 (5, 2)

c. ____ + ____ = 1 (0, 1)

MENTAL MATH Have students name the fractional part:

a. $\frac{1}{2}$ of 10 (5)

b. $\frac{1}{2}$ of 12 (6)

c. $\frac{1}{2}$ of 8 (4)

d. $\frac{1}{2}$ of 50 (25)

e. $\frac{1}{2}$ of 16 (8)

LESSON 79

Name ______________________

Geometric Shapes—Plane Figures

Answers are examples only.

COOPERATIVE LEARNING Work with a partner.

1. Cut to make two right triangles.

2. Cut to make two rectangles.

3. Cut to make two parallelograms.

4. Cut differently to make two parallelograms.

5. Cut to make two triangles.

6. Cut differently to make two triangles.

NOTE TO HOME
Students review properties of two-dimensional figures.

Art Connection List these names of shapes on the chalkboard: two triangles, two squares, two rectangles. Have students work in pairs to draw, cut out, and paste these shapes to create a picture. Have pairs share and compare pictures. Display them on a classroom bulletin board.

RETEACHING

Have students work with partners as they work backwards with pattern blocks* to make the shapes shown on pages 173–174. For example, problem 1 on page 173 has students cut a rectangle to make two right triangles. For reteaching, have students use two right triangle blocks to make a rectangle. Do the same for the remaining shapes on these pages.

*available separately

◆ **LESSON 79 Geometric Shapes—Plane Figures**

Answers are examples only.

7. Cut to make two right triangles.

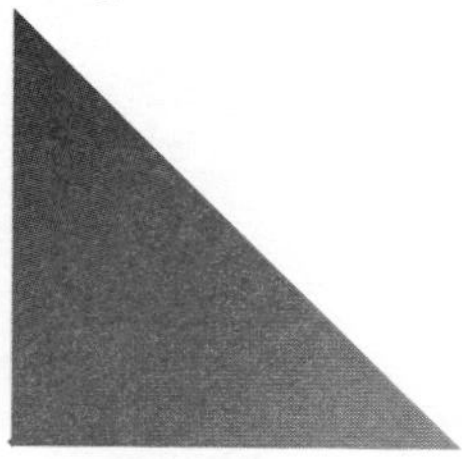

8. Cut to make four squares.

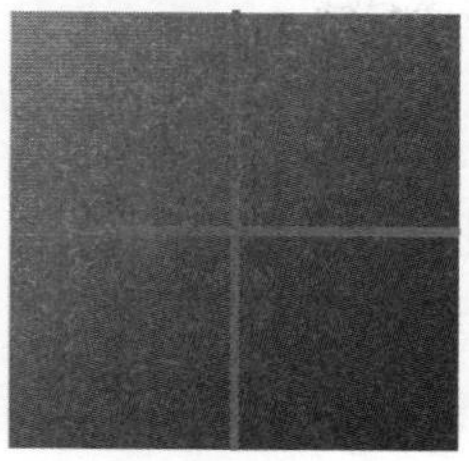

9. Cut to make one right triangle and one triangle that is not a right triangle.

10. Cut to make two triangles that are not right triangles.

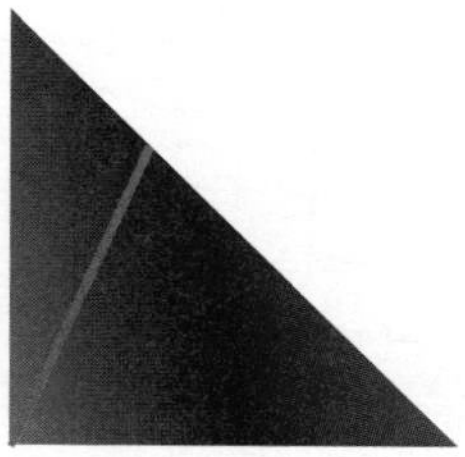

11. Cut to make two pieces from which you can make a rectangle.

12. Cut to make two rectangles that are not squares.

NOTE TO HOME
Students review two-dimensional figures.

❷ Teach

Demonstrate Review geometric terms. Write *right angle* on the chalkboard. Have students find and name an example of a right angle. (corner of a book) Then draw a right angle next to the term on the chalkboard. Then ask what a right triangle is and draw a right triangle. Continue reviewing attributes of a rectangle, parallelogram, and square. Leave the names and figures on the board for students to refer to.

Using the Student Pages Divide students into pairs. Have partners work together to complete the activities on pages 173 and 174. Note that they will have to use one partner's book to do page 173 and the other's to do page 174. Emphasize that the partners should agree in advance where they will cut before they actually cut up the figures. You might want to ask students to draw their cut lines with pencil. When finished, have partners show their figures.

Using the Thinking Story Present one or two new problems from those following "Half a Job" on pages 70–71 of the Thinking Story Book.

❸ Wrap-Up

5 MINUTES

In Closing Ask whether there was more than one way to cut some of the shapes on pages 173–174 and whether there were some that could only be done in one way.

ALTERNATIVE ASSESSMENT

Portfolio Assessment Have students save their shapes in their Math Portfolios.

Assessment Criteria

Did the student . . .

✓ correctly cut at least nine of 12 shapes on pages 173–174?

✓ work cooperatively with a partner?

PRACTICE p. 79

LESSON 79 PRACTICE Name ______________

Draw one or more lines to make the figures. Answers will vary.

1. Make four rectangles.

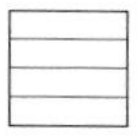

2. Make four squares.

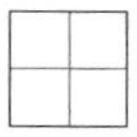

3. Make two right triangles.

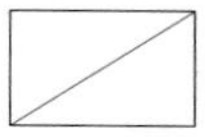

4. Make four right triangles.

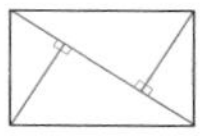

5. Make one rectangle and two right triangles.

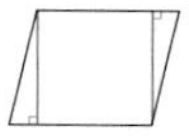

6. Make two triangles.

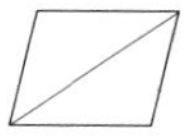

7. Make two right triangles.

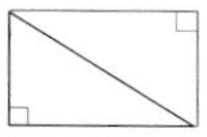

8. Make two triangles that are not right triangles.

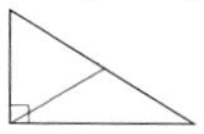

Math Explorations and Applications Level 2 • 79

ENRICHMENT p. 79

LESSON 79 ENRICHMENT Name ______________

Draw lines between the shapes and the things that are the same.

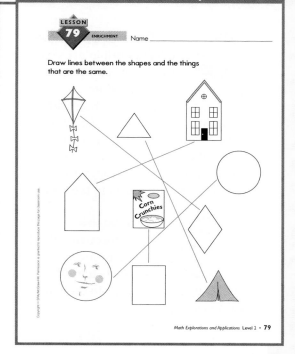

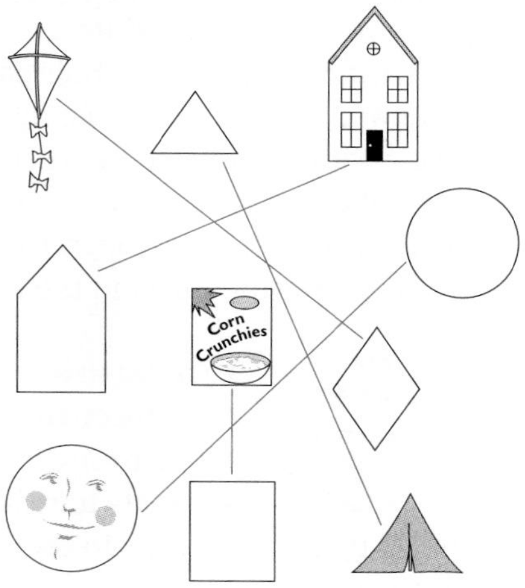

Math Explorations and Applications Level 2 • 79

LESSON 80

Student Edition pages 175–176

Congruent Shapes

LESSON PLANNER

Objectives

- ▶ to help students develop an understanding of congruency
- ▶ to help students identify congruent figures

Context of the Lesson This lesson prepares students for the next lesson, which is on symmetry. Congruency is continued in Lesson 83.

Materials	Program Resources
index cards	Number Cubes
tracing paper	Thinking Story Book, pages 70–71
	Practice Master 80
	Enrichment Master 80
	For extra practice: CD-ROM* Lesson 80

1 Warm-Up

5 MINUTES

Problem of the Day Write the following problem on the chalkboard: Jen ate one half of a pizza. Her brother ate three quarters of a pizza. Who ate more? How can you tell? (Her brother, because $\frac{2}{4}$ is half, so $\frac{3}{4}$ is more than half.)

MENTAL MATH Have students add, using their Number Cubes to respond:

a. 80 + 70 = (150)　　**b.** 40 + 90 = (130)

c. 60 + 60 = (120)　　**d.** 30 + 50 = (80)

e. 50 + 70 = (120)　　**f.** 70 + 70 = (140)

LESSON 80

Name ______________________________

Congruent Shapes

Which are the same shape and same size?
Match the figures.

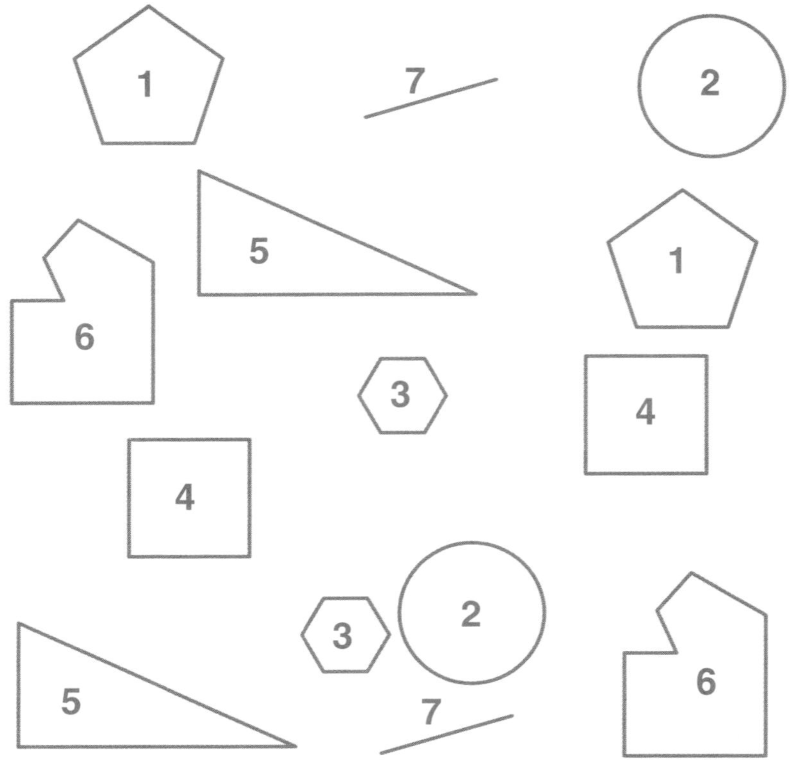

Talk about your answers. Trace to check.

NOTE TO HOME
Students identify congruent (same shape and same size) shapes.

Art Connection Have students work in pairs. One partner cuts an irregular figure from a piece of white construction paper. The other partner traces and cuts out the same figure. Have partners use each figure in a different design and paste them both on one larger sheet of paper. Display partners' drawings around the room.

Literature Connection Read aloud or invite students to read *Circles* by Rose Griffiths to reinforce lesson concepts.

RETEACHING

Draw pairs of congruent circles, triangles, squares, and rectangles on individual index cards. Hold up two index cards at a time. Have students put "thumbs up" if the figures shown are congruent and "thumbs down" if they are not.

*available separately

◆ **LESSON 80** Congruent Shapes

Which are the same shape and same size?

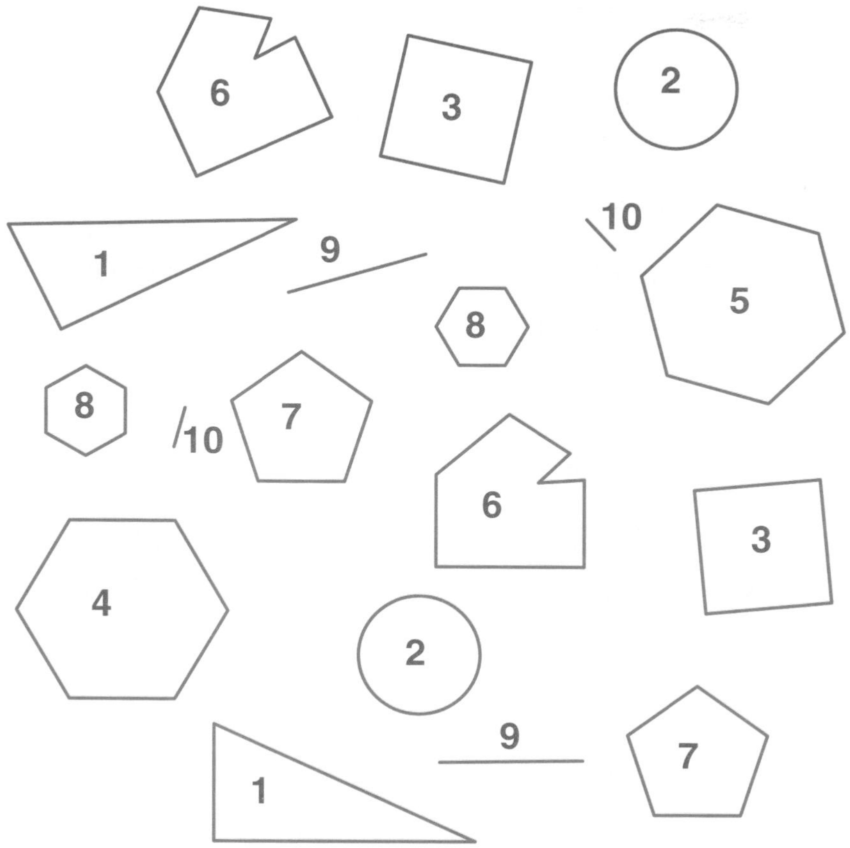

MATH JOURNAL

List some times we have to have congruent shapes. Tell why they are important.

NOTE TO HOME
Students identify congruent shapes.

PRACTICE p. 80

LESSON 80 PRACTICE Name ____________

Which are the same shape and size?
Talk about your answers. Trace to check.

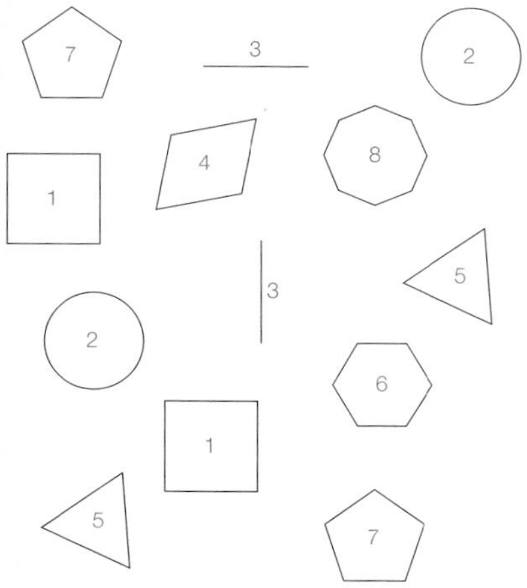

ENRICHMENT p. 80

LESSON 80 ENRICHMENT Name ____________

Look at the lines. Use your ruler and pencil to make the same size lines for the sides of shapes. Make five or more different shapes.

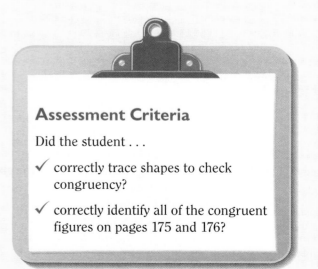

❷ Teach

Demonstrate Have students look at the circle on page 175. Ask them to find another figure on the page that is the same shape and size, or congruent to the circle. After students identify the other circle, discuss ways in which they could prove the figures are congruent. Then show them how to prove the figures are congruent by using tracing paper. Have them trace over one circle and see whether it fits exactly over the other. Repeat this demonstration with the pentagons on this page. Point out that even though the figures are facing different directions they are still congruent. Demonstrate this by having students trace over one pentagon, then seeing whether it fits over the other by turning the tracing.

Using the Student Pages After the demonstration have students write the number 1 inside both pentagons on page 175 to show they are congruent. Have them write number 2 inside both circles. They can continue identifying pairs of congruent shapes on this page and page 176 by writing the same number in or on both shapes. (For example, they can write 3 inside both triangles, and 4 on both straight lines on page 175.) Have students use their tracing paper to check their answers.

Using the Thinking Story Present one or two new problems from those following "Half a Job" on pages 70–71 of the Thinking Story Book.

❸ Wrap-Up

5 MINUTES

In Closing Have students find congruent shapes in the classroom.

ALTERNATIVE ASSESSMENT

Informal Assessment Use students' answers on pages 175–176 to informally assess their understanding of congruency.

Assessment Criteria

Did the student . . .

✓ correctly trace shapes to check congruency?

✓ correctly identify all of the congruent figures on pages 175 and 176?

LESSON 81

Student Edition pages 177–178

Symmetry

LESSON PLANNER

Objectives

- ▶ to review the concept of symmetry
- ▶ to help students recognize and draw lines of symmetry

Context of the Lesson This lesson reviews symmetry, which was introduced in level 1.

Materials	Program Resources
catalogs or magazines (optional)	Number Cubes
index cards	Thinking Story Book, pages 70–71
paper	Practice Master 81
ruler	Enrichment Master 81
scissors	For extra practice: CD-ROM* Lesson 81

1 Warm-Up

5 MINUTES

Problem of the Day Write the following on the chalkboard: You buy a $14 basketball. You pay with two $10 bills. You get back a $5 bill and a $1 bill for change. Is that correct? Why or why not? (Yes, because $20 – $14 = $6 and $5 + $1 = $6.)

MENTAL MATH Have students subtract, using their Number Cubes to respond:

a. 140 – 80 = (60)	**b.** 130 – 90 = (40)
c. 90 – 40 = (50)	**d.** 110 – 90 = (20)
e. 70 – 40 = (30)	**f.** 170 – 90 = (80)

2 Teach

MATH MANIPULATIVES **Demonstrate** Show how to make a figure in which both sides are the same: Fold a sheet of paper, draw half of a circle, cut out the shape and unfold the paper. Explain that the fold through the center of the figure is a line of symmetry. Ask students to draw half of a heart on a folded sheet of paper, cut it out, and unfold it. Have them identify the line of symmetry. Repeat for several other figures of their choice.

LESSON 81

Name ______________________

Symmetry

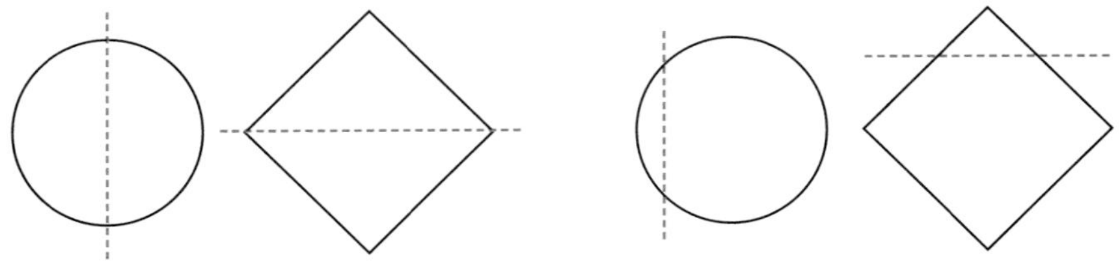

Draw as many lines of symmetry as you can.

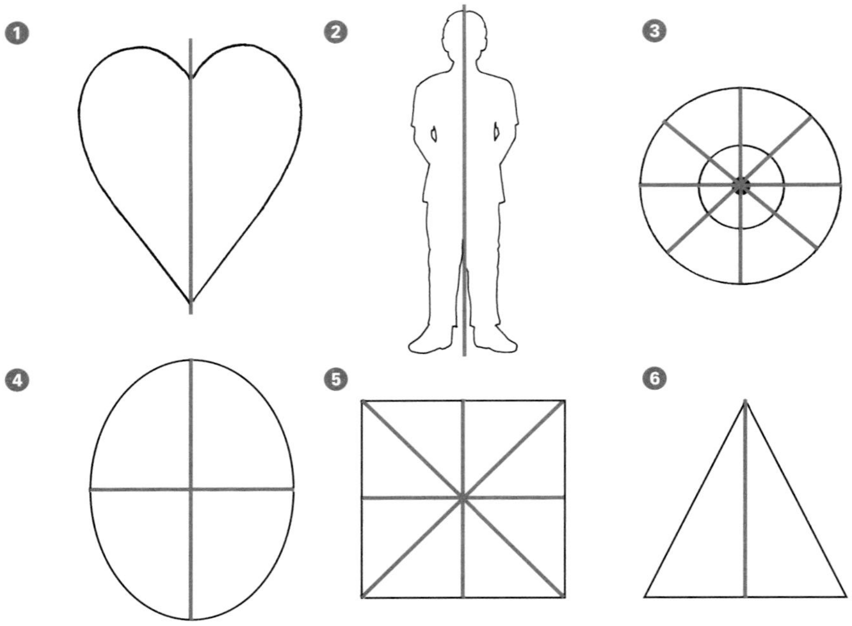

NOTE TO HOME
Students demonstrate their understanding of symmetry by drawing lines of symmetry.

Literature Connection Read aloud or invite students to read *Shapes In Nature* by Judy Feldman to reinforce lesson concepts.

RETEACHING

Draw figures with and without lines of symmetry on individual index cards. Hold up index cards one at a time. Have students show "thumbs up" if the figures have lines of symmetry and "thumbs down" if they do not.

*available separately

◆ **LESSON 81** Symmetry

Use the Mixed Practice on page 382 after this lesson.

Draw as many lines of symmetry as you can.

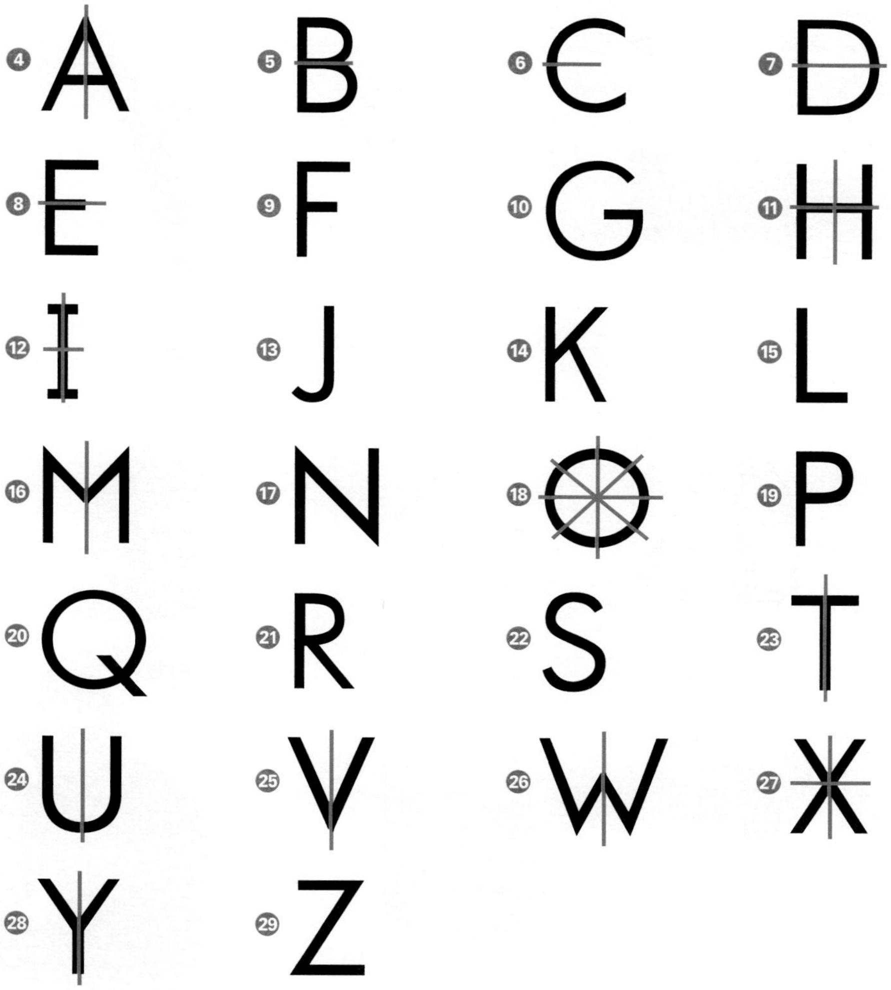

NOTE TO HOME
Students draw lines of symmetry through as many letters as they can.

PRACTICE p. 81

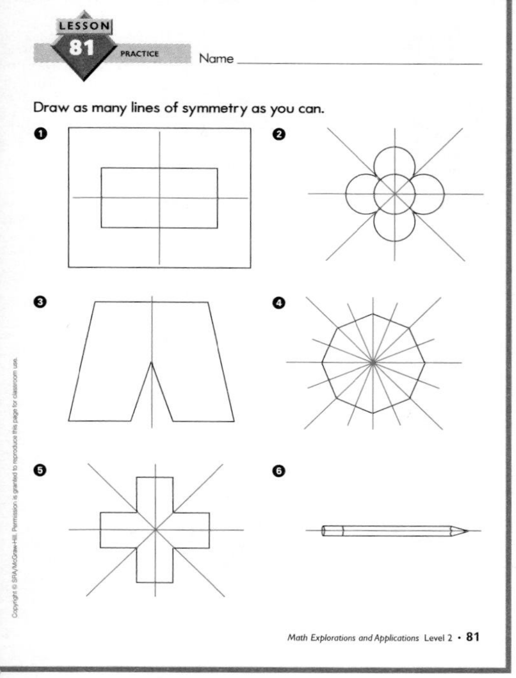
LESSON 81 PRACTICE Name ____________

Draw as many lines of symmetry as you can.

1 2 3 4 5 6

Math Explorations and Applications Level 2 • 81

ENRICHMENT p. 81

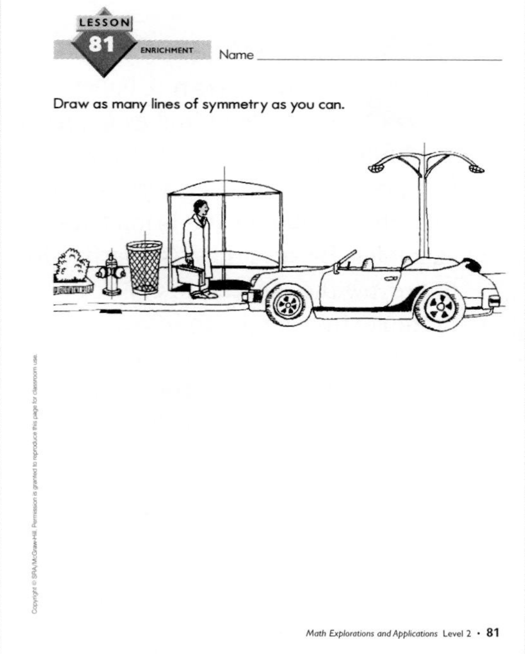
LESSON 81 ENRICHMENT Name ____________

Draw as many lines of symmetry as you can.

Math Explorations and Applications Level 2 • 81

COOPERATIVE LEARNING **Using the Student Pages** Have students look at the first four figures on page 177. Ask them to explain why the lines are and are not lines of symmetry. Next ask students where they think the heart shape's line of symmetry is. Have them draw this line using their rulers. Continue discussing and drawing lines of symmetry for the next two figures, pointing out that the circle has many lines of symmetry. Have students complete the rest of the page independently and compare answers. Students can work in groups to complete page 178. Discuss answers as a class.

Using the Thinking Story Present one or two new problems from those following "Half a Job" on pages 70–71 of the Thinking Story Book.

3 Wrap-Up 5 MINUTES

MATH JOURNAL **In Closing** Ask students to draw any figure of their choice that has a line of symmetry. Have them draw the line of symmetry and label it on the figure.

ALTERNATIVE ASSESSMENT **Portfolio Assessment** Have students save the figures that they made in their Math Portfolios.

Assessment Criteria

Did the student . . .

✓ correctly identify lines of symmetry in figures during the demonstration?

✓ correctly draw at least one line of symmetry for figures and letters on pages 177–178?

GIFTED & TALENTED **Meeting Individual Needs**
Challenge students to find pictures of objects in magazines or catalogs that have lines of symmetry. Invite them to make collages to be displayed on a classroom bulletin board.

LESSON 82

Student Edition pages 179–180

Geometric Shapes—Solid Figures

LESSON PLANNER

Objectives

- ▶ to review names of solid figures
- ▶ to provide opportunities to identify common shapes

Context of the Lesson This is the fourth of five lessons on geometry concepts.

Materials	Program Resources
models of prism, pyramid, sphere, cone, and cylinder*	Number Cubes Reteaching Master Practice Master 82 Enrichment Master 82 For extra practice: CD-ROM* Lesson 82

1 Warm-Up 5 MINUTES

Problem of the Day Write this problem on the chalkboard: What numbers do the letters in the following example stand for? (B = 0; L = 1)

```
  4 B
 -L 5
  25
```

MENTAL MATH Have students add or subtract the following, using Number Cubes to respond.

- **a.** 13 – 6 = (7)
- **b.** 5 + 3 = (8)
- **c.** 12 – 7 = (5)
- **d.** 7 – 4 = (3)
- **e.** 15 – 9 = (6)
- **f.** 9 + 5 = (14)

LESSON 82

Name ______________________

Geometric Shapes—Solid Figures

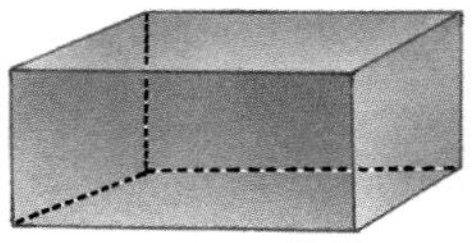
prism

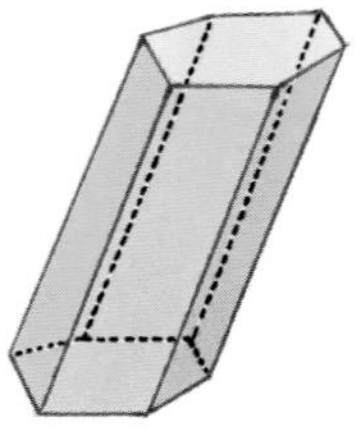
prism

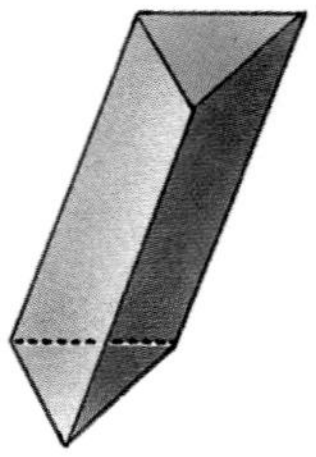
prism

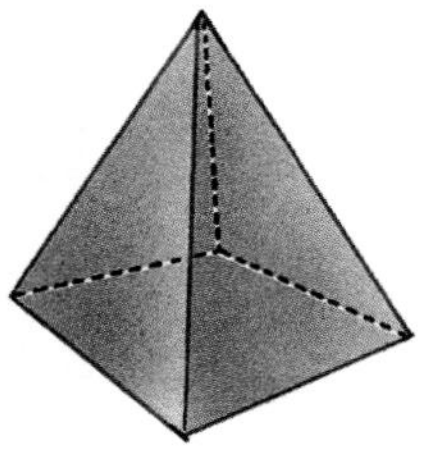
pyramid

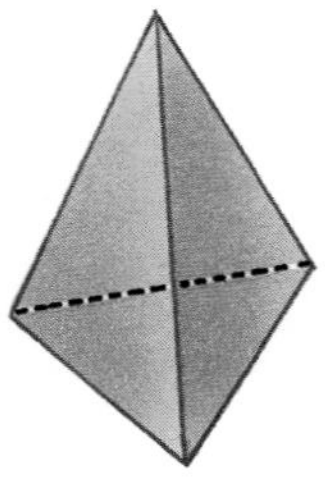
pyramid

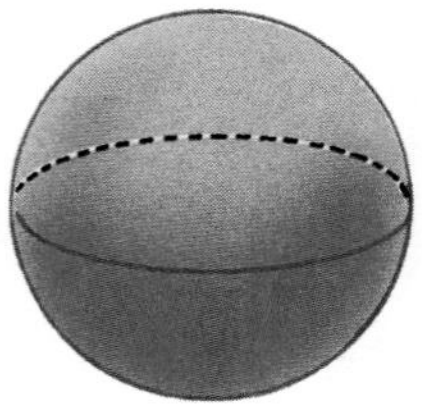
sphere

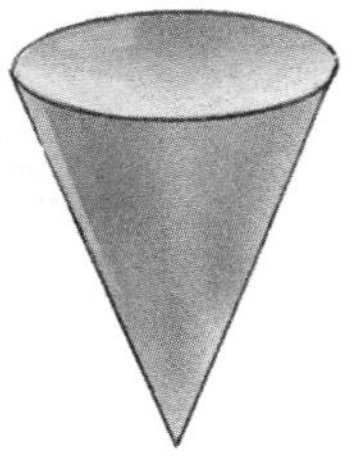
cone

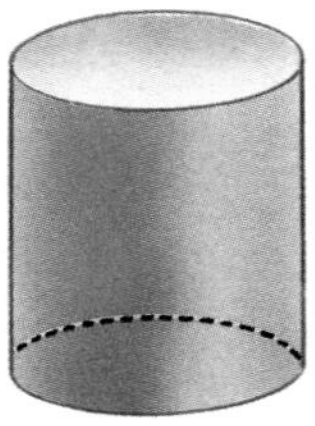
cylinder

NOTE TO HOME
Students are introduced to solid figures.

Real-World Connection Challenge students to find examples of solid figures in the school. Allow them to go on walks with partners around the school building and bring back examples. Be sure they ask permission to borrow the objects they find. For example, they might go into a kindergarten classroom and ask the teacher if they may borrow some shapes like prisms and cylinders to bring back.

RETEACHING p. 22

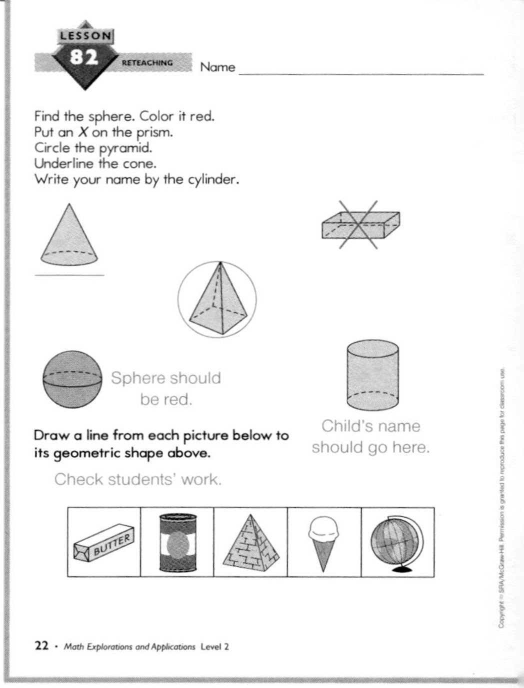
LESSON 82 RETEACHING Name ______________

Find the sphere. Color it red.
Put an X on the prism.
Circle the pyramid.
Underline the cone.
Write your name by the cylinder.

Sphere should be red.

Child's name should go here.

Draw a line from each picture below to its geometric shape above.

Check students' work.

22 • Math Explorations and Applications Level 2

*available separately

◆ **LESSON 82** **Geometric Shapes—Solid Figures**

1. Name at least four objects that are prisms.
   Examples: a box, a building, a dresser

2. Name four spheres.
   Examples: a globe, the earth, a basketball

3. Name two cones and two cylinders.
   Examples of cones: an ice-cream cone, a party hat, a megaphone
   Examples of cylinders: a jar, a garbage pail, a tube

FANTASTIC FACT China is so big that it covers 6 time zones.

NOTE TO HOME
Students identify solid figures.

② Teach

Demonstrate Give informal definitions and examples of the figures shown on page 179. For example, show that the classroom is one big prism. Point out that the ceiling and floor are two congruent polygons. To show a pyramid, cut out a large equilateral triangle. Draw lines to connect the midpoint of each side, then fold along the lines to make a triangular pyramid. Show a globe or ball to model a sphere. Allow students to handle models of each figure.

Using the Student Pages Have students work in groups. Explain that they should use page 179 to help them complete page 180. Encourage them to discuss ideas with family members or friends. Have students share and compare results when finished.

③ Wrap-Up

5 MINUTES

In Closing Draw several figures on the chalkboard and have students identify them without referring to page 179.

ALTERNATIVE ASSESSMENT

Informal Assessment Note which students have the ability to identify solid figures. Reteach students who need more practice.

Assessment Criteria

Did the student . . .

✓ correctly name at least three of four objects for each figure named on page 180?

✓ work cooperatively in a group?

PRACTICE p. 82

LESSON 82 PRACTICE Name ____________

Name each figure.

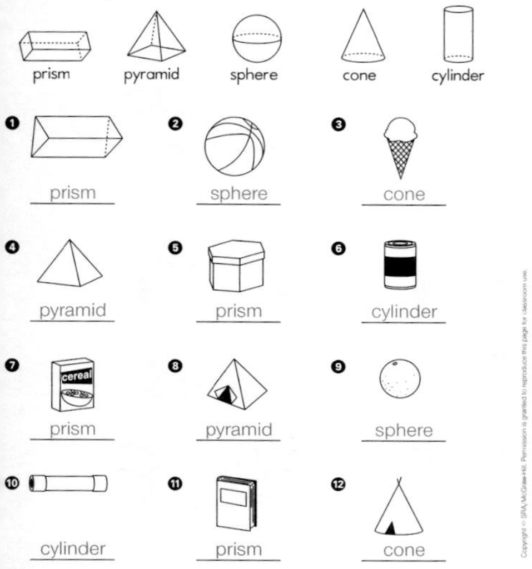

ENRICHMENT p. 82

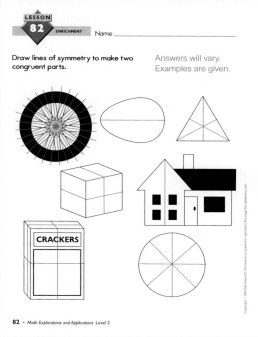

LESSON 82 ENRICHMENT Name ____________

Draw lines of symmetry to make two congruent parts.

Answers will vary. Examples are given.

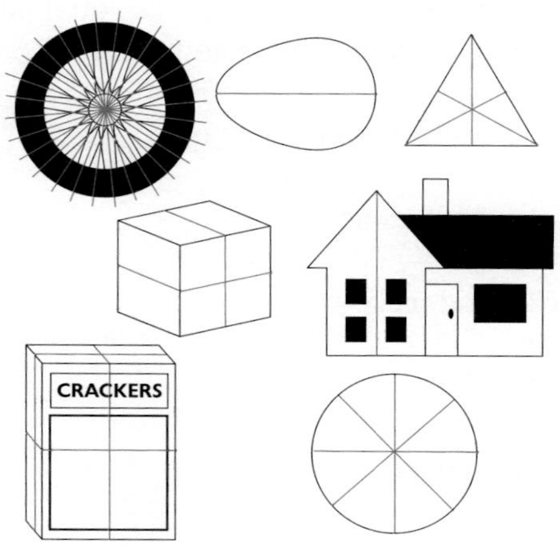

LESSON 83

Student Edition pages 181–182

More Congruency

LESSON PLANNER

Objectives

✓ to review and assess students' understanding of congruency

▶ to provide practice in solving addition and subtraction word problems involving two-digit numbers

Context of the Lesson This lesson continues the topic of congruency that was introduced in Lesson 80, and contains Mastery Checkpoint 11 for this skill.

Materials

congruent articles
ice cube molds (optional)
index cards
play money
rulers
tracing paper
water (optional)

Program Resources

Practice Master 83
Enrichment Master 83
Assessment Master
For extra practice:
CD-ROM* Lesson 83

1 Warm-Up

5 MINUTES

Problem of the Day Write the following problem on the chalkboard: Kenya studied spelling for 15 minutes every night from Monday through Thursday. What is the total amount of time that she studied? (60 minutes or an hour)

MENTAL MATH Have students say whether the first expression is "greater than," "less than," or "equal to" the second expression:

a. 8 + 7 ___ 5 + 6 (greater than)

b. 12 – 4 ___ 5 + 3 (equal to)

c. 30 + 70 ___ 20 + 90 (less than)

d. 15 – 9 ___ 5 + 7 (less than)

e. 14 – 7 ___ 12 – 5 (equal to)

2 Teach

Demonstrate Hold a class discussion and demonstration about real-world objects that are congruent. Show students objects or pictures of congruent objects, such as identical keys, sheets of paper, rulers, pencils, and pens. Remind

LESSON 83

Name ______________________

More Congruency

Which one is not the same shape and same size as the others?

1

2
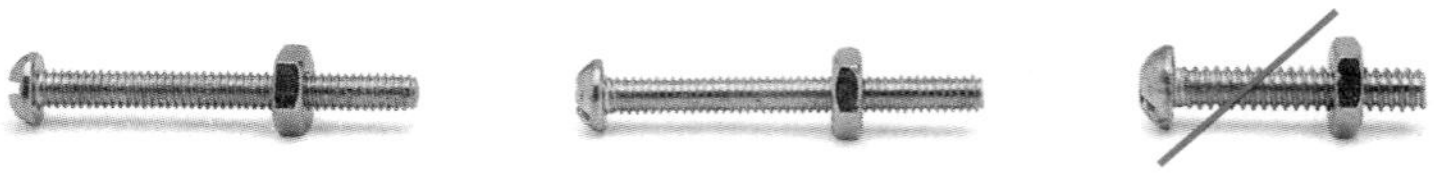

3

4

5

6
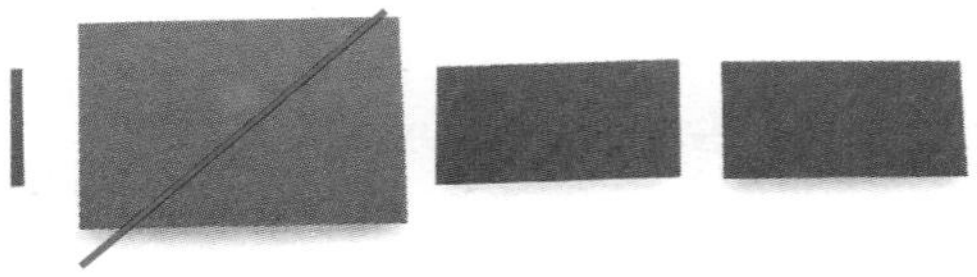

NOTE TO HOME
Students practice recognizing congruent (same shape and same size) objects.

RETEACHING

Have students write "congruent" on one index card and "not congruent" on another. Use play money to reteach congruent shapes by having students hold up the appropriate card as you hold up the following pairs of coins and bills:

$5 bill and $10 bill (congruent)

quarter and dime (not congruent)

nickel and nickel (congruent)

$1 and $20 (congruent)

penny and $1 (not congruent)

PRACTICE p. 83

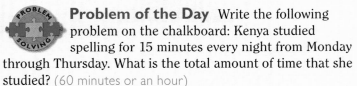

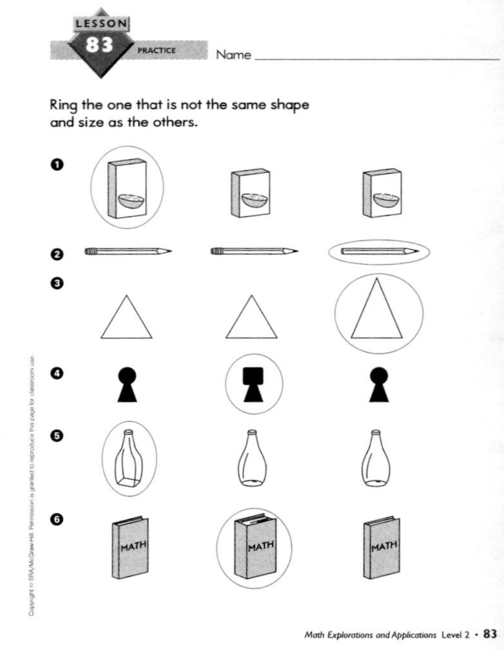
LESSON 83 PRACTICE Name ______

Ring the one that is not the same shape and size as the others.

1

2

3

4

5

6

Math Explorations and Applications Level 2 • 83

*available separately

◆ LESSON 83 Addition and Substraction Checkup

Solve these problems.

7 Jason had 75¢. If he spends 29¢, how much money will he have? 46 ¢

8 Leroy read 18 pages this morning. He read 27 pages this afternoon. How many pages did he read today? 45

9 Sumi has read 45 pages. Her book has 63 pages. How many more pages will she read to finish it? 18

Tell how you know whether you should add or subtract.

NOTE TO HOME
Students review solving two-digit addition and subtraction word problems.

ENRICHMENT p. 83

LESSON 83 ENRICHMENT Name ____________

Ring the things that are the same size and shape.

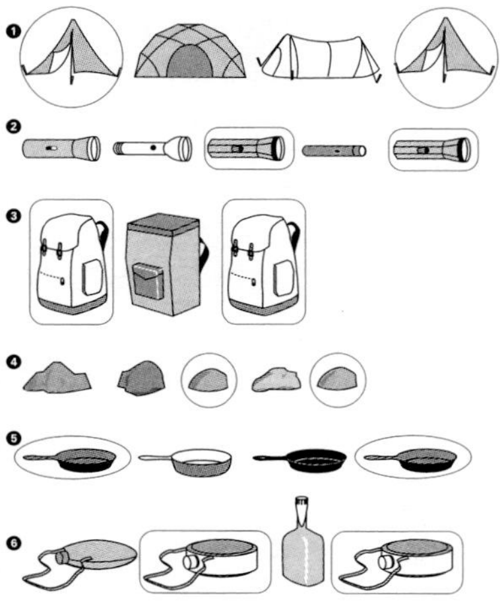

Math Explorations and Applications Level 2 • 83

ASSESSMENT p. 30

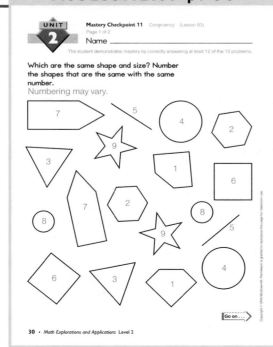

UNIT 2 **Mastery Checkpoint 11** Congruency (Lesson 83)
Page 1 of 2
Name ____________
The student demonstrates mastery by correctly answering at least 12 of the 15 problems.

Which are the same shape and size? Number the shapes that are the same with the same number.
Numbering may vary.

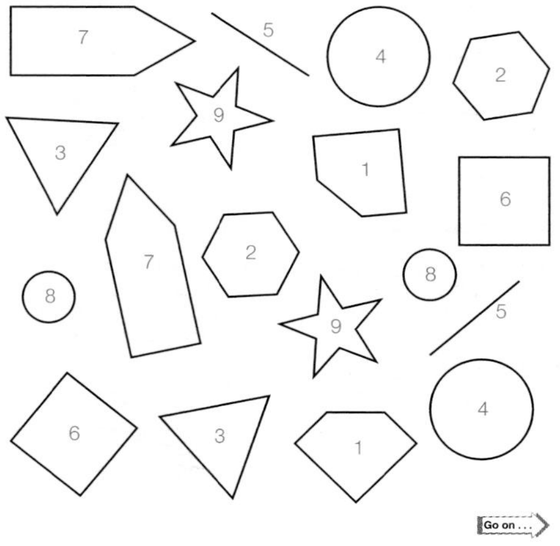

30 • *Math Explorations and Applications* Level 2

students that objects must have the identical shape and size to be congruent. Include objects that are similar in shape and size but not identical to help students distinguish between objects that are and are not congruent. For example, show them two keys that are not made for the same lock and two keys that are. Discuss why one pair is congruent and the other is not.

Using the Student Pages Have students work independently to complete pages 181–182.

3 Wrap-Up (5 MINUTES)

In Closing Have students use their rulers to draw two congruent shapes.

Mastery Checkpoint 11

Use students' answers to pages 181 and 182 and the questions asked during the demonstration to assess their ability to distinguish congruent objects from noncongruent objects and their understanding of how to check for congruency by tracing or placing one object on top of another. You might also wish to use Assessment Masters 31 and 32. Results of this assessment can be recorded on the Mastery Checkpoint Chart.

Assessment Criteria

Did the student . . .

✓ accurately identify examples of congruent objects during the demonstration and discussion?

✓ correctly identify at least five of the six shapes that were not congruent on page 181?

✓ correctly solve the problems on page 182?

Social Studies Connection Take students on a class trip to a local factory, such as a plastic molding, bottle-making, printing, or clothing manufacturer. Focus on the idea that items made in mass production from the same mold are all congruent.

Science Connection Have students make congruent ice cubes. Students need to understand that not only will the molds for the ice cubes have to be identical, but the amount of water they put in each must also be equal.

LESSON 84

Student Edition pages 183–184

Patterns

LESSON PLANNER

Objectives

- ▶ to provide practice with identifying and completing patterns
- ▶ to provide practice with identifying inputs, outputs, and rules in function machines

Context of the Lesson This is the first lesson introducing number patterns.

Materials	**Program Resources**
pattern blocks* (optional)	Practice Master 84
	Enrichment Master 84
	For extra practice: CD-ROM* Lesson 84

1 Warm-Up

5 MINUTES

Problem of the Day Write this sequence on the chalkboard and have students complete the pattern:

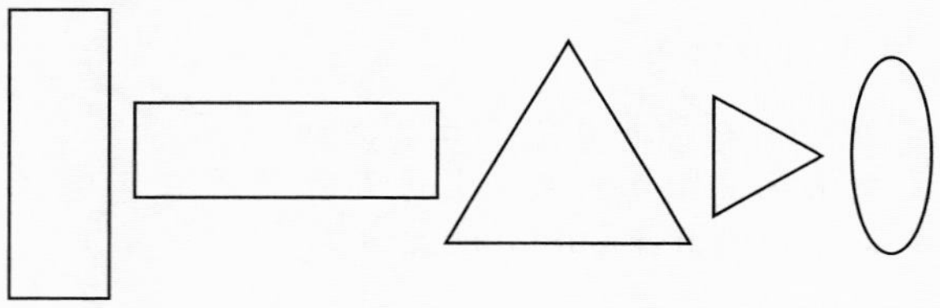

(Answer: oval, lengthwise)

MENTAL MATH Have students write relation signs (<, >, or =) for the following problems:

a. 12 – 6 _____ 7 (<)

b. 13 – 4 _____ 9 (=)

c. 3 + 7 _____ 9 (>)

d. 7 + 9 _____ 8 + 8 (=)

e. 15 – 7 _____ 12 – 5 (>)

LESSON 84

Name ____________________

Patterns

Find a pattern. Fill in the blanks.

1. 1, 3, 5, 4, 6, 8, 7, 9, **11**, **10**, **12**, **14**, **13**, 15
2. 3, 6, 9, 7, 10, 13, 11, **14**, **17**, **15**, **18**, 21
3. 2, 4, 6, 5, 7, 9, 8, 10, **12**, **11**, **13**, **15**, **14**, 16
4. 20, 17, 14, 16, 13, 10, 12, **9**, **6**, **8**, **5**, 2
5. 30, 27, 24, 21, 18, 15, **12**, **9**, **6**, **3**, 0
6. 100, 95, 90, 85, **80**, **75**, **70**, **65**, **60**, **55**, 50
7. 7, 14, 21, 28, **35**, **42**, **49**, **56**, **63**, 70
8. 70, 63, 56, 49, **42**, **35**, **28**, **21**, **14**, **7**, 0

NOTE TO HOME
Students identify and complete patterns.

RETEACHING

If students are having difficulty understanding number patterns, start with shape patterns or very simple number patterns for them to identify. Be sure to discuss and show each pattern before students attempt to tell what comes next.

LEARNING STYLES

Meeting Individual Needs

Have kinesthetic learners work in groups using pattern blocks. Make a pattern for each group using the blocks. Have students work together to figure out the pattern and then continue it. Then have each group make their own pattern and challenge other groups to identify and continue it.

*available separately

◆ **LESSON 84** Patterns

ALGEBRA READINESS

Fill in the blanks.

9
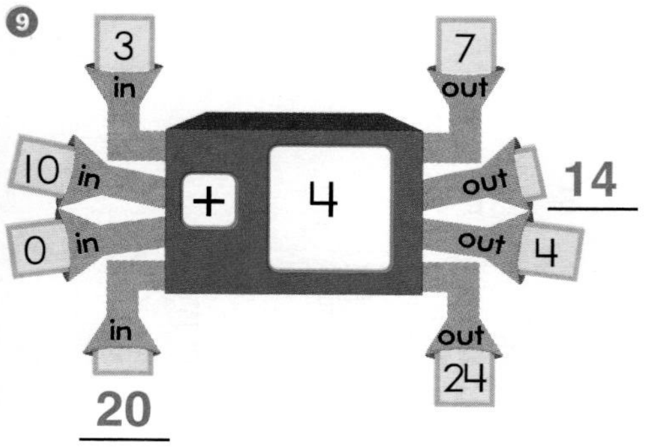

10
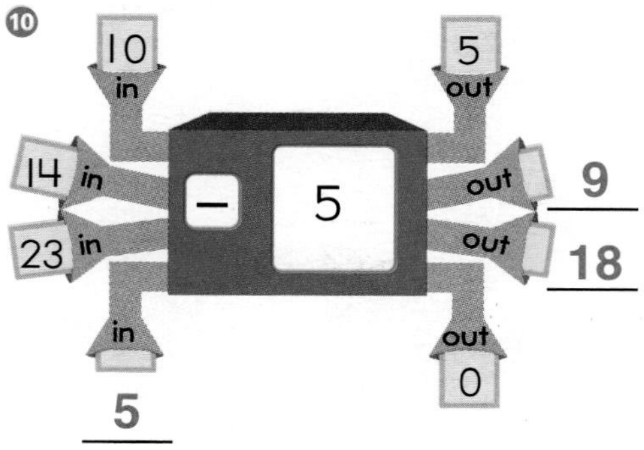

What is the rule? Write it in the box.

11
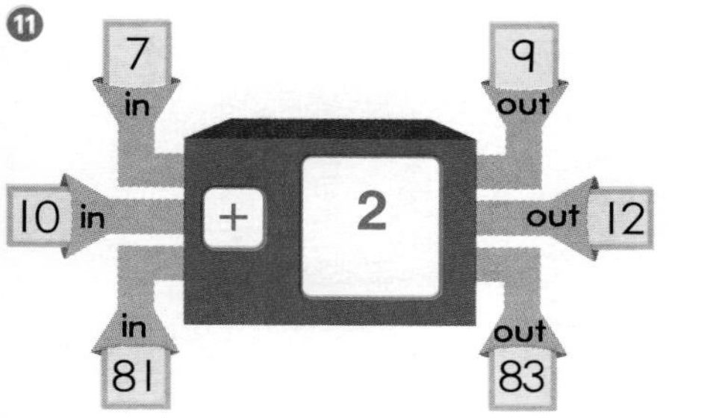

12
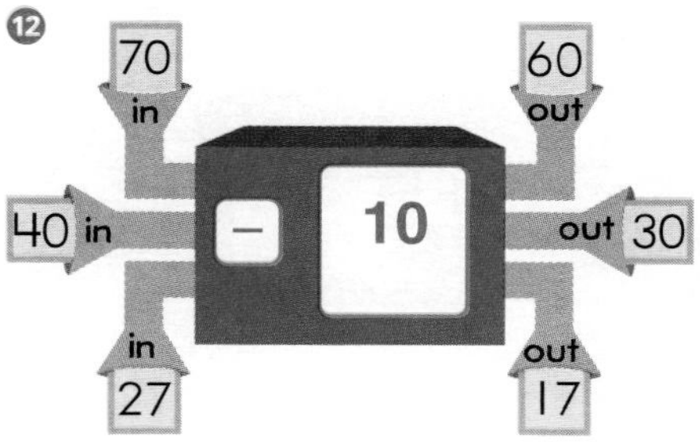

NOTE TO HOME
Students solve problems involving functions.

❷ Teach

Demonstrate Write the following number pattern on the chalkboard: 1, 2, 4, 5, 7, 8, 10, 11, 13, ____, ____, ____, ____, ____, 22 (14, 16, 17, 19, 20). Discuss how to find the pattern in this series of numbers. Write students' suggestions beneath each number. Students should see that the pattern looks like this:

1 2 4 5 7 8 10 11 13

+ 1 + 2 + 1 + 2 + 1 + 2 + 1 + 2

Have students complete the pattern. Point out that because the last number is given they can check to see whether they are correct. You might want to review function machines before assigning pages 183–184.

Using the Student Pages Work through the first pattern on page 183 with the class just as you did in the demonstration. Students should notice that the pattern is + 2 + 2 − 1.

Work the first problem on page 184 with the class before assigning both pages for students to complete on their own. When finished, have students correct their own pages as you explain the correct answers. Encourage students to tell why each answer is correct.

❸ Wrap-Up

5 MINUTES

In Closing Have students make up their own number patterns, then exchange and solve a classmate's by identifying the next three numbers in the pattern.

ALTERNATIVE ASSESSMENT

Performance Assessment Use students' patterns to assess their understanding of patterning.

Assessment Criteria

Did the student . . .

✓ correctly complete six of eight number patterns on page 183?

✓ correctly complete three of four fraction problems on page 184?

PRACTICE p. 84

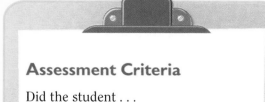

LESSON 84 PRACTICE Name ____________________

Find a pattern. Fill in the blanks.

❶ 6, 12, 18, 24, 30, 36, 42, 48, 54
❷ 65, 60, 55, 50, 45, 40, 35, 30, 25
❸ 13, 14, 16, 17, 18, 20, 21, 22, 23, 25, 26, 27
❹ 40, 38, 36, 35, 33, 31, 30, 28, 26, 25, 23
❺ 4, 8, 12, 16, 20, 24, 28, 32, 36
❻ 90, 81, 72, 63, 54, 45, 36, 27, 18

Fill in the blanks.

❼ In → +6 → Out

In	Out
4	10
8	14
20	26
9	15
23	29

❽ In → −2 → Out

In	Out
12	10
28	26
7	5
18	16
32	30

❾ In → +8 → Out

In	Out
7	15
2	10
12	20
30	38
3	11

84 • *Math Explorations and Applications* Level 2

ENRICHMENT p. 84

LESSON 84 ENRICHMENT Name ____________________

Write the names of five friends in the boxes at the top of the chart. Have your friends tell you their favorite color, favorite food, favorite place, favorite game, and favorite day. Write those favorites in the right boxes under your friends' names.

Answers will vary, but should accurately reflect the answers recorded on the chart.

Then answer the questions below.

❶ Do any friends like the same color? ____________
❷ Do any friends like the same game? ____________
❸ What else can you see from the things you added to the chart? ____________

Friends

Favorite Day					
Favorite Game					
Favorite Place					
Favorite Food					
Favorite Color					

84 • *Math Explorations and Applications* Level 2

LESSON 85

Student Edition pages 185–186

Function Tables

LESSON PLANNER

Objective

▶ to practice identifying inputs, outputs, and rules in function machines

Context of the Lesson This is the second lesson introducing number patterns in function machines. Here students use calculators.

Materials	Program Resources
calculators	Number Cubes
	Practice Master 85
	Enrichment Master 85
	For extra practice: CD-ROM* Lesson 85

1 Warm-Up 5 MINUTES

Problem of the Day Write the following number pattern on the chalkboard. Have students copy it, fill in the missing numbers, and then describe the pattern: 70, 69, 67, 66, 64, ____, 61, 60, ____, 57 (63, 58; Pattern: −1; −2; −1; −2)

MENTAL MATH Complete the table using mental math.

Rule: −2	
In	**Out**
a. 12	(10)
b. 7	(5)
c. 4	(2)
d. 2	(0)
e. 9	(7)

LESSON 85

Name ________________________

Function Tables

ALGEBRA READINESS

Fill in the missing numbers.

1
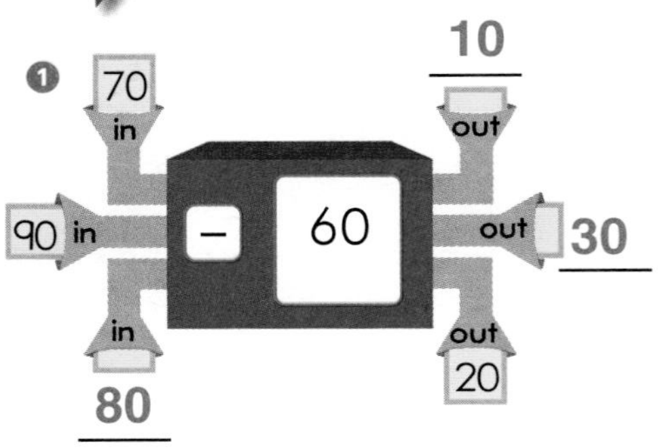

2
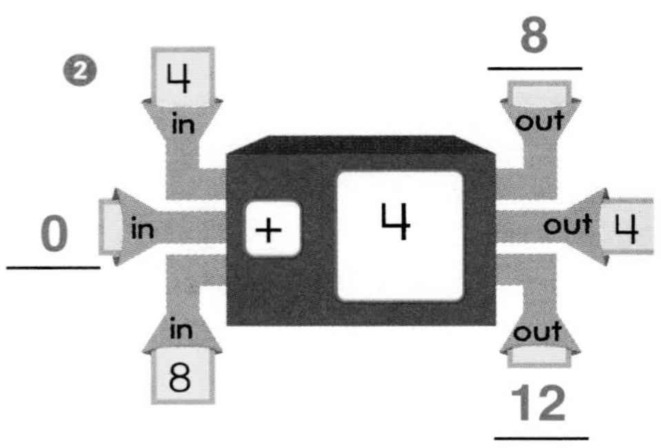

3
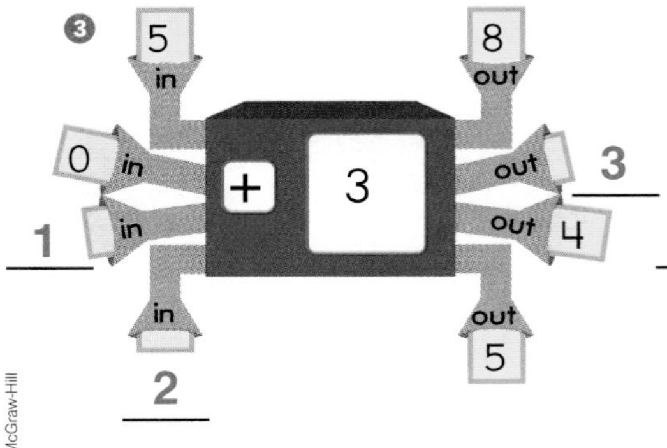

4
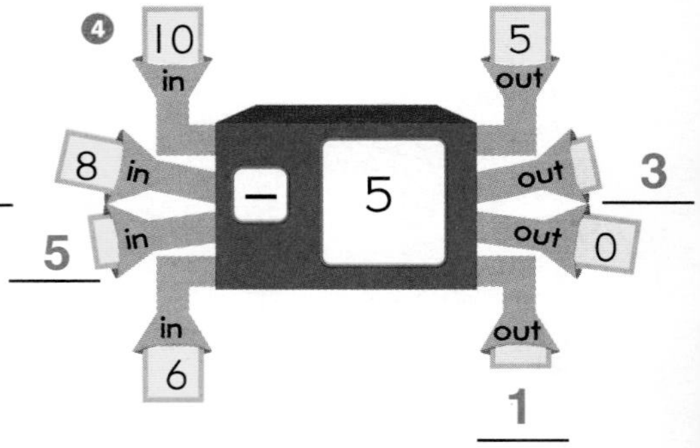

NOTE TO HOME
Students solve problems involving functions.

RETEACHING

Review slowly how to use a calculator to find input and output numbers. Have students always predict the display before pressing the = sign. Then have students who are still having difficulty play the "Function Rule" game with those who understand the concept.

LEARNING STYLES

Meeting Individual Needs

Have kinesthetic learners use base-10 materials to model the numbers in the function tables as they complete the student pages in this lesson. For example, in the first table on page 186 students can model five by showing five craft sticks, and then counting one more stick at a time to see how many they need to make eight. They can repeat this process to complete the rest of the table.

*available separately

◆ LESSON 85 Function Tables

Use the Mixed Practice on page 383 after this lesson.

Figure out the rule. Write it in the space.

5
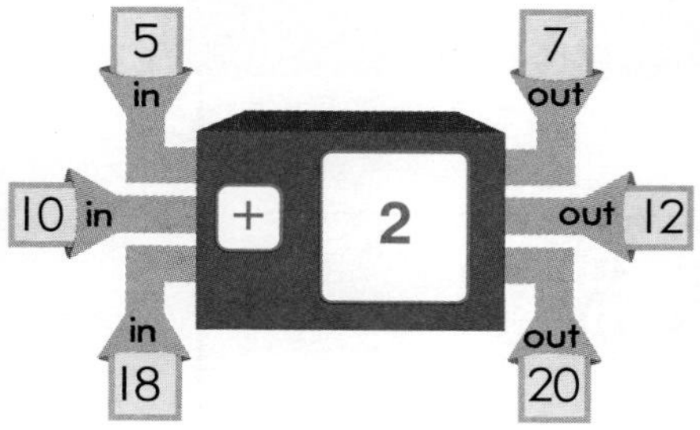

6
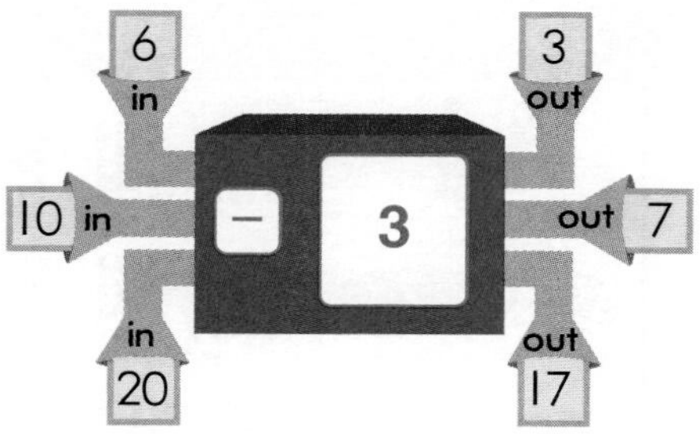

7
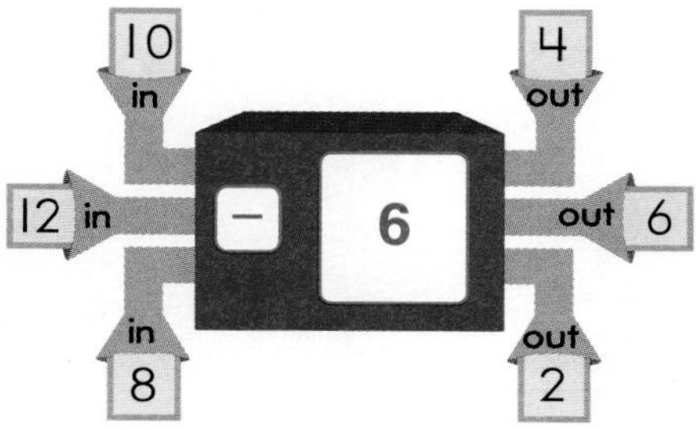

8
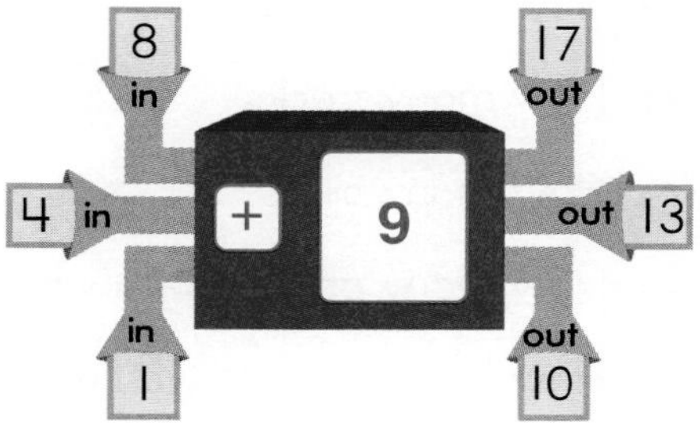

Play the "Function Rule" game.

NOTE TO HOME
Students figure out the function rules.

PRACTICE p. 85

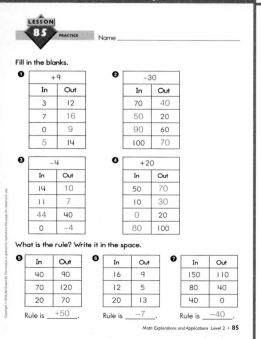

LESSON 85 PRACTICE Name ____________

Fill in the blanks.

1 +9

In	Out
3	12
7	16
0	9
5	14

2 −30

In	Out
70	40
50	20
90	60
100	70

3 −4

In	Out
14	10
11	7
44	40
0	−4

4 +20

In	Out
50	70
10	30
0	20
80	100

What is the rule? Write it in the space.

5

In	Out
40	90
70	120
20	70

Rule is +50.

6

In	Out
16	9
12	5
20	13

Rule is −7.

7

In	Out
150	110
80	40
40	0

Rule is −40.

Math Explorations and Applications Level 2 • 85

ENRICHMENT p. 85

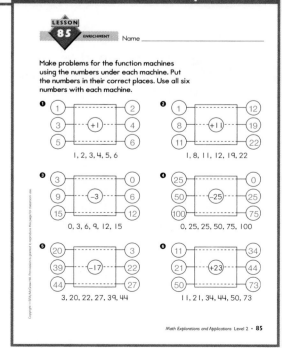

LESSON 85 ENRICHMENT Name ____________

Make problems for the function machines using the numbers under each machine. Put the numbers in their correct places. Use all six numbers with each machine.

1
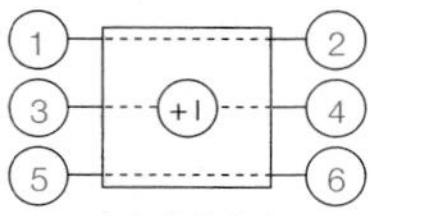

1, 2, 3, 4, 5, 6

2
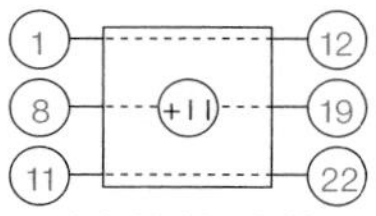

1, 8, 11, 12, 19, 22

3
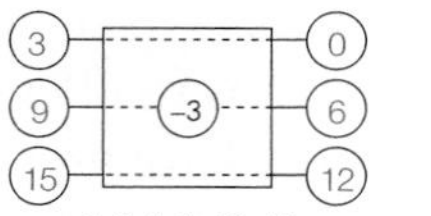

0, 3, 6, 9, 12, 15

4
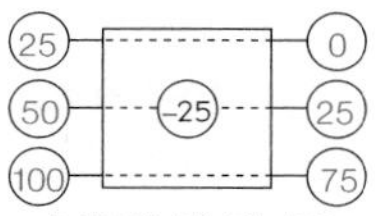

0, 25, 25, 50, 75, 100

5
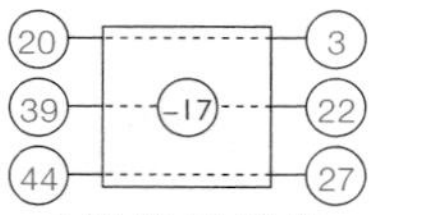

3, 20, 22, 27, 39, 44

6
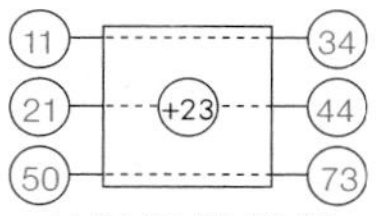

11, 21, 34, 44, 50, 73

Math Explorations and Applications Level 2 • 85

2 Teach

Demonstrate Show students how to use a calculator to apply function rules. Turn on the calculator, clear it, press [+5 =]. Next, press [9 =]. Show the display. (14). Have another student choose a number and press the number and [=]. Tell the class what the display says. Continue until students can figure out what the display will say before you press the [=] and what the function rule is.

Then write a function rule on the chalkboard, such as +8. Have students show with their Number Cubes what will "come out" when you put "in" various numbers. Give students numbers such as 2 (10) and 5 (13). Then using the same function rule have students use their Number Cubes to show what went in when you show the numbers that came out, such as 15 (7) and 12 (4).

Using the Student Pages Have students use their calculators to help them complete the function tables on page 185. For page 186 students write the rule, and then use their calculators to check their answers. Discuss students' strategies and answers when finished.

Introducing the "Function Rule" Game Demonstrate and then have partners play the "Function Rule" game. Without showing the calculator to Player 2, Player 1 sets up the calculator by pressing [on/c], an operation key [+] or [−]; a number, and [=]. Player 1 then presses another number, shows the calculator to player 2, and presses [=]. Player 2 presses another number and [=] and then tries to guess the rule. Players switch roles and repeat.

3 Wrap-Up

5 MINUTES

In Closing Have students make up their own function table by filling in the rule and first column. Have them exchange and complete each other's tables.

ALTERNATIVE ASSESSMENT

Informal Assessment Use students' answers to student pages 186–187 as an informal assessment of their ability to complete function tables.

Assessment Criterion

Did the student . . .

✓ correctly complete 8 of ten function tables on pages 185–186?

LESSON 86

Student Edition pages 187–188

Collecting Data

LESSON PLANNER

Objectives

- to introduce reading charts that use tally marks
- to introduce the use of tally marks to collect and record data

Context of the Lesson This lesson introduces tally marks.

Materials	Program Resources
none	Thinking Story Book, pages 72–75
	Reteaching Master
	Practice Master 86
	Enrichment Master 86
	For extra practice: CD-ROM* Lesson 86

1 Warm-Up

5 MINUTES

Problem of the Day Write this problem on the chalkboard: Fifteen people saw a movie. Three more people liked it than did not like it. How many people did not like it? (6)

MENTAL MATH Have students add or subtract the following problems using mental math.

a. 14 – 9 = (5)
b. 7 + 8 = (15)
c. 4 + 9 = (13)
d. 12 – 5 = (7)
e. 16 – 7 = (9)
f. 6 + 8 = (14)

LESSON 86

Name ______________________

Collecting Data

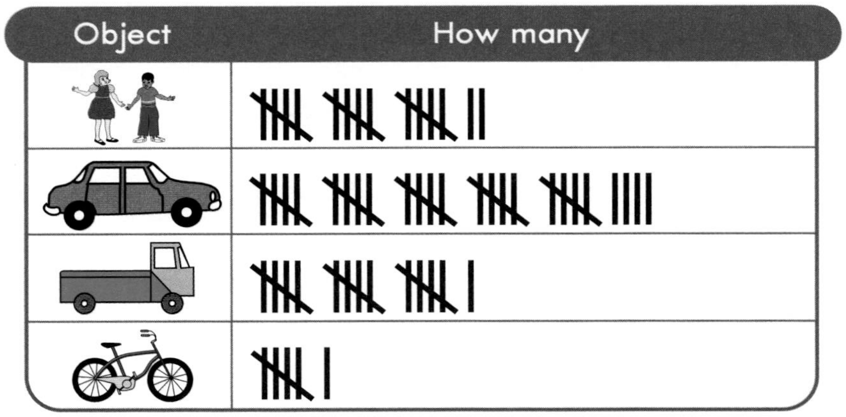
Object
How many

1. How many people? 17
2. How many cars? 29
3. How many trucks? 16
4. How many bikes? 6
5. How many objects with wheels? 51
6. How many objects with motors? 45
7. How many all together? 68

THINKING STORY

Talk about the Thinking Story "The Ten-Minute Wonder."

NOTE TO HOME
Students use tally marks to collect data.

Real-World Connection Have students collect data to find out which letter is used most often in their names. Divide students into small groups. Have them write out the first and last name of each student in the group. Students can then work together to create a chart to show how many times each letter is used in their names. When finished, have groups share data to find out which letter is used most often and which is used least.

RETEACHING p. 23

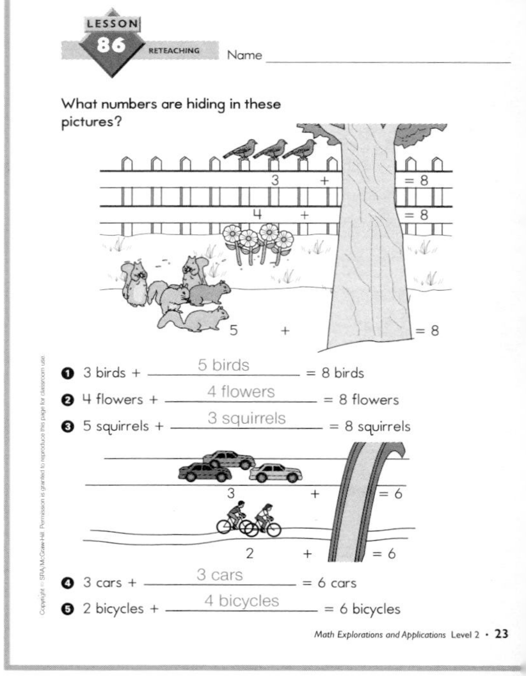
LESSON 86 RETEACHING
Name
What numbers are hiding in these pictures?
3 +
= 8
4 +
= 8
5 +
= 8
1. 3 birds + 5 birds = 8 birds
2. 4 flowers + 4 flowers = 8 flowers
3. 5 squirrels + 3 squirrels = 8 squirrels
3 +
= 6
2 +
= 6
4. 3 cars + 3 cars = 6 cars
5. 2 bicycles + 4 bicycles = 6 bicycles
Math Explorations and Applications Level 2 • 23

*available separately

◆ **LESSON 86** Collecting Data

COOPERATIVE LEARNING Work with friends. Collect data. Make up problems about your data.

Answers will vary depending on data collected.

Object	How many

NOTE TO HOME
Students collect and record data.

❷ Teach

Using the Student Pages Discuss the chart on page 187 with the class. Explain that the person who created this chart recorded what she saw pass the school in one hour. Guide students through questioning or explanation to understand that each tally mark stands for one object and that the fifth tally mark is always drawn across to make it easy to count by fives. Answer the first question with the class. Be sure students explain how they arrived at their answer. Then have them work independently to finish page 187.

COOPERATIVE LEARNING To complete page 188, have students work in small groups. Discuss the kind of data students will collect before assigning this page. For example, groups might count the number of pencils, books, desks, and chairs in one row. When they have finished collecting and recording the data, have them write questions similar to those on page 187 about their own data.

Using the Thinking Story Read aloud the story "The Ten-Minute Wonder" on Thinking Story Book pages 72–75. Stop and discuss the questions asked throughout the story.

❸ Wrap-Up

5 MINUTES

In Closing Have students answer the questions they made up about each other's data.

ALTERNATIVE ASSESSMENT **Portfolio Assessment** Have students save the charts they created on page 188 in their Math Portfolios.

PRACTICE p. 86

LESSON 86 PRACTICE Name ____________

Use the tally marks to answer the questions.

Objects	How Many
☆ (star)	𝍸 𝍸 𝍸 𝍸 II
(apple)	𝍸 𝍸 𝍸 III
(pizza)	𝍸 III
(pear)	𝍸 𝍸 I

❶ How many stars? 22

❷ How many apples? 18

❸ How many pizzas? 8

❹ How many pears? 11

❺ How many things that you can eat? 37

❻ How many fruits? 29

❼ How many objects all together? 59

ENRICHMENT p. 86

LESSON 86 ENRICHMENT Name ____________

Collect data about the lights in your home. Make a chart showing the number of lamps, ceiling lights, wall lights, and lights on (or in) appliances.

Type of Light	Number Found
lamps	
ceiling lights	
wall lights	
appliance lights	

Graph your results.

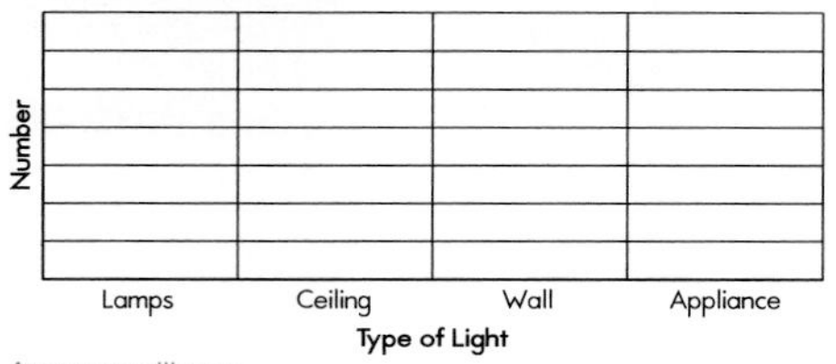

Answers will vary.

Assessment Criteria

Did the student . . .

- ✓ participate in the Thinking Story discussion?
- ✓ correctly answer five of the six remaining questions on page 187?
- ✓ work cooperatively and constructively in the group when collecting data for page 188?
- ✓ correctly record and interpret the data collected on page 188?

STORY 12

THINKING STORY

The Ten-Minute Wonder

It was an especially busy week at Mr. Breezy's dog training school. Errands kept piling up and piling up, and Trixie didn't know how she was going to get all of the work done.

"I want to repair some of the dog cages," said Mr. Breezy. "Here's my plan for getting everything done in a hurry. You need to get on the bus, go to the shopping center, get out of the bus, and buy 25 nails. Then get back on the bus and come back here. That should take about five minutes. Then I'll tell you about the next job."

Did Mr. Breezy give Trixie enough time to do the errand? no

About how much time would it take you to do the errand? Answers will vary; perhaps an hour.

Outside Trixie thought about the errand and the time that Mr. Breezy had said it would take. "It will take me more than an hour to go all the way downtown. But I can do the errand and still please Mr. Breezy."

What do you think Trixie will do? Answers will vary; she could go to a closer store.

"I only have to go around the corner to buy the nails," said Trixie. She ran to the hardware store around the corner and was back in Mr. Breezy's office, with 25 nails in hand, in five minutes. "What's next, Mr. Breezy?" she asked.

Mr. Breezy was delighted that Trixie had been so quick. "Wonderful," he said. "You're just in time to work with some of the dogs. Three of them need to practice sitting up. You need to take one dog to the training yard, give it practice sitting up, then bring it back. Next you get another dog, take it to the training yard, give it practice sitting up, then bring it back. Next you get the third dog, take it to the training yard, give it practice sitting up, and bring it back. I guess that will take you ten minutes."

Do you think Trixie could work with all three dogs, one at a time, in ten minutes? no

How long do you think it would really take to do all that? Answers will vary; perhaps 30 minutes.

Trixie started to get one of the dogs. "It will take longer than ten minutes to do all of this," she thought, looking at all three dogs, "but I know a quicker way."

What could Trixie do to finish the job faster? work with all three dogs at the same time

Trixie took all three dogs to the training yard. By working with the three dogs at the same time, she soon had them sitting up nicely in a row. Ten minutes later the dogs were back in Mr. Breezy's office, sitting up in front of his desk.

"You're right on time again," said Mr. Breezy, "and there's enough time for one more errand before lunch. It's ten minutes to 12 now. You should be finished by noon."

How much time is Mr. Breezy giving Trixie to do this errand? ten minutes

◆ STORY 12 The Ten-Minute Wonder

"Here are five posters showing the dog-training school. They should be pinned up on different floors in that building across the street." He gave the posters to Trixie, one at a time. "This one goes to the fourth floor. So you need to take it first. This one goes to the tenth floor. Take it next. This one goes to the fifth floor. This one goes to the eleventh floor. And the last one goes to the ninth floor."

"I guess you think that this job will take me ten minutes," said Trixie.

"Exactly," said Mr. Breezy. "If you keep this up, I'm going to call you the Ten-Minute Wonder."

"Fourth, tenth, fifth, eleventh, ninth," thought Trixie. "That's going to be a lot of running up and down if I do it that way."

Why will it be a lot of running up and down? because she'll be going to the floors out of order

As she started across the street, Trixie thought, "I'll never make it in ten minutes if I have to go to the fourth floor, then up to the tenth, then back down to the fifth, then way up to the eleventh, and then down to the ninth. There must be an easier way."

How could she make the job take less time? Go to each floor in order, starting at the top.

As Trixie stepped into the elevator of the building where she was supposed to pin up the posters, she had an idea. "I'll go to the highest floor first," she decided.

What floor is that? eleventh

Trixie quickly pinned up the poster on the eleventh floor and started running down the stairs to the ninth floor. But when she got to the tenth floor she remembered something.

What did she remember about the tenth floor? She needed to put up a poster there.

She remembered that a poster was supposed to go up on the tenth floor too, so she pinned one up there, then ran down to the ninth floor and pinned up a poster there. "Just two more posters to go and I still have five minutes," she thought.

Where do the last two posters go? fourth and fifth floors

Which floor should she go to next? fifth

It took Trixie only another minute to go down the stairs to the fifth floor.

"Still four minutes left to put up my last poster," she said. "I guess I'll relax and take the elevator."

How far will she have to ride on the elevator to get to the last place where a poster has to go? one floor down

. . . the end

LESSON 87

Student Edition pages 189–190

Measurement—Thermometers

LESSON PLANNER

Objectives

- ▶ to provide practice in counting by twos
- ▶ to demonstrate how to read thermometers with even-numbered degrees marked

Context of the Lesson This lesson introduces thermometers.

Materials	Program Resources
thermometers marked with even numbers (optional)	Number Cubes Thinking Story Book, pages 76–77 Practice Master 87 Enrichment Master 87 For extra practice: CD-ROM* Lesson 87

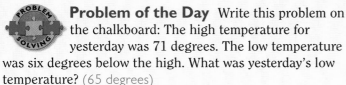

1 Warm-Up

5 MINUTES

Problem of the Day Write this problem on the chalkboard: The high temperature for yesterday was 71 degrees. The low temperature was six degrees below the high. What was yesterday's low temperature? (65 degrees)

MENTAL MATH Present the following addition problems orally. Have students use tally marks to add the numbers. Then have them show their totals with their Number Cubes.

a. 5 + 5 + 2 = (12)

b. 5 + 4 = (9)

c. 5 + 5 + 5 + 1 = (16)

d. 5 + 5 + 5 + 5 + 3 = (23)

e. 5 + 1 = (6)

LESSON 87

Name ______________________

Measurement—Thermometers

Count by twos. Fill in the blanks.

1. 50, 52, 54, 56, 58, 60
2. 0, 2, 4, 6, 8, 10
3. 70, 72, 74, 76, 78, 80
4. 20, 22, 24, 26, 28, 30
5. 100, 102, 104, 106, 108, 110
6. 30, 32, 34, 36, 38, 40
7. 90, 92, 94, 96, 98, 100
8. 10, 12, 14, 16, 18, 20
9. −10, −8, −6, −4, −2, 0
10. −40, −38, −36, −34, −32, −30

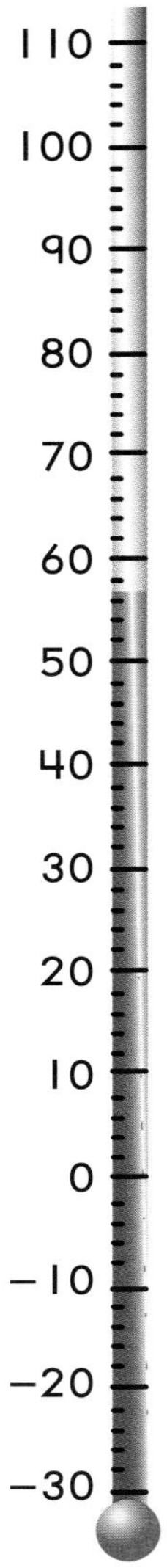

NOTE TO HOME
Students count by twos.

Science Connection Divide the class into groups. Have groups record the daily temperature at the same time each day for two weeks. Encourage groups to decide how they will collect and organize the data. At the end of the two weeks, have groups present their data to the class. Then discuss how the data is the same and how it is different. (The temperatures will be the same, but may differ in the way they are presented.)

RETEACHING

Draw a large thermometer on the chalkboard. Label the temperature markings from 0 through 60, with markings for only the even numbers. First mark off several temperatures and have students tell what temperature each mark stands for. Then have students mark off temperatures you tell them to show.

*available separately

◆ **LESSON 87** Measurement—Thermometers

Use the Mixed Practice on page 384 after this lesson.

Write the temperature.

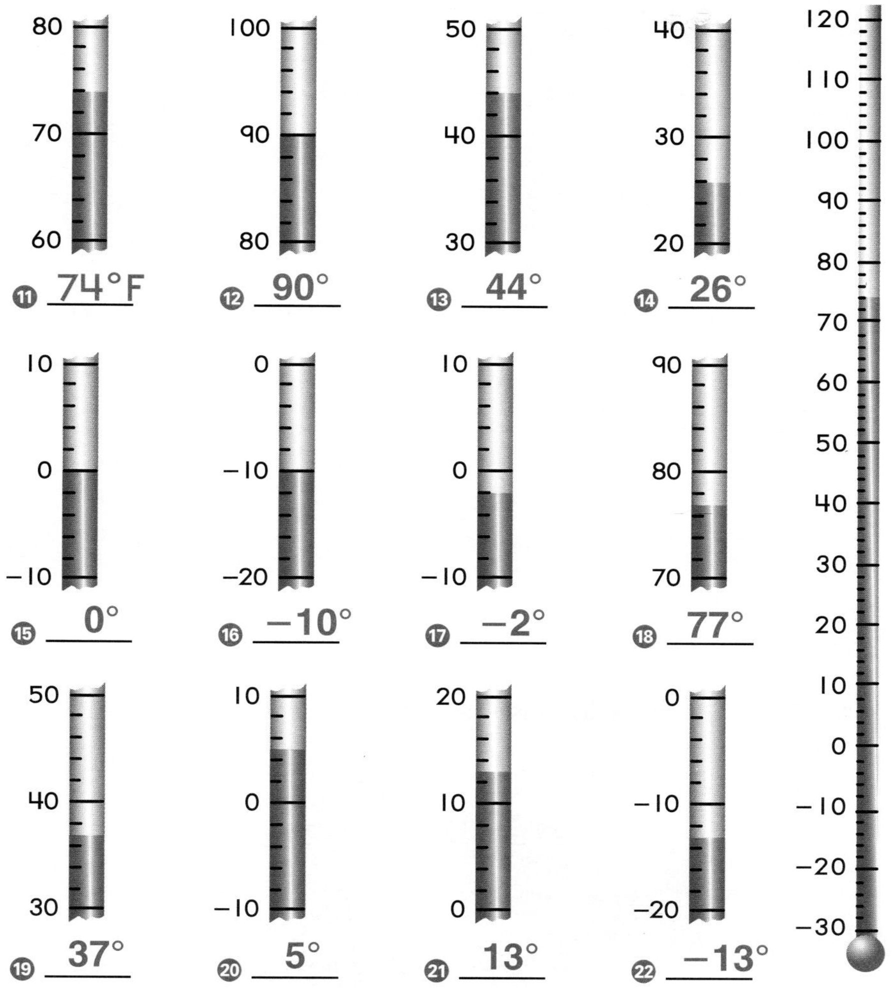

11. 74°F
12. 90°
13. 44°
14. 26°
15. 0°
16. −10°
17. −2°
18. 77°
19. 37°
20. 5°
21. 13°
22. −13°

NOTE TO HOME
Students read a thermometer and count by twos.

❷ Teach

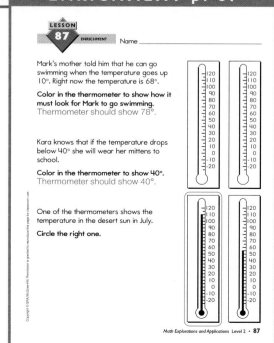

Demonstrate Have students count by twos, first starting at 2 (2, 4, 6, . . .) and then starting in different places such as 40, 42, 44 . . . and 62, 64, 66. . . .

Next, draw a number line on the chalkboard. Label it from −10 through +10. Have the students count on the number line by twos from negative ten to positive ten.

Using the Student Pages Have students look at the thermometer on page 189. Discuss the markings, pointing out that only even-numbered degrees are marked. Count the marks with the class by twos starting at 50 degrees. Point out that because the mercury stops between the mark for 56 and the mark for 58, the thermometer shows 57 degrees. Have students work with partners to complete pages 189 and 190. When they are finished with both pages, have them share and discuss their methods and answers.

If you have thermometers available in your room, let students practice reading them to find the temperature at various times of the day.

Using the Thinking Story Present one or two new problems from those following "The Ten-Minute Wonder" on Thinking Story Book pages 76–77.

❸ Wrap-Up

5 MINUTES

In Closing Ask students to tell what temperatures they think are cold, comfortable, and hot. Discuss their answers as you try to agree upon a general statement about temperature.

ALTERNATIVE ASSESSMENT

Informal Assessment Use students' answers to page 190 to informally assess their ability to read a thermometer.

Assessment Criteria

Did the student . . .

✓ correctly complete eight of the ten problems on page 189?

✓ correctly read ten of 12 thermometers shown on page 190?

PRACTICE p. 87

LESSON 87 PRACTICE Name ____________

Count by twos. Fill in the blanks.

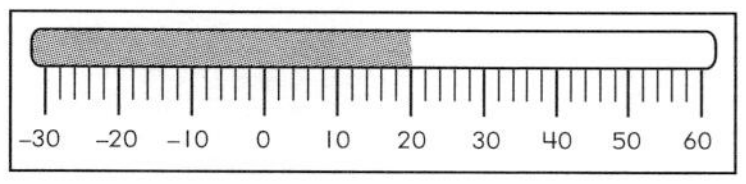

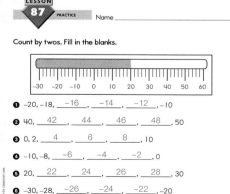

1. −20, −18, −16, −14, −12, −10
2. 40, 42, 44, 46, 48, 50
3. 0, 2, 4, 6, 8, 10
4. −10, −8, −6, −4, −2, 0
5. 20, 22, 24, 26, 28, 30
6. −30, −28, −26, −24, −22, −20
7. 50, 52, 54, 56, 58, 60

Write the temperature.

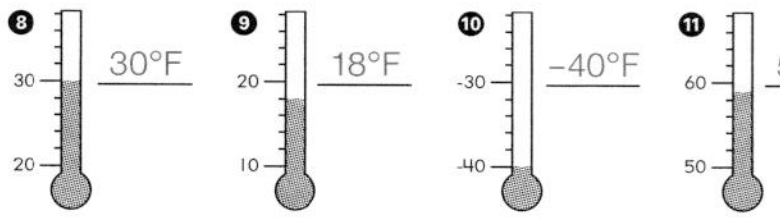

8. 30°F
9. 18°F
10. −40°F
11. 59°F

ENRICHMENT p. 87

LESSON 87 ENRICHMENT Name ____________

Mark's mother told him that he can go swimming when the temperature goes up 10°. Right now the temperature is 68°.

Color in the thermometer to show how it must look for Mark to go swimming.
Thermometer should show 78°.

Kara knows that if the temperature drops below 40° she will wear her mittens to school.

Color in the thermometer to show 40°.
Thermometer should show 40°.

One of the thermometers shows the temperature in the desert sun in July.

Circle the right one.

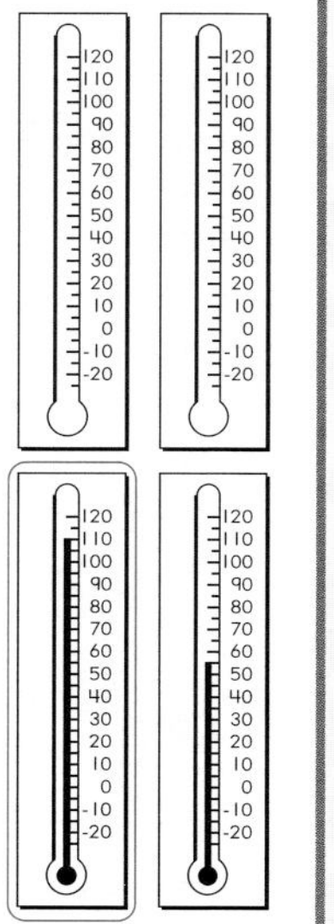

LESSON 88

Student Edition pages 191–194

Unit 2 Review

Using the Student Pages Use this Unit Review as a preliminary unit test to indicate areas in which each student is having difficulty or in which the entire class might need help. If students do well on the Unit Review, you might want to go directly to the next unit. If not, you may spend a day or so helping students overcome their individual difficulties before they take the Unit Test.

The lesson numbers next to each instruction line refer students to specific lessons for additional instruction if students need help. You may also use this information to make additional assignments to reinforce lesson skills and concepts.

Have students complete pages 191 through 194 on their own. Help students who have trouble reading the word problems, if necessary. Each student will need a centimeter ruler to do the problem at the the bottom of page 191.

Unit Project If you have not already assigned the weather information project on pages 200a and 200b, you might want to do so at this time. This project is a good opportunity for students to practice collecting, organizing, displaying, and interpreting visually represented information, develop appropriate methods of collecting information, demonstrate individual techniques for collecting, organizing, and displaying information, and represent information in a variety of forms.

LESSON 88

Name ______________________

Unit 2 Review

Lessons 50 to 55

Solve these problems. Watch the signs.

1. 34 + 27 = **61**	2. 34 − 27 = **7**	3. 83 − 45 = **38**	4. 29 + 36 = **65**
5. 64 + 18 = **82**	6. 33 + 56 = **89**	7. 56 − 33 = **23**	8. 75 − 47 = **28**
9. 12 − 8 = **4**	10. 8 + 12 = **20**	11. 30 + 27 = **57**	12. 6 + 78 = **84**

Lessons 39 and 40

13. How long is the fish? **10** cm

NOTE TO HOME
Students review unit skills and concepts.

◆ LESSON 88 Unit 2 Review

Lesson 70–72

What time is it?

⑭ 7:15

⑮ 6:00

Lesson 73–75

⑯ Color one third.

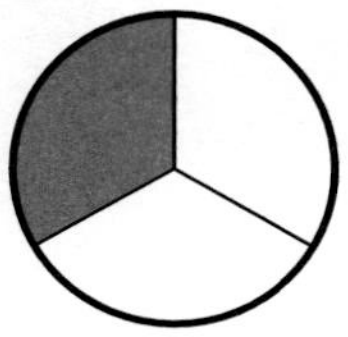

⑰ Color two fifths.

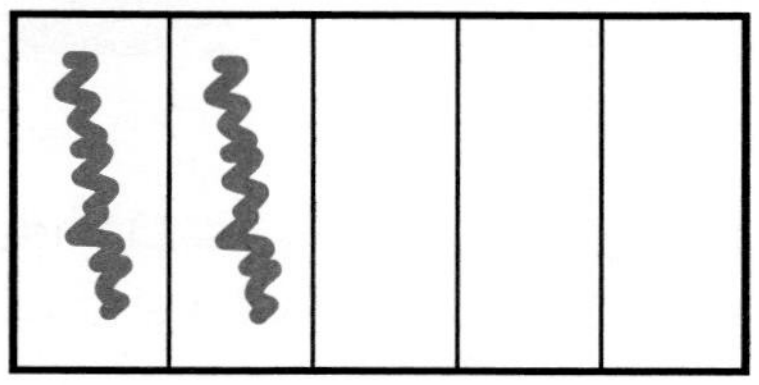

Answers are examples only.

Lesson 56

PROBLEM SOLVING

⑱ Pablo has two dimes. An apple costs 12¢. How much change will Pablo get if he buys an apple? 8 ¢

NOTE TO HOME
Students review unit skills and concepts.

PRACTICE p. 88

LESSON 88 PRACTICE Name

Solve. Watch the signs.

❶ 36 + 17 = 53	❷ 81 − 35 = 46	❸ 74 − 62 = 12	❹ 48 + 26 = 74
❺ 28 + 49 = 77	❻ 30 + 57 = 87	❼ 63 − 44 = 19	❽ 92 − 77 = 15
❾ 90 − 25 = 65	❿ 42 + 42 = 84	⓫ 75 − 57 = 18	⓬ 64 + 28 = 92
⓭ 38 + 43 = 81	⓮ 99 − 69 = 30	⓯ 21 + 49 = 70	⓰ 53 − 14 = 39

ENRICHMENT p. 88

LESSON 88 ENRICHMENT Name

Imagine that you are setting up a display in a toy store window. You will place each of six action figures on a base. The measurements of the figures and bases are shown below.

Use your adding and subtracting skills to answer the questions.

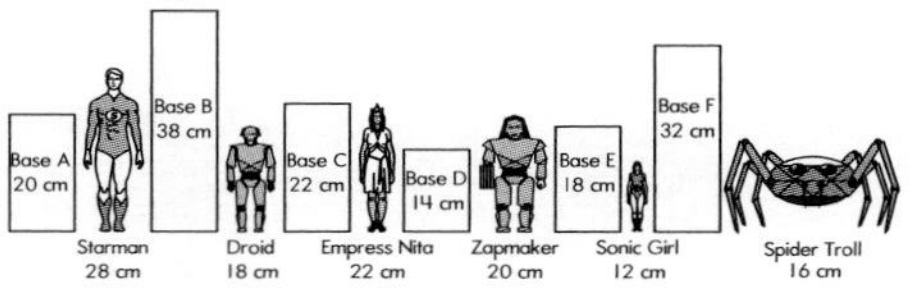

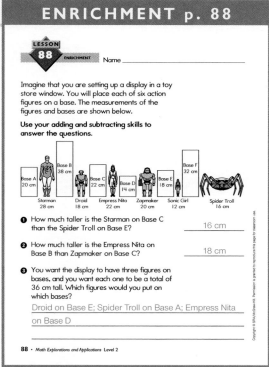

❶ How much taller is the Starman on Base C than the Spider Troll on Base E? 16 cm

❷ How much taller is the Empress Nita on Base B than Zapmaker on Base C? 18 cm

❸ You want the display to have three figures on bases, and you want each one to be a total of 36 cm tall. Which figures would you put on which bases?
Droid on Base E; Spider Troll on Base A; Empress Nita on Base D

◆ LESSON 88 Unit 2 Review

Name ______________________

Lesson 56

19 Jack has 37¢. Jill has 54¢.
Who has more? **Jill**
How much more? **17** ¢
How much do they have all together? **91** ¢

Lesson 63

20 Mrs. Davidson has $35.
Can she buy the jacket and slacks? **no**

21 Suppose she buys the jacket.
How much money will she have left? $ **17**

Lessons 19 and 20

Solve these problems.

22 [7] + 3 = 10

23 6 + [10] = 16

24 5 + [7] = 12

25 10 + [7] = 17

26 10 = [9] + 1

27 12 = [6] + 6

NOTE TO HOME
Students review unit skills and concepts.

◆ **LESSON 89 Unit 2 Test**

Answers are examples only.

7. Color one fifth.

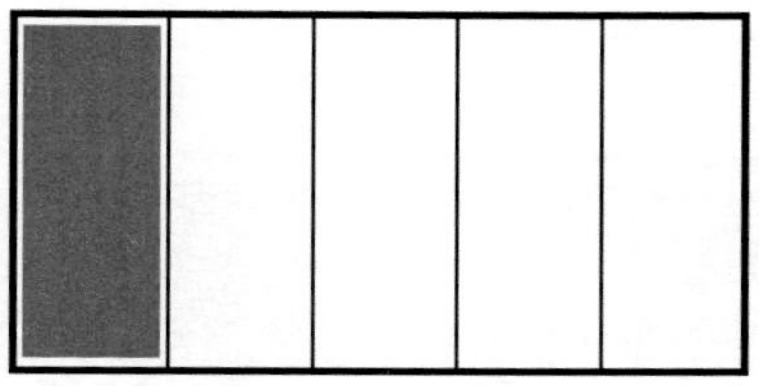

8. Color three fifths.

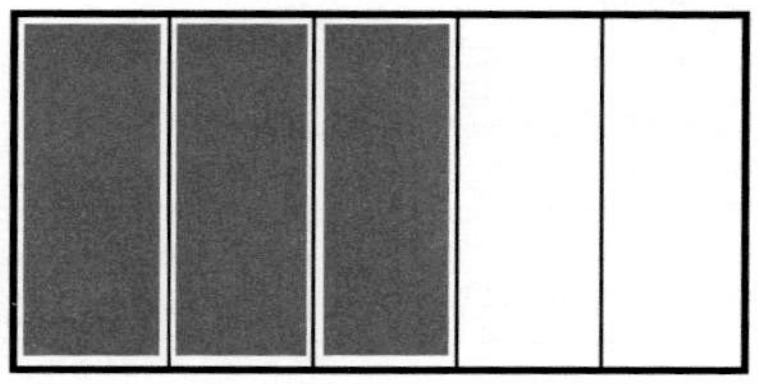

9. Color one quarter.

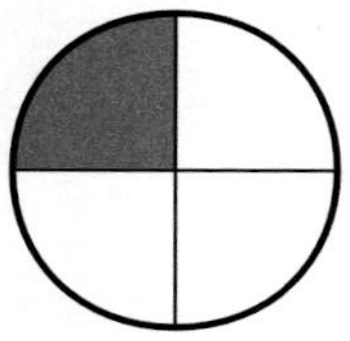

10. Color two thirds.

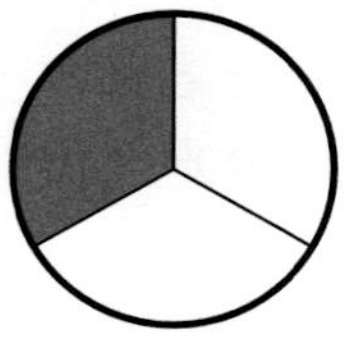

Solve these problems.

11. 4 + **6** = 10
12. **6** + 3 = 9
13. 8 + **8** = 16
14. **10** + 9 = 19
15. 75 − **32** = 43
16. 18 − **15** = 3
17. 26 − **14** = 12
18. 36 − **7** = 29
19. 47 − **26** = 21
20. 50 − **0** = 50

NOTE TO HOME
This test checks unit skills and concepts.

ENRICHMENT p. 89

LESSON 89 ENRICHMENT Name ____________

How big is a mouth? Write your friends' names. Use your centimeter ruler to measure their mouths. Write the sizes beside the names.

Name	Length of Mouth
Answers will vary.	________ centimeters
	________ centimeters
	________ centimeters
	________ centimeters

How big is a smile? Who has the biggest smile? Write your friends' names. Use your centimeter ruler to measure their smiles. Write the sizes beside the names.

Name	Length of Smile
Answers will vary.	________ centimeters
	________ centimeters
	________ centimeters
	________ centimeters

ASSESSMENT p. 32

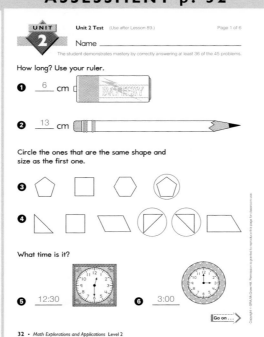

UNIT 2 **Unit 2 Test** (Use after Lesson 89.) Page 1 of 6

Name ____________

The student demonstrates mastery by correctly answering at least 36 of the 45 problems.

How long? Use your ruler.

1. 6 cm

2. 13 cm

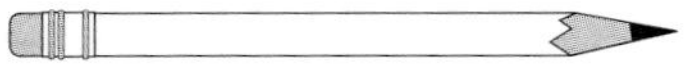

Circle the ones that are the same shape and size as the first one.

3.

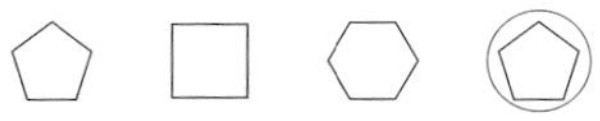

4.

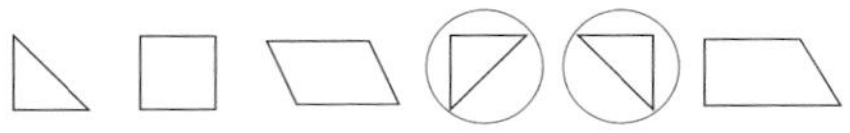

What time is it?

5. 12:30
6. 3:00

Go on . . .

◆ LESSON 89 Unit 2 Test

Solve these problems.

21. Marie has 71¢. Paul has 49¢.

    Who has more? Marie

    How much more? 22 ¢

22. How much for one bat and one ball?
    $ 9

23. How much for two bats and one ball?
    $ 16

24. How much for one glove and one ball?
    $ 17

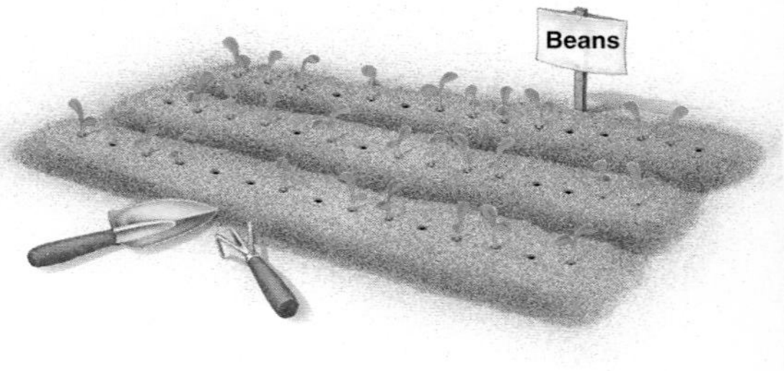

25. Fred planted 45 bean seeds. So far, 29 have sprouted.
    How many have not sprouted? 16

NOTE TO HOME
This test checks unit skills and concepts.

◆ LESSON 89 Unit 2 Test

Watch the signs.

26 $5 + 7 = 12$	27 $8 + 4 = 12$	28 $17 - 9 = 8$	29 $16 - 8 = 8$
30 $28 + 41 = 69$	31 $37 - 25 = 12$	32 $60 - 33 = 20$	33 $66 - 33 = 33$
34 $29 + 41 = 70$	35 $37 - 27 = 10$	36 $18 + 18 = 36$	37 $81 - 39 = 42$
38 $56 - 29 = 27$	39 $35 + 35 = 70$	40 $50 - 25 = 25$	41 $64 + 27 = 91$
42 $30 + 26 = 56$	43 $42 + 18 = 60$	44 $65 - 24 = 41$	45 $41 - 23 = 18$

NOTE TO HOME
This test checks unit skills and concepts.

LESSON 90

Student Edition pages 199–200

Extending the Unit

LESSON PLANNER

Objective

- to provide remediation instruction and enrichment activities

Context of the Lesson This is the second remediation and enrichment lesson in this book. The next will be at the end of Unit 3.

Materials	Program Resources
none	Practice Master 90
	Enrichment Master 90
	For extra practice: CD-ROM* Lesson 90

1 Warm-Up (5 MINUTES)

Problem of the Day Write the following problem on the chalkboard: How many different ways can you make 36 cents with seven or fewer coins ? What are they? (3 dimes, 1 nickel, 1 penny; 2 dimes, 3 nickels, 1 penny; 1 dime, 5 nickels, 1 penny; 3 ways)

MENTAL MATH Have students use mental math to subtract.

a. 60 – 50 = (10)
b. 120 – 80 = (40)
c. 70 – 50 = (20)
d. 140 – 90 = (50)
e. 120 – 60 = (60)

2 Teach

Using the Student Pages Students who need remediation can do activities, play games, and complete extra practice in skills diagnosed in Lesson 89. Enrichment activities for students who have finished remediation or do not need it are included on student pages 199–200. The cross-number puzzle on page 200 should serve as a fun challenge for students who do not need remediation.

LESSON 90

Name ______________________

Extending the Unit

GAME Play the "Roll a Problem" game.

Listen to the directions.

__ __ + __ __	__ __ + __ __	__ __ + __ __	__ __ + __ __
__ __ + __ __	__ __ + __ __	__ __ + __ __	__ __ + __ __
__ __ – __ __	__ __ – __ __	__ __ – __ __	__ __ – __ __
__ __ – __ __	__ __ – __ __	__ __ – __ __	__ __ – __ __

NOTE TO HOME
Students play a game to review skills in addition and subtraction.

COOPERATIVE LEARNING Allow students who do not need remediation to work with those who do to play games that were introduced previously in this unit.

RETEACHING

Give flash-card drills to review addition and subtraction facts and adding and subtracting multiples of ten.

*available separately

◆ LESSON 90 Extending the Unit

Solve the cross number puzzle.

[1] 1	7			[2] 4	1
0			[3] 1	6	
[4] 0	[5] 8		3		
	[6] 6	[7] 5		[8] 5	[9] 3
		7			2

Across

1. 9 + 8 = 17
2. 90 − 49 = 41
3. 9 + 7 = 16
4. 16 − 16 = 0
5. 52 − 44 = 8
6. 83 − 18 = 65
8. 89 − 36 = 53

Down

1. 50 + 50 = 100
2. 18 + 28 = 46
3. 62 − 49 = 13
5. 99 − 13 = 86
7. 23 + 34 = 57
9. 60 − 28 = 32

NOTE TO HOME
Students review addition and subtraction skills.

Why teach it at this time?

Multiplication facts from 0 x 0 through 10 x 10 were introduced in the second-grade program and extensively and methodically taught and practiced in third grade. This series of six lessons should review multiplication facts and show the relationships among sets of facts. Practice for multiplication facts is provided throughout the year.

Using the "Roll a Problem" Game Space for playing this game is provided on page 199. The game was introduced and first played in Lesson 26.

3 Wrap-Up 5 MINUTES

In Closing Have students explain any strategies they used in playing the "Roll a Problem" game.

ALTERNATIVE ASSESSMENT

Informal Assessment Use students' answers to the cross-number puzzle as an informal assessment of their addition and subtraction skills.

Assessment Criteria

Did the student . . .

✓ correctly solve the problems in the "Roll a Problem" game?

✓ correctly complete 80% of the cross-number puzzle on page 200?

UNIT 2

Student Edition pages 200a–200b

Wrap-Up

PRESENTING THE PROJECT

Project Objectives

- to provide practice in collecting, organizing, displaying, and interpreting visually represented information
- to develop appropriate methods of collecting information
- to demonstrate individual techniques for collecting, organizing, and displaying information
- to represent information in a variety of forms, using prepared charts or graph paper to compare the information being represented

Materials

chart paper
drawing paper
markers, crayons, paints
outdoor thermometer or daily newspaper
drawings of thermometers

Students will record weather information over two weeks and then present their information. Students may work individually or in groups; however, students will probably learn more if they work in groups.

Invite students to determine what they want to find out, what information they need, and how and where they will locate and record the information. You might begin with a list of questions that they can answer when they've completed their projects. For example: Which day was warmest? How much rain did we get? How many sunny days did we have? Which day was coolest? Do you see any patterns in the weather? Encourage students to add more questions to the list.

Encourage groups of students to figure out several ways to present the information they have collected, then to decide which they like best. They might choose a variety of graphs; they might draw pictures on a calendar; or they could present the information as a table or as journal entries. Students could use pictures of thermometers and mark each day's high and low temperatures on the thermometers.

Invite students to notice how people, animals, and events are influenced by the weather. In addition to charting weather conditions, they might also keep track of such things as animals they see, what people wear, events that are changed or canceled, or how they feel.

Challenge students to figure out how they might keep track of weather temperature if we did not have thermometers. How would they display that information?

Students might want to begin each day with a recap of the previous day's weather and a forecast for the day. Encourage them to keep track of predictions to see how accurate they are.

Wrapping Up the Project Display all of the information the students have collected and use it to answer the questions they listed at the beginning of the project.

What Is a Math Project? If this is the first time you have used math projects in your classroom, you might want to refer to pages 98a–98b in this Teacher's Guide for more detailed information about effectively implementing and assessing projects.

Assessing the Project Observe while the students collect, record, and graph weather information. Watch to see if they can record weather accurately and interpret the results.

Literature Connection You might want to read *The Cloud Book* by Tommy de Paolo to introduce types of clouds and how they are related to weather.

Technology Connection The software *Graph Power* from Ventura Educational Systems will provide practice for creating graphs and analyzing data.

PACING

PACING THE REST OF THE YEAR

Perhaps you have less than 45 minutes to devote to each lesson. Perhaps you have a slower-than-average class that needs extra time on various lessons. Or, perhaps you simply feel comfortable proceeding at a more leisurely pace. Whatever the reason, a few tips will help you trim the program with the fewest consequences.

Because each unit should take up about one fourth of the school year, you can use the units somewhat as mileposts. From time to time, after each unit or halfway though each unit, do a rough calculation to see whether your pace will allow you to finish the program. If it appears that you won't finish, check the suggestions given below; but don't speed up at the expense of students' understanding. If you are moving at an appropriate pace and yet won't finish the program, that is all right. The material in Unit 4 is reviewed in depth or retaught in Level 3.

MORE THAN 90 DAYS LEFT AFTER UNIT 2

If more than 90 days remain, you'll probably be able to finish the Level 2 program, so you won't need to significantly modify the lesson plans for the rest of the year.

80–90 DAYS LEFT AFTER UNIT 2

If, after you finish Unit 2, 80–90 days remain in the school year, go though the lesson list below and decide which lessons or portions of lessons to omit. The lessons listed may be omitted without creating undue difficulty for students when they enter the third grade. Any of these lessons may be omitted, but if you have to skip only a few lessons, try to choose lessons from later in the year rather than earlier. This will minimize disruption of the lesson continuity. Whenever possible, do the Mental Math exercises of the lessons you omit.

Unit 4

Lesson 151	Approximating Answers
Lesson 152	Counting by 100s and 1000s
Lesson 153	Adding Four-Digit Numbers
Lesson 154	Four-Digit Addition
Lesson 155	Four-Digit Subtraction
Lesson 156	Keeping Sharp
Lesson 157	Applying Addition and Subtraction

If you omit any material from a unit, be sure to modify the Unit Review and Unit Test to take into account the deleted material.

FEWER THAN 80 DAYS LEFT AFTER UNIT 2

If, after you finish Unit 2, fewer than 80 days remain in the school year, omit the items listed below.

Unit 4

Lesson 130	Days of the Week
Lesson 131	Telling Time
Lesson 148	Adding and Subtracting Money
Lesson 151	Approximating Answers
Lesson 152	Counting by 100s and 1000s
Lesson 153	Adding Four-Digit Numbers
Lesson 154	Four-Digit Addition
Lesson 155	Four-Digit Subtraction
Lesson 156	Keeping Sharp
Lesson 157	Applying Addition and Subtraction

Allow plenty of time for remediation outlined in Lesson 159. Depending on how much remediation you foresee, you'll spend from three days to two weeks on this. Be sure you go through the final review and diagnostic test early enough to leave as much time as you think you'll need for remediation.

IF YOU ADMINISTER STANDARDIZED TESTS

You might want to review the test that you will be administering to your students at this time. Note any topics that will be assessed that you have not covered in your mathematics curriculum. You might want to introduce a series of lessons earlier to accommodate your testing schedule.

UNIT 3

Measurement

APPLYING AND ESTIMATING

OVERVIEW

This unit begins with a review of symbols used to compare numbers and a review of adding three numbers. Students extend their ability to tell time to the minute and to tell the number of minutes before the hour. Students practice reading maps and comparing numbers in problem situations. Students informally explore triangles. They also explore sums and differences of odd and even numbers. Students learn about metric and customary units of weight and capacity and solve problems that involve measuring. The unit ends with a lesson on rounding to the tens place.

Integrated Topics in This Unit Include:

- comparing numbers
- adding three addends
- telling time to the nearest half hour, to the minute, and minutes before the hour
- adding columns of numbers
- finding perimeter
- reading maps
- exploring triangles
- identifying odd and even numbers
- investigating sums and differences of odd and even numbers
- measuring weight in metric units
- measuring weight in customary units
- measuring capacity in customary units
- measuring capacity in metric units
- using mental math to add and subtract
- rounding to the tens place

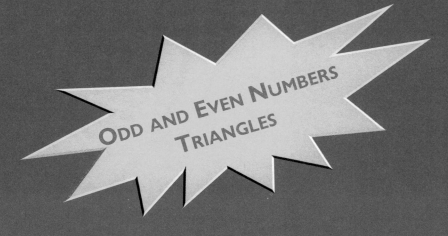

ODD AND EVEN NUMBERS
TRIANGLES

"Measurement is of central importance to the curriculum because of its power to help children see that mathematics is useful in everyday life and to help them develop many mathematical concepts and skills. Measuring is a natural context in which to introduce the need for learning about fractions and decimals, and it encourages children to be actively involved and discussing problems."

—NCTM Curriculum and Evaluation Standards for School Mathematics

GAMES

Motivating Mixed Practice

Games provide **basic math skills** practice in cooperative groups and develop **mathematical reasoning.**

Roll a Problem Game	Lesson 92	page 206
Harder Time Game	Lesson 94	page 210
Harder Time Game	Lesson 95	page 212
Roll a Problem Game	Lesson 97	page 218
Roll a Problem Game	Lesson 98	page 220
Map Game	Lesson 99	page 224
Map Game	Lesson 100	page 226
Odds-Evens Game	Lesson 102	page 230
Roll a Problem Game	Lesson 105	page 236
Measurement Game	Lesson 109	page 244

THINKING STORIES

Integrated Problem Solving

Thinking Stories provide opportunities for students to work in **cooperative groups** and develop **logical reasoning** while they integrate **reading skills** with mathematics.

Ferdie Borrows and Borrows and Borrows	Lesson 91	Thinking Story Book pages 79–83
I Owe You	Lesson 97	Thinking Story Book pages 84–89
Sharing with Cousin Trixie	Lesson 105	Thinking Story Book pages 90–95
More Sharing with Cousin Trixie	Lesson 111	Thinking Story Book pages 96–101

Story Summaries In "Ferdie Borrows and Borrows and Borrows," Ferdie learns that it is not feasible to borrow money in order to pay off debt. The story and story problems will increase students understanding of money.

In "I Owe You," students will gain practical understanding of financial matters as they calculate Mr. Muddle's debt and correct his mathematical errors.

In "Sharing with Cousin Trixie," Trixie, Ferdie, and Portia set out to divide a bottle of soda into three equal parts. As students work out the portions, they will use mathematical reasoning and estimation skills and will develop understanding of division and fractions.

In "More Sharing with Cousin Trixie," Trixie, Ferdie, and Portia have borrowed a bike for an hour and they want to divide that time equally. Students will use division and addition skills to enhance their understanding of time and will gain understanding of fractions.

PROJECT

Making Connections

The Unit Project makes real-world connections. Students work in **cooperative groups** to problem solve and to communicate their findings.

In the Unit Wrap-Up Project students evaluate the information found on kitchen product labels, such as capacity, and to determine why the information is written in so many different ways. Students will learn about units of volume and capacity, such as milliliters and fluid ounces. Students may begin this project any time after Lesson 98.

UNIT 3 MEASUREMENT LESSON PLANS

	LESSON	PACING	PRIMARY OBJECTIVES	FEATURE	RESOURCES	NCTM STANDARDS
91	Less Than, Greater Than **203–204**	1 day	to review and assess the use of <, >, and = to show how numbers are related	Thinking Story	Reteaching Master Practice Master 91 Enrichment Master 91 Assessment Master p. 39	2, 3, 6
92	Three Addends **205–206**	1 day	to demonstrate how basic addition facts are related to adding one-digit and two-digit numbers	Thinking Story, Game	Practice Master 92 Enrichment Master 92	7, 8
93	Telling Time—Nearest Half Hour **207–208**	1 day	to provide practice for telling time to the nearest quarter hour	Thinking Story	Practice Master 93 Enrichment Master 93	10
94	Telling Time—To the Minute **209–210**	1 day	to introduce telling time to the nearest minute	Thinking Story, Game	Practice Master 94 Enrichment Master 94	10
95	Telling Time—Before the Hour **211–212**	1 day	✓ to assess telling time to the nearest minute	Game	Practice Master 95 Enrichment Master 95 Assessment Master pp. 40–41	10
96	Keeping Sharp **213–216**	1 day	to review fractions as related to area as well as inequalities presented in this and previous units		Practice Master 96 Enrichment Master 96	
97	Column Addition. **217–218**	1 day	to review methods of adding columns of numbers	Thinking Story, Game	Practice Master 97 Enrichment Master 97	7, 8
98	Column Addition—Finding Perimeter **219–220**	1 day	✓ to provide practice for and assessment of column addition	Thinking Story, Game	Practice Master 98 Enrichment Master 98 Assessment Master pp. 42–43	8
	Mid-Unit Review **221–222**	1 day			Assessment Master pp. 44–46	
99	Reading Maps **223–224**	1 day	to introduce and provide practice for reading maps	Thinking Story, Game	Reteaching Master Practice Master 99 Enrichment Master 99	1, 2, 3, 4, 9, 10
100	Map Reading **225–226**	1 day	to continue providing experience in reading maps	Thinking Story, Game	Practice Master 100 Enrichment Master 100	1, 2, 3, 4, 9, 10
101	Exploring Triangles. **227–228**	1 day	to help students understand the property of triangles: the length of side 1 + side 2 > the length of side 3		Practice Master 101 Enrichment Master 101	1, 2, 3, 4, 9
102	Odd and Even Numbers. **229–230**	1 day	to present the concept of odd and even numbers	Game	Reteaching Master Practice Master 102 Enrichment Master 102	4, 6, 12
103	Odds and Evens. **231–232**	1 day	to provide practice for and assess students' understanding of identifying odd and even numbers by sight	Game	Practice Master 103 Enrichment Master 103 Assessment Master	4, 6, 8
104	Adding Odds and Evens **233–234**	1 day	to help students discover and use information about addition of odd and even numbers		Practice Master 104 Enrichment Master 104	3, 4, 8
105	Subtracting Odds and Evens **235–236**	1 day	to help students discover and use information about subtraction of odd and even numbers	Thinking Story	Reteaching Master Practice Master 105 Enrichment Master 105	3, 4, 8
106	Kilograms and Grams **237–238**	1 day	to provide experience in and assess understanding of measuring weight in metric units and in converting kilograms to grams	Thinking Story	Practice Master 106 Enrichment Master 106	10
107	Pounds and Ounces **239–240**	1 day	to help students develop an understanding of weight in pounds and ounces		Practice Master 107 Enrichment Master 107	10
108	Using Measurements **241–242**	1 day	to understand the relationship between grams and kilogram		Practice Master 108 Enrichment Master 108	1, 2, 3, 4, 10

LESSON		PACING	PRIMARY OBJECTIVES	FEATURE	RESOURCES	NCTM STANDARDS
109	**Measurement—Capacity** **243–244**	1 day	to introduce customary units of measure for capacity	**Game**	Reteaching Master Practice Master 109 Enrichment Master 109	10
110	**Metric Measurement** **245–246**	1 day	to introduce metric units of measurement for capacity		Practice Master 110 Enrichment Master 110	10
111	**Using Measurements** **247–248**	1 day	to give students more practice in solving realistic measurement problems		Practice Master 111 Enrichment Master 111	1, 2, 3, 4, 10
112	**Shortcuts** **249–250**	1 day	to introduce shortcuts to mental addition and subtraction		Practice Master 112 Enrichment Master 112	3, 4, 5, 7, 8
113	**Round to Ten**. **251–252**	1 day	to provide practice using rounding to estimate sums and differences		Practice Master 113 Enrichment Master 113	5
114	**Unit Review** **253–256**	1 day	to review measurement			
115	**Unit Test**. **257–260**	1 day	to practice measurement		Assessment Master pp. 48–50	
116	**Extending the Unit** **261–262**	1 day	to review measurement	**Project**		

UNIT CONNECTIONS

INTERVENTION STRATEGIES

In this Teacher's Guide there will be specific strategies suggested for students with individual needs—ESL, Gifted and Talented, Special Needs, Learning Styles, and At Risk. These strategies will be provided at the point of use. Here are the icons to look for and the types of strategies that will accompany them:

English as a Second Language

These strategies, designed for students who do not fluently speak the English language, will suggest meaningful ways to present the lesson concepts and vocabulary.

Gifted and Talented

Strategies to enrich and extend the lesson will offer further challenges to students who have easily mastered the concepts already presented.

Special Needs

Students who are physically challenged or who have learning disabilities might require alternative ways to complete activities, record answers, use manipulatives, and so on. The strategies labeled with this icon will offer helpful methods of presenting lesson concepts to these students.

Learning Styles

Each student has a unique learning style. The strategies labeled with this icon address a variety of learning modalities, such as tactile/kinesthetic, visual, and auditory.

At Risk

These strategies highlight the relevancy of math skills and concepts to the world outside the classroom. They are directed toward students that appear to be at risk of dropping out of school before graduation.

TECHNOLOGY CONNECTIONS

The following materials, designed to reinforce and extend lesson concepts, will be referred to throughout this Teacher's Guide. It might be helpful to order this software or check it out of the school media center or local community library.

Look for this **Technology Connection** *icon.*

- *Treasure MathStorm!,* from The Learning Company, Mac, IBM, for grades 2–4 (software)
- *Treasure Galaxy!,* from The Learning Company, Mac, IBM, for grades 1–3 (software)
- *Math Computation I,* from EPC, Mac, for grades 1–5 (software)
- *Pondering Problems,* from Microgram, Mac, IBM, for grades 2–5 (software)
- *Math Journey,* from The Learning Company, Mac, IBM, for grades 1–3 (software)
- *Trudy's Time and Place House,* from Edmark, Mac, IBM, for grades PreK–2 (software)
- *Discover Time,* from Gamco, Mac, for grades 1–5 (software)
- *Clock Shop,* from Nordic Software, Mac, IBM, for grades K–6 (software)

CROSS-CURRICULAR CONNECTIONS

This Teacher's Guide offers specific suggestions for connecting the math skills and concepts presented in the unit with other subject areas and with real-world situations. These strategies will be provided at the point of use.

Look for these icons:

- Geography
- Health
- Social Studies
- Music
- Science
- Math
- Art
- Physical Education
- Language Arts

LITERATURE CONNECTIONS

Relevant fiction and nonfiction books are suggested throughout the Teacher's Guide at the point where they could be used to introduce, reinforce, or extend specific lesson concepts. You might want to locate these books in your school or your local community library.

Look for this **Literature Connection** *icon.*

- *Animal Orchestra* by Scott Gustafson, Contemporary Books, 1988
- *Just Beyond Reach and Other Riddle Poems* by Bonnie Larkin Nims, Scholastic, 1992
- *Time* by Henry Pluckrose, Childrens Press, 1995
- *My First Book of Time* by Claire Llewellyn, Dorling Kindersley, 1992
- *The Cuckoo-Clock Cuckoo* by Annegert Fuchshuber, Carolrhoda Books, 1988
- *Pigs Will Be Pigs* by Amy Axelrod, Four Winds Press, 1994
- *As the Roadrunner Runs* by Gail Hartman, Bradbury Press, 1994
- *As the Crow Flies* by Gail Hartman, Bradbury Press, 1991
- *Number Families* by Jane Jonas Srivastava, Crowell, 1979
- *Rooster's Off to See the World* by Eric Carle, Picture Book Studio, 1972
- *Domino Addition* by Lynette Long, Charlesbridge Pub., 1996
- *Look Both Ways: City Math* pp. 6–12 "The Great Mail Mix Up," Time-Life for Children, 1992
- *What Would Mama Do?* by Judith Ross Enderlee and Stephanie Gordon Tessler, Boyds Mills Press, 1995
- *Capacity* by Henry Pluckrose, F. Watts, 1988

ASSESSMENT OPPORTUNITIES AT-A-GLANCE

LESSON	PORTFOLIO	PERFORMANCE	FORMAL	SELF	INFORMAL	MULTIPLE CHOICE FORMAT	MASTERY CHECKPOINTS	ANALYZING ANSWERS
91			✓				✓	✓
92					✓			
93					✓			
94		✓						
95			✓				✓	
96		✓						
97					✓			
98			✓				✓	
Mid-Unit Review			✓					
99		✓						
100					✓			
101	✓							
102		✓						
103			✓				✓	
104	✓							
105					✓			
106								
107					✓			
108					✓			
109					✓			
110					✓			
111					✓			
112					✓			
113				✓				
114								
Unit Review/ Unit Test			✓		✓			

ASSESSMENT OPTIONS

PORTFOLIO ASSESSMENT

Throughout this Teacher's Guide are suggested activities in which students draw pictures, make graphs, write about mathematics, and so on. Keep students' work to assess growth of understanding as the year progresses.

Lessons 101 and 104

PERFORMANCE ASSESSMENT

Performance assessment items focus on evaluating how students think and work as they solve problems. Opportunities for performance assessment can be found throughout the unit. Rubrics and guides for assessment are in the front of the Assessment Masters book.

Lessons 94, 99, and 102

FORMAL ASSESSMENT

A Mid-Unit Review and a Unit Test help assess students' understanding of concepts, skills, and problem solving. The *Math Explorations and Applications* CD-ROM Test Generator can create additional unit tests at three ability levels. Also, Mastery Checkpoints are provided periodically throughout the unit.

Lessons 91, 95, 98, 103, Mid-Unit Review, Unit Review, and Unit Test

SELF ASSESSMENT

Throughout the program, students evaluate their math skills through self-assessment activities.

Lesson 113

INFORMAL ASSESSMENT

A variety of assessment suggestions are provided, including interviews, oral questions or presentations, and debates. Also, each lesson includes Assessment Criteria—a list of questions about each student's progress, understanding, and participation.

Lessons 92, 93, 97, 100, 105, 107, 109, 110, and 112

MULTIPLE-CHOICE TESTS (STANDARDIZED FORMAT)

Each unit includes a Unit Test in multiple choice format, presenting students with an opportunity to practice taking a test in a standardized test format.

MASTERY CHECKPOINTS

Mastery Checkpoints are provided throughout the unit to assess student proficiency in specific skills. Checkpoints reference appropriate Assessment Masters and other assessment options. Results of these evaluations can be recorded on the Mastery Checkpoint Chart.

Lessons 91, 95, 98, and 103

ANALYZING ANSWERS

Analyzing Answers suggests possible sources of student error and offers teaching strategies for addressing difficulties.

Lesson 91

Look for these icons:

> ***"Grades based on demonstrated depth of mathematical knowledge communicate more about students' developing mathematical understanding than grades based on a student's relative position in the class or on percentage points."***
>
> *—NCTM Assessment Standards*

ASSESSING INDIVIDUAL PROGRESS

WHAT TO EXPECT FROM STUDENTS AS THEY COMPLETE THIS UNIT

INEQUALITIES AND EQUALITIES

By this time students should recognize equalities and inequalities. Use students' responses during the demonstration, their answers to pages 203 and 204, or Assessment Master page 39 to assess students' ability to use relation signs to describe equalities and inequalities.

TELLING TIME

At about this time most students should be able to tell time by using a clock with a conventional face. Use students' answers to pages 211–212 or Assessment Master pages 40 and 41 to assess students' ability to tell time.

COLUMN ADDITION

At about this time most students should be able to add columns of two-digit numbers. Use students' work on pages 219 and 220 or Assessment Master pages 42 and 43 to assess their understanding of column addition.

ODD OR EVEN NUMBERS

By the end of this lesson students should be able to identify odd and even numbers by sight. You can assess their performance during the demonstration or use Assessment Master page 47.

UNIT 3

PROGRAM RESOURCES

THESE ADDITIONAL COMPONENTS OF *MATH EXPLORATIONS AND APPLICATIONS* CAN BE PURCHASED SEPARATELY FROM SRA/MCGRAW-HILL.

LESSON	BASIC MANIPULATIVE KIT	GAME MAT PACKAGE	TEACHER KIT	OPTIONAL MANIPULATIVE KIT	OVERHEAD MANIPULATIVE KIT	*MATH EXPLORATIONS AND APPLICATIONS* CD-ROM	LITERATURE LIBRARY
91						Lesson 91	How Do You Measure Up?
92	Number Cubes			base-10 blocks		Lesson 92	
93	Number Cubes			clock face		Lesson 93	
94		Harder Time Game	clock	clock face		Lesson 94	
95	Number Cubes	Harder Time Game	clock			Lesson 95	
96	Number Cubes					Lesson 96	
97	Number Cubes					Lesson 97	
98	Number Cubes					Lesson 98	
99	Number Cubes					Lesson 99	
100						Lesson 100	
101	Number Cubes					Lesson 101	
102				base-10 blocks		Lesson 102	
103	Number Cubes			base-10 blocks		Lesson 103	
104				counters		Lesson 104	
105						Lesson 105	
106			scale			Lesson 106	
107	Number Cubes					Lesson 107	Here Be Giants
108			balance			Lesson 108	
109	Number Cubes	Measurement Game				Lesson 109	
110	Number Cubes					Lesson 110	
111	Number Cubes					Lesson 111	The Seesaw
112				base-10 blocks		Lesson 112	
113						Lesson 113	

UNIT 3

Student Edition pages 201–202

Measurement

INTRODUCING THE UNIT

Using the Student Pages To help students make the connection between what they learn in school and how it applies to the outside world, ask the students to name some ways that carpenters use math. Then read aloud the paragraph on page 202.

ACTIVITY Give the students drawing paper, pencils, markers or crayons, and graph paper and invite them to design a bookcase. Ask them to label their bookcases to show how tall and wide they are. Then invite the students to share their designs with the class. You may wish to ask the following: "How did you determine the size and shape of your bookcase?" "Are all of the bookcases the same size and shape?" "How will you make sure that the sides, top, bottom, and shelves of your bookcase are straight?" and "What do you need to know to figure out how much wood you need to build your bookcase?"

SCHOOL TO WORK CONNECTION

FYI The following information and discussion ideas will help students see how the skills and concepts they learn in school are used in the world outside the classroom. Use as much of the information and as many of the questions as are appropriate for your students. Remember, discussion questions are designed to promote thinking; students are not expected to be able to answer all of them.

Carpentry is an ancient skill (and art). Prehistoric people shaped wood and bones into weapons and tools and eventually used these materials to create complicated structures, like huts and sheds. Have students consider the following: Ancient people did not know about numbers like we do. "How do you think they figured out how long a bed should be? How might you measure wood without a ruler or tape measure? How might you tell a woodcutter how many trees to cut down?"

UNIT 3

Measurement

APPLYING AND ESTIMATING

- length, weight, and capacity
- approximation
- reading maps
- shapes

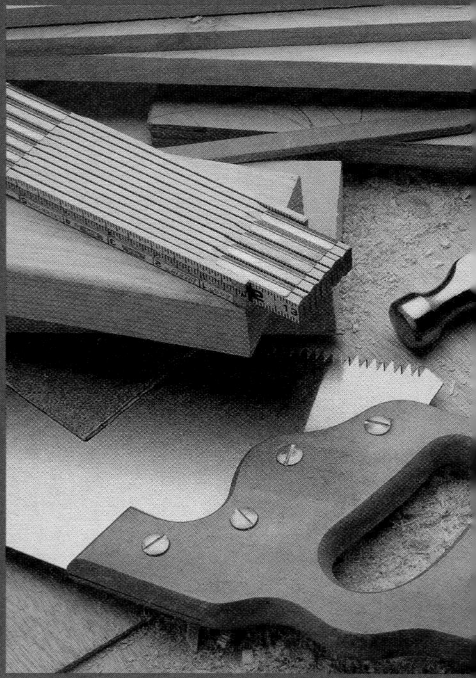

201

PROBLEM SOLVING

*Junior Thinklab™**

Junior Thinklab™ provides a series of creative and logical problem-solving opportunities for individual students. The problems are designed to appeal to different cognitive abilities.

- Use Activity Cards 41–45 with this unit to reinforce ordering skills and concepts.
- Use Activity Cards 46–50 with this unit to reinforce classifying skills and concepts.
- Use Activity Cards 51–55 with this unit to reinforce perception and spatial relations skills and concepts.
- Use Activity Cards 56–60 with this unit to reinforce reasoning and deducing skills and concepts.
- Use Divergent Thinking Activity Sheets 11–15 with this unit to encourage creativity in art and in intellectual activity.

*available separately

SCHOOL TO WORK CONNECTION

Carpenters use math . . .

The tools in this picture help carpenters measure and cut. Carpenters decide what shape pieces they need. Each piece is carefully measured and then cut from a larger piece of wood.

202

Early tools, like the adze (a kind of ax used for scraping wood and stone), were developed in Ancient Egypt, China, and South America. The plane and the lathe are variations of the same idea—both tools are used to cut and shape wood. With the Industrial Revolution in the eighteenth century, power tools vastly increased the amount of work that one person could do. "What would you do to a piece of bone or a hunk of rock to turn it into a cutting tool?" "Pretend that you have to strip the bark off a tree trunk before you can cut it into planks of wood. How could you strip the bark without tools? What kind of tool would help you do the job faster and easier? Tell us about its shape."

Carpentry is a craft and the products are usually created by hand. Basic math skills are necessary if a carpenter is to create a good product. Creating right angles in a bookcase or table requires precise measurement and calculation—even when a carpenter is using power tools. A carpenter must have many skills, and being able to calculate accurately and quickly is as important as being able to use tools. "Pretend that you have to build a cabinet that is four feet tall, three feet wide, and two feet deep. The cabinet has three shelves. How many feet of wood do you need?" "You have a plank of wood 12 feet long. If you cut off 4 feet for a table top, will you have enough left to cut five 2-foot pieces?"

Carpenters must also know a great deal about the materials they work with. They must study the nature of woods, the different kinds of grains, and the ways woods react to stress so that they can identify the right material for each job. These are often problems of science and math.

COOPERATIVE LEARNING **Minds on Math** *Minds on Math* is a series of units covering problem solving, data collection, number sense, measurement, money, and geometry and spatial relations. Each unit provides a series of open-ended projects for individuals or small groups. These projects develop problem-solving and critical-thinking skills, utilize real-world materials, emphasize language, and integrate curriculum areas. Use projects from *Problems to Solve* to emphasize that there is more than one way to look at and solve any problem.

LITERATURE CONNECTION The books *Here Be Giants* and *How Do You Measure Up?* are interesting ways to look at size and measurement. These books are part of the *Math Explorations and Applications* Literature Library*.

Home Connections You may want to send Home Connections Masters 43–44 to families to provide additional activities for them to do together. These activities apply skills and concepts presented in this unit.

*available separately

LESSON 91

Student Edition pages 203–204

Less Than, Greater Than

LESSON PLANNER

Objectives

✓ review and assess the use of <, >, and = signs to show how numbers are related

▶ to introduce the use of < and > in addition and subtraction sentences

Context of the Lesson Equalities and inequalities were introduced in level 1. This is the first presentation of this topic in level 2. This lesson also contains Mastery Checkpoint 12 to assess students' understanding of equalities and inequalities.

Materials	Program Resources
index cards	Thinking Story Book, pages 78–81
	Reteaching Master
	Practice Master 91
	Enrichment Master 91
	Assessment Master
	For extra practice: CD-ROM* Lesson 91

1 Warm-Up

5 MINUTES

Problem of the Day Write this problem on the chalkboard: Jamal rides his bike 2 miles on Monday, 4 miles on Tuesday, and 8 miles on Wednesday. If he keeps to this pattern, how many miles will he ride on Thursday? (16)

MENTAL MATH Have students tell which words belong in the blanks: *greater than, less than,* or *equals:*

a. 7 + 5 _____ 6 + 3 (>) b. 4 + 7 _____ 6 + 5 (=)

c. 2 + 2 _____ 2 + 4 (<) d. 9 + 7 _____ 7 + 6 (>)

e. 4 – 3 _____ 8 – 7 (=) f. 5 + 5 _____ 12 – 2 (=)

2 Teach

Demonstrate Review the relation signs <, >, and = with the class. Remind students that the smaller ends of < and > always point to the lesser number. Point out that the = sign has no smaller end because it means both numbers are the same or equal. Write several problems on the chalkboard and have students put the tips of their fingers together facing in the direction of the lesser number in each pair. For example:

LESSON 91

Name ______________________

Less Than, Greater Than

What is the right sign? Draw <, >, or =.

1. 10 (<) 20
2. 2 (=) 1 + 1
3. 5 (>) 1 + 1
4. 9 (>) 4 + 3
5. 56 (=) 56
6. 4 (<) 5 + 5
7. 12 (<) 21
8. 13 (=) 10 + 3
9. 87 (>) 78
10. 30 (>) 14 + 3
11. 55 (=) 55
12. 22 (=) 20 + 2
13. 0 (<) 99
14. 30 (<) 20 + 20
15. 41 (>) 14
16. 29 (=) 25 + 4
17. 81 (>) 78
18. 19 (<) 91

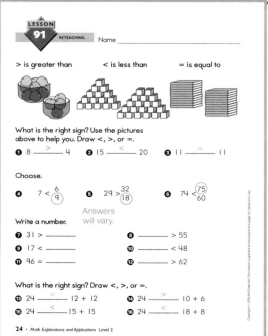

NOTE TO HOME
Students use less than, greater than, and equal signs to show how numbers are related.

RETEACHING p. 24

LESSON 91 RETEACHING Name ______________________

> is greater than < is less than = is equal to

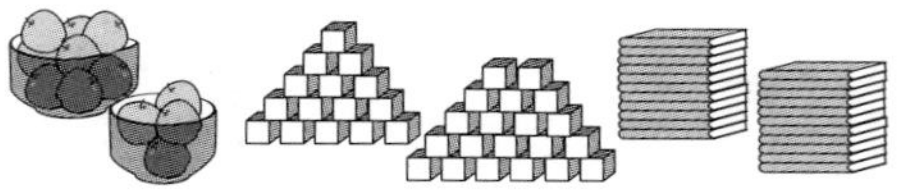

What is the right sign? Use the pictures above to help you. Draw <, >, or =.

1. 8 __>__ 4 2. 15 __<__ 20 3. 11 __=__ 11

Choose.

4. 7 < 6 / (9) 5. 29 > 32 / (18) 6. 74 < (75) / 60

Write a number. Answers will vary.

7. 31 > ______ 8. ______ > 55
9. 17 < ______ 10. ______ < 48
11. 96 = ______ 12. ______ > 62

What is the right sign? Draw <, >, or =.

13. 24 __=__ 12 + 12 14. 24 __>__ 10 + 6
15. 24 __<__ 15 + 15 16. 24 __<__ 18 + 8

PRACTICE p. 91

LESSON 91 PRACTICE Name ______________________

What is the right sign? Draw <, >, or =.

1. 74 (<) 78 2. 39 (<) 93
3. 82 (>) 38 4. 56 (<) 64
5. 45 (<) 51 6. 83 (>) 82
7. 23 (>) 22 8. 36 (<) 46
9. 19 (<) 91 10. 25 (>) 19
11. 64 (=) 64 12. 97 (<) 99
13. 98 (>) 89 14. 41 (>) 39
15. 11 (>) 10 16. 13 (<) 31

*available separately

◆ **LESSON 91** Less Than, Greater Than

What is the right sign? Draw <, >, or =.

19	9 + 8	(>)	7 + 9	20	41 + 3	(<)	49
21	2 + 3	(<)	2 + 4	22	21 − 4	(=)	17
23	20 + 3	(<)	20 + 4	24	6 + 15	(>)	19
25	5 − 3	(>)	5 − 4	26	58 − 7	(>)	49
27	28 − 3	(>)	28 − 4	28	24 + 5	(>)	28
29	5 + 6	(=)	6 + 5	30	15 + 16	(<)	32
31	10 + 3	(<)	10 + 4	32	61 − 3	(>)	57
33	87 + 3	(<)	87 + 4	34	18 + 9	(>)	25
35	10 − 3	(>)	10 − 4	36	37 − 7	(=)	30

THINKING STORY

Talk about the Thinking Story "Ferdie Borrows and Borrows and Borrows."

NOTE TO HOME
Students show number relationships with less than, greater than, or equal signs.

ENRICHMENT p. 91

LESSON 91 ENRICHMENT Name ______________________

Start at the top. Solve the first two problems. Write a less than (<) or greater than (>) sign in the block that is blank to show which answer is greater. Then go on to the next pair of problems. See how fast you can be the big 100 winner!

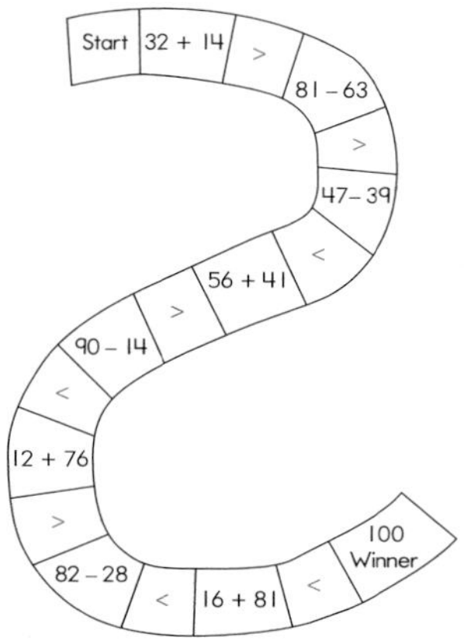

Math Explorations and Applications Level 2 • 91

ASSESSMENT

UNIT 3 **Mastery Checkpoint 12** Inequalities and equalities (Lesson 91)

Name ______________________

The student demonstrates mastery by correctly answering at least 16 of the 20 problems.

What is the right sign?
Draw <, >, or =.

1 32 (>) 23	2 29 (<) 29 + 11
3 42 (>) 41	4 15 (<) 10 + 7
5 13 (<) 30	6 35 (<) 70 + 3
7 6 (<) 60	8 13 (=) 6 + 7
9 49 (=) 49	10 100 (>) 90 + 9
11 0 (<) 50	12 50 (>) 10 + 10
13 22 (>) 9	14 50 (<) 40 + 40
15 88 (<) 91	16 50 (>) 40 + 4
17 37 (<) 73	18 80 (>) 30 + 5
19 42 (>) 17	20 56 (>) 20 + 28

38 • Math Explorations and Applications Level 2

11 ( ) 13 (Students should point the tips of their fingers to the left). Provide several examples of sums and differences as well: 7 + 8 (<) 10 + 9 and 26 − 5 (<) 38 − 5.

Using the Student Pages Have students independently complete pages 203–204. Encourage students to use number sense to solve the problems rather than calculate the exact sums and differences.

Using the Thinking Story Read aloud "Ferdie Borrows and Borrows and Borrows" on pages 78–81 of the Thinking Story Book. Stop and discuss the questions asked throughout the story.

MATH JOURNAL Ask students to write a story about some children who earn money together to buy something special.

3 Wrap-Up

5 MINUTES

In Closing Have students write each sign on an index card and write the definition of the sign on the back and an example of when it is used to show the relationship between two numbers.

ANALYZING ANSWERS You might wish to interview students who get more than five problems wrong on pages 203–204. Have them explain how they arrived at their answers. Check to see whether they are making errors because they cannot remember the signs' meanings or are making computational errors. Reteach accordingly.

Mastery Checkpoint 12

Use students' answers to pages 203 and 204 or Assessment Master 39 to assess their ability to use relation signs to describe equalities and inequalities. Results of this assessment can be recorded on the Mastery Checkpoint Chart.

Assessment Criteria

Did the student . . .

✓ point the tips of his or her fingers in the right direction?

✓ write the correct relation sign in at least 28 of the 36 problems?

✓ participate in the discussion of the Thinking Story?

STORY 13

THINKING STORY

Ferdie Borrows and Borrows and Borrows

Every Saturday morning Ferdie gets an allowance of $1. By the middle of the week, and sometimes sooner, he has usually spent it. Then he has no money left.

One Tuesday after school Ferdie saw a package of baseball cards in a store window. He reached into his pocket and counted his money. "Forty cents. And the price tag says 50¢." Then he had an idea. Maybe he could borrow just enough money to buy the cards.

How much money does Ferdie need to borrow? 10¢

His friend Marcus came by. "Hi, Marcus!" said Ferdie. "Can you lend me 50¢? I need enough money to buy a package of baseball cards."

"Here you are," said Marcus, handing Ferdie 50¢. "But I need it back tomorrow."

Did Ferdie borrow the right amount of money? no

How much money does he have now? 90¢

Ferdie thanked Marcus, hurried to the toy store, and bought the cards.

How much money does Ferdie have left?
40¢

"Borrowing is great!" Ferdie told himself. "A little while ago I didn't have enough money to buy a package of baseball cards, and now I have the cards and 40¢ besides. I only have one little problem."

What problem does Ferdie still have?
He has to pay Marcus back.

The next day at school Marcus asked for his 50¢. Ferdie didn't have that much, of course. All he had was the 40¢ from the day before. But he had an idea. "If borrowing worked so well yesterday," he thought, "it should work again today."

He said to Marcus, "I'll be glad to pay you back 50¢ if you can lend me a dime."

"Sure," said Marcus, giving Ferdie 10¢.

How much money does Ferdie have now?
50¢

"Here's your 50¢," Ferdie said cheerfully, giving Marcus the 40¢ from the day before and the 10¢ he had just borrowed. "I guess that settles my debt, right?"

"But I just lent you 10¢ more," Marcus complained.

"And I gave it back to you," Ferdie said. "So we're even."

Is that right? no

How much money did Ferdie borrow all together? 60¢

How much did Ferdie pay back all together? 50¢

How much money does Ferdie still owe Marcus? 10¢

Marcus was getting confused. "I think I'm losing money on this deal," he said, "but I'm not sure how. Yesterday I lent you 50¢ and you just paid that back to me. Today I lent you a dime and you gave that back to me too."

"That's right," Ferdie said. "It's all fair and square."

"But I know I had 60¢ yesterday," Marcus said. "And now I have just 50¢, and I know I didn't spend any. So I know I've lost a dime."

"That's too bad," Ferdie said. "If I had a dime, I'd lend it to you."

"Wait a minute!" Marcus said, looking at the coins in his hand. "I know what happened. You used the same dime to pay back the 50¢ you owed me and the 10¢ you owed me. You can't use the same money to pay two debts. You borrowed 60¢ from me all together, and you only paid me back 50¢. You still owe me 10¢!"

"Don't get so excited," Ferdie said. "If you think I still owe you 10¢, I'll pay you 10¢. Just wait here a while. I know how to take care of these things."

Ferdie rushed over to his friend Willy. He was about to borrow 10¢ from him to pay Marcus back. But then he stopped and thought, "If I borrow 10¢ from Willy to pay Marcus back, I won't be any better off than I was before."

Why won't Ferdie be any better off?
He'll still owe someone 10¢.

◆ STORY 13 Ferdie Borrows and Borrows and Borrows

"Then I'll owe Willy 10¢," Ferdie thought. So he tried a different plan. He borrowed 20¢ from Willy. Then he found Marcus and paid him back the money he owed him.

How much did Ferdie pay Marcus? ten cents

How much money does Ferdie have left? ten cents

Ferdie looked at the 10¢ he had left. "I was hoping I would have enough left to pay Willy back, but I don't," he thought.

Why doesn't Ferdie have enough left to pay Willy back? He used some money to pay Marcus.

"Borrowing isn't working out as well as I thought," Ferdie said to himself. "I always end up owing people more money than I have. There must be a better way."

While Ferdie was thinking of what to do, he used the 10¢ to buy himself a gumball from a candy machine so that he would have something to do while he was thinking.

How much money does Ferdie have left now? none

How much does he owe? twenty cents to Willy

"Now I owe 20¢ and I don't have any money at all. I'm worse off than I was before. Maybe if I borrowed a lot of money that would help."

After school he went to Ms. Eng's house. "Ms. Eng, could you lend me $10?" he asked.

"What do you need it for?" asked Ms. Eng.

"I need it to pay Willy 20¢ that I owe him."

"And what will you do with all the rest of the money?"

"I'll pay it back to you."

"You'll never get out of debt by borrowing," said Ms. Eng. "I have a better idea how you can get the 20¢ you need."

What other ways are there for Ferdie to get money besides borrowing? Answers will vary; responses include getting paid to do a chore.

"Our sidewalk is badly in need of sweeping," said Ms. Eng. "If you would sweep it for me, I'd gladly pay you 20¢."

"But then how would I pay it back?" Ferdie asked.

Would Ferdie have to pay back the 20¢ to Ms. Eng? no

Why not? He would be earning the money, not borrowing it.

"You don't have to pay it back if you earn it," said Ms. Eng.

Ferdie's eyes popped when he heard that. "Why, earning's even better than borrowing!" he said. "When you borrow money, people keep wanting it back."

. . . the end

LESSON 92

Student Edition pages 205–206

Three Addends

LESSON PLANNER

Objectives

- to demonstrate how basic addition facts are related to adding one-digit and two-digit numbers
- to review adding columns of one-digit numbers
- to provide practice in adding columns of two-digit numbers

Context of the Lesson Adding columns of numbers continues in Lesson 97.

Materials	Program Resources
base-10 materials*	Number Cubes
	Thinking Story Book, pages 82–83
	Practice Master 92
	Enrichment Master 92
	For extra practice: CD-ROM* Lesson 92

1 Warm-Up

5 MINUTES

Problem of the Day Write this problem on the chalkboard: What is the smallest number of coins you can use to make 37 cents? What coins are they? (four; quarter, dime, two pennies)

MENTAL MATH Have students add, using their Number Cubes to respond:

a. 2 + 2 + 3 = (7)
b. 1 + 8 + 4 = (13)
c. 9 + 0 + 7 = (16)
d. 5 + 0 + 1 = (6)
e. 3 + 2 + 6 = (11)
f. 1 + 2 + 1 = (4)

2 Teach

Demonstrate Write the following problems on the chalkboard. Have students solve them and discuss any patterns they see in the addends and sums.

7 + 8 = ____ (15) 17 + 8 = ____ (25)

27 + 8 = ____ (35) 37 + 8 = ____ (45)

After guiding students to see that the units in the addends and sums are the same in each problem, and that the tens

LESSON 92

Name ____________________

Three Addends

Add.

1. 5 + 8 + 4 = 17
2. 7 + 3 + 8 = 18
3. 4 + 8 + 6 = 18
4. 5 + 6 + 7 = 18
5. 8 + 9 + 4 = 21
6. 14 + 10 + 26 = 50
7. 13 + 12 + 14 = 39
8. 21 + 34 + 13 = 68
9. 21 + 18 + 16 = 55
10. 36 + 23 + 12 = 71

GAME

11. ___ ___ + ___ ___ + ___ ___
12. ___ ___ + ___ ___ + ___ ___
13. 19 + 24 + 20 = 63
14. ___ ___ + ___ ___ + ___ ___
15. ___ ___ + ___ ___ + ___ ___
16. 31 + 18 + 27 = 76

NOTE TO HOME
Students learn to add three two-digit numbers.

Literature Connection Read aloud or invite students to read *Just Beyond Reach and Other Riddle Poems* by Bonnie Larkin Nims to reinforce lesson concepts.

RETEACHING

MATH MANIPULATIVES Demonstrate and then have students use base-10 materials to add three addends of two-digit numbers. Have students explain their methods as they manipulate the materials to add the numbers.

*available separately

◆ **LESSON 92** Three Addends

Add. Use shortcuts if you can.

⑰ 27 + 26 + 39 = **92**

⑱ 18 + 24 + 15 = **57**

⑲ 25 + 25 + 25 = **75**

⑳ 24 + 25 + 26 = **75**

㉑ 13 + 20 + 67 = **100**

㉒ 23 + 25 + 27 = **75**

㉓ 20 + 25 + 30 = **75**

㉔ 30 + 16 + 28 = **74**

㉕ 42 + 13 + 17 = **72**

㉖ 18 + 53 + 10 = **81**

March has 31 days.
April has 30 days.
May has 31 days.

㉗ How many days are in March, April, and May all together? **92**

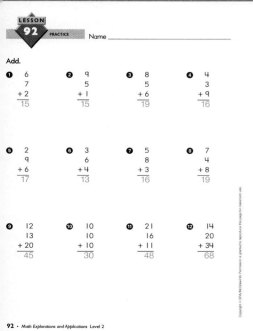

NOTE TO HOME
Students continue adding three two-digit numbers.

increase by one in both the addend and sum, ask students to tell what the next three addends and sums are if they follow the same pattern (47 + 8 = 55; 57 + 8 = 65; and 67 + 8 = 75).

Next demonstrate that students can add a column of three two-digit numbers by either adding the first two numbers and then adding that sum to the third number or by adding the ones and then the tens.

Using the Number Cubes Use Number Cubes to practice addition facts and related two-digit plus one-digit facts (5 + 8 = 13; 15 + 8 = 23), and addition of columns of one-digit and two-digit numbers, such as 4 + 6 + 8 (18) and 15 + 23 +12 (50).

GAME

Introducing the "Roll a Problem" Game: two-digit column addition variation Demonstrate and play this variation of the "Roll a Problem" game. Students can use the bottom of page 205 to play four games.

Using the Student Pages Have students who can work independently complete pages 205–206, while you help those students having difficulty.

Using the Thinking Story Present three problems from those following the story "Ferdie Borrows and Borrows and Borrows" on pages 82–83 of the Thinking Story Book.

3 Wrap-Up

5 MINUTES

In Closing Have students explain their favorite method for adding three addends of two-digit numbers.

ALTERNATIVE ASSESSMENT

Informal Assessment Observe students as they complete pages 205–206 to see who is having difficulty.

Assessment Criteria

Did the student . . .

✓ correctly solve the problems he or she created for the "Roll a Problem" game?

✓ correctly solve at least 20 of the 25 addition problems on pages 205–206?

✓ correctly solve the word problem on page 206?

PRACTICE p. 92

LESSON 92 PRACTICE Name ____

Add.

❶ 6 + 7 + 2 = 15

❷ 9 + 5 + 1 = 15

❸ 8 + 5 + 6 = 19

❹ 4 + 3 + 9 = 16

❺ 2 + 9 + 6 = 17

❻ 3 + 6 + 4 = 13

❼ 5 + 8 + 3 = 16

❽ 7 + 4 + 8 = 19

❾ 12 + 13 + 20 = 45

❿ 10 + 10 + 10 = 30

⓫ 21 + 16 + 11 = 48

⓬ 14 + 20 + 34 = 68

92 • *Math Explorations and Applications* Level 2

ENRICHMENT p. 92

LESSON 92 ENRICHMENT Name ____

In the Olympic Games a gold medal is given for first place, a silver medal for second place, and a bronze medal for third place.

Use your math skills to complete the chart and answer the questions.

Number of Medals Won, Summer of 1996

Country	Gold	Silver	Bronze	Total
Australia	9	9	23	41
China	16	22	12	50
France	15	7	15	37
Germany	20	18	27	65
Italy	13	10	12	35
Russia	26	21	16	63
South Korea	7	15	5	27
United States	44	32	25	101

❶ Which country won the most
a. gold medals? United States
b. silver medals? United States
c. bronze medals? Germany

❷ Which country won more silver medals than it did gold and bronze medals put together? South Korea

❸ Which country won more bronze medals than than it did gold and silver medals put together? Australia

92 • *Math Explorations and Applications* Level 2

LESSON 93

Student Edition pages 207–208

Telling Time—Nearest Half Hour

LESSON PLANNER

Objective

- ▶ to provide practice for telling time to the nearest half hour

Context of the Lesson Telling time was introduced at this grade level beginning in Lesson 70. The topic is continued in Lessons 94, 95, and 131.

Materials	Program Resources
clock with minutes and minute hand visible to students	Number Cubes
toy or paper clocks	Thinking Story Book, pages 82–83
	Practice Master 93
	Enrichment Master 93
	For extra practice: CD-ROM* Lesson 93

1 Warm-Up

5 MINUTES

Problem of the Day Write the following problem on the chalkboard: Tyrone has 24 basketball trading cards and 17 football trading cards. Keisha has 40 trading cards. Who has more trading cards? How many more? (Tyrone, one more than Keisha)

MENTAL MATH Have students add, using their Number Cubes to respond:

a. 2 + 7 + 8 (17)

b. 6 + 8 + 1 (15)

c. 5 + 7 + 3 (15)

d. 4 + 3 + 6 (13)

e. 2 + 5 + 4 (11)

2 Teach

Demonstrate Display several times on a clock and have students tell what time it is, such as 5:00, 8:30, 7:45, and 3:15. Next set the clock at times close to half hours such as 7:59, 12:27, 3:03, and 4:32. Have students tell approximately what time each shows. (8:00, 12:30, 3:00, and 4:30)

LESSON 93

Name ______________________

Telling Time—Nearest Half Hour

What time is it?

1. 7 : 00

2. 2 : 00

3. 3 : 30

4. 5 : 45

5. 9 : 15

6. 12 : 15

7. 4 : 45

8. 7 : 30

9. 6 : 00

NOTE TO HOME
Students practice telling time to the half hour.

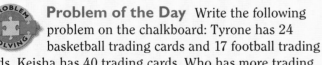

Literature Connection Read aloud or invite students to read *Time* by Henry Pluckrose to reinforce lesson concepts.

RETEACHING

Provide toy clocks or paper clock faces. Tell students to show approximate times on their clocks, such as "about 4:30" or "about 6:00." With volunteers, point out that students can have different answers and still be correct. Encourage students to explain how they decided where to place each hand.

*available separately

◆ **LESSON 93** Telling Time—Nearest Half Hour

Use the Mixed Practice on page 385 after this lesson.

About what time is it? The hands might not be at exactly that time.

Tell the time to the nearest half hour.

10. 2 : 00

11. 4 : 30

12. 4 : 30

13. 10 : 00

14. 12 : 30

15. 7 : 00

16. 5 : 30

17. 8 : 00

18. 11 : 00

FANTASTIC FACT One day on Mercury lasts as long as about eight Earth years.

NOTE TO HOME
Students tell time to the nearest half hour.

PRACTICE p. 93

LESSON 93 PRACTICE Name ____________

What time is it?

1. 8:30
2. 10:45
3. 11:00
4. 1:15
5. 6:30
6. 2:00

About what time is it? The hands may not be exactly on the time. Tell the time to the nearest half hour.

7. 7:30
8. 4:00
9. 10:30
10. 9:30
11. 3:00
12. 11:00

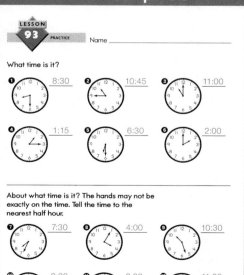

ENRICHMENT p. 93

LESSON 93 ENRICHMENT Name ____________

Hours	Minutes
7, 1, 8, 2, 9, 4, 5, 10, 11, 6, 12, 3	23, 18, 7, 47, 36, 15

Make time. Flip one marker onto an hour tile and another onto a minute tile. Draw the time to the nearest half hour on a clock below. Repeat three more times.

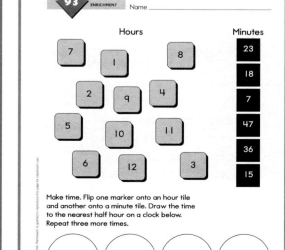

Using the Student Pages Have students write the exact times for each clock shown on page 207. Explain that on page 208 they will write the approximate times to the nearest half hour. You might wish to complete the first problem on each page with the class before students work independently. When finished, go over the answers with students. Encourage them to explain how they decided what time to write for each problem.

Using the Thinking Story Present one or two new problems from those following "Ferdie Borrows and Borrows and Borrows" on pages 82–83 of the Thinking Story Book.

3 Wrap-Up

5 MINUTES

In Closing Have students draw two clocks and show exactly 2:00 on one, and any time that they would read as "about" 2:00 on the other.

ALTERNATIVE ASSESSMENT

Informal Assessment Observe students as they complete the student pages, taking note of which students are still having difficulty telling time to the nearest hour, half hour, or quarter hour.

Assessment Criteria

Did the student . . .

- ✓ write the correct time for seven of the nine clocks shown on page 207?
- ✓ write the correct approximate time for seven of the nine clocks shown on page 208?

SPECIAL NEEDS

Meeting Individual Needs
Students who cannot tell time to the nearest hour, quarter hour, and half hour should receive additional help before they work on page 208.

LESSON 94

Student Edition pages 209–210

Telling Time—To the Minute

LESSON PLANNER

Objective

▶ to introduce telling time to the nearest minute

Context of the Lesson This is the second of three lessons on telling time.

Materials

clock with minutes and minute hand visible to students

toy clock

Program Resources

"Harder Time" Game Mat

Thinking Story Book, pages 82–83

Practice Master 94

Enrichment Master 94

For extra practice:
CD-ROM* Lesson 94

1 Warm-Up

5 MINUTES

Problem of the Day Write the following problem on the chalkboard: Suppose you save five cents on the first day of the week, eight cents on the second day, and 11 cents on the third day. If you keep up this pattern, how much will you save on the seventh day of the week? (23 cents)

MENTAL MATH Have students find the missing number in each problem:

a. 30 + _____ = 60 (30)
b. 20 + _____ = 60 (40)
c. 50 + _____ = 60 (10)
d. 10 + _____ = 60 (50)
e. 40 + _____ = 60 (20)
f. 55 + _____ = 60 (5)

2 Teach

Demonstrate Explain to students that each little line on the clock stands for one minute. Ask "How many minutes in an hour?" (60) "How many little lines in all?" (60) Display several times on a clock and have students tell what time it is, such as 8:00, 8:01, 8:06. Discuss how students can tell the time when the minute hand is on the line just before the 12 and the hour hand is almost at the 9. Students should realize that since there are 60 minutes in an hour, one minute before the 60 will be 59. The clock therefore shows 8:59. Have students explain how they can tell other times, such as 8:33, without counting from the top of the hour each time. (Because they know the six corresponds to 30, they can see that three minutes after that will be 33.)

LESSON 94

Name ______________________________

Telling Time—To the Minute

Accept all reasonable answers.

What time is it?

1 11 : 09

2 6 : 13

3 5 : 54

4 8 : 32

5 12 : 16

6 9 : 44

7 2 : 02

8 7 : 49

NOTE TO HOME
Students learn to tell time to the nearest minute.

RETEACHING

Provide copies of clocks on a sheet of paper for students. Write times on the chalkboard for them to show on their clocks. Correct and discuss each answer before going on to the next.

ESL **Meeting Individual Needs**

Help students learn to count from 1 through 60 in English so that they can say, as well as write, the times shown on the clocks on pages 209 and 210.

*available separately

◆ **LESSON 94** Telling Time—To the Minute

Draw the minute hands.

9 3:27

10 4:51

11 8:04

12 10:40

NOTE TO HOME
Students continue to tell time to the nearest minute.

PRACTICE p. 94

LESSON 94 PRACTICE Name ____________

What time is it?

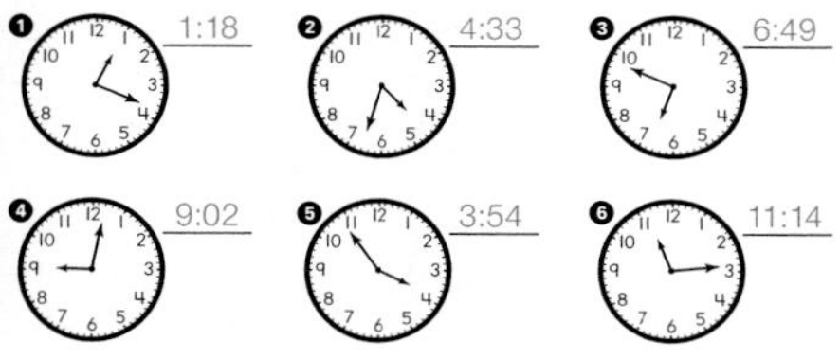

1 1:18 2 4:33 3 6:49

4 9:02 5 3:54 6 11:14

Draw in the minute hand.

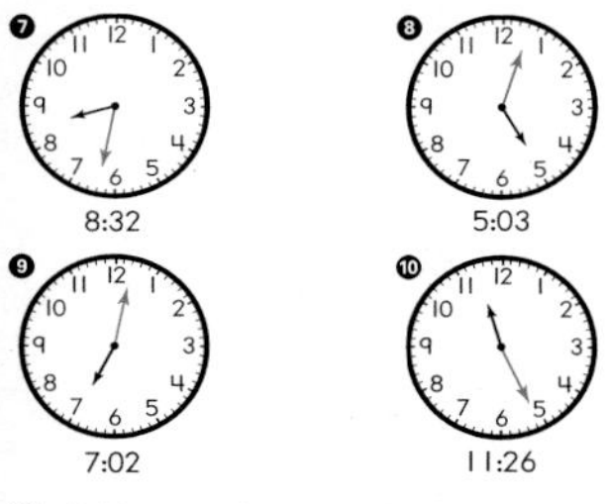

7 8:32 8 5:03

9 7:02 10 11:26

ENRICHMENT p. 94

LESSON 94 ENRICHMENT Name ____________

1 Anna left school at 3:40. She got home one half hour later. Show what time she got home.

2 Anna had told Gena she would call her at 6:30. She called 10 minutes early. Show what time she called.

3 Gena said she is going to a play. She wants to be there by 8:00. She needs 45 minutes to get to the play. Show the time she must leave to be on time.

4 Gena usually goes to bed at 9:15. Her father said she could stay up two hours later tonight. Show the time she will go to bed tonight.

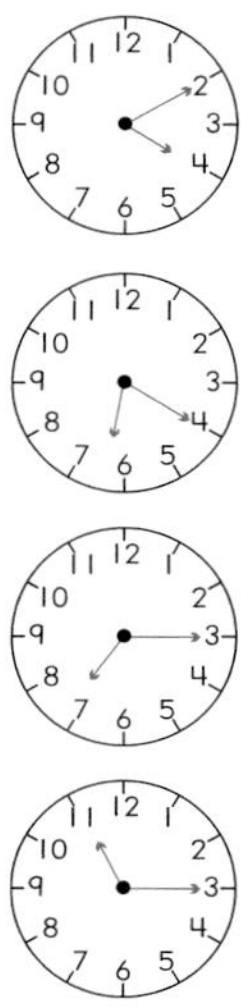

Using the Student Pages Explain that on page 209 students must write the time each clock shows, but on page 210 they must show the time that is written below each clock by drawing a minute hand on each clock. Students who finish early may go directly to playing the "Harder Time" game.

Using the Thinking Story Present one or two questions from those following "Ferdie Borrows and Borrows and Borrows " on pages 82–83 of the Thinking Story Book.

GAME

Introducing a Variation of the "Harder Time" Game Mat Students may play the "Harder Time" game, which they played in Lesson 72. If they need more of a challenge, teach them the variation that involves telling time to the hour, half hour, quarter hour, and nearest minute. Complete directions are on the game mat.

3 Wrap-Up

5 MINUTES

In Closing Display a real analog clock in your classroom. Ask students what time it is at the close of the lesson.

ALTERNATIVE ASSESSMENT

Performance Assessment Observe students as they play the "Harder Time" game and its variation to see who is having difficulty stating the correct times.

Assessment Criteria

Did the student . . .

✓ write the correct time for 6 of the 8 clocks shown on page 209?

✓ correctly draw the minute hand for 3 of the 4 clocks shown on page 210?

✓ correctly state the time when playing the "Harder Time" game?

LEARNING STYLES

Meeting Individual Needs
Kinesthetic learners might need more practice using toy clocks so they can physically move the minute hand to show different times. Then they can draw the minute hands as indicated on page 210.

LESSON 95

Student Edition pages 211–212

Telling Time—Before the Hour

LESSON PLANNER

Objectives

✓ to assess telling time to the nearest minute

▶ to provide practice for telling time as a number of minutes before the hour

Context of the Lesson This lesson, the last of three lessons on telling time until Lesson 131, contains Mastery Checkpoint 13 for this skill.

Materials

clock with minutes and minute hand visible to students

Program Resources

"Harder Time" Game Mat
Number Cubes
Reteaching Master
Practice Master 95
Enrichment Master 95
Assessment Master
For extra practice:
CD-ROM* Lesson 95

1 Warm-Up

5 MINUTES

Problem of the Day Write the following problem on the chalkboard: You plan to study for a half hour. So far you have studied for 12 minutes. How much longer will you study? (18 more minutes)

MENTAL MATH Have students find the missing number in each equation, using their Number Cubes to respond:

a. 57 + ____ = 60 (3) b. 1 + ____ = 60 (59)

c. 50 + ____ = 60 (10) d. 3 + ____ = 60 (57)

e. 59 + ____ = 60 (1)

2 Teach

Demonstrate Explain to students that times that are less than 30 minutes before the hour can be named in different ways. Show students the clock set at 8:50. Ask them what time it shows. (8:50) Then ask how many minutes before nine o'clock it is. (10) Point out that 8:50 can also be said as ten minutes to nine. Repeat for several other times that are less than 30 minutes before the hour.

LESSON 95

Name ____________________

Telling Time—Before the Hour

What time is it? Accept all reasonable answers.

1. 2 : 36

2. 4 : 45

3. 7 : 05

4. 8 : 00

5. 8 : 55

6. 2 : 17

7. 12 : 45

8. 5 : 55

NOTE TO HOME
Students practice telling time to the nearest minute.

RETEACHING p. 25

LESSON 95 RETEACHING Name ____________

In each of the boxes on this page, draw a picture of one of your favorite times of day. Make the clocks show those times. On the lines name those favorite times.

Example: time to go to bed Check students' work.

Math Explorations and Applications Level 2 • 25

PRACTICE p. 95

LESSON 95 PRACTICE Name ____________

What time is it?

1. 11:45
2. 8:55
3. 3:05
4. 12:37
5. 4:00
6. 8:14

How many minutes before the hour?

7. 5 minutes to 5
8. 25 minutes to 9
9. 14 minutes to 12
10. 20 minutes to 2

Math Explorations and Applications Level 2 • 95

*available separately

◆ LESSON 95 Telling Time—Before the Hour

Accept all reasonable answers.

How many minutes before the hour?

9 15 minutes before 1

10 2 minutes before 6

11 25 minutes before 7

12 18 minutes before 11

13 10 minutes before 4

14 5 minutes before 3

15 4 minutes before 9

16 15 minutes before 9

NOTE TO HOME
Students learn to tell how many minutes before the hour a clock shows.

ENRICHMENT p. 95

LESSON 95 ENRICHMENT Name ____

1 Kara got to May's house at a quarter after one. Show the time on the clock.

2 May and Kara made bread, starting at two-thirty. Show the time.

3 The bread dough was ready 40 minutes later. Show the time.

4 They put the bread in the oven at 3:20. It baked for 25 minutes. Show the time they took the bread out of the oven.

Math Explorations and Applications Level 2 • 95

ASSESSMENT p. 39

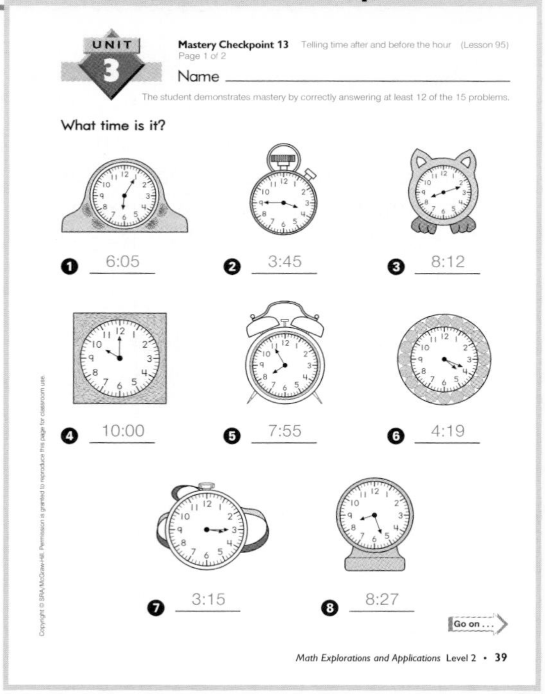
UNIT 3 Mastery Checkpoint 13 Telling time after and before the hour (Lesson 95) Page 1 of 2

Name ____

The student demonstrates mastery by correctly answering at least 12 of the 15 problems.

What time is it?

1 6:05 2 3:45 3 8:12

4 10:00 5 7:55 6 4:19

7 3:15 8 8:27

Go on . . .

Math Explorations and Applications Level 2 • 39

Using the Number Cubes Set the hands of the clock to various times. For each time ask students to show the number of minutes after the hour and then the number of minutes before the next hour. Have students add the two numbers, which will always be a sum of 60.

Using the Student Pages Assign pages 211–212 for students to complete independently. You might wish to complete the first problem on each page with the class to be sure everyone understands what they must do.

Using the Variations of the "Harder Time" Game Mat Have students play one of the variations of the "Harder Time" Game Mat.

3 Wrap-Up 5 MINUTES

In Closing Show a clock that is set to 5:45. Have students write three different ways to say this time. (5:45, a quarter to six, or 15 minutes to six)

Mastery Checkpoint 13

At about this time most students should be able to tell time by using a clock with a conventional face. Use students' answers to pages 211–212 or Assessment Masters 40 and 41 to assess who is still having difficulty telling time. Results of this assessment can be recorded on the Mastery Checkpoint Chart.

Assessment Criteria

Did the student . . .

✓ show the correct Number Cubes when adding sums of 60 minutes?

✓ write the correct time for six of the eight clocks shown on page 211?

✓ write the correct time for five of the seven clocks shown on page 212?

✓ correctly state the time when playing the "Harder Time" game?

LESSON 96

Student Edition pages 213–216

Keeping Sharp

LESSON PLANNER

Objectives

- to review the addition and subtraction of one-, two-, and three-digit numbers
- to review equations involving missing addends
- to review fractions as related to area as well as inequalities and equalities

Context of the Lesson This lesson reviews topics covered in this and previous units.

Materials	Program Resources
none	Number Cubes
	Practice Master 96
	Enrichment Master 96
	For extra practice: CD-ROM* Lesson 96

1 Warm-Up

5 MINUTES

Problem of the Day Present the following problem: Gary flipped a coin 25 times. It landed on heads three more times than it landed on tails. How many times did it land on tails? (11)

MENTAL MATH Have students find the missing number in each equation and use their Number Cubes to respond.

a. 23 + _____ = 30 (7)

b. 1 + _____ = 10 (9)

c. 5 + _____ = 45 (40)

d. 6 + _____ = 20 (14)

e. 9 + _____ = 40 (31)

LESSON 96

Name ______________________

Keeping Sharp

Solve these problems. Watch the signs.

1. 5 + 6 = 11
2. 4 + 9 = 13
3. 8 + 7 = 15
4. 9 + 9 = 18
5. 15 − 8 = 7
6. 13 − 9 = 4
7. 12 − 3 = 9
8. 9 − 2 = 7

Solve.

9. 83 + 72 = 155
10. 26 + 38 = 64
11. 47 + 83 = 130
12. 32 + 69 = 101
13. 98 − 35 = 63
14. 153 − 28 = 125
15. 64 − 37 = 27
16. 56 − 27 = 29

NOTE TO HOME
Students review skills presented in this unit.

COOPERATIVE LEARNING Have students work in pairs. Have them figure out the value of each of their first names by assigning each letter the number value of its place in the alphabet. For example, A=1, B=2, etc. Have each partner find the value of his or her first name, then add the amounts together. See which partners' names have the greatest value.

*available separately

◆ **LESSON 96** Keeping Sharp

ALGEBRA READINESS

Solve these problems.

17. $\boxed{8} = 4 + 4$
18. $\boxed{9} + 5 = 14$
19. $\boxed{9} + 8 = 17$
20. $10 = \boxed{4} + 6$
21. $10 + \boxed{3} = 13$
22. $14 = 7 + \boxed{7}$

What is the right sign? Draw $<$, $>$, or $=$.

23. $8 + 9 \; (>) \; 15$
24. $25 + 35 \; (<) \; 100$
25. $45 - 25 \; (<) \; 30$
26. $50 + 50 \; (=) \; 100$
27. $1000 - 100 \; (>) \; 800$
28. $10 + 7 \; (=) \; 17$
29. $400 + 300 \; (=) \; 700$
30. $100 - 50 \; (<) \; 75$

NOTE TO HOME
Students review skills presented in this unit.

❷ Teach

Demonstrate Write missing number equations on the chalkboard, such as 7 + _____ = 16 and _____ + 8 = 12. Ask students to solve the problems. Then discuss their answers. How can they tell whether they have the right answers?

Then draw several circles on the chalkboard like those on page 215. Ask volunteers to shade or color a given fraction of each circle. Discuss the results to see whether there is general agreement that the shaded parts of the circles represent the fractions requested. Invite students to represent the same fractions using different shading.

Next, write three sentences on the chalkboard without relations signs. Ask volunteers to fill in one of the three signs: *greater than, less than,* or *equal to.* Review, if necessary, the fact that the small end of the inequality sign points to the lesser quantity.

◆ LESSON 96 Keeping Sharp

Teach

Using the Student Pages Have students complete pages 213 through 216 on their own. While they are working, you might want to walk around the room to see which students are having trouble. Students who finish early may play any of the games introduced in the unit so far.

◆ LESSON 96 Keeping Sharp

Name ______________________

Solve each problem two ways.

Answers are examples only.

31 Color $\frac{3}{4}$.

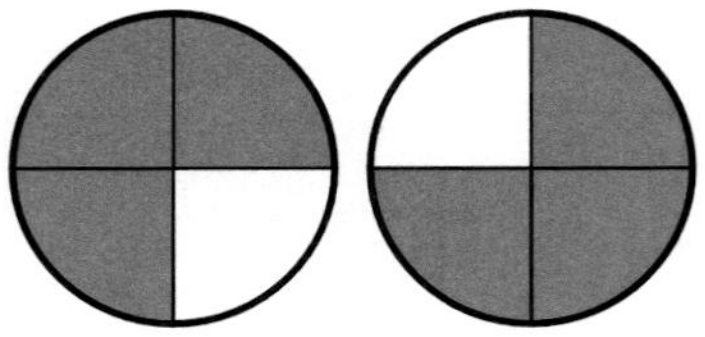

32 Color $\frac{1}{2}$.

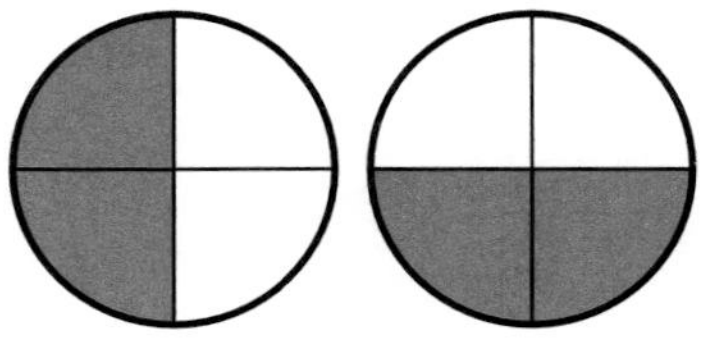

33 Color $\frac{2}{5}$.

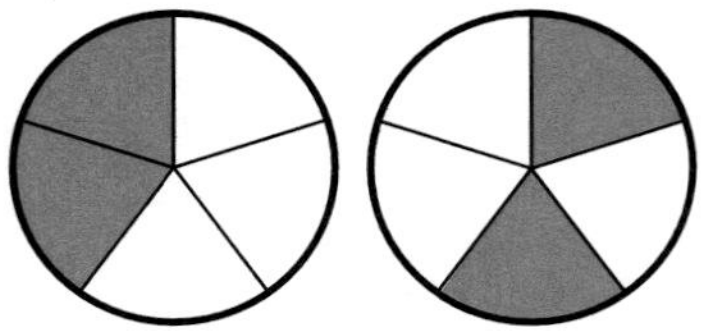

34 Color $\frac{1}{3}$.

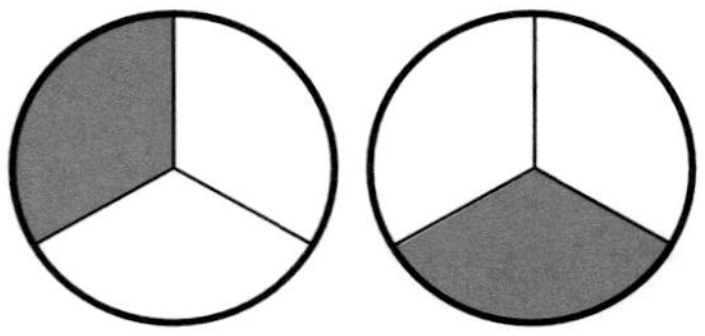

Work these problems. Watch the signs.

35 $66 + 23 = $ **89**

36 $43 + 59 = $ **102**

37 $81 - 22 = $ **59**

38 $30 - 29 = $ **1**

39 $21 + 18 = $ **39**

40 $24 + 19 + 20 = $ **63**

41 $46 + 21 + 18 = $ **85**

42 $27 + 16 + 17 = $ **60**

43 $19 + 9 + 15 = $ **43**

44 $31 + 18 + 27 = $ **76**

NOTE TO HOME
Students review skills presented in this unit.

RETEACHING

Invite students who have trouble with any section of this review to first proofread and correct their errors. You should then try to discover whether carelessness, lack of knowledge, or lack of understanding caused the errors. If the latter, try to develop students' understanding on an individual basis with further work from the appropriate lesson.

◆ LESSON 96 Keeping Sharp

Add.

45. 7 + 8 + 9 = **24**
46. 12 + 15 + 7 = **34**
47. 21 + 10 + 15 = **46**
48. 5 + 35 + 18 = **58**
49. 11 + 32 + 25 = **68**
50. 17 + 17 + 6 = **40**
51. 4 + 9 + 6 = **19**
52. 23 + 19 + 22 = **64**

What time is it? **Accept all reasonable answers.**

53. **2** : **41**

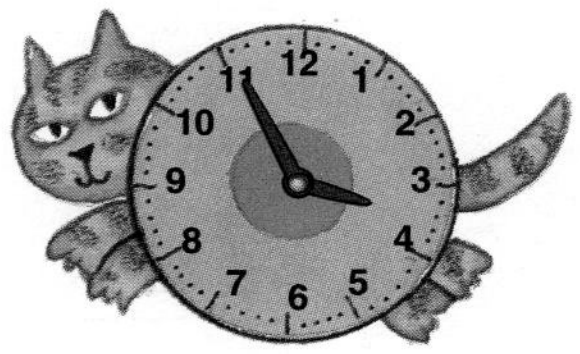

54. **3** : **55**

55. **11** : **09**

56. **8** : **05**

57. **7** : **23**

58. **2** : **28**

NOTE TO HOME
Students review skills presented in this unit.

PRACTICE p. 96

LESSON 96 PRACTICE Name ____________

Solve. Watch the signs.

1. 9 + [7] = 16
2. [6] + 7 = 13
3. [10] + 4 = 14
4. 7 + [3] = 10
5. 18 − 9 = 9
6. 9 + 3 = 12
7. 6 + 5 = 11
8. 14 − 8 = 6
9. 68 + 34 = 102
10. 95 + 45 = 140
11. 72 − 25 = 47
12. 97 − 44 = 53
13. 24 + 46 = 70
14. 80 − 57 = 23
15. 33 − 18 = 15
16. 85 + 68 = 153

What is the right sign? Draw <, >, or =.

17. 35 + 45 (<) 90
18. 60 − 15 (<) 50
19. 25 + 55 (=) 80
20. 8 + 9 (>) 15
21. 100 − 40 (<) 70
22. 10 + 9 (>) 17

96 • *Math Explorations and Applications* Level 2

ENRICHMENT p. 96

LESSON 96 ENRICHMENT Name ____________

The answers and the problems on this page are all mixed up. Draw a line from each problem to the answer it matches.

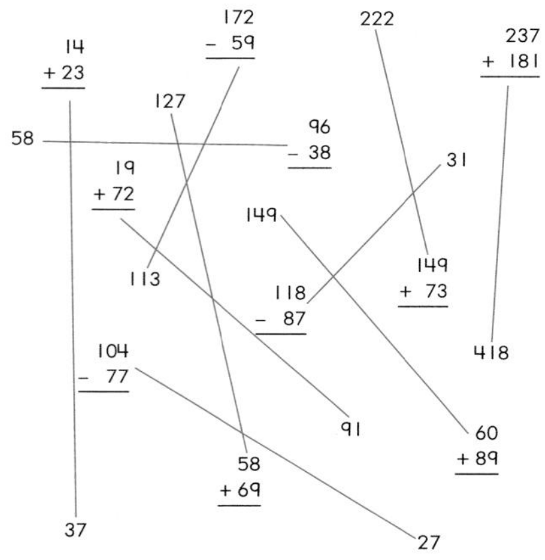

96 • *Math Explorations and Applications* Level 2

3 Wrap-Up (5 MINUTES)

In Closing Discuss with students the problems with which they had difficulty. Invite students to brainstorm methods of improving their skills.

ALTERNATIVE ASSESSMENT

Performance Assessment List four digits on the chalkboard, such as 1, 3, 5, and 7. See which group can make the least sum and the greatest difference using the four digits once. Repeat using other digits.

__ __
+__ __

__ __
+__ __

Assessment Criteria

Did the student . . .

✓ correctly solve at least 48 of the 58 problems on pages 213 through 216?

✓ actively brainstorm methods of improvement after the review exercises?

LESSON 97 Column Addition

Student Edition pages 217–218

LESSON PLANNER

Objective

- ▶ to review methods of adding columns of numbers

Context of the Lesson This is a review and continuation of the topic covered in Lesson 92.

Materials	Program Resources
none	Number Cubes Thinking Story Book, pages 84–87 Practice Master 97 Enrichment Master 97 For extra practice: CD-ROM* Lesson 97

1 Warm-Up (5 MINUTES)

Problem of the Day Write the following problem on the chalkboard: There are 24 students in Mr. Rolling's class and the same number in Ms. Ling's class. There are 27 students in Mrs. Patterson's class. How many students are there in all? (75)

MENTAL MATH Have students add and subtract using their Number Cubes to respond:

a. 8 + 5 = (13)
b. 16 − 8 = (8)
c. 6 + 7 = (13)
d. 11 − 4 = (7)
e. 5 + 4 = (9)
f. 11 − 8 = (3)
g. 8 + 8 = (16)
h. 8 − 5 = (3)

2 Teach

Demonstrate Provide this word problem with four addends: There are 87 students in second grade, 92 in third, 78 in fourth, and 81 in fifth. How many students are there all together? Work with the class to solve the problem. Show the algorithm and the solution on the chalkboard, focusing on regrouping the ones and tens. (87 + 92 + 78 + 81 = 338)

Using the Student Pages Assign pages 217–218 for students to complete independently. When students finish, discuss their methods and solutions, focusing particularly on their strategies for solving the word problems on page 218.

LESSON 97

Name ____________________

Column Addition

Solve these problems. Use shortcuts if you can.

❶ 42 + 86 + 74 = 202	❷ 98 + 76 + 85 = 259	❸ 34 + 29 + 16 = 79	❹ 33 + 53 + 34 = 120
❺ 33 + 33 + 34 + 34 = 134	❻ 25 + 25 + 25 + 25 = 100	❼ 17 + 32 + 21 + 13 = 83	❽ 34 + 63 + 20 + 12 = 129
❾ 76 + 89 + 12 + 96 = 273	❿ 54 + 87 + 69 + 94 = 304	⓫ 75 + 75 + 75 + 75 = 300	⓬ 30 + 30 + 26 + 17 = 103

THINKING STORY Talk about the Thinking Story "I Owe You."

NOTE TO HOME
Students review adding columns of two-digit numbers.

Literature Connection Read aloud or invite students to read *Pigs Will Be Pigs* by Amy Axelrod to reinforce lesson concepts.

RETEACHING

As you walk around the classroom, have students count and record the number of steps you take to measure each of the four sides of the room. Work together to add the numbers in a column. You might wish to draw a map on the chalkboard to show the number of steps you took in each direction.

*available separately

◆ LESSON 97 Column Addition

Solve these problems.

⓭ Mary worked four weeks during the summer. The chart shows how much money she earned. How much money did Mary earn? $ 283

⓮ How far is it from *A* to *B* to *C* to *D* to *E* and back to *A*? 159

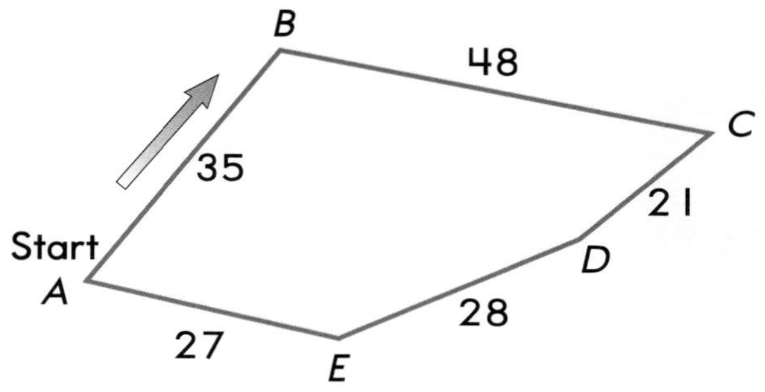

GAME Play the "Roll a Problem" game.

NOTE TO HOME
Students continue reviewing two-digit addition.

PRACTICE p. 97

LESSON 97 PRACTICE Name

Add.

❶ 17 + 28 + 64 = 109	❷ 9 + 62 + 86 = 157	❸ 44 + 84 + 34 = 162
❹ 25 + 15 + 72 + 36 = 148	❺ 30 + 68 + 71 + 11 = 180	❻ 25 + 57 + 36 + 22 = 140
❼ 21 + 86 + 32 + 94 = 233	❽ 75 + 23 + 40 + 17 = 155	❾ 32 + 85 + 16 + 45 = 178

ENRICHMENT p. 97

LESSON 97 ENRICHMENT Name

SILVER	GOLD	BROWN	TAN	BLACK
15 m	16 m	15 m	10 m	20 m

❶ Cal got one roll of brown paper, one roll of gold, and one roll of tan. How much paper did he have? 41 meters

❷ Sandra got one roll of silver and two rolls of black. How much paper did she have? 55 meters

❸ Chuck got two rolls of tan, one roll of gold, and one roll of silver. How much did he have? 51 meters

❹ Barry got three rolls of gold and one roll of brown. How much did he have? 63 meters

❺ Who got the most paper? Barry

❻ Who got the least paper? Cal

❼ Jean needs 61 meters of paper. What will she get? Answers will vary.

GAME **Using the "Roll a Problem" Game** Have students play the game twice. The "Roll a Problem" game was introduced in Lesson 67.

Using the Thinking Story Read aloud the story "I Owe You" on pages 84–87 of the Thinking Story Book. Stop and discuss the questions asked throughout the story. In the story, Mr. Muddle leaves home and forgets to take his wallet or can't remember that he has it in his pocket. Luckily, Mr. Muddle has some honest friends who are good at remembering.

MATH JOURNAL Ask students to write a paragraph explaining what would happen to Mr. Muddle if his friends were as mixed-up as he is.

3 Wrap-Up 5 MINUTES

In Closing Have students make up a problem in which they must add four addends with one or two digits in each. Ask them to solve and trade problems.

ALTERNATIVE ASSESSMENT **Informal Assessment** Use students' solutions to the problems on pages 217–218 as an informal assessment of their ability to add columns of numbers.

Assessment Criteria

Did the student . . .

- ✓ correctly solve 10 of the 12 problems on page 217?
- ✓ correctly solve both word problems on page 218?
- ✓ correctly solve the problems he or she created in the "Roll a Problem" game?
- ✓ participate in the discussion of the Thinking Story?

ESL **Meeting Individual Needs**
Students just learning English might need extra help to understand the chart and map on page 218. Work with these students by having them explain in their own words what each graphic represents.

STORY 14

THINKING STORY

I Owe You

Mr. Muddle usually forgets his wallet when he leaves his house. Even when he remembers that he should take it, he forgets where it is. The only way he can buy things is to borrow money. When he remembers that he owes money, he forgets how much.

Mr. Muddle answered his doorbell one day and found Portia standing there. "I remember that I owe you money for something, but I can't remember what for or how much," said Mr. Muddle.

"I've been delivering your Sunday paper, remember?" said Portia. "You owe me for three weeks. It's $2 for each week."

How much does Mr. Muddle owe? $6

"That's $6," Mr. Muddle said, "but I can't seem to find my wallet right now. Can I pay you tomorrow?"

Portia agreed and returned the next day.

"Here you are," said Mr. Muddle, giving her $12. "Thank you for coming back."

Is Mr. Muddle right? no

How much does he really owe Portia? $6

How much change should Mr. Muddle get? $6

Portia gave Mr. Muddle $6 change. When Mr. Muddle saw the change he remembered something.

What does the change remind him of? the $6 he owed Portia

"You must be mixed up," said Mr. Muddle. "You don't owe me $6. I owe you $6." He gave the $6 back to Portia.

What is Mr. Muddle forgetting? He already paid Portia $6.

What can they do to make things right? Portia can give Mr. Muddle his change.

"Wait, Mr. Muddle," Portia said. "You owed me $6 and you paid me $12. You're forgetting that this $6 is your change. Now take it."

"You're an honest girl," said Mr. Muddle. "And you're good at remembering too."

The next day Mr. Muddle went to the grocery store. He chose three things for a total of $4. "Oops!" he said, as he reached for his wallet. "I seem to have left my wallet at home."

"That's O.K.," said Mrs. Frazier, the owner of the grocery store. "You can owe it to me. That's three things for $4."

That afternoon Mr. Muddle returned and paid Mrs. Frazier $10.

How much does he really owe? $4

How much change should he get? $6

Mrs. Frazier gave him $6 change. Mr. Muddle looked at the money. "You must be mixed up."

"No," said Mrs. Frazier. "That's the right change."

"I'd spend this here," said Mr. Muddle, "but I can't think of six things that I need."

What might have made Mr. Muddle think he needed six things? He thinks everything in the store costs $1.

◆ STORY 14 I Owe You

"I get it," said Mrs. Frazier. "You must think that everything in my store costs $1. But everything has a different price. Your $4 bought three things. Your $6 doesn't have to buy six things. It could buy more and it could buy less."

"Thank you," said Mr. Muddle. "You're an honest woman. And you must be good at remembering. Otherwise you wouldn't be able to remember all the different prices."

Does a grocer really have to remember all the prices? no

Why not? The prices are on the items or the shelves under them.

When Mr. Muddle got home he found Loretta the Letter Carrier waiting for him. "Hi, Mr. Muddle. I've got a letter for you from your brother, but he didn't put enough stamps on it. There's 10¢ postage due."

"Just a minute," said Mr. Muddle, going inside his house. He soon returned. "I'm sorry Loretta, but I can't seem to find my wallet. Can you lend me the 10¢? I'll pay you tomorrow."

Where was Mr. Muddle before he came home? at the grocery store

What did he do there? repay the grocer

Where might his wallet be? in his pocket

When Loretta returned the next day she asked, "Did you find your wallet?"

"It was in my pocket all the time. I'd taken it to the store. Here's 10¢ for the postage due and the 10¢ I borrowed from you," said Mr. Muddle.

How much is Mr. Muddle paying Loretta? 20¢

Is Mr. Muddle mixed up? yes

How? He only owes Loretta 10¢.

"You're mixed up," said Loretta "You owe me only 10¢. You borrowed 10¢ to pay the postage due. You don't owe me any more."

"Thank you, Loretta. You're an honest mail carrier. And you're good at remembering too."

"Mail carriers have to be good at remembering," said Loretta "I, uh . . . I don't suppose you've ever been a mail carrier, have you, Mr. Muddle?"

"Not that I can recall," he said.

What might mail carriers have to remember? addresses, the names of people on their route, when people have moved, and so on

. . . the end

LESSON 98

Student Edition pages 219–220

Column Addition—Finding Perimeter

LESSON PLANNER

Objective

✓ to provide practice for and assessment of column addition

Context of the Lesson This lesson contains Mastery Checkpoint 14 for column addition.

Materials	Program Resources
none	Number Cubes
	Thinking Story Book, pages 88–89
	Practice Master 98
	Enrichment Master 98
	Assessment Masters
	For extra practice: CD-ROM* Lesson 98

1 Warm-Up (5 MINUTES)

Problem of the Day Write the following on the chalkboard and have students complete the patterns:

100, 1, 105, 2, 110, 3, 115, 4, ____, ____, ____ (120, 5, 125)

50, 49, 47, 44, 40, ____, ____, ____ (35, 29, 22)

MENTAL MATH Have students add and subtract using their Number Cubes to respond:

a. 6 + 2 = (8) b. 6 − 3 = (3)

c. 9 + 9 = (18) d. 14 − 6 = (8)

e. 9 + 4 = (13) f. 13 − 4 = (9)

g. 7 + 6 = (13) h. 10 − 6 = (4)

LESSON 98

Name ____________________

Column Addition—Finding Perimeter

Solve these problems.

1. This is part of Mr. Mason's yard. He wants to put a fence around it. What is the perimeter of the yard?

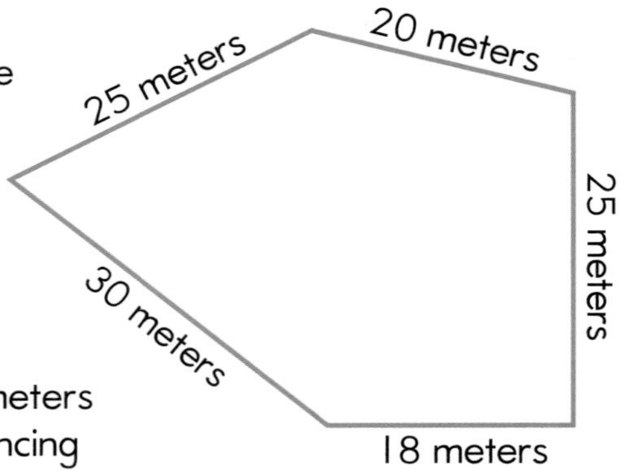

118 meters

2. Each roll of fencing is 25 meters long. How many rolls of fencing does Mr. Mason need?

5

3. The town of Muddleville began 96 years ago. There are 87 people now living in Muddleville. There are also 42 cats in Muddleville.

How many dogs are there in Muddleville? ____

not enough information given

NOTE TO HOME
Students practice solving word problems.

RETEACHING

Review how to add two addends by working with students on several examples such as:

$$\begin{array}{r} 25 \\ +37 \\ \hline (62) \end{array}$$

Once students can work this type of problem, add another addend to each example:

$$\begin{array}{r} 25 \\ 37 \\ +42 \\ \hline (104) \end{array}$$

Discuss how this changes each problem and how to solve them.

PRACTICE p. 98

LESSON 98 PRACTICE Name ____________

Add.

1. 48 + 23 + 77 + 26 = 174
2. 35 + 48 + 3 + 19 = 105
3. 50 + 20 + 10 + 15 = 95
4. 34 + 42 + 27 + 19 = 122
5. 62 + 10 + 30 + 34 = 136
6. 23 + 17 + 58 = 98
7. 29 + 18 + 14 + 55 = 116
8. 18 + 12 + 10 + 59 = 99
9. 32 + 56 + 34 = 122

10. On the Canto family vacation, they drove 43 miles the first day, 69 miles the second day, and 76 miles the third day. How many miles did the Cantos travel in three days? 188

98 • Math Explorations and Applications Level 2

*available separately

◆ **LESSON 98** Column Addition—Finding Perimeter

Use the Mixed Practice on page 386 after this lesson.

Add.

4	5	6	7
64	17	40	10
27	46	40	20
59	73	40	30
+ 12	+ 59	+ 40	+ 40
162	195	160	100

8	9	10	11
34	58	66	22
20	30	20	33
+ 20	+ 10	20	11
74	98	+ 10	+ 10
		136	110

12	13	14	15
23	29	10	18
50	79	97	16
10	88	30	40
+ 28	+ 46	+ 56	+ 17
111	242	183	91

NOTE TO HOME
Students continue practicing two-digit column addition.

❷ Teach

Using the Student Pages Assign pages 219–220 for students to complete independently. When finished, discuss the problem about Muddleville. Students should realize that there is no way to tell how many dogs are in Muddleville. Point out the importance of reading and understanding problems before solving them, rather than simply adding every number presented in the problem.

Using the "Roll a Problem" Game Have students play variations of the "Roll a Problem" game.

Using the Thinking Story Present one or two questions from those following "I Owe You" on pages 88–89 of the Thinking Story Book.

❸ Wrap-Up

5 MINUTES

In Closing Write the following problems on the chalkboard, and have students tell how they are the same and how they are different:

12	12
+24	24
36	+18
	54

Mastery Checkpoint 14

At about this time, most students should be able to add columns of two-digit numbers. Use students' work on pages 219 and 220 or Assessment Masters 42 and 43 to assess their understanding of column addition. Results of this assessment can be listed on the Mastery Checkpoint Chart.

Assessment Criteria

Did the student . . .

- ▶ correctly solve all word problems on page 219?
- ▶ correctly solve ten of the 12 problems on page 220?

ENRICHMENT p. 98

LESSON 98 ENRICHMENT Name ____________________

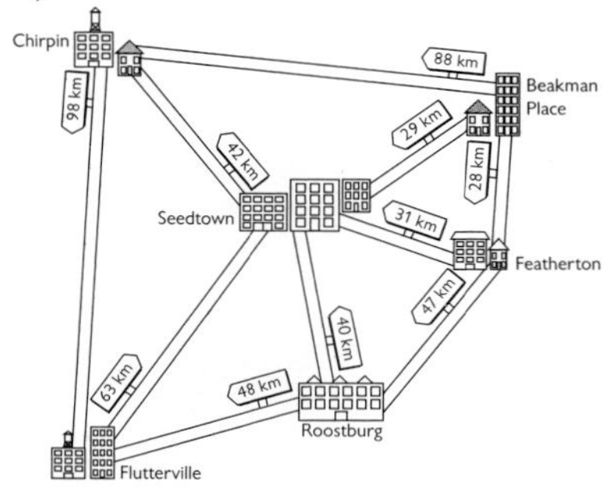

1. A bird flew from Flutterville to Roostberg, then on to Seedtown. How far did it fly? 88 km
2. It flew from Seedtown to Chirpin, then on to Beakman Place and Featherton. How far did it fly? 158 km
3. The bird flew from Featherton to Roostberg, then to Seedtown, then back to Beakman Place. How far did it fly? 116 km
4. It flew from Beakman Place to Seedtown, then to Flutterville and back to Seedtown. How far did it fly? 155 km

98 • *Math Explorations and Applications* Level 2

ASSESSMENT p. 41

UNIT 3

Mastery Checkpoint 14 Column addition (Lesson 98)
Page 1 of 2
Name ____________________

The student demonstrates mastery by correctly answering at least 14 of the 18 problems.

Add.

1	2	3
24	8	50
37	35	50
67	52	50
+ 13	+ 19	+ 50
141	114	200

4	5	6
44	17	3
1	39	60
+ 55	+ 10	20
100	66	+ 10
		93

7	8	9
22	12	31
22	45	9
50	+ 78	26
+ 5	135	+ 53
99		119

Go on . . .

Math Explorations and Applications Level 2 • 41

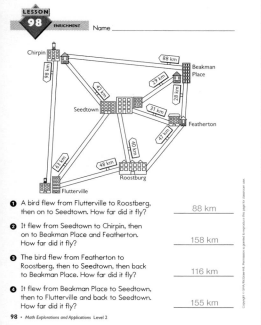

UNIT 3

Student Edition pages 221–222

Mid-Unit Review

The Mid-Unit Review pinpoints troublesome skill areas for students, allowing plenty of time for additional practice and reteaching before the unit ends. If students did not do well on the Mid-Unit Review and have completed additional practice, you might want to use the Mid-Unit Review provided on pages 40–41 in the Assessment Master Book.

Using the Student Pages Have students complete problems 1–25 on pages 221 and 222 on their own. You might treat this review as a formal assessment of students' skills and have students complete this review as a timed test. See suggestions on page 44.

Home Connections You may want to send home Home Connections Masters 45–46 which provide additional activities families can complete together. These activities apply the skills being presented in this unit.

Unit Project This would be a good time to assign the container volume project on pages 262a and 262b. Students may begin working on the project in cooperative groups in their free time as you work through the unit. The Unit Project is a good opportunity for students to compare the capacity of containers, practice using words or symbols to record and interpret information, and compare objects that are the same size but have a different mass or weight and other objects that are of a different size but have the same mass or weight.

UNIT 3

Name ______________________

Mid-Unit Review

What is the right sign? Draw <, >, or =.

1. 30 (<) 40
2. 7 (=) 3 + 4
3. 65 (>) 56
4. 8 (>) 3 + 3

Add.

5. 6 + 3 + 4 = **13**
6. 8 + 4 + 2 = **14**
7. 22 + 37 + 16 = **75**
8. 45 + 16 + 29 = **90**

About what time is it? The hands might not be at exactly that time.

Tell the time to the nearest half hour.

9. 2 : 30

10. 5 : 00

11. 11 : 30

NOTE TO HOME
Students review unit skills and concepts.

What time is it?

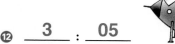

⑫ 3 : 05

⑬ 4 : 12

⑭ Draw in the minute hands to show 5:42.

How many minutes before the hour?

⑮ 15 minutes before 5

⑯ 10 minutes before 8

Add.

⑰ 73	⑱ 35	⑲ 50	⑳ 41
48	26	30	18
39	42	5	29
+ 22	+ 31	+ 40	+ 4
182	134	125	92

NOTE TO HOME
Students review unit skills and concepts.

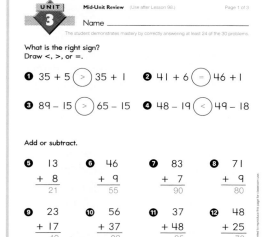

ASSESSMENT p. 44

UNIT 3 **Mid-Unit Review** (Use after Lesson 98.) Page 1 of 3

Name ____________________

The student demonstrates mastery by correctly answering at least 24 of the 30 problems.

What is the right sign?
Draw <, >, or =.

❶ 35 + 5 (>) 35 + 1 ❷ 41 + 6 (=) 46 + 1

❸ 89 − 15 (>) 65 − 15 ❹ 48 − 19 (<) 49 − 18

Add or subtract.

❺ 13 + 8 = 21	❻ 46 + 9 = 55	❼ 83 + 7 = 90	❽ 71 + 9 = 80
❾ 23 + 17 = 40	❿ 56 + 37 = 93	⓫ 37 + 48 = 85	⓬ 48 + 25 = 73
⓭ 37 − 28 = 9	⓮ 48 − 29 = 19	⓯ 56 − 37 = 19	⓰ 50 − 24 = 26

Go on . . .

LESSON 99

Student Edition pages 223–224

Reading Maps

LESSON PLANNER

Objectives

- to introduce and provide practice for reading maps
- to provide experience in adding and comparing numbers in real-world situations

Context of the Lesson This is the first of two lessons that introduce map-reading activities for this grade level. Some basic map-reading experiences were provided in level 1.

Materials	Program Resources
none	"Map" Game Mat
	Number Cubes
	Thinking Story Book, pages 88–89
	Reteaching Master 26
	Practice Master 99
	Enrichment Master 99
	For extra practice: CD-ROM* Lesson 99

1 Warm-Up 5 MINUTES

Problem of the Day Write this problem on the chalkboard: Mike has 35 cents in his pocket. Gina has eight cents more than Mike in her pocket. How much money do they have all together? (78 cents)

MENTAL MATH Have students add and subtract, using their Number Cubes to respond:

a. 7 – 1 = (6)
b. 9 + 6 = (15)
c. 12 – 6 = (6)
d. 7 + 5 = (12)
e. 3 + 8 = (11)
f. 10 – 2 = (8)
g. 8 + 4 = (12)
h. 10 – 5 = (5)

LESSON 99

Name ____________________

Reading Maps

GEOGRAPHY CONNECTION

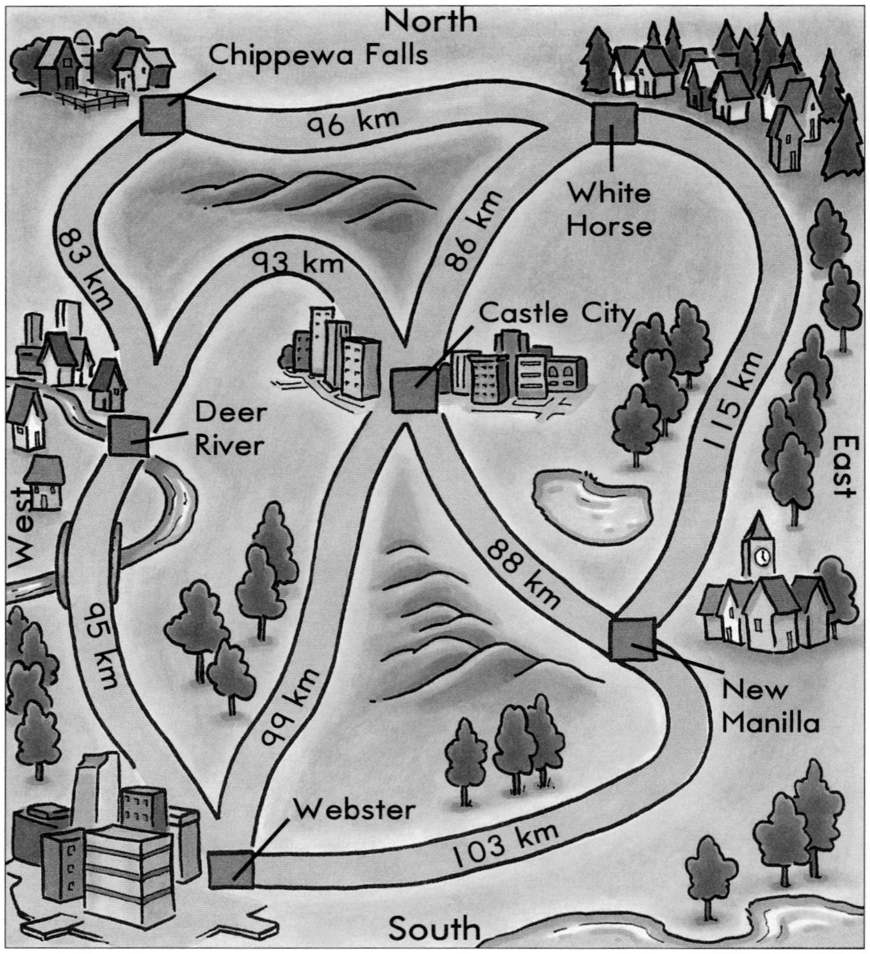

NOTE TO HOME
Students learn to read maps.

Social Studies Connection

Display a political map of the United States. Show students the approximate location of your town. Encourage the students to locate other interesting places on the map, such as Mount Rushmore in the Black Hills of South Dakota or the White House in Washington, D.C. Have students tell which direction they would travel to get to each place from their town.

Literature Connection

Read aloud or invite students to read *As the Roadrunner Runs* by Gail Hartman to reinforce lesson concepts.

RETEACHING p. 26

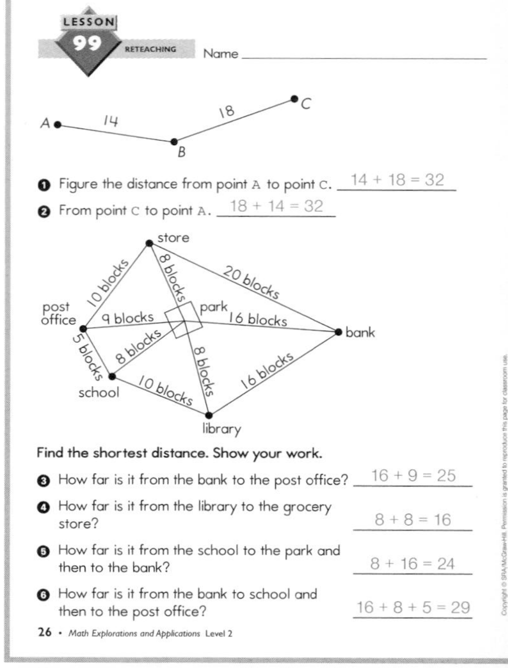
LESSON 99 RETEACHING Name ____________

❶ Figure the distance from point A to point C. 14 + 18 = 32
❷ From point C to point A. 18 + 14 = 32

Find the shortest distance. Show your work.

❸ How far is it from the bank to the post office? 16 + 9 = 25
❹ How far is it from the library to the grocery store? 8 + 8 = 16
❺ How far is it from the school to the park and then to the bank? 8 + 16 = 24
❻ How far is it from the bank to school and then to the post office? 16 + 8 + 5 = 29

26 • Math Explorations and Applications Level 2

*available separately

◆ **LESSON 99** Reading Maps

GEOGRAPHY CONNECTION

Complete the chart. Use the map on page 223 to find the shortest distances.

	Towns	Shortest Distance (kilometers)
1	Chippewa Falls and New Manila	221
2	New Manila and Deer River	181
3	White Horse and Webster	185
4	Chippewa Falls and Webster	178

5. What town is farthest from Castle City? **Chippewa Falls**
6. What town is farthest from Webster? **Chippewa Falls**
7. What town is closest to White Horse? **Castle City**
8. What town is closest to Deer River? **Chippewa Falls**
9. What is the shortest way to get to Deer River from White Horse? **either through Chippewa Falls or Castle City**

GAME

Play the "Map" game.

NOTE TO HOME
Students learn to read maps.

❷ Teach

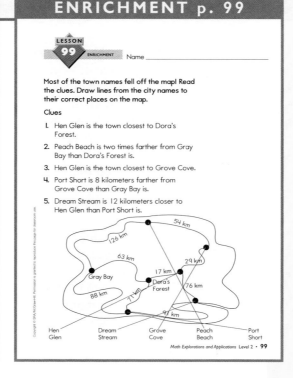

Demonstrate Use the map on page 223 to introduce road distances and directions on maps. Ask questions such as "How far is it from Chippewa Falls to White Horse?" to provide practice for finding distance. To provide experience in using directions, ask questions such as "In which direction do you travel to go from Chippewa Falls to White Horse?" (east)

Using the Student Pages Encourage students to complete page 224 independently. If necessary, do the page with the class, discussing and completing each chart entry one at a time. Point out that road distance between two places is the same no matter from which direction you travel.

Using the Thinking Story Present one or two new problems from those following the story "I Owe You" on pages 88–89 of the Thinking Story Book.

Introducing the "Map" Game Mat Demonstrate and play this game that uses numbers to represent magnitude and direction. Some students might enjoy playing a variation of this game. Complete directions are on the Game Mat.

❸ Wrap-Up

5 MINUTES

In Closing Have students draw a diagram showing the directions North, South, East, and West.

ALTERNATIVE ASSESSMENT

Performance Assessment Observe which students understand directions as they play the "Map" Game Mat.

Assessment Criteria

Did the student . . .

✓ correctly answer the questions you discussed in the demonstration?

✓ correctly complete the chart on page 224?

✓ correctly answer the questions on page 224?

PRACTICE p. 99

LESSON 99 PRACTICE Name ________

Find the shortest distances.

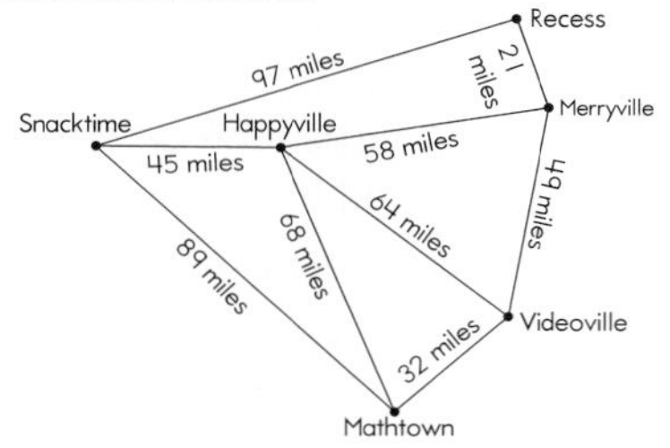

	Town	Shortest Distance (in miles)
1	Snacktime to Videoville	109
2	Merryville to Mathtown	81
3	Snacktime to Merryville	103
4	Mathtown to Recess	102

5. Which town is the farthest from Happyville? Recess
6. Which town is the farthest from Videoville? Snacktime

Math Explorations and Applications Level 2 • **99**

ENRICHMENT p. 99

LESSON 99 ENRICHMENT Name ________

Most of the town names fell off the map! Read the clues. Draw lines from the city names to their correct places on the map.

Clues

1. Hen Glen is the town closest to Dora's Forest.
2. Peach Beach is two times farther from Gray Bay than Dora's Forest is.
3. Hen Glen is the town closest to Grove Cove.
4. Port Short is 8 kilometers farther from Grove Cove than Gray Bay is.
5. Dream Stream is 12 kilometers closer to Hen Glen than Port Short is.

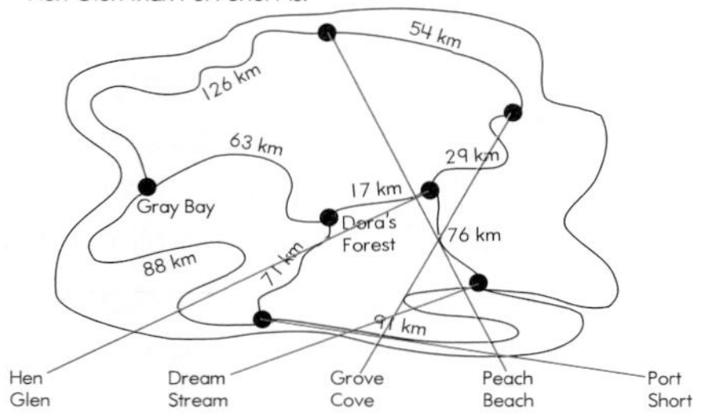

Math Explorations and Applications Level 2 • **99**

LESSON 100

Student Edition pages 225–226

Map Reading

LESSON PLANNER

Objectives

- to continue providing experience in reading maps
- to continue providing experience in adding, subtracting, and comparing numbers

Context of the Lesson This is the second of two lessons that introduce map-reading exercises.

Materials	Program Resources
none	Number Cubes
	"Map" Game Mat
	Thinking Story Book, pages 88–89
	Practice Master 100
	Enrichment Master 100
	For extra practice:
	CD-ROM* Lesson 100

1 Warm-Up

5 MINUTES

Problem of the Day Write this problem on the chalkboard: Jorge lives 14 miles from school. Jenna lives eight miles farther from school than Jorge. How far does Jenna live from school? (22 miles away)

MENTAL MATH Have students add and subtract using their Number Cubes:

a. 7 – 1 = (6)

b. 9 + 6 = (15)

c. 12 – 6 = (6)

d. 7 + 5 = (12)

e. 3 + 8 = (11)

f. 10 – 2 = (8)

g. 8 + 4 = (12)

h. 10 – 5 = (5)

LESSON 100

Name ______________________

Map Reading

GEOGRAPHY CONNECTION

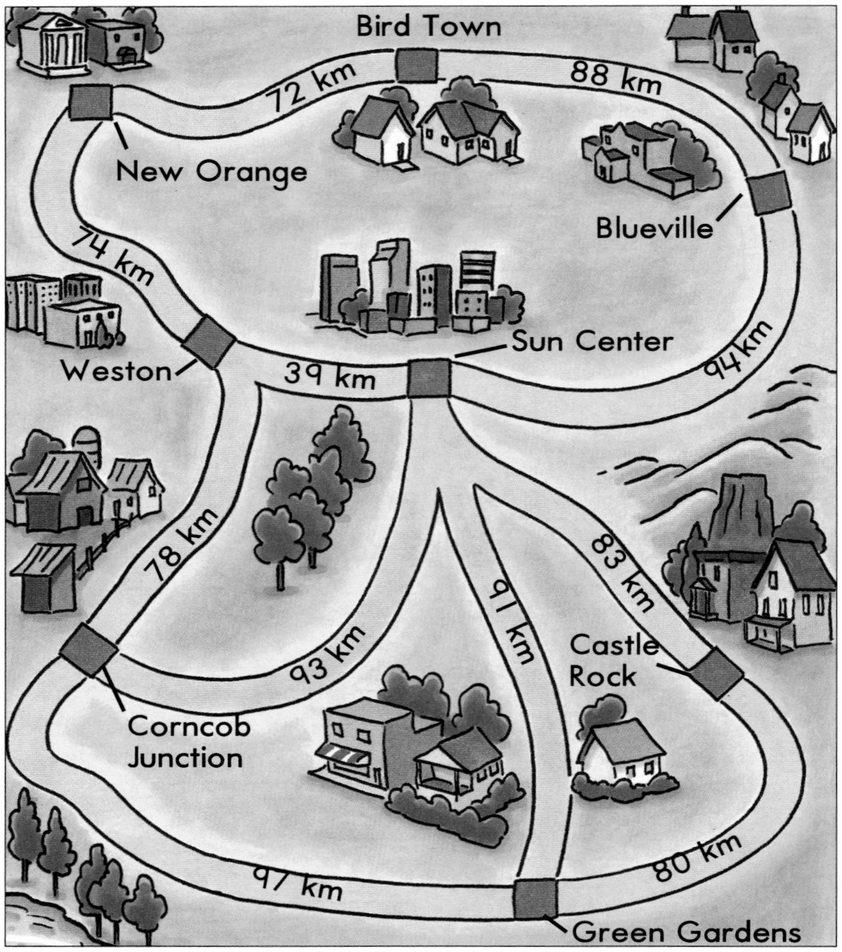

NOTE TO HOME
Students practice reading maps.

CULTURAL DIVERSITY Display a world map. Invite and help students who have relatives in other countries or who were born in countries other than the United States to show where the countries are in relation to the United States. Discuss the distance and direction these students had to travel to come to this country or to go to see their relatives.

Literature Connection Read aloud or invite students to read *As the Crow Flies* by Gail Hartman to reinforce lesson concepts.

RETEACHING

Work with the class to draw a map of the neighborhood surrounding your school. Have students work on their own maps as you draw one on the chalkboard. Ask questions such as, "How shall we show the streets? How shall we show the buildings? How many streets shall we show on our map?" Display completed maps around your classroom.

*available separately

◆ LESSON 100 Map Reading

GEOGRAPHY CONNECTION

Complete the chart. Use the map on page 225 to find the shortest distances.

	Towns	Shortest Distance (kilometers)
1	Blueville and New Orange	160
2	Bird Town and Corncob Junction	224
3	Castle Rock and Corncob Junction	176
4	Green Gardens and New Orange	204

5. Which town is closest to Corncob Junction? Weston
6. Which town is closest to Weston? Sun Center
7. Which town is closest to Sun Center? Weston
8. Which town is farthest from Weston? Green Gardens
9. Which town will you pass through on the road from New Orange to Blueville? Bird Town
10. Take a drive from Corncob Junction through Green Gardens, Sun Center, Weston, and back to Corncob Junction.

    How far did you drive? 305 km

NOTE TO HOME
Students solve word problems that involve reading maps.

② Teach

Demonstrate Use the map on page 225 to review road distances and directions on maps. Ask questions such as, "What is the shortest distance from New Orange to Sun Center?" "How can you tell?" "In which direction do you travel to go from Green Gardens to Corncob Junction?" (west)

Using the Student Pages Encourage students to do the work on page 226 independently. If necessary, do page 226 with the class, discussing and completing each chart entry and question one at a time.

Using the Thinking Story Present two or three new problems from those following the story "I Owe You" on pages 88–89 of the Thinking Story Book.

GAME

Using the "Map" Game Mat Have students play the "Map" game introduced in Lesson 99.

③ Wrap-Up

5 MINUTES

In Closing Have students describe three different routes they could take to go from Corncob Junction to Sun Center.

ALTERNATIVE ASSESSMENT

Informal Assessment Use students' responses to page 226 to informally assess which students understand how to read maps.

PRACTICE p. 100

LESSON 100 PRACTICE Name ______

Find the shortest distances.

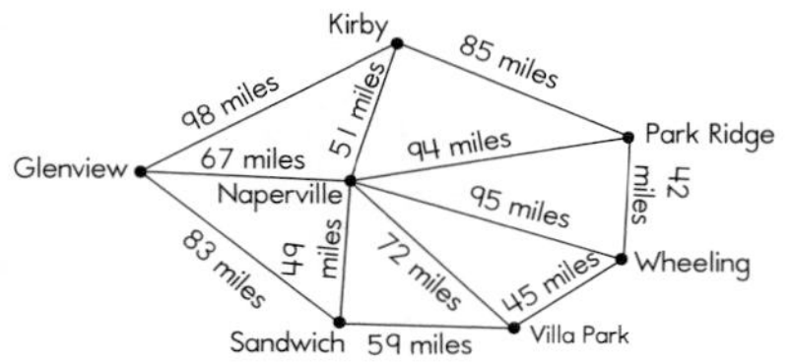

	Town	Shortest Distance (in miles)
1	Villa Park to Glenview	139
2	Wheeling to Kirby	127
3	Park Ridge to Glenview	161
4	Wheeling to Glenview	162

5. Which town is the closest to Naperville? Sandwich
6. Which town is the closest to Villa Park? Wheeling
7. Which town is the closest to Kirby? Naperville

100 • *Math Explorations and Applications* Level 2

ENRICHMENT p. 100

LESSON 100 ENRICHMENT Name ______

Some of the lengths of the walks at the zoo are missing from this map. Read the clues. Write the missing lengths on the walks.

Clues

1. The walk from cats to reptiles is 27 meters shorter than from cats to bears.
2. The total of the walks from cats to apes is 3 meters longer than the one from sea lions to elephants.
3. The walk from elephants to bears is 8 meters longer than the walk from apes to elephants.
4. The walk from birds to zebras is half as long as the walk from cats to bears.
5. The walk from bears to reptiles is half as long as the walk from birds to sea lions.

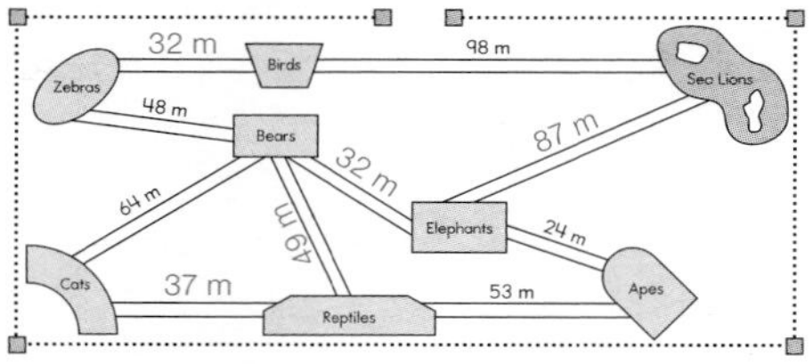

100 • *Math Explorations and Applications* Level 2

Assessment Criteria

Did the student . . .

- ✓ correctly answer the questions you discussed in the demonstration?
- ✓ correctly complete the chart on page 226?
- ✓ correctly answer the questions on page 226?

LESSON 101

Student Edition pages 227–228

Exploring Triangles

LESSON PLANNER

Objectives

- ▶ to help students understand the property of triangles: the lengths of side 1 + side 2 > the length of side 3
- ▶ to provide experience in using equality and inequality signs

Context of the Lesson Students learn about triangles through a process of experimentation and discovery.

Materials	Program Resources
centimeter rulers	Number Strips or strips of paper 9, 6, 5, 4, and 3 centimeters long
	Practice Master 101
	Enrichment Master 101
	For extra practice: CD-ROM* Lesson 101

1 Warm-Up 5 MINUTES

Problem of the Day Write this problem on the chalkboard: There are 21 coins on the floor. There are three more heads than tails. How many are heads? (12)

MENTAL MATH Have students write <, >, or = to solve each problem:

a. 5 + 4 ____ 6 + 2 (>)   b. 7 – 1 ____ 14 – 8 (=)

c. 12 – 3 ____ 10 – 0 (<)   d. 15 – 8 ____ 3 + 3 (>)

e. 7 + 4 ____ 5 + 5 (>)

2 Teach

MATH MANIPULATIVES **Demonstrate** Demonstrate and then have students use any three Number Strips or strips of paper (9, 6, 5, 4, and 3 cm each) to construct as many triangles as they can. As they complete a triangle, have volunteers compare the lengths of the sides of the different triangles they made.

LESSON 101

Name ____________________

Exploring Triangles

Measure the sides of each triangle in centimeters.
Add the lengths of the two shorter sides.
Then write the problem.

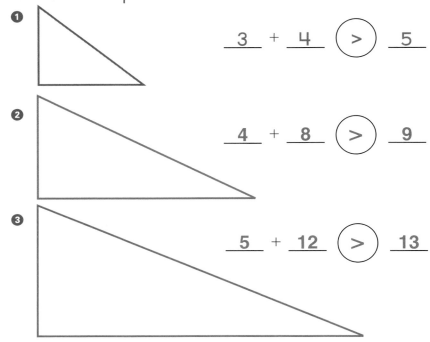

1 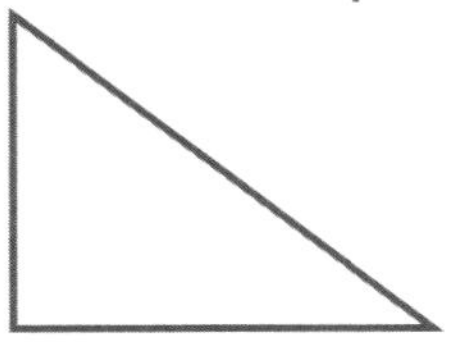

3 + 4 (>) 5

2 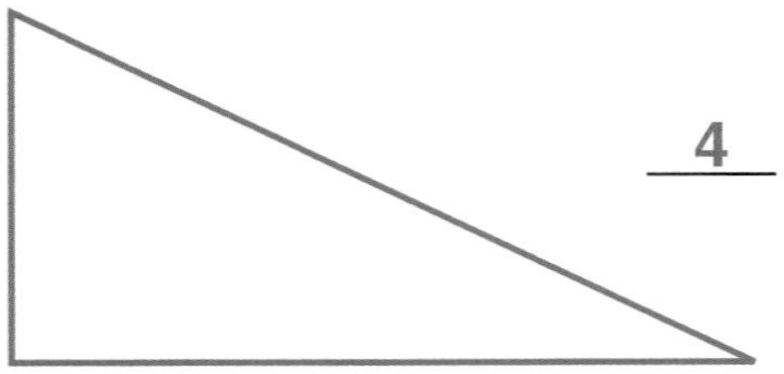

4 + 8 (>) 9

3 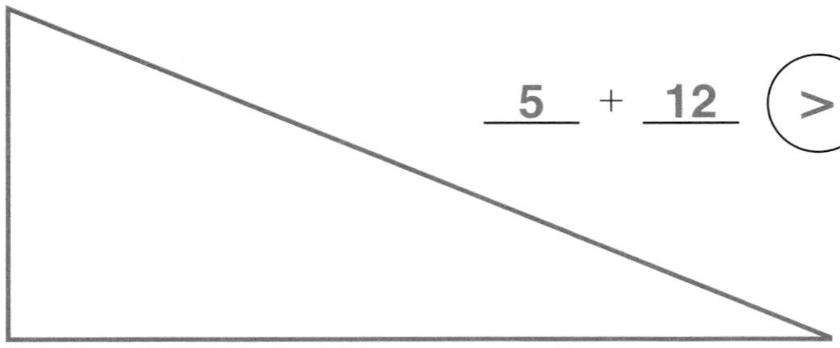

5 + 12 (>) 13

4 Try to make a triangle with strips of paper 9 cm, 6 cm, and 5 cm long. **This is possible.**

5 Now try to make another triangle with strips 9 cm, 4 cm, and 3 cm long. **This is not possible.**

NOTE TO HOME
Students explore properties of the sides of triangles.

RETEACHING

Reteaching of this concept is not recommended at this time because this is an experimentation and discovery lesson.

*available separately

◆ LESSON 101 Exploring Triangles

What is the right sign? Draw <, >, or =.
Is it possible to make a triangle?

6	3 + 4	(>)	5	(yes)	no
7	4 + 6	(>)	5	(yes)	no
8	2 + 10	(>)	10	(yes)	no
9	1 + 10	(>)	10	(yes)	no
10	5 + 6	(>)	10	(yes)	no
11	5 + 5	(=)	10	yes	(no)
12	3 + 4	(<)	10	yes	(no)
13	6 + 6	(>)	6	(yes)	no

NOTE TO HOME
Students continue to explore properties of triangles.

PRACTICE p. 101

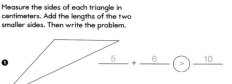

LESSON 101 PRACTICE Name ____________

Measure the sides of each triangle in centimeters. Add the lengths of the two smaller sides. Then write the problem.

1 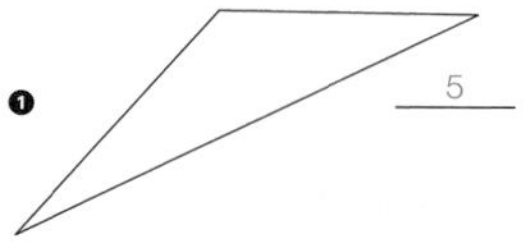 5 + 6 (>) 10

2 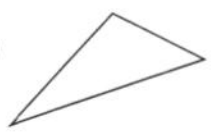 2 + 3 (>) 4

What is the right sign? Draw <, >, or =.
Is it possible to make a triangle?

3	7 + 2	(>)	8	(yes)	no	4	3 + 4	(<)	8	yes	(no)
5	10 + 3	(>)	10	(yes)	no	6	8 + 3	(>)	9	(yes)	no
7	4 + 4	(=)	8	yes	(no)	8	5 + 6	(>)	8	(yes)	no
9	7 + 1	(<)	10	yes	(no)	10	3 + 3	(>)	5	(yes)	no
11	5 + 5	(>)	8	(yes)	no	12	3 + 5	(=)	8	yes	(no)

ENRICHMENT p. 101

LESSON 101 ENRICHMENT Name ____________

Measure the lines in each set of lines. Write yes or no after each set telling whether the lines can make a triangle. Draw the triangles to check your answers.

	Yes or No		Yes or No
1	no	2	yes
3	no	4	yes
5	yes	6	no
7	yes	8	yes

COOPERATIVE LEARNING **Using the Student Pages** Have students work in pairs to complete page 227. Students can use their strips of paper to construct the triangles described at the bottom of the page. Before assigning page 228, discuss the results of the problems on page 227. Guide students to see that the sum of the lengths of two sides of each triangle is always greater than the length of side three. Encourage students to use this rule as they complete page 228. You might wish to complete and discuss the first two problems on this page to be sure students understand this property of triangles.

3 Wrap-Up

5 MINUTES

In Closing Have students tell what they learned about how the length of the sides of triangles are related.

ALTERNATIVE ASSESSMENT **Portfolio Assessment** Have students draw and label the sides of several triangles using their strips of paper. Have them include their triangles in their Math Portfolios.

Assessment Criteria

Did the student . . .

- ✓ make at least three different triangles using strips of paper?
- ✓ correctly complete page 227?
- ✓ correctly answer seven of the eight problems on page 228?

GIFTED & TALENTED

Meeting Individual Needs

Have students find objects or pictures that contain triangles. Ask them to measure and record the lengths of the sides to check that all of the triangles have the property the students discovered in this lesson. Ask students to share their findings with the class.

LESSON 102

Student Edition pages 229–230

Odd and Even Numbers

LESSON PLANNER

Objectives

- to present the concept of odd and even numbers
- to explain how to find half of an even number

Context of the Lesson This is the first of four lessons on odd and even numbers.

Materials	Program Resource
base-10 materials*	Reteaching Master Practice Master 102 Enrichment Master 102 For extra practice: CD-ROM* Lesson 102

1 Warm-Up (5 MINUTES)

Problem of the Day Write this problem on the chalkboard: This year Ben's birthday is on a Monday. He is going to have his party two Saturdays before his birthday. How many days before his birthday will his party be? (9 days)

MENTAL MATH Have students count by twos to complete each of the following:

a. 32, 34, 36, ____ ____ ____ (38, 40, 42)

b. 68, 70, 72, ____ ____ ____ (74, 76, 78)

c. 5, 7, 9, ____ ____ ____ (11, 13, 15)

d. 55, 57, 59, ____ ____ ____ (61, 63, 65)

2 Teach

Demonstrate Show students how to divide a specific number of craft sticks or other base-10 counters in half. Have them count the sticks aloud to see that you have ten sticks total. Then divide them into two equal piles, counting one in one pile and then one in the other, until you have five in each. Repeat with 16 sticks. Explain that when you can divide a number into equal piles with none left over the number is even. Then show that when you try to divide odd numbers equally there is always one left over. Finally, hold

LESSON 102

Name ____________________

Odd and Even Numbers

Ring the odd numbers.
Then write half of each even number.

1. 10 <u>5</u>	2. (11) ____	3. 12 <u>6</u>
4. 14 <u>7</u>	5. (15) ____	6. 16 <u>8</u>
7. 18 <u>9</u>	8. 24 <u>12</u>	9. 20 <u>10</u>
10. 0 <u>0</u>	11. (1) ____	12. (41) ____
13. 4 <u>2</u>	14. (5) ____	15. 2 <u>1</u>
16. 8 <u>4</u>	17. (9) ____	18. 6 <u>3</u>
19. (31) ____	20. 22 <u>11</u>	21. 36 <u>18</u>
22. (25) ____	23. 30 <u>15</u>	24. (27) ____

FANTASTIC FACT A golf ball has more than 400 "dimples."

NOTE TO HOME
Students identify odd and even numbers and find halves.

Literature Connection Read aloud *Number Families* by Jane Jonas Srivastava to reinforce lesson concepts.

RETEACHING p. 27

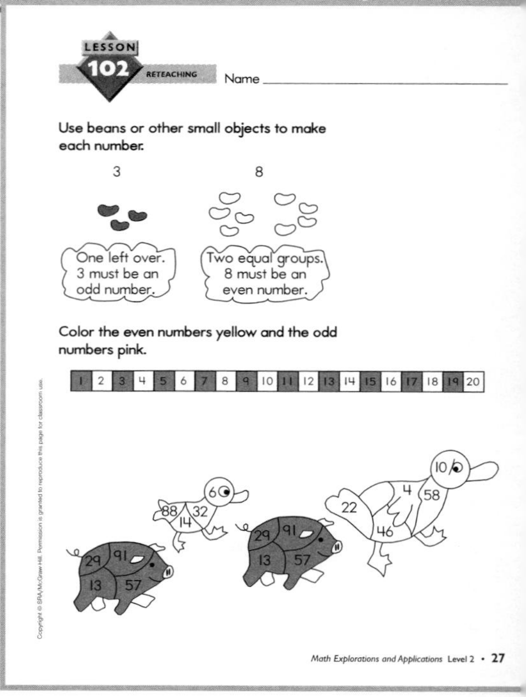
LESSON 102 RETEACHING Name ____________

Use beans or other small objects to make each number.

3 8

One left over. 3 must be an odd number.

Two equal groups. 8 must be an even number.

Color the even numbers yellow and the odd numbers pink.

1 2 3 4 5 6 7 8 9 10 11 12 13 14 15 16 17 18 19 20

Math Explorations and Applications Level 2 • 27

*available separately

◆ LESSON 102 Odd and Even Numbers

Take-Home Activity

GAME

Odds-Evens

Players: Two
Materials: Ten counters

RULES

First Player: You are the "even" player. Choose a number between 0 and 5. Put one hand behind your back with that many fingers extended.

Second Player: You are the "odd" player. Choose a number between 0 and 5. Put one hand behind your back with that many fingers extended.

Both Players: Count "1, 2, 3." Both of you bring your fingers to the front.

Winner: If the total number of fingers showing is even, the "even" player wins. If the total number of fingers showing is odd, the "odd" wins.

Use the Mixed Practice on page 387 after this lesson.

NOTE TO HOME
Students identify odd and even numbers through ten.

up various odd and even numbers of sticks and have students tell whether the numbers are odd or even. When the number is even, have them tell what half is.

GAME **Using the Student Pages** Have students complete page 229 on their own. Allow students to use craft sticks or other counters if needed. Then demonstrate the "Odds-Evens" game on page 230 by playing it with students.

3 Wrap-Up

5 MINUTES

In Closing Ask students to give a definition of *odd* and *even numbers* in their own words. Students should realize that even numbers can be divided evenly into two groups; odd numbers cannot.

ALTERNATIVE ASSESSMENT

Performance Assessment Observe students as they play the game to assess their ability to identify odd and even numbers.

Assessment Criteria

Did the student . . .

✓ correctly complete 20 of the 24 problems on page 229?

✓ correctly identify odd and even numbers when playing the game?

GIFTED & TALENTED

Meeting Individual Needs

Challenge students to take a survey of the classes in your school to find out how many students are in each class. Have them then tell which classes have an odd number of students and which have an even number of students.

PRACTICE p. 102

LESSON 102 PRACTICE Name ______________________

Ring the odd numbers. Then write half of each even number.

1 8 __4__	2 (33) ____	3 (49) ____
4 26 __13__	5 (11) ____	6 40 __20__
7 12 __6__	8 (35) ____	9 (47) ____
10 (9) ____	11 18 __9__	12 10 __5__
13 (15) ____	14 20 __10__	15 14 __7__
16 22 __11__	17 (13) ____	18 28 __14__
19 34 __17__	20 4 __2__	21 (19) ____
22 24 __12__	23 (21) ____	24 60 __30__
25 (45) ____	26 6 __3__	27 (43) ____
28 80 __40__	29 (39) ____	30 (23) ____
31 (17) ____	32 16 __8__	33 2 __1__
34 (25) ____	35 (1) ____	36 0 __0__

ENRICHMENT p. 102

LESSON 102 ENRICHMENT Name ______________________

Ring the number that does not belong in each line.

1	4	6	8	(9)	10	12	14	16
2	11	13	15	17	(20)	21	23	25
3	24	22	20	(19)	18	16	14	12
4	77	75	(74)	73	71	69	67	65

Fill in the missing number in each line.

5	5	10	6	12	7	__14__	8	16
6	22	11	20	10	18	9	16	__8__
7	11	22	12	24	13	26	__14__	28
8	39	37	35	33	31	__29__	27	25
9	9	6	__11__	8	13	10	15	12
10	46	17	44	18	__42__	19	40	20
11	13	23	14	22	15	21	16	__20__
12	1	3	3	__5__	5	7	7	9

LESSON 103

Student Edition pages 231–232

Odds and Evens

LESSON PLANNER

Objective

✓ to provide practice for identifying odd and even numbers by sight

Context of the Lesson This is the second of four lessons on odd and even numbers and contains Mastery Checkpoint 15 for this skill.

Materials	Program Resources
craft sticks or other base-10 materials	Number Cubes Practice Master 103 Enrichment Master 103 Assessment Master For extra practice: CD-ROM* Lesson 103

1 Warm-Up

5 MINUTES

Problem of the Day Write the following on the chalkboard and ask students to complete the patterns:

1, 24, 3, 24, 5, 24, 7, ____, ____, ____, (24, 9, 24)

1, 2, 4, 8, ____, ____, ____, (16, 32, 64)

MENTAL MATH Have students add or subtract, using their Number Cubes to respond:

a. 30 + 70 = (100) **b.** 40 + 80 = (120) **c.** 70 + 90 = (160)

d. 140 – 60 = (80) **e.** 170 – 90 = (80) **f.** 150 – 90 = (60)

2 Teach

Demonstrate Explain that any even number of objects can always be divided into two equal groups. Ask whether *two* is even or odd. Then show that it is even because two items can be divided into two equal piles. Invite volunteers to repeat with other even numbers.

Show that there will always be one stick left over after dividing an odd number of sticks into equal piles.

LESSON 103

Name ____________________

Odds and Evens

Ring the odd numbers.

1. 3   8   7   12   28
2. 41   50   56   59   63

Add. Then ring all the odd numbers.

3. 6 + 5 = 11
4. 2 + 2 = 4
5. 3 + 3 = 6
6. 7 + 8 = 15
7. 9 + 7 = 16
8. 5 + 7 = 12
9. 10 + 5 = 15
10. 6 + 6 = 12
11. 20 + 7 = 27
12. 7 + 7 = 14
13. 29 + 10 = 39
14. 8 + 8 = 16
15. 17 + 14 = 31
16. 12 + 12 = 24
17. 6 + 9 = 15
18. 5 + 5 = 10

NOTE TO HOME
Students explore properties of odd and even numbers.

RETEACHING

Review using sticks or other base-10 materials to demonstrate the single-digit odd and even numbers. Show that two-digit numbers are always odd if their last digit is odd or always even if the last digit is even. Demonstrate with the sticks that any number of tens is always even. Therefore, whether a number is odd or even depends on the digit in the units or ones place.

PRACTICE p. 103

LESSON 103 PRACTICE Name ____________________

1. Ring the odd numbers.

6   5   9   18   11
21   26   33   30   28
44   37   35   50   52

Add. Then ring all the odd numbers.

2. 8 + 5 = 13
3. 6 + 10 = 16
4. 30 + 5 = 35
5. 5 + 5 = 10
6. 9 + 4 = 13
7. 2 + 8 = 10
8. 10 + 10 = 20
9. 7 + 8 = 15
10. 47 + 10 = 57
11. 4 + 4 = 8
12. 3 + 7 = 10
13. 6 + 9 = 15

*available separately

◆ LESSON 103 Odds and Evens

⑲ Ring the even numbers.

0	1	**2**	3	**4**	5	**6**	7	**8**	9
10	11	**12**	13	**14**	15	**16**	17	**18**	19
20	21	**22**	23	**24**	25	**26**	27	**28**	29

Do you see a pattern? Can you use this pattern to decide whether a number is even?

⑳ Ring the even numbers.

60 **88** 97 **100** 247 **356** **482** 611 **998**

㉑ Ring the odd numbers.

3 **7** 12 28 **41** 50 56 **59** **63**

Add. Then ring all the odd numbers.

㉒ 6 + **5** = **9**

㉓ **5** + **7** = 12

㉔ 2 + 2 = 4

㉕ 10 + **5** = **15**

㉖ **3** + **3** = 6

㉗ **7** + **7** = 14

㉘ **7** + 8 = **15**

㉙ **29** + 10 = **39**

㉚ **9** + **7** = 16

㉛ 8 + 8 = 16

NOTE TO HOME
Students explore properties of odd and even numbers.

Demonstrate with sticks to show that adding one to an even number will make that number odd. Show that when students add one stick to an odd number of sticks, the new number will always be even. Point out that 0 is even.

Write different numbers on the chalkboard and have students show "thumbs up" if it is even and "thumbs down" if it is odd. Help students see that the digit in the ones place determines whether the whole number is even or odd.

Using the Student Pages To complete page 231 have students first ring the odd numbers at the top of the page, then do the addition at the bottom of the page. Finally have them ring all of the odd numbers in addition problems including any odd sums. After completing page 232 have students discuss how they arrived at their answers.

3 Wrap-Up (5 MINUTES)

In Closing Have students write a rule for identifying odd and even numbers.

Assessment Criteria

Did the student . . .

✓ correctly identify 21 of the 27 odd numbers on the bottom of page 231?

✓ correctly add eight of the ten problems on page 232?

✓ correctly ring 34 of the 42 odd and even numbers as directed on page 232?

ENRICHMENT p. 103

LESSON 103 ENRICHMENT Name ________________

Fill in the missing numbers.

1	3	5	7	9	11	13	15	17
2	8	10	12	14	16	18	20	22
3	23	21	19	17	15	13	11	9
4	48	46	44	42	40	38	36	34
5	39	41	43	45	47	49	51	53
6	52	54	56	58	60	62	64	66

Ring the problems that add up to odd numbers.

7	31 + 11	**14 + 13**	**8 + 23**
8	13 + 15	17 + 19	**36 + 13**
9	**14 + 23**	12 + 30	51 + 15
10	41 + 19	**8 + 45**	**36 + 15**

ASSESSMENT p. 43

UNIT 3 **Mastery Checkpoint 15** Odd and even numbers (Lesson 103)

Name ________________

The student demonstrates mastery by correctly answering at least 8 of the 10 problems.

Ring the odd numbers.

1	2	**5**	**9**	14	**17**
2	**21**	26	28	**33**	38
3	**43**	44	**45**	46	**47**
4	50	52	**55**	56	**57**
5	**71**	72	74	**77**	**81**

Ring the even numbers.

6	1	3	**4**	5	**6**
7	13	**16**	**18**	21	**22**
8	35	**36**	39	41	**44**
9	**58**	63	75	**82**	**98**
10	81	83	**84**	87	89

Mastery Checkpoint 15

By the end of this lesson students should be able to identify odd and even numbers by sight. You can assess their performance during the demonstration or use Assessment Master 39. You may record the students' scores on the Mastery Checkpoint Chart.

LESSON 104

Student Edition pages 233–234

Adding Odds and Evens

LESSON PLANNER

Objective

▶ to help students discover and use information about addition of odd and even numbers

Context of the Lesson This is the third of four lessons on odd and even numbers.

Materials	Program Resources
counters	Practice Master 104
	Enrichment Master 104
	For extra practice: CD-ROM* Lesson 104

1 Warm-Up

5 MINUTES

Problem of the Day Write this problem on the chalkboard: You want to put three books on a shelf in order. How many different ways can you order them on a shelf? (6)

MENTAL MATH Have students tell whether each number is odd or even:

a. 21 (odd) **b.** 27 (odd)
c. 69 (odd) **d.** 39 (odd)
e. 73 (odd) **f.** 82 (even)
g. 45 (odd) **h.** 91 (odd)
i. 51 (odd) **j.** 30 (even)

2 Teach

Demonstrate Ask students whether they think the sum of two even numbers will be odd or even. Have volunteers come up to the chalkboard and give examples to support their answers. For example, 8 + 10 = 18; 4 + 2 = 6; 6 + 4 = 10. Ask students what they think the rule E + E = E means. (Even + Even = Even) Have students work in groups to complete the following rules by experimenting with adding different numbers:

E + O = ____ (O) O + E = ____ (O) O + O = ____ (E)

LESSON 104

Name ______________________

Adding Odds and Evens

Look at the digits in the ones place.
24
+32

Think: even + even = even
odd + odd = even
even + odd = odd
odd + even = odd

Ring each wrong answer.
(Eight of the answers are wrong.)

1. 18 + 26 = 44
2. 41 + 23 = 75
3. 37 + 58 = 94
4. 67 + 22 = 89
5. 39 + 39 = 78
6. 54 + 19 = 73
7. 47 + 35 = 83
8. 35 + 47 = 83
9. 45 + 45 = 90
10. 78 + 19 = 96
11. 17 + 58 = 74
12. 35 + 28 = 62
13. 35 + 35 = 70
14. 8 + 77 = 86

NOTE TO HOME
Students continue to explore properties of odd and even numbers.

Literature Connection Read aloud or invite students to read *Domino Addition* by Lynette Long to reinforce lesson concepts.

RETEACHING

Remind students that they can tell whether a number is odd or even simply by looking at the ones digit. Have students identify numbers with tens and hundreds as odd or even. Have them write "odd" or "even" on two index cards. Write the following numbers on the chalkboard one at a time: 124, 431, 572, 36, 43, 468. Invite students to hold up the appropriate index card each time.

*available separately

◆ LESSON 104 Adding Odds and Evens

Ring the odd numbers.

15	(3)	6	(9)	12	(15)	18	(21)
16	(7)	10	(13)	16	(19)	22	(25)
17	2	(5)	8	(11)	14	(17)	20

PROBLEM SOLVING

Solve the problems. Ring the odd number answers.

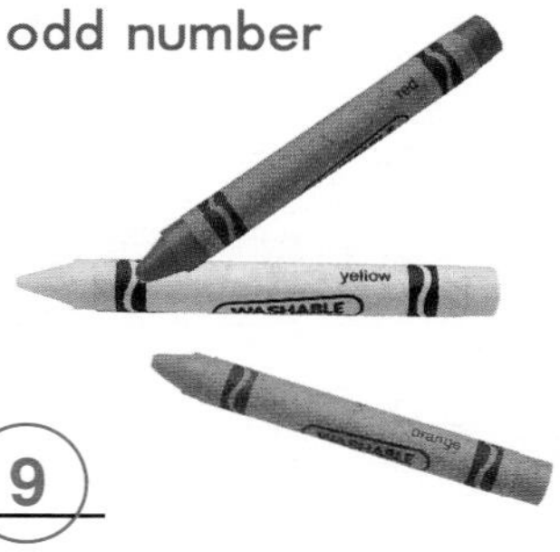

18 Rico has 24 crayons. If he loses 15 of them, how many will be left?

24 (−) 15 = (9)

19 Ashley has 32 jumbo crayons and 48 small crayons. How many crayons in all?

32 (+) 48 = 80

NOTE TO HOME
Students continue exploring properties of odd and even numbers.

PRACTICE p. 104

LESSON 104 PRACTICE Name ______

Ring and correct each wrong answer. Watch the signs. (Eight answers are wrong.)

1 35 + 16 = 51 ______	2 68 + 14 = (83) 82
3 45 − 27 = 18 ______	4 22 − 18 = 4 ______
5 44 − 15 = (28) 29	6 49 + 29 = (77) 78
7 25 + 25 = 50 ______	8 81 − 17 = (65) 64
9 39 + 10 = 49 ______	10 25 + 48 = (74) 73
11 64 + 15 = (80) 79	12 17 + 17 = 34 ______
13 85 − 19 = (67) 66	14 4 + 49 = 53 ______
15 72 − 15 = (56) 57	16 34 − 12 = 22 ______

104 • *Math Explorations and Applications* Level 2

ENRICHMENT p. 104

LESSON 104 ENRICHMENT Name ______

Ring the two numbers on the left that add up to the number on the right.

1	(149)	206	(101)	194	84	250
2	(46)	(48)	66	35	63	94
3	155	62	(86)	114	(87)	173
4	54	(14)	68	(71)	42	85
5	114	168	(212)	98	(102)	314
6	52	81	(70)	54	(37)	107
7	253	69	(382)	401	(95)	477
8	(350)	205	212	(191)	420	541

104 • *Math Explorations and Applications* Level 2

Then write several addition problems on the chalkboard, such as 43 + 53 = ______ (even), and have students tell whether the sums are odd or even by applying the rules they discovered.

Using the Student Pages Have students use what they learned about odd and even sums to complete these pages independently. There are eight errors on page 233.

3 Wrap-Up

5 MINUTES

In Closing Have students say the rules they learned about sums of odd and even numbers.

ALTERNATIVE ASSESSMENT

Portfolio Assessment Have students write and keep the rules about odd and even numbers in their Math Portfolios.

Assessment Criteria

Did the student . . .

✓ find seven of the eight errors on page 233?

✓ ring nine of the 11 odd numbers on page 234?

✓ correctly solve both word problems on page 234?

LEARNING STYLES

Meeting Individual Needs

Have kinesthetic learners use counters to experiment with odd and even numbers. Write the following numbers on the chalkboard: 8, 11, 5, 14. Have students model each number using counters. Tell them to try to separate the counters into two equal groups. Explain that when they can do this, the number is even, and when they cannot, the number is odd. Have students then use the counters to add odd and even numbers and check to see that the sums follow the rules.

LESSON 105

Student Edition pages 235–236

Subtracting Odds and Evens

LESSON PLANNER

Objective

▶ to help students discover and use information about subtraction of odd and even numbers

Context of the Lesson This is the last of four lessons on odd and even numbers.

Materials	Program Resources
none	Thinking Story Book, pages 90–93
	Reteaching Master
	Practice Master 105
	Enrichment Master 105
	For extra practice: CD-ROM* Lesson 105

1 Warm-Up

5 MINUTES

Problem of the Day Write the following problem on the chalkboard: Roberto is taller than Sal, but not as tall as Manuel. Paul is not taller than Roberto or Sal. List the boys in order from shortest to tallest. (Paul, Sal, Roberto, Manuel)

MENTAL MATH Have students tell whether each sum is odd or even:

a. 17 + 46 = (63, odd) **b.** 33 + 19 = (52, even)

c. 51 + 27 = (78, even) **d.** 81 + 11 = (92, even)

e. 62 + 18 = (80, even) **f.** 10 + 71 = (81, odd)

2 Teach

COOPERATIVE LEARNING **Demonstrate** Ask students whether they think the subtraction rules for even and odd numbers will be the same as addition rules. Have them work in small groups to experiment and discuss the following rules:

E – E = _____ (E) O – E = _____ (O)

E – O = _____ (O) O – O = _____ (E)

After groups have arrived at answers they all agree on, have them share and compare their results. Students should realize that the rules are similar to those for addition.

LESSON 105

Name ____________________

Subtracting Odds and Evens

Use what you know about odd and even numbers. Ring each wrong answer. (Nine of the answers are wrong.)

1. 43 – 29 = 15
2. 86 – 34 = 53
3. 27 – 6 = 21
4. 82 – 13 = 58
5. 93 – 6 = 77
6. 100 – 35 = 66
7. 100 – 27 = 73
8. 81 – 59 = 22
9. 50 – 18 = 33
10. 84 – 25 = 58
11. 65 – 37 = 29
12. 100 – 25 = 75
13. 83 – 30 = 53
14. 60 – 54 = 6
15. 27 – 24 = 50
16. 39 – 19 = 21

NOTE TO HOME
Students continue to explore properties of even and odd numbers.

Literature Connection Read aloud or invite students to read the story "The Great Mail Mix-Up" in *Look Both Ways: City Math* by Time-Life, Inc. to reinforce lesson concepts.

Real-World Connection Take a walk around the school neighborhood with students. Have them observe house numbers on both sides of the streets. When you return discuss how odd and even numbers are used in addresses. Generally, odd numbered buildings or homes are on one side of the street and even numbers are on the other.

RETEACHING p. 28

LESSON 105 RETEACHING Name ____________________

You can divide even numbers into two equal groups. These are even numbers: 2, 4, 6, and 8.

You cannot divide odd numbers into two equal groups—you'll always have one left over. These are odd numbers: 1, 3, 5, 7, and 9.

Ring the even numbers. Box the odd numbers.

1. 68 – 24 = 44
2. 75 – 11 = 64
3. 86 – 42 = 44
4. 55 – 13 = 42
5. 78 – 14 = 64

Solve.

6. 69 – 33 = 36
7. 66 – 21 = 45
8. 27 – 15 = 12
9. 65 – 13 = 52
10. 99 – 27 = 72

Solve these problems.

11. What kind of number do you get when you subtract an even number from an even number? even
12. What kind of number do you get when you subtract an odd number from an odd number? odd
13. What happens when you subtract an odd number from and even number or an even number from an odd number? You get an odd number.

28 • *Math Explorations and Applications* Level 2

*available separately

◆ LESSON 105 Subtracting Odds and Evens

Ring each wrong answer.
(Five of the answers are wrong.)

17. 48 + 69 = (106)	18. 73 + 81 = 154	19. 94 − 27 = 67	20. 83 + 72 = 155
21. 96 − 81 = 15	22. 42 + 98 = 140	23. 50 + 50 = 100	24. 26 + 38 = 64
25. 87 − 69 = 18	26. 73 + 86 = (158)	27. 90 − 78 = (21)	28. 98 − 35 = 63
29. 90 − 76 = 14	30. 75 + 25 = (95)	31. 43 − 41 = 2	32. 47 + 83 = (131)

THINKING STORY

Talk about the Thinking Story "Sharing with Cousin Trixie."

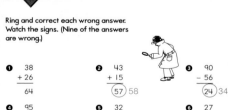

NOTE TO HOME
Students continue to use what they know about odd and even numbers.

Then write several subtraction problems on the chalkboard, such as 33 - 13 = _____ (even), and have students tell whether the sums are odd or even by applying the rules they discovered. Finally, present both addition and subtraction problems and have students identify the answers as odd or even numbers.

Using the Student Pages Have students complete these pages independently. There are nine errors on page 235 and five errors on page 236. Remind students to use the addition and subtraction rules to find the errors, rather than to calculate each problem.

Using the Thinking Story Read aloud the story "Sharing with Cousin Trixie" on pages 90–93 of the Thinking Story Book. Stop and discuss the questions asked throughout the story. In the story, Ferdie has one bottle of soda pop and two cups. With Portia and Cousin Trixie, he works to divide the soda pop equally among the three of them.

MATH JOURNAL

Ask students to write about a time when they shared fairly with others.

3 Wrap-Up

5 MINUTES

In Closing Have students write the rules they learned about subtraction of odd and even numbers.

ALTERNATIVE ASSESSMENT

Informal Assessment Use students' responses to pages 235 and 236 to assess their understanding of the rules.

Assessment Criteria

Did the student . . .

- ✓ identify odd and even sums and differences in the demonstration?
- ✓ ring seven of the nine errors on page 235?
- ✓ ring three of the five errors on page 236?
- ✓ participate in the discussion of the Thinking Story?

LOOKING AHEAD A double-pan balance scale or metric scale will be needed for Lesson 106.

PRACTICE p. 105

LESSON 105 PRACTICE Name ______________

Ring and correct each wrong answer. Watch the signs. (Nine of the answers are wrong.)

1. 38 + 26 = 64	2. 43 + 15 = (57) 58	3. 90 − 56 = (24) 34
4. 95 − 7 = (89) 88	5. 32 + 49 = 81	6. 27 + 89 = (106) 116
7. 87 + 63 = 150	8. 50 − 18 = (42) 32	9. 83 + 46 = 129

10. 36 − 27 = 9 ______
11. 25 + 86 = (101) 111
12. 80 − 46 = (24) 34
13. 79 − 29 = 50 ______
14. 40 − 8 = 32 ______
15. 35 − 14 = (49) 21
16. 24 − 19 = 5 ______
17. 36 + 17 = (19) 53

ENRICHMENT p. 105

LESSON 105 ENRICHMENT Name ______________

Write a number from Jar A and a number from Jar B to make a problem for each sum.

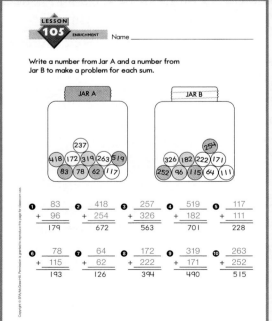

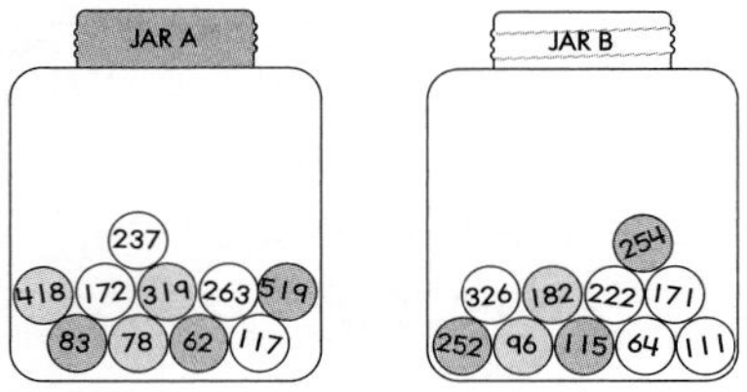

1. 83 + 96 = 179	2. 418 + 254 = 672	3. 257 + 326 = 563	4. 519 + 182 = 701	5. 117 + 111 = 228
6. 78 + 115 = 193	7. 64 + 62 = 126	8. 172 + 222 = 394	9. 319 + 171 = 490	10. 263 + 252 = 515

STORY 15

THINKING STORY

Sharing with Cousin Trixie

[It will be easier for the students to grasp the ideas in this story if you have available two identical drinking glasses and a soft-drink bottle with straight sides.]

One day while his cousin Trixie was staying at his house, Ferdie brought home a bottle of soda pop. He knew that Portia was playing in the park across the street, so he got two plastic cups from the kitchen and took them to the park with him.

"I have some soda pop to share," said Ferdie when he saw Portia.

Cousin Trixie was in the park with Portia. When she noticed the cups and the bottle in Ferdie's hand she said, "Aren't you forgetting something?"

What might Trixie think Ferdie was forgetting? a cup for her

"You need another cup," Trixie said. "There is no way three people can share a bottle of soda pop if there are only two cups."

Is Cousin Trixie right? no

How can the three of them share the soda pop although there are only two cups? One of them can drink out of the bottle.

"One of us can drink out of the bottle," said Portia. "That way we won't need to get another cup."

"But how will we be sure we all get the same amount?" said Ferdie. "It's hard when the cups are one shape and the bottle is another shape."

Why would that make it hard to divide the soda evenly? If all the containers are alike, you can get equal amounts by filling them to the same level; but when the containers are of different sizes or shapes, that doesn't work.

"I have an idea," said Portia. "We'll pour a little in one cup and then a little in the second cup, then a little more in the first cup and a little more in the second cup, and then a little more in the first cup, and then a little more in the second cup–and that way the cups will have the same amount."

"There's something wrong with that," said Ferdie.

What's wrong with Portia's way of dividing the soda? There's no way to know whether the amount in the bottle is the same as in one of the cups.

◆ STORY 15 Sharing with Cousin Trixie

"The two people who get the cups might get the same amount," Cousin Trixie said, "but the person who gets the bottle wouldn't get the same as the others. I have a better idea. I'll show you."

Cousin Trixie took the bottle and poured soda out of it into one of the cups. She poured until the bottle was about half empty. "There. Now the cup and the bottle have the same amount, right?" she said.

Is Cousin Trixie right? Yes, that should be approximately right. [If students disagree, you might try it with an actual bottle and glass, then pour the remainder of the bottle into the other glass to show that the amounts are equal.]

Next Cousin Trixie took the cup that had soda pop in it and poured soda pop from it into the other cup until the two cups were filled to the same level. "Now the cups have the same amount in them too. So everything is even. I'll take the bottle and each of you can have a cup. Is everybody happy?"

"I'm not," said Ferdie.

"Neither am I," said Portia.

Why should Ferdie and Portia be unhappy? Trixie was getting more soda pop than they were.

About how much of the soda pop did each person get? Trixie got half and Ferdie and Portia each got half of a half, or a fourth, of the soda pop.

Can you think of a fairer way to divide the soda pop? [The students' suggestions might be tested with the actual bottle and glasses. A fair way might be to pour soda pop into the glasses until the bottle is only one-third full, then adjust the amounts in the glasses to make them equal. That way each person would get about one third of the bottle.]

. . . the end

LESSON 106

Student Edition pages 237–238

Kilograms and Grams

LESSON PLANNER

Objectives

- ▶ to introduce the gram and kilogram as standard units of weight
- ▶ to explain the relationship between grams and kilograms
- ▶ to provide experience in measuring weight in metric units
- ▶ to provide experience in converting kilograms to grams by counting in thousands

Context of the Lesson This is the first of six lessons on measurement.

Materials	Program Resources
double-pan balance scale* with metric weights or metric scale	Thinking Story Book, pages 94–95 Practice Master 106 Enrichment Master 106 For extra practice: CD-ROM* Lesson 106

1 Warm-Up

5 MINUTES

Problem of the Day Write this problem on the chalkboard: Morgan is third in line. Harry is seven places behind Morgan. Jerry is four places in front of Harry. The teacher told students standing in odd numbered places to sit. Should Morgan sit? Harry? Jerry? (Yes; No; No)

MENTAL MATH Have students tell whether each sum is odd or even:

- **a.** 6 + 4 = (10, even)
- **b.** 8 + 4 = (12, even)
- **c.** 8 − 5 = (3, odd)
- **d.** 6 + 6 = (12, even)
- **e.** 15 − 9 = (6, even)
- **f.** 7 + 5 = (12, even)

2 Teach

Demonstrate Use page 237 as a guide to introduce kilograms and grams. Read the top of page 237 with students. Then ask: "If there are 1000 grams in 1 kilogram,

LESSON 106

Name ______________________

Kilograms and Grams

The kilogram and the gram are units of weight.
There are 1000 grams in 1 kilogram.

How many?

1. 1 kilogram = 1000 grams
2. 2 kg = 2000 g
3. 3 kg = 3000 g
4. 4 kg = 4000 g
5. 10 kg = 10,000 g
6. 5 kg = 5000 g

NOTE TO HOME
Students learn how grams and kilograms are related.

RETEACHING

Take advantage of normal classroom activities that lend themselves to estimating and measuring weights. For example, ask students how much they think the books they will take home might weigh. Then have them weigh them on a metric scale.

*available separately

◆ LESSON 106 Kilograms and Grams

COOPERATIVE LEARNING

How much does it weigh?

Unit ____________

Objects	Estimate Weight	Measure Weight	Difference

FANTASTIC FACT

One ton of recycled waste paper saves 17 trees.

NOTE TO HOME
Students estimate and weigh a variety of objects.

how many grams are there in 2 kilograms?" (2000) Write 2000 on the chalkboard and read the number aloud. Then ask questions such as, "How many grams are there in ten kilograms?" Next, show students how to measure the weight of objects in these units. Complete the items on page 237. Explain that they will use a scale, if available, to measure the weight of various objects just as you did in this demonstration.

COOPERATIVE LEARNING **Using the Student Pages** Have students complete page 237 independently. After they complete page 237, guide them to see that all of the answers are multiples of 10 and that to change kilograms to grams they need only add the correct number of zeros to the number of kilograms given. Have them complete page 238 in small groups.

Using the Thinking Story Present one or two problems from those following "Sharing with Cousin Trixie" on page 94–95 of the Thinking Story Book.

3 Wrap-Up

5 MINUTES

In Closing Have students describe how they change kilograms to grams.

PRACTICE p. 106

LESSON 106 PRACTICE Name ____________

How many grams?

The kilogram and the gram are units of weight. There are 1000 grams in 1 kilogram.

1. 6 kg = 6000 g
2. 4 kg = 4000 g
3. 3 kg = 3000 g
4. 11 kg = 11,000 g

5. Find things to weigh. Estimate first. Then weigh.

Things	Estimate Weight	Measure Weight	Difference

Answers will vary.

106 • *Math Explorations and Applications* Level 2

ENRICHMENT p. 106

LESSON 106 ENRICHMENT Name ____________

Fit these words into the puzzle.

CENTIMETER VALUE
BALANCE DAY
KILOGRAM FAR
METER
YEARS
GRAM

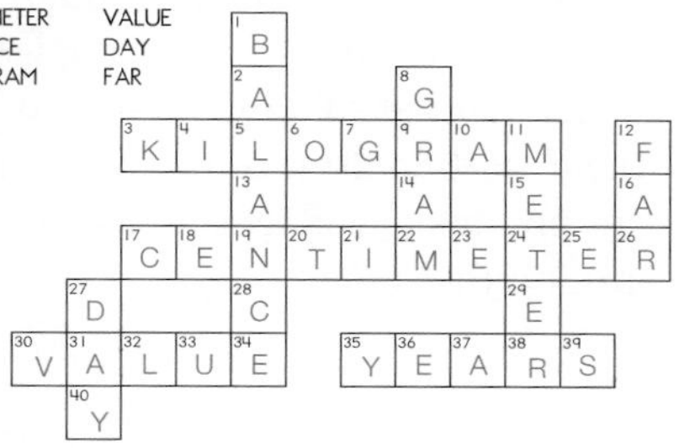

Now find the secret message.

I	T		I	S		E	A	S	Y		
21	24		4	39		18	10	39	35		
T	O		B	E		B	R	A	V	E	
20	6		1	18		1	9	13	30	34	
F	R	O	M		A		S	A	F	E	
12	26	6	22		31		39	13	12	15	
D	I	S	T	A	N	C	E.				
27	21	39	20	13	19	17	34				

106 • *Math Explorations and Applications* Level 2

Assessment Criteria

Did the student . . .

- ✓ correctly solve five of the six problems on page 237?
- ✓ make sensible estimates in the charts on page 238?
- ✓ weigh objects correctly and record the weights on page 238?

LESSON 107

Student Edition pages 239–240

Pounds and Ounces

LESSON PLANNER

Objectives

- ▶ to introduce standard units of measure for weight
- ▶ to help students develop an understanding of weight in pounds and ounces

Context of the Lesson This lesson parallels Lesson 42 in which students learned to measure length in standard units of measure.

Materials	Program Resources
magazine pictures of small and large objects	Number Cubes
supermarket ads (optional)	Practice Master 107
	Enrichment Master 107
	For extra practice: CD-ROM* Lesson 107

1 Warm-Up

5 MINUTES

Problem of the Day Write this problem on the chalkboard: I have two digits. The sum of my digits is 14. The difference between my digits is 2. What number am I? (86)

MENTAL MATH Have students add or subtract the following, using their Number Cubes to respond.

a. 15 – 8 = (7) b. 11 – 7 = (4) c. 5 + 8 = (13)
d. 7 + 3 = (10) e. 16 – 9 = (7) f. 6 + 8 = (14)

2 Teach

Demonstrate Explain to students that there are 16 ounces in a pound. Show several objects, such as a paper clip, piece of chalk, chair, and computer. Ask students to tell whether they would weigh each object in pounds or ounces. Students should realize that the lighter objects would be weighed in ounces, while the heavier ones would be weighed in pounds.

Using the Student Pages Have students complete pages 239 and 240 with a partner. Then go over each page with the class, encouraging students to share and explain how they arrived at their answers.

LESSON 107

Name ______________________________

Pounds and Ounces

The pound and the ounce are units of weight.
There are 16 ounces in 1 pound.

Ring the better answers.

1. How many ounces in a pound? 1 ounces (16 ounces)
2. How much does one grape weigh? 1 pound (1 ounce)
3. How much does a book weigh? (1 pound) 1 ounce
4. How much does a pencil weigh? more than 1 pound (less than 1 pound)
5. How much do you weigh? (more than 1 pound) less than 1 pound

NOTE TO HOME
Students estimate using pounds and ounces.

Real-World Connection Have students look through supermarket ads to find examples of items that are sold by the pound. Have them work in groups to cut out the ads and make collages to display around the room.

RETEACHING

Have students cut out pictures of large and small objects from magazines. Display each picture one at a time and discuss whether you would weigh each object in pounds or ounces.

*available separately

◆ **LESSON 107** Pounds and Ounces

Use the Mixed Practice on page 388 after this lesson.

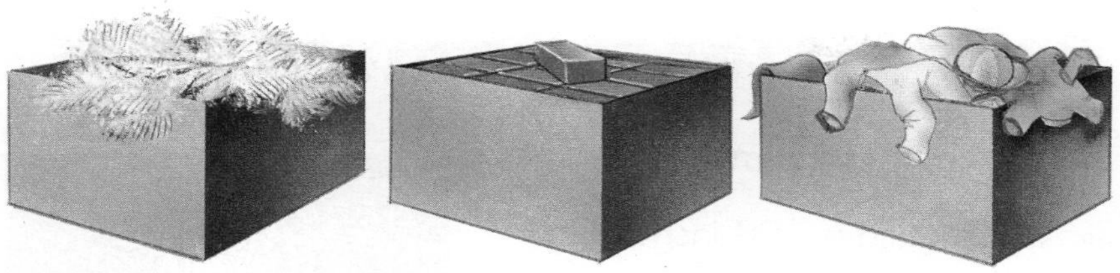

feathers bricks clothes

6. Which box weighs the most? **bricks**
7. Which box weighs the least? **feathers**

Becky weighs more than Libby but less than Goldie.

8. Who weighs the most? **Goldie**
9. Who weighs the least? **Libby**

Martin weighs 112 pounds. Mollie weighs 118 pounds. Maris weighs 99 pounds.

10. Who weighs the most? **Mollie**
11. Who weighs the least? **Maris**

NOTE TO HOME
Students compare weights.

3 Wrap-Up (5 MINUTES)

In Closing Ask students to name something that might weigh 100 pounds and something that might weigh 1 ounce. (possible answers: a person, a grape)

ALTERNATIVE ASSESSMENT

Informal Assessment Use students' responses as they discuss their answers to pages 239 and 240 to informally assess their understanding of standard measurements of weight.

Assessment Criteria

Did the student . . .

✓ correctly answer 4 of 5 questions on page 239?

✓ correctly answer 4 of 6 questions on page 240?

✓ provide sensible explanations for answers?

PRACTICE p. 107

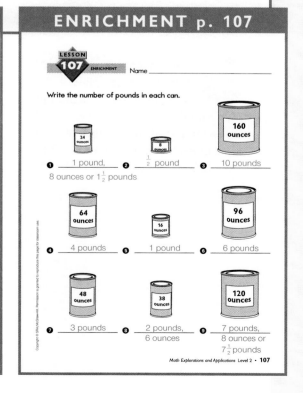

LESSON 107 PRACTICE Name ____________

The pound and the ounce are units of weight. There are 16 ounces in 1 pound.

Change pounds to ounces.

1. 3 pounds = 48 ounces
2. 6 pounds = 96 ounces
3. 9 pounds = 144 ounces
4. 12 pounds = 192 ounces
5. 2 pounds = 32 ounces
6. 4 pounds = 64 ounces
7. 8 pounds = 128 ounces
8. 10 pounds = 160 ounces

ENRICHMENT p. 107

LESSON 107 ENRICHMENT Name ____________

Write the number of pounds in each can.

1. 1 pound, 8 ounces or $1\frac{1}{2}$ pounds

2. $\frac{1}{2}$ pound

3. 10 pounds

4. 4 pounds

5. 1 pound

6. 6 pounds

7. 3 pounds

8. 2 pounds, 6 ounces

9. 7 pounds, 8 ounces or $7\frac{1}{2}$ pounds

LESSON 108

Student Edition pages 241–242

Using Measurements

LESSON PLANNER

Objectives

- ▶ to give students experience measuring kilograms
- ▶ to develop an understanding of the relationship between grams and kilogram
- ▶ to solve realistic measurement problems
- ▶ to review the use of inequality and equality signs

Context of the Lesson This lesson continues measurement activities from Lesson 107.

Materials	Program Resources
craft sticks	Practice Master 108
double-pan balance	Enrichment Master 108
grams weights	For extra practice: CD-ROM* Lesson 108
kilogram weight	

1 Warm-Up (5 MINUTES)

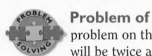

Problem of the Day Write the following problem on the chalkboard: In two years Diana will be twice as old as Jared. Last week Jared turned 6 years old. How old is Diana? (14 years old)

MENTAL MATH Have students fill in the blanks.

a. 13 – _____ = 6 (7)

b. 7 + _____ = 11 (4)

c. _____ + 6 = 12 (6)

d. _____ – 4 = 6 (10)

e. _____ – 7 = 5 (12)

2 Teach

Demonstrate Present examples of realistic measurement problems orally to the class. Illustrate and discuss the solutions. Present problems such as:

A rectangular-shaped garden measures 10 meters on one side and 5 meters on the other. How many meters of fencing would you need to fence in the garden. (Draw a picture on the chalkboard labeling the dimensions of the rectangle and discuss the solution: 10 + 10 + 5 + 5 = 30 meters)

LESSON 108

Name ______________________

Using Measurements

Solve these problems.

1. The branch is 100 inches from the ground. The swing is 30 inches from the ground. About how many inches of rope were used to tie the swing to the branch? __140__

2. Caroline needs 60 meters of rope. Rope comes in packages of 25 meters. How many packages must she buy? __3__

COOPERATIVE LEARNING Do the "Making a Kilogram" activity.

NOTE TO HOME
Students solve problems about measurement.

Real-World Connection Have students look at boxes and other containers of food at home and list the foods and the number of grams in each box or container. Have students bring in and share their lists.

RETEACHING

Show students pictures of various objects and ask whether they would weigh each in grams or kilograms and why.

*available separately

◆ LESSON 108 Using Measurements

Compare methods of solving. Which do you think is easiest?

What is the right sign? Draw <, >, or =.

3. 10 (<) 15
4. 17 − 7 (>) 18 − 18
5. 16 + 1 (<) 16 + 2
6. 122 + 23 (>) 122 + 20
7. 18 − 1 (>) 18 − 5
8. 195 − 95 (>) 195 − 96
9. 25 + 25 (<) 25 + 26
10. 75 + 75 (=) 75 + 75
11. 25 (<) 52
12. 18 + 2 (=) 2 + 18
13. 89 + 5 (<) 89 + 10
14. 19 + 3 (>) 0 + 19
15. 6 + 125 (=) 125 + 6
16. 35 − 1 (>) 35 − 5
17. 999 (=) 998 + 1
18. 675 + 1 (>) 675 + 0

NOTE TO HOME
Students review using less than, greater than, and equal signs.

PRACTICE p. 108

LESSON 108 PRACTICE Name ____________

What is the right sign? Draw <, >, or =.

1. 7 + 4 (<) 7 + 5
2. 36 − 2 (<) 37 − 1
3. 20 − 3 (>) 20 − 5
4. 69 + 2 (=) 70 + 1
5. 15 + 2 (<) 16 + 3
6. 25 − 5 (>) 24 − 5
7. 10 − 7 (>) 10 − 9
8. 71 − 3 (>) 71 − 4
9. 13 + 5 (=) 9 + 9
10. 59 − 9 (<) 95 − 9

PROBLEM SOLVING — **Solve these problems.**

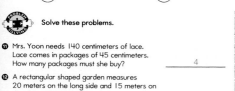

11. Mrs. Yoon needs 140 centimeters of lace. Lace comes in packages of 45 centimeters. How many packages must she buy? 4
12. A rectangular shaped garden measures 20 meters on the long side and 15 meters on the short side. About how many meters of wire would be needed to enclose the garden? 70

ENRICHMENT p. 108

LESSON 108 ENRICHMENT Name ____________

PROBLEM SOLVING — **Solve these problems.**

1. Marit has a purse that weighs 15 ounces. She puts a handful of coins into the purse. Then she finds out that the filled purse weighs $2\frac{1}{2}$ pounds. How much did the coins weigh? 25 ounces
2. Used books are for sale for 50 cents a pound. Ed has three books he wants to buy. One weighs 9 ounces, one weighs four pounds, 3 ounces, and the other weighs $3\frac{1}{4}$ pounds. How much will Ed have to pay for the books? $4
3. The runners passed flags placed at 35-yard marks. Clay passed four flags. How far did he run? 140 yards
4. Kelsey rode her bike 11 miles. Barb rode her bike twice as far as Kelsey. Shanika rode her bike 5 miles less than Barb. How many miles did Shanika ride her bike? 17

Do the "Making a Kilogram" activity with students. Remind them that there are 1000 grams in 1 kilogram. Tell students you want to make a kilogram weight out of craft sticks. Guide them to see that they can first make a bunch of craft sticks that weigh 100 grams. Discuss how to use this information to make a kilogram. Students should realize they can make ten bunches of sticks. Allow them to make the kilogram weight, then check their results on the double balance scale using their weight on one side and a kilogram weight on the other.

Using the Student Pages Have students complete pages 241 and 242 independently. Then go over each page with the class, encouraging students to share and explain how they arrived at their answers.

3 Wrap-Up (5 MINUTES)

In Closing Ask students to give an example of something that might weigh 1 kilogram and something that might weigh 1 gram. (Possible answers: a guinea pig; a paper clip)

ALTERNATIVE ASSESSMENT

Informal Assessment Use students' responses as they discuss their answers to pages 241 and 242 to informally assess their understanding of measurement and inequality and equality signs.

Assessment Criteria

Did the student . . .

✓ show about 1 kilogram in craft sticks during the activity?

✓ correctly answer both problems on page 241?

✓ correctly answer 13 of the 16 problems on page 242?

LESSON 109

Student Edition pages 243–244

Measurement—Capacity

LESSON PLANNER

Objectives

- ▶ to introduce customary units of measure for capacity
- ▶ to demonstrate converting one customary unit of capacity to another

Context of the Lesson This lesson is an introduction to ounces, pints, quarts, and gallons.

Materials

drinking glasses (optional)
measuring cup marked in fluid ounces
pint, quart, and gallon containers
posterboard (optional)
supermarket ads (optional)

Program Resources

"Measurement" Game Mat
Number Cubes
Reteaching Master
Practice Master 109
Enrichment Master 109
For extra practice:
CD-ROM* Lesson 109

1 Warm-Up

5 MINUTES

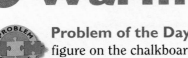

Problem of the Day Draw the following figure on the chalkboard. Challenge students to determine how many rectangles there are. (13; remind students that squares are also rectangles.)

MENTAL MATH Have students add or subtract the following, using their Number Cubes to respond.

a. 170 – 80 = (90)
b. 70 + 50 = (120)
c. 50 + 90 = (140)
d. 120 – 30 = (90)
e. 160 + 80 = (240)
f. 70 + 90 = (160)

LESSON 109

Name ____________________

Measurement—Capacity

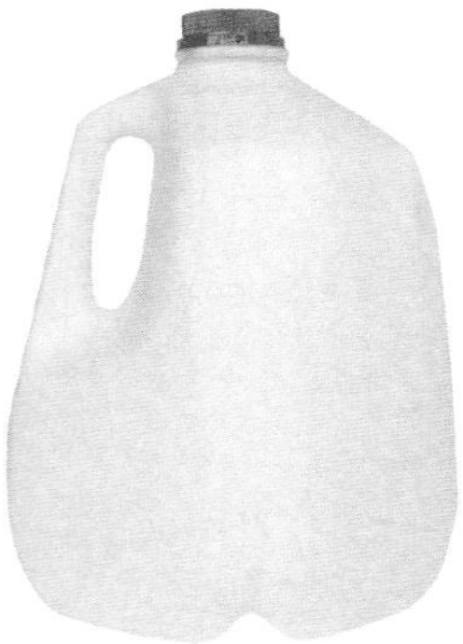

16 fluid ounces = 1 pint
2 pints = 1 quart
4 quarts = 1 gallon

How many?

1. How many fluid ounces in 1 quart? 32
2. How many pints in 1 gallon? 8
3. How many fluid ounces in 1 gallon? 128
4. How many fluid ounces in 2 gallons? 256
5. How many fluid ounces in 3 gallons? 384
6. How many fluid ounces in 4 quarts? 512
7. How many pints in 4 quarts? 8

NOTE TO HOME
Students convert customary units of volume (capacity).

Real-World Connection Have students look through supermarket ads to find pictures of items that are sold in various-sized containers: pints, quarts, gallons. Have them cut the pictures out, paste them on posterboard, and label each with the correct unit of capacity.

Music Connection Invite students to demonstrate how the amount of water in a glass changes the sound it makes when tappped with a spoon. Let volunteers play the glasses. Then have students find how many ounces of water are in each glass.

RETEACHING p. 29

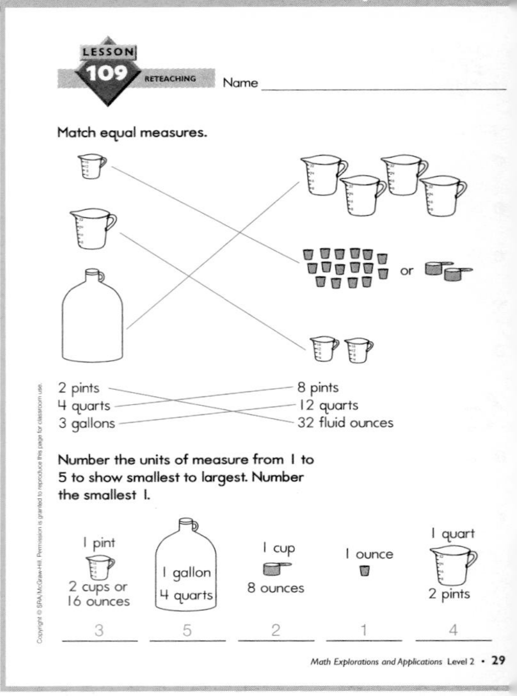
LESSON 109 RETEACHING Name ____________

Match equal measures.

2 pints
4 quarts
3 gallons
8 pints
12 quarts
32 fluid ounces

Number the units of measure from 1 to 5 to show smallest to largest. Number the smallest 1.

1 pint 2 cups or 16 ounces	1 gallon 4 quarts	1 cup 8 ounces	1 ounce	1 quart 2 pints
3	5	2	1	4

Math Explorations and Applications Level 2 • 29

*available separately

◆ **LESSON 109 Measurement—Capacity**

A pint of water weighs about 1 pound.

How much?

8 How much does a quart of water weigh? 2 pounds

9 How much does a gallon of water weigh? 8 pounds

10 How much do 5 gallons of water weigh? 40 pounds

11 How many ounces in a pound? 16

12 How many fluid ounces in a pint? 16

13 How much do you think a fluid ounce of water weighs? 1 ounce or $\frac{1}{8}$ of a pound

GAME

Play the "Measurement" game.

NOTE TO HOME
Students convert customary units of volume (capacity).

2 Teach

Demonstrate Display a gallon and a pint container. Have students predict how many times you will have to fill the pint container in order to fill the gallon container. Pour in one pint, and allow students to change their estimates if they wish. After finding that there are eight pints in a gallon, repeat the same experiment with several other containers.

Using the Student Pages Discuss the first problems on pages 243 and 244 with students before assigning the remainder for them to complete on their own. Demonstrate for students how to use repeated addition to solve the problems. For example, for problem 1 on page 243, explain that because there are 16 ounces in a pint and 2 pints in a quart, then there are 16 + 16, or 32, ounces in a quart.

GAME **Introducing the "Measurement" Game Mat** Introduce and demonstrate the game so that students can play it when they complete pages 243–244. This game provides practice with choosing the appropriate standard unit of measure. Complete directions are on the Game Mat.

3 Wrap-Up

5 MINUTES

In Closing Ask students to give an examples of things that come in quart, pint, and gallon containers.

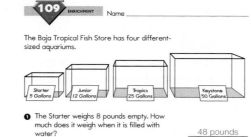

ALTERNATIVE ASSESSMENT **Informal Assessment** Use students' responses as they discuss their answers to pages 243 and 244 to informally assess their understanding of traditional measurements of capacity.

PRACTICE p. 109

LESSON 109 PRACTICE Name ____________

16 fluid ounces = 1 pint 2 pints = 1 quart
4 quarts = 1 gallon

1 How many fluid ounces are in 3 pints? 48
2 How many pints are in 2 quarts? 4
3 How many pints are in 3 quarts? 6
4 How many fluid ounces are in 2 quarts? 64
5 How many fluid ounces are in 3 quarts? 96
6 How many pints are in 1 gallon? 8
7 How many fluid ounces are in 1 gallon? 128

A pint of water weighs about 1 pound.

8 How much does 2 pints of water weigh? 2 pounds
9 How much does a quart of water weigh? 2 pounds
10 How much does 3 quarts of water weigh? 6 pounds
11 How much does a gallon of water weigh? 8 pounds
12 How much does 4 gallons of water weigh? 32 pounds
13 How many ounces are in a pound? 16 ounces
14 How many ounces are in 3 pounds? 48 ounces

ENRICHMENT p. 109

LESSON 109 ENRICHMENT Name ____________

The Baja Tropical Fish Store has four different-sized aquariums.

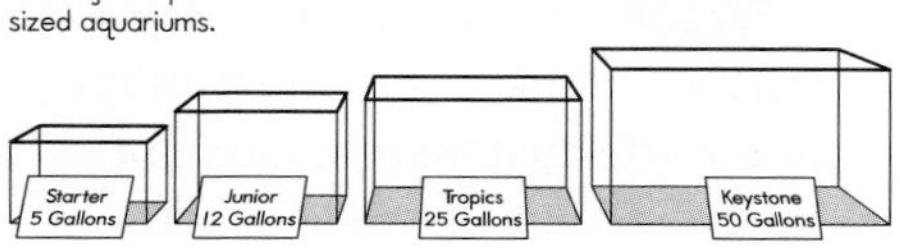

1 The Starter weighs 8 pounds empty. How much does it weigh when it is filled with water? 48 pounds

2 How many fluid ounces of water will the Starter hold? 640

3 How many more quarts does the Tropics hold than the Junior? 52

4 The Junior weighs 15 pounds empty. How much would it weigh if it was half full of water? 63 pounds

5 The Keystone weighs 45 pounds empty, and the Tropics weighs 30 pounds.
a. If the Keystone had 50 quarts and the Tropics was full, which would weigh more? Tropics
b. How much more? 85 pounds

Assessment Criteria

Did the student . . .

✓ provide sensible estimates in the demonstration?

✓ correctly answer four of six remaining questions on page 243?

✓ correctly answer four of five remaining questions on page 244?

Student Edition pages 245–246

LESSON 110

Metric Measurement—Capacity

LESSON PLANNER

Objectives

- ▶ to introduce metric units of measurement for capacity
- ▶ to demonstrate converting one metric unit of capacity to another

Context of the Lesson This lesson is an introduction to milliliters and liters.

Materials	Program Resources
liter containers	Number Cubes
measuring cup marked in milliliters	Practice Master 110
	Enrichment Master 110
	For extra practice: CD-ROM* Lesson 110

1 Warm-Up 5 MINUTES

Problem of the Day Write the following problem on the chalkboard: If you wrote all the even numbers from 1–50, how many times would you write the number 2? the number 3? (15, 5)

MENTAL MATH Write the following on the chalkboard, and have students show the answers with their Number Cubes.

a. 1 quart = _____ pints (2)

b. 1 gallon = _____ quarts (4)

c. 1 gallon = _____ pints (8)

d. 1 pint = _____ ounces (16)

e. 2 quarts = _____ pints (4)

2 Teach

Demonstrate Repeat the demonstration you did in Lesson 109 using containers in metric units of capacity rather than customary units. For example, have students estimate how many times you will fill a container that holds 250 milliliters to fill a liter container. Then fill the container to see whether their estimates were accurate. Again, allow students to adjust their estimates after the first time you pour.

LESSON 110

Name ____________________

Metric Measurement—Capacity

1000 milliliters = 1 liter

1 cubic centimeter = 1 milliliter

1 cubic decimeter = 1 liter

Use a centimeter ruler.

1 Draw a square centimeter.

2 Draw a square decimeter (10 cm on a side).

NOTE TO HOME
Students review metric capacity.

Language Arts Connections Have students work with a partner to discuss their opinions about the customary system of measurement versus the metric system. Have them then work together to write a paragraph telling about which system they prefer, why, and why they think we have two different systems. Encourage partners to share their paragraphs with the class.

RETEACHING

Write the following table on the chalkboard and have students complete the problem. Then correct the answers together:

a. _____ milliliters = 2 liters (2000)

b. 4 liters = _____ milliliters (4000)

c. 5000 milliliters = _____ liters (5)

d. $\frac{1}{2}$ liter = _____ milliliters (500)

*available separately

◆ LESSON 110 Metric Measurement—Capacity

A liter is a little more than a quart.

How many?

3. About how many pints are in a liter? __2__

4. About how many liters are in a gallon? __4__

A liter of water weighs 1 kilogram.

How much?

5. How much does a milliliter of water weigh? __1 gram__

6. How much do 5 liters of water weigh? __5 kg__

PROBLEM SOLVING

7. Sara is having a party. She needs about two gallons of punch. The punch she wants is in liter bottles. How many liters of punch should she buy? __8__

NOTE TO HOME
Students review metric capacity.

Using the Student Pages Read the equivalencies on page 245 with the class; then have them complete the rest of page 245 and page 246 on their own.

3 Wrap-Up (5 MINUTES)

In Closing Ask students to explain how they arrived at their answers to the questions on page 246.

ALTERNATIVE ASSESSMENT

Informal Assessment Use students' responses as they discuss their answers to pages 245 and 246 to informally assess their understanding of metric measurements of capacity.

Assessment Criteria

Did the student . . .

✓ correctly complete page 245?

✓ correctly answer 4 of 5 questions on page 246?

✓ provide sensible estimates in the demonstration?

PRACTICE p. 110

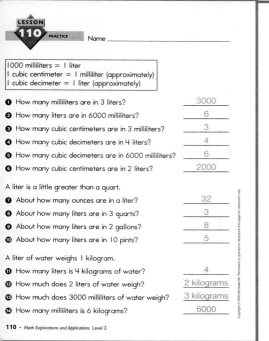

LESSON 110 PRACTICE Name ____________

1000 milliliters = 1 liter
1 cubic centimeter = 1 milliliter (approximately)
1 cubic decimeter = 1 liter (approximately)

1. How many milliliters are in 3 liters? __3000__
2. How many liters are in 6000 milliliters? __6__
3. How many cubic centimeters are in 3 milliliters? __3__
4. How many cubic decimeters are in 4 liters? __4__
5. How many cubic decimeters are in 6000 milliliters? __6__
6. How many cubic centimeters are in 2 liters? __2000__

A liter is a little greater than a quart.

7. About how many ounces are in a liter? __32__
8. About how many liters are in 3 quarts? __3__
9. About how many liters are in 2 gallons? __8__
10. About how many liters are in 10 pints? __5__

A liter of water weighs 1 kilogram.

11. How many liters is 4 kilograms of water? __4__
12. How much does 2 liters of water weigh? __2 kilograms__
13. How much does 3000 milliliters of water weigh? __3 kilograms__
14. How many milliliters is 6 kilograms? __6000__

110 • Math Explorations and Applications Level 2

ENRICHMENT p. 110

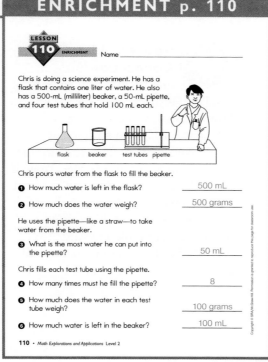

LESSON 110 ENRICHMENT Name ____________

Chris is doing a science experiment. He has a flask that contains one liter of water. He also has a 500-mL (milliliter) beaker, a 50-mL pipette, and four test tubes that hold 100 mL each.

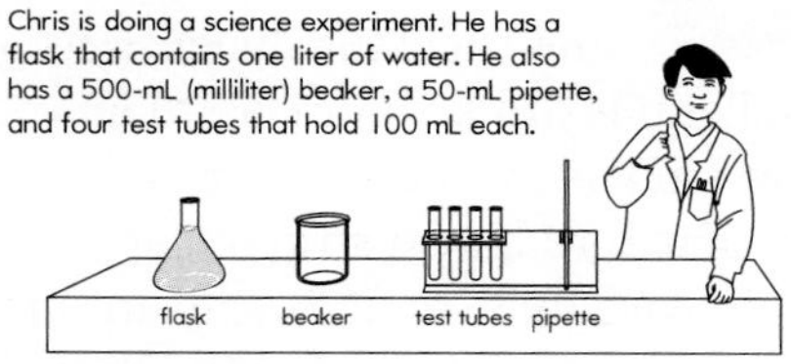

Chris pours water from the flask to fill the beaker.

1. How much water is left in the flask? __500 mL__
2. How much does the water weigh? __500 grams__

He uses the pipette—like a straw—to take water from the beaker.

3. What is the most water he can put into the pipette? __50 mL__

Chris fills each test tube using the pipette.

4. How many times must he fill the pipette? __8__
5. How much does the water in each test tube weigh? __100 grams__
6. How much water is left in the beaker? __100 mL__

110 • Math Explorations and Applications Level 2

LESSON 111

Student Edition pages 247–248

Using Measurements

LESSON PLANNER

Objective

- ▶ to give students more practice in solving realistic measurement problems

Context of the Lesson This is the last lesson on measurement.

Materials	Program Resources
none	Thinking Story Book, pages 96–99
	Number Cubes
	Practice Master 111
	Enrichment Master 111
	For extra practice: CD-ROM* Lesson 111

1 Warm-Up

5 MINUTES

Problem of the Day Present the following problem to the class: I am a two-digit number. The sum of my digits is 13. The difference is 5. What two numbers could I be? (49 or 94)

MENTAL MATH Have students add or subtract.

a. 9 + 6 = (15)

b. 4 + 7 = (11)

c. 8 + 9 = (17)

d. 14 − 6 = (8)

e. 12 − 7 = (5)

f. 11 − 9 = (2)

2 Teach

Demonstrate Present, discuss, and solve realistic measurement problems such as the following:

A boat can hold 200 kilograms. About how many people can safely ride on the boat if each person weighs about 60 kilograms? (3)

LESSON 111

Name ______________________

Using Measurements

1. How many can safely ride in this boat at one time? 3

2. How many can safely ride in this boat at one time? 2

3. Green Pond is 80 meters long. Ginny knows she can swim 250 meters. Can she swim to the end of the pond and back? yes

THINKING STORY Talk about the Thinking Story "More Sharing with Cousin Trixie."

NOTE TO HOME
Students solve problems involving measurement.

Real-World Connection Measure and show the dimensions of a bulletin board in your classroom. Have students work in groups to calculate how long a strip of paper would have to be to fit exactly around the bulletin board as a border. Then, if available, give students supplies to cut and design a strip of paper to be used as the border. Use each group's border on your bulletin board. (Change borders every week until all borders have been displayed.)

RETEACHING

Work in small groups with students who do not understand how to solve the word problems on the student pages. Have students act out the problems, or use concrete objects to demonstrate each solution.

*available separately

◆ LESSON 111 Using Measurement

Solve these problems.

4. You need 25 gallons of paint. Each can holds 10 gallons. How many cans must you buy? **3**

5. You need 12 cups of juice. Each box holds 8 cups. How many boxes of juice must you buy? **2**

6. Spencer's dog Rover is 65 centimeters tall. The bottom of the window is 92 centimeters from the floor. The stool is 30 centimeters high. Can Rover look out the window if he stands on the stool? **yes**

7. A pitcher can hold one gallon. How many quarts of juice will the pitcher hold? **4**

8. At football practice Bryan must run 50 yards. He has run 32 yards. How many more yards must he run? **18**

NOTE TO HOME
Students solve problems about measuring capacity and length.

There are ten people, each weighing about 60 kilograms. There are three boats, each can hold about 200 kilograms. Can all ten people safely ride in the three boats? Why or why not? (No, only nine can ride safely: three in each boat. You can't divide the tenth person among the three boats.)

Using the Student Pages Have students complete pages 247 and 248 independently. Give individual help to those who need it. Give students who finish early a choice of games from among those previously introduced.

Using the Thinking Story Read the story "More Sharing with Cousin Trixie" to the class. Stop and discuss the questions asked throughout the story.

3 Wrap-Up (5 MINUTES)

In Closing Ask students to explain how they used addition and subtraction to solve the problems on pages 247 and 248.

Informal Assessment Use students' responses as they discuss their answers on pages 247 and 248 to informally assess their understanding of realistic measurement problems.

Assessment Criteria

Did the student . . .

✓ correctly solve two of the three problems on page 247?

✓ correctly solve four of the five problems on page 248?

✓ give sensible answers during the demonstration?

PRACTICE p. 111

LESSON 111 PRACTICE Name ____________

Solve these problems.

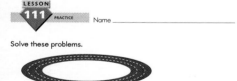

1. One lap around the track is 1400 feet. Joe jogged three laps around the track. How many feet did Joe jog? 4200

2. Eli needs 86 ounces of spaghetti sauce. Each can holds 16 ounces. How many cans must he buy? 6

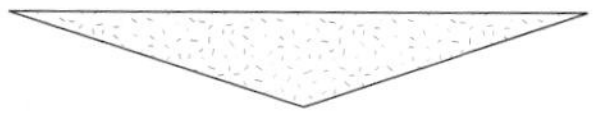

3. Tamara wants to add lace trim to her scarf. The sides are 32 inches, 18 inches, and 18 inches. Will 75 inches of lace be enough? yes

4. An elevator can hold 1200 pounds. If each person weighs about 150 pounds, how many people can the elevator hold? 8

ENRICHMENT p. 111

LESSON 111 ENRICHMENT Name ____________

Movers charge the Browns $2.00 for each pound of weight. Their truck can carry 1100 pounds.

Complete the chart to show how much it will cost to move each item. Then add the weights and the costs.

Items	Weight (in pounds)	Cost to Move (in dollars)
table	45	90
four chairs	56	112
dresser	74	148
couch	187	374
recliner	106	212
stove	440	880
bed	55	110
two end tables	36	72
piano	978	1956
Total	1977	3954

Use the chart to answer these questions.

1. Can all of the furniture go in one trip? no
2. What should go in the second trip? Answers will vary. Possible answer: piano

STORY 16

THINKING STORY

More Sharing With Cousin Trixie

One day when Ferdie and Portia were in the park, Cousin Trixie appeared with a small bag of grapes. "Today I have something we can all share," she said. "And I'll even let you do the dividing, Ferdie."

Ferdie poured the grapes onto a napkin on a park table. He wanted to divide them, but he wasn't quite sure how to do it.

How would you do it? by having each child take one grape in turn, for example

"There might be enough to give everyone six grapes," Ferdie said. "Here are six for you, Trixie, and six for you, Portia, and, oops. . ." He looked at the rest of the grapes. "That leaves only three for me."

How many grapes were there? 15

"It's nice of you to give more to the girls," said Trixie. "But that means that the grapes are not being shared evenly."

How could they make things right? They could start again and pass out the grapes one at a time.

"Why don't we give you the grapes and you can start all over," said Portia.

Is there another way? They could give each other some of their grapes.

"If each of us gives you some of our grapes, it might work out that we all have the same number," said Trixie.

How many grapes do Portia and Trixie each have? six

How many grapes does Ferdie have? three

How many grapes would each girl have to give Ferdie for all of them to have the same number? one

How many grapes would each child have then? five

Portia and Trixie each gave Ferdie one grape. "Now we each have five," said Portia. "That's sharing evenly."

On the way home, they found Manolita riding a bicycle. "What a great bike!" said Ferdie. "May I borrow it?"

"All right," said Manolita. "But only for an hour. I'll come back and get it then."

Ferdie forgot all about the girls and began riding the bicycle.

"Of all the nerve!" said Trixie.

What's wrong? Ferdie didn't offer to share.

"You're not sharing," said Portia.

"How can I share a bicycle?" Ferdie asked. "Only one person can ride it at a time."

How could they share the bicycle? by taking turns

◆ STORY 16 More Sharing With Cousin Trixie

"We'll take turns," Portia suggested. "Trixie can ride it for one minute, then I'll ride it for one minute, then Ferdie can ride it for one minute. Then we'll keep on taking turns for the whole hour."

Can you think of another way?
Take longer turns.

Trixie looked at her watch. "One minute at a time isn't long enough for riding a bike," she said. "I have a better way. Ferdie can ride the bike for 15 minutes, then Portia can ride it for 15 minutes, and then I'll ride it for the rest of the hour."

Is that a fair way to share the bicycle? no

How much time will Trixie have to ride the bicycle? 30 minutes

"That's not fair," Portia said. "If Ferdie and I each have it for 15 minutes, that's just half an hour—and you'll have half an hour all for yourself."

"Then you figure out a better way," Cousin Trixie said huffily.

"Let's each ride it for 30 minutes," Ferdie suggested. "That will be even."

What's wrong with Ferdie's idea? It adds up to an hour and a half.

"That adds up to an hour and a half," Cousin Trixie said. "And we have the bike for only an hour. You'll have to do better than that."

"Then let's try 20 minutes," said Ferdie.

"Twenty and 20 and 20—that should add up to about an hour."

How many minutes does that add up to? 60

Is that an hour? yes

"That's right," said Cousin Trixie. "If we take.the bike for 20 minutes apiece, that will use up the hour exactly. You're learning fast about sharing, Ferdie. Only it's too bad that we had to use up ten of your 20 minutes deciding what we are going to do."

. . . the end

LESSON 112

Student Edition pages 249–250

Shortcuts

LESSON PLANNER

Objective

- ▶ to introduce shortcuts to mental addition and subtraction

Context of the Lesson This lesson focuses on mental math strategies.

Materials	Program Resources
base-10 materials*	Thinking Story Book, pages 100–101
	Practice Master 112
	Enrichment Master 112
	For extra practice: CD-ROM* Lesson 112

1 Warm-Up

5 MINUTES

Problem of the Day Present this problem to the class: You can buy 32 ounces of juice for $1.25 or one quart of the same juice for $1.50. Which is the best buy? Why? (32 ounces; 1 qt is the same amount, but costs more)

MENTAL MATH Have students add or subtract the following using mental math.

a.	10 + 9 = (19)	**b.**	9 + 7 = (16)
c.	17 − 9 = (8)	**d.**	50 + 60 = (110)
e.	110 − 70 = (40)	**f.**	40 + 60 = (100)

2 Teach

Demonstrate Write the following problem on the chalkboard: 37 + 19. Model the problem by showing three bunches of ten and seven more in one pile, and one bunch of ten and nine more in another pile. Then move one counter from the 37 pile to the 19 to model 36 + 20. Demonstrate for students that the sums for both problems are the same. Discuss how changing 37 + 19 to 36 + 20 makes it easier to solve the problem mentally. Repeat with several similar problems such as 42 + 29 and 41 + 30; 39 + 51 and 40 + 50.

LESSON 112

Name ______________________

Shortcuts

Add.

37 + 19

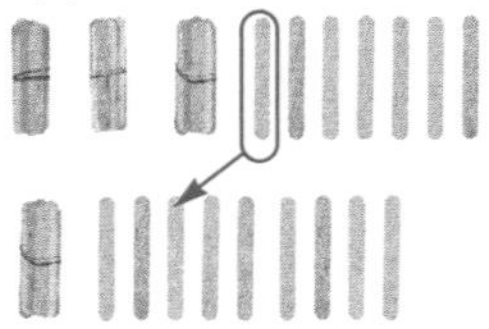

1. Is 37 + 19 the same as 36 + 20? **yes**
2. 37 + 19 = **56**

37 − 19

Subtract 20; put 1 back.

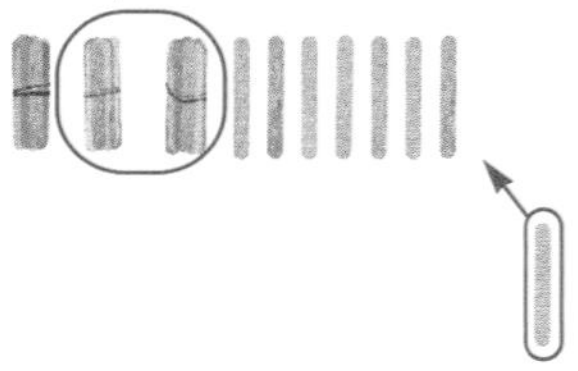

3. Is 37 − 19 the same as 38 − 20? **yes**
4. 37 − 19 = **18**

Use shortcuts to solve these problems.

5. 56 + 29 = **85**
6. 63 + 19 = **82**
7. 54 + 39 = **93**
8. 56 − 29 = **27**
9. 63 − 19 = **44**
10. 54 − 39 = **15**

NOTE TO HOME
Students learn shortcuts to two-digit addition and subtraction.

RETEACHING

Have students work in groups using base-10 materials. Have them show how to change addition and subtraction examples into problems they can solve using mental math. Have them mentally solve each problem after they have changed it. Give practice examples such as: 53 + 39; 53 + 38; 53 + 37; 61 − 19; 61 − 18; 61 − 17. (92; 91; 90; 42; 43; 44)

*available separately

◆ **LESSON 112** Shortcuts **Use the Mixed Practice on page 389 after this lesson.**

Solve these problems. Use shortcuts when you can.

11. 91 − 89 = 2
12. 38 + 42 = 80
13. 91 − 39 = 52
14. 38 + 47 = 85
15. 92 − 89 = 3
16. 28 + 32 = 60
17. 92 − 39 = 53
18. 28 + 37 = 65
19. 73 + 19 = 92
20. 81 − 39 = 42
21. 23 + 19 = 42
22. 51 − 38 = 13
23. 46 + 39 = 85
24. 51 − 39 = 12
25. 46 + 38 = 84
26. 52 − 38 = 14
27. 46 + 37 = 83
28. 47 − 27 = 20

Talk about the ways you did these.

MATH JOURNAL

Describe your shortcuts. What works best for you?

NOTE TO HOME
Students use shortcuts to two-digit addition and subtraction.

PRACTICE p. 112

LESSON 112 PRACTICE Name ____________

Solve these problems.

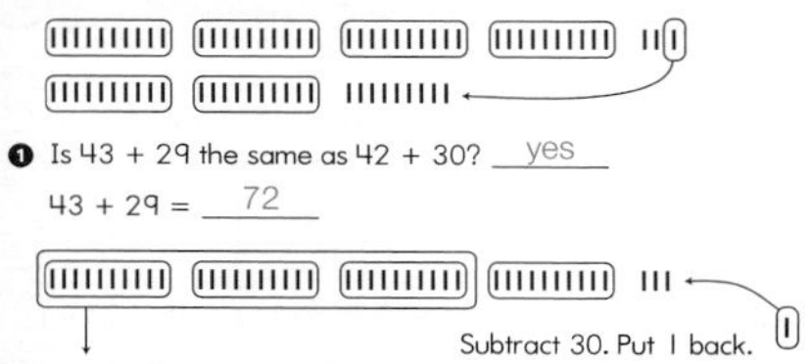

1. Is 43 + 29 the same as 42 + 30? yes
   43 + 29 = 72
2. Is 43 − 29 the same as 44 − 30? yes
   43 − 29 = 14

Solve. Use shortcuts when you can.

3. 45 + 39 = 84
4. 45 − 39 = 6
5. 66 + 19 = 85
6. 66 − 19 = 47
7. 52 + 39 = 91
8. 52 − 39 = 13
9. 31 + 29 = 60
10. 31 − 29 = 2
11. 78 + 22 = 100
12. 71 − 38 = 33

ENRICHMENT p. 112

LESSON 112 ENRICHMENT Name ____________

This very long mathepillar has problems starting at its head and reaching all the way to its tail. Fill in the missing numbers on its back to get to the tail.

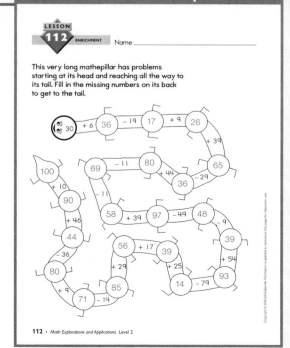

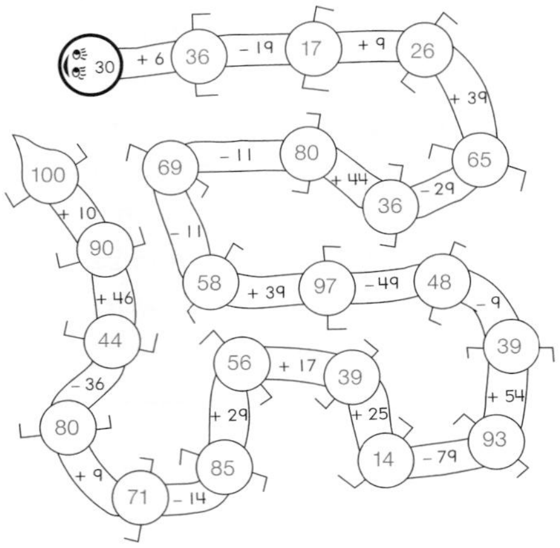

Next, show how to change subtraction problems to easier forms. Write 37 – 19 on the chalkboard, then model the problem using counters. Add one counter to each pile to make 38 – 20. Demonstrate for students that the difference is the same for both problems. Repeat for similar examples. Emphasize that in addition the sum remains the same when we move counters from one addend to the other, but in subtraction we must do the same thing (either add or take away the same number of counters) from each side to keep the difference (18) the same.

Using the Student Pages Have students complete the problems on pages 249 and 250 independently. Correct the problems with the class.

Using the Thinking Story Present one or two new problems from those following "More Sharing With Cousin Trixie" on pages 100–101 of the Thinking Story Book.

3 Wrap-Up

5 MINUTES

In Closing Ask students to explain the shortcut for adding, the shortcut for subtracting, and the difference between them.

ALTERNATIVE ASSESSMENT

Informal Assessment Have students explain how they arrived at their answers to pages 249 and 250 to informally assess their understanding of these mental math strategies.

Assessment Criteria

Did the student . . .

- ✓ correctly solve 23 of 28 problems on pages 249–250?
- ✓ use mental math strategies when appropriate?

LEARNING STYLES

Meeting Individual Needs

Have auditory learners orally explain each step they would follow to mentally add 57 + 29 (move 1 unit from 57 to make 56 + 30 = 86) and mentally subtract 57 – 29 (add 1 unit to both to make 58 – 30 = 28). Allow them to write the steps out as they say them. Then have them say the steps aloud without writing. Finally, have them complete examples mentally.

LESSON 113

Student Edition pages 251–252

Round to Ten

LESSON PLANNER

Objectives

- ▶ to introduce rounding to the nearest ten
- ▶ to provide practice using rounding to estimate sums and differences

Context of the Lesson This lesson continues the focus on mental math strategies of the previous lesson.

Materials	Program Resources
calculators	Thinking Story Book, pages 100–101
	Practice Master 113
	Enrichment Master 113
	For extra practice: CD-ROM* Lesson 113

1 Warm-Up (5 MINUTES)

Problem of the Day Present this problem: Bryan exercised on Saturday for ten minutes. Each night he will exercise five minutes longer. On what night will he exercise for a half hour? (Wednesday)

MENTAL MATH Have students add or subtract the following using mental math.

a. 12 + 19 = (31)
b. 26 – 11 = (15)
c. 47 – 29 = (18)
d. 53 + 39 = (92)

2 Teach

Demonstrate Draw a number line from 20 to 50 on the chalkboard. Ask whether 37 is closer to 30 or 40 (40). Ask whether there is any other multiple of ten that is closer to 37 than 40. Explain that 37 rounded to the nearest ten is 40. Explain to students that they can round numbers to estimate sums and differences. Demonstrate rounding 58 + 27 as 60 + 30, or about 90. Repeat for differences such as 72 – 39, which rounds to 70 – 40 = 30.

Discuss how to round numbers with a five in the ones place. The most common strategy is to round up. Practice several examples: 35 + 17 rounds to 40 + 20 = 60; 81 – 45 rounds to 80 – 50 = 30.

LESSON 113

Name ______________________

Round to Ten

Round to the nearest ten.

1. 73 __70__	2. 84 __80__	3. 99 __100__
4. 7 __10__	5. 3 __0__	6. 6 __10__
7. 54 __50__	8. 90 __90__	9. 56 __60__
10. 61 __60__	11. 88 __90__	12. 12 __10__
13. 35 __30 or 40__	14. 55 __50 or 60__	15. 15 __10 or 20__
16. 73 __70__	17. 42 __40__	18. 5 __0 or 10__
19. 8 __10__	20. 39 __40__	21. 17 __20__
22. 66 __70__	23. 22 __20__	24. 48 __50__

Is 35 closer to 30 or to 40? Talk about it.

NOTE TO HOME
Students round to tens.

SPECIAL NEEDS: Meeting Individual Needs

Provide more practice for students in rounding to the nearest ten only. Do not have them use rounding to estimate sums or differences until they master rounding. Use number lines to demonstrate how to round a two-digit number.

RETEACHING

Display problems in a table to help students keep track of the numbers they are rounding, adding, and subtracting. For example, display the following table for estimating sums:

Problem:	37	+	42	=	
Estimate:	40	+	40	=	80
Problem:					
Estimate:					
Problem:					
Estimate:					
Problem:					
Estimate:					

*available separately

◆ **LESSON 113** Round to Ten

Use the Mixed Practice on page 390 after this lesson.

Estimate answers to the nearest ten. Then calculate the difference between your estimate and the exact answer.

	Estimate	Exact answer	Difference
25 42 + 38 =	80	80	0
26 72 − 28 =	40	44	4
27 81 − 19 =	60	62	2
28 71 + 19 =	90	90	0
29 45 − 25 =	20	20	0
30 45 + 25 =	70	70	0
31 33 + 43 =	70 or 80	76	6
32 87 − 56 =	30	31	1
33 48 + 69 =	120	117	3
34 87 − 63 =	20	24	4

NOTE TO HOME
Students estimate answers by rounding to ten.

PRACTICE p. 113

LESSON 113 PRACTICE Name ______

Round to the nearest ten.

1 8 10 2 87 90 3 42 40
4 57 60 5 14 10 6 25 30
7 60 60 8 51 50 9 36 40
10 29 30 11 45 50 12 63 60

Estimate answers to the nearest ten. Then calculate the difference between your estimate and the exact answer.

		Estimate	Exact Answer	Difference
13	78 − 24	60	54	6
14	32 + 17	50	49	1
15	65 + 18	90	83	7
16	85 − 35	50	50	0
17	24 + 43	60	67	7
18	91 − 29	60	62	2

Math Explorations and Applications Level 2 • 113

ENRICHMENT p. 113

LESSON 113 ENRICHMENT Name ______

The chart below shows the number of floors in some of the world's tallest buildings.

	Sears Tower, Chicago	110
	Empire State Building, New York	102
X	Bank of China, Hong Kong	72
	Chrysler Building, New York	77
	Transamerican Pyramid, San Francisco	48
X	Scotia Plaza, Toronto	68
	World Wide Plaza, New York	53
X	Liberty Square Tower, Los Angeles	75

Round the numbers to the nearest ten and answer the questions using estimates.

1. According to the chart, about how many floors must a building have to be called "one of the world's tallest"? 50
2. Mark an *X* beside three buildings that have about the same number of floors.
3. About how many floors taller is the Sears Tower than the Empire State Building? 10
4. About how much of a difference is there between the tallest and the shortest building on this chart? 62

Math Explorations and Applications Level 2 • 113

Using the Student Pages Have students complete problems 1–24 on page 251 on their own. Discuss the answers, then discuss whether 35 is closer to 30 or to 40. Have students then complete page 252 on their own. Allow them to use calculators to find the exact answers and the differences between their estimates and the exact answer.

Using the Thinking Story Present one or two new problems from those following "More Sharing With Cousin Trixie" on pages 100–101 of the Thinking Story Book.

3 Wrap-Up

5 MINUTES

In Closing Ask students to explain how they would estimate 55 + 28 and 55 – 28. (Round 55 up to 60, 28 up to 30, for about 90 and about 30.)

SELF ASSESSMENT

To assess students' understanding of rounding, have them write a number from one through ten at the bottom of page 252. Explain that they should write eight or above if they completely understand how to round, between four and seven if they understand it but still need some help, and between one and three if they have no understanding of rounding. Reteach as necessary.

Assessment Criteria

Did the student . . .

✓ correctly round 20 of 24 numbers on page 251?

✓ estimate within ten of the exact answer for eight of the ten problems on page 252?

LEARNING STYLES

Meeting Individual Needs

Have visual learners draw number lines to help them round the numbers on pages 251 and 252.

LESSON 114

Student Edition pages 253–256

Unit 3 Review

Using the Student Pages Use this Unit Review as a preliminary unit test to indicate areas in which each student is having difficulty or in which the entire class might need help. If students do well on the Unit Review, you might want to go directly to the next unit. If not, you may spend a day or so helping students overcome their individual difficulties before they take the Unit Test.

The lesson numbers next to each instruction line refer to specific lessons for additional instruction if students need help. You may also use this information to make additional assignments to reinforce lesson skills and concepts.

Have students complete pages 253 through 256 on their own. Help students who have trouble and make note of those who may continue to need special help. You might read the problems on page 255 with students who need help.

Unit Project If you have not already assigned the container volume project on pages 262a and 262b, you might want to do so at this time. This project is a good opportunity for students to compare the capacity of containers, practice using words or symbols to record and interpret information, and compare objects that are the same size but have a different mass or weight and other objects that are of a different size but have the same mass or weight.

LESSON 114

Name ____________________

Unit 3 Review

What time is it?

Lessons 93–95

❶ 1:22

❷ 3:48

❸ 7:12

Lessons 73–75

❹ Color three fourths.

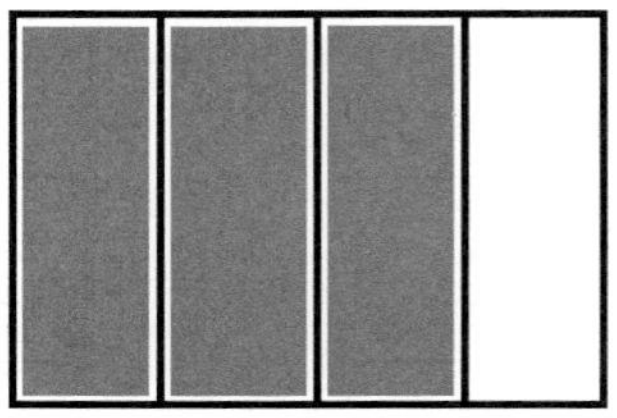

❺ Color one third.

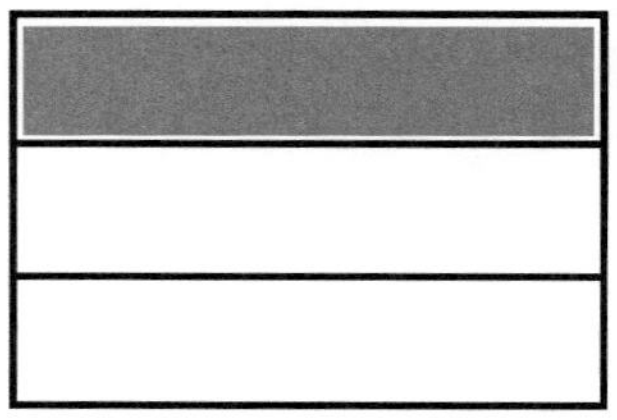

What is the right sign? Draw <, >, or =.

Lesson 91

❻ 8 + 7 (<) 20

❼ 112 (>) 84 + 112

❽ 14 + 26 (=) 26 + 14

❾ 127 (=) 100 + 27

NOTE TO HOME
Students review unit skills and concepts.

◆ LESSON 114 Unit 3 Review

Lessons 102–105

⑩ Ring the odd numbers.

(3) 22 10 (195) 86

(47) (73) (351) 98 352

ALGEBRA READINESS

Solve these problems.

Lessons 104 and 105

⑪ [14] = 10 + 4

⑫ [6] = 10 − 4

⑬ 5 + [8] = 13

⑭ [9] + 8 = 17

⑮ 12 = [5] + 7

⑯ 14 = 5 + [9]

Lesson 112

Solve the problems. Watch the signs.

⑰ 20 − 19 = **1**

⑱ 26 + 18 = **44**

⑲ 91 − 84 = **7**

⑳ 53 + 29 = **82**

FANTASTIC FACT

The longest hiccup attack lasted five years.

NOTE TO HOME
Students review unit skills and concepts.

PRACTICE p. 114

LESSON 114 PRACTICE Name ______________________

What time is it?

❶  4:57

❷  10:18

❸  6:34

What is the right sign? Draw <, >, or =.

❹ 67 + 43 (>) 55

❺ 100 + 38 (=) 138

❻ 12 (<) 5 + 9

❼ 10 + 8 (=) 9 + 9

Ring the odd numbers.

❽ 8 (13) (55) 76 (211) 232

Solve. Watch the signs.

❾ 8 + 8 = 16

❿ 18 − 9 = 9

⓫ 3 + 9 = 12

⓬ 15 − 6 = 9

⓭ 84 − 26 = 58

⓮ 60 − 35 = 25

⓯ 47 + 17 = 64

⓰ 98 − 46 = 52

⓱ 23 + 59 = 82

ENRICHMENT p. 114

LESSON 114 ENRICHMENT Name ______________________

How many triangles can you find? 7

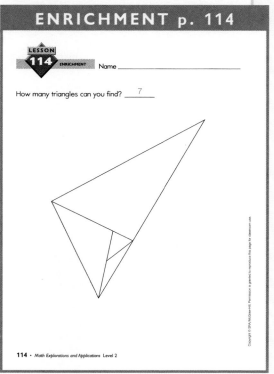

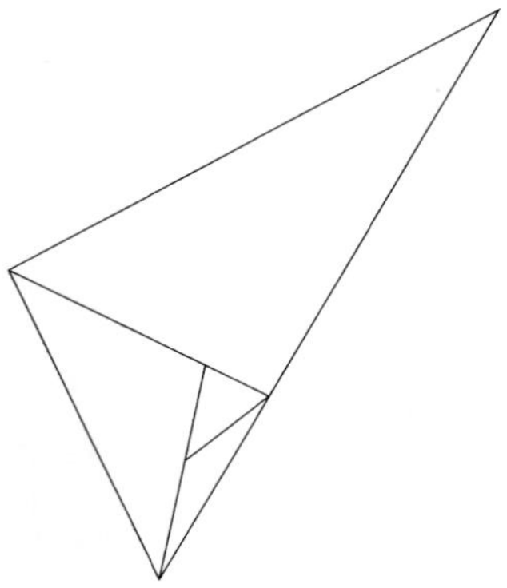

◆ **LESSON 114 Unit 3 Review** Name ______________

Solve these problems.

Lessons 67 and 68

21 George is 53 inches tall. Paula is 48 inches tall.

Who is taller? George

How much taller? 5 inches

22 Mrs. Okomoto works in sales. She drove 75 miles on Monday, 30 miles on Tuesday, and 63 miles on Wednesday. How far did she drive in the three days?

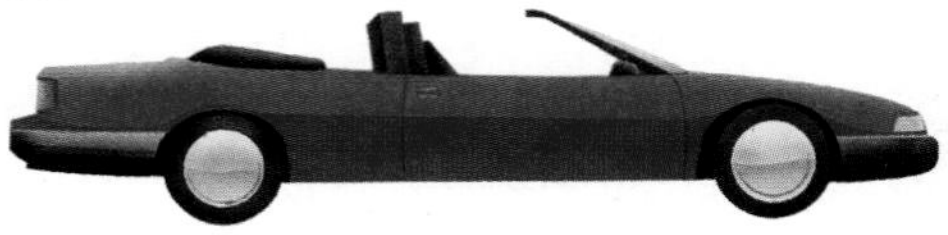

168 miles

23 Mr. Katz has $49. He wants to buy a sweater that costs $85. How much more does he need?

$ 36

24 There are 100 centimeters in 1 meter. How many centimeters are there in 7 meters? 700

NOTE TO HOME
Students review unit skills and concepts.

◆ LESSON 114 Unit 3 Review

Solve these problems. Use shortcuts when you can.

Lesson 96

25. 13 + 17 = **30**
26. 76 − 59 = **17**
27. 18 + 17 = **35**
28. 58 − 28 = **30**
29. 59 + 38 = **97**
30. 35 − 26 = **9**
31. 39 + 43 = **82**
32. 64 − 49 = **15**
33. 38 + 43 = **81**
34. 64 − 19 = **45**

Estimate answers by rounding to the nearest ten. Then calculate the difference between your estimate and the exact answer.

Estimates may vary. Examples are given below.

Lesson 113

	Estimate	Exact answer	Difference
35. 66 − 39 =	30	27	3
36. 18 + 53 =	70	71	1
37. 45 + 55 =	100	100	0
38. 71 − 64 =	10	7	3

NOTE TO HOME
Students continue to review skills presented in this unit.

LESSON 115

Student Edition pages 257–260

Unit 3 Test

Using the Student Pages The Unit Test on Student Edition pages 257 through 260 provides an opportunity to formally evaluate your students' proficiency with skills and concepts developed in this unit. It is similar in content and format to the Unit Review. Students who did well on the Unit Review might not need to take this test. Students who did not do well on the Unit Review should be provided with additional practice opportunities, such as the Mixed Practice pages, before taking the Unit Test. For further evaluation, you might want to have these students also take the Unit Test in multiple choice format, provided on pages 104–109 in the Assessment Master Book.

LESSON 115

Name ______________________

Unit 3 Test

Check your math skills.

Solve these problems. Watch the signs.

1. 8 + 9 = 17
2. 15 − 7 = 8
3. 16 − 6 = 10
4. 8 + 2 = 10
5. 12 − 3 = 9
6. 5 + 7 = 12
7. 8 + [4] = 12
8. [4] + 7 = 11
9. 18 = 9 + [9]
10. 12 = [6] + 6
11. [7] + 0 = 7
12. 9 + [0] = 9
13. [10] = 5 + 5
14. [10] + 3 = 13
15. Ring the odd numbers.

(1) 8 (123) 500 (501)

NOTE TO HOME
This test checks unit skills and concepts.

PRACTICE p. 115

LESSON 115 PRACTICE Name ______________________

Color one fourth.

1. 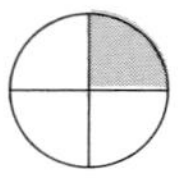

Color three fourths.

2. 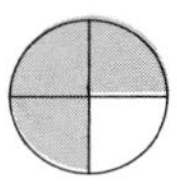

Shaded areas may vary. Check students' work.

Solve. Watch the signs.

3. 8 + [5] = 13
4. 14 = 7 + [7]
5. [10] + 9 = 19
6. 6 + [0] = 6
7. 78 + 44 = 122
8. 45 − 16 = 29
9. 33 + 49 = 82
10. 54 − 21 = 33
11. 66 + 29 = 95

Ring the odd numbers.

12. (3) 16 (307) (481) 614

What is the right sign? Draw <, >, or =.

13. 21 − 5 (<) 20
14. 10 + 10 (=) 20
15. 43 + 19 (>) 60
16. 12 + 36 (=) 36 + 12

◆ LESSON 115 Unit 3 Test

Solve these problems. Watch the signs.

16. $24 + 18 =$ **42**
17. $36 + 87 =$ **123**
18. $59 + 46 =$ **105**
19. $27 + 33 =$ **60**
20. $19 - 12 =$ **7**
21. $82 - 37 =$ **45**
22. $51 - 36 =$ **15**
23. $75 - 16 =$ **59**

What is the right sign? Draw <, >, or =.

24. 18 + 24 (**>**) 30
25. 19 − 7 (**<**) 20
26. 5 + 5 (**=**) 10
27. 8 + 4 (**=**) 4 + 8

Add.

28. $43 + 28 + 62 + 57 =$ **190**
29. $26 + 17 + 30 + 19 =$ **92**
30. $29 + 30 + 43 + 16 =$ **118**
31. $16 + 40 + 29 + 18 =$ **103**

NOTE TO HOME
This test checks unit skills and concepts.

ENRICHMENT p. 115

LESSON 115 ENRICHMENT Name ______

How many triangles can you find? 23

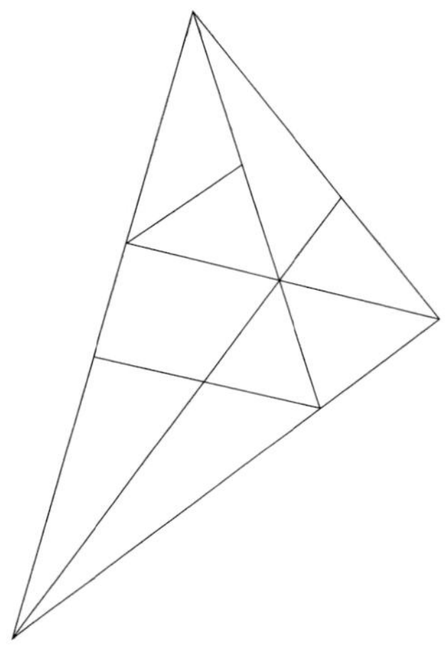

ASSESSMENT p. 47

UNIT 3 — Unit 3 Test (Use after Lesson 115.) Page 1 of 4

Name ______

The student demonstrates mastery by correctly answering at least 36 of the 45 problems.

Work these problems. Watch the signs.

1. 9 + 7 = 16
2. 16 − 9 = 7
3. 6 + 4 = 10
4. 7 + 8 = 15
5. 5 + 6 = 11
6. 19 = 8 + 11
7. 3 + 9 = 12
8. 12 = 6 + 6

Ring the odd numbers.

9. 96 (11) 90 (29) (5)

Solve. Watch the signs.

10. $36 + 14 =$ 50
11. $28 + 37 =$ 65
12. $65 + 13 =$ 78
13. $34 + 24 =$ 58
14. $17 - 13 =$ 4
15. $96 - 77 =$ 19
16. $48 - 21 =$ 27
17. $51 - 26 =$ 25

Go on . . .

◆ **LESSON 115** **Unit 3 Test**

Name ______________________

Solve these problems.

32. The soup costs \$3. The hamburger costs \$5. How much do they cost all together?

\$ 8

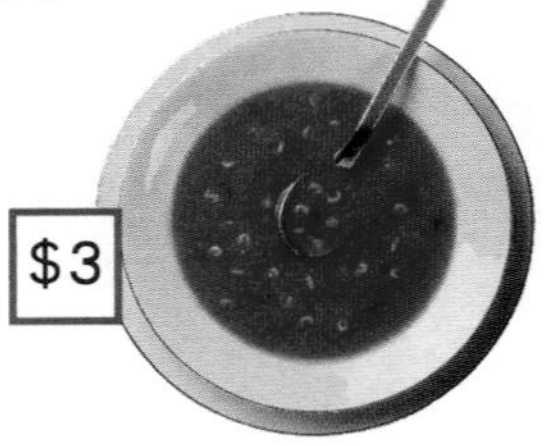

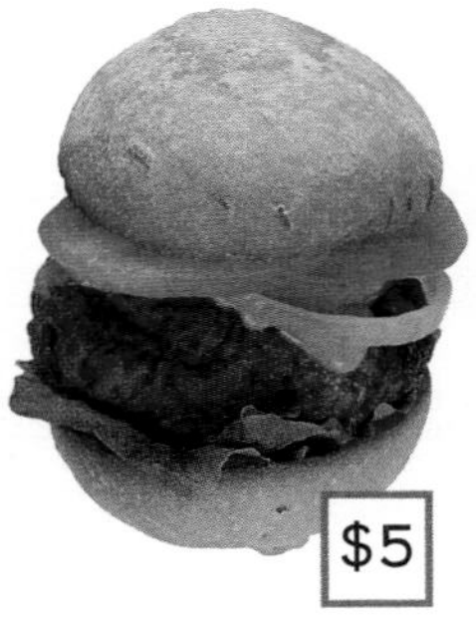

33. The camera costs \$75. The fan costs \$49. How much do they cost all together?

\$ 124

34. The radio costs \$24. Ms. Duffy gave the salesperson \$50. How much change should she get?

\$ 26

NOTE TO HOME
This test checks unit skills and concepts.

◆ LESSON 115 Unit 3 Test

What time is it?

㉟ 4 : 00 ㊱ 5 : 37 ㊲ 9 : 06

㊳ Color one third.

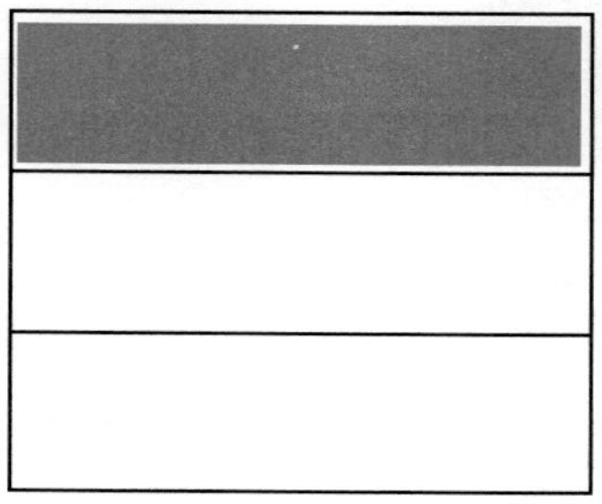

㊴ Color two thirds.

Answers are examples only.

㊵ There are 100 centimeters in 1 meter. How many centimeters are there in 4 meters? 400

NOTE TO HOME
This test checks unit skills and concepts.

LESSON 116

Student Edition pages 261–262

Extending the Unit

LESSON PLANNER

Objective

- ▶ to provide remediation instruction and enrichment activities

Context of the Lesson This is the third remediation and enrichment lesson in this book. The last will be at the end of Unit 4.

Materials	Program Resources
none	Practice Master 116
	Enrichment Master 116
	For extra practice: CD-ROM* Lesson 116

1 Warm-Up 5 MINUTES

Problem of the Day Write the following problem on the chalkboard: Suppose you had 75 cents and lost a nickel. Do you have enough money left to buy a 25-cent eraser and a 45-cent notebook? How can you tell? (Yes, because 75 – 5 = 70 and 25 + 45 = 70.)

MENTAL MATH Have students use mental math to add or subtract.

a. 17 – 8 = (9)

b. 12 – 8 = (4)

c. 15 – 9 = (6)

d. 8 + 7 = (15)

e. 6 + 5 = (11)

LESSON 116

Name ______________________

Extending the Unit

Solve the cross-number puzzle.
Fill in the numbers.

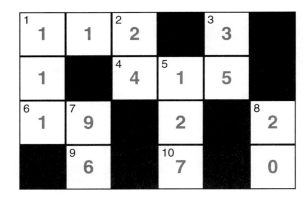

1: 1	1	2: 2	■	3: 3	■
1	■	4: 4	5: 1	5	■
6: 1	7: 9	■	2	■	8: 2
■	9: 6	■	10: 7	■	0

Across

1. 94 + 18 = 112
4. 15 minutes past 4 o'clock 4:15
6. 36 − 17 = 19
8. 2 tens + 6 ones = 26
9. 5:55 is about 6 o'clock
10. Number of centimeters in seven meters 700

Down

1. 86 + 25 = 111
2. 2 tens and 4 ones 24
3. 69 − 34 = 35
5. 69 + 58 = 127
7. 42 + 54 = 96
8. 43 − 23 = 20
10. 26 − 19 = 7

NOTE TO HOME
Students complete a number puzzle.

COOPERATIVE LEARNING Allow students who do not need remediation to work with those who do to play games that were introduced previously in this unit or by doing flash card practice with them.

RETEACHING

Use base-10 materials to reteach addition and subtraction of two-digit numbers. Have students use craft sticks to model and solve problems such as 73 + 46 (119) and 79 – 45 (34).

*available separately

◆ LESSON 116 Extending the Unit

Solve the cross-number puzzle.

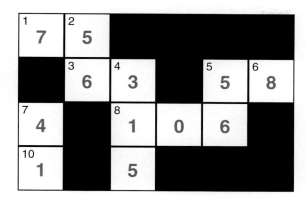

1 7	2 5	■	■	■	■
■	3 6	4 3	■	5 5	6 8
7 4	■	8 1	0	6	■
10 1	■	5	■	■	■

Across

1. 50 + 25 = 75
3. 120 − 57 = 63
5. 85 − 27 = 58
7. 40 = 4 tens
8. 68 + 38 = 106
10. 1:10 is about 1 o'clock

Down

1. 63 − 56 = 7
2. 56 − 19 = 37
4. 45 minutes before 4 o'clock 3:15
5. 43 + 13 = 56
6. 7:55 is 5 minutes before 8
7. 113 − 72 = 41

NOTE TO HOME
Students complete a number puzzle.

❷ Teach

Using the Student Pages Students who need remediation can do activities, play games previously introduced, and complete extra practice in skills diagnosed in Lesson 115. Enrichment activities for students who have finished remediation or do not need it are included on student pages 261 and 262. The cross-number puzzles on these pages should serve as a fun challenge for students who do not need remediation.

❸ Wrap-Up

5 MINUTES

In Closing Have students identify any cross-number puzzle answers they were able to figure out mentally.

ALTERNATIVE ASSESSMENT

Informal Assessment Use students' answers to the cross-number puzzle as an informal assessment of their addition and subtraction skills and their understanding of metric measurement.

Assessment Criterion

Did the student . . .

✓ correctly complete 80% of the cross-number puzzles on pages 261–262?

PRACTICE p. 116

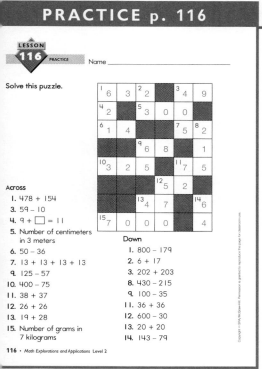

LESSON 116 PRACTICE Name ____________

Solve this puzzle.

1 6	3	2 2	■	3 4	9
4 2	■	5 3	0	0	■
6 1	4	■	■	7 5	8 2
■	■	9 6	8	■	1
10 3	2	5	■	11 7	5
■	■	■	12 5	2	■
■	■	13 4	7	■	14 6
15 7	0	0	0	■	4

Across

1. 478 + 154
3. 59 − 10
4. 9 + □ = 11
5. Number of centimeters in 3 meters
6. 50 − 36
7. 13 + 13 + 13 + 13
9. 125 − 57
10. 400 − 75
11. 38 + 37
12. 26 + 26
13. 19 + 28
15. Number of grams in 7 kilograms

Down

1. 800 − 179
2. 6 + 17
3. 202 + 203
8. 430 − 215
9. 100 − 35
11. 36 + 36
12. 600 − 30
13. 20 + 20
14. 143 − 79

ENRICHMENT p. 116

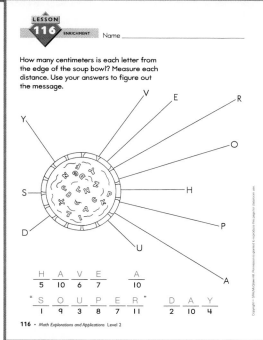

LESSON 116 ENRICHMENT Name ____________

How many centimeters is each letter from the edge of the soup bowl? Measure each distance. Use your answers to figure out the message.

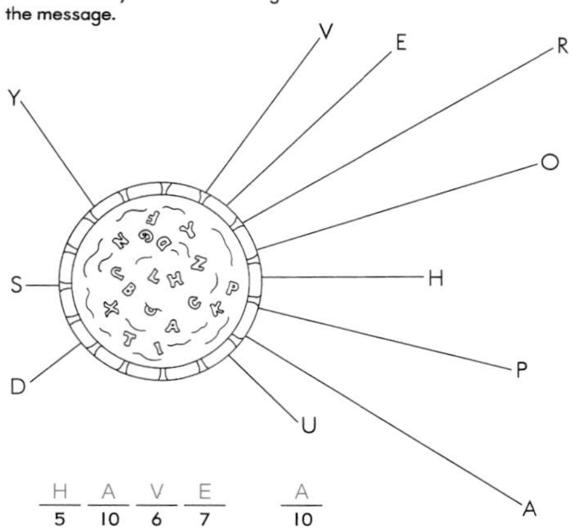

H A V E (5 10 6 7) A (10)
"S O U P E R" (1 9 3 8 7 11) D A Y (2 10 4)

UNIT 3

Student Edition pages 262a–262b

Wrap-Up

PRESENTING THE PROJECT

Project Objectives

- to compare the capacity of containers–similar shape but different capacity, a different shape but identical capacity, regular and irregular shapes
- to provide practice using words or symbols to record and interpret information
- to compare objects that are the same size but have a different mass or weight and other objects that are of a different size but have the same mass or weight

Materials

a variety of empty containers with labels
water
large and small standard measuring utensils
customary and/or metric scales

Students will investigate capacity and weight and explore customary and metric measurements. Introduce the project by displaying a variety of empty containers with labels. Help students find the capacity and/or weight on each label. Make sure the students understand that these numbers refer to the weight or mass of the products in the containers or to the capacity of the containers. Write the unit names and abbreviations on the chalkboard or on chart paper.

Invite the students to use the standard measuring utensils to fill the containers and keep track of how much water they put into each container and how much each weighs. Then, help the students compare the capacities of different sizes and shapes of containers.

Encourage groups of students to figure out the best way to communicate what they discovered as they experimented.

Invite students to survey the containers in their homes, record information about size, shape, capacity, and weight. Encourage students to suggest reasons we use a variety of units of measurement and how we decide when to use them.

Wrapping Up the Project Invite students to use the empty containers and labels to set up a pretend store in the classroom.

What Is a Math Project? If this is the first time you have used math projects in your classroom, you might want to refer to pages 98a–98b in this Teacher's Guide for more detailed information about effectively implementing and assessing projects.

Assessing the Project When students are making lists of products and weights, observe whether they were able to find the numbers, words, and symbols they were asked to find on the containers.

Portfolio Assessment Have students work in twos and draw a picture of a product they might find in the kitchen. The product should have a label and weight. Compile all the drawings into a class book.

Literature Connection You might want to share the book *The Supermarket* by Anne and Harlow Rockwell to set the stage for looking at containers and product packages.

Technology Connection The software *Measure Works* from MECC (Apple, for ages 6–12) will provide practice selecting appropriate units for measuring weight. It can be set for customary or metric units.

UNIT 4

Money and Multiplication

EXPLORING AND PROBLEM SOLVING

OVERVIEW

In this unit students are introduced to the operation of multiplication. Basic facts with factors 0 through 5 are presented and division is related by way of missing factors. Students apply multiplication to a variety of problems. Students collect data from random events and analyze data to predict results. Students also graph variables. Then, they continue their work on the calendar by finding the day of the week for a given number of days in the past or future. Students also learn to solve problems about elapsed time, explore rules for function tables, and apply and identify one- and two-step function rules. Students extend their knowledge of numbers to counting and writing numbers through 1000 and through 10,000. Students extend their computational skills to adding and subtracting three-digit numbers and four-digit numbers. Students also learn to add and subtract money.

Integrated Topics in This Unit Include:

- learning basic multiplication facts for factors 0 through 5
- collecting and organizing data from random events
- making bar graphs and organizing variable data on a graph
- relating division to multiplication
- solving problems about elapsed time
- identifying one- and two-step function rules
- adding and subtracting money
- adding and subtracting three-digit numbers
- counting numbers through 10,000
- adding and subtracting four-digit numbers
- adding two, three, or four addends

DIVISION
MIXED OPERATIONS

"A developmental approach to computation fosters a problem-solving atmosphere in which children are actively involved in using materials, discussing their work, validating solutions, and raising questions. Placing computation in a problem-solving context motivates students to learn computational skills and serves as an impetus for the mastery of paper-and-pencil algorithms."

—NCTM Curriculum and Evaluation Standards for School Mathematics

GAMES

Motivating Mixed Practice

Games provide **basic math skills** practice in cooperative groups and develop **mathematical reasoning.**

Add the Products Game	Lesson 120	page 272
Multiplication Table Game	Lesson 120	page 272
Add the Products Game	Lesson 121	page 274
Multiplication Table Game	Lesson 123	page 278
Harder What's the Problem? Game	Lesson 132	page 298
Choice of Game	Lesson 133	page 299
Rummage Sale Game	Lesson 141	page 317
Choice of Game	Lesson 146	page 329
Harder Rummage Sale Game	Lesson 147	page 332
Make a $10 Bill Game	Lesson 148	page 334
Make 1000 Game	Lesson 150	page 338
Checkbook Game	Lesson 151	page 342
Counting and Writing Numbers Game	Lesson 152	page 344
Roll a Problem Game	Lesson 154	page 348
Four-Digit Addition Game	Lesson 156	page 352
Four Cubes from 10,000 to 0 Game	Lesson 157	page 354

THINKING STORIES

Integrated Problem Solving

Thinking Stories provide opportunities for students to work in **cooperative groups** and develop **logical reasoning** while they integrate **reading skills** with mathematics.

Loretta the Letter Carrier Chooses Sides	Lesson 118	Thinking Story Book pages 102–107
Ferdie's Meterstick	Lesson 126	Thinking Story Book pages 108–113
How Far Up? How Far Down?	Lesson 133	Thinking Story Book pages 114–119
Manolita Changes Things	Lesson 142	Thinking Story Book pages 120–123

Story Summaries In "Loretta the Letter Carrier Chooses Sides," the story and story problems offer students practice using odd and even numbers.

In "Ferdie's Meterstick," the story and story problems enhance students' understanding of measuring and offer a practical demonstration of how parts fit into a whole.

"How Far Up? How Far Down?" explores the concept of negative and positive numbers.

"Manolita Changes Things," focuses on basic addition and division, giving students an opportunity to improve their understanding of how parts make a whole.

PROJECT

Making Connections

The Unit Project establishes more real-world connections. Students work in **cooperative groups** to solve problems and communicate their findings.

In the Unit Project students use a newspaper to identify and use numbers in a variety of ways. Students may begin this project any time after Lesson 129.

UNIT 4

Money and Multiplication Lesson Plans

LESSON		PACING	PRIMARY OBJECTIVES	FEATURE	RESOURCES	NCTM STANDARDS
117	Introduction to Multiplication 265–266	1 day	to introduce and provide experience in multiplication		Reteaching Master Practice Master 117 Enrichment Master 117	7, 8
118	Multiplication—Using Repeated Addition 267–268	1 day	to introduce repeated addition to solve multiplication problems	Thinking Story, Game	Practice Master 118 Enrichment Master 118	7, 8
119	Multiplication—Finding Area 269–270	1 day	to demonstrate how to find area by counting square units	Thinking Story	Practice Master 119 Enrichment Master 119	4, 7, 8, 9
120	Multiplication 271–272	1 day	to introduce multiplication facts for factors 0 through 5	Thinking Story	Practice Master 120 Enrichment Master 120	1, 2, 3, 4, 8
121	Multiplication—Using Pictures 273–274	1 day	to review multiplication facts for factors 0 through 5	Thinking Story, Game	Practice Master 121 Enrichment Master 121	8
122	Applying Multiplication . . . 275–276	1 day	to provide realistic multiplication problems for students to solve	Thinking Story	Practice Master 122 Enrichment Master 122	1, 2, 3, 4, 8
123	Multiplication 277–278	1 day	to provide practice using a multiplication table	Game	Practice Master 123 Enrichment Master 128	8, 13
124	Analyzing Random Events 279–280	1 day	to introduce collecting and organizing data from random events		Practice Master 124 Enrichment Master 124	11
125	Predicting Results 281–282	1 day	to provide practice analyzing and making predictions about data		Practice Master 125 Enrichment Master 125	11
126	Introducing Variability 283–284	1 day	to demonstrate predicting variability	Thinking Story	Practice Master 126 Enrichment Master 126	3, 10, 11, 13
127	Applying Multiplication . . . 285–286	1 day	to provide practice solving missing-factor problems	Thinking Story	Reteaching Master Practice Master 127 Enrichment Master 127 Assessment Master p. 51	1, 2, 3, 4, 7
128	Introducing Division 287–288	1 day	to introduce division	Thinking Story	Reteaching Master Practice Master 128 Enrichment Master 128	4, 7, 8
129	Division and Multiplication 289–290	1 day	to introduce multiplication and division as inverse operations		Practice Master 129 Enrichment Master 129	1, 2, 3, 4, 7, 8
	Mid-Unit Review 291–292	1 day			Assessment Master pp. 52–55	
130	Days of the Week 293–294	1 day	to demonstrate ordering the days of the week	Thinking Story	Practice Master 130 Enrichment Master 130	4, 10
131	Telling Time 295–296	1 day	to introduce basic concepts of telling time		Reteaching Master Practice Master 131 Enrichment Master 131	1, 2, 3, 4, 10
132	Number Sentences 297–298	1 day	to introduce number sentences with mixed operations	Game	Practice Master 132 Enrichment Master 132	1, 2, 3, 4, 6, 7, 8
133	Grouping by Tens 299–300	1 day	to introduce the strategy of grouping by ten for mental addition	Thinking Story, Game	Practice Master 133 Enrichment Master 133	3, 7, 8
134	Multiplication and Division 301–302	1 day	to provide practice in multiplying and dividing	Thinking Story	Reteaching Master Practice Master 134 Enrichment Master 134	3, 8, 13
135	Mixed Operations 303–304	1 day	to provide practice with basic operations using function machines	Thinking Story	Practice Master 135 Enrichment Master 135	3, 8, 13
136	More Mixed Operations . . 305–306	1 day	to provide practice in solving realistic problems involving composite function rules	Thinking Story	Practice Master 136 Enrichment Master 136	3, 8, 13
137	Keeping Sharp 307–308	1 day	to provide review and practice two-digit addition and subtraction		Reteaching Master Practice Master 137 Enrichment Master 137	8
138	Counting through 1000 309–310	1 day	✓ to assess students' ability to count from 0 through 1000		Reteaching Master Practice Master 138 Enrichment Master 138	6

	LESSON	PACING	PRIMARY OBJECTIVES	FEATURE	RESOURCES	NCTM STANDARDS
139	Numbers through 1000 . . . 311–312	1 day	to prepare students to add two three-digit numbers		Practice Master 139 Enrichment Master 139 Assessment Master p. 56	5, 6, 8
140	Introducing Three-Digit Addition 313–314	1 day	to review the relationships among units, tens, and hundreds		Practice Master 140 Enrichment Master 140	4, 7, 8
141	Three-Digit Addition. 313–314	1 day	to review the relationships among units, tens, and hundreds		Practice Master 141 Enrichment Master 141	7, 8
142	More Three-Digit Addition 319–320	1 day	to provide practice adding three-digit numbers	Thinking Story	Reteaching Master Practice Master 142 Enrichment Master 142	1, 2, 3, 4, 8
143	Three-Digit Subtraction . . . 321–324	1 day	to prepare students for learning to subtract three-digit numbers	Thinking Story	Practice Master 143 Enrichment Master 143	7, 8
144	More Three-Digit Subtraction. 325–326	1 day	to reinforce the relationship among units, tens, and hundreds	Thinking Story	Practice Master 144 Enrichment Master 144	1, 2, 3, 4, 7, 8
145	Practicing Three-Digit Subtraction. 327–328	1 day	to practice subtracting three-digit numbers	Thinking Story	Reteaching Master Practice Master 145 Enrichment Master 145	8
146	Three-Digit Addition and Subtraction. 329–330	1 day	to provide practice in adding and subtracting three-digit numbers	Game	Practice Master 146 Enrichment Master 146	1, 2, 3, 4, 8, 11
147	Three-Digit Practice 331–332	1 day	to provide practice with three-digit addition and subtraction	Game	Practice Master 147 Enrichment Master 147	8
148	Adding and Subtracting Money 333–334	1 day	✓ to assess students' ability to form any amount of money up to $10 using coins and bills and up to $1000 using bills	Game	Practice Master 148 Enrichment Master 148 Assessment Master p. 57	1, 2, 3, 4, 8
149	Adding and Subtracting with Three Digits 335–336	1 day	✓ to assess students' ability to add and subtract three-digit numbers		Reteaching Master Practice Master 149 Enrichment Master 149 Assessment Master p. 58	1, 2, 3, 4, 8
150	Practicing Addition and Subtraction. 337–338	1 day	to provide practice in using Mental Math strategies with addition and subtraction	Game	Practice Master 150 Enrichment Master 150	3, 8
151	Approximating Answers . . 339–342	1 day	to provide practice in estimating sums and differences	Game	Practice Master 151 Enrichment Master 151	1, 2, 3, 4, 5
152	Counting by 100s and 1000s. 343–344	1 day	to introduce counting and writing numbers to 10,000	Game	Practice Master 152 Enrichment Master 152	6
153	Adding Four-Digit Numbers. 345–346	1 day	to explore adding four-digit numbers		Practice Master 153 Enrichment Master 153	1, 2, 3, 4, 8
154	Four-Digit Addition 347–348	1 day	to develop proficiency in adding four-digit numbers	Game	Practice Master 154 Enrichment Master 154	6
155	Four-Digit Subtraction 349–350	1 day	to introduce the subtraction of four-digit numbers		Practice Master 155 Enrichment Master 155	6
156	Keeping Sharp 351–352	1 day	to provide practice in adding and subtracting pairs of four-digit numbers	Game	Reteaching Master Practice Master 156 Enrichment Master 156	4, 8
157	Applying Addition and Subtraction. 353–354	1 day	to provide practice with adding and subtracting four-digit numbers		Practice Master 157 Enrichment Master 157	1, 2, 3, 4, 8
158	Unit Review 355–358	1 day	to review skills and concepts			
159	Unit Test. 359–362	1 day	to assess skills and concepts		Assessment Master pp. 59–63	
160	Extending the Unit. 363–364	1 day	to review number concepts	**Project**		

UNIT CONNECTIONS

INTERVENTION STRATEGIES

In this Teacher's Guide there will be specific strategies suggested for students with individual needs–ESL, Gifted and Talented, Special Needs, Learning Styles, and At Risk. These strategies will be provided at the point of use. Here are the icons to look for and the types of strategies that will accompany them:

ESL

English as a Second Language

These strategies, designed for students who do not fluently speak the English language, will suggest meaningful ways to present the lesson concepts and vocabulary.

GIFTED & TALENTED

Gifted and Talented

Strategies to enrich and extend the lesson will offer further challenges to students who have easily mastered the concepts already presented.

SPECIAL NEEDS

Special Needs

Students who are physically challenged or who have learning disabilities might require alternative ways to complete activities, record answers, use manipulatives, and so on. The strategies labeled with this icon will offer helpful methods of presenting lesson concepts to these students.

LEARNING STYLES

Learning Styles

Each student has a unique learning style. The strategies labeled with this icon address a variety of learning modalities, such as tactile/kinesthetic, visual, and auditory.

AT RISK

At Risk

These strategies highlight the relevancy of math skills and concepts to the world outside the classroom. They are directed toward students who appear to be at risk of dropping out of school before graduation.

TECHNOLOGY CONNECTIONS

The following materials, designed to reinforce and extend lesson concepts, will be referred to throughout this Teacher's Guide. It might be helpful to order the software, video and laser disc, or check them out of the school media center or local community library. If the school does not provide Internet access, consider visiting a local library college or business specializing in Internet services. Some students will be able to access the Internet at home.

TECHNOLOGY CONNECTION

Look for this **Technology Connection** *icon.*

- *Home Grade Level Math Programs: Level 2* from Jostens Home Learning, Mac, IBM, for grade 2 (software)
- *Hands-On Math Series: Volumes 1, 2, and 3* from Ventura Educational Systems, Apple, Mac, IBM, for grades 1–8 (software)
- *Math Mystery Theater: Subtraction Roundup* from EdCon/Imperial International, VHS, for grades 2–8 (video)
- *Math For Beginners* from Coronet/MTI, for grades K–3 (laser disc)
- *Math Shop Jr.* from Scholastic, Mac, IBM, for grades 1–4 (software)
- *Eisenhower National Clearinghouse:* http://www.enc.org; Telnet: enc.org (login using the word "guest"); or dial (800) 362-4448 (Internet)

CROSS-CURRICULAR CONNECTIONS

This Teacher's Guide offers specific suggestions for connecting the math skills and concepts presented in the unit with other subject areas and with real-world situations. These strategies will be provided at the point of use.

Look for these icons:

- Geography
- Health
- Social Studies
- Music
- Science
- Math
- Art
- Physical Education
- Language Arts

LITERATURE CONNECTIONS

Relevant fiction and nonfiction books are suggested throughout the Teacher's Guide at the point where they could be used to introduce, reinforce, or extend specific lesson concepts. You might want to locate these books in your school or your local community library.

Look for this **Literature Connection** *icon.*

- *Counting on Frank* by Rod Clement, G. Stevens Children's Books, 1991
- *Each Orange Had 8 Slices* by Paul Giganti Jr., Greenwillow Press, 1992
- *Area* by Jane Jonas Srivastava, Crowell, 1974
- *Too Many Kangaroo Things to Do* by Stuart J. Murphy, HarperCollins, 1996
- *Anno's Mysterious Multiplying Jar* by Masaichiro and Mitsumasa Anno, Philomel Books, 1983
- *Right in Your Own Backyard: Nature Math* pp. 52–53 "Clover Time," Time-Life for Children, 1992
- *Anno's Magic Seeds* by Mitsumasa Anno, Philomel Books, 1994
- *Number Puzzles* by Rose Griffiths, Gareth Stevens Pub., 1995
- *When We Grow Up* by Anne Rockwell, Dutton, 1981
- *The Greatest Guessing Game* by Robert Froman, Crowell, 1978
- *A Remainder of One* by Elinor J. Pinczes, Houghton Mifflin, 1995
- *Take Off With Numbers* by Sally Hewitt pp. 26–29, Raintree Stoeck-Vaughn, 1996
- *Alice in Numberland: Fantasy Math* pp. 26–27 "Alice and the Sevens," Time-Life for Children, 1993
- *The Wonderful Counting Clock* by Cooper Edens, Simon & Schuster Books for Young Readers, 1995
- *How the Second Grade Got $8,205.50 to Visit the Statue of Liberty* by Nathan Zimelman, A. Whitman, 1992
- *The King's Commissioners* by Aileen Friedman, Scholastic, 1994
- *Ready, Set, Hop* by Stuart J. Murphy, HarperCollins, 1996
- *Alice in Numberland: Fantasy Math* pp. 48–53 "Alice's Adventures in Symbolville," Time-Life for Children, 1993
- *Numbers* by John Reiss, Bradbury Press, 1971
- *The Wildlife 1, 2, 3* by Jan Thornhill, Simon & Schuster Books for Young Readers, 1989
- *Who Sank the Boat?* by Pamela Allen, Coward, McCann, 1983
- *Kimako's Story* by June Jordan, Houghton Mifflin, 1981
- *Benjamin's 365 Birthdays* by Judi Barrett, Atheneum, 1992
- *Lunch Money and Other Poems About School* by Carol Diggery Shields, Dutton Children's Books, 1995
- *The Purse* by Kathy Caple, Houghton Mifflin, 1986
- *Alice in Numberland: Fantasy Math* pp. 60–63 "The Missing Number Mystery," Time-Life for Children, 1993
- *Annabelle Swift, Kindergartner* by Amy Schwartz, Orchard Books, 1988

ASSESSMENT OPPORTUNITIES AT-A-GLANCE

LESSON	PORTFOLIO	PERFORMANCE	FORMAL	SELF	INFORMAL	MULTIPLE CHOICE FORMAT	MASTERY CHECKPOINTS	ANALYZING ANSWERS
117					✓			
118		✓						
119					✓			
120		✓						
121	✓							
122					✓			✓
123		✓						
124		✓						
125					✓			
126				✓				
127			✓				✓	
128					✓			
129					✓			
Mid-Unit Review			✓					
130	✓							
131		✓						✓
132					✓			
133								
134	✓							
135	✓			✓				
136					✓			
137								
138		✓						
139			✓				✓	
140					✓			
141		✓						
142				✓				
143					✓			
145					✓			
146		✓			✓			
147		✓						
148			✓				✓	
149			✓				✓	
150		✓						
151					✓			
152					✓			
153				✓				
154		✓						
155					✓			
156		✓						
157				✓				
158								
Unit Review/ Unit Test		✓				✓		

ASSESSMENT OPTIONS

PORTFOLIO ASSESSMENT

Throughout this Teacher's Guide are suggested activities in which students draw pictures, make graphs, write about mathematics, and so on. Keep students' work to assess growth of understanding as the year progresses.

Lessons 121, 130, 134, and 135

PERFORMANCE ASSESSMENT

Performance assessment items focus on evaluating how students think and work as they solve problems. Opportunities for performance assessment can be found throughout the unit. Rubrics and guides for assessment are in the front of the Assessment Masters book.

Lessons 118, 120, 123, 124, 131, 138, 141, 146, 147, 150, 154, and 156

FORMAL ASSESSMENT

A Mid-Unit Review and Unit Test help assess students' understanding of concepts, skills, and problem solving. The *Math Explorations and Applications* CD-ROM Test Generator can create additional unit tests at three ability levels. Also, Mastery Checkpoints are provided periodically throughout the unit.

Lessons 126, 139, 148, 149, Mid-Unit Review, Unit Review, and Unit Test

SELF ASSESSMENT

Throughout the program, students evaluate their math skills through self-assessment activities.

Lessons 126, 136, 142, 153, and 157

INFORMAL ASSESSMENT

A variety of assessment suggestions are provided, including interviews, oral questions or presentation, and debates. Also, each lesson includes Assessment Criteria—a list of questions about each student's progress, understanding, and participation.

Lessons 117, 119, 122, 125, 128, 128, 129, 132, 133, 137, 140, 143, 144, 145, 151, 152, and 155

MULTIPLE-CHOICE TESTS (STANDARDIZED FORMAT)

Each unit includes a Unit Test in multiple choice format, presenting students with an opportunity to practice taking a test in a standardized test format.

MASTERY CHECKPOINT

Mastery Checkpoints are provided throughout the unit to assess student proficiency in specific skills. Checkpoints reference appropriate Assessment Masters and other assessment options. Results of these evaluations can be recorded on the Mastery Checkpoint Chart.

Lessons 126, 139, 148, and 149

ANALYZING ANSWERS

Analyzing Answers suggests possible sources of student error and offers teaching strategies for addressing difficulties.

Lesson 122

Look for these icons:

> *"Assessment is the process of gathering evidence about a student's knowledge of, ability to use, and disposition toward, mathematics and of making inferences from that evidence for a variety of purposes."*
>
> *—NCTM Assessment Standards*

ASSESSING INDIVIDUAL PROGRESS

WHAT TO EXPECT FROM STUDENTS AS THEY COMPLETE THIS UNIT

MULTIPLICATION FACTS

At this time students should demonstrate mastery of the multiplication facts studied so far by answering correctly at least 80% of the problems on pages 285 and 286. You might also assess mastery using Assessment Master page 51.

NUMERICAL SEQUENCE IN THE 0–1000 RANGE

By this time students should be able to write the numbers between 0 and 1000 in correct ascending or descending order. You may use their answers to page 311 or Assessment Master page 56 to assess students. Results of this assessment may be recorded on the Mastery Checkpoint Chart.

FAMILIARITY WITH MONEY

By this time students should be able to form and trade money amounts up to $10, using coins and bills, and up to $1000 using bills. To assess students, observe them as they play the "Make a $10 Bill" game or use Assessment Master page 57.

THREE-DIGIT ADDITION AND SUBTRACTION

By this time students should be able to add and subtract three-digit numbers and apply these skills when solving word problems. To assess students, you may use their answers to pages 335 and 336 or use Assessment Master page 58.

UNIT 4

PROGRAM RESOURCES

THESE ADDITIONAL COMPONENTS OF *MATH EXPLORATIONS AND APPLICATIONS* CAN BE PURCHASED SEPARATELY FROM SRA/MCGRAW-HILL.

LESSON	BASIC MANIPULATIVE KIT	GAME MAT PACKAGE	TEACHER KIT	OPTIONAL MANIPULATIVE KIT	OVERHEAD MANIPULATIVE KIT	*MATH EXPLORATIONS AND APPLICATIONS* CD-ROM	LITERATURE LIBRARY
117	Number Cubes					Lesson 117	Two More
118	Number Cubes					Lesson 118	
119	Number Cubes					Lesson 119	
120	Number Cubes	Multiplication Table Game				Lesson 120	
121	Number Cubes					Lesson 121	
122	Number Cubes					Lesson 122	
123	Number Cubes	Multiplication Table Game			counters	Lesson 123	
124						Lesson 124	
125	Number Cubes			counters		Lesson 125	
126						Lesson 126	
127	Number Cubes					Lesson 127	
128	Number Cubes				base-10 blocks	Lesson 128	
129					bills, coins	Lesson 129	
130	Number Cubes					Lesson 130	
131	Number Cubes			clock face		Lesson 131	
132						Lesson 132	
133	Number Cubes				base-10 blocks	Lesson 133	
134						Lesson 134	
135						Lesson 135	
136	Number Cubes					Lesson 136	
137			base-10 blocks			Lesson 137	
138						Lesson 138	
139						Lesson 139	
140					base-10 blocks	Lesson 140	
141		Rummage Sale Game	base-10 blocks		bills, coins	Lesson 141	
142	Number Cubes		base-10 blocks			Lesson 142	
143			base-10 blocks			Lesson 143	
144			base-10 blocks		bills, coins	Lesson 144	
145						Lesson 145	
146	Number Cubes		base-10 blocks		bills, coins	Lesson 146	
147		Harder Rummage Sale Game				Lesson 147	
148	Number Cubes				bills, coins	Lesson 148	
149	Number Cubes				base-10 blocks	Lesson 149	
150					base-10 blocks	Lesson 150	
151	Number Cubes	Checkbook Game				Lesson 151	
152	Number Cubes				base-10 blocks	Lesson 152	
153	Number Cubes		base-10 blocks			Lesson 153	
154					base-10 blocks	Lesson 154	
155			base-10 blocks			Lesson 155	
156	Number Cubes					Lesson 156	
157	Number Cubes		base-10 blocks			Lesson 157	

UNIT 4

Student Edition pages 263–264

Money and Multiplication

INTRODUCING THE UNIT

Using the Student Pages To help students make the connection between what they learn in school and how it applies to the outside world, ask students to imagine what might happen if a bank teller couldn't add and subtract. Then read aloud the paragraph on page 264.

ACTIVITY Ask students to pretend that they have $100 in a bank account and make up four problems to show money going in and going out of the account. Then invite students to share their problems with the rest of the class. You may wish to use the following discussion questions: "What would happen to your bank account if the teller forgot to add your $10 birthday money?" "Each bank account has a different number. The number tells who the account belongs to. What would happen if the bank teller put the wrong account number on your $10 deposit?" and "What would happen if the bank teller subtracted $100 from your account instead of $10?"

SCHOOL TO WORK CONNECTION

FYI The following information and discussion ideas will help students see how the skills and concepts they learn in school are used in the world outside the classroom. Use as much of the information and as many of the questions as are appropriate for your students. Remember, discussion questions are designed to promote thinking; students are not expected to be able to answer all of them.

Banks are a fairly modern invention. The need for banks did not arise until money was used to represent wealth or value. In the old days, people did not use money. They traded goods and services for things they needed. A farmer might trade a pig for two new pairs of shoes. A baker might trade three loaves of bread for a cup of salt. Teachers were paid with a place to live, food to eat, clothing, and other things students had to give. "What could you trade instead of paying for your lunch in the cafeteria?" "Why wouldn't banks work well when people traded for things they needed?" and "Why do you think people finally started using banks?"

UNIT 4

Money and Multiplication

EXPLORING AND PROBLEM SOLVING

- collecting data
- algebra readiness
- adding and subtracting money
- three-digit addition and subtraction
- four-digit addition and subtraction
- division readiness

263

PROBLEM SOLVING

Junior Thinklab™*

Junior Thinklab™ provides a series of creative and logical problem-solving opportunities for individual students. The problems are designed to appeal to different cognitive abilities.

- Use Activity Cards 61–65 with this unit to reinforce ordering skills and concepts.
- Use Activity Cards 66–70 with this unit to reinforce classifying skills and concepts.
- Use Activity Cards 71–75 with this unit to reinforce perception and spatial relations skills and concepts.
- Use Activity Cards 76–80 with this unit to reinforce reasoning and deducing skills and concepts.
- Use Divergent Thinking Activity Sheets 16–20 with this unit to encourage creativity in art and in intellectual activity.

*available separately

SCHOOL TO WORK CONNECTION

Bank tellers use math . . .

A bank teller keeps track of the money in your account. When you deposit or withdraw money, the teller uses addition and subtraction. A teller also uses skip counting or multiplication when counting money.

Paper money is a promise—it means that you can trade the piece of paper for a certain amount of gold or silver. People buy and sell with money. "Is money or trading easier for most people? Why? Why do you think each piece of money is worth a certain amount? What other things might people use instead of coins and bills? How would you decide how much each thing is worth?"

Excellent math skills are a must in any job that involves money. This is especially true for a bank employee who must avoid even the smallest error in order to keep the public's trust. Today a complex and highly accurate computer system conducts banking transactions, but the system is monitored and operated by people with the ability to do the same calculations and to identify when something has gone wrong.

Keeping a checkbook is a fine way to get a sense of the responsibilities and difficulties of a job in banking. The act of monitoring deposits and withdrawals is a perfect simulation of the basic work that tellers do in a bank. Invite the students to figure out a way to set up a pretend bank in their classroom. Encourage them to set up accounts, keep checkbooks, and take turns acting as customers and tellers.

COOPERATIVE LEARNING **Minds on Math** *Minds on Math* is a series of units covering problem solving, data collection, number sense, measurement, money, and geometry and spatial relations. Each unit provides a series of open-ended projects for individuals or small groups. These projects develop problem-solving and critical-thinking skills, utilize real-world materials, emphasize language, and integrate curriculum areas. Use projects from *Problems to Solve* to emphasize that there is more than one way to look at and solve any problem.

LITERATURE CONNECTION In the book *Half a Slice of Bread and Butter,* brothers use multiplication, division, fractions, and predictions as they learn to share. This book is part of the *Math Explorations and Applications* Literature Library*.

Home Connections You may want to send Home Connections Masters 47–48 to families to provide additional activities for them to do together. These activities apply skills and concepts presented in this unit.

*available separately

LESSON 117

Student Edition pages 265–266

Introduction to Multiplication

LESSON PLANNER

Objective

▶ to introduce and provide experience in multiplication

Context of the Lesson This lesson shows how repeated addition is related to multiplication.

Materials	**Program Resources**
calculators	Number Cubes
craft sticks (optional)	Reteaching Master
	Practice Master 117
	Enrichment Master 117
	For extra practice: CD-ROM* Lesson 117

1 Warm-Up

5 MINUTES

Problem of the Day Write this problem on the chalkboard: Antonio saved 25 cents on Monday and five cents every day after. On which day did he have 50 cents? (Saturday)

MENTAL MATH Have students add the following, using their Number Cubes to respond.

a. 2 + 2 + 2 = (6) **b.** 4 + 4 + 4 = (12)

c. 5 + 5 + 5 + 5 = (20) **d.** 3 + 3 + 3 = (9)

e. 1 + 1 + 1 + 1 + 1 = (5)

2 Teach

Using the Student Pages Work with the class to discuss and solve the first problem on page 265. Have them first add three five times. Then explain that 5×3 is a short way to show adding three five times. Have them use their calculators to multiply 5×3. Discuss whether the calculator answer is the same as their answer when they added three five times and why. Have students complete the rest of page 265 by adding, then using their calculators to do the multiplication. When finished, discuss the answers and check that the addition and multiplication answers are the same.

LESSON 117

Name ____________________

Introduction to Multiplication

Each triangle has three sides.
How many sides are there?

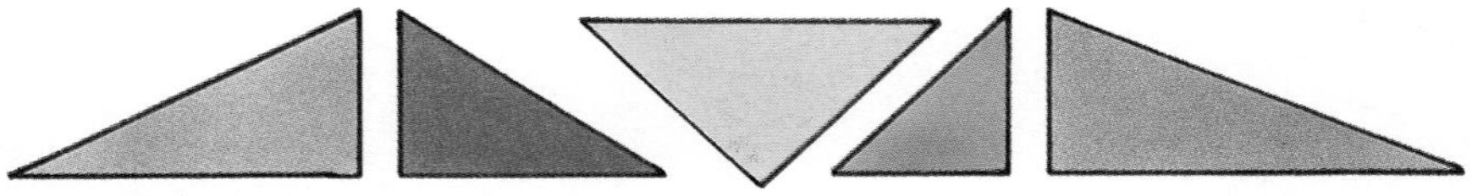

❶ 3 + 3 + 3 + 3 + 3 = 15 ❷ 5×3 = 15

Each car has four tires.
How many tires are there?

❸ 4 + 4 + 4 + 4 = 16 ❹ 4×4 = 16

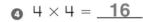

Each box has six pencils.
How many pencils are there?

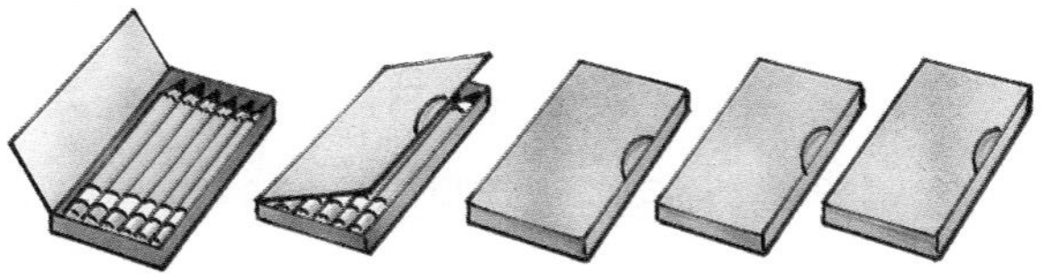

❺ 6 + 6 + 6 + 6 + 6 = 30 ❻ 5×6 = 30

NOTE TO HOME
Students are introduced to multiplication concepts.

RETEACHING p. 30

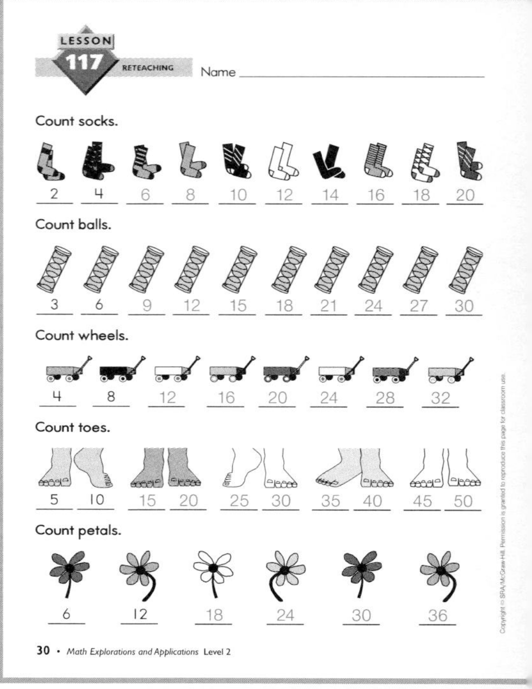

LESSON 117 RETEACHING Name ____________

Count socks.
2 4 6 8 10 12 14 16 18 20

Count balls.
3 6 9 12 15 18 21 24 27 30

Count wheels.
4 8 12 16 20 24 28 32

Count toes.
5 10 15 20 25 30 35 40 45 50

Count petals.
6 12 18 24 30 36

30 • Math Explorations and Applications Level 2

Why teach it at this time?

Introducing multiplication through multiples of ten helps students realize they can solve problems by thinking. Multiplication will be treated in a systematic way to allow students to learn the basic multiplication facts. These facts will be reviewed in level 3. Mastery in level 2 is not essential.

Literature Connection Read aloud *Counting on Frank* by Rod Clement to reinforce lesson concepts.

*available separately

◆ **LESSON 117** Introduction to Multiplication

Skip count to find the missing numbers.
Use manipulatives if you need to.

❼

2	4	6	8	10	12	14	16	18	20

❽ 3 × 2 = 6 ❾ 5 × 2 = 10

❿

3	6	9	12	15	18	21	24	27	30

⓫ 2 × 3 = 6 ⓬ 4 × 3 = 12

⓭

5	10	15	20	25	30	35	40	45	50

⓮ 2 × 5 = 10 ⓯ 8 × 5 = 40

NOTE TO HOME
Students skip count.

Discuss the first problem on page 266 with the class. First have students fill in the boxes by skip counting. Then show them how to use their answers to multiply. Point out that 3 × 2 is the same as skip counting by twos three times; 5 × 2 is the same as skip counting by twos five times. Have students complete the rest of the page on their own; then discuss their answers.

3 Wrap-Up

5 MINUTES

In Closing Ask students whether any addition answers on page 265 were different from the multiplication answers. If they were, find out why. (Either they made an addition error or pressed the wrong keys on the calculator.)

ALTERNATIVE ASSESSMENT

Informal Assessment Use students' answers to the discussion and problems on pages 265–266 as an informal assessment of their understanding of multiplication.

Assessment Criterion

Did the student . . .

✓ correctly solve the remaining problems on pages 265 and 266?

PRACTICE p. 117

LESSON 117 PRACTICE Name ______

Solve these problems.

❶ Each row has six flowers. How many flowers are there?

6 + 6 + 6 + 6 = 24 6 × 4 = 24

❷ Each spider has eight legs. How many legs are there?

8 + 8 + 8 = 24 3 × 8 = 24

❸ Each tree has five apples. How many apples are there?

5 + 5 + 5 + 5 + 5 = 25 5 × 5 = 25

❹ 5 × 4 = 20 ❺ 9 × 4 = 36
❻ 3 × 7 = 21 ❼ 6 × 7 = 42

ENRICHMENT p. 117

LESSON 117 ENRICHMENT Name ______

❶ Roll a 0–5 Number Cube. Write the number. Roll the cube again. Multiply the number you wrote by this number.

Roll the cube until you have written numbers for five problems. Then solve the problems.

Answers will vary.

❷ Roll a 0–5 cube. Write the number. Now roll a 5–10 cube. Multiply the number you wrote by this number.

Roll each cube until you have written numbers for five problems. Then solve the problems.

SPECIAL NEEDS

Meeting Individual Needs
Show students how to model problems similar to those on page 265. For example, have them make three groups of four to model 4 + 4 + 4. Allow them to add the total, then explain that this is the same as 4 x 3, which means "four three times." Have students use models to complete page 265.

LESSON 118

Student Edition pages 267–268

Multiplication—Using Repeated Addition

LESSON PLANNER

Objective

- ▶ to introduce the use of repeated addition to solve multiplication problems

Context of the Lesson This is the second of seven lessons on multiplication concepts.

Materials	**Program Resources**
meterstick	Number Cubes
posterboard	Thinking Story Book, pages 102–105
	Practice Master 118
	Enrichment Master 118
	For extra practice: CD-ROM* Lesson 118

1 Warm-Up

5 MINUTES

Problem of the Day Write this problem on the chalkboard: What is the greatest three-digit even number you can write? What is the least three-digit odd number you can write? (998, 101)

MENTAL MATH Have students fill in the blanks by skip counting by 2s:

a. 2, ____, 6, 8, ____ (4, 10)

b. 20, 22, ____, ____, 28 (24, 26)

c. 44, ____, 48, ____, 52 (46, 50)

d. 12, 14, 16, ____, ____ (18, 20)

e. 88, ____, ____, 94 (90, 92)

f. ____, ____, 70, 72 (66, 68)

2 Teach

Demonstrate Show that repeated addition is the same as multiplication. Ask how many fingers are on one hand. (5) Have four students hold up their hands. Ask them how many fingers are on eight hands. Explain that they can find out by adding five eight times or by multiplying 5 x 8. (40) Repeat

LESSON 118

Name ______________________

Multiplication—Using Repeated Addition

Use these pictures to solve the problems.

3 + 3 + 3 + 3 + 3 + 3

1. 6 × 3 = 18

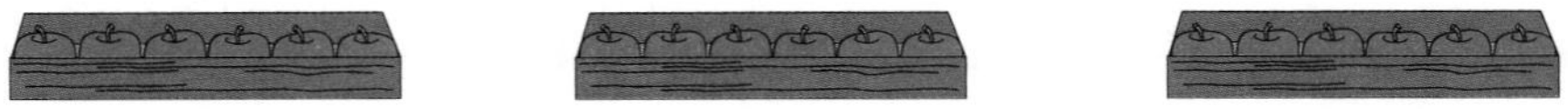

6 + 6 + 6

2. 3 × 6 = 18

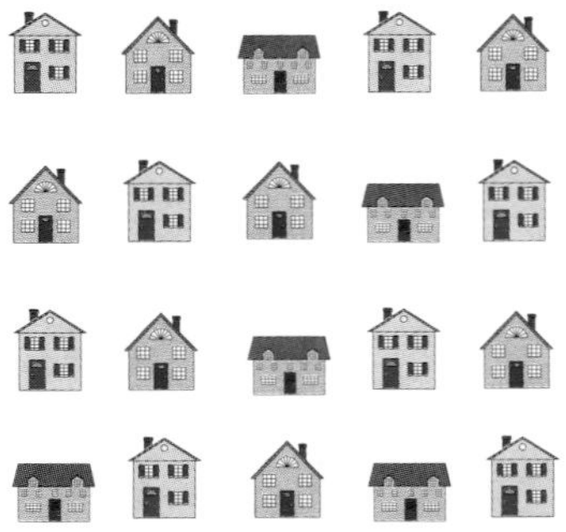

5 + 5 + 5 + 5

3. 4 × 5 = 20

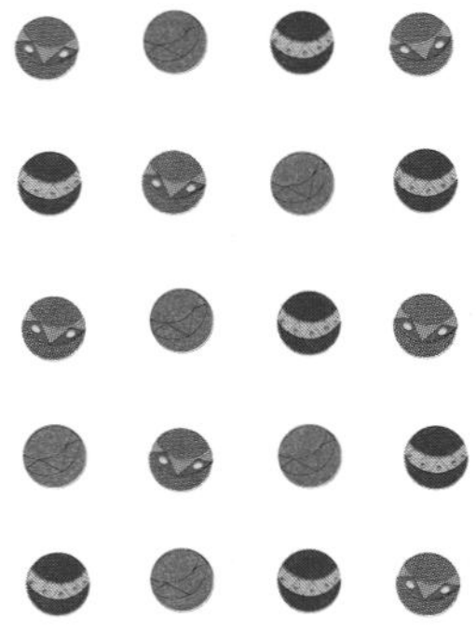

4 + 4 + 4 + 4 + 4

4. 5 × 4 = 20

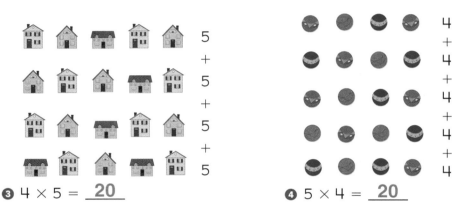

NOTE TO HOME
Students use repeated addition to multiply.

Literature Connection Read or invite students to read *Each Orange Had 8 Slices* by Paul Giganti, Jr. to reinforce lesson concepts.

LEARNING STYLES — Meeting Individual Needs

Kinesthetic learners might need to use base-10 materials to model and solve multiplication problems.

RETEACHING

Draw an 8-cm long line segment on the chalkboard. Ask how long a line segment would be if it were made up of eight such segments. After students suggest answers, draw each of the additional segments and then measure the line to show that it is 64 cm long.

*available separately

◆ LESSON 118 Multiplication—Using Repeated Addition

COOPERATIVE LEARNING Solve these problems. Use the pictures. Work in groups.

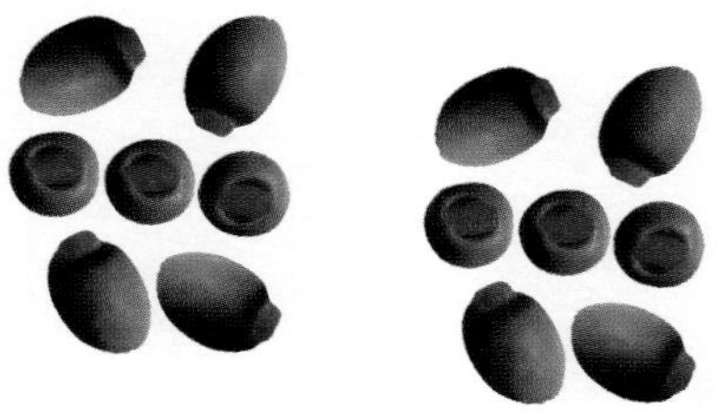

❺ 2 × 7 = 14

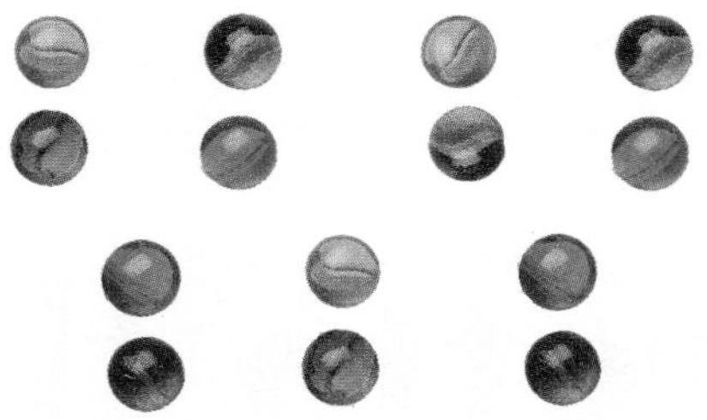

❻ 7 × 2 = 14

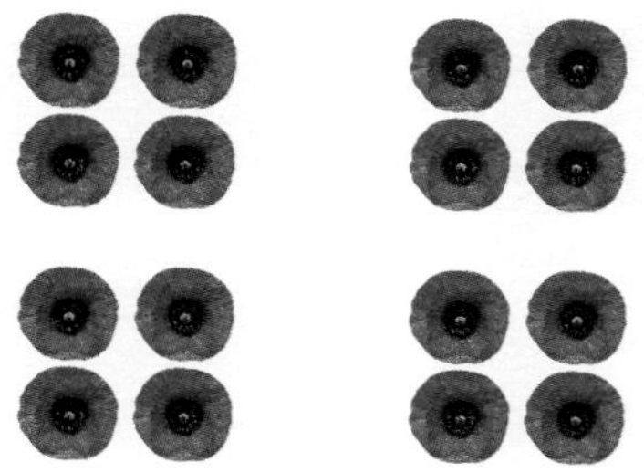

❼ 4 × 4 = 16

❽ 3 × 5 = 15

GAME Play the "Add the Products" game.

THINKING STORY Talk about the Thinking Story "Loretta the Letter Carrier Chooses Sides."

NOTE TO HOME
Students practice multiplication and play a multiplication game.

using an array. Draw a row of five Xs on posterboard. Ask how many Xs would be in six rows. (30) Draw to check answers. Turn the posterboard on its side to show that six rows of five Xs is the same as five rows of six Xs. Again show that 6 x 5 and 5 + 5 + 5 + 5 + 5 + 5 both equal 30. Finally, give a "times 0" problem such as 10 x 0 = 0. Show that no matter how many groups of 0 you have, you still have 0.

COOPERATIVE LEARNING **Using the Student Pages** Have students work in groups to complete pages 267–268. Encourage them to use what they know about repeated addition and arrays to solve the problems. Students can play the "Add the Products" game when they complete pages 267–268.

GAME **Introducing the "Add the Products" Game** This game provides practice with multiplication facts and multidigit addition. Players take turns rolling two 0–5 Number Cubes and multiplying the digits rolled. They record the product as their score, keeping a running total, and the first player to reach or pass 50 wins.

Using the Thinking Story Read aloud "Loretta the Letter Carrier Chooses Sides" on pages 102–105 of the Thinking Story Book.

MATH JOURNAL Ask students to draw a picture that shows several houses on one side of the block. Have them write the numbers on each house. Students can choose any numbers that are consecutive odd or even numbers.

❸ Wrap-Up 5 MINUTES

In Closing Have students draw an array that shows 6 x 8.

ALTERNATIVE ASSESSMENT **Performance Assessment** Observe students play the "Add the Products" game to assess their understanding of multiplication to this point.

Assessment Criteria

Did the student . . .

- ✓ participate in the discussion of the Thinking Story?
- ✓ correctly answer three of the four problems on page 267?
- ✓ correctly answer three of the four problems on page 268?
- ✓ correctly multiply the numbers rolled when playing the "Add the Products" game?

PRACTICE p. 118

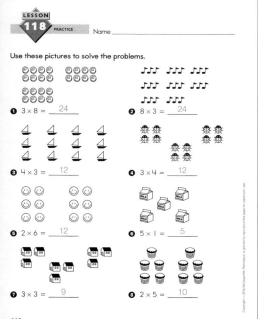

LESSON 118 PRACTICE Name ______

Use these pictures to solve the problems.

❶ 3 × 8 = 24
❷ 8 × 3 = 24
❸ 4 × 3 = 12
❹ 3 × 4 = 12
❺ 2 × 6 = 12
❻ 5 × 1 = 5
❼ 3 × 3 = 9
❽ 2 × 5 = 10

118 • Math Explorations and Applications Level 2

ENRICHMENT p. 118

LESSON 118 ENRICHMENT Name ______

Write the problems.

❶ 6 × 4 = 24
❷ 8 × 5 = 40
❸ 9 × 2 = 18
❹ 7 × 3 = 21

Finish the problems.

❺ 8 × 2 = 16
❻ 12 × 10 = 120
❼ 7 × 4 = 28
❽ 3 × 9 = 27
❾ 16 × 0 = 0
❿ 11 × 3 = 33

118 • Math Explorations and Applications Level 2

STORY 17

THINKING STORY

Loretta the Letter Carrier Chooses Sides

When Loretta was hired as a letter carrier, she was asked a lot of questions, but no one thought to ask her about odd and even numbers. The first day she had a bundle of mail to deliver along Maple Street. She thought, "I'm going to be smart about this." She sorted the mail so that 1 Maple Street was first, 2 Maple Street was next, 3 Maple Street was next, and so on. The first house she came to on Maple Street had a number 2 on it. "That's funny," thought Loretta. "There doesn't seem to be a number 1, although I have mail for it."

Why can't Loretta find number 1? It's on the other side of the street.

Loretta stuffed the mail for 1 Maple Street back into her bag, then delivered the mail to 2 Maple Street. She walked next door with the mail for 3 Maple Street.

Will Loretta find number 3 next door? no

Where is number 3? on the other side of the street

Loretta knocked on the door. When a man opened it, she handed him the mail.

"This is not my mail," the man said, handing it back to Loretta.

Loretta was confused. "I thought this house is number 3. The house next door is number 2."

What is the number of this house? 4

"No," the man answered. "This is number 4. Number 3 is across the street."

"Thank you," said Loretta. She started to cross the street, but there was too much traffic.

What will Loretta have to do? cross at a corner or traffic light

Loretta walked back to the corner and crossed when the traffic light was green. She knocked on the door of the first house.

What is the number of the first house? 1

When a woman answered, Loretta handed her the mail she was holding in her hand.

What number do you think this mail is for? 3

"This is not my mail," the woman said. "My house is number 1. This mail is for number 3, next door." Loretta reached into her bag and gave the woman the mail for number 1. Then she delivered the mail to number 3. She was about to go next door when she remembered that number 4 was across the street. She walked back to the corner to cross at the light.

It took Loretta a long time to deliver the mail on Maple Street that day.

Why did it take her so long? She had to keep going to the corner to cross the street.

Loretta had to keep going back to the corner to cross the street for every new batch of mail she had. If 7 Maple Street was on one side of the street, then, sure enough, 8 Maple Street would be on the other side of the street.

What could Loretta do to deliver the mail faster? Sort the mail by odd and even numbers and go down one side of the street at a time.

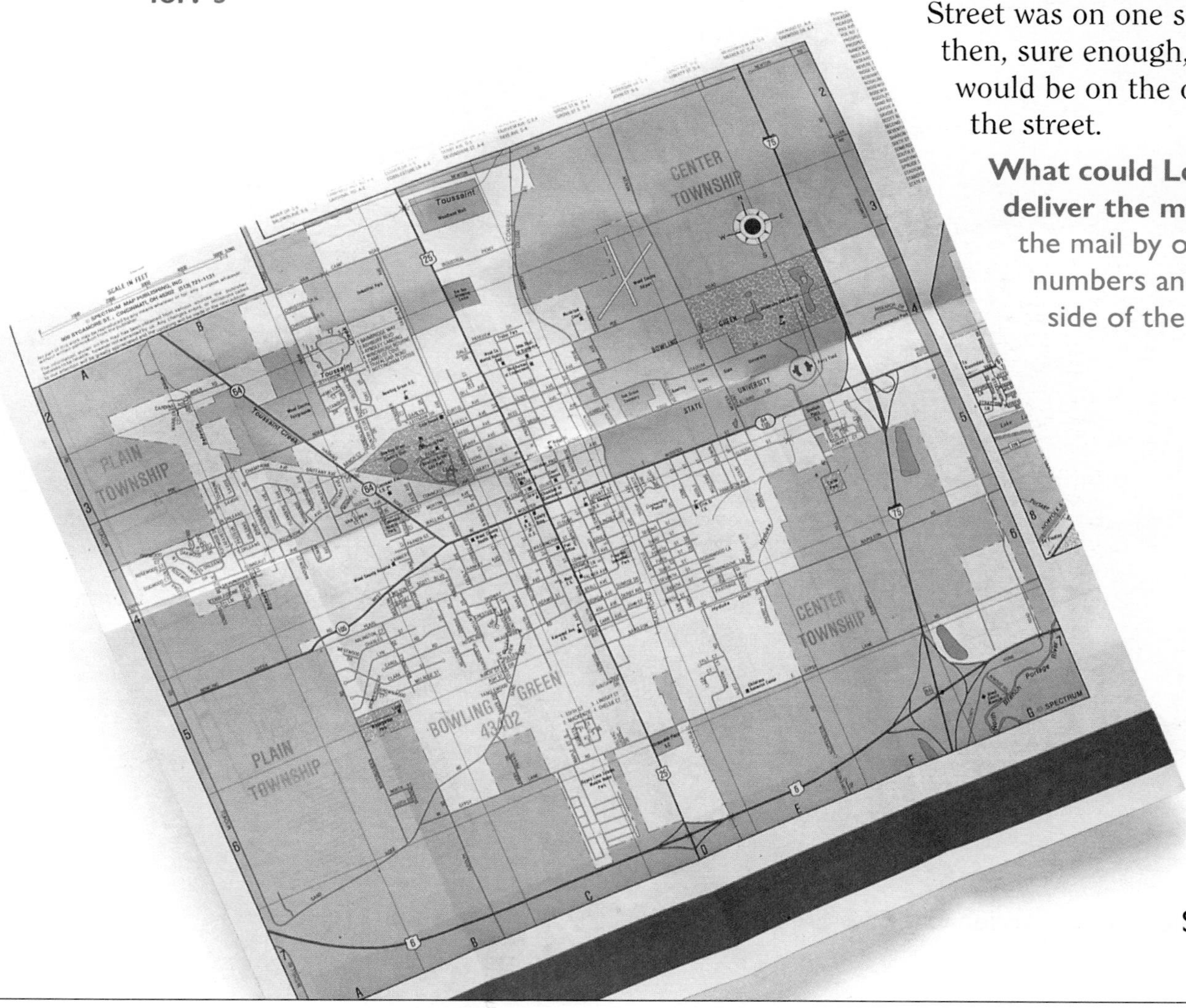

◆ STORY 17 Loretta the Letter Carrier Chooses Sides

"Those must all be even numbers on one side of the street and odd numbers on the other. I wish I knew how to tell which numbers are odd and which numbers are even. I could sort out all the odd numbers first and go down one side of the street, and then do all the even numbers on the other side. That way I wouldn't have to keep crossing the street. But how am I supposed to know which numbers are odd and which are even?"

How would you help Loretta figure it out? skip count

Loretta finally figured out an easy way to sort the mail. She started with number 1, then skipped the next number, then took number 3, skipped the next number, took number 5, and so on.

What numbers are the ones Loretta took—odd or even? odd

The numbers she skipped were 2, 4, 6, 8, and so on.

What numbers are those—odd or even? even

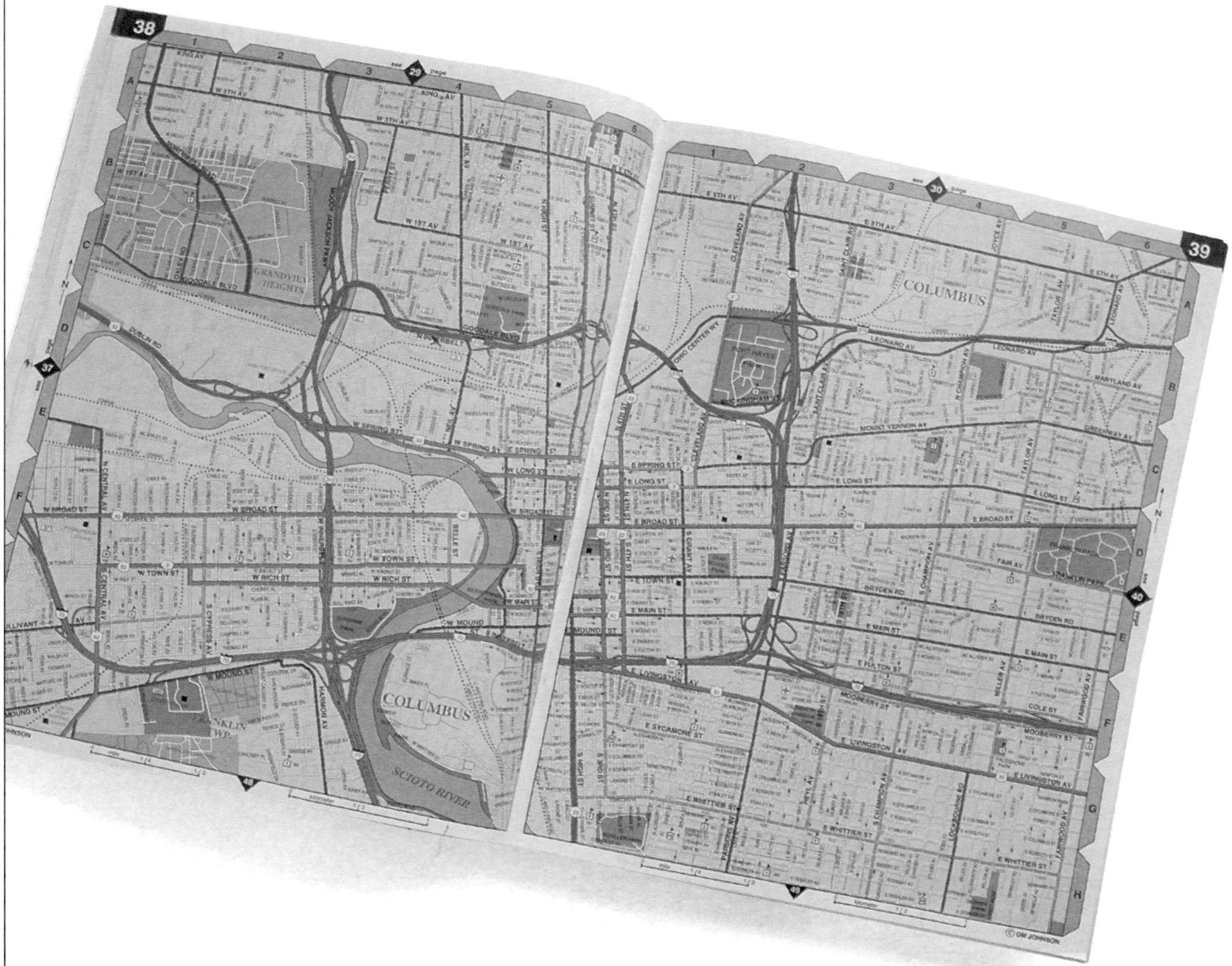

When Loretta sorted her mail that way, she was able to deliver it much faster.

A while later Loretta was given the job of delivering the mail along a street called Park Street. She tried to sort the mail the same way she did for Maple Street–odd numbers first and even numbers second. But there wasn't any mail for 1 Park Street, although there was for 2 Park Street. There wasn't any mail for 3 Park Street either. "That's funny," she said. "There isn't any mail for the odd numbers at all. All of the mail is for the even numbers. The people on the odd-numbered side of the street must not have any friends who write to them."

Can you think of another reason there might not be any mail for the houses with odd numbers? There are no houses on that side of the street.

When Loretta reached Park Street she discovered the reason she had mail for only one side of the street.

"Now I know why they call this Park Street," Loretta thought.

What do you think Loretta saw on the side of the street that wasn't getting any mail? a park running the full length of the street

. . . the end

LESSON 119

Student Edition pages 269–270

Multiplication—Finding Area

LESSON PLANNER

Objective

▶ to demonstrate how to find area by counting square units

Context of the Lesson This is the first lesson introducing area and its relationship to multiplication. Students will learn more about area in Lesson 129.

Materials	**Program Resources**
none	Number Cubes
	Thinking Story Book, pages 106–107
	Practice Master 119
	Enrichment Master 119
	For extra practice: CD-ROM* Lesson 119

1 Warm-Up

5 MINUTES

Problem of the Day Write this problem on the chalkboard: How many 2s will you write if you write the numbers 0–99? Explain how you solved this problem. (19; Possible explanations: made a list of the numbers and counted; added ten 2s in the twenties + nine 2s in the rest of the numbers from 0–99)

MENTAL MATH Have students multiply using mental math:

a. 2 x 3 = (6) **b.** 1 x 4 = (4)

c. 0 x 12 = (0) **d.** 7 x 2 = (14)

e. 8 x 1 = (8) **f.** 6 x 0 = (0)

2 Teach

Demonstrate Draw a 4 x 3 unit grid on the chalkboard. Discuss how to find the area of the rectangular grid by asking the following questions:

▶ How many units long is the figure? (3)

▶ How many units wide is the figure? (4)

LESSON 119

Name ____________________

Multiplication—Finding Area

Count the squares.

❶ The area of the foot is about _______ square units. Accept all reasonable answers.

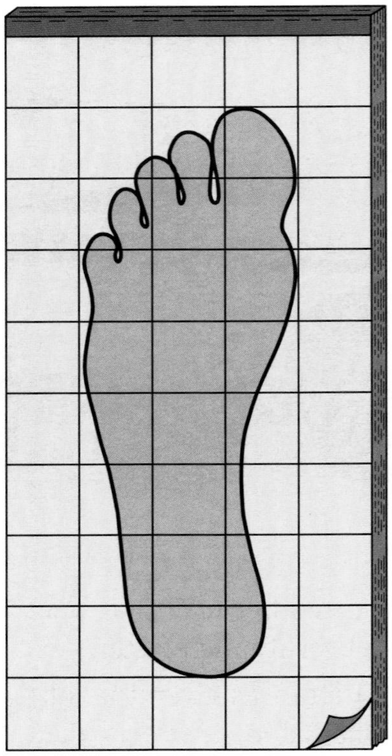

How did you count the squares? Accept all reasonable answers.

❷ The area of the page is 50 square units.

❸ 5 × 10 = 50

NOTE TO HOME
Students are introduced to the concept of area.

Why teach it at this time?

Area is presented here as motivation for multiplication. In Lesson 129 it is presented again, but as an application of multiplication.

Literature Connection Read or invite students to read *Area* by Jane Jonas Srivastava to reinforce the lesson concepts.

RETEACHING

Have students work in pairs. Each pair draws a 6-cm by 8-cm rectangle on cm graph paper. Have students estimate how many cm unit cubes they will need to fill in the rectangle. Then have them fill in the rectangle, count the number of cubes they used, and compare the total number with their estimate. Repeat for several other rectangles or squares.

*available separately

◆ **LESSON 119 Multiplication—Finding Area**

Use the Mixed Practice on page 391 after this lesson.

Use the squares to solve these problems.

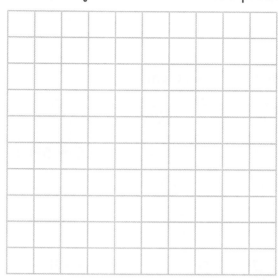

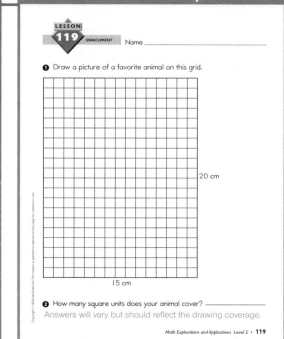

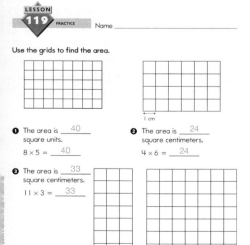

4 The area is 100 square centimeters.

5 10 × 10 = 100

6 The area is 15 square centimeters.

7 5 × 3 = 15

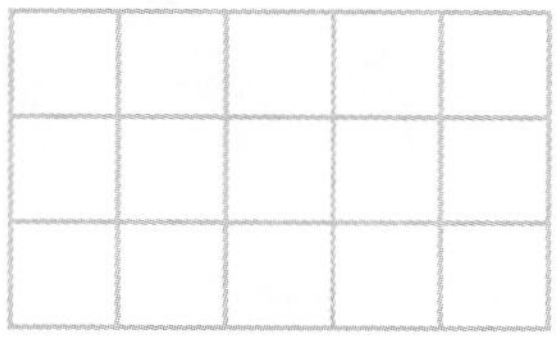

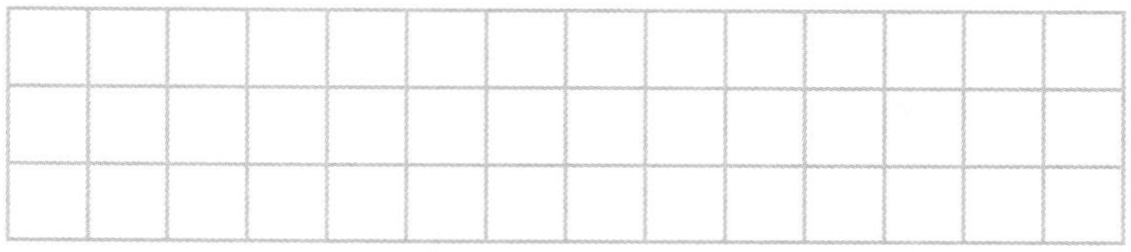

8 The area is 42 square centimeters.

9 3 × 14 = 42

NOTE TO HOME
Students use grids to find area.

PRACTICE p. 119

LESSON 119 PRACTICE Name ____________

Use the grids to find the area.

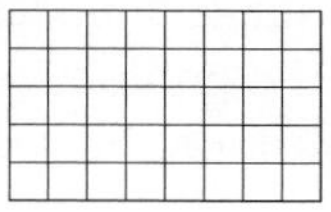

1 The area is 40 square units.
8 × 5 = 40

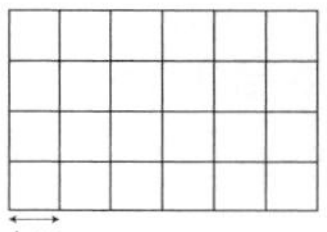

2 The area is 24 square centimeters.
4 × 6 = 24

3 The area is 33 square centimeters.
11 × 3 = 33

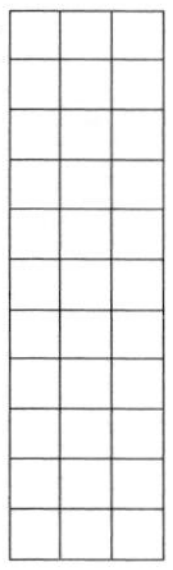

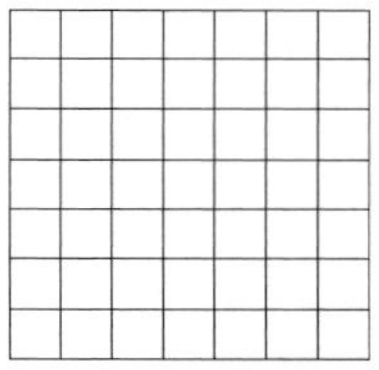

4 The area is 49 square centimeters.
7 × 7 = 49

Math Explorations and Applications Level 2 • 119

ENRICHMENT p. 119

LESSON 119 ENRICHMENT Name ____________

1 Draw a picture of a favorite animal on this grid.

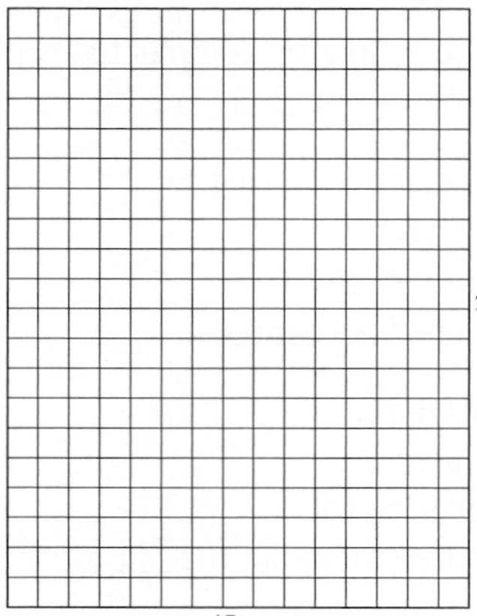

2 How many square units does your animal cover? ____________
Answers will vary but should reflect the drawing coverage.

Math Explorations and Applications Level 2 • 119

▶ The area is the total number of units. What is the area? (12)

▶ How did you find the area? (Possible responses: counted all of the units; multiplied 3 x 4)

Next draw an irregular figure within the grid. Have students estimate the area of the irregular figure. Discuss whether various estimates are sensible.

Using the Number Cubes Give measurements of several rectangles in cm and ask students to find, hide, and show the area of each rectangle using their Number Cubes.

Using the Student Pages Work with the class to discuss and complete page 269. Encourage students to share their methods for first finding the area of the foot, and then the area of the rectangular grid. Discuss how the two areas are related. Ask questions such as: Could the area of the foot be more than 50 units? Why or why not? (No, because the area of the whole rectangle is 50 and the foot is only a part of the whole.) Have students complete page 270 independently and then share and compare their methods and answers.

Using the Thinking Story Present one or two problems from those following the story "Loretta the Letter Carrier Chooses Sides" on pages 106–107 of the Thinking Story Book.

3 Wrap-Up

5 MINUTES

In Closing Ask students how the area of a rectangular grid and multiplication are related. Students should understand that they can multiply the number of units in the length and width of a rectangle to find its area.

ALTERNATIVE ASSESSMENT

Informal Assessment Circulate as students work on page 270. Check their answers to assess their understanding of area.

Assessment Criteria

Did the student . . .

✓ correctly answer the questions you asked pertaining to page 269?

✓ correctly answer 5 of the 6 problems on page 270?

LESSON 120

Student Edition pages 271–272

Multiplication

LESSON PLANNER

Objectives

- to introduce multiplication facts for factors 0 through 5
- to provide practice in solving multiplication word problems

Context of the Lesson This is the fourth of seven lessons on multiplication.

Materials	Program Resources
posterboard	"Multiplication Table" Game Mat
	Number Cubes
	Thinking Story Book, pages 106–107
	Practice Master 120
	Enrichment Master 120
	For extra practice: CD-ROM* Lesson 120

1 Warm-Up

5 MINUTES

Problem of the Day Write the following problem on the chalkboard: I am a two-digit even number. If you add my digits you get 13. If you subtract my digits you get 5. What number am I? (94)

MENTAL MATH Have students multiply using mental math.

a. 1 × 1 = (1)

b. 1 × 5 = (5)

c. 2 × 4 = (8)

d. 1 × 0 = (0)

e. 3 × 2 = (6)

f. 4 × 1 = (4)

g. 1 × 3 = (3)

2 Teach

Demonstrate Draw five rows of three **X**s on the chalkboard. Ask the following questions:

- How can you use this diagram to tell how much five threes are? (Add the 3 **X**s in each of 5 rows: 3 + 3 + 3 + 3 + 3 = 15)

LESSON 120

Name ______________________

Multiplication

Use these pictures to solve the problems.

1 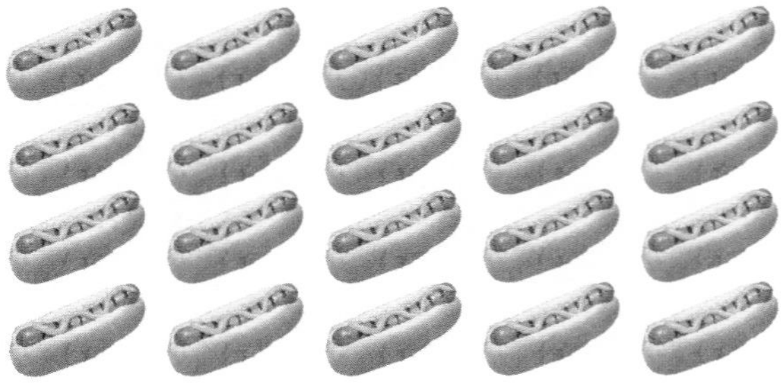

5 + 5 + 5 + 5

4 × 5 = 20

2 

4 + 4 + 4

3 × 4 = 12

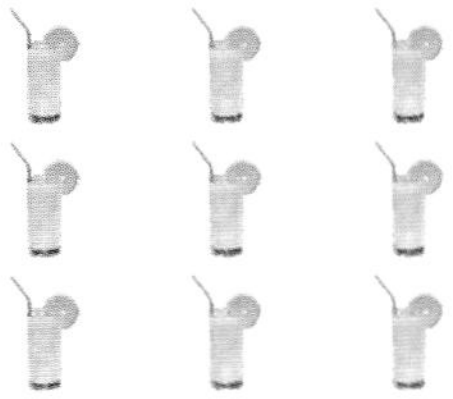

3 + 3 + 3

3 3 × 3 = 9

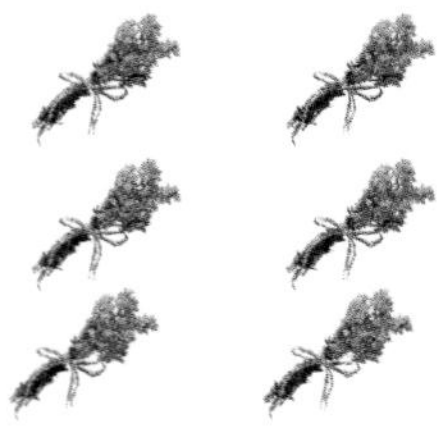

2 + 2 + 2

4 3 × 2 = 6

NOTE TO HOME
Students continue to explore repeated addition to help them multiply.

Real-World Connection Have students work in groups to change the following recipes to feed four people rather than one:

Cheese Sandwich for One
2 slices of bread
3 slices of cheese
1 teaspoon of mayonnaise

Salad for One
4 lettuce leaves
2 slices of tomatoes
2 tablespoons of salad dressing

RETEACHING

Write multiplication facts on the chalkboard such as 4 x 4, 3 x 3, 5 x 2 and 3 x 4. Have students work in groups using Number Cubes to make a model of each fact and then find the product. Check groups as they work on their models.

*available separately

◆ LESSON 120 Multiplication

Use these pictures to solve the problems.

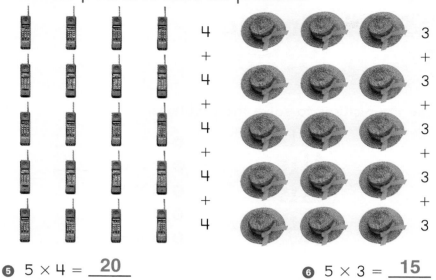

4 + 4 + 4 + 4 + 4

3 + 3 + 3 + 3 + 3

5 $5 \times 4 =$ 20

6 $5 \times 3 =$ 15

Solve this problem.

7 How many cookies do you think are on the tray? 12

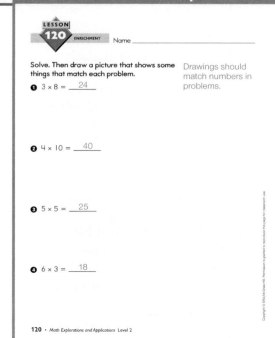

Play the "Multiplication Table" game.

NOTE TO HOME
Students practice multiplication and solve word problems.

PRACTICE p. 120

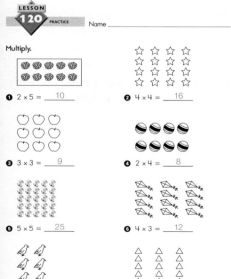

LESSON 120 PRACTICE Name

Multiply.

1 $2 \times 5 =$ 10

2 $4 \times 4 =$ 16

3 $3 \times 3 =$ 9

4 $2 \times 4 =$ 8

5 $5 \times 5 =$ 25

6 $4 \times 3 =$ 12

7 $3 \times 2 =$ 6

8 $5 \times 3 =$ 15

120 • Math Explorations and Applications Level 2

ENRICHMENT p. 120

LESSON 120 ENRICHMENT Name

Solve. Then draw a picture that shows some things that match each problem.

Drawings should match numbers in problems.

1 $3 \times 8 =$ 24

2 $4 \times 10 =$ 40

3 $5 \times 5 =$ 25

4 $6 \times 3 =$ 18

120 • Math Explorations and Applications Level 2

▶ How can you use this diagram to tell how much three fives are? (Turn the diagram so that it shows three rows of five **X**s, then add 5 + 5 + 5 = 15)

Repeat for five fours and four fives and three fours and four threes. You might want to give multiplication problems through 5 x 5 and ask students to find, hide, and show their answers using their Number Cubes.

Using the Student Pages Have students complete pages 271 and 272 independently, and then share and compare their methods and answers.

Introducing the "Multiplication Table" Game Mat Demonstrate the game, which provides practice with multiplication facts in the 0–5 range. Complete directions are on the Game Mat.

Using the Thinking Story Present three new problems from those following the story "Loretta the Letter Carrier Chooses Sides" on pages 106–107 of the Thinking Story Book.

Using the "Add the Products" Game When finished have students play the "Add the Products" game described in Lesson 118.

3 Wrap-Up

5 MINUTES

In Closing Have students draw a diagram using Xs to show 5 x 4.

Performance Assessment Observe students as they play the "Multiplication Table" game to see who solves the multiplication problems correctly.

Assessment Criteria

Did the student . . .

✓ correctly answer the questions you asked during the demonstration?

✓ correctly solve three of the four problems on page 271?

✓ correctly solve two of the three problems on page 272?

LESSON 121

Student Edition pages 273–274

Multiplication—Using Pictures

LESSON PLANNER

Objectives

- to introduce multiplication facts for factors 0 through 5 times 5 through 10
- to review multiplication facts for factors 0 through 5

Context of the Lesson This is the fifth of seven lessons on multiplication.

Materials	Program Resources
none	Number Cubes
	Thinking Story Book, pages 106–107
	Practice Master 121
	Enrichment Master 121
	For extra practice: CD-ROM* Lesson 121

1 Warm-Up

5 MINUTES

Problem of the Day Write this problem on the chalkboard: Matthew works at the library on Mondays. He last went to work on September 30. What date will he work next? (October 7)

MENTAL MATH Provide multiplication problems in which one factor is 1, 2, or 10 and ask students to find, hide, and show their answers using their Number Cubes.

2 Teach

Demonstrate To practice finding multiples of five and ten, have different-sized groups stand at the front of the room with their hands behind their backs as the other students tell how many fingers they have all together. For example, three students with ten fingers is 3 x 10. (30) Then have them hide only one hand each behind their back as students figure out 3 x 5. (15) Repeat with various numbers of students.

LESSON 121

Name ____________________

Multiplication—Using Pictures

Use the pictures to solve the problems.

1. 1 × 6 = 6
2. 2 × 6 = 12
3. 3 × 6 = 18
4. 4 × 6 = 24
5. 5 × 6 = 30

6. 1 × 7 = 7
7. 2 × 7 = 14
8. 3 × 7 = 21
9. 4 × 7 = 28
10. 5 × 7 = 35

11. 1 × 8 = 8
12. 2 × 8 = 16
13. 3 × 8 = 24
14. 4 × 8 = 32
15. 5 × 8 = 40

NOTE TO HOME
Students use pictures to practice multiplication facts.

Literature Connection Read or invite students to read *Anno's Mysterious Multiplying Jar* by Masaichiro and Mitsumasa Anno to reinforce lesson concepts.

SPECIAL NEEDS

Meeting Individual Needs
Allow students to continue to review facts from 0 through 5 by making drawings to represent each fact.

RETEACHING

MATH MANIPULATIVES Write several facts on the chalkboard for multiples of 6–10 mulitiplied by 0–5. Have students work in groups using Number Cubes to make a model of each fact and then find the product. Check groups as they work on their models.

*available separately

◆ LESSON 121 Multiplication—Using Pictures

Use these pictures to solve the problems.

⑯ 1 × 9 = 9

⑰ 2 × 9 = 18

⑱ 3 × 9 = 27

⑲ 4 × 9 = 36

⑳ 5 × 9 = 45

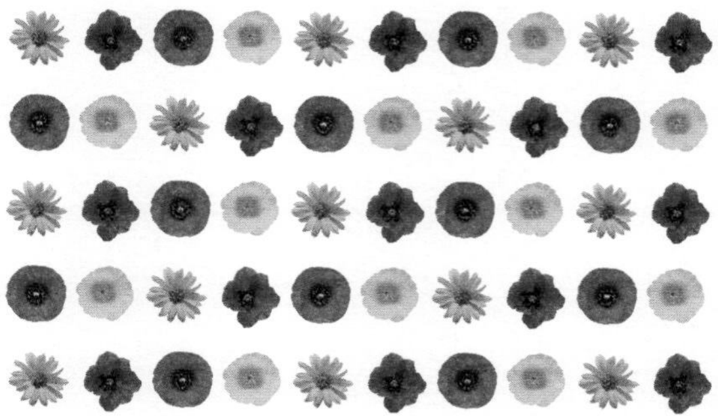

㉑ 1 × 10 = 10

㉒ 2 × 10 = 20

㉓ 3 × 10 = 30

㉔ 4 × 10 = 40

㉕ 5 × 10 = 50

㉖ 9 × 0 = 0	㉗ 3 × 5 = 15
㉘ 5 × 5 = 25	㉙ 3 × 10 = 30
㉚ 5 × 10 = 50	㉛ 5 × 0 = 0

GAME

Play the "Add the Products" game.

NOTE TO HOME
Students practice multiplication facts.

PRACTICE p. 121

LESSON 121 PRACTICE Name ____________

Multiply.

1. 1 × 6 = 6
2. 2 × 6 = 12
3. 3 × 6 = 18
4. 4 × 6 = 24
5. 5 × 6 = 30
6. 1 × 8 = 8
7. 2 × 8 = 16
8. 3 × 8 = 24
9. 4 × 8 = 32
10. 5 × 8 = 40

Math Explorations and Applications Level 2 • 121

ENRICHMENT p. 121

LESSON 121 ENRICHMENT Name ____________

PROBLEM SOLVING Solve these problems.

The winning second-grade class had 17 children. There were eight boys and nine girls.

1. Each girl won five ribbons. How many ribbons did the girls win all together? 45
2. Each boy won four ribbons. How many ribbons did the boys win all together? 32
3. The boys each took two spelling tests, while the girls each took three. How many spelling tests did they take all together? 43
4. Half of the boys took four reading tests each. All of the girls took two reading tests. How many reading tests did they take all together? 34
5. The girls took 36 math tests all together. Each boy took two math tests. How many math tests did the children take all together? 52

Math Explorations and Applications Level 2 • 121

Using the Student Pages Work with the class on page 273 and the top of page 274. Ask questions such as: How many objects are in the first row? (6) the first two rows? (12) Help students complete the facts together through 5 x 10, guiding them to see how each answer can be found using the answer before it. Encourage students to explain how they arrive at each answer. (Some students may count on from the last answer, others may add to the last answer.) Have them do the last six problems independently.

GAME **Using the "Add the Products" Game** As students finish pages 273 and 274, demonstrate and explain the rules for a variation of the "Add the Products" game introduced in Lesson 118. Students use one 0–5 and one 5–10 units cube, multiply the numbers rolled, and keep a running total of their products until one reaches a goal of 150.

Using the Thinking Story Book Present one or two problems from those following "Loretta the Letter Carrier Chooses Sides" on pages 106–107 of the Thinking Story Book.

3 Wrap-Up

5 MINUTES

In Closing Ask students to choose a number between 5 and 10 and write the multiplication facts for that number from 1 through 5. Have them use Xs to draw models to show each fact that they write.

ALTERNATIVE ASSESSMENT **Portfolio Assessment** Have students add the facts and models they drew to their Math Portfolios.

Assessment Criteria

Did the student . . .

✓ correctly answer the questions you asked during the demonstration?

✓ correctly answer at least 18 of 25 problem on pages 273 and 274

LESSON 122

Student Edition pages 275–276

Applying Multiplication

LESSON PLANNER

Objectives

- ▶ to review multiplication facts
- ▶ to provide realistic multiplication problems for students to solve
- ▶ to introduce and use the **×** key on the calculator

Context of the Lesson This is the sixth of seven lessons on multiplication.

Materials	Program Resources
calculators*	Number Cubes
	Thinking Story Book, pages 106–107
	Practice Master 122
	Enrichment Master 122
	For extra practice: CD-ROM* Lesson 122

1 Warm-Up

5 MINUTES

Problem of the Day Write this problem on the chalkboard: If you eat three meals a day, how many meals per week do you eat? How can you find out? (21; 7 × 3 = 21)

MENTAL MATH Have students multiply the following problems using mental math:

a. 1 × 6 = (6) **b.** 5 × 7 = (35)
c. 3 × 8 = (24) **d.** 1 × 7 = (7)
e. 4 × 8 = (32) **f.** 3 × 6 = (18)
g. 5 × 8 = (40) **h.** 1 × 8 = (8)

2 Teach

Demonstrate Give students several oral word problems that involve multiplication. For example: You want to buy tires for three cars. How many tires will you buy? (3 × 4 = 12)

LESSON 122

Name ______________________

Applying Multiplication

Solve these problems.

1. Each child has $6. How much money do they have all together? $ 42
2. Corey read eight pages every day for seven days. How many pages did he read that week? 56
3. There are seven days in one week. How many days are there in five weeks? 35 How many days in six weeks? 42
4. There are four apartments in each building. How many apartments are there in three buildings? 12
5. Lynette bought five action figures. Each figure was $3. How much did Lynette pay in all? $15

NOTE TO HOME
Students practice solving realistic multiplication problems.

Literature Connection To reinforce lesson concepts, read or invite the students to read "Clover Time" in *Right in Your Own Backyard: Nature Math* by Time-Life, Inc.

RETEACHING

Give students practice using their calculators to solve oral word problems involving multiplication.

*available separately

◆ LESSON 122 Applying Multiplication

Fill in the missing numbers in each chart.

6 Sets of Five

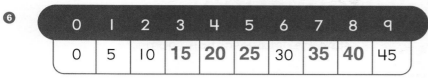

0	1	2	3	4	5	6	7	8	9
0	5	10	**15**	**20**	**25**	30	**35**	**40**	45

7 Sets of Two

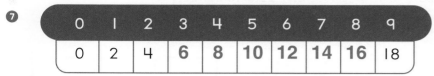

0	1	2	3	4	5	6	7	8	9
0	2	4	**6**	**8**	**10**	**12**	**14**	**16**	18

8 Sets of Three

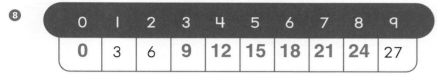

0	1	2	3	4	5	6	7	8	9
0	3	6	**9**	**12**	**15**	**18**	**21**	**24**	27

Use the charts to solve these problems.

9 $4 \times 5 =$ **20** 10 $8 \times 2 =$ **16** 11 $7 \times 3 =$ **21**

Use your calculator to find each answer. Write it in the space.

12 $4 \times 5 =$ **20**

13 $8 \times 2 =$ **16**

14 $7 \times 3 =$ **21**

NOTE TO HOME
Students continue to explore multiplication.

Then invite three students to hold up both hands and one to hold up one hand. Show students how to find the total number of fingers by counting by fives. Point out that when they have many sets of items with the same number in each set, counting by that number will tell how many items there are in all. Next, show students the ☒ key on their calculators and explain that they will use this key on page 276.

Using the Student Pages Students should complete pages 275 and 276 independently. Encourage students to share their answers and methods for both pages.

Using the Thinking Story Book Present one or two problems from those following "Loretta the Letter Carrier Chooses Sides" on pages 106–107 of the Thinking Story Book.

3 Wrap-Up

5 MINUTES

In Closing Ask students what they have discovered about the ☒ key on their calculators.

ANALYZING ANSWERS

Students might need additional help understanding applications of multiplication. Have them make up their own word problems that use multiplication in their solutions.

ALTERNATIVE ASSESSMENT

Informal Assessment Use students' responses to pages 269–270 as an informal assessment of their understanding of multiplication to this point.

Assessment Criteria

Did the student . . .

✓ correctly solve four of the five problems on page 275?

✓ complete the charts on page 276 correctly?

✓ understand how to use a calculator to solve items 12–14 on page 276?

PRACTICE p. 122

LESSON 122 PRACTICE Name ______

Fill in the missing numbers on each chart.

1 Sets of 4

0	1	2	3	4	5	6	7	8	9
0	4	8	12	16	20	24	28	32	36

2 Sets of 7

0	1	2	3	4	5	6	7	8	9
0	7	14	21	28	35	42	49	56	63

3 Sets of 6

0	1	2	3	4	5	6	7	8	9
0	6	12	18	24	30	36	42	48	54

Use the charts to solve these problems.

4 $6 \times 8 =$ 48 5 $4 \times 5 =$ 20 6 $7 \times 2 =$ 14

7 $3 \times 6 =$ 18 8 $8 \times 4 =$ 32 9 $9 \times 6 =$ 54

10 $3 \times 4 =$ 12 11 $2 \times 6 =$ 12 12 $7 \times 8 =$ 56

122 • *Math Explorations and Applications* Level 2

ENRICHMENT p. 122

LESSON 122 ENRICHMENT Name ______

PROBLEM SOLVING

Solve these problems.

1. Each of four tables has five chairs. There are 27 children. How many children cannot sit down at a table? 7
2. The janitor brings one more table and ten more chairs. Now there are five tables with six chairs at each table. How many empty chairs are there? 3
3. All but eight of the children have two forks each. The others have no fork at all. How many forks are there? 38
4. The janitor brings out six stacks of plates, with exactly the same number in each stack. How many plates must he have in each stack for each of the 27 children to have one plate? 5
5. Mr. Jaffray served spaghetti. He said that he had enough to feed six baseball teams. If there are nine players on a baseball team, how many children would the spaghetti feed? 54

122 • *Math Explorations and Applications* Level 2

LESSON 123

Student Edition pages 277–278

Multiplication

LESSON PLANNER

Objectives

- ▶ to provide practice using a multiplication table
- ▶ to provide practice with the multiplication facts

Context of the Lesson In this lesson, students continue practicing multiplication facts.

Materials	Program Resources
counters	"Multiplication" Game Mat
map of U.S.A. (optional)	Number Cubes
	Reteaching Master
	Practice Master 123
	Enrichment Master 123
	For extra practice: CD-ROM* Lesson 123

1 Warm-Up

5 MINUTES

Problem of the Day Write this problem on the chalkboard: If you saved a nickel a day for a week, would you have more or less than 50 cents at the end of the week? How can you tell? (Less, because 5¢ each day for a week is 5 × 7 = 35¢.)

MENTAL MATH Have students multiply.

a. 1 × 5 = (5)

b. 2 × 2 = (4)

c. 3 × 2 = (6)

d. 5 × 3 = (15)

e. 2 × 4 = (8)

f. 3 × 3 = (9)

2 Teach

Using the Student Pages Students should be able to use the multiplication table to complete pages 277 and 278 on their own. Remind them that they used a similar table in addition and subtraction. Demonstrate how to use the table to find 3 × 4. Find the 3 along the left side of the table. Move your finger to the right until it is under 4. Check their answers.

LESSON 123

Name ______________________

Multiplication

GAME Play the "Multiplication" game.

Use the multiplication table to fill in the missing numbers.

❶

0	2	4	6	8	10

❷

0	5	10	15	20	25

❸

0	3	6	9	12	15

FANTASTIC FACT The longest sneezing attack lasted 978 days. If the sneezer sneezed only three times a day, how many sneezes would there be all together?

NOTE TO HOME
Students use a multiplication table.

Literature Connection Read aloud *Anno's Magic Seeds* by Mitsumasa Anno to reinforce lesson concepts.

Social Studies Connection Show students how to read a map grid at this time because it is read the same way as a multiplication table. Provide a map of the United States. Have students locate various states by using the grid locations as shown on the map.

RETEACHING p. 31

LESSON 123 RETEACHING Name ______________

Adam made 3 quarts of lemonade. Each quart needed four lemons. How many lemons were needed all together?

❶ Draw the right amount of lemons in each pitcher.

3 fours 3 × 4 = 12

How many lemons are in 4 quarts?

4 fours 4 × 4 = 16

Grandma knitted Ted five sweaters. Each sweater had six buttons. How many buttons are there all together?

❷ Draw the right number of buttons on each sweater.

5 sixes 5 × 6 = 30

How many buttons are on six sweaters?

36

Math Explorations and Applications Level 2 • 31

*available separately

◆ LESSON 123 Multiplication

Suzanne was selling bags of peanuts for 8¢ each. To help know how much money to collect, she made this chart.

Help Suzanne by completing the chart.

4

Bags	1	2	3	4	5	6	7	8	9	10
Price (in cents)	8	16	24	32	40	48	56	64	72	80

5 What is the price of seven bags of peanuts? 56 ¢

6

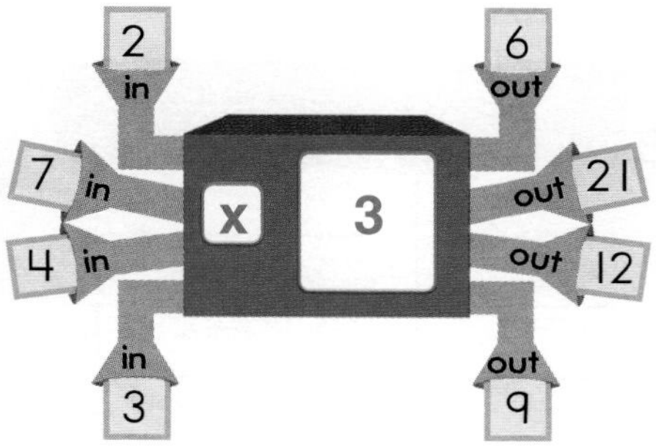

7

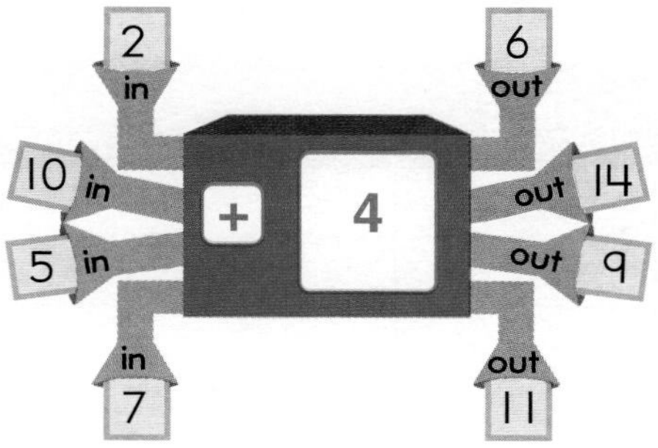

NOTE TO HOME
Students practice multiplication.

Introducing the "Multiplication" Game Mat

Demonstrate the "Multiplication" Game Mat for students. This game provides practice with basic facts, two factors of 5 or less. Complete directions are on the Game Mat.

3 Wrap-Up

5 MINUTES

In Closing Have students tell whether they prefer to solve problems like those on page 278 using repeated addition or multiplication and why.

ALTERNATIVE ASSESSMENT

Performance Assessment Observe students as they play the game to see who can consistently find the correct product after they roll their cubes.

Assessment Criteria

Did the student . . .

- ✓ find the correct product when playing the "Multiplication" Game Mat?
- ✓ correctly complete the tables on page 277?
- ✓ correctly solve all of the problems on page 278?

COOPERATIVE LEARNING Have students work in pairs. Tell each partner to write ten multiplication facts on ten index cards. Then have them exchange cards and write the same number sentence on the other side, but with a missing factor. For example, one side of a card will say 3 × 4 = 12; the other side will say _____ × 4 = 12 or 3 × _____ = 12. Combine both sets of cards and have partners use them as flash cards to practice finding missing factors.

PRACTICE p. 123

LESSON 123 PRACTICE Name ____________

Solve these problems.

1 Li was selling cookies for 9¢ each. To help know how much money to collect, she made this chart. Help Li by completing the chart.

Number of Cookies	1	2	3	4	5	6	7	8
Price (cents)	9	18	27	36	45	54	63	72

How much are six cookies? 54¢

2 Stuart made the following chart to help him know how much to collect for brownies. Help Stuart complete the chart.

Number of Cookies	1	2	3	4	5	6	7	8
Price (cents)	6	12	18	24	30	36	42	48

How much is one brownie? 6¢

Write the rule for each chart.

3

In	Out
4	16
8	32
2	8
5	20

Rule is ×4.

4

In	Out
10	2
15	7
13	5
19	11

Rule is −8.

5

In	Out
6	42
3	21
8	56
4	28

Rule is ×7.

Math Explorations and Applications Level 2 • **123**

ENRICHMENT p. 123

LESSON 123 ENRICHMENT Name ____________

PROBLEM SOLVING **Solve these problems.**

1 Jeb has eight pieces of wood. He can cut each piece into five sections. How many smaller pieces will he have? 40

2 Jeb will make four stools. He must have seven of the smaller pieces of wood for each of the stools. How many pieces will he have left when he has made the stools? 12

3 He knows he can sell the four stools for eight dollars each. How much money will he make? $ 32

4 Jeb must buy some nails before he can start. He needs ten nails that will cost six cents each and eight nails that will cost three cents each. How much money will he spend on nails? 84 ¢

5 He wants to use many colors to paint his stools. He will use seven colors on each stool. He will have to buy at least 7 colors.

Math Explorations and Applications Level 2 • **123**

LESSON 124

Student Edition pages 279–280

Analyzing Random Events

LESSON PLANNER

Objectives

- ▶ to introduce collecting and organizing data from random events
- ▶ to assist students in analyzing and making predictions about data
- ▶ to use tally marks to record frequency of events

Context of the Lesson This is the first of three lessons dealing with collecting and presenting data.

Materials	Program Resources
box, opaque	Practice Master 124
counters, three colors	Enrichment Master 124
paper, three sheets	For extra practice: CD-ROM* Lesson 124

1 Warm-Up

5 MINUTES

Problem of the Day Write the following problem on the chalkboard: Ed bought a box of 24 cookies on Monday. He ate three cookies on that day. He ate three more every day after. On what day did he finish his cookies? (the following Monday)

MENTAL MATH Have students multiply the following using mental math:

a. 1 × 6 = (6)   b. 3 × 7 = (21)

c. 4 × 1 = (4)   d. 2 × 10 = (20)

e. 3 × 8 = (24)   f. 1 × 2 = (2)

g. 8 × 1 = (8)   h. 5 × 7 = (35)

2 Teach

Demonstrate Place seven blue, seven red, and seven yellow counters (or other objects) in the cup or box. Have students predict which color counter you will pick out. Remove it and show it to students. Then go on to the activity, which is illustrated on page 279.

LESSON 124

Name ______________________

Analyzing Random Events

COOPERATIVE LEARNING Do the "Race Across the Room" activity.

Keep track of the colors.

First trial: I predict __________ will win.

Colors	Tallies	Totals

The winner was __________.

Second trial: I predict __________ will win.

Colors	Tallies	Totals

The winner was __________.

NOTE TO HOME
Students learn to collect and organize data.

RETEACHING

Because this is a discovery and experimentation lesson, reteaching is not necessary at this time.

GIFTED & TALENTED

Meeting Individual Needs

Gifted and talented students should be able to solve more complex probability problems. For example, "If there are three apples and three oranges in a box, what are the chances you will pick an apple?" (1 in 2)

*available separately

◆ LESSON 124 Analyzing Random Events

Use the Mixed Practice on page 392 after this lesson.

COOPERATIVE LEARNING Do the "Cube-Rolling" activity.

Keep track of the numbers you roll.

	Tallies	Totals	Class Totals
0			
1			
2			
3			
4			
5			

I am finding a class total for the number ______.

Keep sharp. Solve these problems.

❶ 5 × 10 = ______ ❷ 4 × 6 = ______ ❸ 8 × 3 = ______

❹ 2 × 9 = ______ ❺ 7 × 3 = ______ ❻ 2 × 2 = ______

FANTASTIC FACT One of every 50 Americans lives on a farm, and one of every 33 Americans says he or she doesn't eat candy.

NOTE TO HOME
Students use tally marks to collect data.

PRACTICE p. 124

LESSON 124 PRACTICE Name ____________________

Do the "Cube Rolling" activity.

Keep track of the numbers you roll.

	Tallies	Totals	Class Totals
0			
1			
2			
3			
4			
5			

I predict ________ will be rolled most often. Answers will vary.

The number rolled most often was ________.

124 • Math Explorations and Applications Level 2

ENRICHMENT p. 124

LESSON 124 ENRICHMENT Name ____________________

How many dots are in the big box? Try to make a good estimate without counting very much.

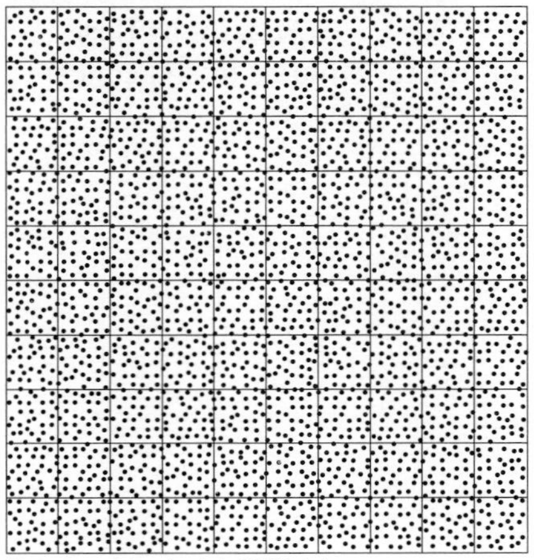

There are approximately 3000 dots. Accept all reasonable answers.

124 • Math Explorations and Applications Level 2

COOPERATIVE LEARNING **Using the Student Pages** Set up a race course with spaces including a start and finish. Tape each of the three color sheets to three students. Explain that each student will move one space each time his or her color is picked out of the box. Have one student keep score on the chalkboard using tally marks to indicate each time a color is drawn. The rest of the students keep track using the "First Trial" chart on page 279. Before beginning to draw objects, have students predict which color will win and write their predictions on their pages. As you draw the object from the container, have students make a tally mark and move a space. Replace the object and shake the container before drawing again. Before the end of the game let students make predictions or change their predictions. Repeat for a second trial.

Have students work in pairs to complete page 280. One partner rolls a 0–5 Number Cube 50 times. The other keeps a tally of each number that comes up. Students may exchange roles after a while. Discuss the results by asking: Did all the numbers come up the same number of times? Were you able to always predict which number would come up?

Next, divide students into six groups and assign one number from 0–5 to each group. Have students read their totals for each number on their charts. Have each group copy the totals for their number and add them to find the class totals. Discuss the results by asking whether they would be exactly the same if the class did the activity again.

3 Wrap-Up (5 MINUTES)

In Closing Ask students what they think a random event is. Have them give examples of other random events. (picking a card from a deck; rolling a die in a game)

ALTERNATIVE ASSESSMENT **Performance Assessment** Observe which students understand how to record and count the tally marks as they do the activities.

Assessment Criteria

Did the student . . .

✓ correctly keep a record of events using tally marks?

✓ correctly find the total number of tally marks for each event on pages 279 and 280?

LESSON 125

Student Edition pages 281–282

Predicting Results

LESSON PLANNER

Objectives

- ▶ to provide practice collecting and organizing data from random events
- ▶ to provide practice analyzing and making predictions about data

Context of the Lesson This is the second of three lessons dealing with collecting and presenting data.

Materials

13 counters (8 blue, 4 red, 1 yellow)

opaque box or cup

sheets of paper with one color on each

Program Resources

Number Cubes

Practice Master 125

Enrichment Master 125

For extra practice: CD-ROM* Lesson 125

1 Warm-Up

5 MINUTES

Problem of the Day Present this problem to the class: If you started at 23 and skip counted aloud by threes, what would be the sixth number you would say? (38)

MENTAL MATH Have students multiply the following using their Number Cubes to respond:

a. 2 × 4 = (8)   **b.** 3 × 5 = (15)

c. 4 × 3 = (12)   **d.** 6 × 2 = (12)

e. 8 × 1 = (8)   **f.** 4 × 4 = (16)

2 Teach

Demonstrate Repeat the "Race Across the Room" activity you did in Lesson 124. However, this time show students you are putting eight blue, four red, and one yellow counter into the container. Discuss the probable results of the race before doing the activity. Have students record the results of the race on a separate sheet of paper. When they finish, ask what the

LESSON 125

Name ____________________

Predicting Results

Answers are examples only.

Do the "Cube-Rolling" activity.

Keep track of the numbers you roll.

My number is ______.

	Tallies	Totals	Class Totals
5	I	1	20
6	卌 I	6	43
7	卌 I	6	65
8	卌 卌 III	13	70
9	卌 IIII	9	148
10	卌 卌 IIII	14	150
11	卌	5	133
12	卌	5	89
13	III	3	49
14	卌 II	7	57
15	I	1	16

NOTE TO HOME
Students keep a tally of sums they roll.

Literature Connection Read aloud *Number Puzzles* by Rose Griffiths to reinforce lesson concepts.

RETEACHING

This is a discovery and experimentation lesson, as was Lesson 124; therefore, reteaching is not necessary at this time.

*available separately

◆ LESSON 125 Predicting Results

Chuck and Maggie were doing the "Cube-Rolling" activity, but they decided to subtract rather than add. They used these cubes:

1. What is the least difference they could roll? **0**
2. What is the greatest difference they could roll? **10**
3. Which difference do you think will be rolled most often? _____

COOPERATIVE LEARNING Do the "Cube Rolling" activity.

Difference	Tallies	Totals	Class Totals

4. What difference was rolled the most? _____
5. Was your prediction close? __________

NOTE TO HOME
Students do the "Cube-Rolling" activity using subtraction.

PRACTICE p. 125

LESSON 125 PRACTICE Name ____________

Do the "Cube Rolling" activity.

Keep track of the numbers you roll.

	Tallies	Totals	Class Totals
5			
6			
7			
8			
9			
10			
11			
12			
13			
14			
15			

I predict the sum of ______ will be rolled most often.

The sum rolled most often was ______. Answers will vary.

ENRICHMENT p. 125

LESSON 125 ENRICHMENT Name ____________

Use a calculator to count from the starting number. Write the next five numbers.

Count by:

2s	0	2	4	6	8	10
2s	1	3	5	7	9	11
3s	5	8	11	14	17	20
5s	27	32	37	42	47	52
11s	46	57	68	79	90	101

Think about these questions. Ring your answers.

1. If you start at 0 and count by 2s, will you reach 15? yes (no)
2. If you start at 5 and count by 2s, will you reach 25? (yes) no
3. If you start at 39 and count by 2s, will you reach 112? yes (no)
4. If you start at 35 and count by 5s, will you reach 140? (yes) no
5. If you start at 31 and count by 4s, will you reach 102? yes (no)

Now use the calculator to check your answers. Put boxes around the right answers.

results might be if you do not return the counter to the container after each draw. (Students should realize that they can predict the results of the race without even drawing counters because there are more blue ones than any other color.)

Using the Student Pages Divide the class into 11 pairs or small groups. Repeat the "Cube Rolling" activity of Lesson 124. This time have students roll the 0–5 and 5–10 cubes at the same time, and record the sums on page 281. Assign each group or pair of students a number from 5–15. Have students read aloud their totals for each number on their charts. Have each group copy the totals for their number, then add them to find the class totals. Read aloud all class totals for students to copy. Discuss whether the results are what the students expected and why.

Discuss questions 1–3 on page 282 with the class. Repeat the "Cube Rolling" activity by subtracting the lesser Number Cube from the greater. Again, discuss the results and compare students' predictions to the actual results.

3 Wrap-Up

5 MINUTES

In Closing Ask students to explain how they predicted who would win the "Race Across the Room."

ALTERNATIVE ASSESSMENT

Informal Assessment Observe which students give sensible answers to questions about predicting events.

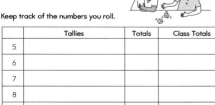

Assessment Criteria

Did the student . . .

✓ correctly keep a record of events using tally marks?

✓ correctly find the total number of tally marks for each event on pages 281 and 282?

✓ give sensible answers to questions 1–5 on page 282?

LESSON 126

Student Edition pages 283–284

Introducing Variability

LESSON PLANNER

Objectives

- ▶ to introduce making bar graphs
- ▶ to demonstrate organizing variable data on a bar graph
- ▶ to demonstrate predicting variability
- ▶ to provide practice in measuring length

Context of the Lesson Variability is related to the experiments students did in Lessons 124 and 125 on random events.

Materials	Program Resources
pencils (60), 30 sharpened to various lengths, and 30 unsharpened	Thinking Story Book, pages 108–111 Practice Master 126 Enrichment Master 126 For extra practice: CD-ROM* Lesson 126

1 Warm-Up 5 MINUTES

Problem of the Day Write the following problem on the chalkboard: Al is three years older than Bill. Carl is two years older than Al. Bill will be 10 in two years. How old are all three boys now? (Al is 11, Carl is 13, and Bill is 8)

MENTAL MATH Have students add, subtract, and multiply the following problems using mental math:

- **a.** 8 + 5 = (13)
- **b.** 4 × 8 = (32)
- **c.** 11 − 3 = (8)
- **d.** 9 × 1 = (9)
- **e.** 6 + 7 = (13)
- **f.** 5 + 4 = (9)
- **g.** 9 − 4 = (5)
- **h.** 3 × 5 = (15)
- **i.** 2 × 1 = (2)
- **j.** 8 + 8 = (16)
- **k.** 13 − 8 = (5)

LESSON 126

Name ______________________

Introducing Variability

COOPERATIVE LEARNING How long is a used pencil? Keep track of the centimeters.

Answers are examples only.

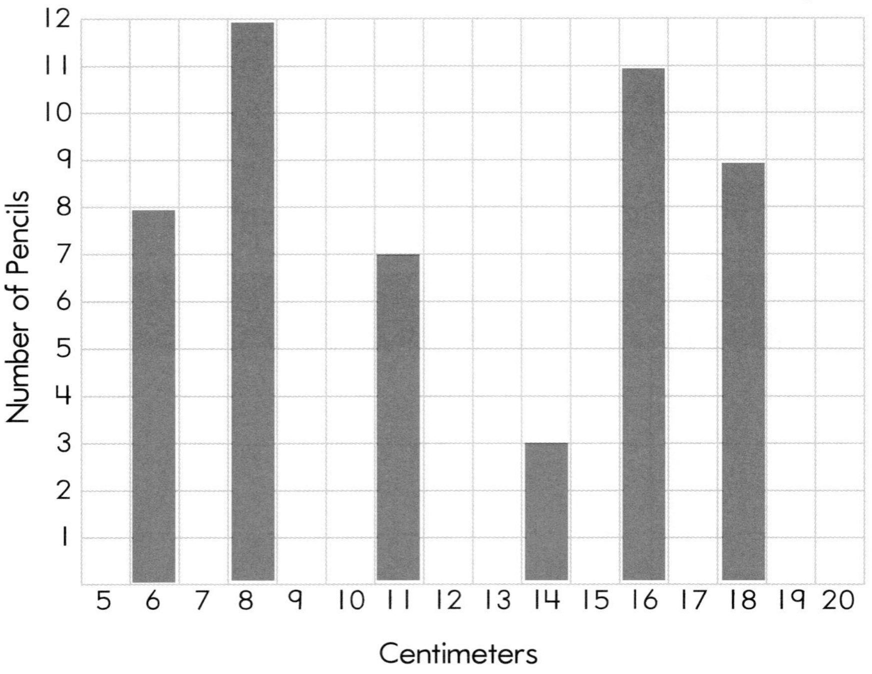

THINKING STORY Talk about the Thinking Story "Ferdie's Meterstick."

NOTE TO HOME
Students collect data and make a bar graph.

Language Arts Connection Have students make bar graphs showing the number of times each vowel appears in a selected paragraph of a story they have read.

RETEACHING

Because this is a discovery and experimentation lesson, reteaching is not necessary at this time.

*available separately

◆ **LESSON 126** Introducing Variability

COOPERATIVE LEARNING

How long is a new pencil?
Keep track of the centimeters.

Answers shown are samples only.

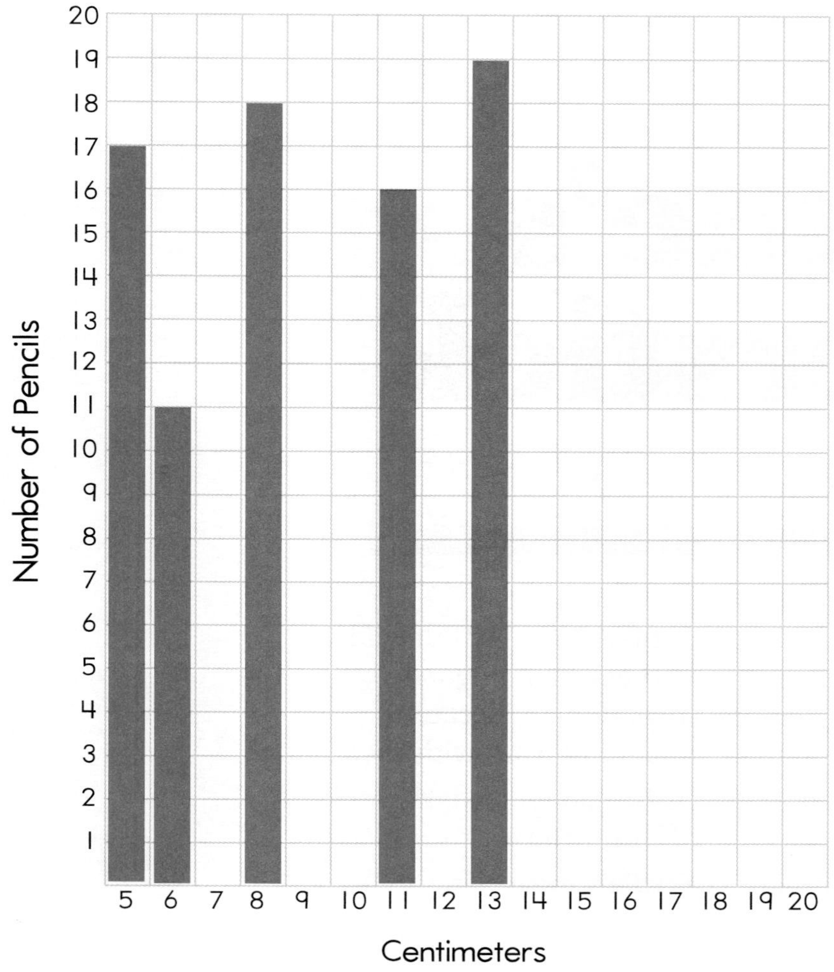

NOTE TO HOME
Students create, explore, and interpret bar graphs.

PRACTICE p. 126

LESSON 126 PRACTICE Name ____________

How long is your hand? Answers will vary.

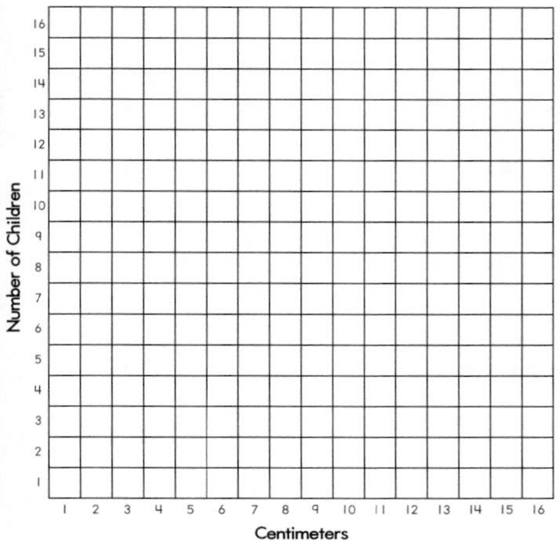

126 • *Math Explorations and Applications* Level 2

ENRICHMENT p. 126

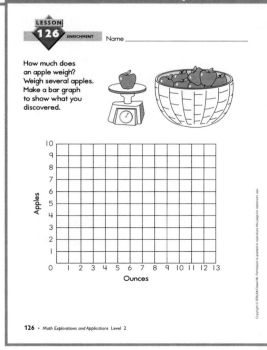

LESSON 126 ENRICHMENT Name ____________

How much does an apple weigh? Weigh several apples. Make a bar graph to show what you discovered.

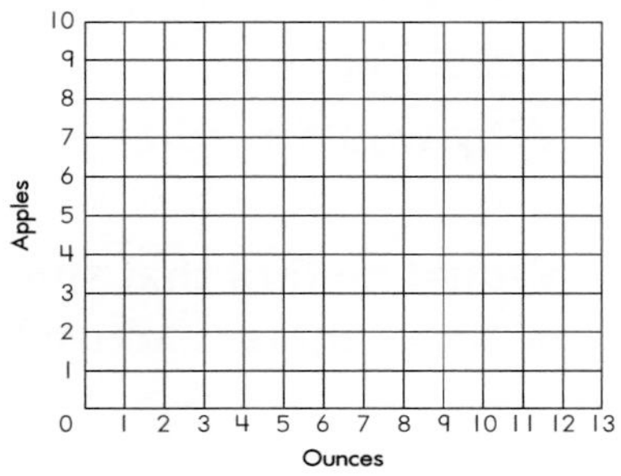

126 • *Math Explorations and Applications* Level 2

2 Teach

COOPERATIVE LEARNING **Using the Student Pages** Draw a chart on the chalkboard like the one on page 283. Distribute several used, sharpened pencils to each student. Have students measure their pencils and record the lengths on a separate sheet of paper. Then have each student call out the lengths of his or her pencils. Demonstrate at the chalkboard and have students at the same time mark off a box on the graph for each length called out. When finished, compare graphs. They should all be the same.

Repeat for page 284. Discuss and compare the data shown on both graphs by asking questions such as:

- ▶ What is the length of the longest pencil on the first graph? on the second graph?
- ▶ What is the length of the shortest pencil on the first graph? on the second graph?
- ▶ What conclusions can you make about used and new pencils based on these graphs? (Guide students to see that the second graph shows little or no variation compared to the first.)

Using the Thinking Story Read aloud "Ferdie's Meterstick" to the class on pages 108-111 of the Thinking Story Book. Discuss the questions asked throughout the story.

3 Wrap-Up

5 MINUTES

In Closing Ask students to name another set of objects they think would result in the same kind of variability as the lengths of the used pencils. (Example: heights of students, length of different pieces of used chalk)

SELF ASSESSMENT

Have students write a sentence at the bottom of each page indicating whether they understand how to make a bar graph. Have students who do not understand fully how to make a bar graph brainstorm strategies for learning.

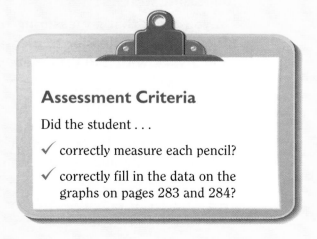

Assessment Criteria

Did the student . . .

✓ correctly measure each pencil?

✓ correctly fill in the data on the graphs on pages 283 and 284?

STORY 18

THINKING STORY

Ferdie's Meterstick

One day Ms. Arthur gave every child in the class a wooden ruler. "This is a meterstick," she said. "Do you all know how many centimeters there are in a meter?"

Do you know? 100

"One hundred!" shouted all the students in the class except Ferdie.

"Eighty!" shouted Ferdie.

"One hundred is right," said Ms. Arthur. "There are 100 centimeters in a meter."

"Well, there should be 80," said Ferdie, who never liked to admit that he was wrong. "Eighty is a smaller number, and a meterstick with 80 centimeters is easier to measure with."

Do you think that a measuring stick with 80 centimeters is easier to measure with than a stick with 100 centimeters? Why or why not? Answers will vary; possibilities include that it is easier to add 100s than 80s.

"You can take these metersticks home with you tonight and measure things around the house with them," Ms. Arthur said. "Be sure to bring them back in good condition tomorrow, though, because we're going to do a lot of work with them."

That night Ferdie had an idea. He broke 20 centimeters off his meterstick.

How long was Ferdie's measuring stick then? 80 cm

"Eighty centimeters is a better length for a measuring stick," Ferdie said to himself. "Who needs those extra 20 centimeters anyway?"

The next day Ms. Arthur gave the students their first measuring job. They were to find out how many meters wide the room was. The students all got down on the floor and moved their metersticks along, counting the number of meters. They all agreed that the room was about 8 meters across–all except Ferdie.

Why would Ferdie get a different answer? His measuring stick is shorter.

Would he find that the room was more or fewer meters across? more

"This room is 10 meters across," said Ferdie. "The rest of you must have counted wrong."

The next measuring job was even more fun. Each child measured how far his or her desk was from the classroom door.

"My desk is the farthest from the door!" Ferdie bragged.

"No, it isn't," said Marcus. "See, our desks are next to each other, but mine is farther out than yours."

"I measured and my desk is 3 meters from the door," said Ferdie. "How far away is yours?"

"Just $2\frac{1}{2}$ meters," Marcus said sadly. "But I still think my desk is farther."

Whose desk is really farther from the door? Marcus's

How do you know? Marcus's desk is farther out.

Why does it seem to Ferdie that his desk is farther? Ferdie measured the distance with his shorter measuring stick.

◆ STORY 18 Ferdie's Meterstick

The last thing the children did was the most fun. Each child stood behind a line, ran a few steps, and jumped as far as possible. A chalk mark was made to show where each child landed.

"I jumped $2\frac{1}{2}$ meters," Ferdie announced.

"That can't be true," said Manolita, "because my chalk mark is just as far from the line as yours. And I jumped only 2 meters."

"You may think that you jumped as far as I did, but this proves you didn't," said Ferdie. "Metersticks don't lie."

"If you don't believe me, come and measure my chalk mark yourself," said Ferdie.

Manolita took her own meterstick and measured from the starting line to the chalk mark that showed where Ferdie landed.

About what will the distance be, according to Manolita's meterstick? 2 meters

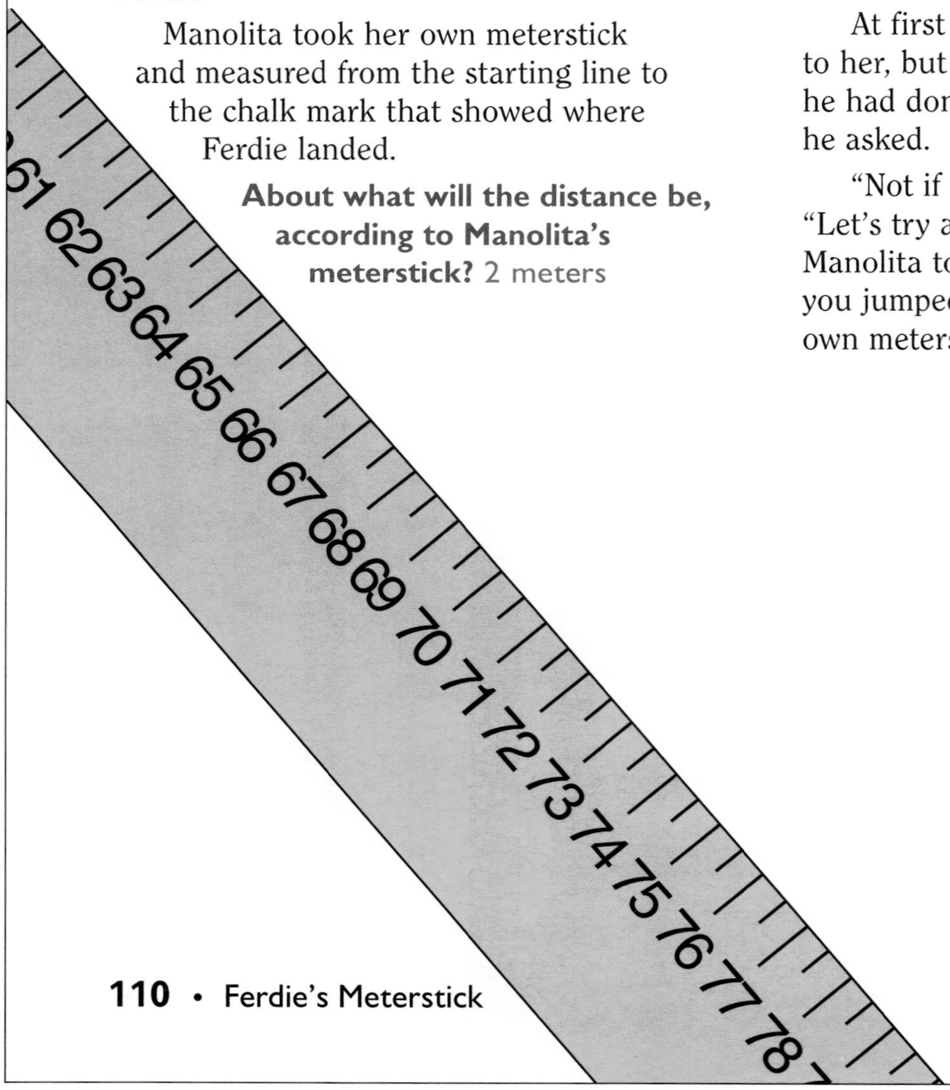

"Just as I thought!" said Manolita. "Two meters—the same distance that I jumped. And you said $2\frac{1}{2}$ meters. That's crazy!"

"You didn't do it right," said Ferdie. "You measured my jump with your meterstick. We're all supposed to measure our jumps with our own metersticks. That's what Ms. Arthur said."

Does it usually make any difference what meterstick you use? a little, because not all metersticks are exactly the same length, but generally not enough to notice

"Something does seem a little strange here," said Ms. Arthur. "Could I have a look at that meterstick of yours, Ferdie?"

At first Ferdie didn't want to show it to her, but then he did and explained what he had done. "Did I ruin my meterstick?" he asked.

"Not if you use it right," Ms. Arthur said. "Let's try a little experiment. I want you and Manolita to measure how many centimeters you jumped. Each of you should use your own meterstick."

Manolita measured the distance from the starting line to her chalk mark. It was exactly two meterstick lengths.

How many centimeters is that? 200

How can you figure that out? 100 + 100 = 200

Ferdie measured the distance from the starting line to his chalk mark. It was two lengths of his meterstick and 40 centimeters more.

How many centimeters is that? 200

How can you figure that out? 80 + 80 is 160, and 40 more is 200

"We both jumped 200 centimeters," Ferdie and Manolita said.

"Now," said Ms. Arthur, "I'd like you both to trade metersticks and measure your jumps in centimeters again."

What answers do you think they will get this time? the same

"It's 200 centimeters no matter which meterstick you use!" said Ferdie. "My meterstick works. Yipee!"

Why do you get the same answer with both metersticks? They both measure in centimeters.

On whose meterstick were the centimeters easier to figure out? Manolita's

Why? It's easier to add 100 + 100 than 80 + 80 + 40.

. . . the end

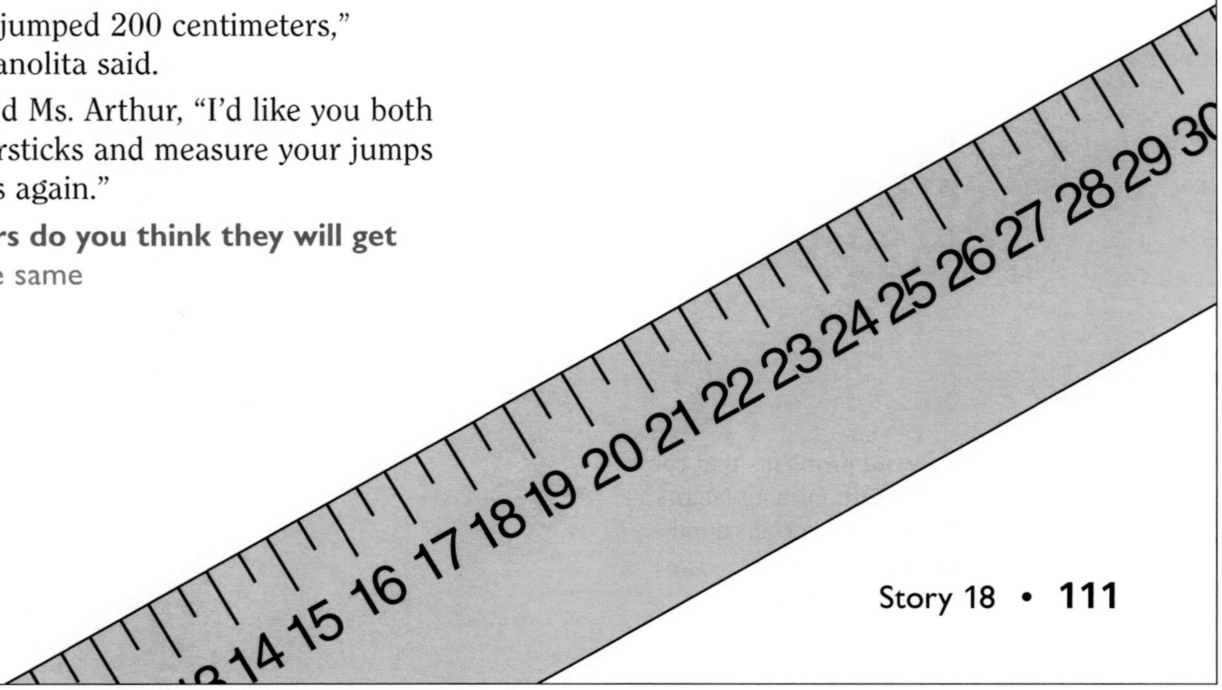

LESSON 127

Student Edition pages 285–286

Applying Multiplication

LESSON PLANNER

Objective

✓ to provide practice solving missing-factor problems

Context of the Lesson This lesson helps students discover the relationship between multiplication and division. This lesson also contains the 16th Mastery Checkpoint, which assesses students' mastery of the multiplication facts.

Materials	Program Resources
none	Number Cubes
	Thinking Story Book, pages 112–113
	Practice Master 127
	Enrichment Master 127
	Assessment Master
	For extra practice: CD-ROM* Lesson 127

1 Warm-Up

5 MINUTES

Problem of the Day Write this problem on the chalkboard: How many sections would you have if you folded a square in half three times and then unfolded it? (8)

MENTAL MATH Have students add, subtract, or multiply, using mental math.

a. 16 – 9 = (7)
b. 12 – 9 = (3)
c. 6 + 8 = (14)
d. 4 + 7 = (11)
e. 3 × 6 = (18)
f. 4 × 3 = (12)

2 Teach

Demonstrate Discuss several word problems that can be solved by writing number sentences with missing factors. For example, say: If I multiply five times a certain number, I will get 35. What is that number? 5 × _____ = 35 (7) Have

LESSON 127

Name ________________________

Applying Multiplication

Work these problems.

There are five crayons in one box.

1. How many crayons are there in two boxes? 10
2. How many crayons in three boxes? 15
3. How many crayons in four boxes? 20
4. How many crayons in five boxes? 25

One pizza costs $4.

5. How much do six pizzas cost? $ 24
6. How much do four pizzas cost? $ 16

NOTE TO HOME
Students solve multiplication problems.

RETEACHING

Begin by writing several multiplication equations on the chalkboard. Then have students close their eyes as you erase one factor. See who can name the factor that is missing. Repeat until you have erased a factor in each equation. Then have students write the missing factor in each equation.

PRACTICE p. 127

LESSON 127 PRACTICE Name __________

Solve.

1. 5 × [2] = 10
2. [7] × 4 = 28
3. 9 × [4] = 36
4. [5] × 7 = 35
5. 3 × [7] = 21
6. [5] × 6 = 30
7. 8 × [5] = 40
8. [9] × 1 = 9
9. 1 × [3] = 3
10. [3] × 8 = 24
11. 6 × [6] = 36
12. [8] × 5 = 40
13. 2 × [8] = 16
14. [3] × 9 = 27
15. 4 × [9] = 36
16. [3] × 2 = 6
17. 7 × [1] = 7
18. [4] × 3 = 12

Math Explorations and Applications Level 2 • 127

*available separately

◆ LESSON 127 Applying Multiplication

Use manipulatives to help solve these problems. Check to be sure your answers make sense.

7. Nancy wants to buy 15 balloons. They come five to a box. How many boxes must she buy?

   5 × [3] = 15

8. Miriam needs to put 28 pictures in her album. She wants to put four pictures on each page. How many pages will she need?

   4 × [7] = 28

9. Courtney wants to earn $40. She can make $5 a week. How many weeks will it take her?

   5 × [8] = 40

ALGEBRA READINESS

Solve these problems.

10. 4 × [2] = 8
11. 5 × [3] = 15
12. [2] × 4 = 8
13. 5 × [4] = 20
14. 10 × [5] = 50
15. 5 × [5] = 25

NOTE TO HOME
Students solve multiplication problems with missing factors.

students explain how they would solve the problem. Continue with real-life situations, such as: Erasers cost eight cents each. How many erasers can I buy with 40 cents?
____ × 8 = 40 (5)

Using the Student Pages Have students complete pages 285 and 286 independently. When finished, have them work in pairs to correct each other's answers by checking that the multiplication equations are correct. Finally, discuss answers with the class as a whole.

Using the Thinking Story Present one or two new problems from those following "Ferdie's Meterstick," on pages 112–113 of the Thinking Story Book.

3 Wrap-Up (5 MINUTES)

In Closing Ask students to summarize what they learned in this lesson by telling what a missing factor is and how to check if you wrote the correct missing factor in a number sentence.

Mastery Checkpoint 16

At this time, students should demonstrate mastery of the multiplication facts studied so far by correctly answering at least 12 of 15 problems on pages 285 and 286. You might also assess mastery using Assessment Masters 51 and 52. Results of this assessment may be recorded on the Mastery Checkpoint Chart.

ENRICHMENT p. 127

LESSON 127 ENRICHMENT Name ________

Use a calculator to count up or down from the starting number. Write the next five numbers.

Count:

up by 3s	0	3	6	9	12	15
down by 2s	29	27	25	23	21	19
down by 2s	75	73	71	69	67	65
up by 99s	0	99	198	297	396	495
down by 2s	5	3	1	−1	−3	−5

Think about these questions. Ring your answers.

1. If you start at 15 and count up by 2s, will you reach 100? yes (no)
2. If you start at 24 and count down by 5s, will you reach 0? yes (no)
3. If you start at 100 and count down by 3s, will you reach 0? yes (no)
4. If you start at 20 and count up by 7s, will you reach 34? (yes) no
5. If you start at 1000 and count down by 200s, will you reach 0? (yes) no

ASSESSMENT p. 51

UNIT 4 Mastery Checkpoint 16 Multiplication facts (Lesson 127)
Page 1 of 2
Name ________
The student demonstrates mastery by correctly answering at least 32 of the 40 problems.

Work these problems.

1. 3 × 5 = 15
2. 6 × 2 = 12
3. 8 × 2 = 16
4. 7 × 3 = 21
5. 4 × 5 = 20
6. 5 × 4 = 20
7. 8 × 0 = 0
8. 9 × 9 = 81
9. 5 × 7 = 35
10. 3 × 3 = 9
11. 6 × 6 = 36
12. 7 × 6 = 42
13. 4 × 3 = 12
14. 10 × 6 = 60
15. 8 × 4 = 32
16. 5 × 9 = 45
17. 2 × 7 = 14
18. 8 × 8 = 64
19. 7 × 8 = 56
20. 9 × 6 = 54

Go on . . .

Assessment Criteria

Did the student . . .

✓ correctly solve five of six problems on page 285?

✓ correctly solve seven of nine problems on page 286?

LESSON 128

Student Edition pages 287–288

Introducing Division

LESSON PLANNER

Objectives

- to introduce division
- to demonstrate division as the inverse of multiplication
- to provide practice with multiplication facts

Context of the Lesson Division is introduced in this lesson and then combined with multiplication in Lesson 129.

Materials	Program Resources
base-10 materials	Number Cubes
index cards, 22 (two each)	Reteaching Master
tape	Practice Master 128
	Enrichment Master 128
	For extra practice: CD-ROM* Lesson 128

1 Warm-Up

5 MINUTES

Problem of the Day Write the following problem on the chalkboard: Using each digit only once, fill in the blanks with the digits 6, 7, 8 and 9 to make the greatest possible sum: □ + □ (97 + 86 or 96 + 87)

MENTAL MATH Have students add, subtract, and multiply the following problems using mental math:

a. 8 + 5 = (13) **b.** 4 x 8 = (32) **c.** 11 – 3 = (8)
d. 6 + 7 = (13) **e.** 9 x 1 = (9) **f.** 5 + 4 = (9)
g. 9 – 4 = (5) **h.** 3 x 5 = (15) **i.** 8 + 8 = (16)

2 Teach

Demonstrate Display 30 objects of the base-10 materials. Tell five students that you want to divide the objects equally among them. Have students predict how many each will receive; then give out the objects to check their answers. Guide students to see that they each get six objects because 5 x 6 = 30.

LESSON 128

Name ______________________

Introducing Division

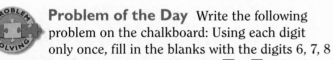

COOPERATIVE LEARNING Do the "Missing Factor Puzzle" activity.

1. What number is hidden? _____

Solve these problems.

2. I paid 21¢ for seven candles.
How much would one candle cost? 3 ¢

There are seven days in one week.

Sun	Mon	Tues	Wed	Thur	Fri	Sat
1	2	3	4	5	6	7
8	9	10	11	12	13	14
15	16	17	18	19	20	21
22	23	24	25	26	27	28
29	30	31				

3. How many weeks are there in 14 days? 2
4. How many weeks are there in 35 days? 5
5. How many weeks are there in 49 days? 7
6. How many weeks are there in 28 days? 4

NOTE TO HOME
Students play a game and begin to learn about division.

LEARNING STYLES

Meeting Individual Needs

Visual learners may need to make drawings to show division facts. Work with students by drawing sets of shapes and then ringing groups within the set. For example, ask students to draw a set of 12 squares. Have them ring groups of four squares to see how much 12 ÷ 4 is.

RETEACHING p. 32

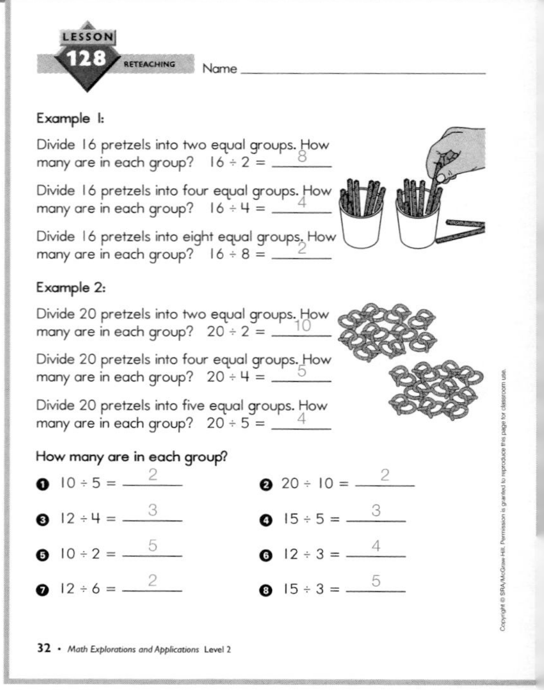
LESSON 128 RETEACHING Name ______________________

Example 1:

Divide 16 pretzels into two equal groups. How many are in each group? 16 ÷ 2 = 8

Divide 16 pretzels into four equal groups. How many are in each group? 16 ÷ 4 = 4

Divide 16 pretzels into eight equal groups. How many are in each group? 16 ÷ 8 = 2

Example 2:

Divide 20 pretzels into two equal groups. How many are in each group? 20 ÷ 2 = 10

Divide 20 pretzels into four equal groups. How many are in each group? 20 ÷ 4 = 5

Divide 20 pretzels into five equal groups. How many are in each group? 20 ÷ 5 = 4

How many are in each group?

1. 10 ÷ 5 = 2
2. 20 ÷ 10 = 2
3. 12 ÷ 4 = 3
4. 15 ÷ 5 = 3
5. 10 ÷ 2 = 5
6. 12 ÷ 3 = 4
7. 12 ÷ 6 = 2
8. 15 ÷ 3 = 5

32 • Math Explorations and Applications Level 2

Copyright © SRA/McGraw-Hill. Permission is granted to reproduce this page for classroom use.

*available separately

◆ LESSON 128 Introducing Division

COOPERATIVE LEARNING Use coins or counters to act these out in a group.

Solve these problems.

❼ 12 cents are to be divided equally among three children. How many cents for each child?

$12 \div 3 =$ 4

❽ 24 cents are to be divided equally among four children. How many cents for each child?

$24 \div 4 =$ 6

❾ 32 cents are to be divided equally among eight children. How many cents for each child?

$32 \div 8 =$ 4

❿ 15 cents are to be divided equally among three cups. How many cents in each cup?

$15 \div 3 =$ 5

NOTE TO HOME
Students use coins or counters to learn about division.

Write $30 \div 5 = 6$ on the chalkboard and explain what each number in the number sentence represents. Repeat with other numbers, including having some objects left over.

Using the Number Cubes Give students multiplication facts to find, hide, and show their answers. After each multiplication fact give the related division fact. For example, $3 \times 10 = ?$ then $30 \div 3 = ?$

COOPERATIVE LEARNING **Introducing the "Missing Factor Puzzle" Activity** Have two students come to the front of the room. Attach a number to each student's back. Ask each player to look at the other player's number. Then have the class tell the product of the two numbers. Each player must then figure out what number is on his or her back. Repeat with several pairs of students.

MATH MANIPULATIVES **Using the Student Pages** Work the opening problem on page 287 with the class. Have students work in groups and use base-10 materials to complete the remaining problems on both pages.

❸ Wrap-Up (5 MINUTES)

In Closing Have students make up their own word problems that can be solved using division. Students can share and solve each other's problems.

ALTERNATIVE ASSESSMENT **Informal Assessment** Use students' answers on the Student Edition pages to assess their understanding of division.

PRACTICE p. 128

LESSON 128 PRACTICE Name ____________

Solve these problems.

❶ Maxine bought eight apples for 72¢. How much did each apple cost? 9¢

There are three feet in one yard.

❷ How many yards are there in 15 feet? 5

❸ How many yards are there in 27 feet? 9

❹ How many yards are there in 18 feet? 6

❺ Fifteen marbles are to be divided equally among five children. How many marbles are there for each child? $15 \div 5 =$ 3

128 • Math Explorations and Applications Level 2

ENRICHMENT p. 128

LESSON 128 ENRICHMENT Name ____________

❶ Bob and Ginny each get an allowance of 75 cents a week. Each put one third of their allowance in their own bank at home. Draw coins to show the money they put in the bank all together.

❷ Selena put in the same amount of money each week for seven weeks. At the end of the time, she had 56 cents. Draw the money she put in her bank each week.

❸ Gary went to his bank on the night stand six times. Each time he put in nine cents. Draw the money he had in the bank after the six visits.

128 • Math Explorations and Applications Level 2

Assessment Criteria

Did the student . . .

✓ correctly name the number on his or her back when doing the activity?

✓ correctly solve the last 4 problems on page 287?

✓ correctly solve 3 of the 4 problems on page 288?

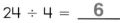

LESSON 129

Student Edition pages 289–290

Division and Multiplication

LESSON PLANNER

Objectives

- to introduce multiplication and division as inverse operations
- to demonstrate use of the area of a rectangle to solve missing-factor problems
- to provide practice in solving word problems involving missing factors, multiplication, and money

Context of the Lesson This lesson uses students' knowledge of area and multiplication to continue division practice.

Materials	**Program Resources**
play money	Practice Master 129
flash cards (optional)	Enrichment Master 129
	For extra practice: CD-ROM* Lesson 129

1 Warm-Up (5 MINUTES)

Problem of the Day Write this problem on the chalkboard: There are six rows of desks in the second-grade classroom. Each row has four desks. There is a student at every desk except two. How many students are in this class? (22)

MENTAL MATH Have students find the missing factors in each of the following.

a. 3 × ____ = 9 (3) **b.** 2 × ____ = 8 (4)

c. ____ × 5 = 15 (3) **d.** 7 × ____ = 35 (5)

e. 4 × ____ = 24 (6) **f.** ____ × 4 = 16 (4)

2 Teach

Demonstrate Draw a six-by-four unit rectangle on the chalkboard. Review how to use multiplication to find its area. (6 × 4 = 24 square units) Next, draw a rectangle on the chalkboard and label one side seven units long. Tell students

LESSON 129

Name ______________________

Division and Multiplication

Solve these problems.

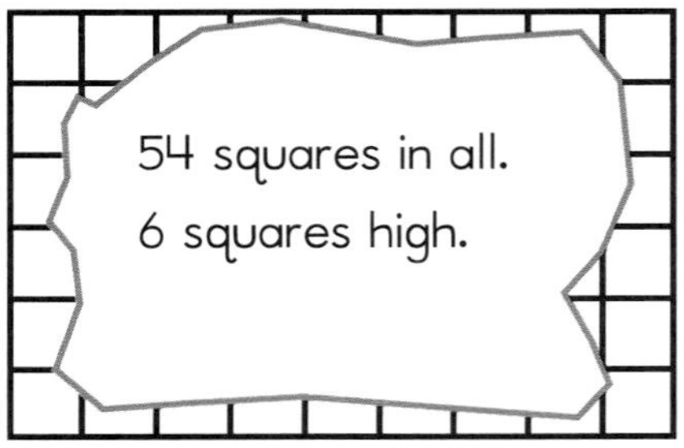

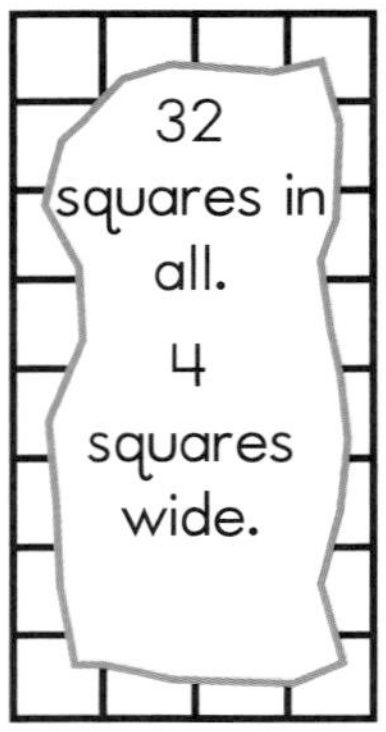

❷ How many squares long? __9__ squares long

❸ How many squares high? __8__ squares high

Sharpen your skills. Remember the doubles!

❹ 1 + 1 = __2__

❺ 2 + 2 = __4__

❻ 3 + 3 = __6__

❼ 4 + 4 = __8__

❽ 5 + 5 = __10__

❾ 6 + 6 = __12__

❿ 7 + 7 = __14__

⓫ 8 + 8 = __16__

⓬ 9 + 9 = __18__

⓭ 10 + 10 = __20__

NOTE TO HOME
Students explore division and review adding doubles.

Literature Connection Read aloud *A Remainder of One* by Elinor J. Pinczes and *Take Off with Numbers* by Sally Hewitt to reinforce lesson concepts.

RETEACHING

Have students look back at page 290. Tell them that instead of selling strawberries for $3 a basket, Paul sold them for $2 a basket. Work with students to see how this changes the table they must create for problem 14. Write the table on the chalkboard, have students complete it, and then ask questions similar to those in problems 15–18.

*available separately

◆ LESSON 129 Division and Multiplication

Use the Mixed Practice on page 393 after this lesson.

Use play money to help solve these problems. Check to be sure your answers make sense.

⓮ Paul sells baskets of strawberries for $3 a basket. He made this chart to help him know how much to collect. Help Paul by completing the chart.

Number of baskets	1	2	3	4	5	6	7	8	9	10
Price (dollars)	3	6	9	12	**15**	**18**	**21**	**24**	**27**	**30**

Use the chart to answer these questions.

⓯ Sara bought five baskets. What did she pay?

3 × 5 = **15**

⓰ Megan paid $24. How many did she buy?

8 × 3 = 24

⓱ Raulito paid $9. How many did he buy?

3 × 3 = 9

⓲ Late in the season Paul raised his prices. Then he sold five baskets of strawberries for $20. What was the new price? **$4 per box**

5 × **4** = 20

NOTE TO HOME
Students solve word problems.

PRACTICE p. 129

LESSON 129 PRACTICE Name ______

Use play money to help solve these problems. Check to be sure your answers make sense.

❶ Donna was selling magazines for $4 each in March. She made this chart to help her know how much money to collect. Help Donna by completing the chart.

Number of Magazines	1	2	3	4	5	6	7	8	9	10	11	12
Price (dollars)	4	8	12	16	20	24	28	32	36	40	44	48

Use the chart to answer these questions.

❷ Mrs. Brown bought eight magazines. How much did she pay?

8 × 4 = 32

❸ Mr. Delgado paid $16. How many magazines did he buy?

4 × 4 = 16

❹ Beth paid $28. How many magazines did she buy?

7 × 4 = 28

Math Explorations and Applications Level 2 • 129

ENRICHMENT p. 129

LESSON 129 ENRICHMENT Name ______

Answer these questions.

❶ Marg and Leann are covering the wall with paper for a mural. They will need 96 squares in all. Marg says the wall is eight squares high. How many squares long is it? 12

❷ The mural will show fun things that children do for every month of the year. Each small group of children will do two months. There are 24 children in three classes all together. How many will be in each small group? 4 children

❸ Each month will cover the same number of squares on the mural. Remember there are 96 squares. How many will each month use? 8 squares

❹ The markers come in packages of five. Ms. Fenster needs markers for 24 students. How many packages must she buy? 5

❺ How many markers will be left over? 1

Math Explorations and Applications Level 2 • 129

the area is 42 square units. Ask how they can use this information to find the length of the other side without measuring. Guide students to see that this is a missing-factor problem. (7 × 6 = 42; therefore the other side is 6 units long.) Provide several more problems of this type.

Using the Student Pages Have students complete page 289 independently. After checking answers, have students work with partners using play money to solve the remaining problems on this page. Then have them solve the problems on page 290.

❸ Wrap-Up

5 MINUTES

In Closing Ask students to explain how they solved problems 15 through 18 on page 290.

ALTERNATIVE ASSESSMENT

Informal Assessment Use students' answers to these pages to informally assess their ability to find missing factors and solve multiplication problems involving money.

Assessment Criteria

Did the student . . .

✓ correctly solve all of the problems on page 289?

✓ correctly solve four of five problems on page 290?

SPECIAL NEEDS

Meeting Individual Needs

Some students will need extra practice to learn multiplication facts. They can use flash cards, Number Cubes, or, if available, a computer program such as *Math Blaster.*

UNIT 4

Student Edition pages 291–292

Mid-Unit Review

The Mid-Unit Review pinpoints troublesome skill areas for students, allowing plenty of time for additional practice and reteaching before the unit ends. If students did not do well on the Mid-Unit Review and have completed additional practice, you might want to use the Mid-Unit Review provided on pages 47–48 in the Assessment Master Book.

Using the Student Pages Have students complete problems 1–12 on pages 291 and 292 on their own. You might treat this review as a formal assessment of students' skills and have students complete this review as a timed test. See suggestions on page 44.

Home Connections You may want to send home Home Connections Masters 49–50 which provide additional activities families can complete together. These activities apply the skills being presented in this unit.

Unit Project This would be a good time to assign the newspaper numbers project on pages 364a and 364b. Students may begin working on the project in cooperative groups in their free time as you work through the unit. The Unit Project is a good opportunity for students to practice counting numbers from a starting point other than one, recognize and write the numerals 0 to 10 and 0 to 20, experience saying and reading numbers, and practice discussing numbers and how they are used to measure, count, order, quantify, and label.

UNIT 4

Name ______________________

Mid-Unit Review

Solve these problems. Use the pictures.

1. 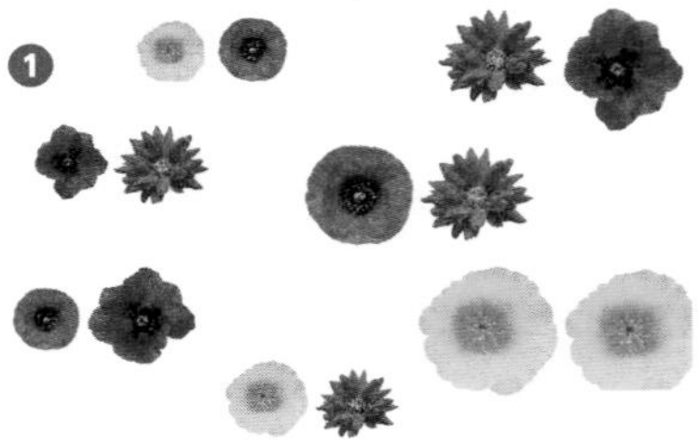

$7 \times 2 =$ 14

2. 

$3 \times 8 =$ 24

Use the squares to solve these problems.

3. 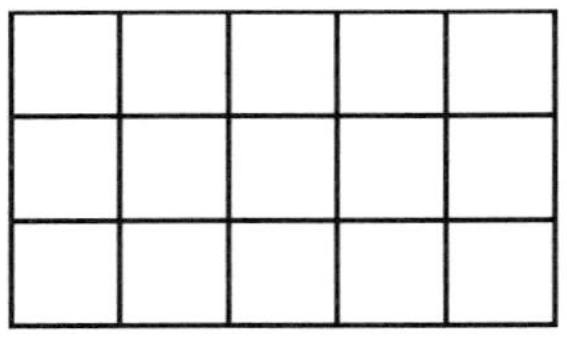

The area is 15 square centimeters.

4. 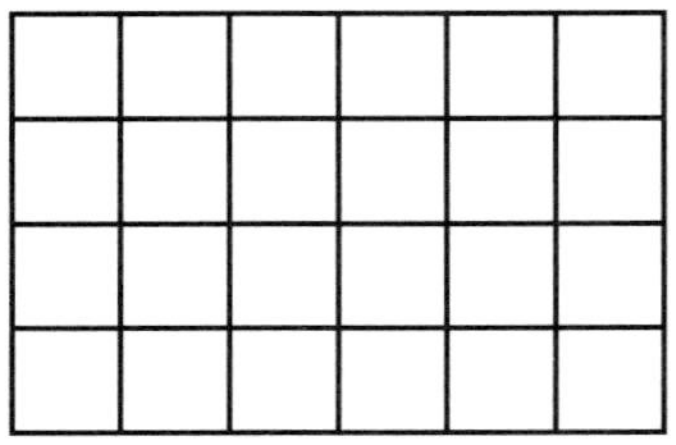

The area is 24 square centimeters.

NOTE TO HOME
Students review unit skills and concepts.

❺ Fill in the missing numbers in the chart.

0	1	2	3	4	5	6	7	8	9
0	4	8	**12**	**16**	20	**24**	**28**	32	36

Use the chart above to solve these problems.

❻ 3 × 4 = **12** ❼ 4 × 7 = **28**

❽ 4 × 9 = **36**

❾ José made the following chart to help him know much to charge for balloons. Help José by completing the chart.

Number of balloons	1	2	3	4	5	6	7	8	9	10
Price (cents)	6	**12**	18	**24**	30	**36**	**42**	48	**54**	60

❿ What is the price of nine balloons? **54¢**

⓫ Kelly bought eight balloons.
She gave José 50¢.
How much did she get back? **2¢**

⓬ Daniel bought one balloon for his sister, two for his mother, and one for his aunt.
How much did he pay? **24¢**

NOTE TO HOME
Students review unit skills and concepts.

ASSESSMENT p. 53

UNIT 4 **Mid-Unit Review** (Use after Lesson 129.) Page 1 of 3

Name ____________________

The student demonstrates mastery by correctly answering at least 28 of the 34 problems.

Solve these problems.

❶ 15 − 9 = 6 ❷ 8 + 7 = 15
❸ 12 − 3 = 9 ❹ 5 + 6 = 11
❺ 6 × 5 = 30 ❻ 8 × 3 = 24
❼ 4 × 7 = 28 ❽ 2 × 6 = 12
❾ 3 × 5 = 15 ❿ 6 × 7 = 42
⓫ 35 ÷ 7 = 5 ⓬ 48 ÷ 6 = 8
⓭ 16 ÷ 4 = 4 ⓮ 21 ÷ 3 = 7
⓯ 27 ÷ 9 = 3 ⓰ 12 ÷ 2 = 6

Find the missing numbers.

⓱ 7 + [9] = 16 ⓲ [4] + 9 = 13
⓳ 19 − [11] = 8 ⓴ 15 − [10] = 5
㉑ [6] + 9 = 15 ㉒ 13 + 7 = [20]

Go on ...

Math Explorations and Applications Level 2 • 53

LESSON 130

Student Edition pages 293–294

Days of the Week

LESSON PLANNER

Objectives

- to provide practice using a calendar
- to demonstrate ordering the days of the week
- to introduce telling what day it will be or was given a number of days in the future or past

Context of the Lesson This and the next lesson review the calendar and time, focusing on the modular structure of both.

Materials

monthly calendar, current month

Program Resources

Thinking Story Book, pages 112–113

Practice Master 130

Enrichment Master 130

For extra practice: CD-ROM* Lesson 130

1 Warm-Up (5 minutes)

Problem of the Day Write the following problem on the chalkboard: Fruit rolls cost three for $1. How many fruit rolls can you buy if you have $3? (9)

MENTAL MATH Have students multiply, divide, add, and subtract the following problems using mental math:

a. 2 + 3 = (5)
b. 9 – 0 = (9)
c. 1 × 4 = (4)
d. 14 ÷ 2 = (7)
e. 5 + 4 = (9)
f. 8 – 1 = (7)
g. 2 × 2 = (4)
h. 35 ÷ 5 = (7)
i. 10 + 6 = (16)

2 Teach

Demonstrate Display a calendar for the current month. Review how to read the calendar by having students identify each of the following days: today, yesterday, two days ago, five days ago, tomorrow, and next week. Have on hand the preceding and following month's calendar to refer to if necessary.

LESSON 130

Name ______________________________

Days of the Week

Fill in the missing days.

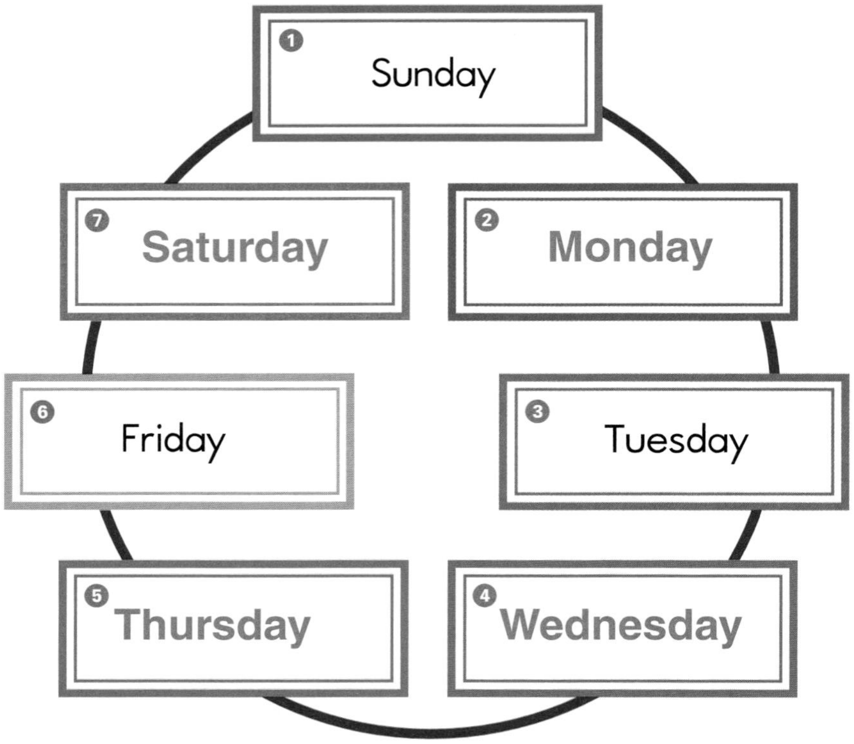

NOTE TO HOME
Students practice ordering the days of the week.

Literature Connection To reinforce lesson concepts, read or invite the students to read "Alice and the Sevens" in *Alice in Numberland: Fantasy Math* by Time-Life, Inc.

RETEACHING

Because this concept is not formalized at this level, reteaching is not considered necessary at this time.

*available separately

◆ LESSON 130 Days of the Week

Draw a ring around the day it is today.

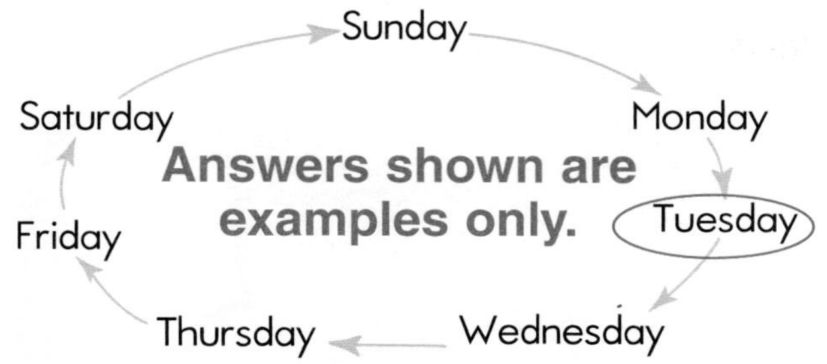

Use today to complete the chart. Write the day it was and the day it will be.

Number of Days	Day It Was	Day It Will Be
1	⑧ Monday	⑨ Wednesday
3	⑩ Saturday	⑪ Friday
6	⑫ Wednesday	⑬ Monday
7	⑭ Tuesday	⑮ Tuesday
8	⑯ Monday	⑰ Wednesday
14	⑱ Tuesday	⑲ Tuesday
21	⑳ Tuesday	㉑ Tuesday
69	㉒ Wednesday	㉓ Monday
70	㉔ Tuesday	㉕ Tuesday
71	㉖ Monday	㉗ Wednesday

NOTE TO HOME
Students learn to identify days of the week by using multiples.

PRACTICE p. 130

LESSON 130 PRACTICE Name ______________________

❶ Draw a circle around the day it is today. Answers will vary.

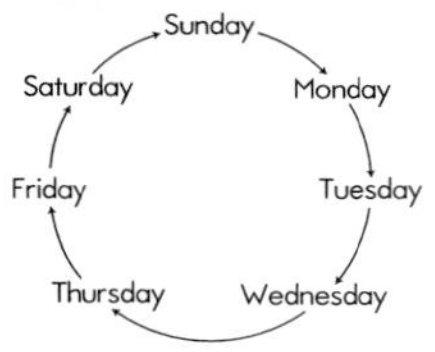

❷ Now complete the chart. Show the day it was and the day it will be.

Number of Days	Day It Was	Day It Will Be
1		
2		
5		
7		
9		
14		
28		
35		

ENRICHMENT p. 130

LESSON 130 ENRICHMENT Name ______________________

July						
Sun.	Mon.	Tue.	Wed.	Thu.	Fri.	Sat.

Use the calendar above to help you answer these questions.

❶ Ray and his family will be leaving for vacation in four days. Today is Thursday. On what day will they leave? Monday

❷ Their vacation will last for 12 days, including the day they leave and the day they get home. On what day will they get home? Friday

❸ Ray has saved $24 to spend on his vacation. He wants to spend the same amount each day so that he always has some money left. If the vacation is 12 days long, how much can he spend each day? $2

❹ If Ray is careful to spend the same amount every day, how much will he have left at the end of Sunday? $10

❺ Ray and his family will get to Texas on a Wednesday and then drive for three nights and three days to Mexico. On what day will they arrive in Mexico? Saturday

Using the Student Pages Complete page 293 with the class. Discuss how the numbers can help identify the days. Ask questions such as, "What is the second day of the week?" Guide students to see that the same day of the week occurs every 7 days. For example, ask them to name what day it was 7 days ago, 14 days ago, 21 days from now, and 70 days from now. Encourage students to explain their answers. (Possible explanation: Every 7 days you get back to the same day, so 10 x 7 or 2 x 7 or 3 x 7 days ago is still the same day of the week as today.) Use this concept to help students identify the day it will be 75 days from today. (70 days will be the same day as today, so count 5 days from today.)

Have students complete page 294 in pairs. Have them complete one column before going on to the next. You might want to work several examples with them before they begin work with their partners.

Using the Thinking Story Present one or two new problems from "Ferdie's Meterstick," on pages 112–113 of the Thinking Story Book.

3 Wrap-Up 5 MINUTES

In Closing Have students write an explanation for how they would name the day that is 37 days from today.

ALTERNATIVE ASSESSMENT

Portfolio Assessment Have students save their completed charts on page 294 in their Math Portfolios.

Assessment Criteria

Did the student . . .

✓ correctly name the days during the demonstration?

✓ correctly label the days on page 293?

✓ correctly complete 18 out of 20 answers on page 294?

LOOKING AHEAD You will need a large working clock for Lesson 131.

LESSON 131

Student Edition pages 295–296

Telling Time

LESSON PLANNER

Objective

▶ to introduce basic concepts of telling time

Context of the Lesson This lesson uses the modular system of time just as Lesson 130 used the modular system of the calendar.

Materials	Program Resources
clock with movable hands	Number Cubes
map of U.S.A. (optional)	Reteaching Master
	Practice Master 131
	Enrichment Master 131
	For extra practice: CD-ROM* Lesson 131

1 Warm-Up

5 MINUTES

Problem of the Day Write the following problem on the chalkboard: Tara covered her 24-square-foot table top with a sheet of plastic that was 3 feet wide. How long did the plastic have to be to cover the whole table top? Why? (At least 8 ft long, because if it were less there would not be 24 square ft.)

MENTAL MATH Have students divide the following numbers, using their Number Cubes to respond.

a. 12 ÷ 4 = (3) **b.** 21 ÷ 3 = (7)
c. 30 ÷ 5 = (6) **d.** 24 ÷ 4 = (6)
e. 10 ÷ 2 = (5) **f.** 14 ÷ 7 = (2)

2 Teach

Demonstrate Show students a clock set to 12:00. Explain that it is 12 noon. Work with students to calculate what time it will be in one hour, two hours, five hours, 12 hours, and 24 hours. Be sure students understand which answers are A.M. and which are P.M. Repeat to find the time it was one hour ago, two hours ago, and so on.

LESSON 131

Name ____________________

Telling Time

The time now is 4:00 P.M.

Complete the chart. Show the time it was and the time it will be.

Number of Hours	Time It Was	Time It Will Be
1	3:00 P.M.	5:00 P.M.
2	❶ 2:00 P.M.	❷ 6:00 P.M.
4	❸ 12:00 noon	❹ 8:00 P.M.
8	❺ 8:00 P.M.	❻ 12:00 midnight
12	❼ 4:00 P.M.	❽ 4:00 P.M.
24	❾ 4:00 P.M.	❿ 4:00 P.M.
36	⓫ 4:00 P.M.	⓬ 4:00 P.M.
48	⓭ 4:00 P.M.	⓮ 4:00 P.M.
72	⓯ 4:00 P.M.	⓰ 4:00 P.M.
73	⓱ 3:00 P.M.	⓲ 5:00 P.M.

NOTE TO HOME
Students learn to identify the time after a specific number of hours have passed.

Literature Connection Read aloud *The Wonderful Counting Clock* by Cooper Edens to reinforce lesson concepts.

Social Studies Connection Display a large map of the United States. Discuss the time zones. Point to different states as you tell students how many hours later or earlier it is in one state than the other. For example, ask questions such as "If it is 9 A.M. in California, what time is it in New York?" (12 noon) Explain that it is three hours earlier in California than New York.

RETEACHING p. 33

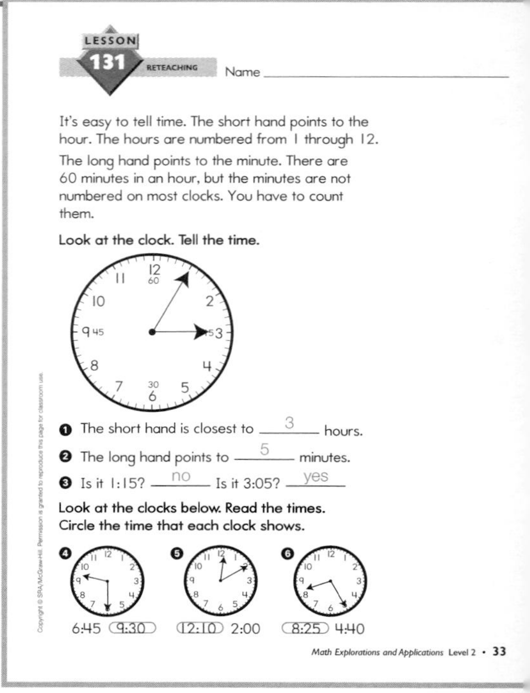
LESSON 131 RETEACHING Name ____________________

It's easy to tell time. The short hand points to the hour. The hours are numbered from 1 through 12.
The long hand points to the minute. There are 60 minutes in an hour, but the minutes are not numbered on most clocks. You have to count them.

Look at the clock. Tell the time.

❶ The short hand is closest to 3 hours.
❷ The long hand points to 5 minutes.
❸ Is it 1:15? no Is it 3:05? yes

Look at the clocks below. Read the times. Circle the time that each clock shows.

❹ 6:45 (9:30) ❺ (12:10) 2:00 ❻ (8:25) 4:40

Copyright © SRA/McGraw-Hill. Permission is granted to reproduce this page for classroom use.

Math Explorations and Applications Level 2 • 33

*available separately

◆ LESSON 131 Telling Time

⑲ Mrs. Fontana gave her class an assignment on Friday and said it must be finished in eight days.

What day of the week will that be? Saturday

⑳ What's wrong with Mrs. Fontana's assignment? She made the assignment due on a weekend when no one is in school.

COOPERATIVE LEARNING How many seconds does it take? First estimate. Write in the chart below. Then work in small groups to check.

㉑ Count to 50

㉒ Count to 25

㉓ Say the sentence at the bottom of the page clearly.

㉔ Say the sentence at the bottom of this page clearly twice.

Task	Estimate (in seconds)	Measure (in seconds)
㉑		
㉒		
㉓		
㉔		

She sells sea shells by the seashore.

NOTE TO HOME
Students practice solving problems involving elapsed time.

Then, use a clock to demonstrate the modular system of time. Show students that every 12 hours the hour has the same name but in the opposite part of the day. For example, if it is 10 A.M. now, in 12 hours it will be 10 P.M., and 12 hours ago it was 10 P.M. Show students that every 24 hours the time will have the same name.

Using the Student Pages Work with students to complete the first column on the table on page 295. Discuss how you arrive at each answer. Have students work independently to complete the second column.

Have students work in small groups to complete the problems and do the activity on page 296.

3 Wrap-Up 5 MINUTES

In Closing Ask students to explain their methods and give their results for solving the problems and doing the activity on page 296.

ALTERNATIVE ASSESSMENT **Performance Assessment** Observe which students can accurately keep time for the tasks their classmates perform in the activity on page 296.

Assessment Criteria

Did the student . . .

✓ correctly complete seven of the nine remaining blanks in the table on page 295?

✓ work cooperatively in groups to complete page 296?

PRACTICE p. 131

LESSON 131 PRACTICE Name ____________

The time now is 6:00 P.M.

Complete the chart. Show the time it was and the time it will be.

❶

Number of Hours	Time It Was	Time It Will Be
1	5:00 P.M.	7:00 P.M.
2	4:00 P.M.	8:00 P.M.
5	1:00 P.M.	11:00 P.M.
6	12:00 NOON	12:00 MIDNIGHT
12	6:00 A.M.	6:00 A.M.
24	6:00 P.M.	6:00 P.M.
36	6:00 A.M.	6:00 A.M.

❷ Lana goes to school at 8:00 A.M. She is in school for seven hours. What time is school over for the day? 3:00 P.M.

❸ Carlos goes to bed at 9:00 P.M. He sleeps for ten hours. What time does Carlos get up? 7:00 A.M.

❹ Mrs. Meyers goes to work at 10:00 A.M. She works for eight hours. What time is she done with work? 6:00 P.M.

ENRICHMENT p. 131

LESSON 131 ENRICHMENT Name ____________

❶ Write the times of your day in the chart below. Tell whether the time is A.M. or P.M.

What I Do	Time
wake up	
go to school	
eat lunch	
get home from school	
play with friends	
eat dinner	
go to bed	

Now imagine some different times and answer the questions.

❷ If you went to school five hours earlier, what time would that be? ________

❸ If you ate lunch three hours later, what time would you eat? ________

❹ If you got home from school 13 hours later, what time would you play? ________

❺ If you went to bed six hours earlier, what time would that be? ________

Answers will vary. Answers should reflect relationships to the times listed on the chart.

LESSON 132

Student Edition pages 297–298

Number Sentences

LESSON PLANNER

Objectives

- ▶ to introduce number sentences with mixed operations that result in the same solution
- ▶ to provide practice solving multistep word problems involving mixed operations

Context of the Lesson Number sentences and equations involving mixed operations are introduced in this lesson as a challenge. Mastery by all students is not expected.

Materials	Program Resources
none	Practice Master 132
	Enrichment Master 132
	For extra practice: CD-ROM* Lesson 132

1 Warm-Up

5 MINUTES

Problem of the Day Write this problem on the chalkboard: You had 75 cents on Monday. You spent 20 cents on Tuesday and 32 cents on Wednesday. Can you still buy a 25-cent bag of chips? Why? (No, because you only have 23¢ left.)

MENTAL MATH Have students add, subtract, multiply, or divide the following.

a. 30 ÷ 6 = (5) **b.** 12 ÷ 6 = (2)

c. 5 × 3 = (15) **d.** 6 × 3 = (18)

e. 14 − 8 = (6) **f.** 12 − 7 = (5)

2 Teach

Demonstrate Ask students to make up an addition problem with 10 as the answer. Focus on the fact that there is more than one correct answer. (6 + 4, 5 + 5, etc.) Repeat for subtraction, multiplication, and division. Then invite students to create several equations using mixed operations that produce the same answer. For example, 10 − 4 + 4 ; 2 × 3 + 4; 7 + 5 − 2.

LESSON 132

Name ______________________

Number Sentences

Write three number sentences that give the number shown as the answer.

Answers given are examples only.

10 ❶ 5 + 3 + 6 − 4 = 10

❷ 25 − 15 = 10

❸ 5 + 1 + 4 = 10

8 ❹ 16 − 8 = 8

❺ 18 − 5 − 5 = 8

❻ 6 + 4 − 2 = 8

5 ❼ 15 − 6 − 7 + 4 = 5

❽ 25 − 15 = 10

❾ 5 + 10 = 5

GAME

Play the "Harder What's the Problem?" game.

NOTE TO HOME
Students learn to create different number sequences with the same answer.

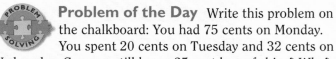

Literature Connection Read aloud *How the Second Grade Got $8,205.50 to Visit the Statue of Liberty* by Nathan Zimelman to reinforce lesson concepts.

RETEACHING

Show students step by step how to make different number sentences with an answer of 12:

Write: 3 + 4 + 5 = 12. Then ask for a number sentence with two numbers that equal 12. For example: 6 + 6 = 12.

Then take one number from a 6 and write: 5 + 6 + _____ = 12.

Ask what number is missing. Fill in the blank to show a new number sentence with an answer of 12: 5 + 6 + 1 = 12.

Repeat with simple subtraction examples.

*available separately

◆ LESSON 132 Number Sentences

Write a number sentence for each problem. Then solve the problem.

13. Mary earned $5 on Monday, $7 on Tuesday, and $4 on Wednesday. How many dollars did she earn in the three days? $ 16

14. Samantha had nine marbles. She bought two more. Then she gave three away. Then she got three more. How many marbles does Samantha have now? 11

15. John earned $3 a day for seven days. How many dollars has he earned? $ 21

16. There were 20 apples on the tree. Abby picked three apples a day for five days. One apple fell off the tree. How many apples are on the tree? 4

NOTE TO HOME
Students solve word problems.

PRACTICE p. 132

LESSON 132 PRACTICE Name ______

1. Write three number sentences that give the number shown as the answer.

An example for the first number has been done for you.

Answers shown are examples only.

(6) 8 + 2 + 1 − 5 = 6

10 ÷ 2 + 3 − 2 = 6

1 + 2 + 3 = 6

(12) 2 + 8 + 3 − 1 = 12

4 × 5 − 8 = 12

3 × 2 + 3 × 2 = 12

2. Jeremy has six marbles. His sister gives him four more marbles. Jeremy gives two marbles to a friend. He shares the remaining marbles equally with his sister. How many marbles do Jeremy and his sister each have? 4

3. Anne has 25¢. She finds a nickel. She then buys a pack of gum for 15¢ and a piece of candy for 3¢. How much money does Anne have left? 12¢

132 • *Math Explorations and Applications* Level 2

ENRICHMENT p. 132

LESSON 132 ENRICHMENT Name ______

Write a number sentence that shows how the numbers changed.

1. School was over for the day. Ms. Maloney's class had 28 children. After class she was having a meeting with nine children. When the bell rang, 14 children left the room right away. Then 11 more left a little later. Soon six of them came back.
28 − 14 − 11 + 6 = 9

2. There were 12 children remaining at the bus stop. At first there were 20 children. Parents picked up 11 of those children. Then four more children came, but one girl had to go back to get her books.
20 − 11 + 4 − 1 = 12

3. The bus was empty by 4:00 P.M. Earlier there were seven people on it. Then 12 children got on. At one stop six people got off. At another stop 13 people got off.
7 + 12 − 6 − 13 = 0

132 • *Math Explorations and Applications* Level 2

COOPERATIVE LEARNING **Using the Student Pages** Have students work in pairs to complete pages 297 and 298. Instruct partners that they must both agree on each number sentence before writing it. Encourage partners to discuss and share their reasoning for each answer.

Note: The solution to the last word problem on page 298 requires more than one operation. Because students have not yet formally learned solving mixed addition and multiplication problems, have them explain what they did and why.

GAME **Introducing the "Harder What's the Problem" Game** This game provides practice with making number sentences and using mathematical reasoning. Divide the class into small groups of two to five. Begin by having player 1 write a number sentence and show it to the other players in the group. Each player in turn then tries to write a different number sentence with the same answer. Each number sentence must have at least two operation signs (same or different). Players then check each others' number sentences for accuracy. Every player with a correct number sentence is a winner in the round. Players repeat the rounds, taking turns as the player who writes the first number sentence.

3 Wrap-Up (5 MINUTES)

In Closing Have partners share and compare their methods and answers to problems on pages 297–298.

ALTERNATIVE ASSESSMENT **Informal Assessment** Use students' responses to pages 297–298 to informally assess their understanding of creating different number sentences with the same solution.

Assessment Criteria

Did the student . . .

✓ write correct number sentences for the numbers on page 297?

✓ correctly solve three of the four problems on page 298?

✓ write accurate number sentences when playing the "Harder What's the Problem?" game?

LESSON 133

Student Edition pages 299–300

Grouping by Tens

LESSON PLANNER

Objective

▶ to introduce the strategy of grouping by ten for mental addition

Context of the Lesson As in Lesson 112, students learn additional shortcuts to help them use mental math in addition.

Materials	Program Resources
base-10 counters*	Number Cubes
	Thinking Story Book, pages 114–117
	Practice Master 133
	Enrichment Master 133
	For extra practice: CD-ROM* Lesson 133

1 Warm-Up

5 MINUTES

Problem of the Day Write this problem on the chalkboard: The sum of the numbers that the two hands of a clock are pointing to is six. If both hands are pointing to the same number, what time is it? (3:15)

MENTAL MATH Have students add, subtract, multiply, or divide the following using mental math.

a. 30 ÷ 5 = (6) **b.** 21 ÷ 3 = (7)

c. 5 x 5 = (25) **d.** 2 x 3 = (6)

e. 14 – 5 = (9) **f.** 13 – 7 = (6)

2 Teach

Demonstrate Write: 10 + 10 + 10 + 10 = on the chalkboard. Ask students to answer the problem using mental math. (40) Then write: 3 + 7 + 4 + 6 + 5 + 5 + 2 + 8 =. Ask how to add these numbers using mental math. Guide students to see that if they group the addends into sums of ten, the answer is the same as the answer to the first problem. (40) Give students several more problems that include sums of ten in the addend. Remind them that they

LESSON 133

Name ____________________

Grouping by Tens

Solve these problems. Use shortcuts if you can.

1. 1 + 3 + 7 + 9 = 20
2. 6 + 7 + 4 = 17
3. 4 + 6 + 7 + 3 + 5 + 5 + 9 + 1 = 40
4. 1 + 2 + 3 + 4 + 5 + 6 + 7 + 8 + 9 = 45
5. 1 + 3 + 5 + 7 + 9 = 25
6. 6 + 7 + 4 + 3 = 20
7. 8 + 2 + 9 + 1 + 7 + 3 + 6 + 4 + 10 = 50
8. 4 + 6 + 2 + 8 + 3 + 7 = 30
9. 7 + 3 + 1 + 9 + 5 + 5 + 3 = 33
10. 5 + 5 + 6 + 4 + 1 + 9 + 7 = 37

MATH JOURNAL

Ring one problem. In your Math Journal tell what shortcuts you used.

NOTE TO HOME
Students use patterns to add mentally.

GIFTED & TALENTED

Meeting Individual Needs

Challenge students to mentally solve this problem and explain how they did it: 1 + 2 + 3 + 4 + 5 + 6 + 7 + 8 + 9 = (45). Students can pair end numbers to make ten until they get to the middle: 1 + 9; 2 + 8; 3 + 7; and 4 + 6 = 10 + 10 + 10 + 10. Then add the 5: 40 + 5 = 45.

RETEACHING

Use base-10 materials to show how to regroup 1 + 4 + 9 + 6. Have students make groups of ten wherever they can (1 + 9 and 4 + 6), then trade them for a bunch of ten. Discuss how this makes it easier to add the numbers. Repeat for several similar problems.

*available separately

◆ **LESSON 133 Grouping by Tens**

Use the Mixed Practice on page 394 after this lesson.

Solve these problems. Use mental math where you can. Many are easier than they look.

11. $4 + 1 + 3 + 2 + 5 + 0 + 2 + 3 =$ **20**
12. $10 + 9 + 8 + 2 + 1 + 10 =$ **40**
13. $2 + 4 + 6 + 8 + 10 =$ **30**
14. $20 + 40 + 60 + 80 + 100 =$ **300**
15. $21 + 19 + 32 + 18 =$ **90**
16. $3 \times 3 \times 3 =$ **27**
17. $2 \times 2 \times 2 \times 2 =$ **8**
18. $9 + 1 + 10 + 19 + 1 + 30 =$ **70**
19. $42 + 8 + 5 + 6 + 5 + 4 =$ **70**
20. Tell the easy way to solve one of these problems.

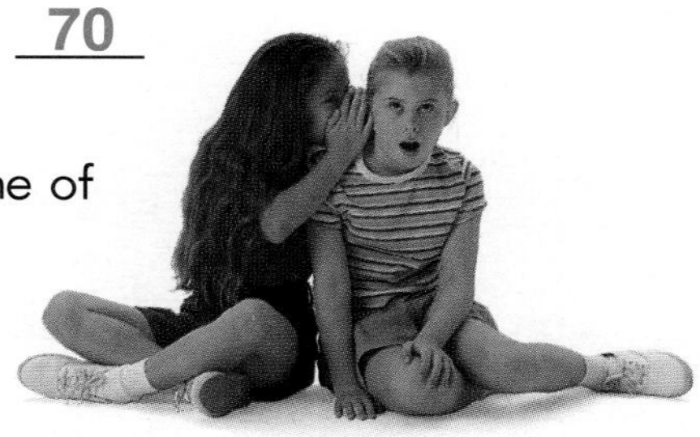

THINKING STORY

Talk about the Thinking Story "How Far Up, How Far Down?"

NOTE TO HOME
Students use mental math.

PRACTICE p. 133

LESSON 133 PRACTICE Name ____________

Solve. Use shortcuts if you can.

1. $2 + 8 + 6 + 4 =$ 20
2. $3 + 5 + 5 + 7 =$ 20
3. $5 + 4 + 1 + 10 + 3 =$ 23
4. $2 + 1 + 8 + 9 + 5 =$ 25
5. $6 + 3 + 5 + 5 + 7 + 4 =$ 30
6. $5 + 5 + 5 + 5 + 3 + 7 =$ 30
7. $10 + 6 + 3 + 4 + 7 + 5 =$ 35
8. $2 + 10 + 8 + 10 + 5 + 10 + 5 =$ 50
9. $1 + 5 + 2 + 7 + 3 + 5 + 9 + 8 =$ 40

Math Explorations and Applications Level 2 • 133

ENRICHMENT p. 133

LESSON 133 ENRICHMENT Name ____________

Figure out a rule that tells what number comes next. Write the number and the rule. The first problem has been done for you.

Number Pattern	Rule
837, 825, 813, 801, 789, **777**	**−12**
46, 77, 108, 139, 170, 201, 232	+31
37, 136, 235, 334, 433, 532, 631	+99
25, 39, 53, 67, 81, 95, 109	+14
793, 695, 597, 499, 401, 303, 205	−98
999, 924, 849, 774, 699, 624, 549	−75
437, 462, 487, 512, 537, 562, 587	+25
972, 947, 922, 897, 872, 847, 822	−25
412, 399, 386, 373, 360, 347, 334	−13

Make up your own problems. Try them on a friend.

Math Explorations and Applications Level 2 • 133

can add the numbers in any order. For example: 2 + 7 + 8 can be added as (2 + 8) + 7 or 10 + 7 = 17. Give students problems similar to those on the chalkboard and have them find, hide, and show their answers with their Number Cubes. Also give further practice with basic addition, subtraction, multiplication, and division facts.

Using the Student Pages Have students work independently to complete pages 299 and 300. Invite volunteers to share their answers to problem 20 on page 300.

Using the Thinking Story Read aloud the story "How Far Up? How Far Down?" on pages 114–117 of the Thinking Story Book. Stop and discuss the questions asked throughout the story.

3 Wrap-Up

5 MINUTES

In Closing Have students make up a problem with four or more addends that they can solve using mental math. Have students exchange and mentally solve each other's problems.

ALTERNATIVE ASSESSMENT

Informal Assessment Use students' responses to pages 299 and 300 to informally assess their understanding of mental math strategies.

Assessment Criteria

Did the student . . .

✓ correctly solve eight of ten problems on page 299?

✓ demonstrate an understanding of how and when to use mental math shortcuts?

✓ correctly solve eight of ten problems on page 300?

✓ participate in the Thinking Story discussion?

STORY 19

THINKING STORY

How Far Up? How Far Down?

"Don't forget, kids," said Ferdie and Portia's mother. "We've all got dentist appointments this afternoon. We're seeing a new dentist in an office downtown." Ferdie and Portia had forgotten about their appointments, but they were glad to be trying someone new.

It was easy finding the new dentist's building, but all the nearby parking places were filled. Because they were running late, Ferdie and Portia's mother decided to drop her children off at the front door while she looked elsewhere for a place to park.

Seeing a security guard at the door, she told her children to get directions to the dentist's office from him. "I'll meet you in the dentist's office in a couple of minutes," she said.

As Ferdie and Portia climbed out of the car, they looked up at the building. "This building has four floors," said Portia, counting to herself. "Our dentist's office is on the third floor across from the elevator," she reminded Ferdie. "Let's ask the guard where the elevator is."

The guard directed the children inside the lobby and to the right. Ferdie and Portia rushed into the elevator, each one hoping to push the elevator button first. But when they saw all the buttons, they stopped and wondered. The buttons looked like this:

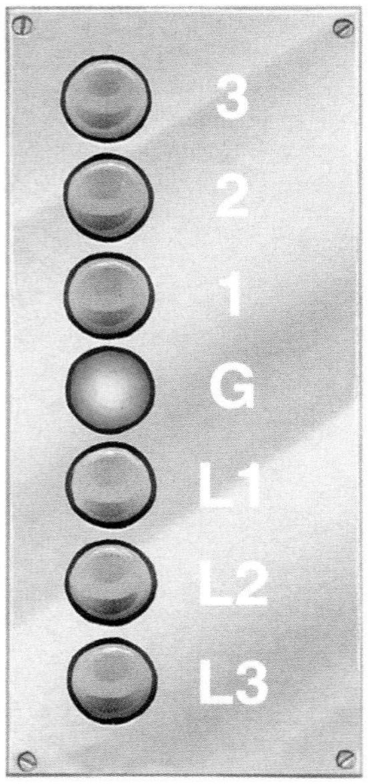

[Draw a picture of the buttons on the chalkboard.]

"I don't understand," said Portia. "The building has four stories, but there's no button for the fourth floor. And there are eight buttons altogether. This is a weird building."

What ideas do you have about what the different buttons stand for? The building has four floors up and four floors down.

While Ferdie and Portia were still trying to figure out the buttons, a woman got into the elevator and asked them what floor they wanted.

"Third," said Ferdie.

"Third up or third down?" the woman asked.

"Your guess is as good as mine," said Ferdie, who looked quite puzzled.

"We'll try third up," said the woman, "because that's the floor I'm going to."

The elevator began to rise. When the children got out on the third floor they went to the door right across from the elevator. There wasn't a sign on the door, so the children knocked. Soon an older woman came to the door. "I'm sorry, but this isn't a dentist's office," the woman said, "but there is a dentist on L3."

"Where is that, please?" asked Ferdie.

"That's six floors down from here," the woman said.

"This doesn't make any sense at all," Ferdie moaned, as they went back and got into the elevator again.

"The building is only four stories high. How can his office be six floors down from here?"

How could that be possible? There could be floors below ground.

"I have an idea," said Portia. "These buttons marked L1, L2, L3, and L4—maybe they're down below the ground. In fact, now I'm almost sure what G stands for."

"Let's press it and find out," said Ferdie.

Where do you think they will end up when they press button G? where they started

Ferdie pressed the button marked G and the elevator started down. When the door opened they found themselves on the floor where they had come in. "G must stand for 'ground,' " Ferdie said.

"But now we have to find the dentist's office," said Portia, "and the woman told us to try six floors down from where she was."

What button should they push to go six floors down from where the woman was? L3

◆ STORY 19 How Far Up? How Far Down?

They pressed L3 and the elevator started down again. “His office must be way down under the ground!” said Ferdie. “How strange.”

When the elevator let them out on floor L3, they checked the door just ahead of them. It was their new dentist’s office.

“We found it!” Ferdie cheered. “I hope Mom doesn’t get lost,” he said as they walked in.

“Where have you two been?” the children heard a voice say as they walked into the waiting room. It was their mother, who had begun to get nervous about their whereabouts.

After Ferdie and Portia explained what had happened, they noticed something peculiar about the waiting room. There was a large picture window at one end with a view of a lovely courtyard with flowers.

Do you find anything strange about that?
The office is below ground level.

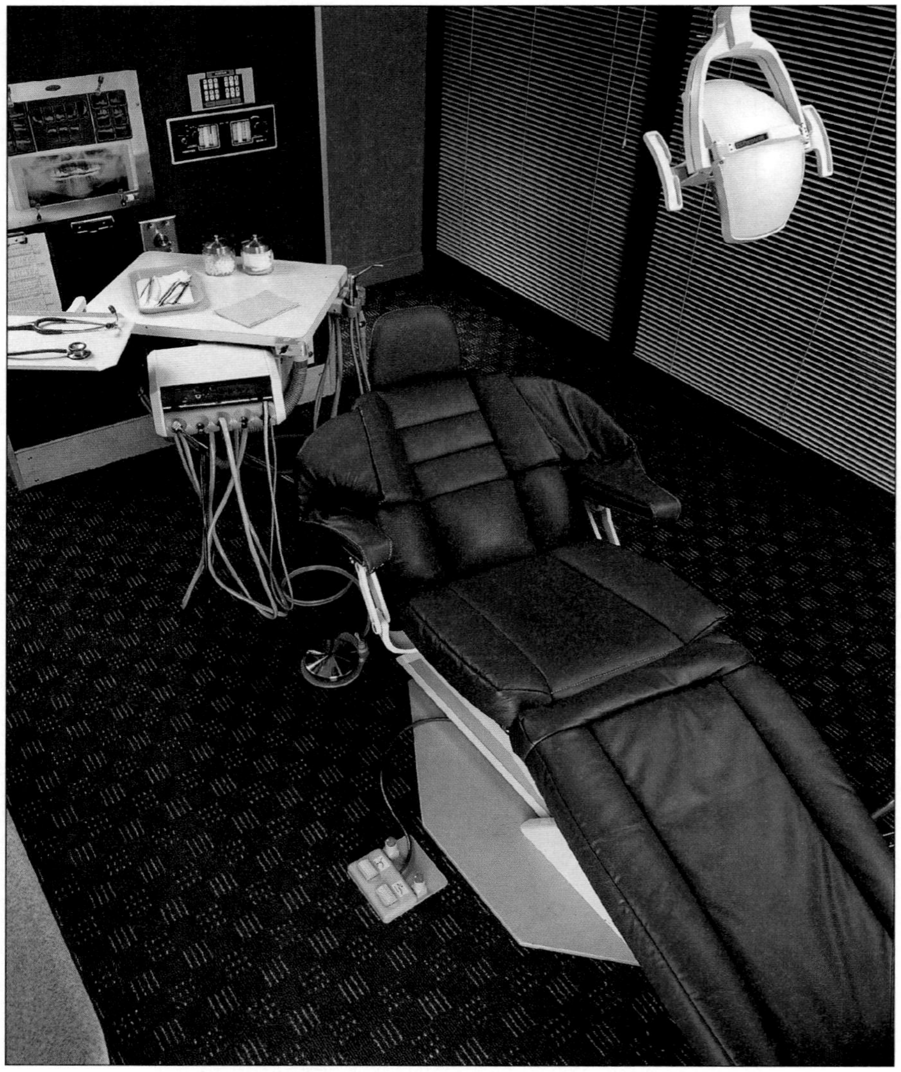

"How can we be three levels below the ground and see flowers and everything?" asked Ferdie.

The receptionist, who had overheard Ferdie's question, responded. "That's what's special about this building," she explained. "It's built on the side of a very steep hill. Where you came in was at the top of the hill. There are more floors below the top of the hill than there are above it."

After their examinations, Ferdie and Portia's mother had hers. This left the children with nothing to do while they waited. "You might want to visit the big aquarium on the second floor," said the dentist. "Some people visit this building just to see the aquarium," he explained.

"Can we, Mom?" the children asked their mother.

"It's fine with me," she said. "Just don't stay too long. I'll be finished here shortly."

Ferdie and Portia raced out the door. Portia waited for the elevator, but Ferdie said, "I'm not going to bother with that. This is floor 3 and the aquarium is on floor 2. That's just one floor down. I'll see you there, slowpoke!" And he rushed off down the stairs.

What floor will Ferdie find himself on? L4

Which way do you have to go to get to floor 2? up

How many floors away is it? five

When the elevator came, Portia pressed the button for floor 2. The elevator went up and up and let her out two floors above the top of the hill. She had a long time to look at the aquarium before Ferdie finally came puffing up the stairs.

How many floors up did Ferdie have to come? six, if he came straight up from L4

"Where have you been, slowpoke?" Portia asked Ferdie when she finally spotted him coming down the hall.

"Oh, just checking out the place," said Ferdie, still trying to catch his breath. "I've got this place all figured out," he said confidently.

"Sure you do, Ferdie," said Portia, knowing her brother all too well. "Come on. We better head back down to the dentist's office to meet Mom."

"Are you sure that's not up?" Ferdie asked, scratching his head.

. . . the end

LESSON 134

Student Edition pages 301–302

Multiplication and Division

LESSON PLANNER

Objectives

- ▶ to provide practice in multiplying and dividing
- ▶ to demonstrate how to identify patterns in determining a function machine rule

Context of the Lesson This lesson uses the function machine for multiplication and division as it was used in Lesson 11 to reinforce addition and subtraction skills.

Materials	**Program Resources**
none	Thinking Story Book, pages 118–119
	Reteaching Master
	Practice Master 134
	Enrichment Master 134
	For extra practice: CD-ROM* Lesson 134

1 Warm-Up

5 MINUTES

Problem of the Day Write this problem on the chalkboard: How many different pairs of factors can you write that have a product of 12? (1 × 12; 2 × 6; 3 × 4: 3 pairs of factors)

MENTAL MATH Have students write the relation signs <, >, or = for the following problems.

a. 2 x 3 ____ 4 (>) **b.** 12 ÷ 2 ____ 10 (<)

c. 4 x 5 ____ 25 (<) **d.** 14 ÷ 2 ____ 7 (=)

e. 6 x 3 ____ 12 (>)

2 Teach

Demonstrate You might want to repeat the activity you did in Lesson 11, but this time give the person in the box multiplication and division rules to apply rather than addition and subtraction rules.

LESSON 134

Name ____________________

Multiplication and Division

Find the function rules.

1
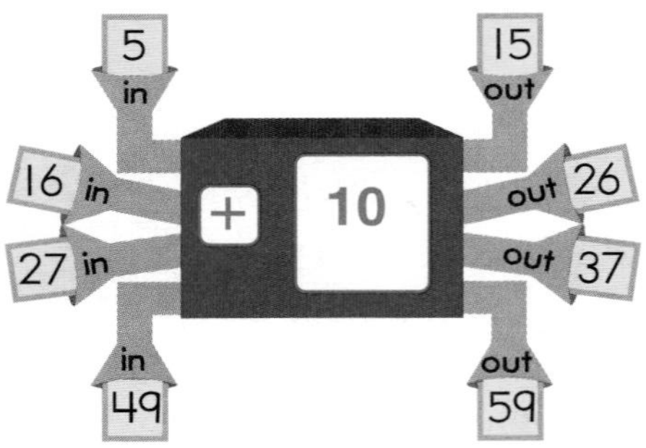

2
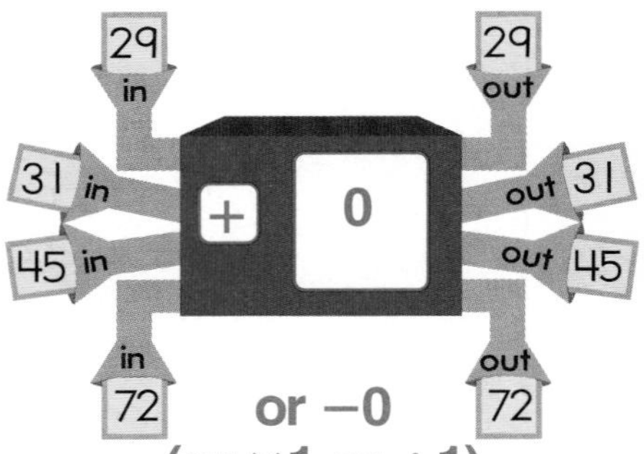

or −0
(or ×1 or ÷1)

3
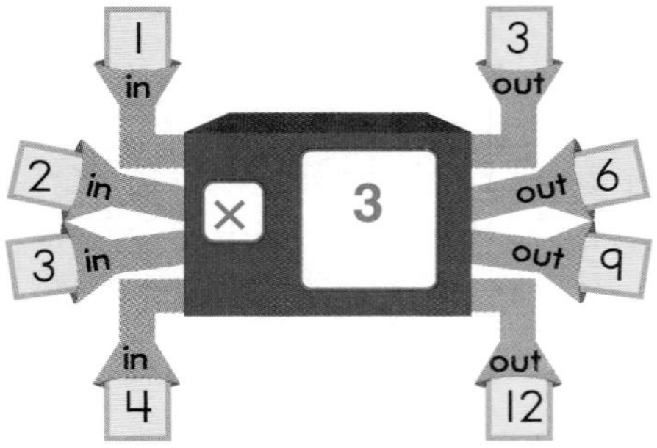

4
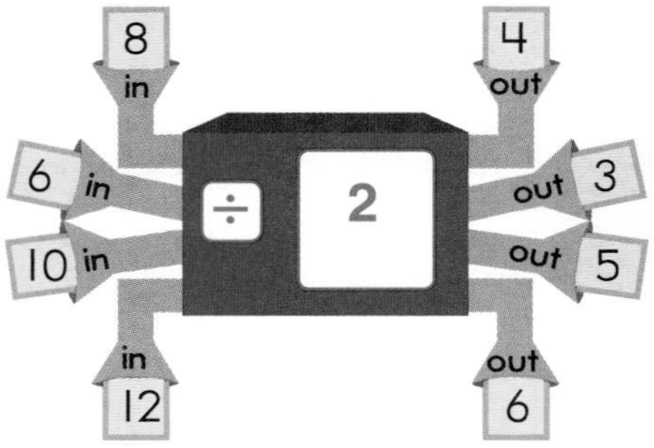

NOTE TO HOME
Students find multiplication and division function rules.

Literature Connection Read or invite students to read *Ready, Set, Hop* by Stuart J. Murphy to reinforce lesson concepts.

RETEACHING p. 34

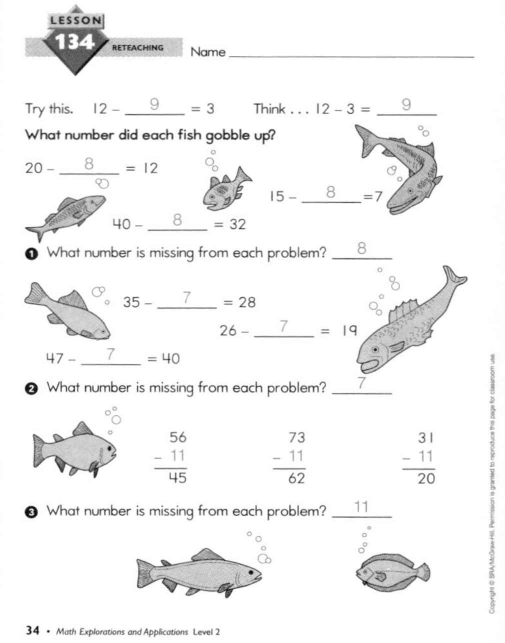
LESSON 134 RETEACHING Name ____________

Try this. 12 – 9 = 3 Think . . . 12 – 3 = 9

What number did each fish gobble up?

20 – 8 = 12
15 – 8 = 7
40 – 8 = 32

1 What number is missing from each problem? 8

35 – 7 = 28
26 – 7 = 19
47 – 7 = 40

2 What number is missing from each problem? 7

56 – 11 = 45
73 – 11 = 62
31 – 11 = 20

3 What number is missing from each problem? 11

34 • Math Explorations and Applications Level 2

*available separately

◆ **LESSON 134 Multiplication and Division**

COOPERATIVE LEARNING

Fill in the missing numbers. Then find the function rules.

5

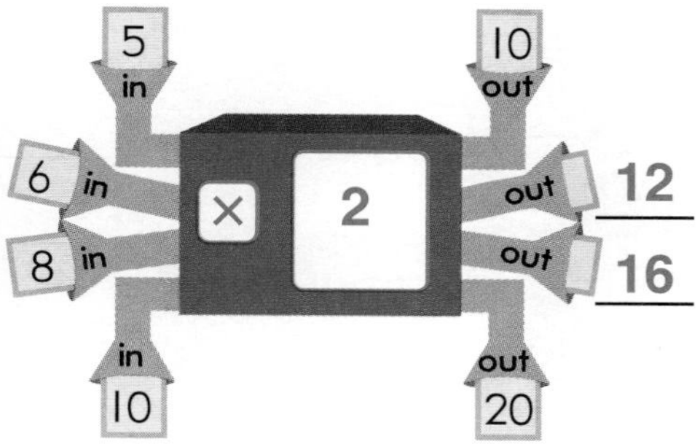

6

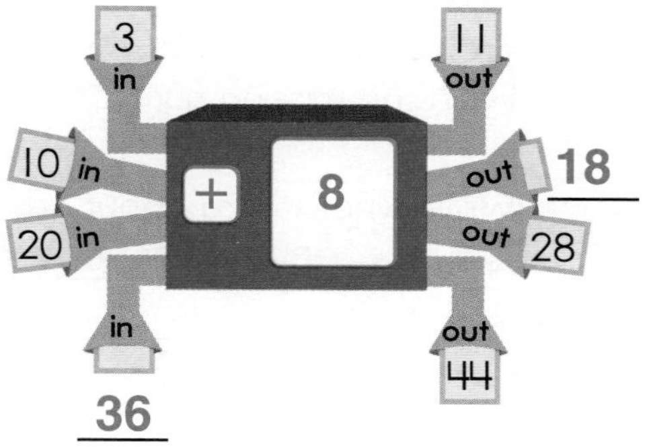

Make up your own function rule problems. Challenge a friend to solve them.

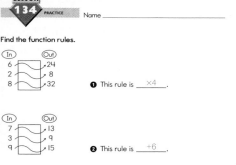

7

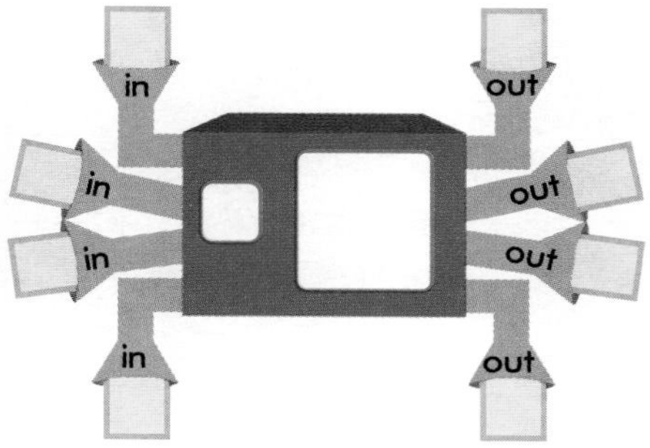

8

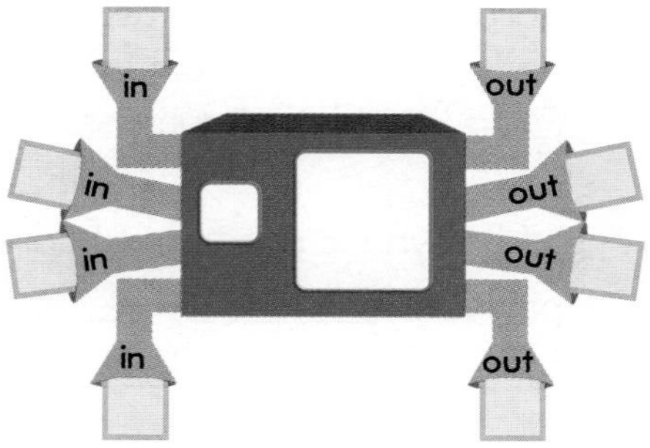

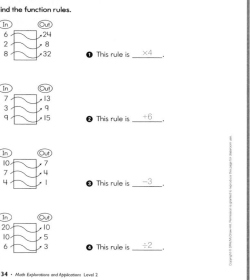

Function rules and answers will vary.

NOTE TO HOME
Students find and create function rules.

PRACTICE p. 134

LESSON 134 PRACTICE Name ______________

Find the function rules.

In	Out
6	24
2	8
8	32

1. This rule is ×4.

In	Out
7	13
3	9
9	15

2. This rule is +6.

In	Out
10	7
7	4
4	1

3. This rule is −3.

In	Out
20	10
10	5
6	3

4. This rule is ÷2.

ENRICHMENT p. 134

LESSON 134 ENRICHMENT Name ______________

Each of the four machines below has a rule. The products of that rule appear on the right. On the left write the numbers that went into the machines.

In	Rule	Out	In	Rule	Out
16	÷8	2	3	×4	12
56		7	5		20
0		0	40		160
40		5	1		4
80		10	7		28
17	−13	4	30	÷6	5
14		1	42		7
30		17	0		0
343		330	72		12
728		715	54		9

Using the Student Pages Work the first problem on each page with the class to be sure everyone understands what to do. Then have students work independently to complete the pages. When finished, have students share and compare answers. Encourage students to give reasons for the answers.

Using the Thinking Story Present one or two problems from those following "How Far Up? How Far Down?" on pages 118–119 of the Thinking Story Book.

3 Wrap-Up

5 MINUTES

In Closing Have students make up function rules and create a machine as shown on the pages. Students can then exchange problems and try to figure out each other's rules.

ALTERNATIVE ASSESSMENT

Portfolio Assessment Have students put the function machines they created in their Math Portfolios as an assessment of their understanding of function machines.

Assessment Criteria

Did the student . . .

- ✓ find all of the rules for the functions on pages 301–302?
- ✓ make up function rules and accurately make tables for them?
- ✓ accurately identify other students' function rules?

ESL

Meeting Individual Needs
At this time, consider reviewing key vocabulary with students who are just learning English. Before assigning pages 301–302, encourage students to explain in their own words what they think they must do. You can then work in small groups with students to help them complete the pages as the rest of the class works independently.

LESSON 135

Student Edition pages 303–304

Mixed Operations

LESSON PLANNER

Objectives

- to provide practice with basic operations using function machines
- to identify and demonstrate the use of composite functions (functions involving more than one operation)
- to provide practice identifying patterns

Context of the Lesson This lesson expands on the skills students learned and applied in Lesson 134.

Materials	Program Resources
none	Thinking Story Book, pages 118–119 Practice Master 135 Enrichment Master 135 For extra practice: CD-ROM* Lesson 135

1 Warm-Up 5 MINUTES

Problem of the Day Write this problem on the chalkboard: All of Mr. Ridman's cars' tires are flat, except one. He has six cars. How many new tires will he need? (23)

MENTAL MATH Have students add the following numbers, using mental math.

a. 2 + 6 + 8 = (16) **b.** 7 + 4 + 3 = (14)

c. 1 + 6 + 4 + 9 = (20) **d.** 3 + 4 + 5 + 7 + 6 + 5 = (30)

e. 6 + 7 + 4 = (17)

2 Teach

Demonstrate Ask students to find as many ways as they can to get from 6 to 11 using addition and subtraction. Guide them to see they can use a variety of operations just as they did when they wrote different number sentences

LESSON 135

Name ______________________

Mixed Operations

1. Kevin was making hard function problems. His rule is +9 − 4. Fill in the missing numbers.

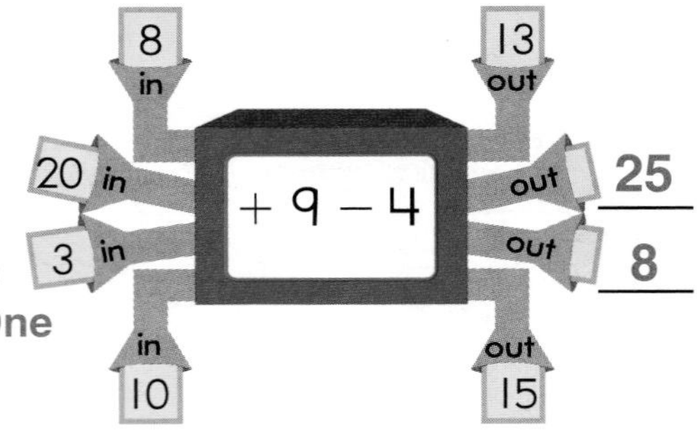

2. Write what's hard about Kevin's problem. **Answers will vary. One possible response is that there are two operations to perform.**

3. Write what's easy about Kevin's problem. **Answers will vary. One possible response is that you could simplify the rule to +5.**

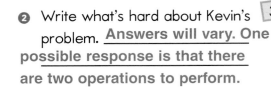

4. Lorena was also trying to make hard function problems. Here's her problem. The rule is × 3 − 1. Fill in the missing numbers.

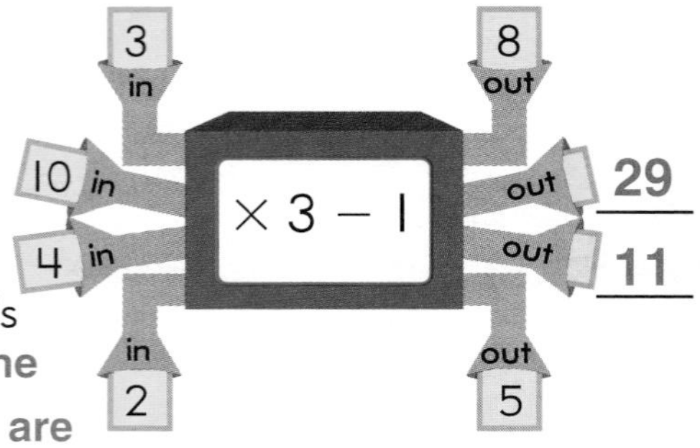

5. Write what's hard about Lorena's problem. **Answers will vary. One possible response is that there are two operations to perform.**

6. Write what's easy about Lorena's problem. **Answers will vary. One possible response is that the −1 operation is easy.**

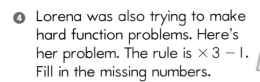

NOTE TO HOME
Students practice mixed operation function rules.

Literature Connection Read aloud "Alice's Adventures in Symbolville" in *Alice in Numberland: Fantasy Math* from Time-Life, Inc. to reinforce lesson concepts.

SPECIAL NEEDS Meeting Individual Needs
Students might not be able to find rules with more than one operation. Provide further practice using simple function tables as on pages 301–302.

RETEACHING

Reteaching composite function tables is not essential, because this lesson is an introduction to the concept. Students are not expected to master it at this time.

*available separately

◆ **LESSON 135 Mixed Operations**

COOPERATIVE LEARNING Work with a partner to solve these problems. They are harder than they look.

7

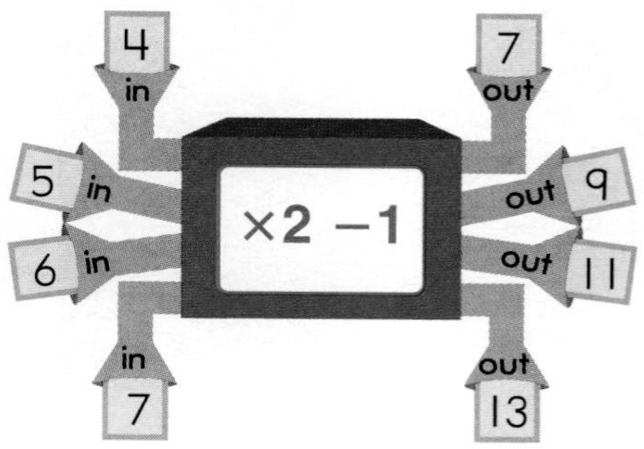

8

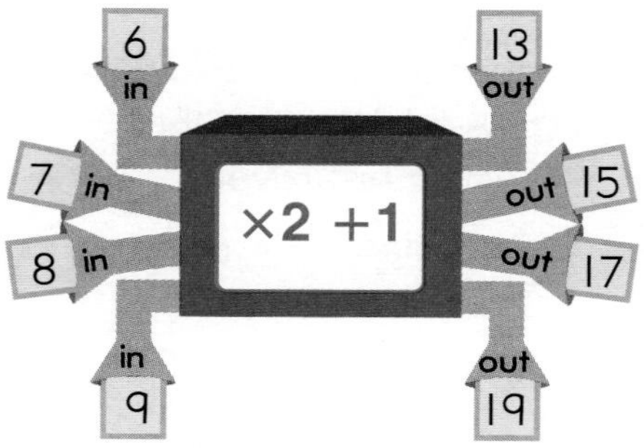

Make up your own function rule problems. Challenge a friend to solve them.

9

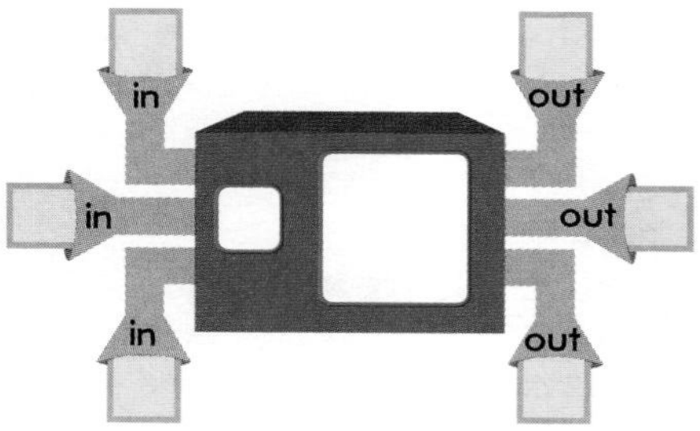

10

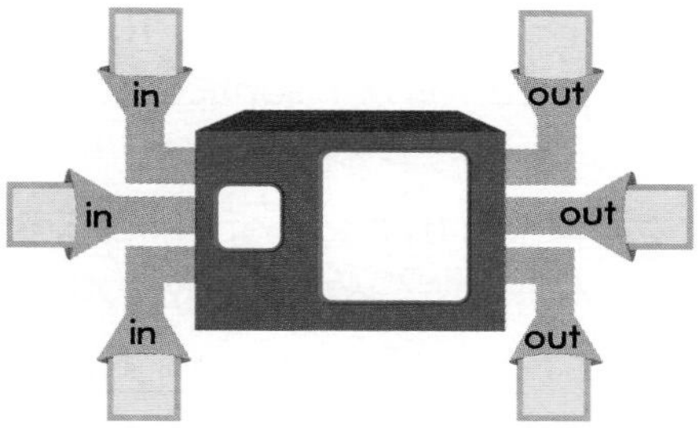

Function rules and answers will vary.

NOTE TO HOME
Students solve mixed operation function rules.

with the same solution. For example, they could start at six, then add seven and subtract two; start at six, then add eight and subtract three; or start at six, subtract three and add eight. Have students then find the rule that would only include one operation. (+ 5)

Using the Student Pages Discuss the opening problem on page 303. Point out that it is similar to the demonstration you just completed. Discuss the remainder of this page and work with students to complete it.

Then divide students into pairs and ask them to complete the problems on page 304. Have partners make up their own function problems and exchange them with other partners to solve. Explain that when classmates can predict the output for every possible input, they have identified the rule, even if it is in a different form. When students are finished, ask them to share their results.

Using the Thinking Story Present one or two new problems from those following "How Far Up? How Far Down?" on pages 118–119 of the Thinking Story Book.

3 Wrap-Up 5 MINUTES

In Closing Ask whether any students made up a rule that they think is very hard to guess. If so, challenge the whole class to identify it.

ALTERNATIVE ASSESSMENT

Portfolio Assessment Have students put the function tables they created in their Math Portfolios as an assessment of their understanding of composite function machines.

PRACTICE p. 135

LESSON 135 PRACTICE Name ____

Find the function rules.

In	Out
4	5
7	2
2	7

1 This rule is subtract the number from 9.

In	Out
8	8
4	4
0	0

2 This rule is +0. or −0 or ×1

In	Out
9	3
4	8
7	5

3 This rule is subtract the number from 12.

In	Out
7	11
2	6
5	9

4 This rule is +4.
5 Another rule is +6 −2.

ENRICHMENT p. 135

LESSON 135 ENRICHMENT Name ____

Solve these first. Use a calculator.

1 34 + 34 + 34 = 102
2 26 + 26 + 26 = 78
3 39 + 39 + 39 + 39 = 156
4 25 + 27 = 52
5 42 + 89 = 131
6 49 + 49 = 98
7 56 + 56 + 56 = 168

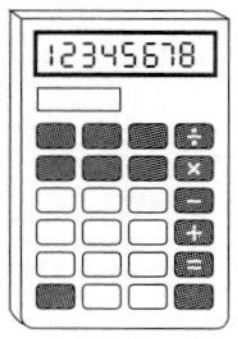

Solve these next. Do not use a calculator.

8 35 + 35 + 35 = 105
9 27 + 27 + 27 = 81
10 38 + 38 + 38 + 38 = 152
11 26 + 26 = 52
12 41 + 89 = 130
13 49 + 48 = 97
14 56 + 56 + 57 = 169

Assessment Criteria

Did the student . . .

✓ find all of the rules for the functions on pages 303–304?

✓ make up function rules and accurately make tables for them?

✓ accurately identify other students' function rules?

LESSON 136

Student Edition pages 305–306

More Mixed Operations

LESSON PLANNER

Objectives

- ▶ to provide practice in solving realistic problems involving composite function rules
- ▶ to provide practice in simplifying rules

Context of the Lesson This lesson presents realistic situations in which students can apply skills learned in Lesson 135.

Materials	Program Resources
calculators*	Number Cubes
graph paper (optional)	Thinking Story Book, pages 118–119
	Practice Master 136
	Enrichment Master 136
	For extra practice: CD-ROM* Lesson 136

1 Warm-Up

5 MINUTES

Problem of the Day Write this problem on the chalkboard: If you ride your bike three miles every weekday and four miles each day on the weekend, how many miles do you ride your bike each week? (23 miles per week)

MENTAL MATH Write the following problems on the chalkboard and have students fill in the blanks using their Number Cubes to respond.

a. 2 × _____ = 14 (7)

b. 21 ÷ _____ = 7 (3)

c. _____ × 4 = 16 (4)

d. _____ × 3 = 15 (5)

e. 24 ÷ _____ = 6 (4)

f. _____ ÷ 4 = 3 (12)

LESSON 136

Name ____________________

More Mixed Operations

1. Matt charges $3 per hour for mowing lawns, plus $1 to cover the cost of his travel.

   Complete the chart to show how much Matt should collect.

Matt's Lawn Mowing Service Price Chart

Hours	1	2	3	4	5	6	7	8
Charge (dollars)	4	7	10	13	16	19	22	25

2. Allison also mows lawns. She estimates how long a job will take. Then she charges a fixed price for her service.

3. Which method of charging is fairer, Matt's or Allison's? Write why you think so. Matt's method is fairer because he works by the hour. Allison may overestimate the time needed to mow a lawn and might therefore overcharge a customer.

NOTE TO HOME
Students complete function charts.

Social Studies Connection Have students draw maps on graph paper using each square as a block. Have them all start at the same point. Then give them directions such as: Go north three blocks. Go west two blocks. Go south three blocks. Go east four blocks. After students draw their maps, ask them to rewrite the directions to make them simpler. (In this case, starting at the same point and simply going east two blocks will put them at the same end point as the complicated directions.)

RETEACHING

Change the data in problem 1 on page 305 and have students write a table for each change you make. Discuss how these changes affect the final charge each time. For example, have Matt charge $2 per hour and $2 for the cost of travel. Be sure students understand that he does not charge $2 travel cost for each hour he mows the lawn, but charges this fee only once per job. Repeat several times with different data.

*available separately

◆ LESSON 136 More Mixed Operations

Answers are examples only.

Kenji was busy making hard function problems. Use a calculator to see why they really aren't so hard. Then write an easy rule for each problem.

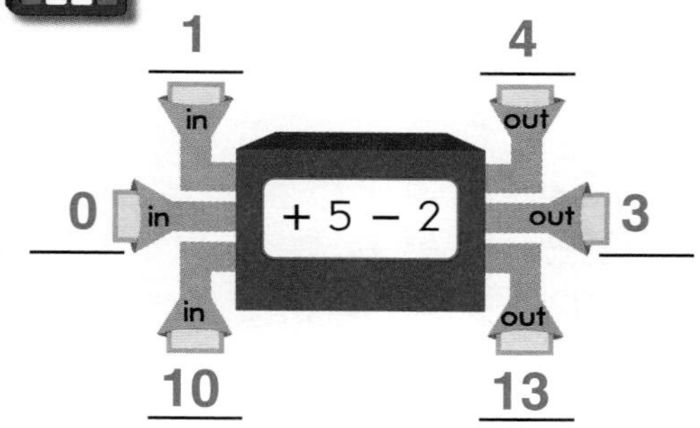

❹ The easy rule is +3.

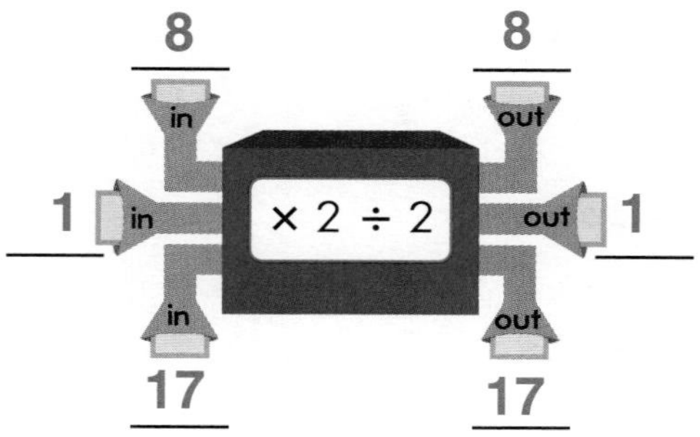

❺ The easy rule is ×1, ÷1, +0 or 0.

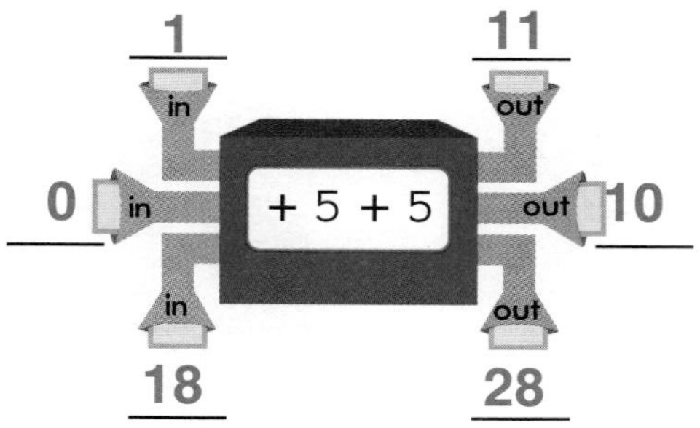

❻ The easy rule is +10.

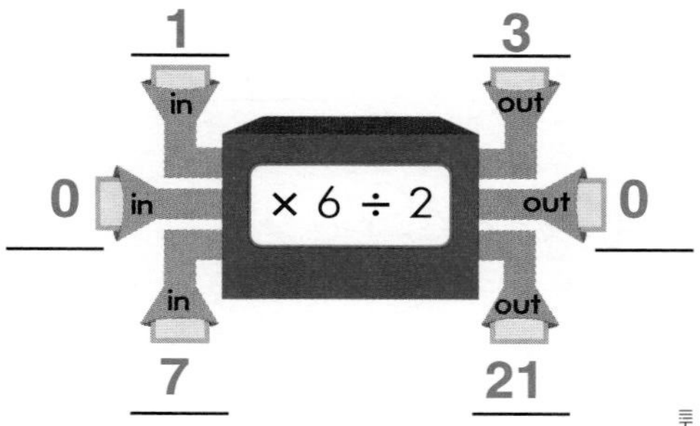

❼ The easy rule is ×3.

NOTE TO HOME
Students find function rules.

PRACTICE p. 136

LESSON 136 PRACTICE Name ________________

Fill in the missing numbers.

❶

+20	
In	Out
30	50
50	70
10	30
80	100

❷

−6	
In	Out
8	2
12	6
21	15
10	4

❸

+8	
In	Out
10	18
7	15
5	13
2	10

What is the rule? Write it in the space.

❹

In	Out
130	80
100	50
80	30
60	10

Rule is −50.

❺

In	Out
4	10
8	14
14	20
20	26

Rule is +6.

❻

In	Out
0	30
60	90
90	120
110	140

Rule is +30.

136 • *Math Explorations and Applications* Level 2

ENRICHMENT p. 136

LESSON 136 ENRICHMENT Name ________________

Look at the distance guide for the Centerville bus station. Write what route or routes each driver might have taken. Keep in mind that each driver started in Centerville, but not all of the drivers returned to Centerville.

Town	Distance from Centerville (in kilometers)
Oak Park	3
Baytown	7
Clayton	8
Rockport	2

❶ Paula drove 23 kilometers.
Paula drove to Clayton and back, then to Baytown, or to Rockport and back five times, then to Oak Park.

❷ Kirby drove 13 kilometers.
Kirby drove to Oak Park and back, then to Baytown.

❸ Dayton drove 19 kilometers.
Dayton drove to Clayton and back, then to Oak Park or to Rockport and back four times, then to Rockport, or to Oak Park and back twice and then to Baytown.

❹ Kavri drove 12 kilometers.
Kavri drove to Rockport and back three times, or to Oak Park and back twice.

136 • *Math Explorations and Applications* Level 2

❷ Teach

Demonstrate Copy the following table on the chalkboard:

Input	Output
3	6
4	8
5	10

Tell students the rule for this table is × 4 ÷ 2. Work the problems with the students. Then ask how to simplify this rule and still make it work for the table on the chalkboard. Guide students to see that × 2 will give the same results.

Using the Student Pages Discuss and complete page 305 with the class. Ask whether Matt's rule can be simplified. (no) When discussing which method of charging is more fair, accept all reasonable answers. Have students use their calculators to complete page 306 independently.

Using the Thinking Story Present one or two new problems from those following "How Far Up? How Far Down?" on pages 118–119 of the Thinking Story Book.

❸ Wrap-Up

5 MINUTES

In Closing Ask students to describe another realistic situation by using a hard function rule similar to the one on page 305.

SELF ASSESSMENT

Have students show "thumbs up" if they feel they understand composite function rules and "thumbs down" if they do not.

Assessment Criteria

Did the student . . .

✓ give sensible responses to the questions on page 305?

✓ find three of four easy rules on page 306?

LESSON 137

Student Edition pages 307–308

Keeping Sharp

LESSON PLANNER

Objective

- ▶ to provide review and practice of two-digit addition and subtraction

Context of the Lesson This lesson provides review of two-digit addition and subtraction in preparation for three- and four-digit addition and subtraction.

Materials	Program Resources
base-10 counters (optional)	Reteaching Master Practice Master 137 Enrichment Master 137 For extra practice: CD-ROM* Lesson 137

1 Warm-Up

5 MINUTES

Problem of the Day Write this problem on the chalkboard: What two numbers each have two digits whose sum is seven and difference is one? (43 and 34)

MENTAL MATH Have students add or subtract the following using mental math.

a. 20 + 15 = (35)

b. 45 – 20 = (25)

c. 30 + 22 = (52)

d. 67 – 20 = (47)

e. 33 + 40 = (73)

2 Teach

Using the Student Pages Have students explain how to solve problem 1 on page 307 and problem 11 on page 308. Then have them complete the pages independently.

LESSON 137

Name ______________________

Keeping Sharp

$$\begin{array}{r} {\scriptstyle 1} \\ 27 \\ +\ 65 \\ \hline 2 \end{array}$$

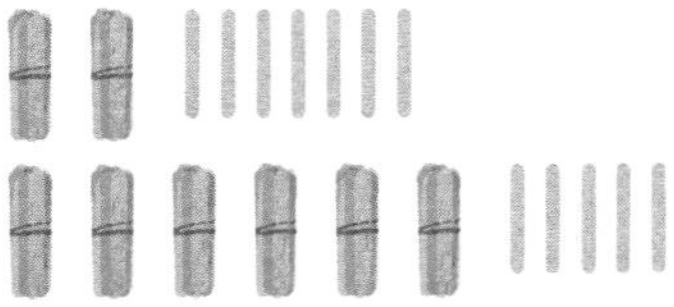

$$\begin{array}{r} {\scriptstyle 1} \\ 27 \\ +\ 65 \\ \hline 92 \end{array}$$

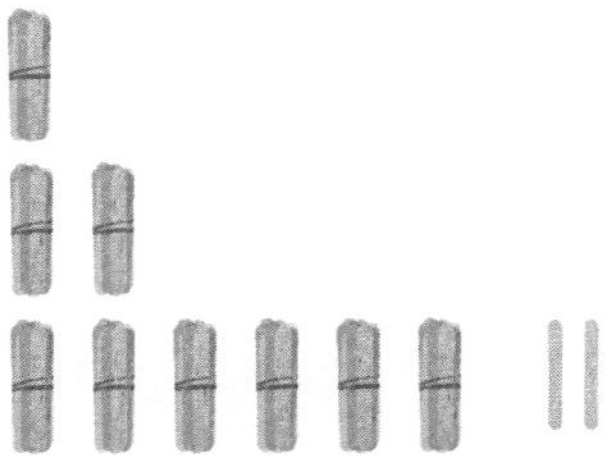

Solve.

1. 54 + 35 = 89
2. 65 + 28 = 93
3. 35 + 35 = 70
4. 24 + 24 = 48
5. 82 + 9 = 91
6. 26 + 27 = 53
7. 25 + 29 = 54
8. 43 + 37 = 80
9. 99 + 34 = 133
10. 32 + 27 = 59

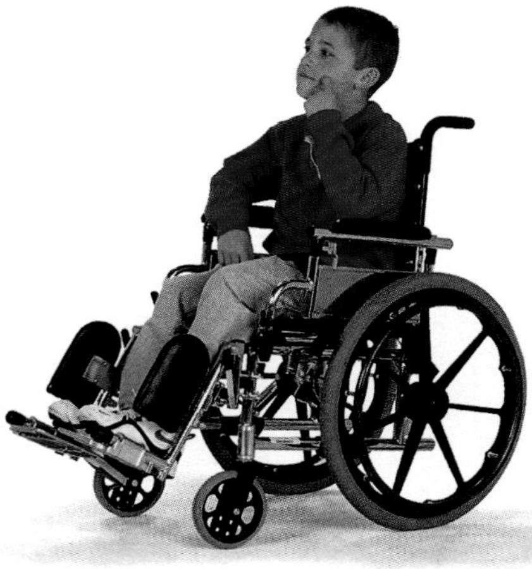

NOTE TO HOME
Students review two-digit addition.

RETEACHING p. 35

LESSON 137 RETEACHING Name ______________________

Solve. Write the letter for each problem above its answer in the puzzle below.

E $\begin{array}{r} 53 \\ +\ 28 \\ \hline \end{array}$ I $\begin{array}{r} 64 \\ +\ 16 \\ \hline \end{array}$ R $\begin{array}{r} 45 \\ +\ 34 \\ \hline \end{array}$

G $\begin{array}{r} 72 \\ -\ 46 \\ \hline \end{array}$ T $\begin{array}{r} 58 \\ -\ 31 \\ \hline \end{array}$ O $\begin{array}{r} 85 \\ -\ 57 \\ \hline \end{array}$

H $\begin{array}{r} 56 \\ +\ 27 \\ \hline \end{array}$ R $\begin{array}{r} 50 \\ -\ 25 \\ \hline \end{array}$ U $\begin{array}{r} 39 \\ +\ 43 \\ \hline \end{array}$

Y It is sunny and 91° degrees in Washington, D. C.
It is rainy and 67° in Hartford, Connecticut.
How much warmer is it in Washington, D. C.?
24°

Math Puzzle

Y	O	U'	R	E		R	I	G	H	T!
24	28	82	25	81		79	80	26	83	27

*available separately

◆ LESSON 137 Keeping Sharp

3 13
~~4~~~~3~~
− 25

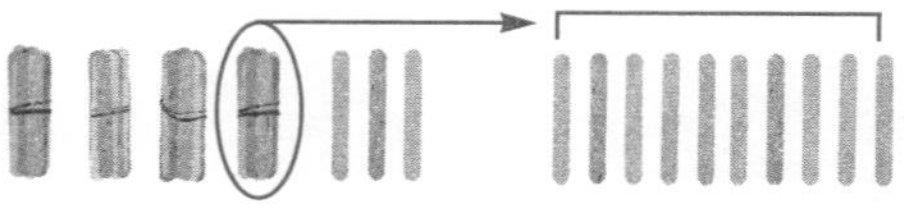

3 13
~~4~~~~3~~
− 25
18

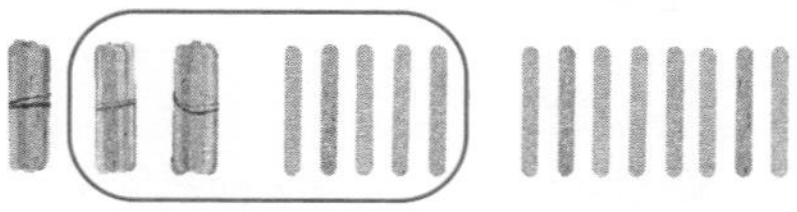

Solve.

⑪ 82 − 75 = 7

⑫ 23 − 23 = 0

⑬ 45 − 17 = 28

⑭ 62 − 25 = 37

⑮ 50 − 25 = 25

⑯ 54 − 29 = 25

⑰ 65 − 18 = 47

⑱ 65 − 19 = 46

⑲ 56 − 29 = 27

⑳ 83 − 27 = 56

㉑ 46 − 23 = 23

㉒ 97 − 34 = 63

㉓ 62 − 32 = 30

㉔ 50 − 35 = 15

㉕ 93 − 86 = 7

㉖ 27 − 8 = 19

NOTE TO HOME
Students review two-digit subtraction.

PRACTICE p. 137

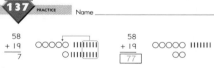

LESSON 137 PRACTICE Name ____________

58 + 19 = 7 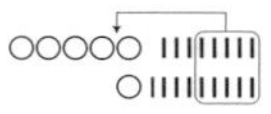 58 + 19 = 77 

Solve.

❶ 34 + 47 = 81 ❷ 62 + 25 = 87 ❸ 16 + 29 = 45 ❹ 98 + 24 = 122 ❺ 86 + 8 = 94

❻ 32 + 32 = 64 ❼ 45 + 18 = 63 ❽ 33 + 9 = 42 ❾ 25 + 25 = 50 ❿ 36 + 41 = 77

32 − 17  32 − 17 = 15 

⓫ 74 − 26 = 48 ⓬ 60 − 35 = 25 ⓭ 37 − 18 = 19 ⓮ 88 − 46 = 42 ⓯ 26 − 26 = 0

⓰ 34 − 18 = 16 ⓱ 45 − 16 = 29 ⓲ 65 − 49 = 16 ⓳ 54 − 21 = 33 ⓴ 38 − 29 = 9

Math Explorations and Applications Level 2 • **137**

ENRICHMENT p. 137

LESSON 137 ENRICHMENT Name ____________

The ancient Romans used letters, called Roman numerals, to show numbers. They then used some simple addition and subtraction to group letters to show other numbers. Look at the chart for the letters and the numbers they stand for.

Letter	Number
I	1
V	5
X	10
L	50
C	100

If the value of a letter is greater, you add another letter to its right. For example for 7 (5 + 1 + 1), you write VII in Roman numerals.

If the value of a letter is less, you add a letter to its left. For example for 4 (5 − 1), you write IV in Roman numerals.

Write the numbers for these Roman numerals.

❶ XIV 14 ❷ XXIX 29 ❸ LXVI 66

❹ XC 90 ❺ XLVIII 48 ❻ XXX 30

Write the Roman numerals for these numbers.

❼ 8 VIII ❽ 25 XXV ❾ 96 XCVI

❿ 88 LXXXVIII ⓫ 39 XXXIX ⓬ 53 LIII

Math Explorations and Applications Level 2 • **137**

③ Wrap-Up (5 MINUTES)

In Closing Ask students to identify any problems they were able to solve mentally. For example, some students might suggest that 99 + 34 is the same as 100 + 33; 82 + 9 is the same as 81 + 10; 54 − 29 is the same as 55 − 30; and 65 − 19 is the same as 66 − 20.

ALTERNATIVE ASSESSMENT

Informal Assessment Use students' answers to pages 307 and 308 as an informal assessment of their ability to add and subtract two-digit numbers.

Assessment Criteria

Did the student . . .

✓ correctly complete 20 of the 26 problems on pages 307–308?

✓ use shortcuts when adding and subtracting?

SPECIAL NEEDS

Meeting Individual Needs

Students who are still having difficulty adding and subtracting two-digit numbers might benefit from using base-10 materials to complete these pages.

Whenever possible, addition and subtraction. should be taught at about the same time so that learners can contrast the two and so that problems can be presented that are not all solved by using the same operation.

—Stephen S. Willoughby,
Mathematics Education for a Changing World

LOOKING AHEAD You will need 600–1000 craft sticks for Lesson 139.

LESSON 138

Student Edition pages 309–310

Counting Through 1000

LESSON PLANNER

Objective

▶ to demonstrate how to count, say, write, and recognize numbers through 1000

Context of the Lesson This is the first of two lessons on counting through 1000.

Materials	**Program Resources**
index cards, 5 x 8 (50)	Reteaching Master
index cards, 5 x 4 (20)	Practice Master 138
	Enrichment Master 138
	For extra practice: CD-ROM* Lesson 138

1 Warm-Up

5 MINUTES

Problem of the Day Write the following problems on the chalkboard and have students complete each sentence:

a. A penny is to a dime as a _____ is to a dollar. (dime)

b. 57 is to 75 as 15 is to _____ (51)

c. 12 inches is to a foot as 36 inches is to _____ (a yard or 3 feet)

MENTAL MATH Have students add by grouping tens using mental math:

a. 1 + 2 + 7 + 5 + 5 = (20)

b. 2 + 2 + 1 + 5 = (10)

c. 7 + 1 + 1 + 1 + 2 + 8 = (20)

d. 1 + 9 + 3 + 7 + 5 = (25)

e. 8 + 2 + 5 + 5 + 10 = (30)

2 Teach

Demonstrate Distribute index cards to groups of students. Have them work together to draw 100 cookies on each of 30 large index cards. Then have them draw ten sets of 10 cookies and one set of each number 1 through 9 cookies on the smaller cards.

LESSON 138

Name ____________________

Counting Through 1000

Write how many cookies are in each group.

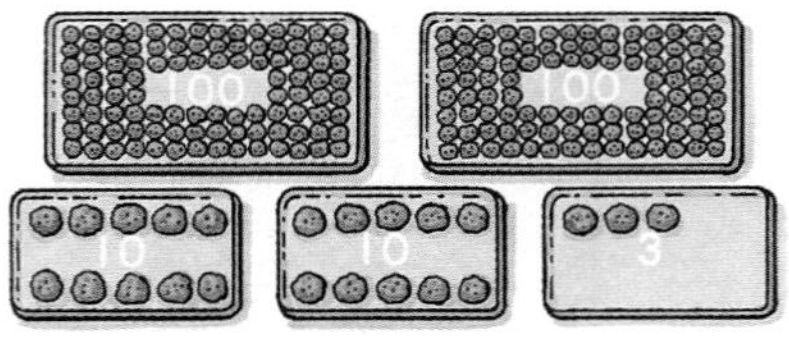

❶ 223

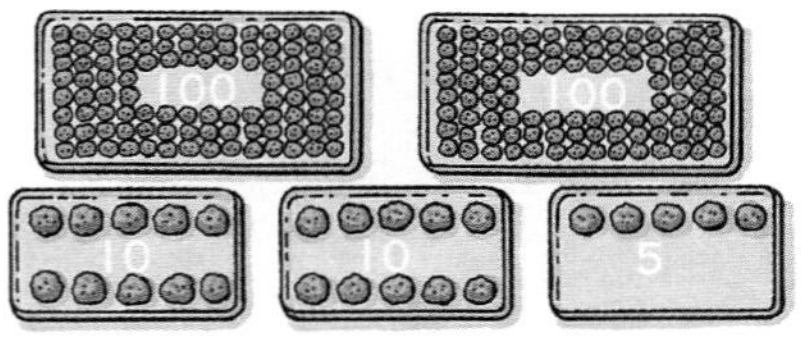

❷ 225

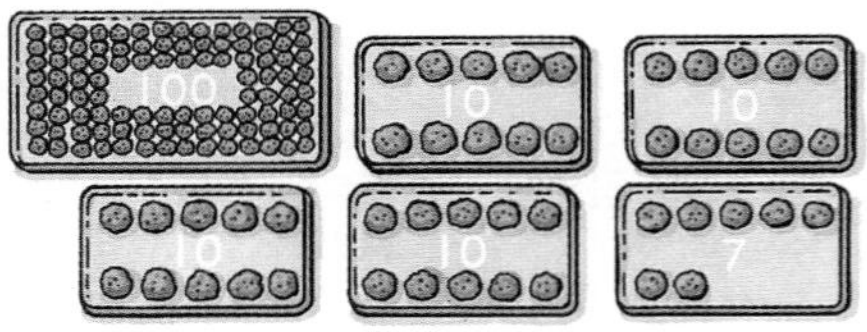

❸ 147

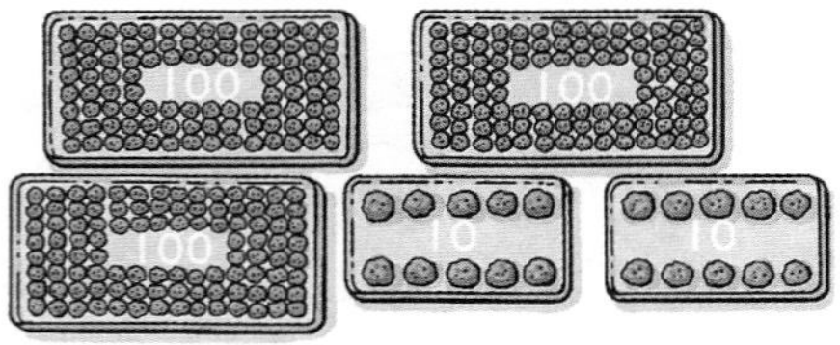

❹ 320

GAME Play the "Harder Counting and Writing Numbers" game.

NOTE TO HOME
Students learn to count hundreds, tens, and ones.

Literature Connection Read or invite students to read *Numbers* by John Reiss to reinforce lesson concepts.

RETEACHING p. 36

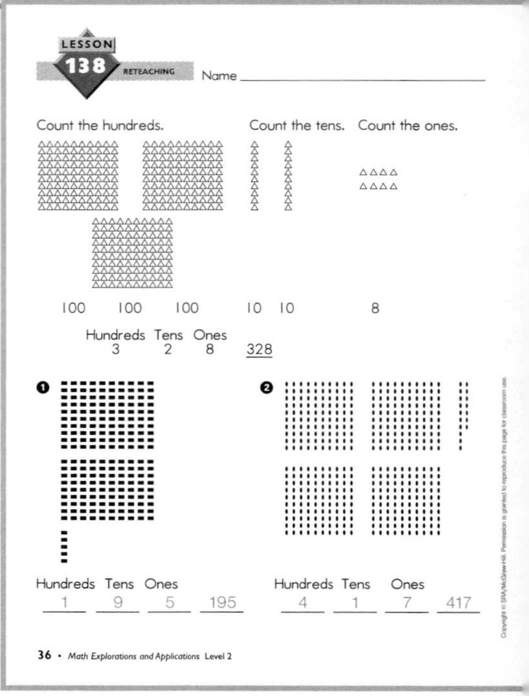
LESSON 138 RETEACHING Name ____________

Count the hundreds. Count the tens. Count the ones.

100 100 100 10 10 8

Hundreds 3 Tens 2 Ones 8 328

❶ Hundreds 1 Tens 9 Ones 5 195

❷ Hundreds 4 Tens 1 Ones 7 417

36 • Math Explorations and Applications Level 2

*available separately

◆ LESSON 138 Counting Through 1000

Use the Mixed Practice on page 395 after this lesson.

Draw pictures to show the number of cookies. Instead of drawing 100 cookies on some sheets, you may write 100 like this. [100]

❺ 253 cookies

100	100	10	10	10	10	10	1	1	1

❻ 307 cookies

100	100	100	1	1	1	1	1	1	1

Fill in the missing numbers.

❼	132	133	134	135	136	137	138
❽	177	178	179	180	181	182	183
❾	398	399	400	401	402	403	404

NOTE TO HOME
Students show and count numbers from 0–1000.

PRACTICE p. 138

LESSON 138 PRACTICE Name ____________

Draw pictures to show the number of triangles. Instead of drawing 100 triangles, you may write 100 like this: [100].

❶ 265 triangles

[100] [10] [10] [10]
[100] [10] [10] [10] △ △ △ △ △

❷ 318 triangles

△ △ △ △
[100] [100] [100] [10] △ △ △ △

❸ 804 triangles

[100] [100] [100] [100]
[100] [100] [100] [100] △ △ △ △

Fill in the missing numbers.

❹

145	146	147	148	149	150
151	152	153	154	155	156

❺

258	259	260	261	262	263
264	265	266	267	268	269

❻

630	631	632	633	634	635
636	637	638	639	640	641

138 • *Math Explorations and Applications* Level 2

ENRICHMENT p. 138

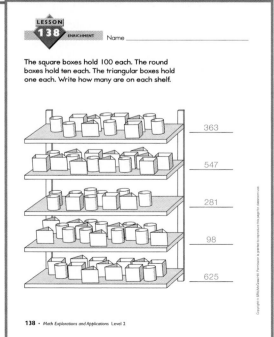

LESSON 138 ENRICHMENT Name ____________

The square boxes hold 100 each. The round boxes hold ten each. The triangular boxes hold one each. Write how many are on each shelf.

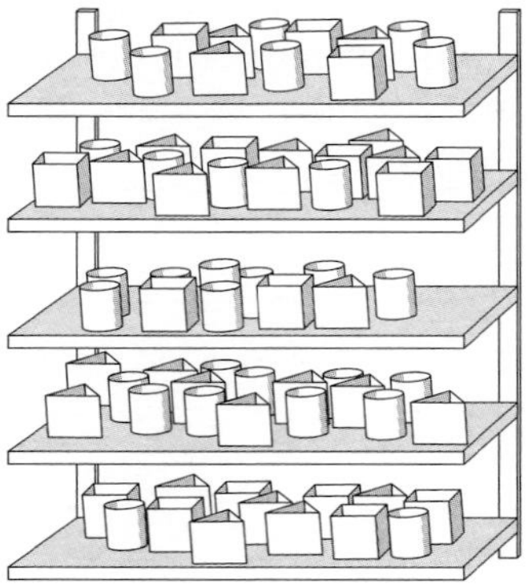

363

547

281

98

625

138 • *Math Explorations and Applications* Level 2

Using the "cookie sheets," work with students to count and name various numbers of cookies. For example, have students show 100 cookies using the ten cards with 10 cookies on each. Then show one set of 100. Ask students which set shows more.

Continue by having students show numbers using the "cookie sheets." Then write a three-digit number, such as 123, on the chalkboard. Guide students to see that this number is read as one hundred twenty-three and means one hundred, two tens, and three ones. Repeat with other three-digit numbers.

Using the Student Pages Assign pages 309–310 for students to complete on their own. You might want to work the first problem on each page with the class.

GAME **Introducing the "Harder Counting and Writing Numbers" Game** Demonstrate this game in which students count and write in the 0–1000 range. The lead player chooses a starting and ending number between 0 and 1000 (for example, 285 and 325). He or she then counts on and writes either 1, 2, or 3 numbers from the starting number (for example, 286, 287). The other player counts on and writes 1, 2, or 3 more numbers. The players take turns counting on and writing. The player who counts to and writes the ending number wins.

3 Wrap-Up

5 MINUTES

In Closing Have students write and draw a model of the number 541.

ALTERNATIVE ASSESSMENT

Performance Assessment Observe students as they play the game to see whether they can correctly write and count the numbers.

Assessment Criteria

Did the student . . .

✓ correctly complete the problems on page 309?

✓ correctly complete four of five problems on page 310?

✓ correctly write and count on when playing the game?

LESSON 139

Student Edition pages 311–312

Numbers Through 1000

LESSON PLANNER

Objectives

- ✓ to assess students' ability to count from 0 through 1000
- ▶ to introduce estimating numbers from 0 through 1000 on a number line
- ▶ to introduce estimating the number of items in various sets
- ▶ to provide practice with addition and subtraction facts

Context of the Lesson This is the second of two lessons on counting through 1000. It contains Mastery Checkpoint 17 for this skill.

Materials

craft sticks (600–1000)

rubber bands

Program Resources

Practice Master 139

Enrichment Master 139

Assessment Master

For extra practice:
CD-ROM* Lesson 139

1 Warm-Up

5 MINUTES

Problem of the Day Write the following problem on the chalkboard: Tanya rode her bike 18 miles on Monday and 15 miles on Tuesday. Kenya rode 30 miles in the two days. Who rode farther? How much farther? (Tanya, by three miles)

MENTAL MATH Have students add the following by grouping tens and using mental math:

a. 6 + 9 + 4 = (19)

b. 1 + 3 + 7 + 9 + 9 = (29)

c. 5 + 5 + 6 + 4 + 4 = (24)

d. 2 + 2 + 2 + 2 + 2 + 10 = (20)

2 Teach

Demonstrate Draw a number line on the chalkboard with 0 and 1000 as endpoints. Have students label the number line with three-digit numbers. Then, have them show various numbers, such as 500, 200, 300, and 700. Then ask what number might fall between 200 and 300. Have students label that number (for example, 250). Continue for other numbers.

LESSON 139

Name ______________________

Numbers Through 1000

Count up or count down. Fill in the missing numbers.

1	97	98	99	100	101	102	103	104
2	706	707	708	709	710	711	712	713
3	843	842	841	840	839	838	837	836
4	704	703	702	701	700	699	698	697
5	413	412	411	410	409	408	407	406

COOPERATIVE LEARNING Do the "How Many Sticks?" activity.

6 Guess ________

7 First estimate ________

8 Last estimate ________

Answers will vary.

NOTE TO HOME
Students practice counting from 0–1000.

RETEACHING

Use the cookie sheet cards students made in Lesson 138 to review counting sets of items between 100 and 1000. Have students work in groups. First, write a number on the chalkboard. Have the groups show the number using the cookie sheet cards. Then use the cards to show various sets and have students write out the number.

PRACTICE p. 139

LESSON 139 PRACTICE Name ______________________

Count up or count down. Fill in the missing numbers.

1	517	518	519	520	521	522	523	524
2	236	237	238	239	240	241	242	243
3	174	173	172	171	170	169	168	167
4	869	870	871	872	873	874	875	876
5	646	645	644	643	642	641	640	639
6	383	384	385	386	387	388	389	390
7	96	97	98	99	100	101	102	103
8	762	761	760	759	758	757	756	755
9	104	103	102	101	100	99	98	97
10	498	499	500	501	502	503	504	505

*available separately

◆ LESSON 139 Numbers Through 1000

Check your math skills.

9. 2 + 3 = 5
10. 2 + 4 = 6
11. 3 + 2 = 5
12. 13 − 7 = 6
13. 5 − 1 = 4
14. 8 + 2 = 10
15. 6 + 2 = 8
16. 5 + 1 = 6
17. 7 − 3 = 4
18. 8 − 3 = 5
19. 10 + 5 = 15
20. 3 + 7 = 10
21. 6 + 6 = 12
22. 9 − 3 = 6

Number correct ☐

NOTE TO HOME
Students review addition and subtraction skills.

ENRICHMENT p. 139

LESSON 139 ENRICHMENT Name ______

Fill in the missing number in each line.

26	30	34	38	42	46	50
200	198	196	194	192	190	188
814	813	812	811	810	809	808
97	100	103	106	109	112	115
615	610	605	600	595	590	585

Write three lines of numbers in a pattern, leaving blanks that a friend can fill in.

______

______

______

Math Explorations and Applications Level 2 • 139

ASSESSMENT p. 56

UNIT 4 Mastery Checkpoint 17 Numerical sequence (0–1000) (Lesson 139)

Name ______

The student demonstrates mastery by correctly filling in all of the missing numbers.

Count up or count down. Fill in the missing numbers.

1	66	67	68	69	70	71	72	73
2	397	398	399	400	401	402	403	404
3	553	552	551	550	549	548	547	546
4	803	802	801	800	799	798	797	796
5	213	212	211	210	209	208	207	206
6	117	118	119	120	121	122	123	124
7	300	299	298	297	296	295	294	293
8	666	667	668	669	670	671	672	673

56 • Math Explorations and Applications Level 2

COOPERATIVE LEARNING **Introducing the "How Many Sticks?" Activity** Place between 600 and 1000 craft sticks in a pile on the floor or a table. Have students guess how many sticks there are. They can record their guesses on the bottom of page 311. Discuss guesses. Next have students work together using rubber bands to group the sticks into bunches of 10. Place the sticks in a pile again in bunches of 10 with any ones left over. Have students write their first estimates in the space on page 311 and discuss whether this estimate is more accurate than their guess and why. Finally have students group the sticks in bunches of 100 with any tens and ones left over and place them again in one pile. Have them write their last estimates on the page, discuss them, then count the hundreds, then tens, then ones.

Using the Student Pages Have students complete page 311 on their own. Point out that they must count down for the last three rows of missing numbers. You might want to use page 312 as a speed test. Give students about four to five minutes to complete the work. Then, as you read out the correct answers, have students correct their papers and write the number of correct answers at the bottom of the page.

3 Wrap-Up

5 MINUTES

In Closing Have students write the numbers between 688 and 705 in order.

Mastery Checkpoint 17

By this time students should be able to write the numbers between 0 and 1000 in correct ascending or descending order. You can use their answers to page 311 or Assessment Master 56 to assess students. Results of this assessment may be recorded on the Mastery Checkpoint Chart.

Assessment Criteria

Did the student . . .

- ✓ write the numbers in a reasonable place on the number line?
- ✓ correctly fill in 18 of the 19 spaces on page 311?
- ✓ correctly complete all of the problems on page 312?

LESSON 140

Student Edition pages 313–314

Introducing Three-Digit Addition

LESSON PLANNER

Objectives

- to prepare students to add two three-digit numbers
- to demonstrate working with money up to $1000

Context of the Lesson This is the introductory lesson for three-digit addition, which is the topic of the next several lessons.

Materials
base-10 materials

Program Resources
Practice Master 140
Enrichment Master 140
For extra practice:
CD-ROM* Lesson 140

1 Warm-Up

5 MINUTES

Problem of the Day Write the following problem on the chalkboard: A video game costs $25. If six friends chip in $4 each, can they buy the game? Why or why not? (No, because they will only have $24.)

MENTAL MATH Have students multiply and divide using mental math:

a. 5 x 7 = (35)
b. 3 x 8 = (24)
c. 4 x 8 = (32)
d. 4 x 1 = (4)
e. 2 x 2 = (4)
f. 9 x 10 = (90)
g. 4 ÷ 2 = (2)

2 Teach

Demonstrate Review with students the addition algorithm for adding problems. Use this problem and others similar to it to work through with the class.

$$\begin{array}{r} {}^{1}4 \\ +\ 8 \\ \hline 12 \end{array}$$

LESSON 140

Name ______________________

Introducing Three-Digit Addition

9 tens and 3 tens = 1 hundred and 2 tens

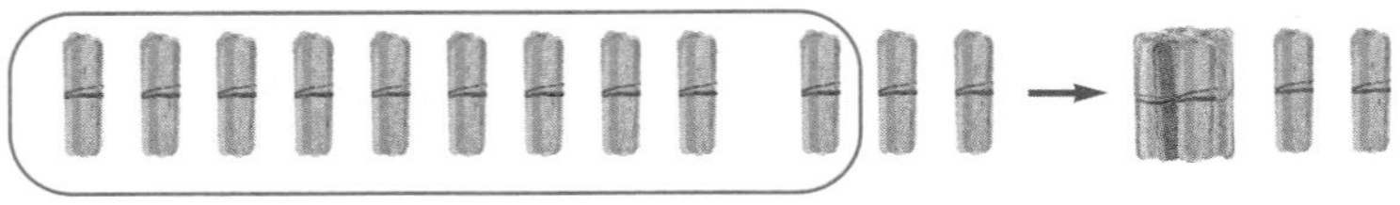

Write the correct number less than ten in each blank.

1. 7 and 6 = 1 tens and 3
2. 7 tens and 6 tens = 1 hundreds and 3 tens
3. 5 and 7 = 1 tens and 2
4. 5 tens and 7 tens = 1 hundreds and 2 tens
5. 3 and 8 = 1 tens and 1
6. 3 tens and 8 tens = 1 hundreds and 1 tens
7. 6 and 9 = 1 tens and 5
8. 6 tens and 9 tens = 1 hundreds and 5 tens

NOTE TO HOME
Students regroup tens and hundreds.

SPECIAL NEEDS

Meeting Individual Needs

Work with students in small groups, using base-10 materials, to first solve addition problems adding units, such as 8 + 5 and 7 + 6. When students understand when to regroup, have them use the base-10 materials to solve the same problems, but add tens rather than units: 8 tens + 5 tens and 7 tens + 6 tens. Discuss how the methods are similar.

RETEACHING

Review the meaning of place value by having students first practice problems similar to the following:

14 = _____ tens and _____ (1, 4)

140 = _____ hundreds, and _____ tens, and_____ (1, 4, 0)

After reviewing place value, use base-10 materials to add units + units and tens + tens, demonstrating how to regroup when necessary.

*available separately

◆ LESSON 140 Introducing Three-Digit Addition

Write the correct number less than ten in each box.

9 tens [1] 7 + 6 = [3]

10 tens [1] 5 + 8 = [3]

11 tens [1] 8 + 8 = [6]

12 hundreds [1] 7 tens + 6 tens = [3] tens

13 hundreds [1] 5 tens + 8 tens = [3] tens

14 hundreds [1] 9 tens + 7 tens = [6] tens

15 hundreds [1] 3 tens + 8 tens = [1] tens

16 tens [1] 8 + 3 = [1]

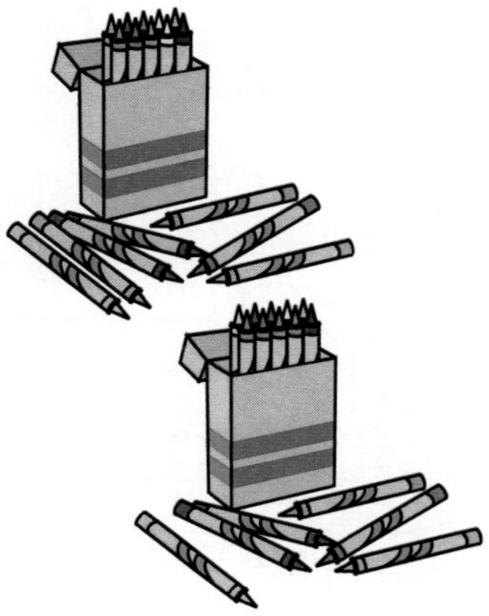

NOTE TO HOME
Students add numbers and regroup.

PRACTICE p. 140

LESSON 140 PRACTICE Name ____________

Write the correct number less than ten in each blank.

1. 5 and 9 = 1 tens and 4 ones
5 tens and 9 tens = 1 hundreds and 4 tens
2. 8 and 8 = 1 tens and 6 ones
8 tens and 8 tens = 1 hundreds and 6 tens
3. 4 and 7 = 1 tens and 1 ones
4 tens and 7 tens = 1 hundreds and 1 tens
4. 6 and 8 = 1 tens and 4 ones
6 tens and 8 tens = 1 hundreds and 4 tens
5. 8 and 5 = 1 tens and 3 ones
8 tens and 5 tens = 1 hundreds and 3 tens
6. 3 and 9 = 1 tens and 2 ones
3 tens and 9 tens = 1 hundreds and 2 tens

140 • *Math Explorations and Applications* Level 2

ENRICHMENT p. 140

LESSON 140 ENRICHMENT Name ____________

Ring the rolls that show the amount of the number at the end of the line.

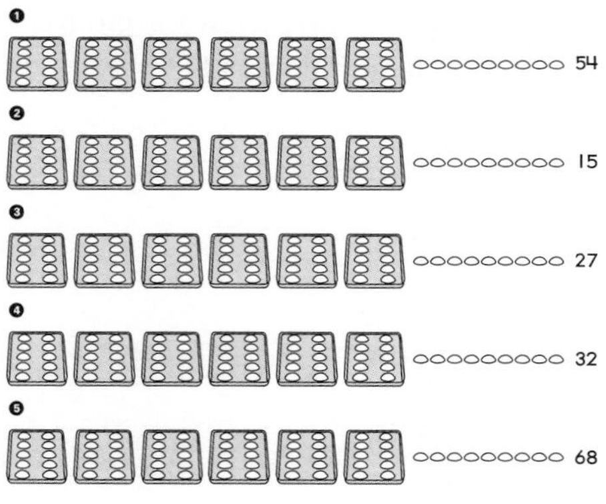

Students should ring: 5 pans of rolls, 4 singles
1 pan of rolls, 5 singles
2 pans of rolls, 7 singles
3 pans of rolls, 2 singles
6 pans of rolls, 8 singles

140 • *Math Explorations and Applications* Level 2

Remind students that they can write the number of tens from the addition in the ones column at the top of the tens column. Then explain that the same thing can be done when adding tens by adding the number of hundreds from the tens column. Present the following problem to demonstrate this:

$$\begin{array}{r} {}^{1}4 \text{ tens} \\ +\ 8 \text{ tens} \\ \hline 12 \text{ tens} \end{array}$$

Give students additional practice by having them complete problems similar to the following:

5 tens + 8 tens = ____ hundred and ____ tens (1, 3)

3 tens + 9 tens = ____ hundred and ____ tens (1, 2)

Using the Student Pages Discuss the problem at the top of page 313 with students. Be sure everyone understands why three tens and nine tens equal one hundred and two tens. Have students complete the remaining problems on pages 313 and 314 independently. Allow students to use base-10 materials, such as the cookie sheet cards they made, to help them complete these pages.

3 Wrap-Up 5 MINUTES

In Closing Have students draw a model to show 5 tens + 9 tens.

ALTERNATIVE ASSESSMENT

Informal Assessment Use students' responses to pages 313–314 to assess their understanding of regrouping tens to hundreds.

Assessment Criteria

Did the student . . .

✓ correctly complete seven of eight problems on page 313?

✓ correctly fill in 14 of the 16 boxes on page 314?

LESSON 141

Student Edition pages 315–318

Three-Digit Addition

LESSON PLANNER

Objectives

- to review the relationship among units, tens, and hundreds
- to demonstrate how this relationship relates to the addition of two three-digit numbers

Context of the Lesson The idea of adding three-digit numbers is introduced here and is continued in the next lesson.

Materials	Program Resources
base-10 materials*	"Rumage Sale" Game Mat
cookie sheet models	Practice Master 141
play money*	Enrichment Master 141
	For extra practice: CD-ROM* Lesson 141

1 Warm-Up

5 MINUTES

Problem of the Day Write the following problem on the chalkboard: John is not shorter than Craig. Craig is shorter than Sam, who is shorter than John. Write the boys' names in order from shortest to tallest. (Craig, Sam, John)

MENTAL MATH Write the following problems on the chalkboard, and have students fill in the blanks.

a. 7 + ____ = 11 (4)

b. 6 + ____ = 15 (9)

c. ____ − 4 = 6 (10)

d. ____ − 7 = 5 (12)

e. ____ × 6 = 18 (3)

f. 24 ÷ ____ = 4 (6)

LESSON 141

Name ______________________________

Three-Digit Addition

Use sticks to add.

325 + 289 = __?__ Write what you did.

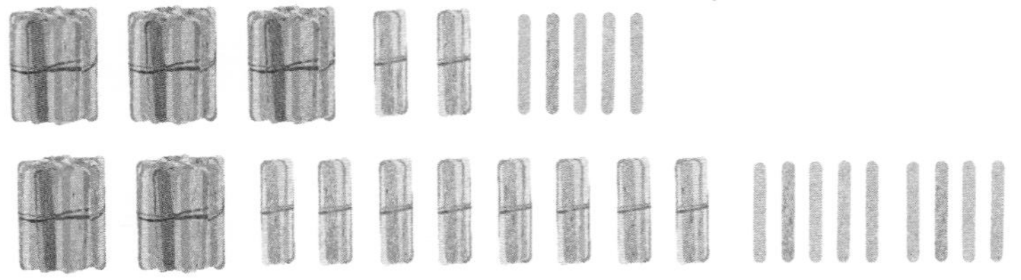

325
\+ 289

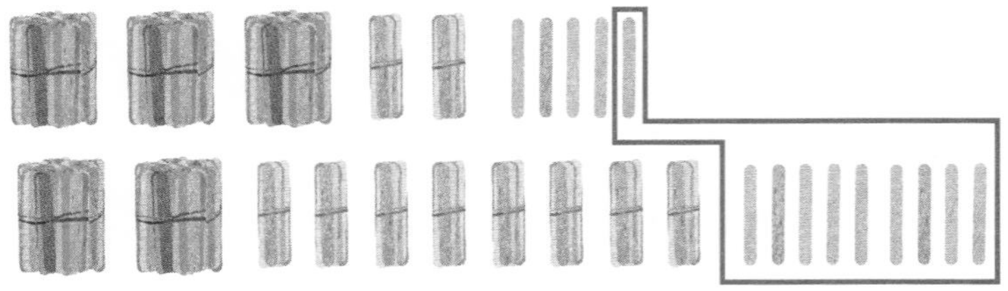

1
325
\+ 289
4

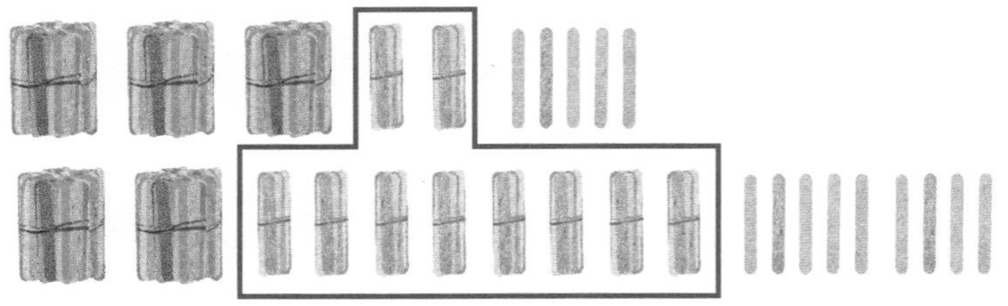

1 1
325
\+ 289
14

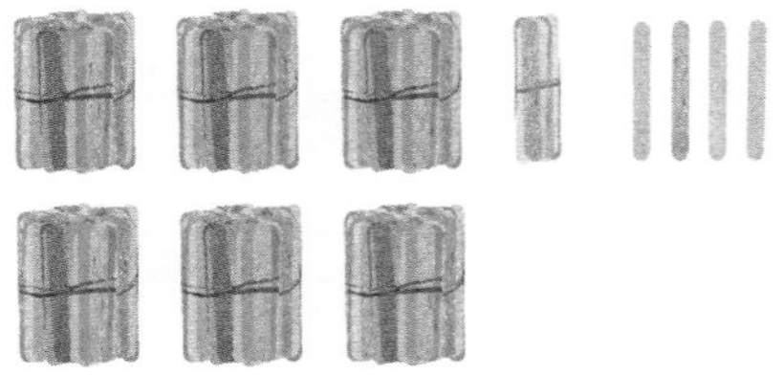

1 1
325
\+ 289
14

NOTE TO HOME
Students learn how to use models to help them add three-digit numbers.

Literature Connection Read aloud *Kimako's Story* by June Jordan to reinforce lesson concepts.

Social Studies Connection Display the following mileage chart on the chalkboard:

	New York	Philadelphia	Atlanta
Boston	206	296	1,037
New York		100	841
Philadelphia	100		741

Show students how to read the table, then work together to solve problems similar to the following: If I drove from Boston to New York and then to Philadelphia, how many miles would I have driven? (206 + 100 = 306)

*available separately

◆ **LESSON 141 Three-Digit Addition**

Solve these problems.

❶ How many cookies? 578

253
+ 325

$355
+ 264

❷ How much money? $ 619

Draw pictures or use manipulatives to add. Record your answer.

❸ 103 + 457 = 560

❹ $271 + 660 = 931

❺ 525 + 347 = 872

Play the "Rummage Sale" game.

NOTE TO HOME
Students use models to add three-digit numbers.

❷ Teach

Demonstrate Write the following two examples on the chalkboard:

3	300
+5	+500
(8)	(800)

Have students solve both. Demonstrate the answer to the second problem using cookie sheet models or other base-10 materials. Then demonstrate the same procedure using problems similar to the following:

57	570
+38	+380
(95)	(950)

Guide students to recognize that 57 tens + 38 tens has an answer related to 57 + 38. Then use craft sticks or cookie sheet models to show how to solve 487 + 389. (876) Discuss how this is similar to adding two-digit numbers. (regrouping when necessary)

Using the Student Pages Discuss each step shown on page 315 with the class. Ask:

- ▶ What is pictured in the first step? (3 hundreds, 2 tens, 5 ones + 2 hundreds, 8 tens, and 9 ones)
- ▶ Why are the ones circled in the next step? (They make a group of ten.)
- ▶ How is the third step like the one before it? How is it different? (Another group of ten is circled; this is a group of tens, the step before was a group of ones.)
- ▶ What sum does the last step show? (6 hundreds, 1 ten, 4 ones)

Following a similar procedure, discuss how to solve the first two problems on page 316. Then have students work in pairs or small groups using base-10 materials to model and solve the last three problems on this page. Discuss each step as students model the problems. Ask:

- ▶ Do we need to regroup? Why or why not?
- ▶ If we need to regroup, what should we do?

Introducing the "Rumage Sale" Game Demonstrate the game, which provides practice changing money and regrouping. Complete directions are on the Game Mat.

◆ LESSON 141 Three-Digit Addition

Teach

Using the Student Pages Discuss the examples on page 317 and have students work in groups, again using models to complete the last three examples.

Have students work independently to complete page 318. Then have them share and compare their answers.

> *Observation of game-playing activity resembles observation of real-life-out-of-school activities as closely as anything we are likely to see in school. Such observation will often give greater insight into a child's thought patterns than anything else the teacher can do.*
>
> —Stephen S. Willoughby,
> *Mathematics Education for a Changing World*

◆ LESSON 141 Three-Digit Addition Name ____________

Here is another way of thinking about adding large numbers.

229	2 hundreds 2 tens and 9
+ 163	1 hundred 6 tens and 3
392	3 hundreds 8 tens and 12
or	or
392	3 hundreds 9 tens and 2

Solve.

6.

347	3 hundreds 4 tens and 7
+ 572	+ 5 hundreds 7 tens and 2
919	8 hundreds 11 tens and 9
	or
	9 hundreds 1 tens and 9

7.

273	2 hundreds 7 tens and 3
+ 419	+ 4 hundreds 1 tens and 9
692	6 hundreds 8 tens and 12
	or
919	6 hundreds 9 tens and 2

8.

623	6 hundreds 2 tens and 3
+ 189	+ 1 hundreds 8 tens and 9
812	7 hundreds 10 tens and 12
	or
	6 hundreds 1 tens and 2

NOTE TO HOME
Students add by expanded counting.

RETEACHING

Have students work in groups using play money to model three-digit addition problems. Demonstrate how to do addition problems, such as $145 + $487 ($632), by trading ten $1 bills for one ten and ten $10 bills for one hundred. Have students work together to solve similar problems.

◆ LESSON 141 Three-Digit Addition

Add.

9. 327 + 269 = 596	10. 700 + 800 = 1500	11. 205 + 304 = 509
12. 200 + 500 = 700	13. 432 + 385 = 817	14. 689 + 219 = 908
15. 434 + 656 = 1090	16. 287 + 342 = 629	17. 250 + 250 = 500
18. 100 + 300 = 400	19. 100 + 250 = 350	20. 507 + 103 = 610

NOTE TO HOME
Students add three-digit numbers with and without regrouping.

3 Wrap-Up 5 MINUTES

In Closing Ask students to explain how adding three-digit numbers is like adding two-digit numbers and how it is different.

ALTERNATIVE ASSESSMENT

Performance Assessment Observe which students understand how to use base-10 materials to model three-digit addition problems.

Assessment Criteria

Did the student . . .

- ✓ correctly answer the discussion questions during the demonstration and on pages 315–317?
- ✓ correctly solve the problems at the bottom of pages 316–317?
- ✓ correctly solve nine of 12 problems on page 318?

PRACTICE p. 141

LESSON 141 PRACTICE Name ____________

1. 488 + 131 = 619 — 4 hundreds, 8 tens and 8 ones + 1 hundred, 3 tens and 1 one = 6 hundreds, 1 ten and 9 ones

2. 217 + 218 = 435 — 2 hundreds, 1 ten and 7 ones + 2 hundreds, 1 ten and 8 ones = 4 hundreds, 3 tens and 5 ones

Solve.

3. 509 + 191 = 700	4. 725 + 194 = 919	5. 446 + 464 = 910	6. 139 + 243 = 382
7. 257 + 367 = 624	8. 326 + 492 = 818	9. 212 + 199 = 411	10. 687 + 209 = 896

ENRICHMENT p. 141

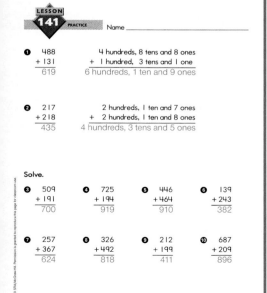

LESSON 141 ENRICHMENT Name ____________

Imagine that you must show a number by making a drawing. Draw a picture on the line that shows the same amount as the total of the numbers on the left. Draw a tree to stand for 100, a house for ten, and a bush for one.

128 + 194 = 322

29 + 415 = 444

130 + 33 = 163

219 + 287 = 506

LESSON 142

Student Edition pages 319–320

More Three-Digit Addition

LESSON PLANNER

Objective

▶ to provide practice adding three-digit numbers

Context of the Lesson This is third lesson involving three-digit addition.

Materials	Program Resources
base-10 materials*	Number Cubes
	Thinking Story Book, pages 120–123
	Reteaching Master
	Practice Master 142
	Enrichment Master 142
	For extra practice: CD-ROM* Lesson 142

1 Warm-Up (5 MINUTES)

Problem of the Day Write the following problem on the chalkboard: Name a three-digit number in which the sum of the digits is 13, the number is greater than 500, and no two digits are the same. (Answers vary. Possible answers: 562, 643, 724)

MENTAL MATH Have students add the following using mental math:

a. 6 + 5 = (11) **b.** 7 + 5 = (12)

c. 3 + 8 = (11) **d.** 8 + 4 = (12)

e. 8 + 7 = (15) **f.** 5 + 2 = (7)

2 Teach

Demonstrate Write several three-digit addition problems on the chalkboard and have students explain how to solve them. For example:

300	538	497
+700	+269	+596
1000	807	1093

If students are having difficulty, show how to solve the problems using base-10 materials.

LESSON 142

Name ____________________

More Three-Digit Addition

Add.

❶ 432 + 158 = 590	❷ 276 + 395 = 671	❸ 403 + 608 = 1011
❹ 302 + 708 = 1010	❺ 536 + 492 = 1028	❻ 507 + 394 = 901
❼ 574 + 687 = 1261	❽ 325 + 244 = 569	❾ 345 + 655 = 1000
❿ 625 + 264 = 889	⓫ 493 + 388 = 881	⓬ 449 + 106 = 555

Talk about the Thinking Story "Manolita Changes Things."

NOTE TO HOME
Students add three-digit numbers.

Literature Connection Read or invite students to read *Benjamin's 365 Birthdays* by Judi Barrett to reinforce lesson concepts.

RETEACHING p. 37

LESSON 142 RETEACHING Name ____________________

Example:

208
+ 115

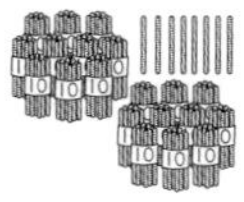

2 hundreds 0 tens and 8
+ 1 hundred 1 ten and 5
3
Add the ones. Rewrite if you can.

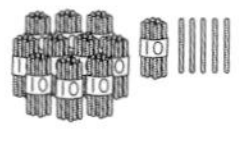

2 hundreds 0 tens and 8
+ 1 hundred 1 ten and 5
2 tens and 3
Add the tens.

2 hundreds 0 tens and 8
+ 1 hundred 1 ten and 5
3 hundreds 2 tens and 3
Add the ones. or 323

Add.

❶ 246 + 326 = 572	❷ 474 + 172 = 646	❸ 357 + 218 = 575	❹ 580 + 143 = 723
❺ 229 + 267 = 496	❻ 445 + 384 = 829	❼ 276 + 186 = 462	❽ 385 + 169 = 554

*available separately

◆ **LESSON 142 More Three-Digit Addition**

Use the Mixed Practice on page 396 after this lesson.

Add.

⑬ 547 + 382 = **929**	⑭ 659 + 147 = **806**	⑮ 506 + 384 = **890**
⑯ 521 + 87 = **608**	⑰ 43 + 812 = **855**	⑱ 342 + 9 = **351**
⑲ 8 + 642 = **650**	⑳ 125 + 125 = **250**	㉑ 250 + 250 = **500**
㉒ 600 + 300 = **900**	㉓ 704 + 200 = **904**	㉔ 704 + 20 = **724**

FANTASTIC FACT

In one season professional football teams use over 300 miles of adhesive tape.

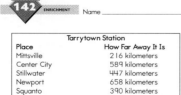

NOTE TO HOME
Students add one-, two-, and three-digit numbers.

PRACTICE p. 142

LESSON 142 PRACTICE Name ____________

Add.

❶ 318 + 655 = 973	❷ 438 + 193 = 631	❸ 532 + 488 = 1020
❹ 290 + 670 = 960	❺ 425 + 475 = 900	❻ 627 + 89 = 716
❼ 363 + 887 = 1250	❽ 505 + 85 = 590	❾ 583 + 446 = 1029
❿ 536 + 227 = 763	⓫ 225 + 116 = 341	⓬ 367 + 46 = 413
⓭ 195 + 8 = 203	⓮ 68 + 281 = 349	⓯ 847 + 175 = 1022

142 • *Math Explorations and Applications* Level 2

ENRICHMENT p. 142

LESSON 142 ENRICHMENT Name ____________

Tarrytown Station

Place	How Far Away It Is
Mittsville	216 kilometers
Center City	589 kilometers
Stillwater	447 kilometers
Newport	658 kilometers
Squanto	390 kilometers

❶ One messenger drove from Tarrytown to Mittsville to get a package. His friend drove from Tarrytown to Newport. How far did they drive all together? 874 kilometers

❷ How far did they drive, including the trips back to Tarrytown? 1748 kilometers

❸ A salesperson drove from Center City to Tarrytown, then on to Squanto. How far did she drive? 979 kilometers

❹ A bus driver left Stillwater to drive to Tarrytown. After 350 kilometers he stopped to pick up Mr. Green. He drove to Tarrytown, then on to Mittsville, where Mr. Green got off the bus. How far did Mr. Green travel? 313 kilometers

❺ The state crew paved the highway to Center City in June, the highway to Stillwater in July, and the highway to Squanto in October. How many kilometers did the crew pave in the summer? 1036

142 • *Math Explorations and Applications* Level 2

Using the Student Pages Have students complete pages 319–320 on their own. Individually help students who are still having difficulty.

Using the Thinking Story Read aloud the story "Manolita Changes Things" on pages 120–123 of the Thinking Story Book. Discuss the questions asked throughout the story.

❸ Wrap-Up (5 MINUTES)

In Closing Have students make up a word problem in which they must add two three-digit numbers. Have them exchange and solve each other's problems.

SELF ASSESSMENT

Have students correct their own work as you read aloud the answers to pages 319 and 320. Invite them to brainstorm ways to improve their skills.

Assessment Criteria

Did the student . . .

✓ participate in the discussion of the Thinking Story?

✓ correctly solve 11 of 12 problems on page 319?

✓ correctly solve 11 of 12 problems on page 320?

LEARNING STYLES

Meeting Individual Needs

Work with auditory learners. Encourage them to orally explain each step they complete as they solve addition problems on pages 319–320. Ask them to explain why they do each step. For example, ask questions such as "Why did you write a one on the top of the tens column?"

STORY 20

THINKING STORY

Manolita Changes Things

Manolita Mudancia wants to be just like her father. Because her father is always changing things, Manolita tries to change things too.

Manolita had 16 photographs that she had taken. She wanted to make a photo album for them, pasting one photograph onto each page. But all she could find were two square sheets of black construction paper. "I have only enough paper to take care of two pictures," she moaned. Then she added, "Oh, I forgot something. This is enough paper for four pictures."

How can Manolita put four pictures onto two sheets of paper if she puts only one picture on a page? Answers may vary; possibilities include pasting one picture on each side of the paper.

Manolita had forgotten that she could put a picture on to each side of the sheet of paper, just as there are words on both sides of the paper in most books. But she didn't want to put just four pictures in her book. She wanted to put all 16 pictures in, and she still wanted only one picture on each page.

"I think I can change this paper a little to make more pages," Manolita thought. "That's what my dad would do."

How can Manolita make more pages?

She can cut the sheets in half.

Manolita took a pair of scissors and cut each sheet of paper down the middle.

How many sheets of paper does Manolita have now? four

How many pictures can she put on to the sheets now, with one picture on a side? eight

Manolita figured out that she had enough pages for eight of her pictures. "But that doesn't take care of all my pictures," she said.

How many pictures would she still have left? eight

What can Manolita do to get just the right number of pages? She can cut all the sheets in half again.

Manolita took the four sheets of paper and cut each one across the middle so that it made two square sheets.

How many sheets of paper does Manolita have now? eight

How many pictures can she put on the sheets now, with one picture to a side? sixteen

"I did it!" Manolita said happily. "I changed those two sheets of paper a little and now I have eight sheets–just enough to put my 16 pictures on. And the pages are all nice and square, just like the ones I started with."

Are they exactly like the ones she started with? no

How are they different? They're smaller.

◆ STORY 20 Manolita Changes Things

But Manolita's troubles were not over. When she tried to put the pictures on to the pages, she found that the pages were a little too small for the pictures. "This is terrible," she said. "I just wanted to make more pages. I didn't want to make them smaller."

Why are the pages smaller? Each one is just a part of the sheet of paper she started with.

Mr. Mudancia came in and asked Manolita what was wrong.

"I'm trying to make a photo album for my pictures," Manolita said, "but the pages are too small. Could you change them a little to make them bigger?"

"Sorry," Mr. Mudancia said. "I don't know any way to do that. But I can change something else a little so that your pictures will fit on the pages."

What else can be changed? the pictures

How? Encourage students to identify a variety of creative solutions.

Mr. Mudancia took the scissors and cut the edges off one of the pictures. "There," he said. "Now you have a smaller picture, but it fits on the page."

"That's great," Manolita said. "Now I'll have a little book that I can carry in my pocket. We really know how to change things to make them better, don't we, Dad?"

"You're getting the idea," Mr. Mudancia said, changing his face a little so that it looked proud and happy.

What do you think Mr. Mudancia did to change his face? He smiled.

. . . the end

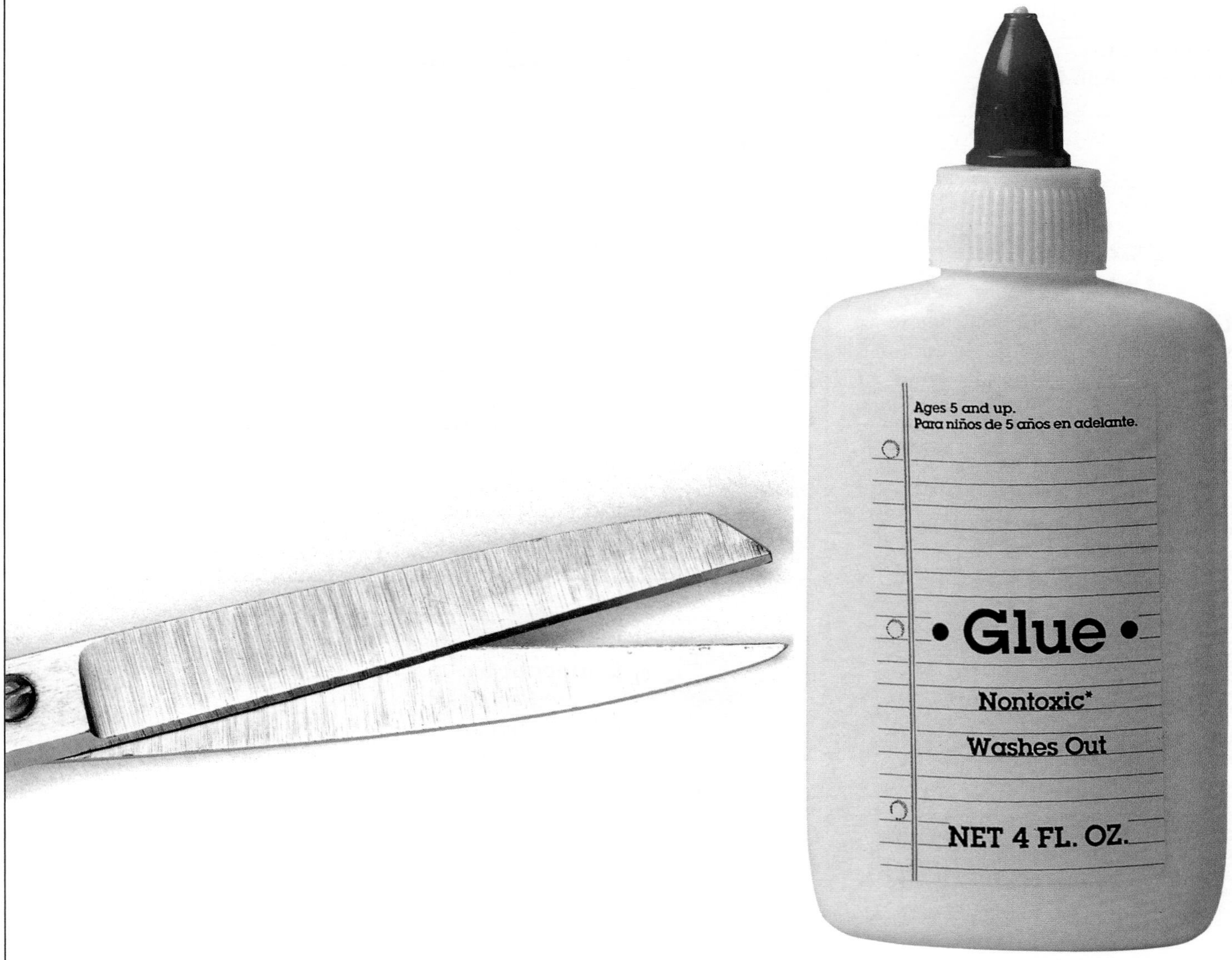

Ages 5 and up.
Para niños de 5 años en adelante.
• Glue •
Nontoxic*
Washes Out
NET 4 FL. OZ.

LESSON 143

Student Edition pages 321–324

Three-Digit Subtraction

LESSON PLANNER

Objective

- ▶ to prepare students for learning to subtract three-digit numbers

Context of the Lesson This topic is introduced in this lesson and continued in the next several lessons.

Materials	Program Resources
base-10 materials*	Thinking Story Book, pages 124–125
	Practice Master 143
	Enrichment Master 143
	For extra practice: CD-ROM* Lesson 143

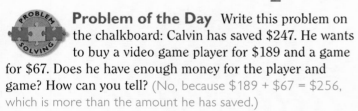

1 Warm-Up (5 MINUTES)

Problem of the Day Write this problem on the chalkboard: Calvin has saved $247. He wants to buy a video game player for $189 and a game for $67. Does he have enough money for the player and game? How can you tell? (No, because $189 + $67 = $256, which is more than the amount he has saved.)

MENTAL MATH Have students add the following problems using mental math.

a. 300 + 400 = (700)

b. 600 + 700 = (1300)

c. 500 + 900 = (1400)

d. 200 + 600 = (800)

e. 700 + 700 = (1400)

LESSON 143

Name ______________________

Three-Digit Subtraction

Rewrite to show more tens.

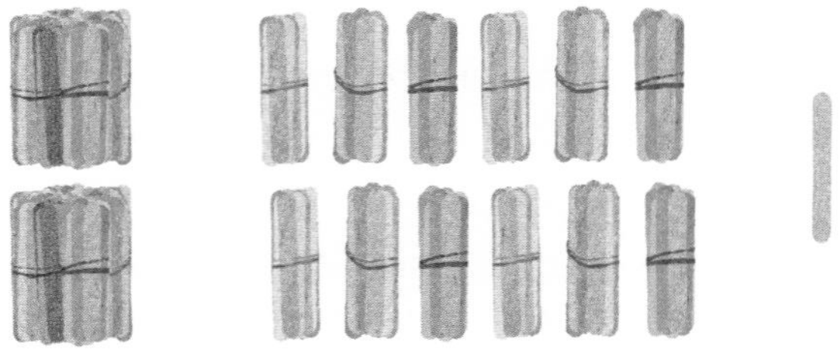

321 = 2 hundreds, 12 tens, and 1

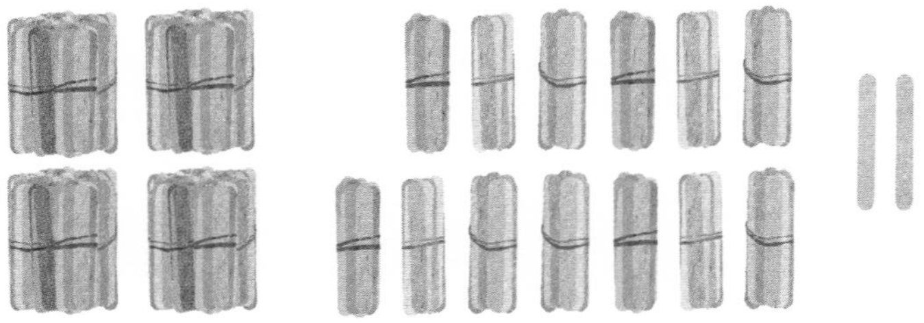

1. 532 = 4 hundreds, 13 tens, and 2

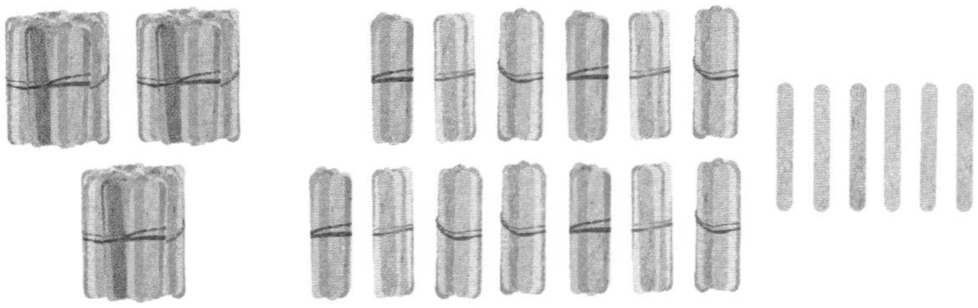

2. 436 = 3 hundreds, 13 tens, and 6

NOTE TO HOME
Students regroup hundreds to tens.

Literature Connection Read aloud *A Remainder of One* by Elinor J. Pinczes and *Take Off with Numbers* by Sally Hewitt to reinforce lesson concepts.

*available separately

◆ LESSON 143 Three-Digit Subtraction

Subtract.

350 − 70 = ___?___

```
 350
+ 70
```

I can't take 7 tens from 5 tens.

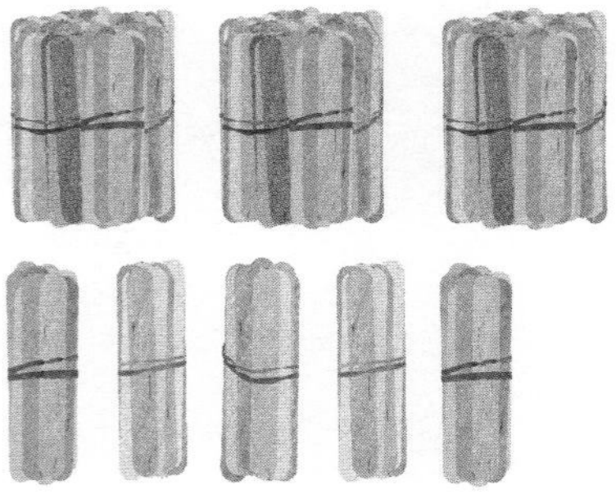

I can undo a bundle of one hundred.

```
 2 15
 3̸5̸0
+  70
```

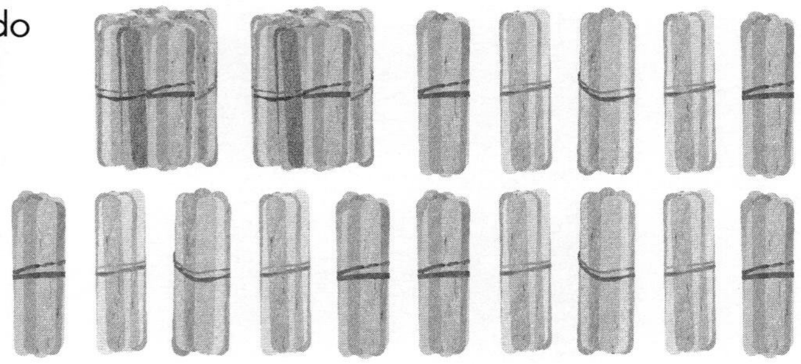

Now I can take away 7 tens.

```
 2 15
 3̸5̸0
+  70
 280
```

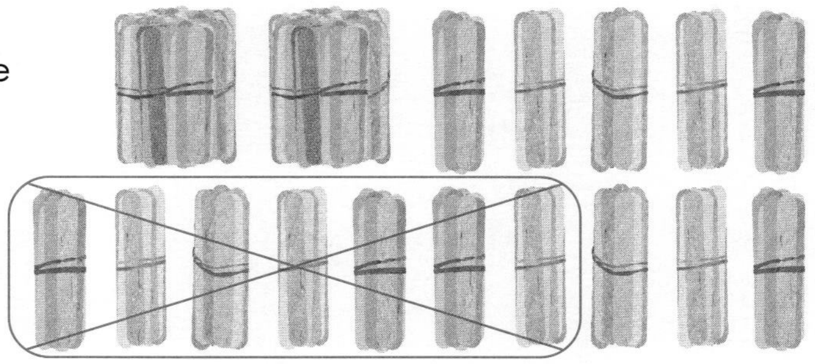

NOTE TO HOME
Students learn how to model subtraction by regrouping sticks.

❷ Teach

Demonstrate Demonstrate how to solve problems similar to the following with the class. Discuss how they are related:

```
  13        130
 - 8       - 80
 (5)       (50)
```

Next use base-10 materials to demonstrate how to solve problems such as:

```
  43        430
 - 8       - 80
 (35)      (350)
```

Remind students that 43 is four tens and three or three tens and 13. Demonstrate this by showing the regrouping in the example on the chalkboard and with base-10 materials. Do the same with 430 - 80. Repeat with similar problems.

Using the Student Pages Discuss the first problem shown on page 321 with the class. Ask: How were the hundreds regrouped in this problem? (1 hundred was taken from 3 hundreds and changed to 10 tens, then added to the 2 tens that were already there.) You might want to demonstrate this problem using base-10 materials as well.

Have students complete the other two examples on this page and then discuss their answers before going on to the next page.

Next, discuss the steps on page 322 with the class. Ask: Were you able to subtract the digits in the ones place? How? (Yes, 0 – 0 = 0) Why is there a 15 over the 5 and a 2 over the 3? (1 hundred was taken from the 3 hundreds and changed to 10 tens, which was added to the 5 tens. This left 2 hundreds in the hundreds and 15 tens in the tens.)

◆ LESSON 143 Three-Digit Subtraction

Teach

Using the Student Pages For page 323, discuss the first example, pointing out that you can subtract the ones, but must regroup to subtract the tens. Have students complete the remaining examples on this page. When finished, have them share their methods and answers before going on to the next page.

Finally, have students work independently to complete page 324. Allow them to use base-10 materials if they need to. Then have them share and compare their answers.

Using the Thinking Story Present one or two new problems from those following "Manolita Changes Things," on pages 124–125 of the Thinking Story Book.

> *Whenever possible, addition and subtraction. should be taught at about the same time so that learners can contrast the two and so that problems can be presented that are not all solved by using the same operation.*
>
> –Stephen S. Willoughby, *Mathematics Education for a Changing World*

◆ LESSON 143 Three-Digit Subtraction

Name ______________________________

Solve each problem in three steps. The first one is done for you.

Can you subtract? Regroup if you have to.

Can you subtract?

3 240 − 90 — yes / (no)

1 14
~~2~~~~4~~0
−90
150

4 530 − 70 — (yes) / no

4 13
~~5~~~~3~~0
−70
460

5 720 − 350 — (yes) / no

6 12
~~7~~~~2~~0
−350
460

6 840 − 210 = 630 — (yes) / no

NOTE TO HOME
Students practice regrouping.

RETEACHING

Present a demonstration similar to the one at the beginning of this lesson. However, this time use play money to show students how to regroup.

GIFTED & TALENTED

Meeting Individual Needs

Provide further practice with subtraction of three-digit multiples of ten, but do not give students the examples in pairs as on page 324. For example, rather than having them find 15 – 7 and then 150 – 70, have them only solve problems such as 150 – 70.

*available separately

◆ **LESSON 143** Three-Digit Subtraction

Subtract.

You may rewrite the numbers when it helps you.

7. 15 − 7 = 8   150 − 70 = 80

8. 12 − 5 = 7   120 − 50 = 70

9. 35 − 7 = 28   350 − 70 = 280

10. 62 − 5 = 57   620 − 50 = 570

11. 13 − 9 = 4   130 − 90 = 40

12. 14 − 8 = 6   140 − 80 = 60

13. 43 − 9 = 34   430 − 90 = 340

14. 94 − 8 = 86   940 − 80 = 860

NOTE TO HOME
Students use patterns to subtract three-digit numbers.

PRACTICE p. 143

LESSON 143 PRACTICE Name ____________

Subtract. Rewrite the numbers when it helps you.

1. 18 − 9 = 9	2. 180 − 90 = 90	3. 13 − 5 = 8	4. 130 − 50 = 80
5. 26 − 8 = 18	6. 260 − 80 = 180	7. 43 − 7 = 36	8. 430 − 70 = 360
9. 35 − 6 = 29	10. 350 − 60 = 290	11. 57 − 8 = 49	12. 570 − 80 = 490
13. 62 − 3 = 59	14. 620 − 30 = 590	15. 81 − 5 = 76	16. 810 − 50 = 760

ENRICHMENT p. 143

LESSON 143 ENRICHMENT Name ____________

Subtract the tens packages from the numbers.

1. 986 − Tens 65 = 336
2. 713 − Tens 70 = 13
3. 190 − Tens 9 = 100
4. 356 − Tens 34 = 16
5. 296 − Tens 21 = 86
6. 441 − Tens 14 = 300
7. 303 − Tens 3 = 273
8. 522 − Tens 45 = 72

3 Wrap-Up (5 MINUTES)

In Closing Have students explain how different pairs of examples on page 324 are related. For example, ask how 15 - 7 is related to 150 - 70. Students should realize that 15 - 7 = 8 and 15 tens - 7 tens = 8 tens or 80.

ALTERNATIVE ASSESSMENT

Informal Assessment Use students' answers to page 324 as an informal assessment of their ability to subtract three-digit numbers that are multiples of ten.

Assessment Criteria

Did the student . . .

✓ correctly answer the discussion questions during the demonstration and on pages 321–324?

✓ correctly solve the problems on pages 322 and 323?

✓ correctly solve 14 of 16 problems on page 324?

LEARNING STYLES

Meeting Individual Needs
Work in small groups with your auditory learners, explaining each step for subtracting three-digit numbers. Then have them explain the steps to you as they demonstrate how to subtract several of the problems on page 324.

LESSON 144

Student Edition pages 325–326

More Three-Digit Subtraction

LESSON PLANNER

Objectives

- ▶ to reinforce students' understanding of the relationship among units, tens, and hundreds
- ▶ to provide practice in subtracting three-digit numbers

Context of the Lesson This topic is continued in the next several lessons. Students should have a basic idea of when and how to regroup, using base-10 materials when necessary.

Materials	Program Resources
base-10 materials	Number Cubes
play money	Thinking Story Book, pages 124–125
	Practice Master 144
	Enrichment Master 144
	For extra practice: CD-ROM* Lesson 144

1 Warm-Up

5 MINUTES

Problem of the Day Write this problem on the chalkboard: Grandma came to visit on Monday. She plans to stay for 16 days. On what day of the week will she leave? (Wednesday)

MENTAL MATH Have students multiply and divide, using their Number Cubes to respond.

a. 4 x 6 = (24) **b.** 3 x 5 = (15) **c.** 2 x 7 = (14)

d. 25 ÷ 5 = (5) **e.** 12 ÷ 2 = (6) **f.** 15 ÷ 3 = (5)

2 Teach

Demonstrate Demonstrate how to solve problems similar to the following.

$$\begin{array}{r} 436 \\ -214 \\ \hline (222) \end{array}$$

LESSON 144

Name ______________________

More Three-Digit Subtraction

Use play money to subtract.

626 − 252 = ?

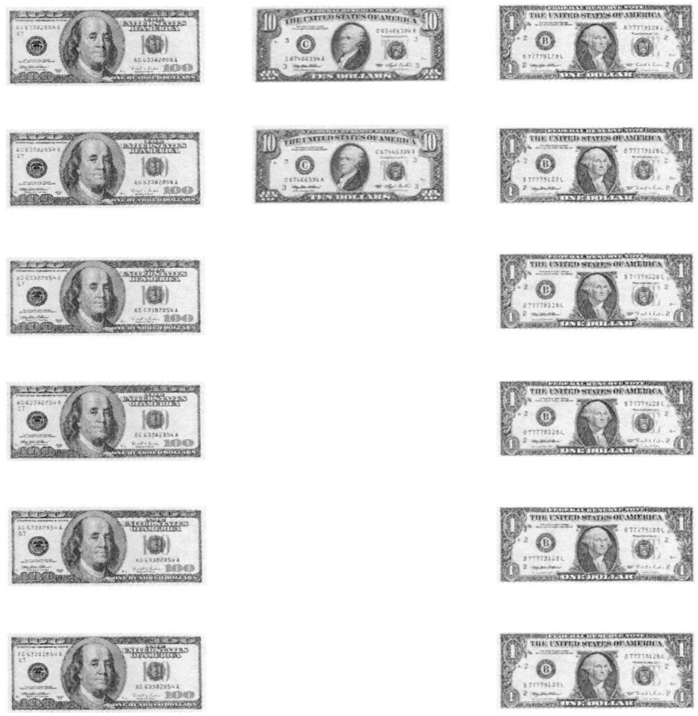

Write what you did.

626
− 252

5 12
~~6~~~~2~~6
− 252

5 12
~~6~~~~2~~6
− 252
374

NOTE TO HOME
Students use play money to learn how to subtract with regrouping.

SPECIAL NEEDS

Meeting Individual Needs

Some students will need more practice subtracting three-digit multiples of ten before going on. Allow these students to practice simpler subtraction examples using base-10 materials before having them complete page 326.

RETEACHING

Demonstrate how to subtract \$753–\$76 one step at a time. Use play money to show each step. Start by showing students seven \$100 bills, five \$10 bills, and three \$1 bills. Then write the problem on the chalkboard. Ask whether you can subtract the units. Show how you must change a \$10 bill for ten ones, and then record this step in the example on the chalkboard. Subtract the ones, and repeat for the tens. Then subtract the tens. Repeat step by step for several more problems.

*available separately

◆ LESSON 144 More Three-Digit Subtraction

Solve these problems. Use play money to help.

❶ Mrs. Mazingo had $357 in the bank. She took out $165. How many dollars does she have in the bank now? **$192**

❷ Mr. Ebert had $275 in his bank account. Then he put in $156. How many dollars does he have in the bank now? **$431**

❸ The girls' basketball team needs $500 to travel to the finals. So far, they have earned $250. How many more dollars do they need? **$250**

❹ Mr. Culyer drove 257 miles to visit his sister. About how many miles will the round trip be? **$514**

NOTE TO HOME
Students solve three-digit addition and subtraction money problems.

Next, use base-10 materials to show how to subtract in problems similar to each of the following. Focus on why regrouping both tens and hundreds is sometimes necessary.

531	304	562
−228	−123	−379
(303)	(181)	(183)

Then, use base-10 materials to show students how to subtract examples such as 703 − 285. (418)

Using the Student Pages Discuss the steps on page 325 with the class. Ask: Were you able to subtract the digits in the ones place? How? (Yes, 6 − 2 = 4) Why is there a 12 over the 2 and a 5 over the 6? (1 hundred was taken from the 6 hundreds and changed to 10 tens, which was added to the 2 tens. This made 5 hundreds in the hundreds and 12 tens in the tens.)

Have students solve the word problems on page 326 independently, then share and compare answers.

Using the Thinking Story Present one or two new problems from those following, "Manolita Changes Things" on pages 124–125 of the Thinking Story Book.

❸ Wrap-Up (5 MINUTES)

In Closing Have students make up their own word problems involving three-digit subtraction, solve them, and then exchange and solve each other's problems.

ALTERNATIVE ASSESSMENT

Informal Assessment Circulate about the room as students complete page 326 to make sure that they understand how to regroup.

Assessment Criteria

Did the student . . .

✓ correctly answer the discussion questions during the demonstration and on page 325?

✓ correctly solve three of the four problems on page 326?

PRACTICE p. 144

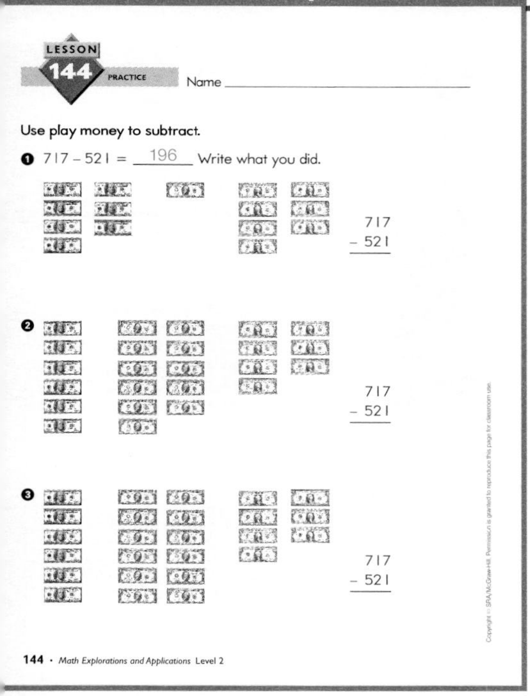

LESSON 144 PRACTICE Name ____________

Use play money to subtract.

❶ 717 − 521 = 196 Write what you did.

717
− 521

❷

717
− 521

❸

717
− 521

144 • *Math Explorations and Applications* Level 2

ENRICHMENT p. 144

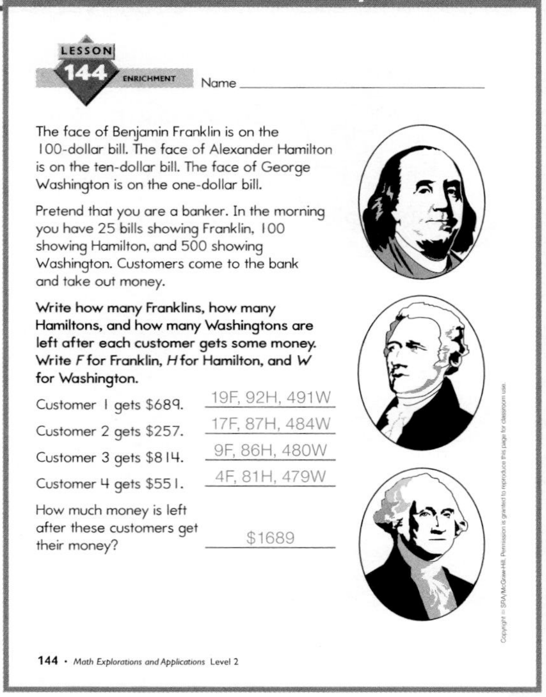

LESSON 144 ENRICHMENT Name ____________

The face of Benjamin Franklin is on the 100-dollar bill. The face of Alexander Hamilton is on the ten-dollar bill. The face of George Washington is on the one-dollar bill.

Pretend that you are a banker. In the morning you have 25 bills showing Franklin, 100 showing Hamilton, and 500 showing Washington. Customers come to the bank and take out money.

Write how many Franklins, how many Hamiltons, and how many Washingtons are left after each customer gets some money. Write *F* for Franklin, *H* for Hamilton, and *W* for Washington.

Customer 1 gets $689. 19F, 92H, 491W

Customer 2 gets $257. 17F, 87H, 484W

Customer 3 gets $814. 9F, 86H, 480W

Customer 4 gets $551. 4F, 81H, 479W

How much money is left after these customers get their money? $1689

144 • *Math Explorations and Applications* Level 2

LESSON 145

Student Edition pages 327–328

Practicing Three-Digit Subtraction

LESSON PLANNER

Objective

▶ to provide practice in subtracting three-digit numbers

Context of the Lesson This is the third lesson involving three-digit subtraction.

Materials	Program Resources
base-10 materials*	Number Cubes
	Thinking Story Book, pages 124–125
	Reteaching Master
	Practice Master 145
	Enrichment Master 145
	For extra practice: CD-ROM* Lesson 145

1 Warm-Up

5 MINUTES

Problem of the Day Write the following question on the chalkboard: You pay for a $12 game and a $5 book with two $10 bills. How much change will you get back? ($3)

MENTAL MATH Have students add and subtract the following, using their Number Cubes to respond:

a. 14 – 7 = (7)
b. 4 + 5 = (9)
c. 6 + 5 = (11)
d. 8 + 7 = (15)
e. 12 – 9 = (3)
f. 8 + 4 = (12)

2 Teach

Demonstrate Write a variety of three-digit subtraction problems on the chalkboard and have students explain how to solve them. For example:

600	207	461
-400	-184	-328
(200)	(23)	(133)

If students are having difficulty, show them how to solve these problems using base-10 materials. Have students check each answer by using addition.

LESSON 145

Name ____________________

Practicing Three-Digit Subtraction

Subtract. The first one has been done for you.

❶ 473 − 218 = 255 (6 13)	❷ 675 − 384 = 291	❸ 582 − 272 = 310
❹ 504 − 217 = 287	❺ 608 − 319 = 289	❻ 705 − 204 = 501
❼ 600 − 357 = 243	❽ 200 − 169 = 31	❾ 410 − 328 = 82
❿ 892 − 538 = 354	⓫ 479 − 265 = 214	⓬ 503 − 247 = 256

NOTE TO HOME
Students subtract three-digit numbers with and without regrouping.

Literature Connection Read or invite students to read *The Purse* by Kathy Caple to reinforce lesson concepts.

RETEACHING p. 38

LESSON 145 RETEACHING

Name ____________________

Example:

240
– 180

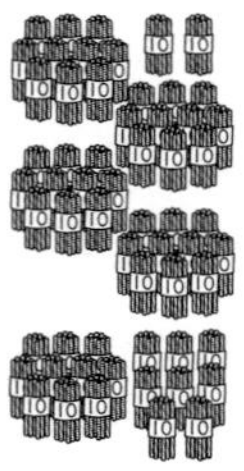

4 hundreds 2 tens and 0 – 1 hundred 8 tens and 0 0	First subtract the ones.
3 hundreds 12 tens and 0 (4 and 2 crossed out) – 1 hundred 8 tens and 0 4 tens and 0	Next, look at the tens. Will you need to get more tens? Go to the hundreds. Subtract the tens.
3 hundreds 12 tens and 0 (4 and 2 crossed out) – 1 hundred 8 tens and 0 2 hundreds 4 tens and 0	Subtract the hundreds. 240

Subtract.

❶ 396 − 182 = 214	❷ 864 − 235 = 629	❸ 539 − 174 = 365	❹ 810 − 234 = 576
❺ 542 − 221 = 321	❻ 461 − 133 = 328	❼ 222 − 104 = 118	❽ 668 − 249 = 419

38 • *Math Explorations and Applications* Level 2

*available separately

◆ LESSON 145 Practicing Three-Digit Subtraction

Subtract.

13. 863 − 398 = 465 (regrouped: 7 15 13)
14. 408 − 372 = 36
15. 604 − 257 = 347
16. 621 − 358 = 263
17. 429 − 275 = 154
18. 599 − 389 = 210
19. 212 − 87 = 125
20. 300 − 25 = 275
21. 516 − 248 = 268
22. 250 − 25 = 225
23. 397 − 209 = 188

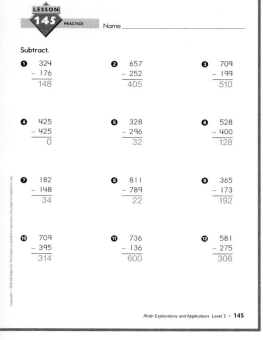

FANTASTIC FACT When the Apollo astronauts walked on the moon, they left footprints that will last for ten million years.

NOTE TO HOME
Students subtract from three-digit numbers.

PRACTICE p. 145

LESSON 145 PRACTICE Name ____________

Subtract.

1. 324 − 176 = 148
2. 657 − 252 = 405
3. 709 − 199 = 510
4. 425 − 425 = 0
5. 328 − 296 = 32
6. 528 − 400 = 128
7. 182 − 148 = 34
8. 811 − 789 = 22
9. 365 − 173 = 192
10. 709 − 395 = 314
11. 736 − 136 = 600
12. 581 − 275 = 306

ENRICHMENT p. 145

LESSON 145 ENRICHMENT Name ____________

Use a centimeter ruler to find the perimeter of each figure. Then figure out the coded message.

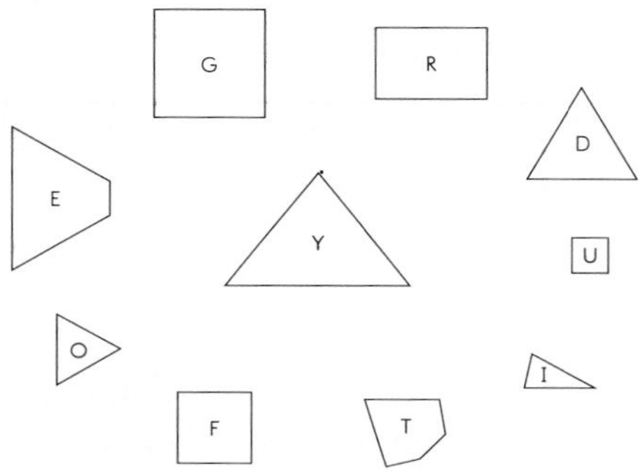

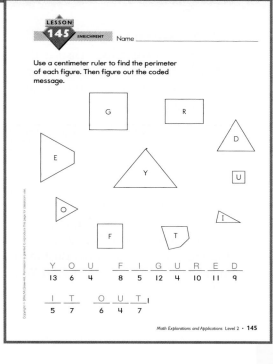

Y O U   F I G U R E D
13 6 4   8 5 12 4 10 11 9

I T   O U T !
5 7   6 4 7

Using the Student Pages Discuss the completed examples on pages 327–328 and then assign the rest of each page for students to complete independently. Provide individual help for students who are having difficulty.

Using the Thinking Story Present one or two new problems from those following "Manolita Changes Things" on pages 124–125 of the Thinking Story Book.

3 Wrap-Up (5 MINUTES)

In Closing Have students make up a word problem in which they must subtract two three-digit numbers. Have them exchange and solve each other's problems.

ALTERNATIVE ASSESSMENT

Informal Assessment Have students correct their own work as you read aloud the answers to pages 327 and 328. Observe students' corrections to assess who is still having difficulty subtracting three-digit numbers.

Assessment Criteria

Did the student . . .

✓ correctly solve ten of 12 problems on page 327?

✓ correctly solve 9 of 11 problems on page 328?

LEARNING STYLES

Meeting Individual Needs
Work with auditory learners as you did when teaching three-digit addition. Encourage them to orally explain each step as they solve the problems on pages 327–328, and to explain how they know when to regroup.

LESSON 146

Student Edition pages 329–330

Three-Digit Addition and Subtraction

LESSON PLANNER

Objectives

- to provide practice in adding and subtracting three-digit numbers
- to provide practice in solving addition and subtraction word problems

Context of the Lesson This is the first lesson in which students practice both addition and subtraction problems.

Materials	Program Resources
base-10 materials*	Number Cubes
play money* (optional)	Practice Master 146
	Enrichment Master 146
	For extra practice: CD-ROM* Lesson 146

1 Warm-Up

5 MINUTES

Problem of the Day Write this problem on the chalkboard: On Monday Evan goes to work at 11:00 A.M. He begins work each day one hour earlier than the day before. What time does Evan go to work on Friday? (7:00 A.M.)

MENTAL MATH Have students add, subtract, multiply, and divide the following, using their Number Cubes to respond.

a. $4 \times 7 =$ (28)
b. $3 \times 6 =$ (18)
c. $15 \div 5 =$ (3)
d. $12 \div 4 =$ (3)
e. $15 - 7 =$ (8)
f. $12 - 8 =$ (4)
g. $6 + 9 =$ (15)
h. $4 + 7 =$ (11)

LESSON 146

Name ____________________

Three-Digit Addition and Subtraction

Solve these problems. Watch the signs.

1. $28 + 37 =$ 65
2. $97 + 84 =$ 181
3. $85 - 26 =$ 59
4. $215 + 346 =$ 561
5. $397 + 284 =$ 681
6. $571 - 222 =$ 349
7. $402 - 204 =$ 198
8. $674 + 88 =$ 762
9. $417 - 205 =$ 212
10. $1000 - 250 =$ 750
11. $317 + 239 =$ 556
12. $412 - 195 =$ 217

NOTE TO HOME
Students practice mixed three-digit addition and three-digit subtraction problems.

Social Studies Connection Display the table you used in the Social Studies Connection in Lesson 141 as shown below.

	New York	Philadelphia	Atlanta
Boston	206	296	1,037
New York		100	841
Philadelphia	100		741

This time ask questions that require subtraction to answer. For example: How much farther is it from Boston to Philadelphia than from Boston to New York? (296 – 206 = 90 miles farther)

RETEACHING

Use play money or base-10 materials to review how to add and subtract three-digit numbers.

*available separately

◆ **LESSON 146** Three-Digit Addition and Subtraction

Use the Mixed Practice on page 397 after this lesson.

Every year Big City has a 15-mile marathon. Records of the marathon are kept. Last year these were the records.

	Total Number	Male	Female	12–17	18–39	40–65	66+
Start	745	347	398	128	439	165	13
Finish	525	239	286	88	335	99	3

Answer these questions. If you don't have enough information, write an X.

13. How many people finished the race? **525**
14. How many didn't finish? **220**
15. How many people younger than 40 finished? **423**
16. How many 18-year-old boys finished the race? **X**
17. How many males didn't finish? **108**
18. How many females younger than 40 finished? **X**

MATH JOURNAL

Write your own problems. Challenge a friend to solve them.

NOTE TO HOME
Students practice addition, subtraction, and reading charts.

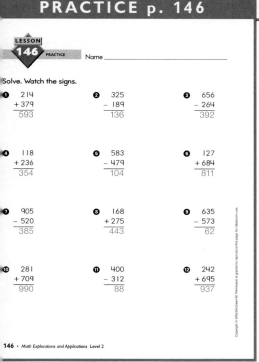

PRACTICE p. 146

LESSON 146 PRACTICE Name ____________

Solve. Watch the signs.

1. 214 + 379 = 593
2. 325 − 189 = 136
3. 656 − 264 = 392
4. 118 + 236 = 354
5. 583 − 479 = 104
6. 127 + 684 = 811
7. 905 − 520 = 385
8. 168 + 275 = 443
9. 635 − 573 = 62
10. 281 + 709 = 990
11. 400 − 312 = 88
12. 242 + 695 = 937

ENRICHMENT p. 146

LESSON 146 ENRICHMENT Name ____________

Part of each problem is missing. Complete the problem.

1. 44 + 155 = 199
2. 87 − 63 = 24
3. 62 + 117 = 179
4. 663 − 276 = 387
5. 568 − 189 = 379
6. 164 + 99 = 263
7. 1010 − 899 = 111
8. 824 − 25 = 799
9. 345 + 273 = 618
10. 174 + 90 = 264
11. 386 − 118 = 268
12. 904 + 79 = 983
13. 892 − 144 = 748
14. 335 + 163 = 498
15. 477 + 76 = 553
16. 128 − 7 = 121
17. 459 + 110 = 569
18. 976 − 761 = 215
19. 884 + 49 = 933
20. 101 + 108 = 209

2 Teach

Demonstrate Demonstrate and review how to solve several three-digit addition and three-digit subtraction problems by crossing out tens and hundreds and regrouping when necessary.

Using the Student Pages Have students who are able complete pages 329 and 330 independently as you work in small groups with students who still need help.

3 Wrap-Up

5 MINUTES

In Closing Let half the class make up word problems involving three-digit subtraction, and the other half make up problems involving three-digit addition. Have them solve their own problems then exchange and solve each other's.

ALTERNATIVE ASSESSMENT

Performance Assessment Use students' answers to pages 329–330 to assess their ability to solve addition and subtraction problems.

Assessment Criteria

Did the student . . .

✓ correctly solve ten of 12 problems on page 329?

✓ correctly answer all of the questions on page 330?

SPECIAL NEEDS

Meeting Individual Needs

To help students complete the Math Journal activity on page 330, allow them to use the questions on this page as a model for their own problem. Work with students to make up other questions for their Math Journal entries using the data shown on this page.

LESSON 147

Student Edition pages 331–332

Three-Digit Practice

LESSON PLANNER

Objective

- ▶ to provide practice with three-digit addition and subtraction

Context of the Lesson This is the second lesson in which students practice mixed examples of three-digit addition and subtraction.

Materials	Program Resources
base-10 materials	"Harder Rummage Sale" Game Mat Practice Master 147 Enrichment Master 147 For extra practice: CD-ROM* Lesson 147

1 Warm-Up (5 MINUTES)

Problem of the Day Write the following problem on the chalkboard: Write a three-digit number that is the same number written backwards and forwards and whose digits add up to the sum of seven. (Possible answers: 313, 232, 151)

MENTAL MATH Have students add and subtract the following using mental math:

a. 5 + 2 = (7) **b.** 11 – 5 = (6) **c.** 7 – 4 = (3)
d. 1 + 7 = (8) **e.** 8 + 9 = (17) **f.** 5 + 3 = (8)
g. 14 – 9 = (5) **h.** 12 – 9 = (3)

2 Teach

Using the Student Pages Use page 331 to review the algorithms for three-digit addition and subtraction. Have students read and explain each step of the three examples. If you wish, have them explain the steps using play money to show regrouping. For example, to show why 1 is written in the tens column in the first example, students can use twelve $1 bills to show that 7 + 5 = 12; then trade ten of the bills for one $10 bill. Do the same for all three problems. Assign page 332 for students to complete independently. Give individual help to those students who are still having difficulty. Have students who finish early go on to the game.

LESSON 147

Name ______________________

Three-Digit Practice

Look at this example of how to add.

Step 1	Step 2	Step 3
1 257 +375 2	1 1 257 +375 32	1 1 257 +375 632

Look at this example of how to subtract.

Step 1	Step 2	Step 3
5 15 3~~65~~ – 179 6	15 2 ~~5~~ 15 ~~365~~ – 179 86	15 2 ~~5~~ 15 ~~365~~ – 179 186

Look at this example of how to subtract.

Step 1	Step 2
6 9 18 ~~708~~ –469	6 9 18 ~~708~~ –469 239

NOTE TO HOME
Students review how to add and subtract three-digit numbers with regrouping.

Social Studies Connection Make copies of an outline map of the United States with labels for the following locations and distances: New York City to Atlanta, 841 miles; Atlanta to Chicago, 674 miles; New York City to Chicago, 802 miles; Chicago to Denver, 996 miles. Have students work in pairs to plan a trip starting in any city and driving to two other cities. Have them tell the total number of miles they would drive on their trip.

RETEACHING

Some students might still need help using base-10 materials to review how to add or subtract three-digit numbers. Work with these students in small groups. First have them use base-10 hundreds, tens, Number Cubes, or craft sticks to solve the addition models shown on page 331. When they have mastered addition, have them work with the materials to solve the subtraction models on that page.

*available separately

◆ LESSON 147 Three-Digit Practice

Solve these problems. Watch the signs.

❶ 69 + 58 = **27**	❷ 173 − 94 = **79**	❸ 289 + 347 = **636**
❹ 620 − 438 = **182**	❺ 200 − 83 = **117**	❻ 547 + 123 = **670**
❼ 250 + 750 = **1000**	❽ 482 − 303 = **179**	❾ 487 − 99 = **388**
❿ 487 + 99 = **586**	⓫ 487 + 101 = **588**	⓬ 343 − 218 = **125**
⓭ 527 + 109 = **636**	⓮ 175 − 69 = **106**	⓯ 398 − 157 = **241**

GAME Play the "Harder Rummage Sale" game.

NOTE TO HOME
Students review three digit addition and subtraction.

GAME **Introducing the "Harder Rummage Sale" Game Mat** Demonstrate and play this game which involves changing $1000, $100, and $10 bills for those of smaller denominations. Complete directions are on the Game Mat.

3 Wrap-Up (5 MINUTES)

In Closing Have students make up and solve a three-digit addition algorithm and a three-digit subtraction algorithm in which they do not have to regroup. Then have them make up two more in which they do have to regroup.

ALTERNATIVE ASSESSMENT

Performance Assessment Observe students as they play the "Harder Rummage Sale" game to see who is having difficulty making the correct change.

Assessment Criteria

Did the student . . .

✓ correctly solve 13 of 15 problems on page 332?

✓ make the correct change during the "Harder Rummage Sale" game?

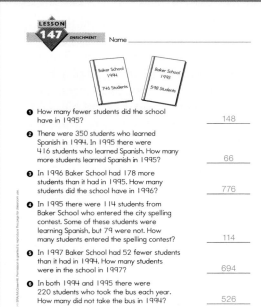

PRACTICE p. 147

LESSON 147 PRACTICE Name ______

Solve. Watch the signs.

❶ 43 + 57 = 100	❷ 430 + 570 = 1000	❸ 738 + 249 = 987
❹ 100 − 43 = 57	❺ 100 − 57 = 43	❻ 900 − 430 = 470
❼ 863 − 359 = 504	❽ 407 − 218 = 189	❾ 342 + 107 + 68 + 259 + 7 + 246 = 1029

Math Explorations and Applications Level 2 • 147

ENRICHMENT p. 147

LESSON 147 ENRICHMENT Name ______

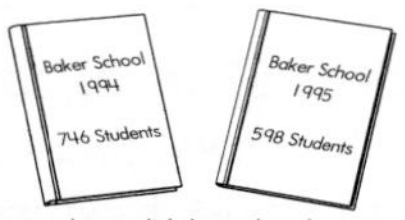

❶ How many fewer students did the school have in 1995? 148

❷ There were 350 students who learned Spanish in 1994. In 1995 there were 416 students who learned Spanish. How many more students learned Spanish in 1995? 66

❸ In 1996 Baker School had 178 more students than it had in 1995. How many students did the school have in 1996? 776

❹ In 1995 there were 114 students from Baker School who entered the city spelling contest. Some of these students were learning Spanish, but 79 were not. How many students entered the spelling contest? 114

❺ In 1997 Baker School had 52 fewer students than it had in 1994. How many students were in the school in 1997? 694

❻ In both 1994 and 1995 there were 220 students who took the bus each year. How many did not take the bus in 1994? 526

❼ How many did not take the bus in 1995? 378

Math Explorations and Applications Level 2 • 147

LESSON 148

Student Edition pages 333–334

Adding and Subtracting Money

LESSON PLANNER

Objectives

✓ to assess students' ability to form any amount of money up to $10 using coins and bills, and up to $1000 using bills

▶ to apply three-digit addition and subtraction to money situations

Context of the Lesson This is the third lesson on three-digit addition and subtraction. It contains Mastery Checkpoint 18 for this skill.

Materials	**Program Resources**
play money*	Number Cubes
	Practice Master 148
	Enrichment Master 148
	Assessment Master
	For extra practice: CD-ROM* Lesson 148

1 Warm-Up

5 MINUTES

Problem of the Day Write the following problem on the chalkboard: Will went on vacation on Monday. His vacation lasted 15 days. On which day of the week did his vacation end? (Tuesday)

MENTAL MATH Have students mentally add and subtract, using their Number Cubes to respond:

a. 6 − 3 = (3) b. 9 + 9 = (18) c. 9 − 5 = (4)
d. 8 +7 = (15) e. 6 + 4 = (10) f. 8 − 0 = (8)

2 Teach

Demonstrate Tell students that one dollar is worth 100 cents. Guide them to use this information to tell how many cents are in various dollar amounts; for example, $2 (200 cents) and $1.26. (126 cents) Then write several amounts on the chalkboard such as 257 cents, and have students show the same amount using a $ and decimal point. ($2.57)

LESSON 148

Name ______________________

Adding and Subtracting Money

Play the "Make a $10 Bill" game.

Write how much.

1. 100 cents 
2. 500 cents 
3. 200 cents 
4. 600 cents 
5. 1000 cents 
6. 150 cents 

7. 150 cents = $ 1.50
8. $1.25 = 125 cents
9. 175 cents = $ 1.75
10. $ 2.38 = 238 cents
11. 96 cents = $ 0.75
12. $1.76 = 176 cents
13. 243 cents = $ 2.43
14. $0.54 = 54 cents

NOTE TO HOME
Students change dollars to cents and cents to dollars.

RETEACHING

To help students who have difficulty playing the "Make a $10 Bill" game, have students make a specific amount of money, such as $7.58, using play bills and coins. Then have them make the same amount using different bills and coins. Continue this activity, gradually increasing the complexity of the amounts up to $10 and up to $1000 using bills only.

PRACTICE p. 148

LESSON 148 PRACTICE Name ______________________

Change cents to dollars.
There are 100 cents in 1 dollar.

1. 336 cents = $ 3.36
2. $5.72 = 572 cents
3. 185 cents = $ 1.85
4. $4.11 = 411 cents

Solve these problems.

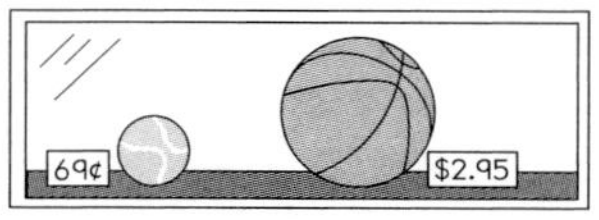

5. How many cents do the basketball and tennis ball cost all together? 295 + 69 = 364 ¢

6. Jerome has a $5 bill. He bought the basketball and tennis ball. How much change did he get? 500 − 364 = 136 ¢

148 • Math Explorations and Applications Level 2

*available separately

◆ LESSON 148 Adding and Subtracting Money

Solve these problems.

⑮ How many cents do the doll and the hat cost all together?

650¢ + 75¢ = 725 ¢

⑯ Leslie has $9.

Suppose she buys the doll and the hat.

How much change will she get?

$$\begin{array}{r} 900¢ \\ -\ 725¢ \\ \hline \end{array}$$

900¢ − 725¢ = 175 ¢

⑰ How long are both tables together? 362 cm

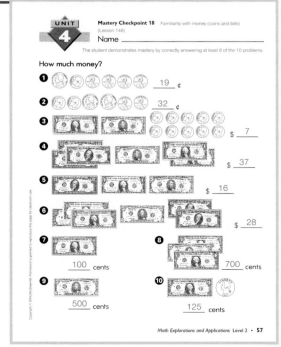

$$\begin{array}{r} 181 \\ +\ 181 \\ \hline 362 \end{array}$$

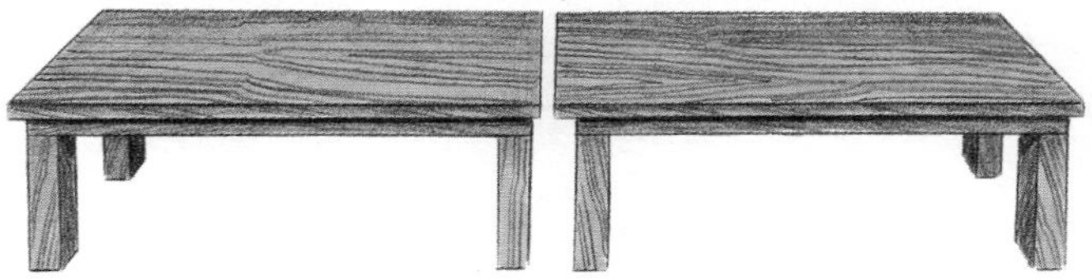

NOTE TO HOME
Students solve problems involving money and measurement.

ENRICHMENT p. 148

LESSON 148 ENRICHMENT Name ____

❶ Wendy cleaned out some drawers and found seven hundred forty-two pennies. Write the dollars and cents she will get at the bank. $7.42

❷ Tell what paper bills and coins she can get for her pennies.
seven one-dollar bills, four dimes, and two pennies; or other combinations that make $7.42

❸ Andrew found six quarters, six dimes, and sixty-six pennies. Write the dollars and cents he will get at the bank. $2.76

❹ Andrew wants mostly paper money. Tell what paper bills and what other coins he can get from his coins.
two one-dollar bills, seven dimes, and 6 pennies, or other combinations that make $2.76

❺ Claire had $123.46 in her bank account. How many ten-dollar bills could she get if she took her money out of the bank? 12

❻ How many one-dollar bills could she get? 123

148 • Math Explorations and Applications Level 2

ASSESSMENT p. 57

UNIT 4 **Mastery Checkpoint 18** Familiarity with money (coins and bills) (Lesson 148)
Name ____
The student demonstrates mastery by correctly answering at least 8 of the 10 problems.

How much money?

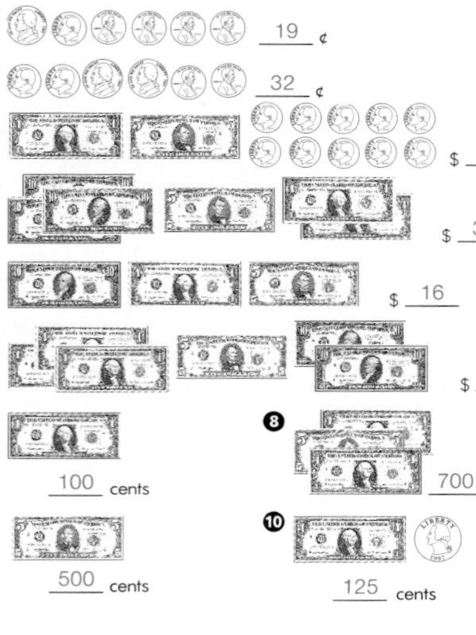

❶ 19 ¢
❷ 32 ¢
❸ $ 7
❹ $ 37
❺ $ 16
❻ $ 28
❼ 100 cents
❽ 700 cents
❾ 500 cents
❿ 125 cents

Math Explorations and Applications Level 2 • 57

Introducing the "Make a $10 Bill" Game Demonstrate and play the "Make a $10 Bill" game, which provides practice changing coins and bills up to $10. You will need: six $1 bills, two $5 bills, and one $10 bill; 10 pennies, 5 nickels, 10 dimes, and 4 quarters per player; and four 0–5 and 5–10 Number Cubes. First, divide the players into groups of two or three and put all of the money into a central pile. Players take turns rolling four cubes, adding the numbers rolled, and taking that amount of money from the bank in the largest possible denominations. Players continue taking turns rolling cubes and trading their money whenever they can for coins or bills of larger denominations. The first player who trades for the $10 bill wins.

Using the Student Pages Assign pages 333 and 334 for students to complete independently. Give individual help to those students who are having difficulty.

3 Wrap-Up

5 MINUTES

In Closing Have students describe two different ways they can combine coins and bills to make $6.45.

Mastery Checkpoint 18

By this time students should be able to form and trade money amounts up to $10 using coins and bills, and up to $1000 using bills. To assess students, observe them as they play the "Make a $10 Bill" game or use Assessment Master 57. Results of this assessment may be recorded on the Mastery Checkpoint Chart.

Assessment Criteria

Did the student . . .

- ✓ correctly trade money amounts during the "Make a $10 Bill" game?
- ✓ correctly solve 12 of 14 problems on page 333?
- ✓ correctly solve the three word problems on page 334?

LESSON 149

Student Edition pages 335–336

Adding and Subtracting with Three Digits

LESSON PLANNER

Objectives

✓ to assess student's ability to add and subtract three-digit numbers

▶ to provide practice solving word problems involving addition and subtraction of three-digit numbers

Context of the Lesson This is the last lesson that completely involves three-digit addition and subtraction; however, further practice is included in subsequent lessons. This lesson contains Mastery Checkpoint 19 for this skill.

Materials	Program Resources
base-10 materials	Number Cubes
	Reteaching Master
	Practice Master 149
	Enrichment Master 149
	Assessment Master
	For extra practice: CD-ROM* Lesson 149

1 Warm-Up 5 MINUTES

Problem of the Day Write this problem on the chalkboard: Leroy plans to save $1 each day every day for one year. So far he has saved $187. How much more will he save by the end of the year? ($178)

MENTAL MATH Have students add and subtract the following problems using mental math:

a. 16 – 12 = (4)
b. 6 + 5 = (11)
c. 5 + 2 = (7)
d. 9 + 6 = (15)
e. 9 – 3 = (6)
f. 7 + 2 = (9)
g. 10 – 10 = (0)
h. 9 + 7 = (16)

LESSON 149

Name ____________________

Adding and Subtracting with Three Digits

Solve these problems. Watch the signs.

❶ 291 − 187 = 104	❷ 356 + 294 = 650	❸ 869 − 334 = 535	❹ 487 + 202 = 689
❺ 125 + 125 = 250	❻ 834 − 78 = 756	❼ 63 + 159 = 222	❽ 547 − 123 = 424
❾ 425 + 58 = 483	❿ 483 + 108 = 591	⓫ 737 − 146 = 591	⓬ 200 − 183 = 17
⓭ 728 − 108 = 620	⓮ 700 − 243 = 457	⓯ 65 + 387 = 452	⓰ 398 − 127 = 271

NOTE TO HOME
Students practice mixed three-digit addition and subtraction problems.

RETEACHING p. 39

LESSON 149 RETEACHING Name ____________________

First add the ones. Rewrite if you need to. Add the tens. Rewrite if you need to. Add the hundreds.

❶ 238 + 143 = 381	❷ 495 + 244 = 739	❸ 361 + 720 = 1081	❹ 543 + 235 = 778

Look at the ones. Will you need to rewrite? Subtract the ones. Look at the tens. Rewrite if you need to. Subtract the tens.

❺ 780 − 190 = 590	❻ 554 − 204 = 350	❼ 612 − 141 = 471	❽ 813 − 245 = 568

Write number sentences and then solve.

❾ Marco saved $160 for his family's vacation. Lupe saved $217. How much more did Lupe save? 217 – 160 = 57

❿ Ms. Smith rewarded her students for extra work done in reading. Miriam earned 120 bonus points reading books at home. Al earned 187 points by reading to younger students. How many points did these two students earn all together? 120 + 187 = 307

PRACTICE p. 149

LESSON 149 PRACTICE Name ____________________

Solve. Watch the signs.

❶ 48 + 325 = 373	❷ 429 − 183 = 246	❸ 537 + 128 = 665
❹ 690 − 370 = 320	❺ 195 + 425 = 620	❻ 627 − 235 = 392
❼ 363 + 285 = 648	❽ 577 + 35 = 612	❾ 623 − 446 = 177

❿ The Kendo family drove 354 miles to Orlando, Florida. The next day they drove 268 miles. How many miles did they drive all together? 622

⓫ The Morris family flew 465 miles. They flew the same number of miles on their return trip. How many miles did they fly round-trip? 930

⓬ Mr. Santos is 175 centimeters tall. His brother is 148 centimeters tall. How much taller is Mr. Santos than his brother? 27 centimeters

*available separately

◆ LESSON 149 Adding and Subtracting with Three Digits

Solve these problems.

⑰ How many cents do the car and the airplane cost all together?
__796__ ¢

$2.98

$4.98

⑱ Kim is 190 centimeters tall. Two years ago he was 172 centimeters tall. How much did he grow in the two years?
__18__ cm

⑲ There are 365 days in 1998 and the same number in 1999. How many days are there in both years?
__730__ days

⑳ Mel rode his horse 24 miles on Monday. He rode another 27 miles on Tuesday. How many miles did he ride all together?
__51__ miles

NOTE TO HOME
Students solve word problems.

❷ Teach

Demonstrate List the following items and prices on the chalkboard:

Book: $3.75

Box of pencils: $2.25

Pencil sharpener: $3.27

Work with students to make up and solve problems about the different items. Include problems in which students can estimate to solve. For example: I have $5. Do I have enough to buy the pencils and book?

Using the Student Pages Assign pages 335 and 336 for students to complete independently. Tell students that these pages are a test to see how well they can add and subtract three-digit numbers.

❸ Wrap-Up

5 MINUTES

In Closing Have students describe a time in their lives when they might need to add or subtract money amounts.

Mastery Checkpoint 19

By this time students should be able to add and subtract three-digit numbers and apply these skills when solving word problems. To assess students , you can use their answers to pages 335 and 336 or use Assessment Master 58. Results of this assesment may be recorded on the Mastery Checkpoint Chart.

ENRICHMENT p. 149

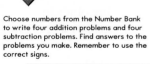

LESSON 149 ENRICHMENT Name ____________

Choose numbers from the Number Bank to write four addition problems and four subtraction problems. Find answers to the problems you make. Remember to use the correct signs.

Number Bank

789	624	95	404	581	78
99	65	982	560	29	900
212	359	701	54	448	848
145	284	307	678	813	723

Adding

Answers will vary but should be correct answers to problems students have written.

Subtracting

Math Explorations and Applications Level 2 • 149

ASSESSMENT p. 58

UNIT 4 **Mastery Checkpoint 19** Three-digit addition and subtraction (Lesson 149)

Name ____________

The student demonstrates mastery by correctly answering at least 13 of the 16 problems.

Work these problems. Watch the signs.

❶ 342 + 256 = 598	❷ 809 − 386 = 423	❸ 182 + 378 = 560	❹ 500 − 344 = 156
❺ 726 + 185 = 911	❻ 35 + 182 = 217	❼ 391 − 291 = 100	❽ 620 − 539 = 81
❾ 445 − 237 = 208	❿ 317 + 25 = 342	⓫ 381 + 296 = 677	⓬ 753 − 68 = 685
⓭ 812 − 15 = 797	⓮ 998 − 108 = 890	⓯ 222 + 678 = 900	⓰ 678 − 222 = 456

58 • Math Explorations and Applications Level 2

Assessment Criteria

Did the student . . .

✓ correctly solve 14 of 16 problems on page 335?

✓ correctly solve three of the four word problems on page 336?

LESSON 150

Student Edition pages 337–338

Practicing Addition and Subtraction

LESSON PLANNER

Objectives

- to review adding and subtracting multiples of 100
- to provide practice in using mental math strategies with addition and subtraction

Context of the Lesson This lesson provides practice adding and subtracting with multiples of 100 in preparation for counting by 100s.

Materials	Program Resources
base-10 materials*	Practice Master 150
	Enrichment Master 150
	For extra practice: CD-ROM* Lesson 150

1 Warm-Up

5 MINUTES

Problem of the Day Write this problem on the chalkboard: Hank is six years old. He is twice as old as his younger brother, Wally. When Wally is five, will Hank be ten? Why or why not? (No, Hank will always be 3 years older. When Wally is 5, Hank will be 8.)

MENTAL MATH Have students add and subtract the following using mental math.

a. 30 + 70 = (100)
b. 50 + 80 = (130)
c. 90 + 40 = (130)
d. 140 – 80 = (60)
e. 110 – 50 = (60)
f. 100 – 80 = (20)

2 Teach

Demonstrate Discuss and practice mental math strategies to solve examples such as: four hundreds + five hundreds (9 hundreds or 900); 400 + 499 (899); 399 + 499 (400 + 498 or 898).

LESSON 150

Name ______________________

Practicing Addition and Subtraction

These problems are easier than they look. Can you solve them in your head?

Add.

1. 300 + 400 = 700
2. 300 + 399 = 699
3. 299 + 400 = 699
4. 299 + 399 = 698
5. 200 + 500 = 700
6. 201 + 499 = 700
7. 499 + 201 = 700
8. 499 + 202 = 701

Subtract.

9. 400 − 100 = 300
10. 400 − 99 = 301
11. 399 − 99 = 300
12. 401 − 99 = 302
13. 375 − 100 = 275
14. 374 − 99 = 275
15. 373 − 98 = 275
16. 372 − 97 = 275

NOTE TO HOME
Students solve addition and subtraction problems in their head.

RETEACHING

Review mental math strategies such as adding a number to one addend and taking it away from the other to mentally add sums such as 299 + 215. (300 + 214 = 514) Subtraction strategies include taking away or adding a number to both numbers: 370 - 231 = 369 - 230 = 139.

Literature Connection Read aloud or invite students to read *A More or Less Fish Story* by Joanne and David Wylie to reinforce lesson concepts.

GIFTED & TALENTED

Meeting Individual Needs

Have students work in groups to estimate their ages in days. Then ask them to find their exact ages and compare their estimates with their exact answers.

*available separately

◆ LESSON 150 Practicing Addition and Subtraction

GAME

Take-Home Activity

Make 1000

Players: Two

Materials: Two 0–5 Number Cubes, two 5–10 Number Cubes, pencil, and paper

RULES

Leader: Choose and write down any number between 250 and 750. This will be the starting number.

Player: Your are going to get as close to 1000 as you can without going over 1000. Roll all four cubes and make a one-, two- or three-digit number. Add your number to the leader's number. If you roll a 10, roll again.

Leader: Roll all four cubes and make a number. Add your number to the starting number.

Winner: The winner of the round is the person who gets closest to 1000 without going over.

NOTE TO HOME
Students approximate and solve problems involving multidigit addition and subtraction.

Using the Student Pages Have students complete page 337 independently, using any mental math strategies that they can.

GAME **Introducing the "Make 1000" Game** Demonstrate how to play the "Make 1000" game on page 338 for two players, which involves estimating sums and differences and solving three-digit addition and subtraction problems. First have player 1 write down any number between 250 and 750. Then player 2 rolls four cubes (if a 10 is rolled, that cube is rolled again) and uses one or more of the cubes to make a one-, two-, or three-digit number. Player 2 then adds this number to the starting number, trying to get a sum as close to 1000 as possible without going over. Players switch roles and repeat. The player with the highest number under 1000 wins the round. To play a variation involving subtraction, players record how close they each come to 1000 on each turn, and at the end of the game add the differences. The player with the lesser sum wins.

3 Wrap-Up (5 MINUTES)

In Closing Have students explain their strategies for choosing the number between 250 and 750 when playing the "Make 1000" game.

ALTERNATIVE ASSESSMENT

Performance Assessment Observe students as they play the game to see who can accurately add and subtract and correctly use mental math strategies.

Assessment Criteria

Did the student . . .

✓ correctly add and subtract when playing the "Make 1000" game?

✓ correctly solve 12 of 16 problems on page 337?

✓ use mental math strategies when appropriate?

PRACTICE p. 150

LESSON 150 PRACTICE Name ____________

Solve these problems quickly. Watch the signs.

1. 700 + 400 = 1100
2. 900 − 400 = 500
3. 500 + 500 = 1000
4. 800 − 200 = 600
5. 600 + 600 = 1200
6. 1000 − 800 = 200
7. 700 + 800 = 1500
8. 600 + 700 = 1300
9. 1600 − 800 = 800
10. 500 + 900 = 1400
11. 1200 − 900 = 300
12. 1400 − 500 = 900

150 • Math Explorations and Applications Level 2

ENRICHMENT p. 150

LESSON 150 PRACTICE Name ____________

Solve these problems quickly. Watch the signs.

1. 700 + 400 = 1100
2. 900 − 400 = 500
3. 500 + 500 = 1000
4. 800 − 200 = 600
5. 600 + 600 = 1200
6. 1000 − 800 = 200
7. 700 + 800 = 1500
8. 600 + 700 = 1300
9. 1600 − 800 = 800
10. 500 + 900 = 1400
11. 1200 − 900 = 300
12. 1400 − 500 = 900

Copyright © SRA/McGraw-Hill. Permission is granted to reproduce this page for classroom use.

150 • Math Explorations and Applications Level 2

LESSON 151

Student Edition pages 339–342

Approximating Answers

LESSON PLANNER

Objectives

- to provide practice in estimating sums and differences
- demonstrate the use of estimating to recognize incorrect sums and differences
- to provide practice in solving addition and subtraction word problems

Context of the Lesson This lesson builds on concepts and skills of estimation taught in Lesson 150.

Materials	Program Resources
world map (optional)	"Checkbook" Game Mat
	Number Cubes
	Practice Master 151
	Enrichment Master 151
	For extra practice: CD-ROM* Lesson 151

1 Warm-Up (5 MINUTES)

Problem of the Day Write this problem on the chalkboard: Mr. Ruiz works five days per week in an office three miles from his house. How many miles does he travel to and from work every week? (30)

MENTAL MATH Have students multiply the following, using their Number Cubes to respond.

a. 4 × 6 = (24)
b. 7 × 2 = (14)
c. 3 × 8 = (24)
d. 5 × 6 = (30)
e. 3 × 7 = (21)
f. 9 × 8 = (72)

LESSON 151

Name ______________________

Approximating Answers

Three answers are given for each problem. Only one of the answers is correct. Put a check mark under the correct answer. Explain why your answers make sense.

❶ 98 + 103

101	201	301
	✔	

❷ 407 + 398

605	705	805
		✔

❸ 489 + 312

599	701	801
		✔

❹ 482 + 312

694	704	794
		✔

❺ 306 + 247

453	503	553
		✔

❻ 694 + 156

750	800	850
		✔

❼ 398 − 199

99	199	299
	✔	

❽ 98 − 21

67	77	87
	✔	

❾ 803 − 198

605	705	805
✔		

❿ 507 − 208

299	399	499
✔		

⓫ 895 − 494

301	401	501
	✔	

⓬ 1000 − 750

250	350	450
✔		

NOTE TO HOME
Students practice adding and subtracting mentally.

Literature Connection Read aloud *A Bag Full of Pups* by Dick Gackenbush to reinforce lesson concepts.

*available separately

◆ **LESSON 151** Approximating Answers

Use the Mixed Practice on page 398 after this lesson.

Solve these problems.

13 Max has a $10.00 bill.
He will buy flowers for $1.98.
How much change should he get?
Ring the correct answer.

$2.02 ($8.02) $10.02

14 Karen earned $3.25 yesterday.
She earned $4.50 today.
How much did she earn in the two days?
Ring the correct answer.

$6.05 $7.05 ($7.75)

89¢ a bunch

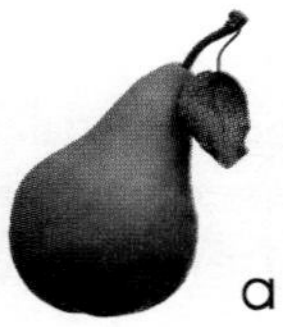

75¢ a pound

15 Jim has $5. Does he have enough money to buy

2 pounds of strawberries? **yes**

3 bunches of grapes? **yes**

3 pounds of pears? **yes**

4 pounds of strawberries? **no**

$1.79 a pound

NOTE TO HOME
Students solve word problems using mental math.

Geography Connection Display a world map, and have students who either came from other countries or have relatives in other countries name and find those countries on the map. Then estimate how far away each country is from your city by estimating the sum of distances between several intermediate locations.

2 Teach

Demonstrate Discuss and demonstrate how to estimate sums and differences of three-digit numbers. For example, write the following on the chalkboard:

$$\begin{array}{r} 392 \\ +206 \\ \hline (598) \end{array}$$

Explain that 392 is almost 400 and 206 is a little more than 200; therefore, the sum is about 400 + 200 or 600. Repeat this procedure for several more addition and subtraction problems.

Next, give students word problems that require only an estimate rather than an exact answer. For example: There are 473 children in a school. The lunchroom manager must order enough cookies for each child to have two. About how many cookies should the manager order?

Discuss whether the estimate should be more or less than the exact answer and why. Then ask students to estimate the answer. Students should realize that the estimate should be greater than the exact answer to be sure there are enough cookies. 500 + 500 = 1000 is a good estimate.

Using the Student Pages Discuss with students how they can use estimation to solve the problems on pages 339 and 340. Then have them complete the pages independently.

> *Most people who find themselves in a situation that requires mathematics either don't recognize that good decisions depend on mathematical thought or don't make the best decisions because they are unable or unwilling to think mathematically.*
>
> —Stephen S. Willoughby, *Mathematics Education for a Changing World*

◆ LESSON 151 Approximating Answers

Teach

Using the Student Pages Have students complete page 341 on their own. Students can use the grid on page 342 to record the results of the "Checkbook" game.

Introducing the "Checkbook" Game Mat Demonstrate and play the game, which involves adding and subtracting two-digit and three-digit numbers and maintaining a record. Complete directions can be found on the Game Mat.

◆ LESSON 151 Approximating Answers

Name ______________________

Solve these problems. If you use a calculator, you must push all the keys and signs shown.

16. 10 + 10 + 10 + 10 + 10 = **50**

17. 20 + 20 + 20 + 20 + 20 = **100**

18. 300 + 200 = **500**

19. 300 + 199 = **499**

20. 299 + 199 = **498**

Write C if you would use a calculator to work these problems. Write N if you would not. Then work each problem.

21. (**N**) 75 + 25 = **100**

22. (**N**) 76 + 25 = **101**

23. (**N**) 5 + 5 = **10**

24. (**C**) 372 + 469 = **841**

NOTE TO HOME
Students assess the difficulty of math problems.

RETEACHING

Write several problems on the chalkboard with incorrect sums or differences. Have students explain how they can use mental math or estimation to tell why each is wrong. Present problems similar to the following:

$$\begin{array}{r} 324 \\ +\,145 \\ \hline 312 \end{array}$$ (incorrect because the sum is less than one of the addends)

$$\begin{array}{r} 450 \\ -\,125 \\ \hline 591 \end{array}$$ (incorrect because the difference is greater than the minuend)

◆ LESSON 151 Approximating Answers

GAME

Play the "Checkbook" game.

"Earn" means to add money to the balance.

"Pay" means to subtract money to the balance.

Date	Earn	Pay	Balance
Start			$1000
Totals			

NOTE TO HOME
Students play a game in which they keep a checkbook balance.

3 Wrap-Up (5 MINUTES)

In Closing Have students describe a real-life situation in which they may need only an estimate rather than an exact answer.

ALTERNATIVE ASSESSMENT

Informal Assessment Use students' answers on the records they kept for the "Checkbook" game to informally assess their ability to add and subtract. To assess their ability to estimate, use their answers to student pages 339 and 340.

Assessment Criteria

Did the student . . .

- ✓ correctly solve ten of 12 problems on page 339?
- ✓ correctly answer five of six questions on page 340?
- ✓ correctly solve all of the problems on page 341?
- ✓ keep an accurate record when playing the "Checkbook" game?

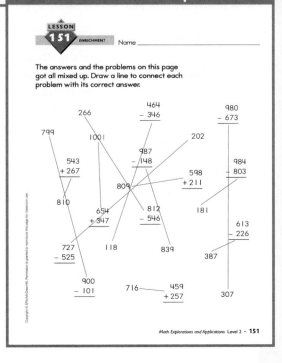

PRACTICE p. 151

LESSON 151 PRACTICE Name ____________________

Three answers are given for each problem. Only one of the answers is correct. Try to find each correct answer by estimating. Put a check mark under the correct answer.

1. 75 + 75 — 70, 150 ✔, 350
2. 307 + 616 — 523, 823, 923 ✔
3. 583 + 219 — 602, 802 ✔, 100
4. 219 + 219 — 438 ✔, 808, 838
5. 425 + 371 — 796 ✔, 625, 846
6. 647 + 135 — 682, 702, 782 ✔
7. 350 − 175 — 75, 175 ✔, 375
8. 904 − 326 — 378, 478, 578 ✔
9. 726 − 519 — 207 ✔, 407, 607
10. 193 − 68 — 25, 125 ✔, 225
11. 857 − 399 — 158, 458 ✔, 858
12. 600 − 235 — 65, 365 ✔, 565

ENRICHMENT p. 151

LESSON 151 ENRICHMENT Name ____________________

The answers and the problems on this page got all mixed up. Draw a line to connect each problem with its correct answer.

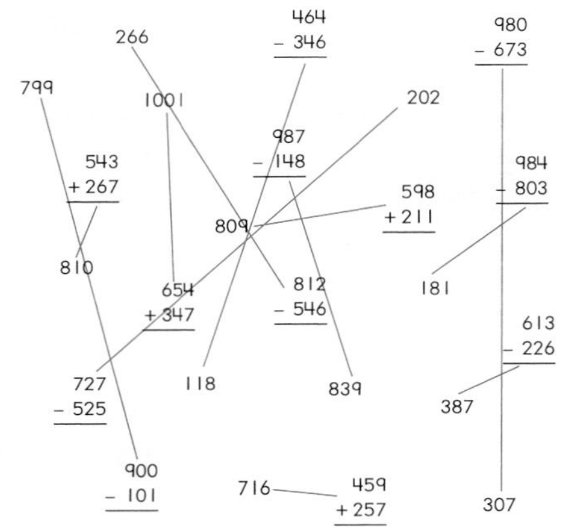

LESSON 152

Student Edition pages 343–344

Counting by 100s and 1000s

LESSON PLANNER

Objectives

- ▶ to introduce counting and writing numbers to 10,000
- ▶ to introduce positioning numbers on a number line through 10,000

Context of the Lesson This lesson introduces students to numbers they will use in four-digit addition and subtraction, which is taught in the next several lessons.

Materials	Program Resources
base-10 materials*	Number Cubes Practice Master 152 Enrichment Master 152 For extra practice: CD-ROM* Lesson 152

1 Warm-Up

5 MINUTES

Problem of the Day Write the following problem on the chalkboard: Each container holds up to three tennis balls. You have 20 tennis balls. What is the fewest number of containers you need to put all the tennis balls in containers? (7)

MENTAL MATH Have students divide the following, using Number Cubes to respond.

a. 21 ÷ 3 = (7) **b.** 28 ÷ 4 = (7)

c. 32 ÷ 4 = (8) **d.** 25 ÷ 5 = (5)

e. 12 ÷ 4 = (3) **f.** 14 ÷ 2 = (7)

2 Teach

Demonstrate Write 100 on the chalkboard. Have students read it aloud. Then write 1500 and ask whether anyone can read it. Although we often read numbers in the thousands as hundreds (i.e., fifteen hundred), teach the

LESSON 152

Name ____________________

Counting by 100s and 1000s

Count up. Fill in the missing numbers.

1	4763	4764	4765	4766	4767	4768
2	5387	5388	5389	5390	5391	5392
3	996	997	998	999	1000	1001
4	2018	2019	2020	2021	2022	2023
5	3097	3098	3099	3100	3101	3102

Count down. Fill in the missing numbers.

6	4325	4324	4323	4322	4321	4320
7	3102	3101	3100	3099	3098	3097
8	2004	2003	2002	2001	2000	1999

NOTE TO HOME
Students learn to count through 10,000.

Literature Connection Read aloud *If You Made a Million* by David M. Schwartz to reinforce lesson concepts.

Real-World Connection Have students order sports events on a number line from the earliest to the most recent event. For example, have students order the following events:

NBA Champions: 1996–Chicago Bulls; 1970–New York Knicks; 1989–Detroit Pistons; 1982–Los Angeles Lakers. (1970, 1982, 1989, 1996)

RETEACHING

Demonstrate and have students model four-digit numbers using base-10 materials. Then have students use the materials to determine where the numbers belong on a number line.

*available separately

◆ LESSON 152 Counting by 100s and 1000s

Count up or down. Fill in the missing numbers.

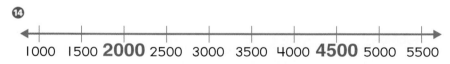

9	100	200	300	400	500	600
10	1000	2000	3000	4000	5000	6000
11	1000	1500	2000	2500	3000	3500
12	4500	4000	3500	3000	2500	2000

Write the missing numbers on each line.

13 1000 2000 **3000** 4000 5000

14 1000 1500 **2000** 2500 3000 3500 4000 **4500** 5000 5500

NOTE TO HOME
Students count by 100s and 1000s.

PRACTICE p. 152

LESSON 152 PRACTICE Name ____________

Count up or down. Fill in the missing numbers.

1	1017	1018	1019	1020	1021	1022	1023
2	3900	4000	4100	4200	4300	4400	4500
3	4630	4629	4628	4627	4626	4625	4624
4	5300	5200	5100	5000	4900	4800	4700
5	6009	6010	6011	6012	6013	6014	6015
6	9975	9974	9973	9972	9971	9970	9969
7	6500	7000	7500	8000	8500	9000	9500
8	3000	3500	4000	4500	5000	5500	6000

ENRICHMENT p. 152

LESSON 152 ENRICHMENT Name ____________

Fill in the missing numbers.

1	3001	2999	2997	2995	2993	2991
2	832	834	836	838	840	842
3	1060	1070	1080	1090	1100	1110
4	9996	9994	9992	9990	9988	9986
5	4001	4002	4003	4004	4005	4006
6	3000	2999	2998	2997	2996	2995
7	6050	6040	6030	6020	6010	6000
8	750	800	850	900	950	1000

students to read them as thousands (one thousand, five hundred). Guide students to read this number and then others similar to the following: 1100, 1900, 5000, 7000, 7200, and 7234.

Next, guide students to find the numbers that come before and after each of the following: 8346, 8399, 8999, 8099, 8909, 1900, 7790, and 5500. Then draw a number line on the chalkboard from 0–10,000 marking multiples of 1000. Have students show the approximate location of various four-digit numbers such as 2500, 4300, 2436. Include some three-digit numbers, too.

Using the Student Pages Explain to students that on page 343 they will need to count up for the top five problems and count down for the bottom three. Tell them to decide for themselves which way they must count for each problem on page 344. Then have students complete the pages independently. When they finish, ask them to share and compare answers.

3 Wrap-Up

5 MINUTES

In Closing Have students explain how they decided whether to count up or count down when completing the problems on page 344.

ALTERNATIVE ASSESSMENT

Informal Assessment Use students' answers on pages 343–344 to informally assess their understanding of four-digit numbers.

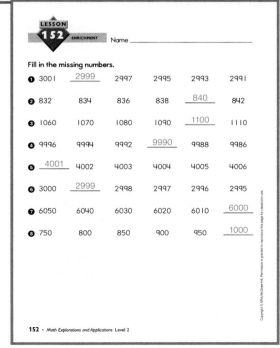

Assessment Criteria

Did the student . . .

✓ correctly fill in six of eight rows of numbers on page 343?

✓ correctly fill in three of four rows at the top of page 344?

✓ correctly fill in the number lines on page 344?

LESSON 153

Student Edition pages 345–346

Adding Four-Digit Numbers

LESSON PLANNER

Objective

▶ to explore adding four-digit numbers

Context of the Lesson This lesson introduces students to discovering methods for adding four-digit numbers. The algorithm for adding 4-digit numbers will be introduced in Lesson 154.

Materials	Program Resources
base-10 materials	Number Cubes Practice Master 153 Enrichment Master 153 For extra practice: CD-ROM* Lesson 153

1 Warm-Up

5 MINUTES

Problem of the Day Write the following problem on the chalkboard: You need to study for an hour and a half for a math test. You want to study a half hour each night. If your test is on Friday, on which night should you start to study for the test? (Tuesday)

MENTAL MATH Have students add, subtract, multiply, and divide the following:

a. 7 + 8 = (15)
b. 5 + 9 = (14)
c. 16 − 7 = (9)
d. 14 − 8 = (6)
e. 3 x 6 = (18)
f. 4 x 7 = (28)
g. 21 ÷ 3 = (7)
h. 16 ÷ 4 = (4)

LESSON 153

Name ______________________

Adding Four-Digit Numbers

Solve these problems.

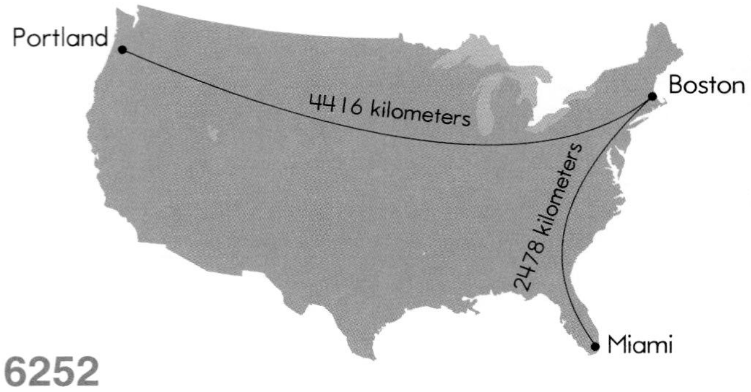

1. Margo has 2734 baseball cards. Roy has 3518 cards. How many cards do Margo and Roy have all together? 6252

GEOGRAPHY CONNECTION

2. How many kilometers is it from Portland to Boston? 4416

from Boston to Miami? 2478

from Portland to Boston to Miami? 6894

from Miami to Boston to Portland? 6894

FANTASTIC FACT

The National Basketball Association uses over 1100 basketballs each season.

NOTE TO HOME
Students solve problems involving addition of four-digit numbers.

RETEACHING

Because the standard four-digit algorithm will be formally taught in the next lesson, reteaching is not essential at this point.

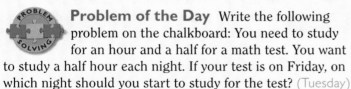

SPECIAL NEEDS

Meeting Individual Needs

Students having difficulty understanding how to add four-digit numbers might need a review and extra practice in addition of two- and three-digit numbers. Work in small groups with these students, encouraging them to explain each step as they solve problems. Encourage them to then use the same methods to add four-digit numbers.

*available separately

◆ **LESSON 153 Adding Four-Digit Numbers**

How well do you know our first president?

Complete the chart to show about how old he was.

Event	Date	About how old?
❸ Born	1732	0
❹ Married	1759	27
❺ Became First President	1789	57
❻ Re-elected President	1792	60
❼ Died	1799	67

❽ About how many years ago was George Washington born? 265 (in 1997)

Challenge: Find out more about George Washington. Make a larger chart to show how old he was when he did other things.

NOTE TO HOME
Students make calculations from a chart.

② Teach

Demonstrate Write two problems similar to those on page 345. Have students use any method they choose to solve them (including using base-10 materials). Then have them share, compare, and decide which methods are best and why. Sample problems to write on the chalkboard are:

- Kim saved 2584 baseball cards and Juanita saved 3063. How many cards are there all together? (5647)
- It is 3493 kilometers from San Francisco to Chicago by the short route and 4897 kilometers by the scenic route. If I drive the short route to Chicago and the scenic route back, how many kilometers is that all together? (8390) (You might want to draw a map on the chalkboard to illustrate this problem.)

Using the Student Pages Have students solve the problems on pages 345–346 using any method they choose. Then have them share and compare methods and results.

③ Wrap-Up

5 MINUTES

In Closing Have students explain which method they prefer to solve four-digit addition problems.

SELF ASSESSMENT

Have students raise their hands if they think they could add any two four-digit numbers you gave them. Observe which students feel confident at this point.

Assessment Criteria

Did the student . . .

✓ correctly solve 4 of the 5 questions on page 345?

✓ correctly solve 5 of the 6 problems on page 346?

✓ describe sensible methods of adding four-digit numbers?

PRACTICE p. 153

LESSON 153 PRACTICE Name ______

PROBLEM SOLVING Solve these problems.

❶ Angel has a collection of 2487 stamps. His friend Sean has 1736 stamps. How many stamps do Angel and Sean have all together? 4223

❷ Sara has $25.76 and her sister has $13.89. How much can Sara and her sister spend on a present for their mother? $39.65

❸ Mrs. Thomas bought a skirt for $29.99 and a blouse for $16.99. How much did she spend on the skirt and blouse all together? $46.98

❹ Jaime swam 1650 yards on Saturday and 1975 yards on Sunday. How many yards did Jaime swim over the weekend? 3625

ENRICHMENT p. 153

LESSON 153 ENRICHMENT Name ______

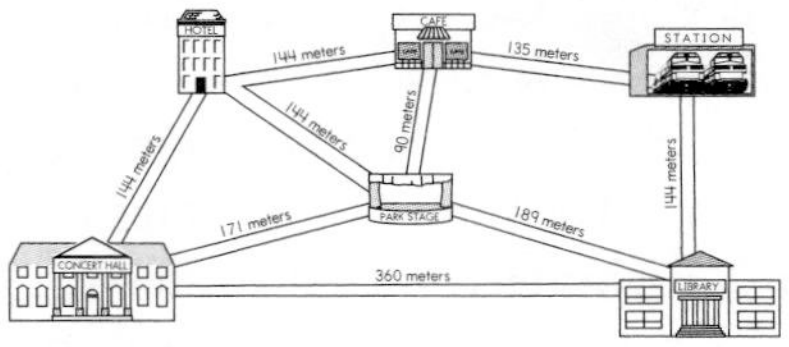

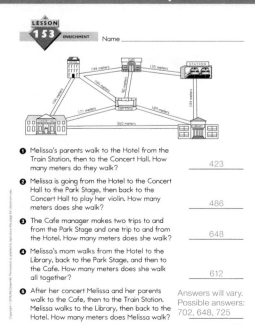

❶ Melissa's parents walk to the Hotel from the Train Station, then to the Concert Hall. How many meters do they walk? 423

❷ Melissa is going from the Hotel to the Concert Hall to the Park Stage, then back to the Concert Hall to play her violin. How many meters does she walk? 486

❸ The Cafe manager makes two trips to and from the Park Stage and one trip to and from the Hotel. How many meters does she walk? 648

❹ Melissa's mom walks from the Hotel to the Library, back to the Park Stage, and then to the Cafe. How many meters does she walk all together? 612

❺ After her concert Melissa and her parents walk to the Cafe, then to the Train Station. Melissa walks to the Library, then back to the Hotel. How many meters does Melissa walk? Answers will vary. Possible answers: 702, 648, 725

LESSON 154

Student Edition pages 347–348

Four-Digit Addition

LESSON PLANNER

Objective

▶ to develop proficiency in adding four-digit numbers

Context of the Lesson This is the last lesson in four-digit addition. The next lesson introduces four-digit subtraction.

Materials	Program Resources
base-10 materials*	Practice Master 154
	Enrichment Master 154
	For extra practice: CD-ROM* Lesson 154

1 Warm-Up

5 MINUTES

Problem of the Day Write this problem on the chalkboard: What is the largest four-digit odd number you can write in which all four digits are different? What is the least four-digit even number you can write in which all four digits are different? (9875; 1024)

MENTAL MATH Have students add, subtract, multiply, and divide the following problems using mental math:

a. 9 − 2 = (7)
b. 30 ÷ 6 = (5)
c. 4 + 4 = (8)
d. 3 × 10 = (30)
e. 15 − 5 = (10)
f. 25 ÷ 5 = (5)
g. 9 × 10 = (90)
h. 11 − 8 = (3)

2 Teach

Demonstrate Copy the problem from the top of page 347 onto the chalkboard. Work with students to solve the problem in the expanded form and then in standard form. Point out that you can solve four-digit addition problems using the same methods the class used for solving two- and three-digit addition problems. Have students explain when and how to regroup each number as you complete the problem on the chalkboard.

LESSON 154

Name ______________________

Four-Digit Addition

Solve these problems.

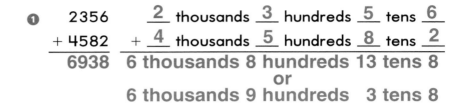

	1 thousands 5 hundreds 1 tens 7
3587	3 thousands 5 hundreds 8 tens 7
+ 4605	+ 4 thousands 6 hundreds 0 tens 5
8192	8 thousands 1 hundreds 9 tens 2

❶

2356	2 thousands 3 hundreds 5 tens 6
+ 4582	+ 4 thousands 5 hundreds 8 tens 2
6938	6 thousands 8 hundreds 13 tens 8
	or
	6 thousands 9 hundreds 3 tens 8

❷

3047	3 thousands 0 hundreds 4 tens 7
+ 2659	+ 2 thousands 6 hundreds 5 tens 9
5706	5 thousands 6 hundreds 9 tens 16
	or
	5 thousands 7 hundreds 0 tens 6

GAME Play the "Roll a Problem" game.

__ __ __ __
\+ __ __ __ __

__ __ __ __
\+ __ __ __ __

NOTE TO HOME
Students show how to add four-digit numbers.

Real-World Connection Tell students to pretend they have $5000 to spend on computers for school. Let students use sales catalogs or brochures from stores selling electronic equipment. Have them work with a partner to buy two items from the brochures. See which partners can buy the best computers and printers without spending more than $5000.

RETEACHING

Review adding two- and three-digit numbers using base-10 materials. Have students practice explaining when and how to regroup. Then use the base-10 materials and the same procedure to add four-digit numbers. Ask students how the methods are the same (as in regrouping whenever you have more than ten in one column) and how they are different (in four-digit addition by adding thousands, which is not done in the other two addition problems).

*available separately

◆ LESSON 154 Four-Digit Addition

Solve these problems.

❸ 2030 + 3506 = **5536**	❹ 4278 + 2356 = **6634**	❺ 3472 + 5689 = **9161**
	❻ 5555 + 6666 = **12,221**	❼ 9021 + 6483 = **15,504**
	❽ 2500 + 2500 = **5000**	❾ 8104 + 5166 = **13,270**
❿ 3047 + 1099 = **4146**	⓫ 4251 + 4152 = **8403**	⓬ 3300 + 4711 = **8011**

NOTE TO HOME
Students practice adding four-digit numbers.

PRACTICE p. 154

LESSON 154 PRACTICE Name ____________

Add.

❶ 1278 + 2253 = 3531
1 thousand + 2 thousands; 2 hundreds, 2 hundreds; 7 tens, 5 tens; 8 ones, 3 ones

❷ 4082 + 3127 = 7209
4 thousands + 3 thousands; 0 hundreds, 1 hundred; 8 tens, 2 tens; 2 ones, 7 ones

❸ 5175 + 2896 = 8071	❹ 6038 + 2774 = 8812	❺ 3578 + 2491 = 6069
❻ 5656 + 2437 = 8093	❼ 5800 + 2500 = 8300	❽ 4119 + 1798 = 5917

ENRICHMENT p. 154

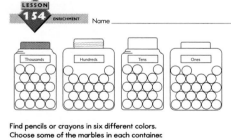

LESSON 154 ENRICHMENT Name ____________

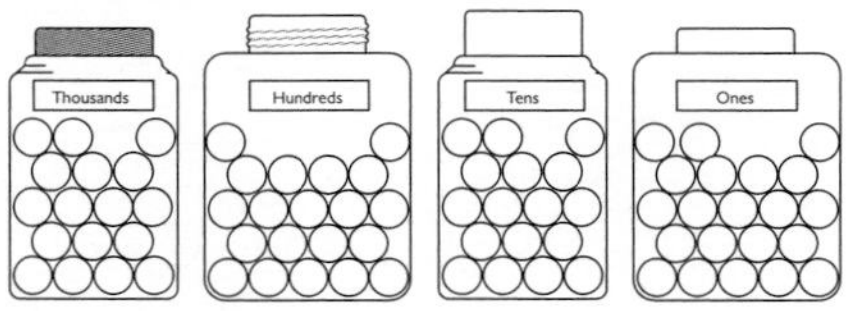

Find pencils or crayons in six different colors. Choose some of the marbles in each container. Color those marbles with one color. Do the same with the other five colors.

Then on the lines below use the same colors to write the numbers they make.

Answers will vary, but numbers near the bottom should correspond to the marbles counted in the jars above.

If necessary use base-10 materials to show what is happening. For example, to show 7 + 5 in the units, show that if you add $7 and $5, you have twelve $1 bills that can be traded for one $10 and two $1 bills.

Using the Student Pages Assign the four-digit addition problems on pages 347–348 for students to complete independently. After correcting the problems students can go on to play the "Roll a Problem" game.

Using the "Roll a Problem" Game Have students use the grids found on page 347 to play a four-digit addition variation of the game. If they have time for more than two games have them use separate sheets of paper.

3 Wrap-Up

5 MINUTES

In Closing Have students make up a word problem that can be solved using four-digit addition. Have them solve their problems and then exchange papers and solve a classmate's problem.

ALTERNATIVE ASSESSMENT

Performance Assessment Use students' responses to pages 347 and 348 to assess their ability to add four-digit numbers.

Assessment Criteria

Did the student . . .

✓ correctly solve both problems on page 347?

✓ correctly solve 10 of the 10 problems on page 348?

✓ correctly solve problems in the "Roll a Problem" game?

LESSON 155

Student Edition pages 349–350

Four-Digit Subtraction

LESSON PLANNER

Objective

▶ to introduce the subtraction of four-digit numbers

Context of the Lesson This is the only lesson that focuses solely on four-digit subtraction.

Materials	**Program Resources**
base-10 materials*	Practice Master 155
	Enrichment Master 155
	For extra practice: CD-ROM* Lesson 155

1 Warm-Up

5 MINUTES

Problem of the Day Write the following problem on the chalkboard: Would you rather have two \$1000 bills or one \$1000 bill and eight \$100 bills? Why? (two \$1000 bills, because \$2000 is more than \$1800)

MENTAL MATH Have students count both forward and backward using mental math:

a. 36, 37, ____, ____, ____, 41, ____, ____, 44

b. 5, 10, ____, ____, 25, 30, ____, ____, 45

c. 2, 4, ____, ____, ____, 12, 14, ____, 18

d. 100, 99, ____, ____, ____, 95, 94, ____, ____, 91

e. 10, 20, ____, ____, ____, ____, 70, 80, ____, ____

f. 54, ____, 52, 51, ____, ____, ____, 47, 46, ____

2 Teach

Demonstrate Divide the class into groups. Give each group play money to facilitate solving several word problems similar to the following: Pablo saved \$2584 and Maria saved \$3063. Who saved more? How much more? (Maria saved \$479 more.)

LESSON 155

Name ______________________

Four-Digit Subtraction

Solve these problems. The first one has been done for you.

1.
```
    9
 2 10 15 13
  3 0 6 3
– 2 5 8 4
  -------
    4 7 9
```

9 hundreds
2 thousands 10 hundreds 15 tens 13
3 thousands 0 hundreds 6 tens 3
– 2 thousands 5 hundreds 8 tens 4
4 hundreds 7 tens 9

2. 4783 – 2651 = **2132**

__4__ thousands __7__ hundreds __8__ tens __3__
– __2__ thousands __6__ hundreds __5__ tens __1__
2 thousands 1 hundred 3 tens 2

3. 8074 – 2356 = **5722**

7 thousands 10 hundreds
__8__ thousands __0__ hundreds __7__ tens __4__
– __2__ thousands __3__ hundreds __5__ tens __6__
5 thousands 7 hundreds 2 tens 2

4. 8525 – 2475 = **6050**

5. 8943 – 356 = **8587**

6. 7583 – 2583 = **5000**

NOTE TO HOME
Students show how to subtract four-digit numbers.

RETEACHING

Review subtracting two- and three-digit numbers using base-10 materials. Have students practice explaining when and how to trade. Then use the base-10 materials and the same procedure to subtract four-digit numbers. Ask students how the methods are the same (trading or borrowing whenever there is not enough in one column to subtract from) and how they are different (in four-digit subtraction thousands are subtracted, which is not done in two- and three-digit subtraction problems).

*available separately

◆ LESSON 155 Four-Digit Subtraction

Use the Mixed Practice on page 399 after this lesson.

Solve these problems.

7. 5000 − 2500 = **2500**
8. 4278 − 2846 = **571**
9. 3472 − 2333 = **3671**
10. 3871 − 2566 = **1305**
11. 1478 − 1185 = **293**
12. 7802 − 4056 = **3746**
13. 8222 − 2550 = **5672**
14. 7000 − 4000 = **3000**
15. 5310 − 2173 = **3137**
16. 4000 − 1234 = **2766**
17. 7456 − 1435 = **6021**
18. 9412 − 3571 = **5841**
19. 2932 − 1414 = **1518**

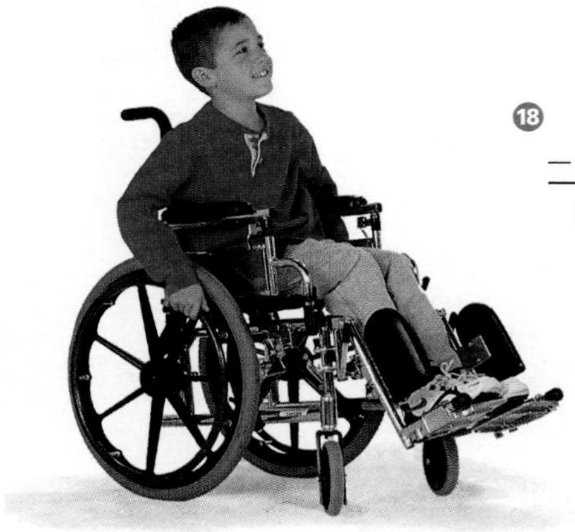

NOTE TO HOME

Students continue subtracting four-digit numbers.

PRACTICE p. 155

LESSON 155 PRACTICE Name ____________

Subtract.

1. 7500 − 6050 = 1450
2. 3981 − 1995 = 1986
3. 6000 − 3725 = 2275
4. 2119 − 1375 = 744
5. 8456 − 2364 = 6092
6. 9027 − 5129 = 3898
7. 4478 − 2186 = 2292
8. 3025 − 2910 = 115
9. 6127 − 4376 = 1751
10. 8521 − 1245 = 7276
11. 7000 − 2500 = 4500
12. 9099 − 8591 = 508

Math Explorations and Applications Level 2 • 155

ENRICHMENT p. 155

LESSON 155 ENRICHMENT Name ____________

The tall buildings stand for thousands. The medium-size buildings are hundreds. The small buildings are tens, and the phone booths stand for ones. The windows show how many thousands, hundreds, tens, and ones.

Solve the problems. Give the answers by making your own drawings.

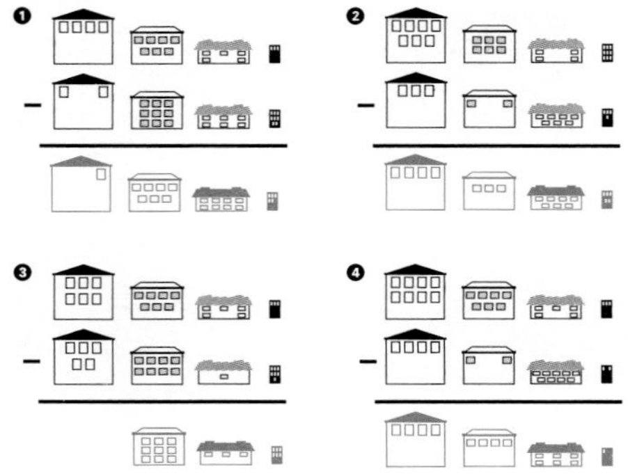

Math Explorations and Applications Level 2 • 155

When finished, demonstrate how to use pencil and paper to solve four-digit subtraction problems both in standard form and in expanded form, just as you demonstrated four-digit addition in Lesson 154. Again, point out the similarities between two- and three-digit subtraction. You might want to use thousands, hundreds, tens, and ones models to demonstrate each step.

Using the Student Pages Assign pages 349 and 350 for students to complete independently. Check students' work as they complete the problems.

3 Wrap-Up (5 MINUTES)

In Closing Have students make up a word problem that can be solved using four-digit subtraction. Have them solve their problems and then exchange and solve a classmate's problem.

ALTERNATIVE ASSESSMENT

Informal Assessment Use students' responses to pages 349 and 350 to informally assess their ability to subtract four-digit numbers.

Assessment Criteria

Did the student . . .

✓ correctly solve the word problems during the demonstration?

✓ correctly solve five of the six problems on page 349?

✓ correctly solve 11 of the 13 problems on page 350?

GIFTED & TALENTED

Meeting Individual Needs

Challenge students to write a paragraph giving examples of how to use addition to check answers in four-digit subtraction. Students should realize that they can use the same method for four-digit subtraction as they did when using addition to check two-digit subtraction. Allow volunteers to demonstrate their methods to the class.

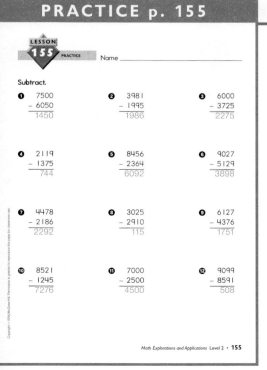

LESSON 156 Keeping Sharp

Student Edition pages 351–352

LESSON PLANNER

Objectives

- to provide practice in adding and subtracting pairs of four-digit numbers
- to introduce adding columns of four-digit numbers

Context of the Lesson This lesson introduces column addition using four-digit numbers.

Materials	Program Resources
none	Number Cubes
	Reteaching Master
	Practice Master 156
	Enrichment Master 156
	For extra practice: CD-ROM* Lesson 156

1 Warm-Up (5 minutes)

Problem of the Day Write the following problem on the chalkboard: Mrs. Ming wants to put a fence around her pool. She wants to fence an area six yards long and three yards wide. She plans on buying 20 yards of fence. Is that enough? How can you tell? (Yes, the perimeter is 6 + 6 + 3 + 3 = 18 yards, so 20 yards is enough.)

MENTAL MATH Have students estimate the sums and differences in the following problems.

a. 29 + 21 = (30 + 20 = 50)

b. 47 + 12 = (50 + 10 = 60)

c. 105 + 298 = (100 + 300 = 400)

d. 292 – 111 = (300 – 100 = 200)

e. 712 – 387 = (700 – 400 = 300)

2 Teach

Demonstrate Write the following problem on the chalkboard:

$$\begin{array}{r} 1142 \\ 5550 \\ +2502 \\ \hline (9194) \end{array}$$

LESSON 156

Name ______________________

Keeping Sharp

Solve these problems. Watch the signs.

1. 4653 + 208 = 4861	2. 4653 − 208 = 4445	3. 3489 − 2438 = 1051	4. 846 + 7259 = 8105
5. 8000 − 2386 = 5614	6. 6173 + 3827 = 10,000	7. 4823 + 1759 + 2427 = 9009	8. 1958 + 66 + 3471 = 5495
9. 125 + 1625 + 2125 + 3125 = 7000	10. 1642 + 871 + 2169 = 4682	11. 2000 + 1776 + 1492 = 5268	12. 4952 + 3000 + 1586 + 2 = 9540
13. 2958 + 37 + 416 = 3411	14. 4821 + 2307 + 219 = 7347	15. 215 + 18 + 4721 = 4954	16. 400 + 30 + 2 = 432

GAME Play the "Four-Digit Addition" game.

NOTE TO HOME
Students add and subtract multiple digits.

Literature Connection Read aloud "Math My Way" from *Lunch Money and Other Poems About School* by Carol Differey Shields to reinforce lesson concepts.

RETEACHING p. 40

LESSON 156 RETEACHING Name ______________________

Work the ones, tens, hundreds, and thousands in that order. Rewrite whenever you need to.

1. 6409 + 3238 = 9647	2. 3290 + 2185 = 5475	3. 1700 + 4595 = 6295	4. 5847 + 1638 = 7485	5. 7968 + 469 = 8437
6. 3575 − 1327 = 2248	7. 4752 − 2461 = 2291	8. 7081 − 1432 = 5649	9. 8316 − 5138 = 3178	10. 6900 − 3148 = 3752

Find the answers to the problems above in the puzzle below. They may be written across, backwards, up, down, or diagonally.

7	4	6	9	5	1	6	7	5	4
3	1	7	8	4	8	3	9	8	7
7	0	5	4	7	5	2	0	4	9
5	6	4	3	1	6	1	2	7	6
2	3	8	7	7	4	3	8	4	3
7	0	9	2	2	9	1	5	2	8

40 • *Math Explorations and Applications* Level 2

*available separately

◆ LESSON 156 Keeping Sharp

Suppose a wealthy person donated $8500 to your school to purchase playground equipment.

Complete the chart to show what you would buy. Make sure that you do not spend more than $8500.

Answers shown are examples only.

Item	How many?	Total Price
sandbox	1	$2795
teeter totter	1	$3450
rubber tire swings	2	$1990
Totals		$8235

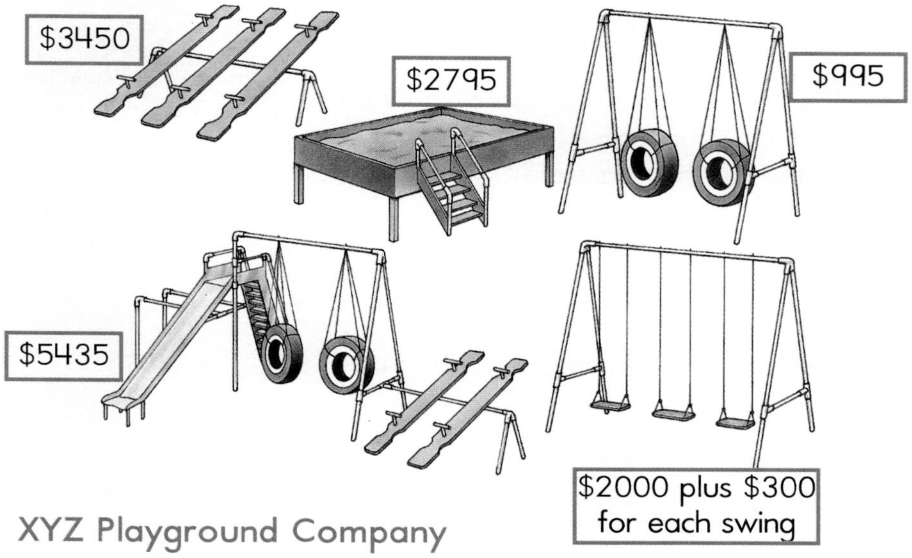

XYZ Playground Company

All prices include shipping and setting up. Schools do not pay tax.

NOTE TO HOME
Students subtract and budget money.

Have students suggest and demonstrate different ways to solve it. They might suggest: add two numbers first and then add that sum to the third number; or add the units, then tens, then hundreds, then thousands.

Using the Student Pages Have students complete page 351 and 352 on their own and share and compare answers.

Introducing the "Four-Digit Addition" Game Demonstrate the "Four-Digit Addition" game. Player 1 rolls all four Number Cubes twice, generating a four-digit number with each roll. The smallest number represents the thousands. The player uses the remaining numbers for any place value of his or her choice, and then adds the two numbers he or she created and records the sum. The other players repeat this procedure, and the player with the highest sum at the end wins. A "Harder Four-Digit Addition" game can be played by having the players take turns rolling the cubes once to make four-digit numbers. Each player keeps a running total of his or her own score. The player to reach 10,000 or more first wins the game.

3 Wrap-Up (5 MINUTES)

In Closing Have students explain which method they prefer for solving four-digit addition problems that have three or more addends.

ALTERNATIVE ASSESSMENT

Performance Assessment Observe which students can correctly add their scores as they play the "Four-Digit Addition" game.

Assessment Criteria

Did the student . . .

✓ correctly add the scores as he or she played the game?

✓ correctly solve 13 of 16 problems on page 351?

✓ correctly complete the chart on page 352?

PRACTICE p. 156

LESSON 156 PRACTICE Name ______

Solve. Watch the signs.

1. 1386 + 1275 + 3600 = 6261
2. 2461 + 3782 + 1158 = 7401
3. 6043 + 1895 + 2153 = 10,091
4. 5097 − 2509 = 2588
5. 2986 − 1597 = 1389
6. 3219 − 1225 = 1994
7. 2710 + 2187 + 3529 = 8426
8. 4814 + 1366 + 1616 = 7796
9. 3312 + 5891 + 1325 = 10,528
10. 3650 − 2450 = 1200
11. 4815 − 3913 = 902
12. 6597 − 798 = 5799

156 • Math Explorations and Applications Level 2

ENRICHMENT p. 156

LESSON 156 ENRICHMENT Name ______

These animals must be rescued from a flood and taken to a different part of the jungle. Look at the chart to see how much the animals weigh.

The animal trailer can carry up to 12,000 kilograms. Work math problems to find out which animals can be carried for each trip. Write the animals that will go on each trip and how much each group of animals will weigh.

Animal	Weight
elephant	5800 kilograms
hippo	2300 kilograms
rhino	2800 kilograms
zebra	300 kilograms

Answers will vary, but some examples are as follows:

1. two elephants—11,600 kilograms
2. one elephant, two zebras—6400 kilograms
3. one elephant, two rhinos, two zebras—12,000 kilograms
4. one elephant, two hippos, four zebras—11,600 kilograms
5. one hippo—2300 kilograms
6. two elephants, one zebra—11,900 kilograms
7. one elephant, two rhinos, two zebras—12,000 kilograms
8. three hippos, four zebras—8100 kilograms

156 • Math Explorations and Applications Level 2

LESSON 157

Student Edition pages 353–354

Applying Addition and Subtraction

LESSON PLANNER

Objectives

- ▶ to demonstrate solving realistic problems involving addition and subtraction of four-digit numbers
- ▶ to provide practice with adding and subtracting four-digit numbers

Context of the Lesson This is the last lesson on four-digit numbers.

Materials	Program Resources
base-10 materials*	Number Cubes
	Practice Master 157
	Enrichment Master 157
	For extra practice: CD-ROM* Lesson 157

1 Warm-Up 5 MINUTES

Problem of the Day Write the following problem on the chalkboard, then have students complete the patterns:

1534, 1634, 1734, ____, ____, ____ (1834, 1934, 2034)

2458, 2448, 2438, ____, ____, ____ (2428, 2418, 2408)

MENTAL MATH Have students multiply, divide, and subtract the following using mental math:

a. 4 × 8 = (32) **b.** 8 × 4 = (32) **c.** 32 ÷ 8 = (4)

d. 32 ÷ 4 = (8) **e.** 14 − 6 = (8) **f.** 17 − 8 = (9)

2 Teach

Demonstrate Present and discuss realistic situations in which students must add or subtract four-digit numbers. For example, have them tell what year they were born and calculate what year it will be when they are 15, 20, and 75 years old.

LESSON 157

Name ______________________

Applying Addition and Subtraction

SOCIAL STUDIES CONNECTION Solve these problems.

1. Antonio was born in 1994. When will he be 95 years old? 2089

2. The United States was "born" in 1776. When will the United States be 250 years old? 2026

3. Thomas Jefferson was born in 1743. He died in 1826. How old was he when he died?

   82 or 83 years old

   How old would he be today? 253 or 254 years old (in 1997)

NOTE TO HOME
Students solve four-digit word problems.

RETEACHING

Give students who are having difficulty understanding the word problems similar problems with smaller numbers. Have them act out or draw pictures to solve them. Gradually, increase the difficulty of the problems. Students who are having difficulty adding and subtracting should be given further practice using base-10 materials to solve four-digit addition and subtraction problems.

*available separately

◆ **LESSON 157** Applying Addition and Subtraction **Use the Mixed Practice on page 400 after this lesson**

Solve these problems.

❹ There are 1440 minutes in one day.

How many minutes are there in two days? 2880

How many minutes are there in three days? 4320

SOCIAL STUDIES CONNECTION

❺ Columbus discovered America in 1492. How many years ago was that? 505 (in 1997)

❻ The Pilgrims first came to America in 1620. How many years ago was that? 377 (in 1997)

❼ Mrs. Phillips wants to buy this car. She has saved $4500. How much more money does she need?

$4957

GAME

Play the "Four Cubes from 10,000 to 0" game.

NOTE TO HOME
Students solve four-digit problems.

Include some money problems, such as, "Ms. Malito saved $3500. She wants to buy a boat for $4800. How much more does she need?" ($1300)

Introducing the "Four Cubes from 10,000 to 0" Game Demonstrate and play the "Four Cubes From 10,000 to 0" game to provide practice subtracting four-digit numbers. First, divide the students in groups of two to five students. Each player writes the number 10,000 on a sheet of paper. In turn, each player rolls all four cubes to form a four-digit number. The lowest number must be in the thousands place, but the other numbers can be assigned any other place value. If a 10 is rolled, the cube is rolled again. The player subtracts the four-digit number from the 10,000 on the paper. Play continues until the first player reaches 0 or less.

To vary the game, players roll two four-digit numbers and subtract one from the other. The player who has the least difference that is still greater than 0 is the winner.

Using the Student Pages Assign pages 353–354 for students to complete independently.

❸ Wrap-Up

5 MINUTES

In Closing Have volunteers explain and demonstrate how to add and subtract four-digit numbers.

SELF ASSESSMENT

Ask students to brainstorm ways they can improve their addition and subtraction skills.

PRACTICE p. 157

LESSON 157 PRACTICE Name ______

Solve these problems.

❶ A local charity had a goal of raising $6500 at a fund-raising dinner. So far, the charity has collected $4678. How much more money is needed for it to reach its goal? $1822

Allentown —2453 km— Bakersville —1697 km— Century City

❷ It is 2453 kilometers from Allentown to Bakersville. It is 1697 kilometers from Bakersville to Century City. How far is it from Allentown to Century City? 4150 kilometers

There are 1760 yards in 1 mile.

❸ How many yards are there in 2 miles? 3520

❹ How many yards are there in 4 miles? 7040

0001386 0008279

❺ Mrs. Cooper's car odometer had 1386 kilometers at the beginning of the year. At the end of the year the odometer read 8279 kilometers. How many kilometers did she drive in that year? 6893

Math Explorations and Applications Level 2 • 157

ENRICHMENT p. 157

LESSON 157 ENRICHMENT Name ______

ACME AUTO COMPANY

Dear Car Owner,

Today the meter in your car shows that you have driven 20,500 miles. You should have the oil changed every time you have driven 3000 more miles. You should get new tires when you have driven 15,000 more miles. Happy driving!

The People at Acme Auto

❶ What should the car's meter show when the car owner gets the oil changed the next time? 23,500

❷ It costs $18 to get the car's oil changed. If the car owner gets the oil changed five times, how much money will she pay all together? $90

❸ What should the car's meter show when the car owner gets new tires? 35,500

❹ The car owner got four new tires for $240. How much did each tire cost? $60

❺ The car owner decided to sell the car when the meter showed 57,550 miles. How many miles did she drive from the time of the letter from Acme Auto Company? 37,050

Math Explorations and Applications Level 2 • 157

Assessment Criteria

Did the student . . .

✓ correctly solve the word problems during the demonstration?

✓ correctly solve 2 of the 3 problems on page 353?

✓ correctly solve 3 of the 4 problems on page 354?

LESSON 158

Student Edition pages 355–358

Unit 4 Review

Using the Student Pages Use this Unit Review as a preliminary unit test to indicate areas in which each student is having difficulty or in which the entire class might need help. If students do well on the Unit Review, you might want to go directly to the next unit. If not, you may spend a day or so helping students overcome their individual difficulties before they take the Unit Test.

The lesson numbers next to each instruction line refer to the specific lessons for additional instruction if students need help. You may also use this information to make additional assignments to reinforce lesson skills and concepts.

Have students complete pages 355 through 358 on their own.

Unit Project If you have not already assigned the newspaper numbers project on pages 364a and 364b, you might want to do so at this time. Students can begin working on the project in cooperative groups in their free time as you work through the unit. The Unit Project is a good opportunity for students to practice counting numbers from a starting point other than one, recognize and write the numerals 0 to 10 and 0 to 20, experience saying and reading numbers, and practice discussing numbers and how they are used to measure, count, order, quantify, and label.

LESSON 158

Name ____________________

Unit 4 Review

Solve these problems. Watch the signs.

Lessons 123–129

1. 8 + 4 = **12**
2. 14 − 7 = **7**
3. 8 + 7 = **15**
4. 19 − 10 = **9**
5. 8 + 9 = **17**
6. 6 + 9 = **15**
7. 5 + [**8**] = 13
8. 10 = [**6**] + 4
9. [**8**] + 7 = 15
10. 9 + [**8**] = 17
11. 5 × 5 = **25**
12. 4 × 4 = **16**
13. 15 ÷ 5 = **3**
14. 3 × 5 = **15**
15. 8 × 6 = **48**
16. 12 ÷ 4 = **3**

NOTE TO HOME
Students review unit skills and concepts.

◆ LESSON 158 Unit 4 Review

Fill in the missing numbers.

Lesson 152

17

59	60	61	62	63	64	65

18

896	897	898	899	900	901	902

19

5048	5049	5050	5051	5052	5053

What is the right sign? Draw <, >, or =.

Lessons 152–154

20 65 (>) 56

21 972 + 4 (>) 952 + 4

22 8078 + 5 (=) 5 + 8078

23 541 + 5 (<) 541 + 10

NOTE TO HOME
Students review unit skills and concepts.

PRACTICE p. 158

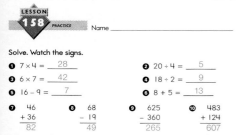

LESSON 158 PRACTICE Name ____________

Solve. Watch the signs.

1. 7 × 4 = 28
2. 20 ÷ 4 = 5
3. 6 × 7 = 42
4. 18 ÷ 2 = 9
5. 16 − 9 = 7
6. 8 + 5 = 13
7. 46 + 36 = 82
8. 68 − 19 = 49
9. 625 − 360 = 265
10. 483 + 124 = 607
11. 5173 + 3426 = 8599
12. 5173 − 3426 = 1747
13. 845 − 499 = 346

Fill in the missing numbers.

14

498	499	500	501	502	503	504

15

6237	6238	6239	6240	6241	6242

What is the right sign? Draw <, >, or =.

16. 236 + 8 (<) 11 + 236
17. 673 (>) 637
18. 9 + 8 (=) 10 + 7
19. 4035 + 20 (<) 4035 + 200
20. Tammy bought seven pencils for 8¢ each. How much did they cost all together? 56¢

158 • *Math Explorations and Applications* Level 2

ENRICHMENT p. 158

LESSON 158 ENRICHMENT Name ____________

If you add the numbers in the correct way, you will always get the same sum. In this case, the sum is 502. Try to figure out the combinations. The first one is done for you. Answers will vary.

101	× 102	103	104	105	106	107	108	× 109	110
111	♦ 112	• 113	114	115	116	117	• 118	♦ 119	120
121	122	123	124	125	126	127	128	129	130
131	♦ 132	• 133	134	135	136	137	• 138	♦ 139	140
141	× 142	143	144	145	146	147	148	× 149	150

Now make your own number puzzle like the one above. If you know the pattern, you can start with any number.

Start with any number. Number the boxes consecutively. The sum will vary depending on the starting number.

158 • *Math Explorations and Applications* Level 2

◆ **LESSON 158 Unit**

Name ______________________

Solve these problems. Watch the signs.

Lessons 153–157

(24) 29 + 67 = **96**

(25) 37 − 29 = **8**

(26) 595 − 435 = **160**

(27) 333 + 666 = **999**

(28) 4072 − 1286 = **2786**

(29) 4072 + 1286 = **5358**

(30) 125 + 125 + 125 + 125 = **500**

(31) 461 + 39 + 15 = **515**

(32) Eight goldfish cost $2.
How much does each goldfish cost? **25** ¢

NOTE TO HOME
Students review unit skills and concepts.

◆ LESSON 158 Unit 4 Review

Solve these problems.

Lessons 153–157

33 Los Amigos School put on a play.
It gave two shows.
1255 tickets were sold on Monday.
1347 tickets were sold on Tuesday.
How many tickets were sold all together? 2602

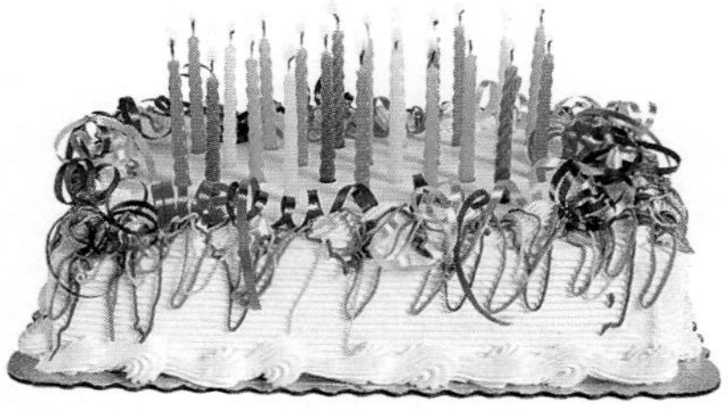

34 Eileen is seven years old.
How old will she be in 27 years? 34

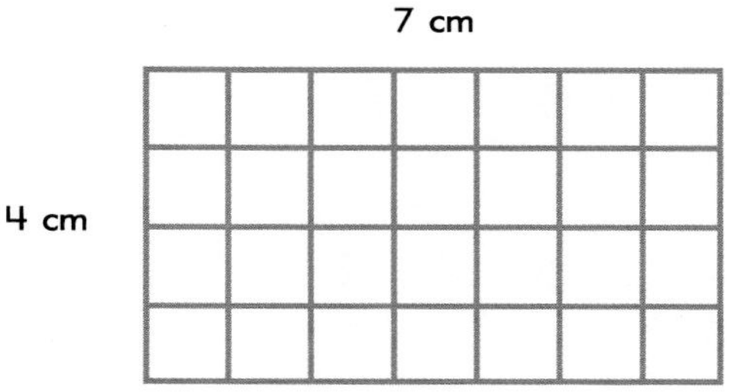

Lesson 119

35 The area is 28 square centimeters.

NOTE TO HOME
Students review unit skills and concepts.

LESSON 159

Student Edition pages 359–362

Unit 4 Test

Using the Student Pages The Unit Test on Student Edition pages 359 through 362 provides an opportunity to formally evaluate your students' proficiency with skills and concepts developed in this unit. It is similar in content and format to the Unit Review. Students who did well on the Unit Review might not need to take this test. Students who did not do well on the Unit Review should be provided with additional practice opportunities, such as the Mixed Practice pages, before taking the Unit Test. For further evaluation, you might want to have these students also take the Unit Test in multiple choice format, provided on pages 110–120 in the Assessment Master Book.

LESSON 159

Name ____________________

Unit 4 Test

ALGEBRA READINESS

Check your math skills.
Solve these problems.

1. 16 − 7 = **9**
2. 2 + 9 = **11**
3. 14 − 9 = **5**
4. 5 + 8 = **13**
5. 8 + [**5**] = 13
6. 12 = [**8**] + 4
7. [**5**] + 7 = 12
8. 11 = 5 + [**6**]
9. 5 × 7 = **35**
10. 9 × 9 = **81**
11. 6 × 8 = **48**
12. 2 × 7 = **14**
13. 7 × 8 = **56**
14. 10 ÷ 2 = **5**
15. 3 × 4 = **12**
16. 24 ÷ 8 = **3**

NOTE TO HOME
This test checks unit skills and concepts.

PRACTICE p. 159

LESSON 159 PRACTICE Name ____________________

Solve. Watch the signs.

1. 15 − 8 = 7
2. 9 + 4 = 13
3. 6 × 5 = 30
4. 24 ÷ 4 = 6
5. 8 × 4 = 32
6. 16 ÷ 8 = 2
7. 27 + 49 = 76
8. 85 − 36 = 49
9. 947 + 518 = 1465
10. 614 − 479 = 135
11. 4038 + 2890 = 6928
12. 4038 − 2890 = 1148
13. 813 − 677 = 136

Fill in the missing numbers.

14.

797	798	799	800	801	802	803

15.

3248	3249	3250	3251	3252	3253

What is the right sign? Draw <, >, or =.

16. 93 + 15 (<) 20 + 93
17. 245 (<) 417
18. 219 + 8 (>) 219 + 7
19. 3125 + 20 (=) 3125 + 20
20. Shannon bought nine tops for 54¢. How much did each top cost? 6¢

◆ LESSON 159 Unit 4 Test

Fill in the missing numbers.

17

77	78	79	80	81	82	83

18

296	297	298	299	300	301	302

19

5088	5089	5090	5091	5092	5093

What is the right sign? Draw <, >, or =.

20. 54 + 4 (<) 64 + 5

21. 735 (>) 537

22. 9025 + 1 (<) 9025 + 3

23. 735 + 15 (=) 15 + 735

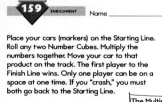

NOTE TO HOME
This test checks unit skills and concepts.

ENRICHMENT p. 159

LESSON 159 ENRICHMENT Name ____________

Place your cars (markers) on the Starting Line. Roll any two Number Cubes. Multiply the numbers together. Move your car to that product on the track. The first player to the Finish Line wins. Only one player can be on a space at one time. If you "crash," you must both go back to the Starting Line.

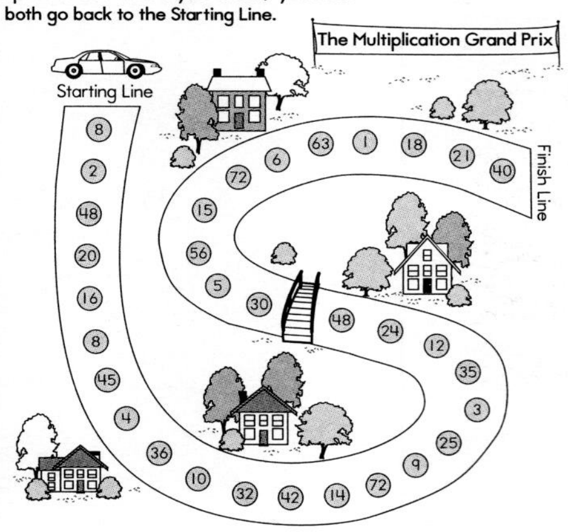

Math Explorations and Applications Level 2 • 159

ASSESSMENT p. 59

UNIT 4 **Unit 4 Test** (Use after Lesson 160.) Page 1 of 5

Name ____________

The student demonstrates mastery by correctly answering at least 40 of the 50 problems.

Solve.

1. 18 − 9 = 9
2. 11 − 3 = 8
3. 8 + 3 = 11
4. 6 + 7 = 13
5. 9 + [6] = 15
6. [7] + 7 = 14
7. 13 = [6] + 7
8. 10 = 4 + [6]
9. 4 × 3 = 12
10. 5 × 7 = 35
11. 3 × 6 = 18
12. 6 × 2 = 12
13. 4 × 8 = 32
14. 2 × 8 = 16
15. 15 ÷ 3 = 5
16. 27 ÷ 9 = 3
17. 24 ÷ 6 = 4
18. 12 ÷ 3 = 4

Go on . . .

Math Explorations and Applications Level 2 • 59

◆ **LESSON 159 Unit 4 Test** Name ____________________

Solve these problems. Watch the signs.

24. $28 + 59 = 87$

25. $74 - 69 = 5$

26. $973 + 809 = 1782$

27. $627 - 438 = 189$

28. $2483 + 3567 = 6065$

29. $4076 - 1284 = 2792$

30. $25 + 25 + 25 + 25 = 100$

31. $2500 + 2500 + 2500 + 2500 = 10{,}000$

32. $380 + 4627 + 1212 + 400 = 6619$

33. Taro bought three stickers. They cost 4¢ each. How much did they cost all together? __12__ ¢

NOTE TO HOME
This test checks unit skills and concepts.

◆ LESSON 159 Unit 4 Test

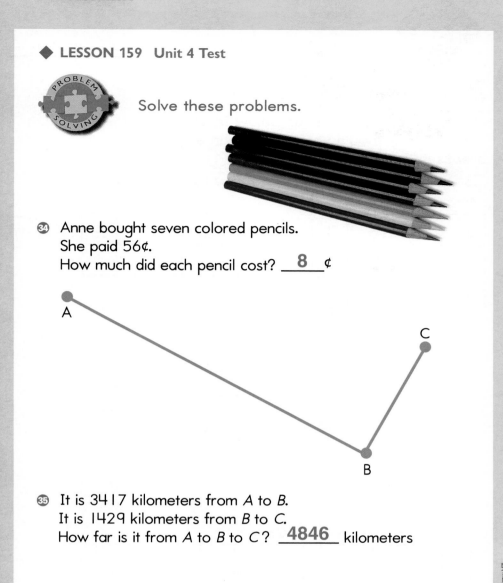

Solve these problems.

34 Anne bought seven colored pencils.
She paid 56¢.
How much did each pencil cost? 8 ¢

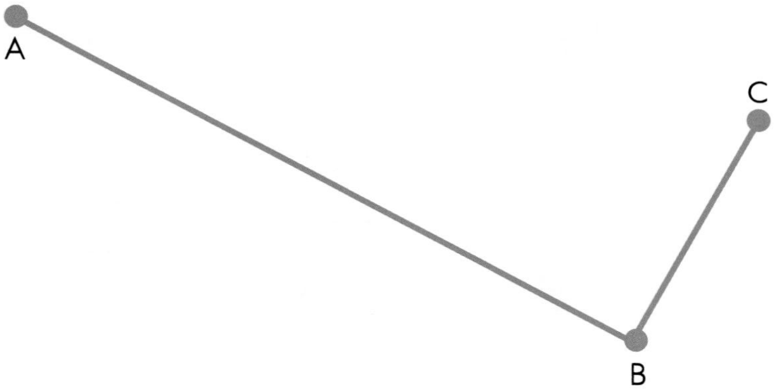

35 It is 3417 kilometers from *A* to *B*.
It is 1429 kilometers from *B* to *C*.
How far is it from *A* to *B* to *C*? 4846 kilometers

NOTE TO HOME
This test checks unit skills and concepts.

LESSON 160

Student Edition pages 363–364

Extending the Unit

LESSON PLANNER

Objective

- to provide remediation instruction and enrichment activities

Context of the Lesson This is the last remediation and enrichment lesson in this book.

Materials

straight edge ruler

Program Resources

Practice Master 160

Enrichment Master 160

For extra practice: CD-ROM* Lesson 160

1 Warm-Up

5 MINUTES

Problem of the Day Write the following problem on the chalkboard: Matt has 24 trading cards. He buys five more. Can he share them equally among his three friends if he keeps 8 cards for himself? Why or why not? (Yes, because he has 29 cards. If he keeps eight for himself, he has 21 left. He can give each of his friends seven cards.)

MENTAL MATH Have students use mental math to add or subtract.

a. 4 x 3 = (12)

b. 6 x 4 = (24)

c. 5 x 2 = (10)

d. 18 ÷ 3 = (6)

e. 20 ÷ 5 = (4)

LESSON 160

Name ____________________

Extending the Unit

Multiply. Then use the code below to solve the riddle, "What should you do when an elephant breaks its toe?"

2 × 4	8	C
4 × 4	16	A
4 × 3	12	L
3 × 4	12	L

2 × 2	4	T
3 × 3	9	H
5 × 4	20	E

1 × 4	4	T
2 × 3	6	O
5 × 3	15	W

4 × 1	4	T
2 × 5	10	R
1 × 3	3	U
1 × 1	1	C
5 × 5	25	K

Code

1	3	4	6	8	9	10	12	15	16	20	25
C	U	T	O	C	H	R	L	W	A	E	K

NOTE TO HOME
Students practice multiplication facts as they solve a puzzle.

COOPERATIVE LEARNING Allow students who do not need remediation to work with those who do to play games that reinforce the skills. Or, have them work together using flash cards to drill addition, subtraction, multiplication, and division facts.

RETEACHING

Continue working with small groups on specific skills. As you are working with the groups, have the other students play their choice of games introduced throughout the year.

*available separately

◆ **LESSON 160** Extending the Unit

Write the total number of steps you need to take to reach the goal. If you will not reach the goal, write N.

	Goal	First Two Steps	Total Steps
1	20	0, 2, 4	10
2	20	0, 5, 10	4
3	197	0, 2, 4	N
4	200	0, 5, 10	40

Fill in the missing numbers.

5. 3 + 3 + 3 + 3 + 3 + 3 = 18
6. 6 + 6 + 6 = 18
7. 6 × 3 = 18
8. 3 × 6 = 18
9. Ring the even numbers. Put a square around the numbers divisible by 5.

23 [45] (16) [(30)] (0) 9 (14) [(200)] 197 63

NOTE TO HOME
Students explore multiplication, addition, and division.

PRACTICE p. 160

LESSON 160 PRACTICE Name ____________

1. How many times do you have to count to reach the goal? If you will not reach the goal, write *N*.

Goal	First Two Steps	Total Steps
45	0 → 5 → 10	9
32	0 → 4 → 8	8
140	0 → 10 → 20	14
137	0 → 4 → 8	N
56	0 → 7 → 14	8

Fill in the missing numbers.

2. 4 + 4 + 4 + 4 + 4 + 4 + 4 = 28
3. 7 + 7 + 7 + 7 = 28
4. 7 × 4 = 28
5. 4 × 7 = 28
6. 5 + 5 + 5 + 5 + 5 + 5 = 30
7. 6 + 6 + 6 + 6 + 6 = 30
8. 5 × 6 = 30
9. 6 × 5 = 30
10. Circle the even numbers. Put a square around the numbers that are divisible by ten.

(62) [(120)] 37 59 (44) [(100)] 13 55 [(90)] (8)

ENRICHMENT p. 160

LESSON 160 ENRICHMENT Name ____________

Draw a line from 1 on one side to 1 on another side. Then draw lines from 2 to 2, 3 to 3, and so on.

Do this for all three sides of the triangle.

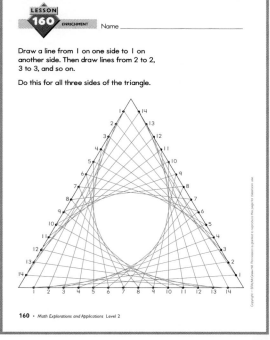

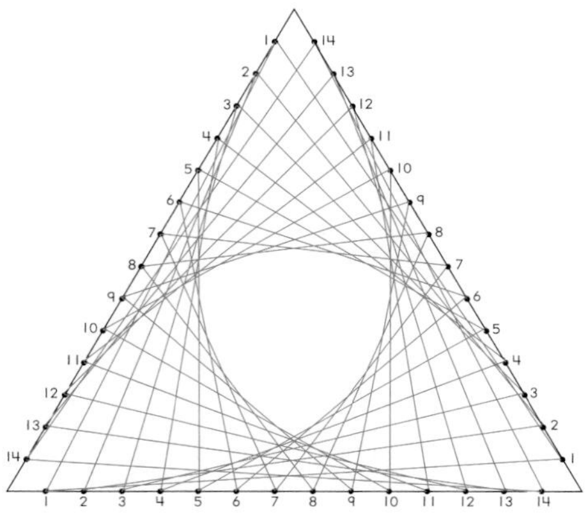

2 Teach

Using the Student Pages Students who need remediation can do activities, play games previously introduced, and complete extra practice in skills as diagnosed in Lesson 159. Enrichment activities for students who have finished remediation or do not need it are included on student pages 363 and 364.

For the puzzle on page 363 students work multiplication problems to solve a riddle. Students use the code at the bottom of the page to fill in the blanks beside each problem.

Students may use calculators to complete the problems on page 364.

3 Wrap-Up

5 MINUTES

In Closing Challenge students to find patterns in each part on page 364. For example, in Part A students will see that numbers ending in 0 are divisible by 2 and 5. In Part B, they will discover the commutative property of multiplication (the order of the factors does not change the product: 6 x 3 = 3 x 6). In Part C, they will see that numbers divisible by 5 always end in a 5 or 0.

ALTERNATIVE ASSESSMENT

Portfolio Assessment Have students save page 363 in their portfolios as an informal assessment of their knowledge of multiplication facts.

Assessment Criteria

Did the student . . .

✓ correctly solve problems and use the code to answer the riddle on page 363?

✓ correctly complete at least 80% of page 364?

UNIT 4

Student Edition pages 364a–364b

Wrap-Up

PRESENTING THE PROJECT

Project Objectives

- to provide practice in discussing numbers and how they are used to measure, count, order, quantify, and label
- to provide practice in counting numbers from a starting point other than one
- to recognize and write the numerals 0–10 and 0–20
- to provide experiences for students in saying and reading numbers

Materials

highlighters

newspaper advertising supplements

advertising flyers for grocery stores, pharmacies, and department stores

In this project, students will read advertising materials to identify and use numbers in a variety of ways. Begin by giving each student an advertising supplement or flyer. Then, ask the students to highlight all the numbers they find on any one page. Invite students to work in pairs and discuss the ways numbers are used in advertising.

Invite students to compare unit prices on similar products and decide which product they would buy and why.

Challenge students to figure out costs per ounce on products such as cereal, shampoo, milk, candy, and fruit, and to compare prices and weights or volumes to find the best buy.

Encourage students to find the best deal on items sold in multipacks, such as soda and toilet paper.

Wrapping Up the Project Tell each group of students to pretend that they have $100 to spend and invite them to investigate, calculate, and make a decision. They might want to share flyers from other groups so that they have a wider range of choices.

What Is a Math Project? If this is the first time you have used math projects in your classroom, you might want to refer to pages 98a–98b in this Teacher's Guide for more detailed information about effectively implementing and assessing projects.

ALTERNATIVE ASSESSMENT

Assessing the Project Observe the students as they are using their advertising pages. Students should recognize the different ways numbers are used.

LITERATURE CONNECTION

Literature Connection You may want to read *A Chair for My Mother* by Vera Williams or *Alexander, Who Used to Be Rich Last Sunday* by Judith Viorst to reinforce money concepts.

TECHNOLOGY CONNECTION

Technology Connection The software *The Coin Changer* from Heartsoft (Apple, IBM, Mac, for grades K–6) provides further practice with skip counting by ones, fives, and tens.

Name ______________________

Mixed Practice

Pages 1–10

Count up or count down. Fill in the missing numbers.

❶ 79 80 81 82 ❷ 49 50 51 52

❸ 18 19 20 21 ❹ 60 59 58 57

How much money?

❺  $ 37

❻  $ 31

❼  $ 42

❽ There are 30 days in April. Fill in the missing numbers.

April

Sunday	Monday	Tuesday	Wednesday	Thursday	Friday	Saturday
		1	2	3	4	5
6	7	8	9	10	11	12
13	14	15	16	17	18	19
20	21	22	23	24	25	26
27	28	29	30			

NOTE TO HOME
Students practice skills from pages 1–10.

Mixed Practice

Pages 1–20

❶ Write the number that comes after 69. 70

❷ Write the number that comes before 90. 89

Solve these problems.

❸ 87 − 3 = 84 ❹ 62 + 2 = 64 ❺ 19 − 3 = 16 ❻ 42 + 0 = 42

❼ 7 + 9 = 16 ❽ 9 + 4 = 13

❾ 6 + 5 = 11 ❿ 3 + 8 = 11

PROBLEM SOLVING

Use play money to act out the stories.

⓫ I had $54.
I found $5 more.
How much money do I have now? $ 59

⓬ I had $18.
I lost $3.
How much money do I have left? $ 15

NOTE TO HOME
Students practice skills from pages 1–20.

Name ______________________

Mixed Practice

Pages 1–30

Solve these problems.

❶ 3 + 8 = 11 ❷ 10 + 5 = 15 ❸ 7 + 8 = 15 ❹ 4 + 6 = 10 ❺ 5 + 4 = 9

❻ 6 + 8 = 8 + 6 ❼ 9 + 6 = 6 + 9

❽ 6 + 6 = 12 ❾ 8 + 9 = 17

❿ 7 + 8 = 15 ⓫ 4 + 6 = 10

⓬ 5 + 9 = 14 ⓭ 7 + 7 = 14

⓮ Write the number before 71. 70

PROBLEM SOLVING

Solve. Write a number sentence.

⓯ There are six red balls and seven yellow balls. How many balls all together?

6 + 7 = 13

⓰ Sheila had nine cents. Juan gave her five cents more. How much does she have now?

9 + 5 = 14 ¢

NOTE TO HOME
Students practice skills from pages 1–30.

Mixed Practice

Pages 1–40

Solve these problems.

❶ 4 + 6 = 10 ❷ 8 + 7 = 15 ❸ 6 + 9 = 15 ❹ 8 + 8 = 16 ❺ 7 + 5 = 12

ALGEBRA READINESS

❻ 8 − 6 = 2 ❼ 9 − 3 = 6

❽ 12 − 0 = 12 ❾ 7 − 4 = 3

❿ 6 + [8] = 14 ⓫ [8] + 7 = 15

⓬ [3] + 10 = 13 ⓭ [6] + 4 = 10

PROBLEM SOLVING

Solve.

⓮ Seven birds are on a wire.
Four more land. How many birds now? 11

⓯ Two more birds land. How many now? 13

⓰ Six more land. How many birds now? 19

NOTE TO HOME
Students practice skills from pages 1–40.

Name ____________________

Mixed Practice

Pages 1–50

Solve these problems.

1. 6 + 4 = 10
2. [3] + 6 = 9
3. [4] + 6 = 10
4. 9 − 6 = 3
5. 10 − 4 = 6
6. 8 + [8] = 16
7. 10 − [6] = 4
8. 16 − 8 = 8
9. 17 − 8 = 9
10. 12 − 4 = 8
11. 7 − 3 = 4
12. 14 + 10 = 24
13. 8 − 4 = 4

Write a subtraction sentence to solve.

14. There are seven eggs. Four broke. How many are eggs are left?
 7 − 4 = 3
15. Nine lights are on. Turn five off. How many lights are on now?
 9 − 5 = 4

NOTE TO HOME
Students practice skills from pages 1–50.

Mixed Practice

Pages 1–60

1. 12 − 9 = 3
2. 11 − 6 = 5
3. 18 − 9 = 9
4. 14 − 5 = 9
5. 13 − 6 = 7
6. 10 − 6 = 4
7. 15 − 10 = 5
8. 17 − 8 = 9
9. 12 − 11 = 1
10. 15 − 9 = 6
11. 3 − 6 = 3
12. 9 − 4 = 5
13. 16 − 7 = 9
14. 11 − 7 = 4

PROBLEM SOLVING

Solve these problems.

15. You have 16 vases. Nine break. How many vases are left? 7
16. There are 12 children. Five are girls. How many are boys? 7
17. You bake 18 pies. Nine are hot. How many are not hot? 9
18. You plant 15 rosebushes. One does not grow. How many did? 14

NOTE TO HOME
Students practice the skills from pages 1–60.

Name ____________________

Mixed Practice

Pages 1–70

Use the graphs to answer the questions.

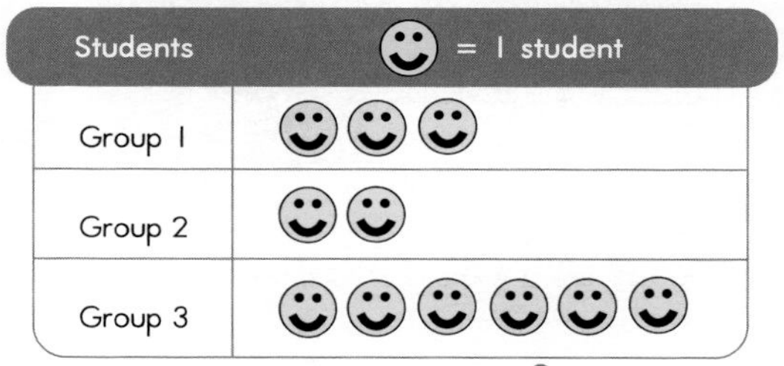

1. How many students are in group 2? 2
2. Which group has the most students? 3
3. How many more students are in Group 3 than in Group 1? 3 more

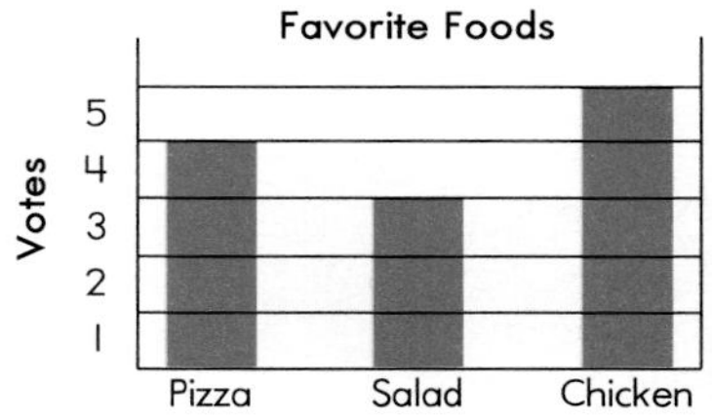

4. Which food got the most votes? chicken
5. Which food got three votes? salad
6. How many votes for pizza? 4

NOTE TO HOME
Students practice skills from pages 1–70.

Mixed Practice

Pages 1–78

Use the graph to answer the questions.

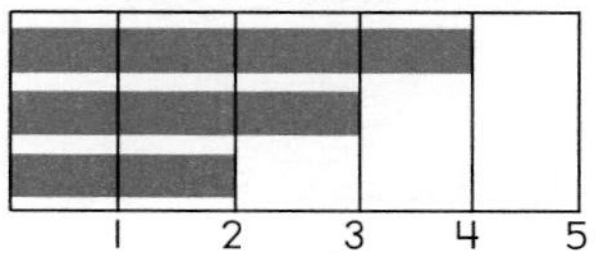

1. How many votes did chocolate get? 4
2. How many votes were there in all? 9
3. Which flavor got two votes? strawberry

How much money?

4.  28 ¢
5.  $ 31

Show each amount with coins.
Draw as few coins as you can.

6. 43¢ (25) (10) (5) (1) (1) (1)

NOTE TO HOME
Students practice skills from pages 1–78.

Name ______________________

Mixed Practice

Pages 1–90

How long? Measure.

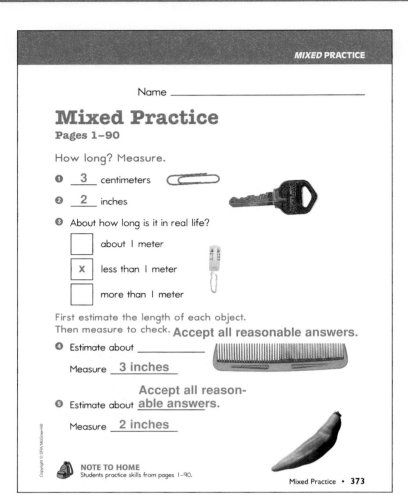

1. 3 centimeters 
2. 2 inches 
3. About how long is it in real life?

- [ ] about 1 meter
- [x] less than 1 meter
- [ ] more than 1 meter

First estimate the length of each object.
Then measure to check. **Accept all reasonable answers.**

4. Estimate about ____________ 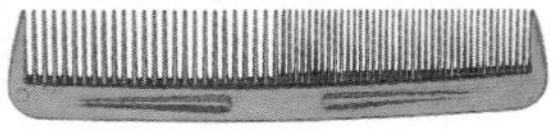

   Measure 3 inches

5. Estimate about **Accept all reasonable answers.**

   Measure 2 inches

NOTE TO HOME
Students practice skills from pages 1–90.

Mixed Practice

Pages 1–98

Name the object.

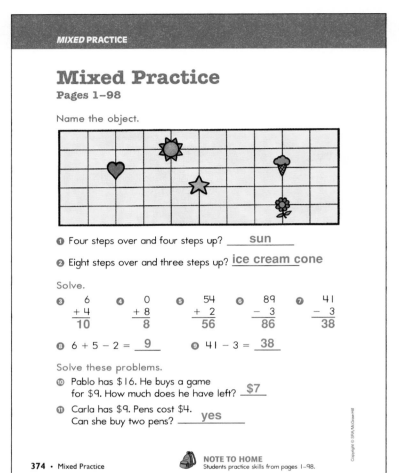

1. Four steps over and four steps up? sun
2. Eight steps over and three steps up? ice cream cone

Solve.

3. $6 + 4 = 10$
4. $0 + 8 = 8$
5. $54 + 2 = 56$
6. $89 - 3 = 86$
7. $41 - 3 = 38$
8. $6 + 5 - 2 =$ 9
9. $41 - 3 =$ 38

Solve these problems.

10. Pablo has \$16. He buys a game for \$9. How much does he have left? \$7
11. Carla has \$9. Pens cost \$4. Can she buy two pens? yes

NOTE TO HOME
Students practice skills from pages 1–98.

Name ______________________

Mixed Practice

Pages 1–110

Write the standard name for each of these.

1. 8 tens and 12 = 92
2. 3 tens and 14 = 44

Use sticks or other objects to solve.

3. 42 + 26 = 68
4. 35¢ + 17¢ = 52 ¢

Use sticks to add. Write what you did.

5. $24 + 17 = 41$

   2 tens and 4
   \+ 1 tens and 7
   3 tens and 11
   or 4 tens and 1

Add.

6. $24 + 47 = 71$
7. $19 + 13 = 32$
8. $25 + 25 = 50$
9. $31 - 14 = 45$
10. $72 + 19 = 91$
11. $29 + 7 = 36$
12. $77 + 77 = 154$
13. $41 + 13 = 54$

NOTE TO HOME
Students practice skills from pages 1–110.

Mixed Practice

Pages 1–120

Use the table. Solve the probler

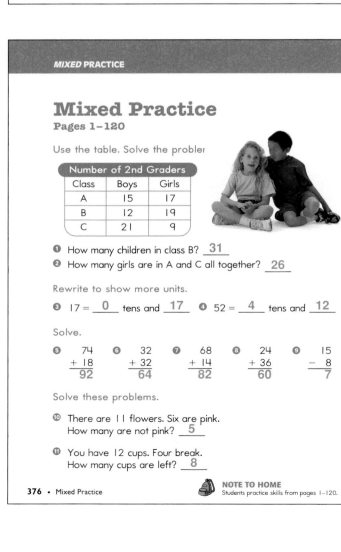

Number of 2nd Graders

Class	Boys	Girls
A	15	17
B	12	19
C	21	9

1. How many children in class B? 31
2. How many girls are in A and C all together? 26

Rewrite to show more units.

3. 17 = 0 tens and 17
4. 52 = 4 tens and 12

Solve.

5. $74 + 18 = 92$
6. $32 + 32 = 64$
7. $68 + 14 = 82$
8. $24 + 36 = 60$
9. $15 - 8 = 7$

Solve these problems.

10. There are 11 flowers. Six are pink. How many are not pink? 5
11. You have 12 cups. Four break. How many cups are left? 8

NOTE TO HOME
Students practice skills from pages 1–120.

Name ______________________

Mixed Practice
Pages 1–130

Use sticks or other objects to subtract.

1. 100 − 60 = 40
2. 90 − 70 = 20
3. 40 − 0 = 40
4. 20 − 10 = 10
5. 30 − 20 = 10

Use sticks to help. Write what you did.

6. 60 − 27 = 33
   6 tens and 0
   − 2 tens and 7
   = 3 tens and 3

7. 90 − 25 = 65
   9 tens and 0
   − 2 tens and 5
   = 6 tens and 5

Solve these problems.

8. 60 − 29 = 31
9. 40 − 37 = 3
10. 84 − 49 = 35
11. 19 − 12 = 7
12. 45 − 13 = 32

NOTE TO HOME
Students practice skills from pages 1–130.

Mixed Practice
Pages 1–140

Solve.

1. 65 − 39 = 26
2. 21 − 12 = 9
3. 19 − 18 = 1
4. 71 − 54 = 17
5. 55 − 10 = 45
6. 56 − 30 = 26
7. 80 − 15 = 65
8. 23 − 19 = 4
9. 92 − 29 = 63
10. 70 − 19 = 51

PROBLEM SOLVING

Solve these problems.

11. Leroy has $47. Sara has $62. How much less money does Leroy have than Sara? $ 15 less
12. Janell is 60 inches tall. Steven is 12 inches shorter. How tall is Steven? 48 inches

Add.

13. 73 + 42 = 115
14. 45 + 25 = 70
15. 46 + 39 = 85
16. 64 + 17 = 81
17. 70 + 18 = 88
18. 63 + 27 = 90
19. 32 + 18 = 50
20. 50 + 25 = 75
21. 29 + 23 = 52
22. 13 + 56 = 69

NOTE TO HOME
Students practice skills from pages 1–140.

Name ______________________

Mixed Practice
Pages 1–150

What time is it?

1. 
   quarter after 6
   half past ____
   quarter to ____

2. 
   quarter after ____
   half past 1
   quarter to ____

Draw the hands.

3. 2:00 
4. 9:30 

Solve these problems. Watch the signs.

5. 43 − 27 = 16
6. 43 + 27 = 70
7. 37 + 54 = 91
8. 90 − 17 = 73
9. 64 − 25 = 39
10. 39 + 45 = 84

NOTE TO HOME
Students practice skills from pages 1–150.

Mixed Practice
Pages 1–158

What time is it?

1. 
   3 : 45
2. 
   8 : 15

Draw the hands.

3. 6:45 
4. 4:15 

Color one quarter $\left(\frac{1}{4}\right)$ of each figure.

5. 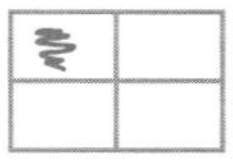
6. 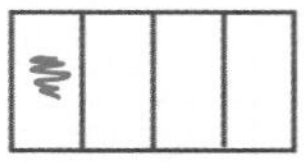
7. 

Answers are examples.

Color two thirds $\left(\frac{2}{3}\right)$ of each figure.

8. 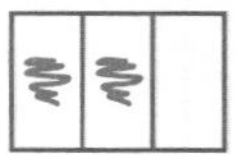
9. 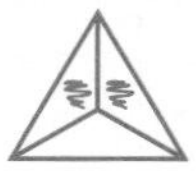
10. 

NOTE TO HOME
Student practice skills from pages 1–158.

Name ______________________

Mixed Practice

Pages 1–170

What fraction is shaded?

❶ $\frac{1}{4}$ 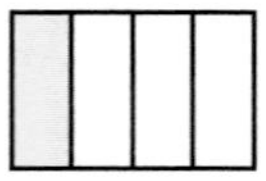

❷ $\frac{2}{3}$ 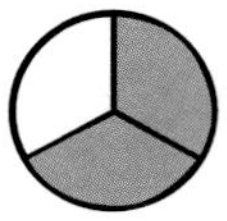

What fraction of the set is blue?

❸ $\frac{1}{6}$ 

❹ $\frac{1}{4}$ 

Complete the chart. Use play coins to help.

	Make this amount.	Use this kind of coin.	How many coins?
❺	$1	quarters	4
❻	50¢	nickels	10

Name the figures.

❼ 1 square 

❽ 2 triangles 

❾ 1 triangle 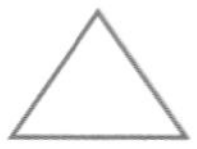

❿ 2 triangles 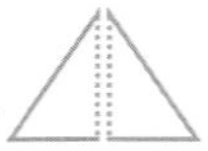

Mixed Practice

Pages 1–178

Which are the same shape and size? Circle your answer.

❶ ❷ 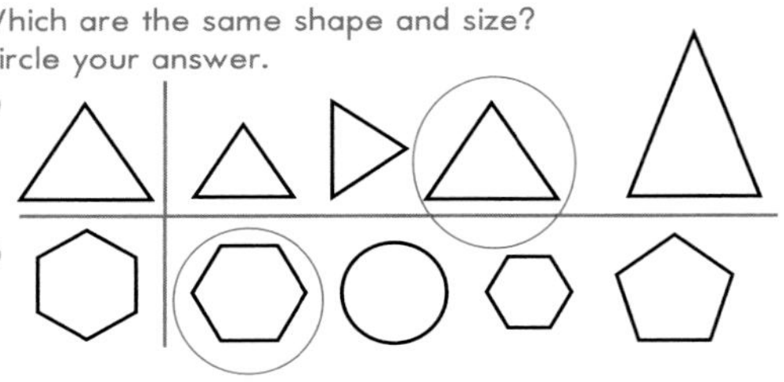

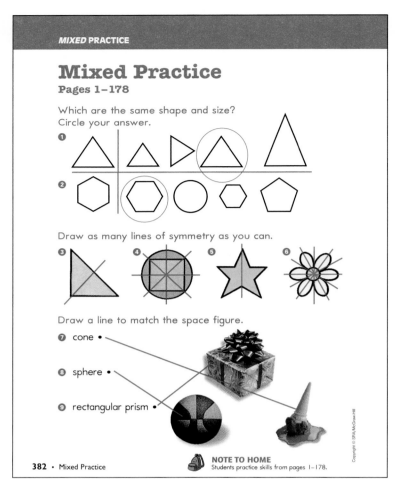

Draw as many lines of symmetry as you can.

❸ ❹ ❺ ❻ 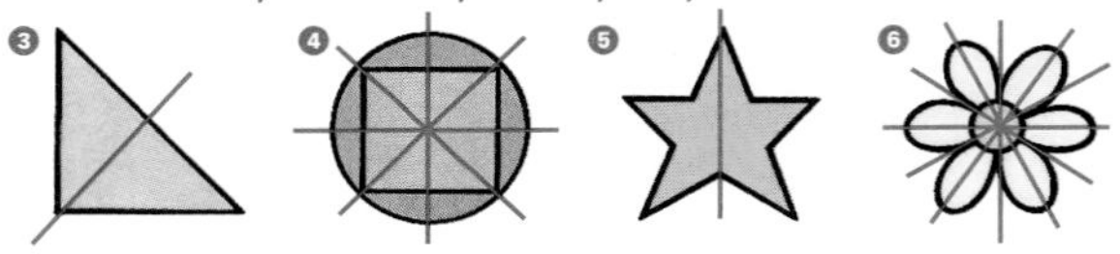

Draw a line to match the space figure.

❼ cone •

❽ sphere •

❾ rectangular prism •

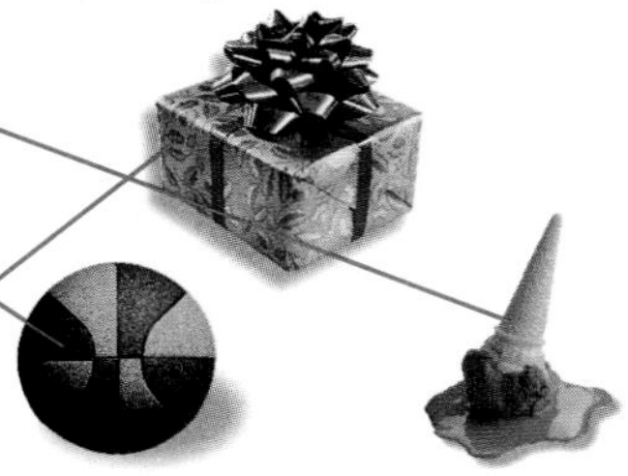

Name ______________________

Mixed Practice

Pages 1–186

What goes next?

❶ A A A B B B A __A__ __A__ __B__

❷ D E E F F F G __G__ __G__ __G__

Complete the chart. Use patterns to help.

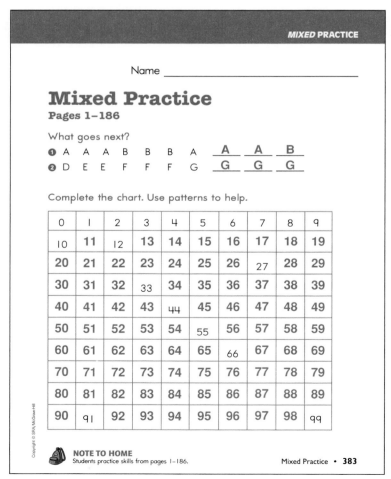

0	1	2	3	4	5	6	7	8	9
10	11	12	13	14	15	16	17	18	19
20	21	22	23	24	25	26	27	28	29
30	31	32	33	34	35	36	37	38	39
40	41	42	43	44	45	46	47	48	49
50	51	52	53	54	55	56	57	58	59
60	61	62	63	64	65	66	67	68	69
70	71	72	73	74	75	76	77	78	79
80	81	82	83	84	85	86	87	88	89
90	91	92	93	94	95	96	97	98	99

Mixed Practice

Pages 1–190

Write the rule.

❶ 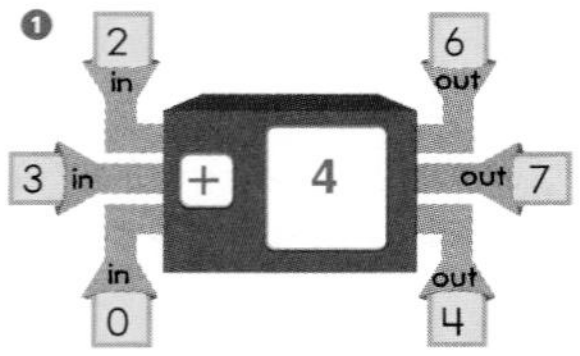

❷ 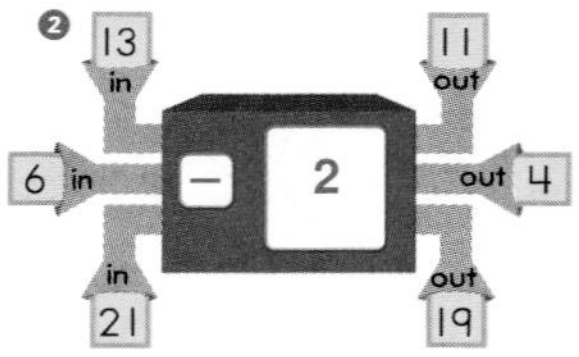

What temperature?

❸ 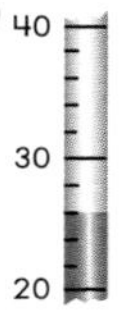

26 degrees

❹ 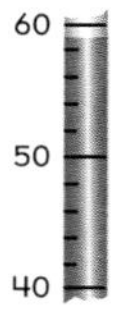

59 degrees

What time is it?

❺ 
12 : 00

❻ 
7 : 45

Name ______________________

Mixed Practice

Pages 1–208

What is the right sign? Draw <, >, or =.

❶ 25−4 [<] 25−2   ❷ 12 + 5 [<] 12 + 9

About what time is it? Tell the time to the nearest half hour.

❸  8 : 00

❹  11 : 30

❺  8 : 00

Draw the minute hands.

❻  2:24

❼  5:56

❽  7:07

Solve these problems.

❾ 26 + 26 = 52

❿ 18 + 27 = 45

⓫ 73 + 14 = 87

⓬ 59 − 7 = 52

⓭ 86 − 39 = 47

NOTE TO HOME
Students practice skills from pages 1–208.

Mixed Practice

Pages 1–220

Complete the chart. Use the map to find the shortest distances. Answer the questions.

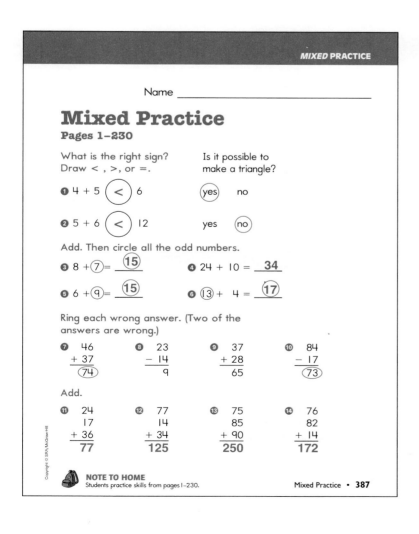

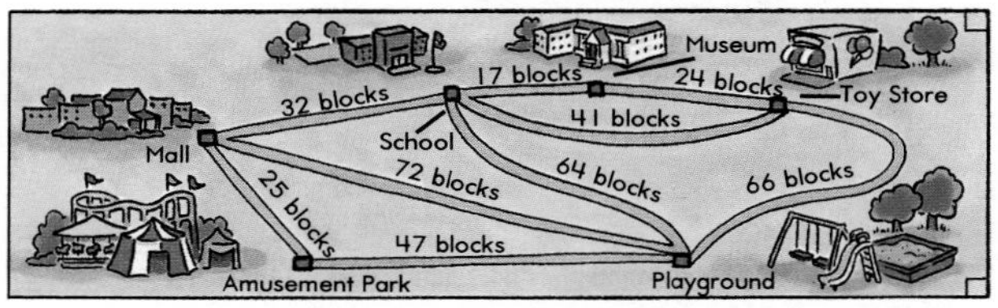

		Shortest Distance
❶	mall to museum	49 blocks
❷	museum to playground	81 blocks
❸	school to toy store	41 blocks

❹ What is farthest from the mall? toy store

❺ What is farthest from the toy store? mall

❻ What is the shortest way from the mall to the toy store? Past the school and the museum

NOTE TO HOME
Students practice skills from pages 1–220.

Name ______________________

Mixed Practice

Pages 1–230

What is the right sign? Draw <, >, or =.

❶ 4 + 5 (<) 6

❷ 5 + 6 (<) 12

Is it possible to make a triangle?

❶ (yes) no

❷ yes (no)

Add. Then circle all the odd numbers.

❸ 8 + (7) = (15)

❹ 24 + 10 = 34

❺ 6 + (9) = (15)

❻ (13) + 4 = (17)

Ring each wrong answer. (Two of the answers are wrong.)

❼ 46 + 37 = (74)

❽ 23 − 14 = 9

❾ 37 + 28 = 65

❿ 84 − 17 = (73)

Add.

⓫ 24 + 17 + 36 = 77

⓬ 77 + 14 + 34 = 125

⓭ 75 + 85 + 90 = 250

⓮ 76 + 82 + 14 = 172

NOTE TO HOME
Students practice skills from pages 1–230.

Mixed Practice

Pages 1–240

How much does it weigh?

❶ 

- [ ] about a pound
- [X] less than a pound
- [ ] more than a pound

❷ 

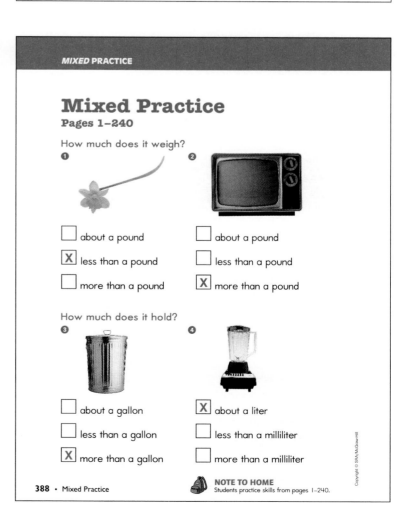

- [ ] about a pound
- [ ] less than a pound
- [X] more than a pound

How much does it hold?

❸ 

- [ ] about a gallon
- [ ] less than a gallon
- [X] more than a gallon

❹ 

- [X] about a liter
- [ ] less than a milliliter
- [ ] more than a milliliter

NOTE TO HOME
Students practice skills from pages 1–240.

Name ______________________

Mixed Practice

Pages 1–250

Round to the nearest ten.

❶ 54 <u>50</u> ❷ 37 <u>40</u> ❸ 96 <u>100</u> ❹ 45 <u>50 or 40</u>

Round to the nearest ten. Then add.

❺ 84 + 27
<u>80</u> + <u>30</u> = <u>110</u>

❻ 54 + 91
<u>50</u> + <u>90</u> = <u>140</u>

PROBLEM SOLVING

Solve these problems.

❼ Craig swam 50 feet across the pool. Robin swam the same distance. Then she swam 75 more feet.
How far did Robin swim? <u>125</u> feet

❽ One dog weighs 54 pounds. The other dog weighs 48 pounds. About how many pounds do they weigh all together?
<u>100</u>

❾ Grandma is 72 years old. Little Hector is six years old. How much older is Grandma?
<u>66</u>

NOTE TO HOME
Students practice skills from pages 1–250.

Mixed Practice

Pages 1–260

Fill in the missing numbers.

❶

○○○ ○○○	○○○ ○○○	○○○ ○○○	○○○ ○○○	○○○ ○○○	○○○ ○○○	○○○ ○○○	○○○ ○○○
6	12	18	24	30	36	42	48

Solve these problems.

❷ A video game costs \$49. The video game player costs \$99. How much all together? \$<u>148</u>

❸ Dora needs 85 cents. She has 47 cents. How much more does she need? <u>38</u> ¢

Solve these problems. Watch the signs.

❹ 34 + 46 + 12 = 92

❺ 50 + 80 + 30 = 160

❻ 12 + 91 + 42 = 145

❼ 19 + 47 + 78 = 144

❽ 78 − 43 = 35

❾ 40 − 16 = 24

❿ 25 − 2 = 23

⓫ 91 − 8 = 83

NOTE TO HOME
Students practice skills from pages 1–260.

Name ______________________

Mixed Practice

Pages 1–270

How many?

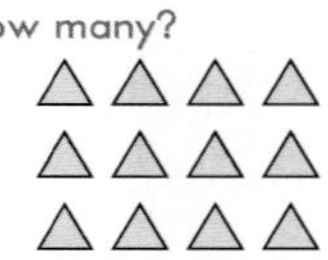

❶ 4 × 3 = <u>12</u>

❷ 6 × 4 = <u>24</u>

Find the area.

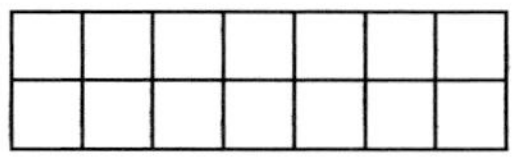

❸ The area is <u>14</u> square centimeters.
7 × 2 = <u>14</u>

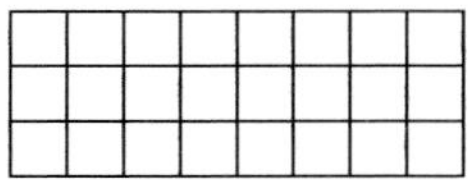

❹ The area is <u>24</u> square centimeters.
8 × 3 = <u>24</u>

Solve these problems.

❺ Pencils are 8 cents each.
How much are four pencils? <u>32</u> cents

❻ Five students each carry four books.
How many books? <u>20</u>

NOTE TO HOME
Students practice skills from pages 1–270.

Mixed Practice

Pages 1–280

Use cubes or sticks to solve these problems.

❶ Take 15 cubes. Divide them into five groups.
How many cubes in each group? <u>3</u> 5 × [3] = 15

❷ Take 20 cubes. Divide them into five groups.
How many cubes in each group? <u>4</u> 5 × [4] = 20

❸ Roll a Number Cube 20 times. Fill in the chart.

Number	Tallies	Totals
1		
2		
3		
4		
5		
6		

Answers will depend on numbers rolled by students.

Solve this problem.

❹ One book costs \$4.
How much do three books cost? \$<u>12</u>
How much do five books cost? \$<u>20</u>

NOTE TO HOME
Students practice skills from pages 1–280.

Name ____________________

Mixed Practice

Pages 1–290

Use coins or objects to act these out in a group.

1. Fourteen cents are to be divided equally between two children. How many cents for each child?

   14 ÷ 2 = 7

2. Twenty-one cents are to be divided equally among three children. How many cents for each child?

   21 ÷ 3 = 7

Complete the chart.

Today is Monday.

Number of days	Day it was	Day it will be
1	Tuesday	Wednesday
3	Thursday	Friday
6	Sunday	Monday
7	Monday	Tuesday

NOTE TO HOME
Students practice skills from pages 1–290.

Mixed Practice

Pages 1–300

Solve these problems.

1. 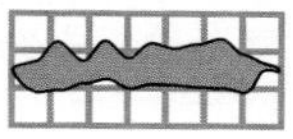

   How many units long? 7

2. 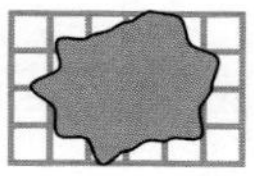

   How many units long? 4 or 5

Write two number sentences that give the number shown as an answer.

3. 3 × 3 = 9   18 ÷ 2 = 9
4. 21 ÷ 3 = 7   14 ÷ 2 = 7

Solve these problems. Use shortcuts if you can.

5. 4 + 2 + 1 + 6 + 3 + 7 = 23
6. 9 + 1 + 3 + 6 + 4 + 2 + 8 = 33

What is the rule?

7. 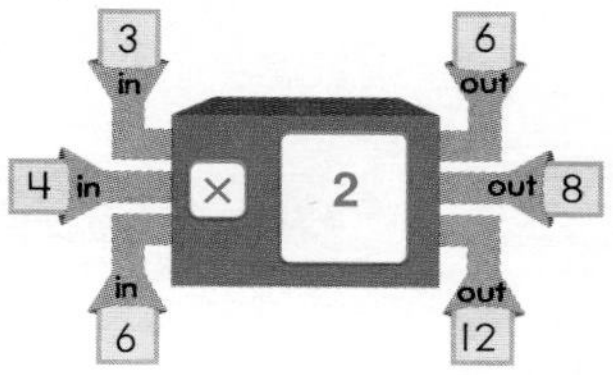

NOTE TO HOME
Students practice skills from pages 1–290.

Name ____________________

Mixed Practice

Pages 1–310

Fill in the missing numbers.

1.

885	884	883	882	881	880	879	878	877

Write the correct number in each blank.

2. 4 and 7 = 4 tens and 7
3. 4 tens and 7 tens = 1 hundreds and 1 tens

Rewrite the problem. Then solve.

4. 425   4 hundreds and 2 tens and 5 ones
   \+ 157   + 1 hundreds and 5 tens and 7 ones

   5 hundreds and 7 tens and 12 ones or
   5 hundreds and 8 tens and 2 ones
   or 582

NOTE TO HOME
Students practice skills from pages 1–310.

Mixed Practice

Pages 1–320

Add.

1. 563 + 474 = 1037
2. 748 + 257 = 1005
3. 903 + 487 = 1390
4. 327 + 495 = 822

Subtract.

5. 400 − 212 = 188
6. 750 − 607 = 143
7. 607 − 418 = 189
8. 298 − 143 = 155

Rewrite to show more tens.

9. 431 = 3 hundreds and 13 tens and 1
10. 752 = 6 hundreds and 15 tens and 2

Solve these problems.

11. A television costs $400. Ramón has $275. How much more does he need to buy the T.V.?

    $125

12. There are 342 students in the school. There are 157 boys. How many are girls?

    185

NOTE TO HOME
Students practice skills from pages 1–320.

Name ____________________

Mixed Practice

Pages 1–330

Solve these problems quickly. Watch the signs.

1. 600 − 200 = 400
2. 600 + 200 = 800
3. 700 − 400 = 300
4. 500 − 300 = 200

Solve these problems. Watch the signs.

5. 497 − 384 = 113
6. 900 − 472 = 428
7. 384 − 144 = 240
8. 807 + 139 = 946

Solve.

9. How much do the juice and milk cost all together? 648 ¢
10. How much more does the juice cost than the milk? 50 ¢

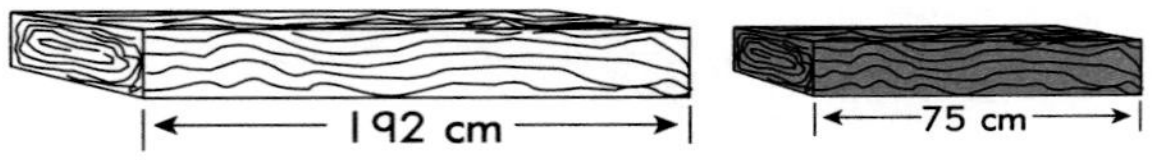

11. How long are both planks together? 267 cm

NOTE TO HOME
Students practice skills from pages 1–330.

Mixed Practice

Pages 1–340

Ring the correct answer. Try to find each correct answer using mental math.

1. 97 + 204 — 101 201 (301)
2. 407 + 358 — 865 (765) 755
3. 702 − 198 — (504) 604 704

Count up or count down. Fill in the missing numbers.

4	2762	2761	2760	2759	2758	2757
5	3998	3999	4000	4001	4002	4003

Fill in the boxes.

6. 100 200 300 [400] 500 [600]
7. 1000 [2000] [3000] 4000 5000

Add.

8. 3572 + 4109 = 7681
9. 5074 + 6181 = 11,255
10. 3500 + 3500 = 7000

NOTE TO HOME
Students practice skills from pages 1–340.

Name ____________________

Mixed Practice

Pages 1–350

Solve these problems.

1. 4285 + 5609 = 9894

4 thousands 2 hundreds 8 tens and 5
\+ 5 thousands 6 hundreds 0 tens and 9
= 9 thousands 8 hundreds 9 tens and 4

2. 7063 − 1245 = 5818

7 thousands 0 hundreds 6 tens and 3
− 1 thousands 2 hundreds 4 tens and 5
= 5 thousands 8 hundreds 1 tens and 8

Solve.

3. Neil Armstrong landed on the moon in 1969. How many years ago was that? 28 (in 1997)
4. Henry was born in 1953. He was married in 1981. How old was he when he got married? 28

NOTE TO HOME
Students practice skills from pages 1–350.

Mixed Practice

Pages 1–356

Solve these problems. Watch the signs.

1. 37 + 49 + 56 = 142
2. 6000 − 1430 = 4570
3. 21 + 68 + 12 = 101
4. 5000 − 1013 = 3987

5. 3 × 7 = 21
6. 15 ÷ 3 = 5
7. 6 × 2 = 12

Solve.

8. There are 24 hours in one day. How many hours in two days? 48
9. There are 365 days in one year. How many days in two years? 730
10. Seven days in one week. How many days in four weeks? 28
11. How old will you be in 2007? 18 years old

Answers will range between 17 and 19 in 1997.

NOTE TO HOME
Students practice skills from pages 1–356.

A

addition sentence

$4 + 1 = 5$

area 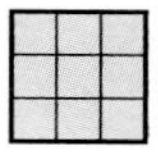

C

circle 

cone 

commutative property

$2 + 3 = 5$

$3 + 2 = 5$

congruent

cube 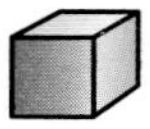

D

difference

$10 - 5 = 5$

F

fraction

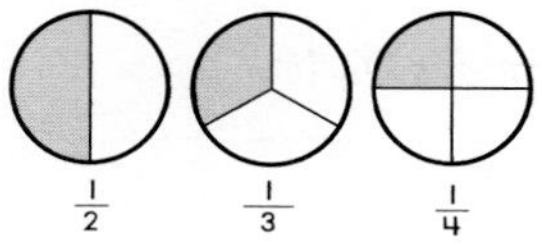

function machine

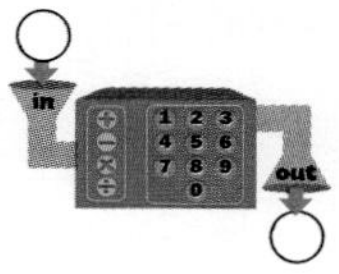

G

greater than

$46 > 12$

L

less than

$10 < 65$

N

number cube 

number line

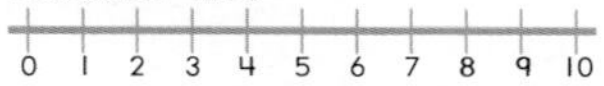

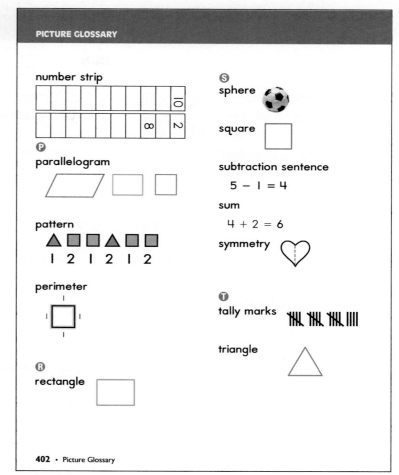

number strip

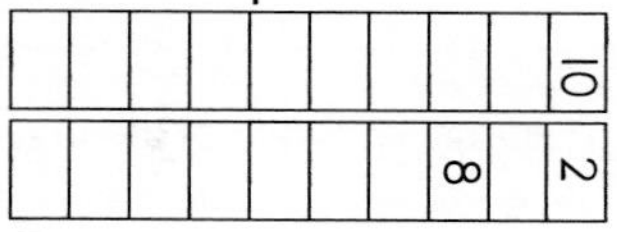

P

parallelogram

pattern

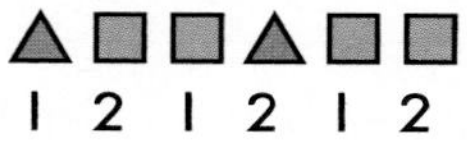

perimeter

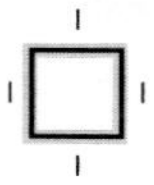

R

rectangle 

S

sphere 

square 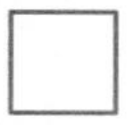

subtraction sentence

$5 - 1 = 4$

sum

$4 + 2 = 6$

symmetry 

T

tally marks 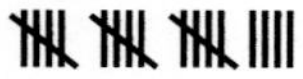

triangle 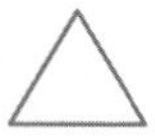

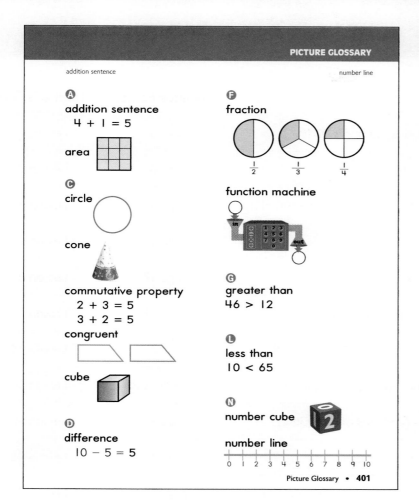

GAME DIRECTORY

Game	Principal Skills	Begin Using* Student's Edition	Teacher's Guide
Tracing and Writing Numbers	Tracing, writing, ordering, and finding numbers 0–10	page 3	Lesson 1
Counting and Writing Numbers	Counting and writing numbers 0–100	page 6	Lesson 2
Yard Sale**	Changing money ($1 bills for $10 bills, $10 bills for $100 bills)	page 8	Lesson 3
Calendar	Using a monthly calendar	page 10	Lesson 4
Frog Pond	Adding with two addends of 10 or less	page 17	Lesson 8
Addition Table	Using an addition table with two addends of 5 or less	page 28	Lesson 13
Harder Addition Table	Using an addition table with two addends of 0–5 or 5–10		Lesson 14
Roll a 15	Adding two, three, or four numbers (0–10) in sequence	page 38	Lesson 18
Missing Number	Solving missing-addend problems (addends of 10 or less)	page 40	Lesson 19
Roll 20 to 5	Subtracting 10 or less from numbers through 20	page 47	Lesson 22
Space	Solving addition and missing-addend problems with sums of 10 or less	page 51	Lesson 24
Harder Space	Solving addition, subtraction, missing-addend, missing-minuend, and missing-subtrahend problems with numbers of 10 or less		Lesson 24
What's the Problem?	Solving addition and subtraction problems; making different number sentences that give the same answer	page 55	Lesson 26
Roll a Number Sentence	Chain calculations that involve both addition and subtraction	page 68	Lesson 32
Get to 100 by Tens or Ones	Adding mentally with numbers through 100	page 76	Lesson 36
Pennies, Nickels, Dimes	Changing money (pennies for nickels and nickels for dimes)		Lesson 37
Roll a Number	Using place value and intuitive notions of probability	page 80	Lesson 38
Dot-Square	Developing geometric intuition	page 97	Lesson 46
Make 10 Bingo	Finding pairs of addends that make 10	page 107	Lesson 50
Get to 100 with the 5–10 Cube	Adding one-digit numbers to two-digit numbers	page 110	Lesson 51
Harder Yard Sale	Changing money ($100 and $10 bills for smaller denominations); regrouping for multidigit subtraction		Lesson 57
Add or Subtract a 10	Adding or subtracting multiples of ten in the 0–100 range	page 124	Lesson 58

GAME DIRECTORY

Game	Principal Skills	Begin Using* Student's Edition	Teacher's Guide
Three-Cube Subtraction	Subtracting two-digit numbers from two-digit numbers that are multiples of ten	page 128	Lesson 60
Four-Cube Addition	Adding two two-digit numbers	page 132	Lesson 62
Four-Cube Subtraction	Subtracting with two-digit numbers	page 132	Lesson 62
Roll a Problem	Adding subtracting multidigit numbers; using intuitive notions of probability	page 141	Lesson 67
Time	Telling time to the hour and half hour	page 150	Lesson 70
Harder Time	Telling time to the hour, half hour, and quarter hour	page 156	Lesson 72
Fraction	Recognizing fractional areas of a circle; recognizng which fractional areas when combined are more than half the area of a circle	page 163	Lesson 75
Map	Using numbers to represent magnitude and direction; using compass directions	page 224	Lesson 99
Odds-Evens Game	Identifying odd and even numbers through ten	page 230	Lesson 102
Measurement	Choosing the appropriate standard unit of measure	page 244	Lesson 109
Add the Products	Multiplying with one number from 0–5 and the other number from 5–10; multiplying with two numbers from 5–10	page 268	Lesson 118
Harder Multiplication Table	Multiplying one number from 0–5 and the other from 5–10; multiplying two numbers from 5–10	page 272	Lesson 120
Multiplication Table	Multiplying two numbers from 0–5 using a multiplication table	page 272	Lesson 120
Harder What's the Problem?	Using addition, subtraction, multiplication, and division to make different number sentences with the same answers	page 297	Lesson 132
Harder Counting and Writing Numbers	Counting in the 0–1000 range; writing numbers in the 0–1000 range	page 309	Lesson 138
Rummage Sale	Changing money ($1, $10, and $100 bills for those of larger denominations); regroupoing in preparation for multidigit addition	page 316	Lesson 141
Harder Rummage Sale	Changing money (various bills and coins)	page 332	Lesson 147
Make a $10 Bill	Changing money (coins and bills for those of larger denominations up to $10)	page 333	Lesson 148

GAME DIRECTORY

Game	Principal Skills	Begin Using* Student's Edition	Begin Using* Teacher's Guide
Make 1000	Approximating answers to multidigit addition and subtraction problems; solving multidigit addition and subtraction problems	page 338	Lesson 150
Checkbook	Adding and subtracting two-digit and three-digit numbers; maintaining a record of money transactions	page 342	Lesson 151
Harder Checkbook	Adding and subtracting decimal numbers; maintaining a record of money transactions		Lesson 151
Four-Digit Addition	Adding four-digit numbers	page 351	Lesson 156
Harder Four-Digit Addition	Adding four-digit numbers		Lesson 156
Four Cubes from 10,000 to 0	Subtracting four-digit numbers	page 354	Lesson 157

***These games and their variations should be used many times throughout the year. Feel free to use them again any time after they are introduced.**
****Games in red are from the Game Mat set.**

ADDITION TABLE GAME

Math Focus:
- Practicing basic facts–using two addends of 5 or less
- Using an addition table

Object of the Game: To have more counters at the end of the game

Players: Two

MATERIALS

Two cubes

36 counters or pennies

SET UP

- Every circle on the mat must be covered with a counter.
- Players roll the 0-5 number cube. The person who rolls the higher number goes first.

HOW TO PLAY

1. Players take turns rolling both cubes and making addition sentences out of the numbers. For example, if a 4 and a 2 are rolled, the player could say either "4 plus 2 equals 6" or "2 plus 4 equals 6."
2. After giving the addition sentence, players check their answers by looking under the appropriate counter. If correct, the player keeps the counter; if incorrect, the player replaces the counter.
3. Once the counter on a circle has been won, the circle remains empty. A player who cannot make an addition sentence that applies to a *covered circle* cannot win a counter that turn.
4. The player with more counters at the end of the game wins.

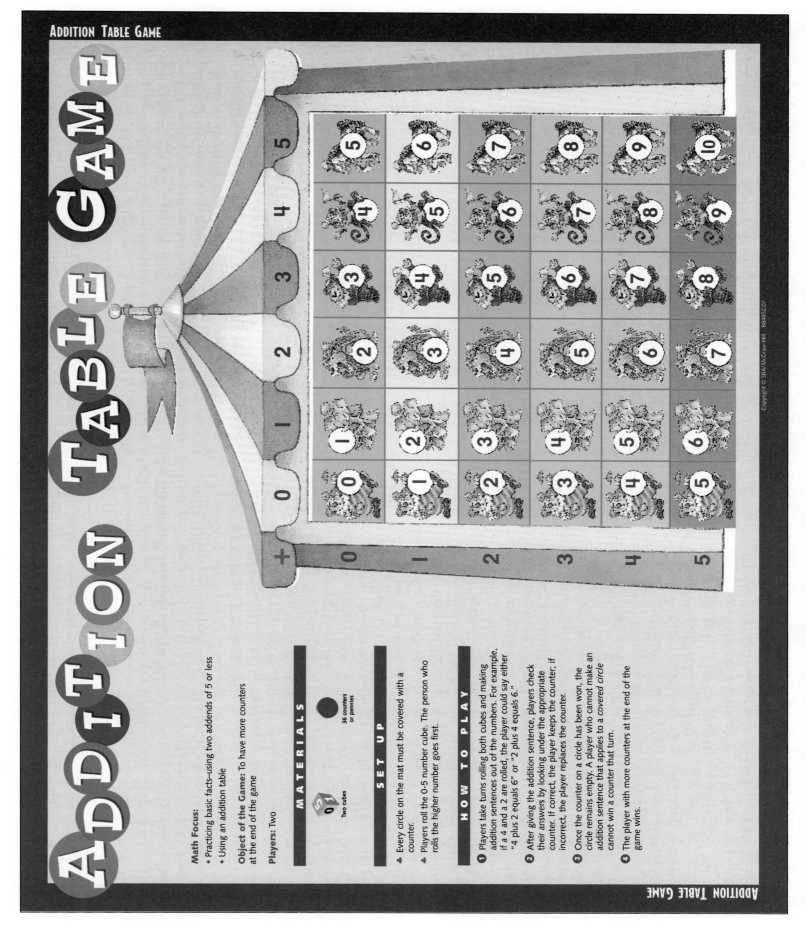

+	0	1	2	3	4	5
0	0	1	2	3	4	5
1	1	2	3	4	5	6
2	2	3	4	5	6	7
3	3	4	5	6	7	8
4	4	5	6	7	8	9
5	5	6	7	8	9	10

ADDITION TABLE GAME

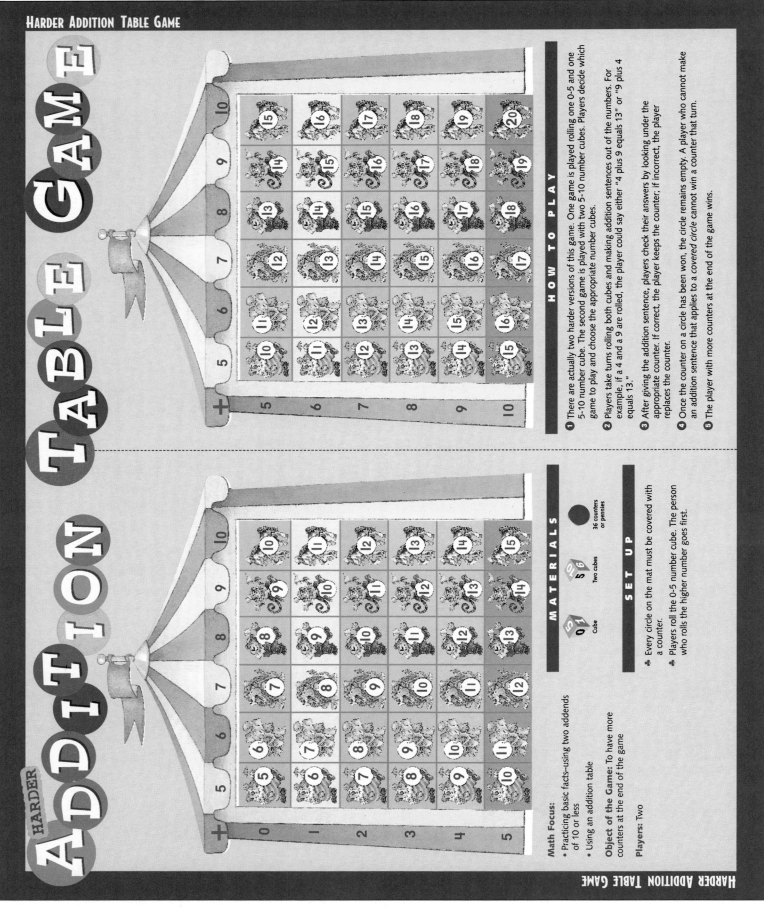

HARDER ADDITION TABLE GAME

+	5	6	7	8	9	10
0	5	6	7	8	9	10
1	6	7	8	9	10	11
2	7	8	9	10	11	12
3	8	9	10	11	12	13
4	9	10	11	12	13	14
5	10	11	12	13	14	15

+	5	6	7	8	9	10
5	10	11	12	13	14	15
6	11	12	13	14	15	16
7	12	13	14	15	16	17
8	13	14	15	16	17	18
9	14	15	16	17	18	19
10	15	16	17	18	19	20

Math Focus:

- Practicing basic facts–using two addends of 10 or less
- Using an addition table

Object of the Game: To have more counters at the end of the game

Players: Two

MATERIALS

SET UP

- ♣ Every circle on the mat must be covered with a counter.
- ♣ Players roll the 0-5 number cube. The person who rolls the higher number goes first.

HOW TO PLAY

1. There are actually two harder versions of this game. One game is played rolling one 0-5 and one 5-10 number cube. The second game is played with two 5-10 number cubes. Players decide which game to play and choose the appropriate number cubes.
2. Players take turns rolling both cubes and making addition sentences out of the numbers. For example, if a 4 and a 9 are rolled, the player could say either "4 plus 9 equals 13" or "9 plus 4 equals 13."
3. After giving the addition sentence, players check their answers by looking under the appropriate counter. If correct, the player keeps the counter; if incorrect, the player replaces the counter.
4. Once the counter on a circle has been won, the circle remains empty. A player who cannot make an addition sentence that applies to a *covered circle* cannot win a counter that turn.
5. The player with more counters at the end of the game wins.

Math Focus: Using a monthly calendar

Object of the Game: To be the first to reach FINISH

Players: Two or three

MATERIALS

Cube

Place marker and counter of the same color per player

SET UP

- Players place their counters on one of the days of the week. Players must choose different days.
- The players then put their place markers on START.
- Players roll the 0-5 number cube. The person who rolls the highest number goes first.

HOW TO PLAY

1. Players take turns rolling the cube and advancing through the 31 days of the month. Players must say aloud the day of the week where they land.
2. A player who lands on an opponent's chosen day must either return to START if still within the first seven days of the month or go back seven days. The player remains on this space until the next roll.
3. If a player is already on an opponent's chosen day and rolls a 0, he or she must move back another seven days.
4. The first player to reach FINISH wins.

CALENDAR GAME

CHECKBOOK GAME

Math Focus:
- Adding and subtracting two-digit and three-digit numbers
- Maintaining a record of money transactions

Object of the Game: To have the largest balance at the end of the month

Players: Two or three

MATERIALS

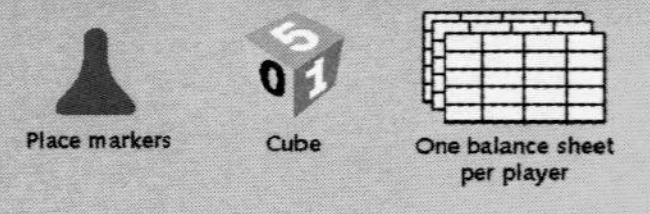

SET UP

- Photocopies of the balance sheet for the "Harder Checkbook Game" can be handed out to students.
- Players prepare their balance sheets by writing "Start" on the first line under DATE and "$1000" on the first line under BALANCE.
- Players put their place markers on START.
- Players roll the 0-5 number cube. The person who rolls the highest number goes first.

HOW TO PLAY

1. Players take turns rolling the cube and moving their markers the number of spaces indicated.
2. Players follow the directions on the spaces where they land, entering the date and all payments or earnings on their balance sheets and recalculating their balances.
3. Play continues until all the players have either reached FINISH or run out of money.
4. The player with the largest balance at the end of the game is declared the winner. The other players then check the addition and subtraction in the winner's balance sheet. If the balance does not check, the player with the highest correct balance becomes the winner.

SAMPLE BALANCE SHEET

Date	Earn	Pay	Balance
Start			$1000
3		-$26	$974
8	+$23		$997
11			
4	+$50		$1047
6		-$20	$1027
Totals	+$73	-$46	$1027

CHECKBOOK GAME

HARDER CHECKBOOK GAME

Math Focus:
- Adding and subtracting two-digit, three-digit, and four-digit numbers
- Maintaining a record of money transactions

Object of the Game: To have the largest balance at the end of the month

Players: Two or three

MATERIALS

SET UP

- Photocopies of the sample balance sheet can be handed out to students.
- Players prepare their balance sheets by writing "Start" on the first line under DATE and "$1000" on the first line under BALANCE.
- Players put their place markers on START.
- Players roll the 0-5 number cube. The person who rolls the highest number goes first.

HOW TO PLAY

1. Players take turns rolling the cube and moving their markers the number of spaces indicated.
2. Players follow the directions on the spaces where they land, entering the date and all payments or earnings on their balance sheets and recalculating their balances.
3. Play continues until all the players have either reached FINISH or run out of money.
4. The player with the largest balance at the end of the game is declared the winner. The other players then check the addition and subtraction in the winner's balance sheet. If the balance does not check, the player with the highest correct balance becomes the winner.

SAMPLE BALANCE SHEET

Date	Earn	Pay	Balance

HARDER CHECKBOOK GAME

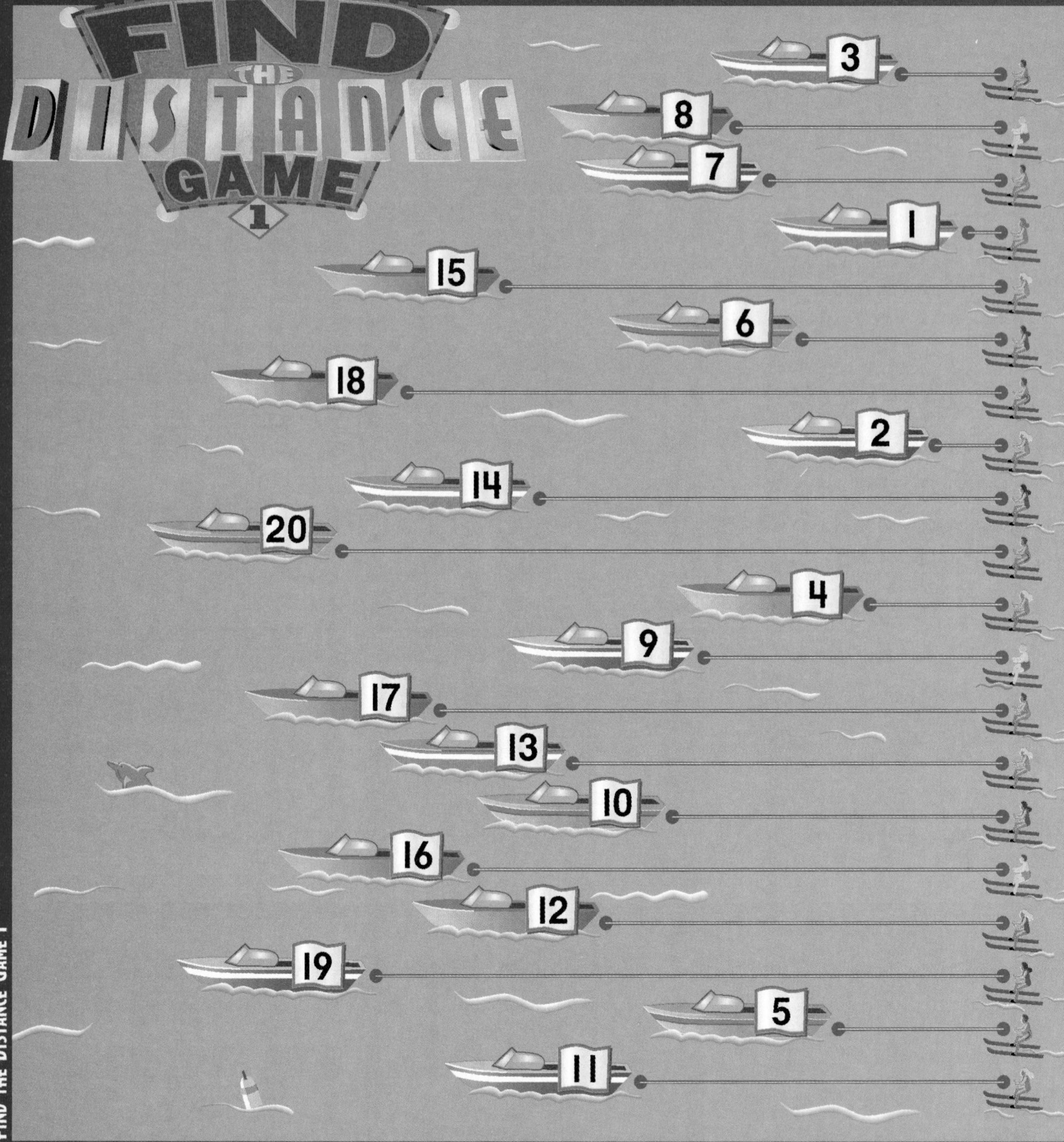

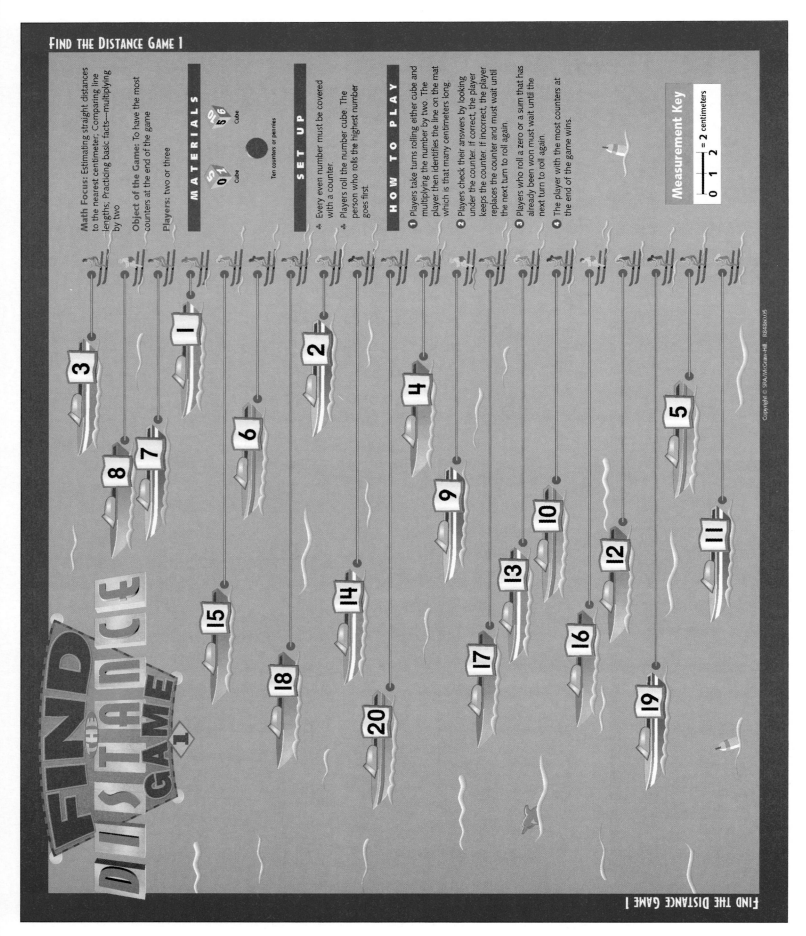

Math Focus: Estimating straight distances to the nearest centimeter; Comparing line lengths; Practicing basic facts—multiplying by two

Object of the Game: To have the most counters at the end of the game

Players: two or three

MATERIALS

Cube

Cube

Ten counters or pennies

SET UP

- Every even number must be covered with a counter.
- Players roll the number cube. The person who rolls the highest number goes first.

HOW TO PLAY

1. Players take turns rolling either cube and multiplying the number by two. The player then identifies the line on the mat which is that many centimeters long.
2. Players check their answers by looking under the counter. If correct, the player keeps the counter. If incorrect, the player replaces the counter and must wait until the next turn to roll again.
3. Players who roll a zero or a sum that has already been won must wait until the next turn to roll again.
4. The player with the most counters at the end of the game wins.

Measurement Key

0 1 2 = 2 centimeters

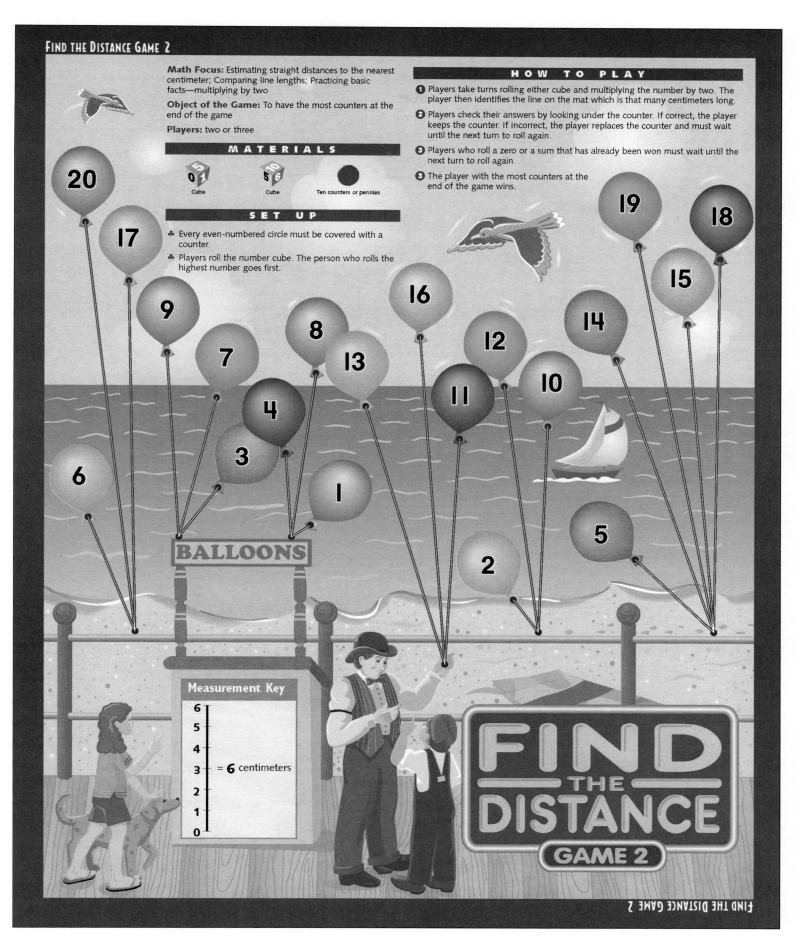

Math Focus: Estimating straight distances to the nearest centimeter; Comparing line lengths; Practicing basic facts—multiplying by two

Object of the Game: To have the most counters at the end of the game

Players: two or three

MATERIALS

Cube | Cube | Ten counters or pennies

SET UP

- Every even-numbered circle must be covered with a counter.
- Players roll the number cube. The person who rolls the highest number goes first.

HOW TO PLAY

1. Players take turns rolling either cube and multiplying the number by two. The player then identifies the line on the mat which is that many centimeters long.
2. Players check their answers by looking under the counter. If correct, the player keeps the counter. If incorrect, the player replaces the counter and must wait until the next turn to roll again.
3. Players who roll a zero or a sum that has already been won must wait until the next turn to roll again.
3. The player with the most counters at the end of the game wins.

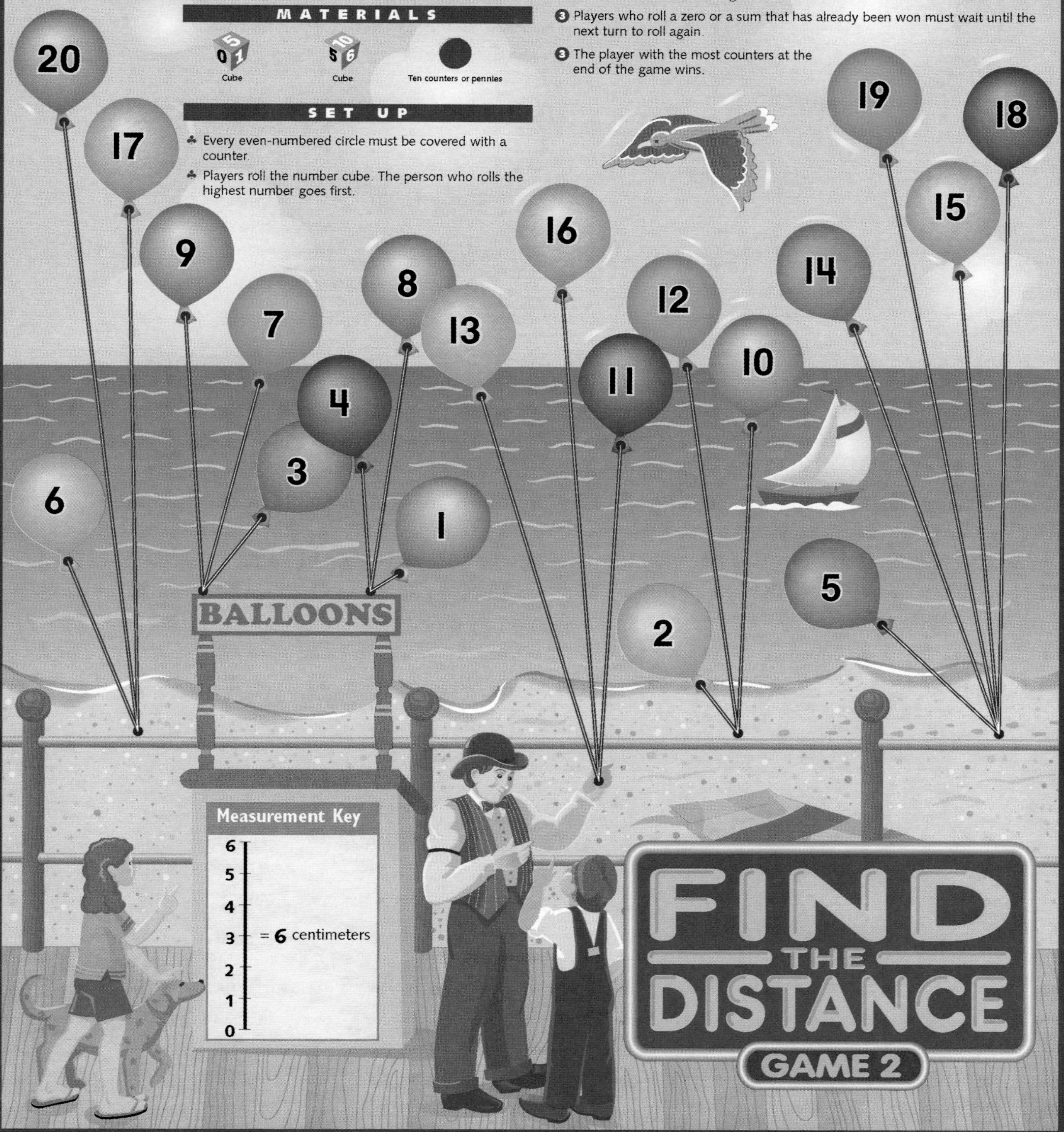

FIND THE DISTANCE GAME 2

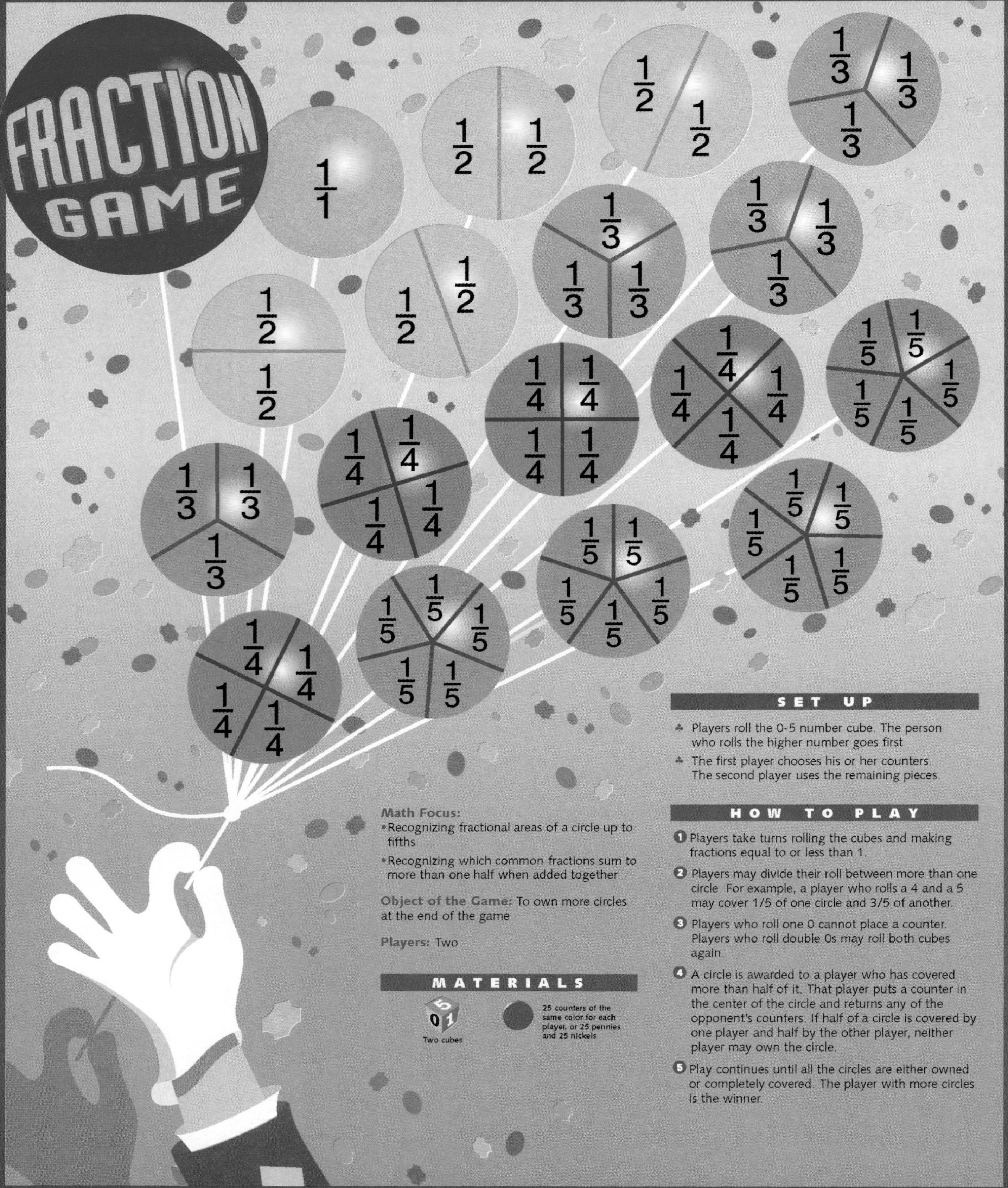

Math Focus:
- Recognizing fractional areas of a circle up to fifths
- Recognizing which common fractions sum to more than one half when added together

Object of the Game: To own more circles at the end of the game

Players: Two

MATERIALS

Two cubes

25 counters of the same color for each player, or 25 pennies and 25 nickels

SET UP

- Players roll the 0-5 number cube. The person who rolls the higher number goes first.
- The first player chooses his or her counters. The second player uses the remaining pieces.

HOW TO PLAY

1. Players take turns rolling the cubes and making fractions equal to or less than 1.
2. Players may divide their roll between more than one circle. For example, a player who rolls a 4 and a 5 may cover 1/5 of one circle and 3/5 of another.
3. Players who roll one 0 cannot place a counter. Players who roll double 0s may roll both cubes again.
4. A circle is awarded to a player who has covered more than half of it. That player puts a counter in the center of the circle and returns any of the opponent's counters. If half of a circle is covered by one player and half by the other player, neither player may own the circle.
5. Play continues until all the circles are either owned or completely covered. The player with more circles is the winner.

FRACTION GAME

FROG POND GAME

Math Focus: Practicing basic math–using two addends of 10 or less

Object of the Game: To have the most counters at the end of the game

Players: Two or three

MATERIALS

Place markers
Cube
20 counters or pennies per player

SET UP

- Every circle on the mat must be covered with a counter.
- Extra counters are placed on the space marked BANK.
- Players put their place markers on GO.
- Players roll the 0-5 number cube. The person who rolls the highest number goes first.

HOW TO PLAY

1. Players take turns rolling the cube and moving their markers the number of spaces indicated.
2. After landing on a space, a player may win the counter there by correctly completing the addition sentence.
3. Players check their answers by lifting the counters. If correct, the player keeps the counter. If incorrect, the player replaces the counter and remains on that space.
4. A player cannot win a counter if there is none in a space. A player who gives an incorrect answer and rolls a 0 on the next turn can try again to win the counter.
5. Players collect two counters from the bank each time they pass or land on GO.
6. The player with the most counters at the end of the game wins.

HARDER FROG POND GAME

Math Focus: Solving mixed addition and subtraction fact problems

Object of the Game: To have the most counters at the end of the game

Players: Two or three

MATERIALS

Place markers, Cube, 20 counters or pennies per player

SET UP

- Every circle on the mat must be covered with a counter.
- Extra counters are placed on the space marked BANK.
- Players roll the 0-5 number cube. The person who rolls the highest number goes first.

HOW TO PLAY

1. Players take turns rolling the cube and moving their markers the number of spaces indicated.
2. After landing on a space, a player may win the counter there by correctly completing the addition or subtraction sentence.
3. Players check their answers by lifting the counters. If correct, the player keeps the counter. If incorrect, the player replaces the counter and remains on that space.
4. A player cannot win a counter if there is none in a space. A player who gives an incorrect answer and rolls a 0 on the next turn can try again to win the counter.
5. Players collect two counters from the bank each time they pass or land on GO.
6. The player with the most counters at the end of the game wins.

HARDER FROG POND GAME

MAP GAME

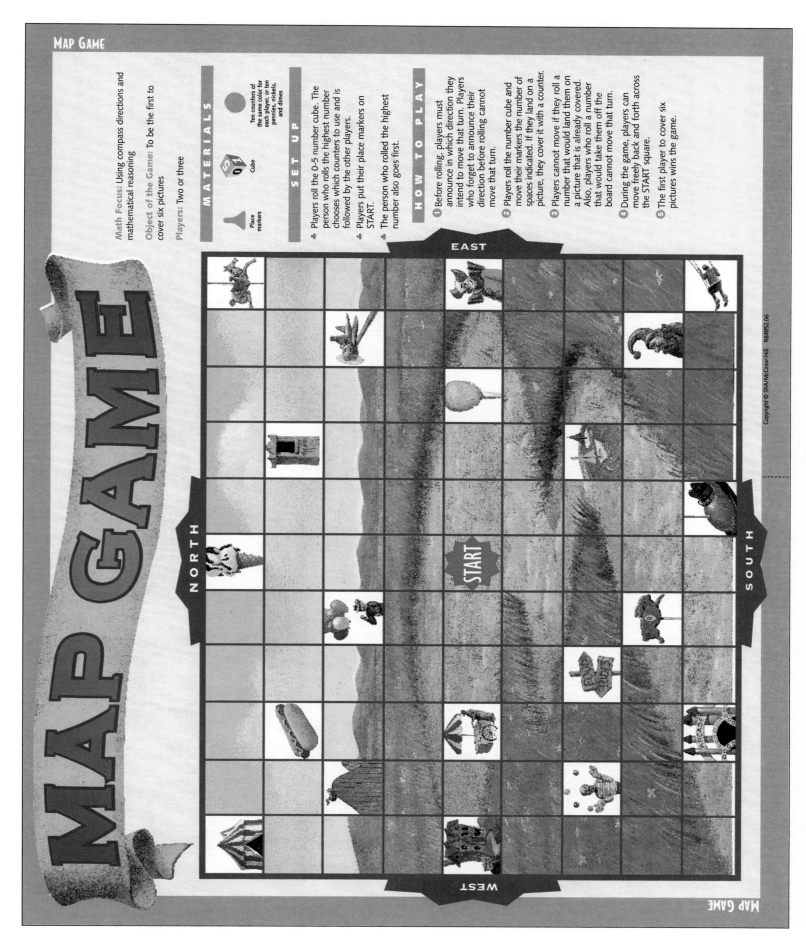

Math Focus: Using compass directions and mathematical reasoning

Object of the Game: To be the first to cover six pictures

Players: Two or three

MATERIALS

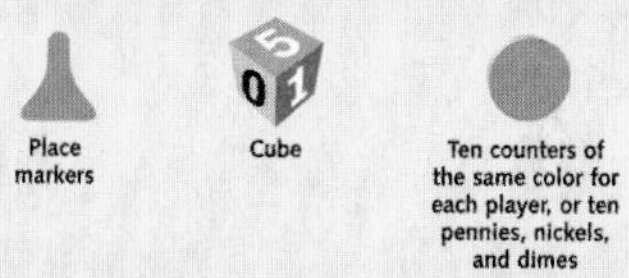

SET UP

- Players roll the 0-5 number cube. The person who rolls the highest number chooses which counters to use and is followed by the other players.
- Players put their place markers on START.
- The person who rolled the highest number also goes first.

HOW TO PLAY

1. Before rolling, players must announce in which direction they intend to move that turn. Players who forget to announce their direction before rolling cannot move that turn.
2. Players roll the number cube and move their markers the number of spaces indicated. If they land on a picture, they cover it with a counter.
3. Players cannot move if they roll a number that would land them on a picture that is already covered. Also, players who roll a number that would take them off the board cannot move that turn.
4. During the game, players can move freely back and forth across the START square.
5. The first player to cover six pictures wins the game.

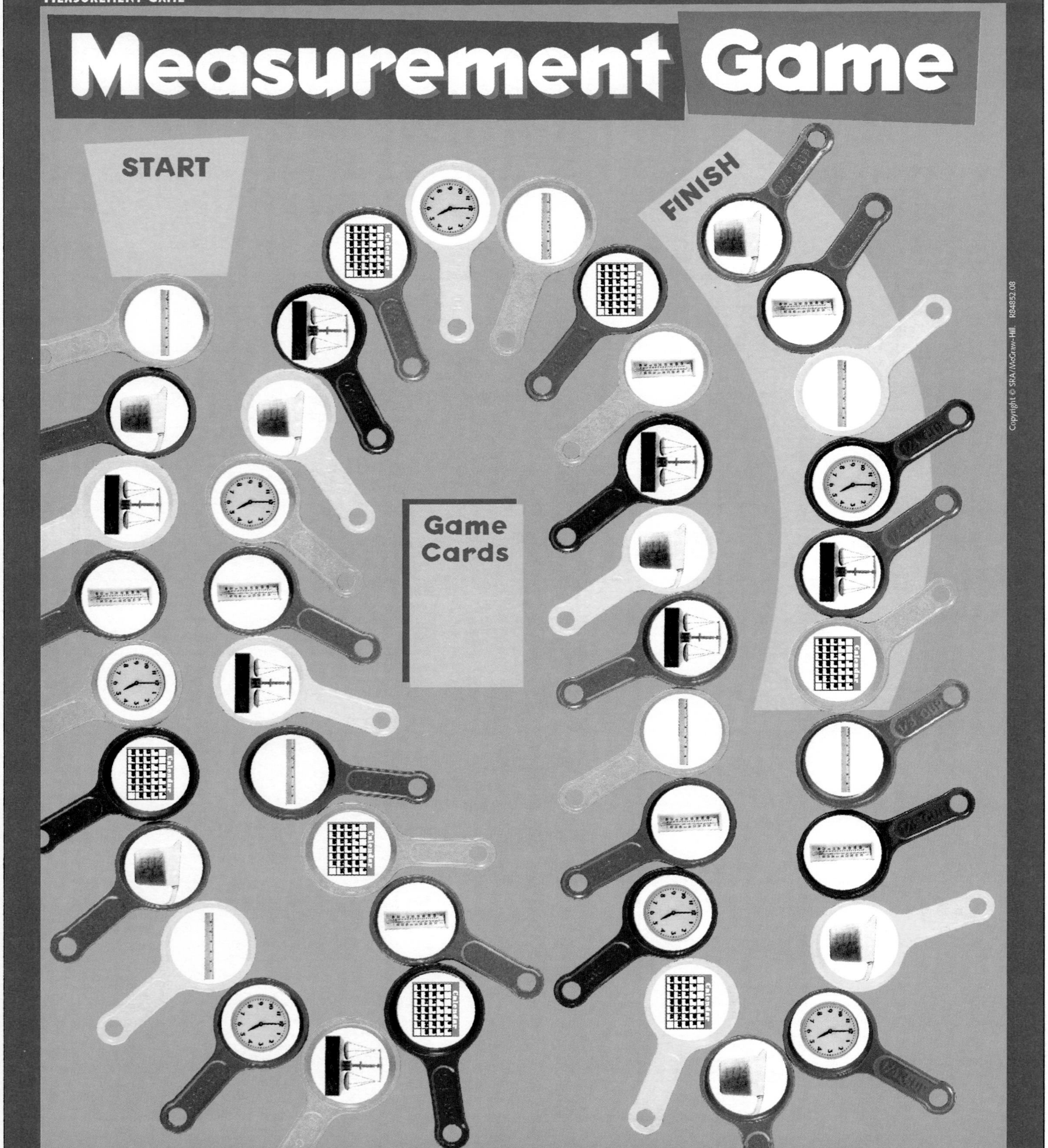

MEASUREMENT GAME

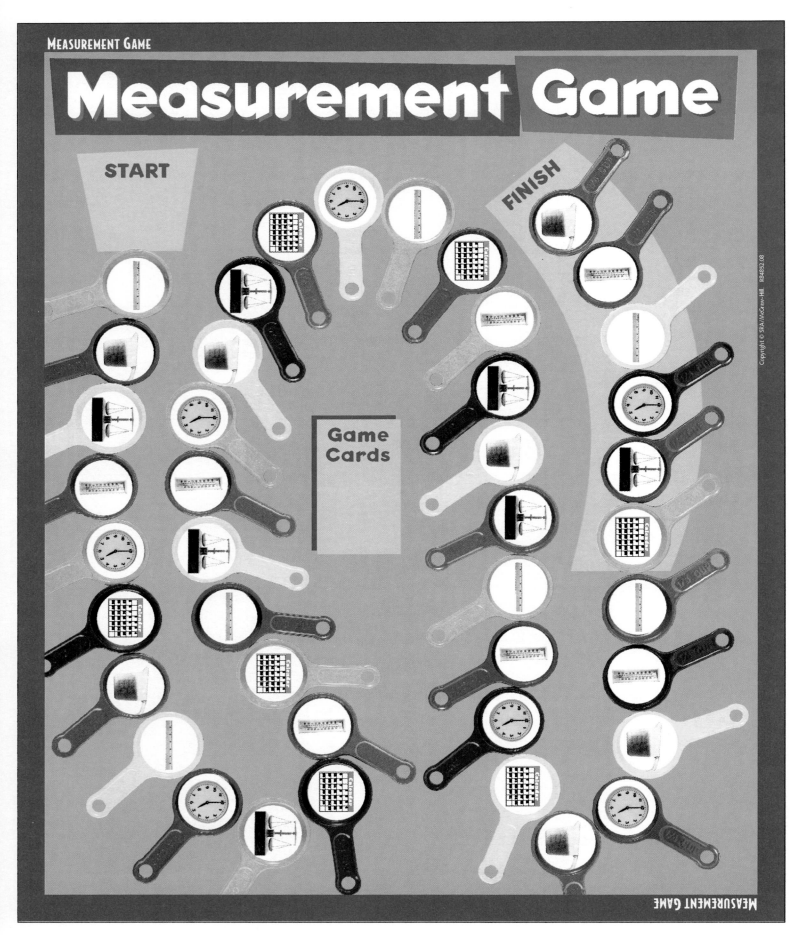

How to Play Measurement Game

Math Focus: Choosing the appropriate measuring instrument

Object of the Game: To be the first to reach FINISH

Players: Two or three

MATERIALS

Place markers Cube 24 game cards

SET UP

- ▶ Copy one set of game cards for each group and cut them out. You may want to mount each card on half of an index card and laminate them for durability.
- ▶ The game cards are placed face down on the rectangle marked GAME CARDS.
- ▶ Players put their place markers on START.
- ▶ Each player rolls the number cube. The person who rolls the highest number goes first.

HOW TO PLAY

1. Players take turns selecting the top card and deciding which measuring instrument would best answer the question.
2. Players move their markers forward on the game mat to the nearest correct measuring instrument. If players move to an incorrect instrument, they must go back to the space where they started.
3. If the card cards are used up, they are reshuffled and play continues.
4. The first player to enter the FINISH area wins the game.

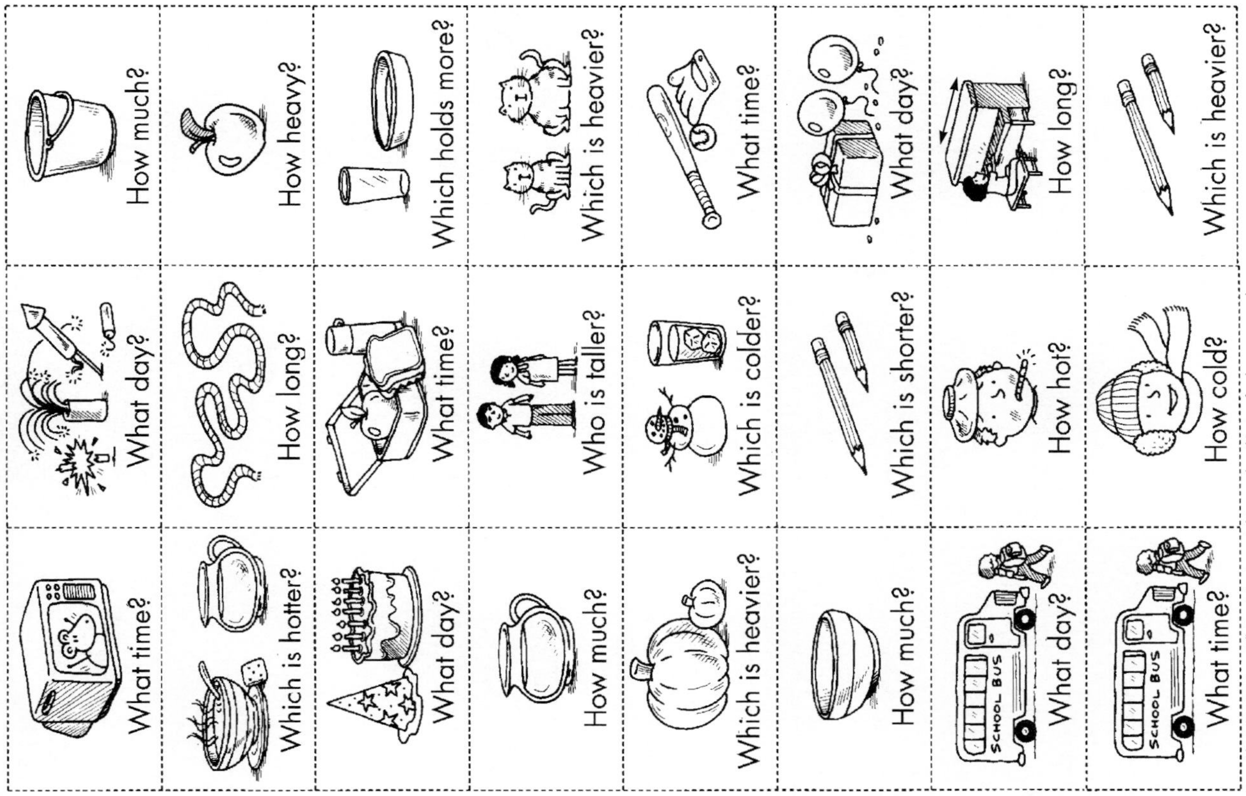

Multiplication Table Game

Math Focus:
- Practicing basic facts–multiplying two factors of 5 or less
- Using a multiplication table

Object of the Game: To have more counters at the end of the game

Players: Two

MATERIALS

Two cubes

36 counters or pennies

SET UP

- Every circle on the mat must be covered with a counter.
- Players roll the 0-5 number cube. The person who rolls the higher number goes first.

HOW TO PLAY

1. Players take turns rolling both cubes and making multiplication sentences out of the numbers. For example, if a 4 and a 2 are rolled, the player could say either "4 times 2 equals 8" or "2 times 4 equals 8."
2. After giving the multiplication sentence, players check their answers by looking under the appropriate counter. If correct, the player keeps the counter; if incorrect, the player replaces the counter.
3. Once the counter on a circle has been won, the circle remains empty. A player who cannot make a multiplication sentence that applies to a covered circle cannot win a counter that turn.
4. The player with more counters at the end of the game wins.

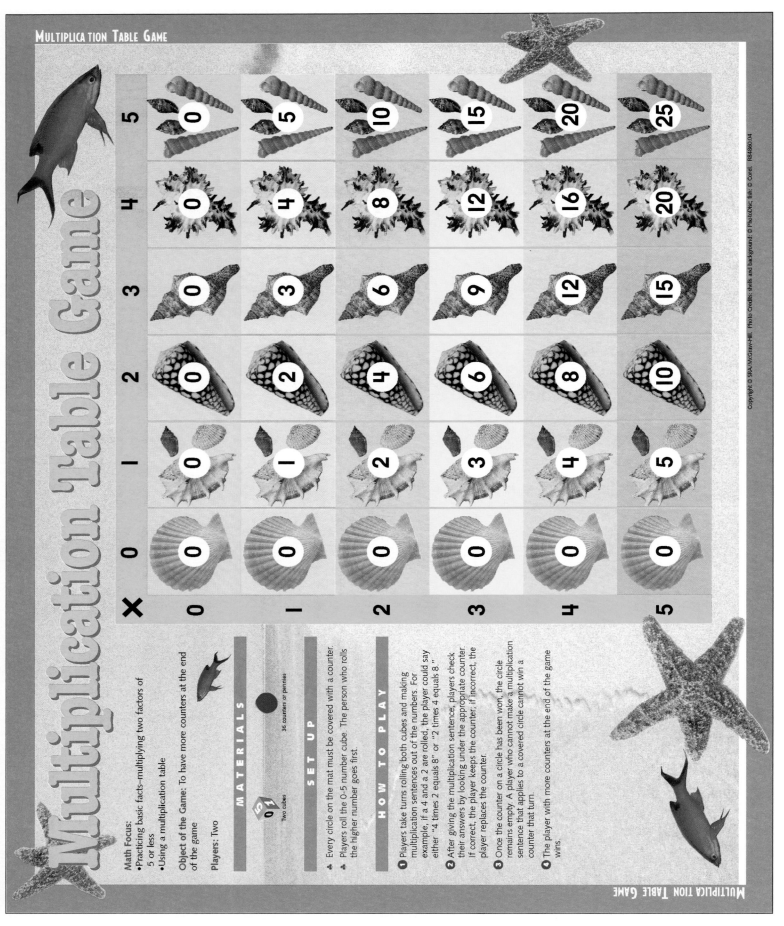

×	0	1	2	3	4	5
0	0	0	0	0	0	0
1	0	1	2	3	4	5
2	0	2	4	6	8	10
3	0	3	6	9	12	15
4	0	4	8	12	16	20
5	0	5	10	15	20	25

MULTIPLICATION TABLE GAME

HARDER Multiplication Table Game

Math Focus:
- Practicing basic facts–multiplying two factors of 10 or less
- Using a multiplication table

Object of the Game: To have more counters at the end of the game

Players: Two

MATERIALS

SET UP

- Every circle on the mat must be covered with a counter.
- Players roll the 0-5 number cube. The person who rolls the higher number goes first.

HOW TO PLAY

1. There are actually two harder versions of this game. One game is played rolling one 0-5 and one 5-10 number cube. The second game is played with two 5-10 number cubes. Players take turns rolling both cubes and making multiplication sentences out of the numbers. For example, if a 4 and a 9 are rolled, the player could say either "4 times 9 equals 36" or "9 times 4 equals 36."
2. After giving the multiplication sentence, players check their answers by looking under the appropriate counter. If correct, the player keeps the counter; if incorrect, the player replaces the counter.
3. Once the counter on a circle has been won, the circle remains empty. A player who cannot make a multiplication sentence that applies to a covered circle cannot win a counter that turn.
4. The player with more counters at the end of the game wins.

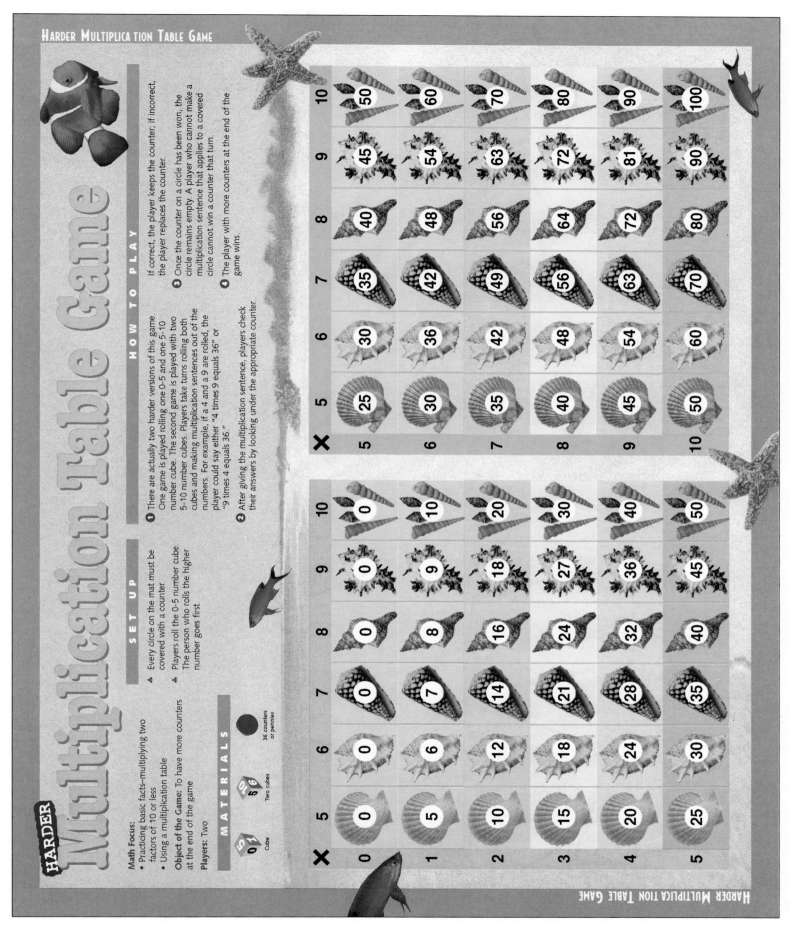

×	5	6	7	8	9	10
0	0	0	0	0	0	0
1	5	6	7	8	9	10
2	10	12	14	16	18	20
3	15	18	21	24	27	30
4	20	24	28	32	36	40
5	25	30	35	40	45	50

×	5	6	7	8	9	10
5	25	30	35	40	45	50
6	30	36	42	48	54	60
7	35	42	49	56	63	70
8	40	48	56	64	72	80
9	45	54	63	72	81	90
10	50	60	70	80	90	100

HARDER MULTIPLICA TION TABLE GAME

SET UP

- Players sort the money into piles next to the game mat.
- Players put their place markers on GO.
- Players roll the 0-5 number cube. The person who rolls the highest number goes first.

HOW TO PLAY

1. Players take turns rolling the cube and moving their place markers the number of spaces indicated.
2. After landing on a space, the player says the price of the object pictured there and collects that amount from the money next to the game mat. Players must count the bills aloud.
3. Players do not collect money for passing or landing on GO.
4. Players should keep their $1, $10, and $100 bills in separate piles. They must trade up whenever possible: ones for tens, tens for hundreds, and hundreds for a thousand. The first player to collect a $1000 bill wins the game.

Math Focus:
- Changing money ($1, $10, $100)
- Practicing regrouping in preparation for multidigit addition

Object of the Game: To be the first player to collect a $1000 bill

Players: Two or three

MATERIALS

Place markers

Cube

Per player:
ten $1 bills
ten $10 bills
ten $100 bills
one $1000 bill

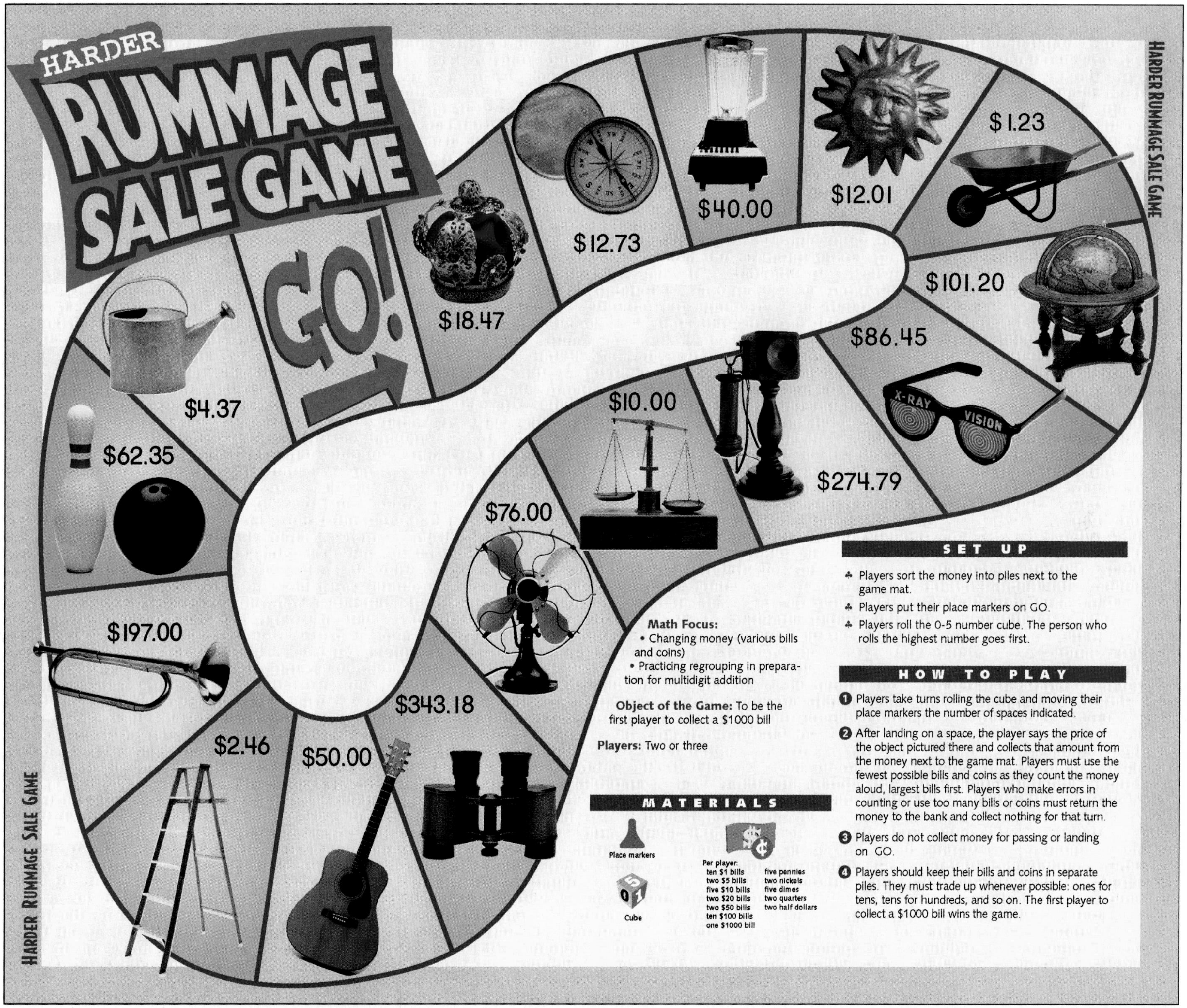

Math Focus:
- Changing money (various bills and coins)
- Practicing regrouping in preparation for multidigit addition

Object of the Game: To be the first player to collect a $1000 bill

Players: Two or three

MATERIALS

Place markers

Cube

Per player:
ten $1 bills
two $5 bills
five $10 bills
two $20 bills
two $50 bills
ten $100 bills
one $1000 bill

five pennies
two nickels
five dimes
two quarters
two half dollars

SET UP

- Players sort the money into piles next to the game mat.
- Players put their place markers on GO.
- Players roll the 0-5 number cube. The person who rolls the highest number goes first.

HOW TO PLAY

1. Players take turns rolling the cube and moving their place markers the number of spaces indicated.
2. After landing on a space, the player says the price of the object pictured there and collects that amount from the money next to the game mat. Players must use the fewest possible bills and coins as they count the money aloud, largest bills first. Players who make errors in counting or use too many bills or coins must return the money to the bank and collect nothing for that turn.
3. Players do not collect money for passing or landing on GO.
4. Players should keep their bills and coins in separate piles. They must trade up whenever possible: ones for tens, tens for hundreds, and so on. The first player to collect a $1000 bill wins the game.

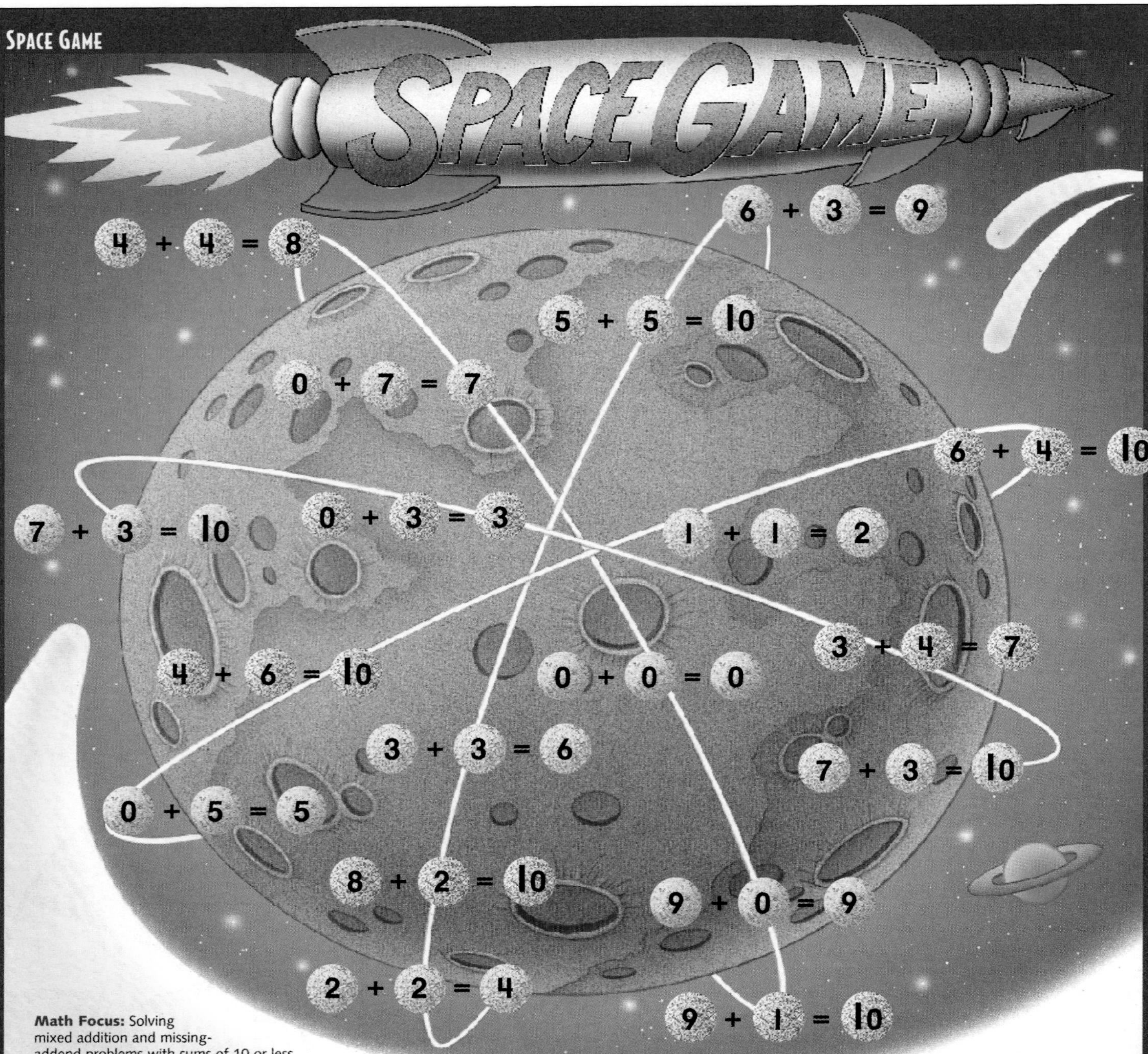

Math Focus: Solving mixed addition and missing-addend problems with sums of 10 or less

Object of the Game: To have the most counters at the end of the game

Players: Two or three

MATERIALS

Cube

Cube

18 counters or pennies

SET UP

- Players cover any one number in each equation.
- Players roll the 0-5 number cube. The person who rolls the highest number goes first.

HOW TO PLAY

1. Players take turns rolling either cube and using the number rolled to complete one of the equations on the mat. The player must correctly say the entire equation.
2. Players check their answers by looking under the counters. If correct, the player keeps the counter. If incorrect, the player replaces the counter.
3. The player with the most counters at the end of the game wins.

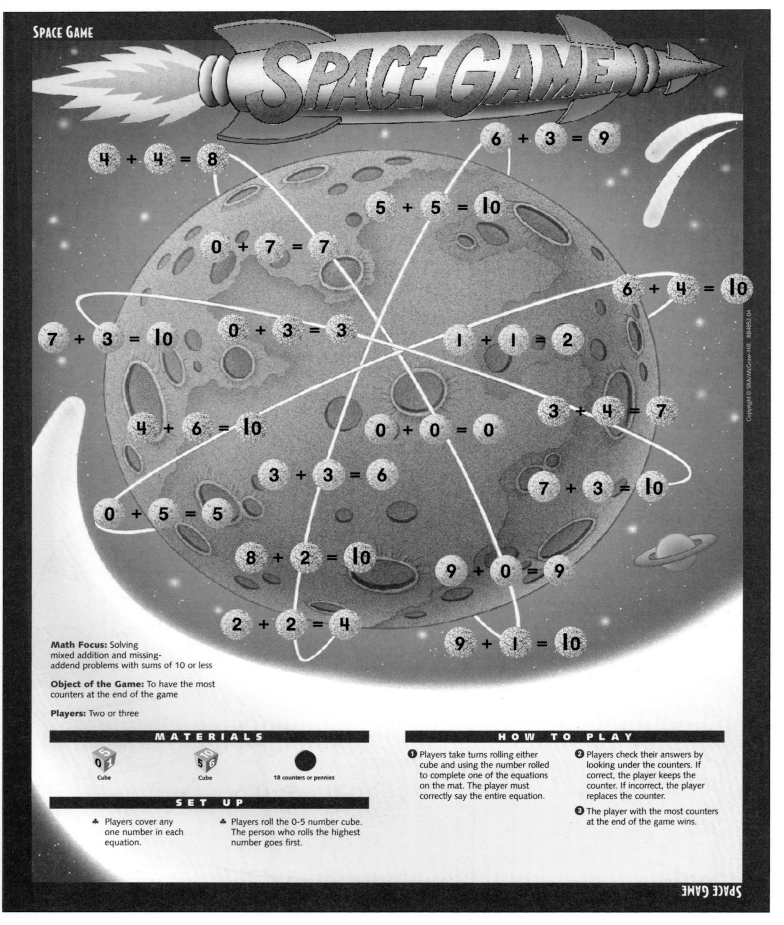

SPACE GAME

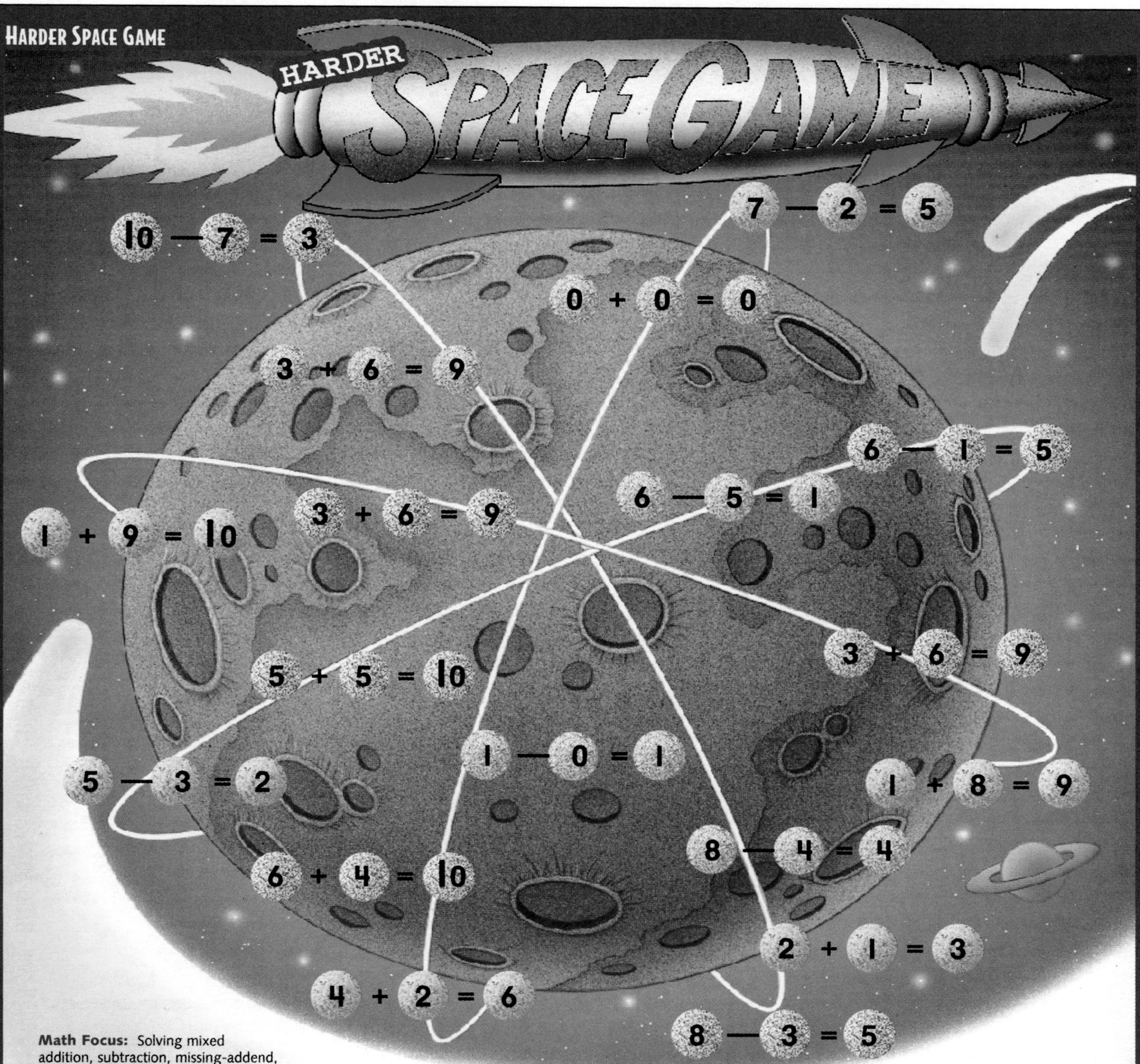

Math Focus: Solving mixed addition, subtraction, missing-addend, -minuend, and -subtrahend problems with numbers of 10 or less

Object of the Game: To have the most counters at the end of the game

Players: Two or three

MATERIALS

- Cube (0–5)
- Cube (5–10)
- 18 counters or pennies

SET UP

- Players cover any one number in each equation.
- Players roll the 0-5 number cube. The person who rolls the highest number goes first.

HOW TO PLAY

1. Players take turns rolling either cube and using the number rolled to complete one of the equations on the mat. The player must correctly say the entire equation.
2. Players check their answers by looking under the counters. If correct, the player keeps the counter. If incorrect, the player replaces the counter.
3. The player with the most counters at the end of the game wins.

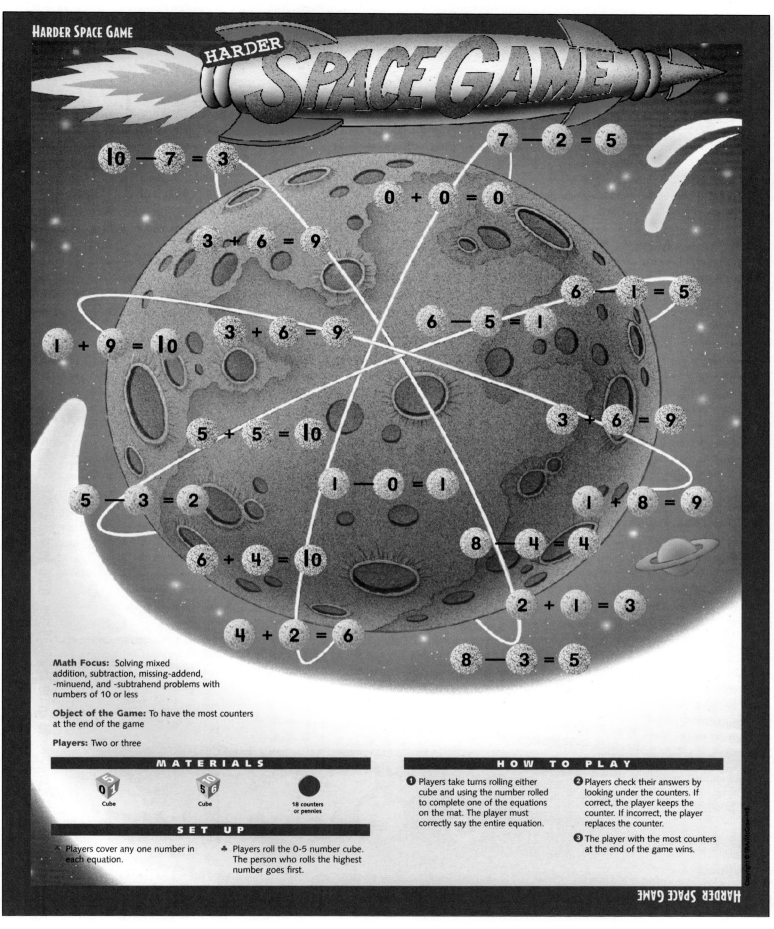

HARDER SPACE GAME

TIME GAME

Math Focus: Telling time to the hour, half hour, and quarter hour

Object of the Game: To have the most counters at the end of the game

Players: Two or three

MATERIALS

Place markers

Cube

16 counters or pennies

SET UP

- The small answer circles must be covered with counters.
- Players put their place markers on GO.
- Players roll the 0-5 number cube. The person who rolls the highest number goes first.

HOW TO PLAY

1. Players take turns rolling the cube and moving their place markers the number of spaces indicated.
2. After landing on a space, a player may win the counter there by correctly saying the time shown on the clock.
3. Players check their answers by lifting the counters. If correct, the player keeps the counter. If incorrect, the player replaces the counter.
4. A player cannot win a counter if there is none in a space. A player who gives an incorrect answer and rolls a 0 on the next turn can try again to win the counter.
5. Players who land on STOP must, if possible, place one of their own counters on an empty answer circle.
6. Players who land on GO may move to any unoccupied space on the mat and try to win a counter there if one is present.
7. The game ends when all counters have been won. The player with the most counters wins.

TIME GAME

HARDER TIME GAME

Math Focus: Telling time to five-minute intervals

Object of the Game: To have the most counters at the end of the game

Players: Two or three

MATERIALS

SET UP

- The red answer circles in each space must be covered by a counter.
- Players put their place markers on the space marked GO.
- Players roll the 0-5 number cube. The person who rolls the highest number goes first.

HOW TO PLAY

1. Players take turns rolling the cube and moving their place markers the number of spaces indicated. Players must correctly state the time indicated on the clock in each space where they land.
2. Players check their answers by looking under the counter. If correct, the player keeps the counter; if incorrect, the player replaces the counter.
3. A player who gives an incorrect answer and then rolls a 0 on the next turn may try again to win the counter.
4. Players who land on empty circles cannot win a counter and must wait until the next turn to roll again.
5. Players who land on the space marked PENALTY must, if possible, place one of their own counters on an empty circle.
6. The player with the most counters at the end of the game wins.

HARDER TIME GAME

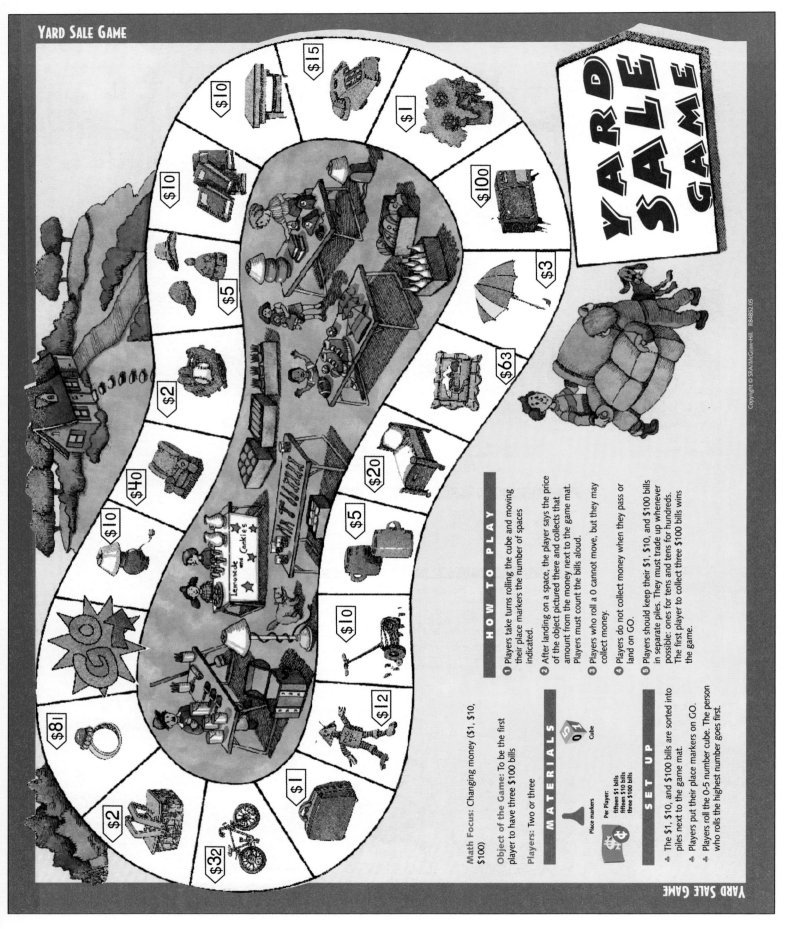

Math Focus: Changing money ($1, $10, $100)

Object of the Game: To be the first player to have three $100 bills

Players: Two or three

MATERIALS

Place markers

Cube

Per Player:
fifteen $1 bills
fifteen $10 bills
three $100 bills

SET UP

- The $1, $10, and $100 bills are sorted into piles next to the game mat.
- Players put their place markers on GO.
- Players roll the 0-5 number cube. The person who rolls the highest number goes first.

HOW TO PLAY

1. Players take turns rolling the cube and moving their place markers the number of spaces indicated.
2. After landing on a space, the player says the price of the object pictured there and collects that amount from the money next to the game mat. Players must count the bills aloud.
3. Players who roll a 0 cannot move, but they may collect money.
4. Players do not collect money when they pass or land on GO.
5. Players should keep their $1, $10, and $100 bills in separate piles. They must trade up whenever possible: ones for tens and tens for hundreds. The first player to collect three $100 bills wins the game.

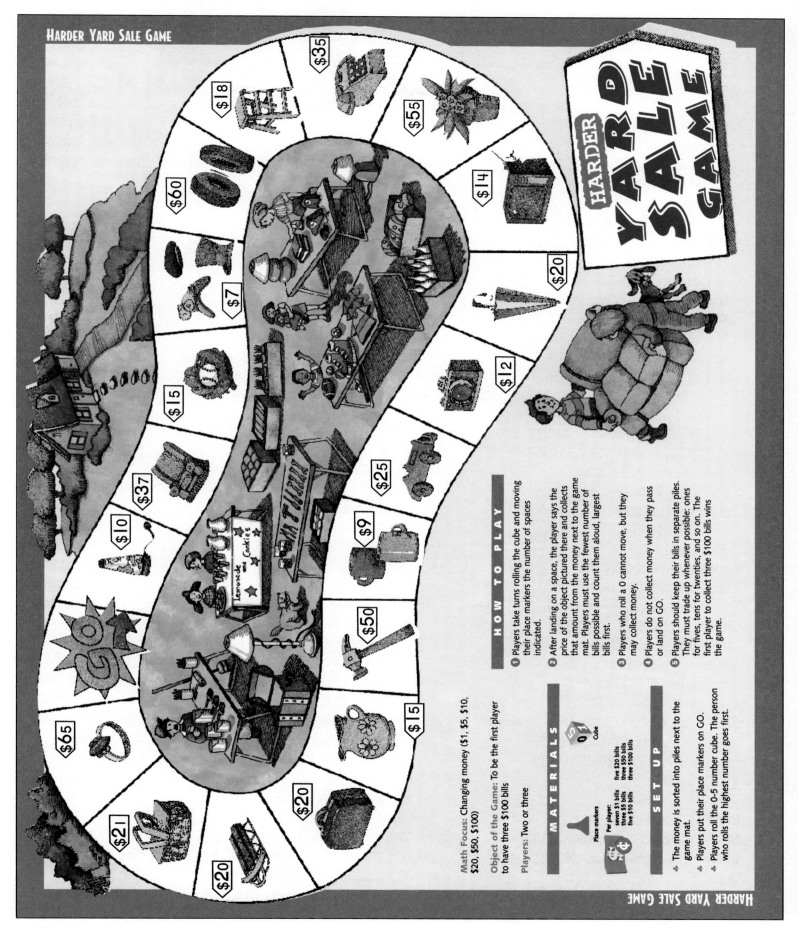

Math Focus: Changing money ($1, $5, $10, $20, $50, $100)

Object of the Game: To be the first player to have three $100 bills

Players: Two or three

MATERIALS

Place markers

Cube

Per player:
- seven $1 bills
- three $5 bills
- five $10 bills
- five $20 bills
- three $50 bills
- three $100 bills

SET UP

- The money is sorted into piles next to the game mat.
- Players put their place markers on GO.
- Players roll the 0-5 number cube. The person who rolls the highest number goes first.

HOW TO PLAY

1. Players take turns rolling the cube and moving their place markers the number of spaces indicated.
2. After landing on a space, the player says the price of the object pictured there and collects that amount from the money next to the game mat. Players must use the fewest number of bills possible and count them aloud, largest bills first.
3. Players who roll a 0 cannot move, but they may collect money.
4. Players do not collect money when they pass or land on GO.
5. Players should keep their bills in separate piles. They must trade up whenever possible: ones for fives, tens for twenties, and so on. The first player to collect three $100 bills wins the game.

HARDER YARD SALE GAME

INDEX

D

E

F

G

H

M

Q

R

S

SCOPE & SEQUENCE

	LESSON AND TITLE	ADDITION/ SUBTRACTION	ALGEBRA READINESS	FRACTION/ DECIMALS	GEOMETRY	MEASUREMENT	MULTIPLICATION/ DIVISION	NUMERATION	PROBABILITY/ STATISTICS/ GRAPHING	PROBLEM SOLVING	RATIO/ PROPORTION/ PERCENT
1	Counting and Writing Numbers							✓		✓	
2	More Counting and Writing							✓		✓	
3	Counting and Regrouping Money	✓				✓		✓		✓	
4	Numbers on the Calendar	✓				✓		✓		✓	
5	Writing Numbers	✓						✓		✓	
6	Adding and Subtracting by Counting	✓						✓		✓	
7	Counting Up or Down	✓						✓		✓	
8	Addition Facts	✓						✓		✓	
9	Double Addends	✓								✓	
10	Addition Facts Review	✓	✓							✓	
11	Commutative Property	✓	✓					✓		✓	
12	Reviewing Addition Facts	✓				✓				✓	
13	Addition Table	✓								✓	
14	Practicing Addition Facts	✓								✓	
15	Addition Fact Review	✓	✓							✓	
16	Additional Practice	✓	✓							✓	
17	Addition Checkpoint	✓								✓	
18	Subtracting Involving 0, 1, and 2	✓								✓	
19	Missing Addends	✓	✓							✓	
20	Functions	✓	✓					✓		✓	
21	Missing Addends and Subtraction	✓	✓							✓	
22	Using an Addition Table to Subtract	✓	✓							✓	
23	Adding and Subtracting	✓				✓				✓	
24	Subtraction Facts	✓								✓	
25	Reviewing Subtraction Facts	✓								✓	
26	Practicing Subtraction Facts	✓								✓	
27	More Subtraction Practice	✓								✓	
28	Subtraction Checkpoint	✓				✓				✓	
29	Using a Calculator	✓	✓							✓	
30	Addition and Subtraction	✓								✓	
31	Applying Addition and Subtraction	✓								✓	
32	Adding and Subtracting Three Numbers	✓								✓	
33	Pictographs	✓	✓						✓	✓	
34	Vertical Bar Graphs	✓						✓	✓	✓	
35	Horizontal Bar Graphs	✓						✓	✓	✓	
36	Place Value–Base Ten	✓						✓		✓	
37	Place Value–Using Money							✓	✓	✓	
38	Counting by Tens	✓						✓		✓	
39	Measuring Length–Centimeters	✓			✓	✓				✓	
40	Measurement–Meters and Centimeters	✓				✓				✓	
41	Measuring Length–Inches	✓				✓				✓	
42	Measurement–Yards, Feet, and Inches	✓				✓				✓	

SCOPE & SEQUENCE

	LESSON AND TITLE	ADDITION/ SUBTRACTION	ALGEBRA READINESS	FRACTION/ DECIMALS	GEOMETRY	MEASUREMENT	MULTIPLICATION/ DIVISION	NUMERATION	PROBABILITY/ STATISTICS/ GRAPHING	PROBLEM SOLVING	RATIO/ PROPORTION/ PERCENT
43	Estimating Length				✓	✓				✓	
44	Measurement–Perimeter	✓			✓	✓				✓	
45	Unit 1 Test	✓	✓			✓		✓		✓	
46	Extending the Unit	✓									
47	Graphs	✓				✓			✓	✓	
48	Place Value	✓						✓		✓	
49	Adding Tens and Ones	✓						✓		✓	
50	Adding Two-Digit Numbers	✓						✓		✓	
51	Two-Digit Numbers	✓				✓		✓		✓	
52	Adding with Renaming	✓						✓		✓	
53	Two-Digit Addition	✓								✓	
54	More Two-Digit Addition	✓								✓	
55	Practicing Two-Digit Addition	✓						✓		✓	
56	Keeping Sharp	✓								✓	
57	Renaming Tens as Ones	✓						✓		✓	
58	Subtracting Multiples of Ten	✓								✓	
59	Subtracting Two-Digit Numbers from Multiples of Ten	✓								✓	
60	Two-Digit Subtraction	✓				✓				✓	
61	Subtracting Two-Digit Numbers	✓								✓	
62	Practicing Two-Digit Subtraction	✓		✓						✓	
63	Applying Subtraction	✓								✓	
64	Subtracting with Money	✓	✓	✓						✓	
65	Checking Subtraction	✓								✓	
66	Subtraction Check	✓				✓				✓	
67	Addition and Subtraction	✓								✓	
68	Practice Adding and Subtracting	✓								✓	
69	Check Your Adding and Subtracting	✓								✓	
70	Telling Time–Hour and Half Hour	✓		✓		✓		✓		✓	
71	Telling Time–Quarter Hour	✓		✓		✓				✓	
72	Telling Time–Halves and Quarters	✓		✓		✓				✓	
73	Fractions–Halves and Quarters	✓		✓						✓	
74	Halves, Quarters, and Thirds	✓		✓						✓	
75	Fifths and Other Fractions	✓		✓						✓	
76	Fractions and Geometry			✓	✓	✓				✓	
77	Fractions	✓		✓						✓	
78	Fractions of Numbers	✓		✓						✓	
79	Geometric Shapes–Plane Figures	✓	✓	✓	✓					✓	
80	Congruent Shapes	✓		✓	✓					✓	
81	Symmetry	✓			✓					✓	
82	Geometric Shapes–Solid Figures	✓			✓					✓	
83	More Congruency	✓			✓					✓	
84	Patterns	✓	✓		✓			✓		✓	

SCOPE & SEQUENCE

LESSON AND TITLE		ADDITION/ SUBTRACTION	ALGEBRA READINESS	FRACTION/ DECIMALS	GEOMETRY	MEASUREMENT	MULTIPLICATION/ DIVISION	NUMERATION	PROBABILITY/ STATISTICS/ GRAPHING	PROBLEM SOLVING	RATIO/ PROPORTION/ PERCENT
85	Function Tables	✓								✓	
86	Collecting Data	✓							✓	✓	
87	Measurement–Thermometers	✓				✓		✓		✓	
88	Unit 2 Review	✓		✓		✓		✓		✓	
89	Unit 2 Test	✓		✓	✓	✓				✓	
90	Extending the Unit	✓								✓	
91	Less Than, Greater Than	✓						✓		✓	
92	Three Addends	✓								✓	
93	Telling Time–Nearest Half Hour	✓		✓		✓				✓	
94	Telling Time–To the Minute	✓	✓			✓				✓	
95	Telling Time– Before the Hour	✓	✓			✓				✓	
96	Keeping Sharp	✓	✓	✓		✓		✓		✓	
97	Column Addition	✓								✓	
98	Column Addition–Finding Perimeter	✓			✓	✓				✓	
99	Reading Maps	✓			✓	✓				✓	
100	Map Reading	✓			✓	✓				✓	
101	Exploring Triangles	✓			✓	✓		✓		✓	
102	Odd and Even Numbers	✓		✓				✓		✓	
103	Odds and Evens	✓						✓		✓	
104	Adding Odds and Evens	✓						✓		✓	
105	Subtracting Odds and Evens	✓						✓		✓	
106	Kilograms and Grams	✓				✓				✓	
107	Pounds and Ounces	✓				✓				✓	
108	Using Measurements	✓				✓		✓		✓	
109	Measurement–Capacity	✓			✓	✓				✓	
110	Metric Measurement–Capacity	✓				✓				✓	
111	Using Measurements	✓				✓				✓	
112	Shortcuts	✓		✓						✓	
113	Round to Ten	✓						✓		✓	
114	Unit 3 Review	✓	✓	✓		✓		✓		✓	
115	Unit 3 Test	✓		✓		✓		✓	✓	✓	
116	Extending the Unit	✓				✓				✓	
117	Introduction to Multiplication	✓					✓			✓	
118	Multiplication–Using Repeated Addition	✓					✓	✓		✓	
119	Multiplication–Finding Area				✓	✓	✓			✓	
120	Multiplication	✓					✓			✓	
121	Multiplication–Using Pictures	✓					✓			✓	
122	Applying Multiplication						✓			✓	
123	Multiplication						✓			✓	
124	Analyzing Random Data	✓					✓		✓	✓	
125	Predicting Results	✓							✓	✓	
126	Introducing Variability	✓				✓			✓	✓	
127	Applying Multiplication	✓	✓	✓			✓			✓	

SCOPE & SEQUENCE

	LESSON AND TITLE	ADDITION/ SUBTRACTION	ALGEBRA READINESS	FRACTION/ DECIMALS	GEOMETRY	MEASUREMENT	MULTIPLICATION/ DIVISION	NUMERATION	PROBABILITY/ STATISTICS/ GRAPHING	PROBLEM SOLVING	RATIO/ PROPORTION/ PERCENT
128	Introducing Division	✓					✓			✓	
129	Division and Multiplication	✓	✓		✓	✓	✓			✓	
130	Days of the Week	✓				✓	✓			✓	
131	Telling Time					✓	✓			✓	
132	Number Sentences	✓					✓			✓	
133	Grouping by Tens	✓						✓		✓	
134	Multiplication and Division	✓	✓				✓			✓	
135	Mixed Operations	✓	✓				✓			✓	
136	More Mixed Operations	✓	✓				✓			✓	
137	Keeping Sharp	✓								✓	
138	Counting Through 1000	✓						✓		✓	
139	Numbers Through 1000	✓						✓		✓	
140	Introducing Three-Digit Addition	✓					✓	✓		✓	
141	Three-Digit Addition	✓						✓		✓	
142	More Three-Digit Addition	✓								✓	
143	Three-Digit Subtraction	✓								✓	
144	More Three-Digit Subtraction	✓					✓	✓		✓	
145	Practicing Three-Digit Subtraction	✓								✓	
146	Three-Digit Addition and Subtraction	✓				✓	✓			✓	
147	Three-Digit Practice	✓								✓	
148	Adding and Subtracting Money	✓		✓						✓	
149	Adding and Subtracting with Three Digits	✓								✓	
150	Practicing Addition and Subtraction	✓								✓	
151	Approximating Answers	✓		✓			✓			✓	
152	Counting by 100s and 1000s						✓	✓		✓	
153	Adding Four-Digit Numbers	✓		✓		✓	✓			✓	
154	Four-Digit Addition	✓					✓			✓	
155	Four-Digit Subtraction	✓						✓		✓	
156	Keeping Sharp	✓				✓	✓			✓	
157	Applying Addition and Subtraction	✓					✓	✓		✓	
158	Unit 4 Review	✓				✓	✓	✓		✓	
159	Unit 4 Test	✓	✓				✓	✓		✓	
160	Extending the Unit	✓					✓			✓	